TEACHING HIGH SCHOOL SCIENCE:

A
Sourcebook
for the
Physical
Sciences

ALEXANDER JOSEPH
PROFESSOR OF PHYSICS, HEAD, DEPARTMENT OF
MATHEMATICS AND PHYSICS, BRONX COMMUNITY
COLLEGE, CITY UNIVERSITY OF NEW YORK;
INSTRUCTOR, HARVARD UNIVERSITY, NSF ACADEMIC
YEAR INSTITUTE 1959–60; CO-DIRECTOR, NSF PHYSICS
INSTITUTE, NEW YORK UNIVERSITY 1960–61, CITY
COLLEGE-BRONX COMMUNITY COLLEGE 1961–62;
CONSULTANT, PHYSICAL SCIENCE STUDY COMMITTEE;
FORMERLY INSTRUCTOR IN PHYSICS, BRONX HIGH
SCHOOL OF SCIENCE

PAUL F. BRANDWEIN
DIRECTOR, DIVISION OF EDUCATION, CONSERVATION
FOUNDATION;
SENIOR GENERAL EDITOR AND CONSULTANT TO
SCHOOLS, HARCOURT, BRACE & WORLD;
STEERING COMMITTEE, PHYSICAL SCIENCE STUDY
COMMITTEE AND BIOLOGICAL SCIENCES CURRICULUM
STUDY;
FORMERLY CHAIRMAN, DEPARTMENT OF SCIENCE,
FOREST HILLS HIGH SCHOOL

EVELYN MORHOLT
CHAIRMAN, DEPARTMENT OF BIOLOGY AND GENERAL
SCIENCE, FORT HAMILTON HIGH SCHOOL, BROOKLYN;
CURRICULUM CONSULTANT, NEW YORK CITY

HARVEY POLLACK
TEACHER OF PHYSICS, FOREST HILLS HIGH SCHOOL;
CURRICULUM ADVISER AND STAFF WRITER, NEW YORK
INSTITUTE OF TECHNOLOGY;
CONTRIBUTING EDITOR, *ELECTRONICS ILLUSTRATED*

JOSEPH F. CASTKA
CHAIRMAN, SCIENCE DEPARTMENT, MARTIN VAN BUREN
HIGH SCHOOL, QUEENS, NEW YORK;
ASSISTANT PROFESSOR, CHEMISTRY AND GENERAL
SCIENCE, C. W. POST COLLEGE, LONG ISLAND UNIVERSITY

HARCOURT, BRACE & WORLD, INC.

NEW YORK / BURLINGAME

COVER PHOTOGRAPH   Visual representation of speech.
A three-dimensional model (*side view*) of a
sound pressure wave that is created when a human
voice speaks into a research apparatus designed by
IBM scientists. This apparatus is used to
study possible ways of controlling data processing
machines with the human voice.
Erich Hartmann, Magnum, courtesy of IBM.

Preface

It is our hope that the multitude of demonstration and laboratory procedures as well as the numerous suggestions for projects and experiments in this volume will fit the variety of teaching situations found in our schools. The topics to which various procedures apply were selected on the basis of a study of more than 40 courses in general science, chemistry, physics, and earth science—including the course developed by the Physical Science Study Committee and such information as we had available relating to the chemistry courses now being developed.

All of the techniques have been tested in actual class situations; we have tried to describe them in adequate detail to invite trial under the variety of conditions we have found to exist in the nation's classrooms and laboratories.

This volume is one of a series. There are two companion volumes now available: *Teaching High School Science: A Book of Methods,* by P. F. Brandwein, F. G. Watson, and P. E. Blackwood (Harcourt, Brace, 1958), and *Teaching High School Science: A Sourcebook for the Biological Sciences,* by E. Morholt, P. F. Brandwein, and A. Joseph (Harcourt, Brace, 1958).

We have thought of the series as *one* text really; an exposition of teaching methods and curricular approaches is, to our mind, inadequate unless accompanied by exposition of specific approaches, in procedure and technique.

It is very clear that this volume, like the others, could not have been possible without the dedicated effort of the profession. We have borrowed heavily, and where we have been able to ferret out the original contribution we have given credit to the author. But too often these techniques are in a kind of public domain.

Certainly some of the descriptions will be found wanting; surely better ones exist. We should consider it a privilege to receive suggestions for improvement of the work and to include the contribution in a revised edition with appropriate credit.

The opportunity we have sought in adding this volume to the two others is that of serving our colleagues, the nation's teachers of science.

ALEXANDER JOSEPH
PAUL F. BRANDWEIN
EVELYN MORHOLT
HARVEY POLLACK
JOSEPH F. CASTKA

Contents

The number and letter preceding the headings refer to chapters, sections, and subsections: the first number stands for the chapter, the number following the decimal is the section within the chapter, and a letter refers to a subsection within the section.

Material at the end of each chapter is designed to supplement the chapter. This section provides Capsule Lessons, Books and Pamphlets, Films and Filmstrips, and Free and Inexpensive Materials.

A listing of the tables that appear in this book is given on p. 620 in the appendix.

Chapter 15   Consumer chemistry / 301

Section *Three*   PHYSICS

Patterns in the use of laboratory

techniques and procedures

Teaching is a personal invention. Each teacher will have his own ways of using the great variety of techniques and procedures described in this book; he will use them selectively. He will use some of them as the basis for individual laboratory work, for group work, for field trips, for projects, and for his own demonstrations, as well as for many other approaches. No one can reasonably hope to include in one book all the individual procedures and the patterns in which they are used, and their variations, which different teachers have found practicable. The purpose of this introduction is to indicate how teachers in groups or as individuals have used the procedures included in this book to build their personal invention—their teaching technique.

An example of techniques and procedures within a unit

Clearly the technique, and procedure, the device—whatever it is—fits within a *pattern,* the *curricular pattern.* A teacher or group of teachers plans a unit of work. At the end of the unit the students are to have mastery of a large idea, perhaps of a concept. In planning to help students achieve learning of this large concept or idea, the teacher uses all methods and techniques at his disposal, fitting them in to meet the total philosophy and practice, both administrative and pedagogical, of his school.

As an example, let us examine a specific unit in physics prepared by a committee of teachers. These teachers have selected techniques for specific purposes; of course, not all the available techniques are used. It is our purpose in this introduction to show that *techniques are not used in isolation but are part and parcel of the teaching development within a unit.* We have selected a unit on *Heat* as taught in a physics course of study. We have, however, condensed the unit to save space (Table 0-1).

Examples of techniques and procedures within a total curricular pattern

More and more teachers are realizing the need for examining the entire curricular range—from kindergarten through high school. One result of this examination is to avoid repetition of experiences in the same context. For instance, teachers in a given school system know what is going on in elementary school and

TABLE 0–1
Outline of one unit of a physics syllabus: heat[1]

topic	*pupil experiences*
I. Thermometry and expansion coefficients	
A. Thermometry	Demonstration of Galileo's thermometer (*18.1, 3.1*)[2]
1. Temperature: meaning of temperature—Galileo's thermometer—temperature and kinetic theory—centigrade and Fahrenheit thermometer—range of the mercury thermometer—fever and hydrogen thermometer—Kelvin scale	Demonstration of water, alcohol, mercury thermometers (*3.1, 18.1*)
	Demonstration of Charles' law (*1.3, 18.2*)
	Demonstration or discussion of hydrogen thermometer
B. Expansion coefficients	Demonstration of maximum density of water (*4.6*)
1. Charles' law	
2. Gay-Lussac's law	Demonstration of expansion of liquids (*1.3, 4.6, 18.2*)
C. Expansion of liquids and solids	
1. Expansion of liquids: measuring expansion coefficients, etc.	Demonstration of ball and ring (*18.2*)
2. Expansion of solids: linear coefficient of expansion	Demonstration of compound bar-thermostat (*18.2*)
	EXPERIMENTS
3. Applications of expansion: thermostats, etc.	1. Thermometers: fixed points (*18.1*)
	2. Charles' law (*18.2*)
	3. Coefficient of linear expansion (*18.2*)
II. Work and heat energy	
A. Mechanical equivalent of heat	Demonstrate heat
1. Wasted heat and work	by friction (*17.3, 17.4*)
2. Heat units	from electricity (*17.3*)
3. Mechanical equivalent: Joule's experiment—heat by compression, conservation	from compression (bicycle pump, *18.8*)
	from chemicals (*17.3, 8.2*)
	Demonstrate or discuss mechanical equivalent of heat (*18.6*)
B. Specific heat	Demonstrate toy heat engine (*18.8*)
1. Definition	Discuss heat units: calorie and Btu—heat content of fuels—value of specific heat data (*18.1–18.8*)
2. Method of mixtures	
3. Caloric content: food—fuels	EXPERIMENTS
	1. Specific heat of lead (*18.4*)
	2. Heat value of city gas (*18.4*)
III. Change of state	
A. Fusion	Demonstrate change of state (*2.2, 4.6, 4.7, 8.2, 18.5*)
1. Energy change	
2. Heat of fusion: value for ice	Demonstrate sublimation (*2.2*)
3. Melting points: crystalline substances—amorphous substances	Discuss applications of heat of fusion and heat of vaporization (*18.4*)
4. Change of volume in fusion	Discuss operation of electric refrigerator, artificial ice (*18.5*)
5. Effect of pressure on melting point	
B. Evaporation and vapors	Discuss freezing of water and expansion effect (*4.6, 8.1*)
1. Effect of temperature on evaporation	

[1] Part of an outline of Unit II of *Course of Study in Physics: Grades Eleven and Twelve*, Cincinnati Public Schools, Cincinnati, O., 1952.
[2] The italic numbers in parentheses refer to sections in *this* sourcebook in which a description of the specific technique is given. The first number represents the chapter of the book; the numbers following the decimal refer to the section within the chapter.

topic	pupil experiences

2. Sublimation
3. Saturation: saturated vapor
4. Influence of air on evaporation
C. Hygrometry
  1. Condensation: dew—frost—fog—clouds
  2. Humidity determinations: dew point—relative humidity
D. Boiling
  1. Heat of vaporization; heat of condensation
  2. Definition of boiling point; effect of pressure on boiling point
  3. Refrigeration
  4. Liquefaction of gases
  5. Distillation: ordinary and fractional
  6. Cooling solutions; freezing mixtures
E. Steam engines
  1. Modern steam engine and steam turbine
F. Internal-combustion engines
  1. Gas engine: auto—clutch—differential—carburetor
  2. Airplane engine: jet
  3. Diesel and semi-diesel
	Take trips to ice plant (see Field Trips, below in Introduction)
	Demonstrate ice bomb; effect of pressure on ice (4.6); boiling at reduced pressure and pressure cooker (4.6, 18.4)
	Demonstrate distillation (4.7); fractional distillation (14.3)
	Demonstrate cooling by evaporation (18.5, 8.5, 3.2)
	Discuss steam vs. electric vs. diesel power (18.8)
	Demonstrate cloud formation and vapor pressure (3.1, 3.2)
	Demonstrate hygrometer, relative humidity, freezing points (3.2); air conditioning (18.4, 8.2)
	
	EXPERIMENTS
	1. Heat of fusion of ice (18.4)
	2. Dew point and relative humidity (3.2)
	3. Effect of pressure on boiling point (4.6)
	Pupil reports on diesel, steam, jet, and other engines (18.8, Chapter 24)
	Discussion of modern auto internal-combustion engines (18.8, 24.1)
	Discussion of Carnot cycle; steam engine (18.8)

IV. Transference of heat
A. Conduction
  1. In solids; in liquids; in gases
  2. Davy safety lamp
B. Convection
  1. In liquids; in gases
  2. Winds and ocean currents
C. Radiation
  1. Nature; radiation and absorption
  2. Dewar flask
D. Heating and ventilation
  1. Principle of ventilation
  2. Heating plants: hot air—hot water—steam—radiant energy
	Demonstrate conduction in solids, liquids (18.3)
	Demonstrate transfer of heat and Davy safety lamp (18.3)
	Demonstrate convection in liquids and gases (18.3); Thermos bottle (18.3); ventilation boxes (18.3)
	Discuss home insulation (18.3, 18.7)
	
	Discussion and reports; demonstrations (18.7, 23.2)

build on the experiences made available earlier.

Note, for instance, the range of activities exemplified in the following curricular plan.[3] Clearly, if teachers follow this plan—or prepare their own plan—grade level for grade level, it would be well to know what went on in prior work, so that greater growth in learning can be achieved.

By studying this one *area* (magnetism and electricity) of the total curricular plan, teachers recognize that through the

[3] Adapted from *Science Curriculum Bulletins, Kindergarten to Grade 6,* Seattle Public Schools, Seattle, Wash.

grades many broad concepts of magnetism and electricity as well as their application in everyday living are developed in a sequential pattern. Many times, in fact, the activity may seem similar (for example, field trips), but students' perception increases as they have more meaningful experiences. Youngsters "see" more as they grow and know more.

Those children who have had some of these experiences in the primary grades bring a richer knowledge of the interrelations among magnetism, electricity, and electromagnetism to their class work in high school physics.

We have selected only a few of the activities in these topics that are suggested for each grade level. A similar development may be undertaken for any other unit or broad concept that we teach at the high school level. In any event students come to high school with experiences gained in the elementary grades.

Kindergarten

One unit: Things may be moved in different ways
MAGNETS PICK UP OR PULL SOME THINGS (Chapter 21)[4]

1. Magnets pick up articles made of iron and steel.

2. They will not pick up paper, wood, glass, copper, silver, brass, gold, rubber, cork, silk.

3. The pull of a magnet will go through many things, including glass and paper.

4. The pull of a magnet is strongest at its ends.

5. Some magnets are stronger than others; a strong magnet will pull from a distance.

Encourage the boys and girls to play freely with different kinds of magnets and various substances. (It should be fun to make and play with a magnetic fish pond rigged up by fastening paper clips to the backs of cardboard fish and using a magnet as "bait" on a long fishing pole.)

ELECTRICITY (Chapters 21, 22)

We run toy electric trains. We turn lights on

[4] The chapter references in parentheses refer to chapters in this sourcebook.

and off as needed. We turn the heater on and off. We ride on the trolley. We watch our mothers use such electrical equipment as washing machines, irons, vacuum cleaners, egg beaters, stoves, toasters, etc.

First grade

One unit: Electricity (Chapters 18, 21, 22)

1. Building an appreciation value of a great power.

2. Electricity is one of our best helpers. (a) Discuss all the ways that electricity helps us in our homes. (b) Discuss all the ways that electricity helps us in school. Note the thermostat. Visit the boiler room to see how the custodian uses electricity to control heat in the building. (c) Electricity lights the streets, runs the trolleys, and helps perform many other community services. (d) How does electricity reach us?

One unit: Magnets (Chapter 21)

1. Magnets attract some things, such as iron and steel, but not others. (*Note:* Course of study gives review of activities of type listed under kindergarten grade.)

2. Use a magnet to pull small toy automobiles or other playthings made of iron.

3. Make a boat from cork and paper; put a small piece of steel (a needle) in it; then, without touching it, move the boat over the water by moving a magnet near the boat.

4. Steel scissors and steel needles can be magnetized by stroking them in one direction with a magnet. Make a magnet for your own use. Report on experiments in which magnets are used at home.

5. The magnetic compass is helpful in finding directions. Interview a Boy Scout to find out how he uses a compass. Show compasses which belong to parents and explain their use.

Second grade

Units: Evaporation; Air is Real; Weather Chart and Weather Conditions; Day and Night; Seasonal Changes and Their Effects on Plants and Animals (Chapters 3, 5)

Third grade

1. Where is a magnet the strongest?[5] (Chapter 21)

The ends of a magnet are called its poles.
A magnet will attract for some distance.
Some magnets are stronger than others.

We can make a magnet by rubbing a piece of hard steel with a magnet.

2. What kinds of magnets are there?

The most common magnets are the bar magnets and the natural magnet or lodestone. These magnets are called permanent magnets because the magnetism cannot be turned off and on.

The electromagnet is a temporary magnet. The magnetism can be turned off and on.

3. Will a magnet's force pass through things?

A magnet's force will attract through a material it does not attract.

A tin can will be attracted by a magnet because it is made of iron with only a thin coating of tin.

4. How can we show that the force of a magnet extends around the magnet?

The region around the magnet in which the magnetic force is exerted is called the magnetic field.

The lines are called the magnetic lines of force.

5. Why is one end of the magnet marked N and the other marked S?

The north-seeking pole of the magnet is marked with N; the south-seeking pole is marked S.

6. How do magnets act toward each other?

7. What use do we make of a compass?

The needle in a compass is a magnet; a compass needle points north and south.

8. How can we use electricity to make a magnet?

An electromagnet can be made by using a coil of insulated wire, an iron core, and a current of electricity.

An electromagnet is a magnet only when electricity is flowing through the coil of wire.

9. Does an electromagnet have poles?

An electromagnet has poles.

10. How can an electromagnet be made stronger?

An electromagnet can be made stronger by increasing the number of turns of wire and by increasing the current of electricity.

Fourth grade

Units: Plants and Animals Grow; How Your Body Works; The Earth, Sun, and Moon (Chapter 5);

[5] Consult course of study for complete descriptions of suggested activities.

The Solid Part of the Earth—Rocks and Minerals (Chapter 4); *The Liquid Part of the Earth—Water* (Chapters 2, 3, 4); *The Gaseous Part of the Earth —Air* (Chapter 3)

Fifth grade

Units: Seasons and Seasonal Change (Chapter 5); *Weather* (Chapter 3); *Our Changing Earth* (Chapter 4); *Machines* (Chapter 17); *Gardening* (Chapters 4, 12)

Sixth grade

One unit: Magnets and Magnetism (Chapter 21)

A check list of previous science experiences is offered "in order to take a child from where he is and not to repeat unnecessarily. From this inventory you may find that you will not need to try any of the experiences in this section. On the other hand, to many members of the group these experiences may be new and/or they have many misconceptions that may need revising."

More elaborate demonstrations are suggested, including Oersted's experiment.

One unit: Electricity (Chapters 21, 22)

1. How to make electromagnets; uses of electromagnets; putting electromagnets to work— door bell, telegraph, telephone, electric motors; sources of electric current—chemical action, turbine and generated electricity; galvanoscope; Faraday's experiments; dynamo.

2. Experiences with electric circuits—closed circuits and switch; transformer; electricity produces heat and light; parallel and series circuits; fluorescent tubes; short circuits, insulation, fuses; safety rules.

Seventh and eighth grades

Unit: Making Work Easier[6]

HOW CAN ELECTRICITY MAKE WORK EASIER?

What is electricity (21.1, 21.3)

How can electricity be produced from chemicals? (13.1, 13.2)

How can electricity be made from magnetism? (21.5, 21.6, 21.6f)

How can electricity be made to do work? (21.5, 22.1, 22.2, 13.3)

[6] Since the previous course of study was K-6, we have adapted a unit from *General Science 7–8–9,* Board of Education, New York City, 1959.

Ninth grade

Unit: Improving Communication[7]

HOW MAY SIGNALS BE SENT BY MEANS OF WIRES AND RADIO WAVES?

How does an electric gong work? (21.5)

How does a simple telegraph circuit work? (22.1)

How does a telephone work? (22.1)

How are radio waves used to send messages? (22.2)

IN WHAT WAYS ARE RADIO AND TELEVISION ALIKE AND DIFFERENT? (22.2)

Suggestions for individual and committee projects: telegraph key and sounder; electric chime; code practice oscillator; crystal or one-tube radio set; transistor radio; photoelectric counter. (Chapters 21, 22)

With an understanding of the curriculum pattern from kindergarten through ninth grade, teachers of physics can plan a sequence for a unit on electricity.

Eleventh or twelfth grade: physics

Unit: Electricity[8] (Chapter 21)

I. Static electricity
Electrostatic forces; Atomic structure (6.2, 6.3); Nature of an electric charge

II. The electric current
Conditions necessary for a current; The ampere; The volt; Conductors, insulators, and laws of resistance; Ohm's law; The ohm; Circuits—series, parallel, series-parallel combinations, internal resistance and line drop; Electrical power and energy—heat, the watt, the volt and energy, electrical energy (17.5, 21.5, Chapters 13, 21, 22)

III. (Topical outline of magnetism omitted here)

IV. Induced electromotive force
Factors determining its magnitude; Lenz's law; Generators; Motors

Unit: Alternating Current and Electronics (Chapters 21, 22)

I. Alternating current circuits
A. Measuring a.c.: A.c. meters; Ohm's law

B. Inductance: Induced e.m.f.; inductance; factors determining current

C. Mutual induction: Induction coils; transformers; power transmission

D. Capacitors and capacitance: Dependence of charge on e.m.f. and capacitance; factors determining capacitance; effects of capacitors in d.c. circuits; effect of capacitors in a.c. circuits

E. Resonant circuits: Transfer of energy between L and C; frequency determined by L and C; response to excitation

II. Vacuum tubes (Chapter 22)
Thermionic emission; Diodes and their construction; Triodes and their construction

III. Radio
The RF carrier; Modulation: AM, FM; Transmission; The receiver

IV. Television
Frequencies used; Picture formation

V. Optional: applications of electrons
Photoelectric effect; Conduction in gases; X-rays; Transistors

An examination of the sequence of ideas developed in the areas of magnetism and electricity throughout the grades (as already described for kindergarten through high school physics) reveals many basic concepts as well as applications that need not be repeated in the same context in senior high school classes.

It will be found that many of the *theoretical* aspects of physics can be developed in greater detail in high school physics. Study of many courses of instruction and of patterns used throughout the country indicates a wide variety of approaches. Observe the manner in which the more theoretical aspects of physical science are developed in the experimental course developed by the Physical Science Study Committee of Educational Services, Inc., at Massachusetts Institute of Technology.[9]

Descriptions of some techniques in

[7] Ibid.

[8] Adapted from one unit of *Physics Course of Study,* New York State Education Department, Albany, N.Y., 1957.

[9] *Physics,* Physical Science Study Committee, D. C. Heath, Boston, 1960.

teaching a course whose curriculum pattern has a PSSC orientation are presented in this book. Observe the sequence of topics on wave mechanics in the PSSC course.

Water waves: Ripple-tank techniques (20.2); the study of waves (20.2b)

Straight and circular waves: Propagation of waves, reflection of straight and circular waves, circular waves in an ellipse (20.2b)

Refraction: Refraction, demonstrating a refracted beam of light, Snell's law (20.1d)

Dispersion: Prisms, student-made prisms (20.1e); color dispersion by a prism (20.5a)

Diffraction: Huygens' principle and diffraction in the ripple tank (20.2b); thin film diffraction (20.5b)

Interference: Interference in the ripple tank (20.5b)

Interference from a two-point source: Two-point interference in the ripple tank (20.5b)

Shape of nodal lines: Study of waves in the ripple tank (20.5b)

Wave lengths, source separation, and angles: Interference in the ripple tank (20.2b); measuring the wave length of any part of the visible spectrum (20.5b)

Phase: Standing waves in the ripple tank (20.2b)

As youngsters have advanced through a total curriculum pattern in science, there has been more often an emphasis on things they can see, manipulate, and build —areas within the scope of physics rather than of chemistry per se. However, students have some introductory facts and some broad concepts about rocks and minerals, water, and air and its gaseous composition.

Teachers planning a curriculum sequence in chemistry will build upon the concepts gleaned in lower grades. And if chemistry is taught as a twelfth-grade subject after physics, students come to chemistry classes with a wealth of experiences, so that more theoretical work can be developed in chemistry. Teachers will

want to peruse the Chemical Education Materials Study (CHEM Study) which was initiated at the University of California in 1960 with Dr. Glenn Seaborg as chairman. The current director of the CHEM Study is Dr. J. Arthur Campbell. Another study under way is the Chemical Bonds Approach Course (CBAC) for beginning chemistry students. The current director of the CBAC study is Dr. Lawrence Strong, Earlham College, Richmond, Ind.[10]

Examples of techniques and procedures within the lesson

Just as the use of techniques and procedures is expressed in teaching patterns known as "syllabuses" or "courses of study" or "curriculums," so the use of various laboratory and field techniques and procedures may be expressed in patterns in the classroom. Again this depends on the special situation in which the teacher finds himself, and his personal preferences. There is no one best way, and no one way. *Below are various ways, just for example.*

As a self-demonstration. Many teachers use procedures which give students directions to guide them in a learning activity. The following guide to activity, described in the text on p. 257, can be revised by the teacher so that it is addressed to the student. Questions to test understandings may be incorporated, and the whole guide mimeographed for distribution.

WET CELL: Students can make a wet-type sal ammoniac cell by standing a carbon rod and a strip of zinc sheeting (or the zinc case of an old dry cell) in a jar of saturated ammonium chloride solution. The zinc should be clean. A carbon rod from an old dry cell may be used; it

[10] Many of the techniques useful for developing some of the traditional as well as the more theoretical aspects of chemistry are presented in this book in Chapters 1, 2, 3, 4, and 6–15.

should first be heated to red heat to drive out impurities and then cooled before using. This cell will provide current for several hours. The cell can be renewed by reheating the carbon rod to depolarize it.

How could you establish continuous depolarization? What difference is there in the operating life of a cell with and without a depolarizer?

As an exercise in planning an experiment. Sometimes a teacher may modify a technique described as a demonstration, and thereby turn it to another purpose.

VARYING THE ACTIVITY SERIES OF METALS. GROUP II: Instead of having students read a technique in advance, some teachers will, on occasion, elicit methodology from students. For example, after students examine the periodic table, they can explore the generalization that in a given period progress from left to right in the periodic system results in a decrease in metallic properties.

In a study of Group II, students can be given materials and asked to devise a method for showing the varying activity of magnesium, calcium, and sodium. See method described on p. 121.

As a specific exercise in planning controls. Students learn to use this method of scientists by "doing."

SIMULATING LAVOISIER'S EXPERIMENT. Students may simulate Lavoisier's work in which mercury is heated to form mercuric oxide. Use a Florence flask fitted with a one-hole cork which carries a ¼″ diameter delivery tube bent to the shape shown in Fig. 7–3A. Place a weighed quantity (1 to 5 grams) of mercury in the flask. Arrange the delivery tube in a basin of mercury or water, and place a glass cylinder over the end of the tube as shown. Now remove some air from the cylinder by means of a small rubber tube and exhaust pump. (A rubber tube and mouth suction can also do the job.) Mark the level of the liquid which has risen into the cylinder. Heat the Florence flask on an electric heating device or a Bunsen burner arranged so that the flask is heated slowly and continuously. After several days of slow heating, students should see that some mercury has disappeared and that some

red mercuric oxide has formed. The volume of gas in the cylinder will decrease, indicating the removal of a gas.

The complete description is given on pp. 131–32.

As a simple investigation. This kind of activity may be used as a teacher demonstration or a student project.[11]

HOW CAN CHARLES' LAW BE DEMONSTRATED? A group of students may build the apparatus for this investigation. They will need to prepare a scale marked in millimeters on a piece of cardboard. To this attach a closed-end "J" manometer which has been prepared as follows. Partially fill it with the oil used in a vacuum pump (available from scientific supply houses). Heat its closed end with a candle (a Bunsen burner is too hot) to drive the trapped air into the oil. Allow to cool. This may have to be repeated several times until the length of trapped air measures between 2½″ and 3½″ (See Fig. 1–8). Attach the inverted tube and a centigrade thermometer to the cardboard scale in such a manner that the mm scale lies along the column of trapped air. Thin copper wire can be used to make the attachment. Insert the cardboard and its tubes into 1½″ diameter test tube which in turn is suspended from a ring stand into a beaker of water. The water level should be above the J-tube. Add ice to the water.

The complete description is given on pp. 9–10.

As a plan for a field trip. Throughout this book, specific procedures are suggested for undertaking field trips to industrial plants, museums, planetariums, and other places of interest. For example, suggestions have been made to plan trips to quarries, excavations, a chlorination plant concerned with the purification of water. Trips may be made by a class, by individual students on weekends, or as a club activity. Be sure to obtain permission notes from parents if the trip is under the supervision of teachers.

[11] You will find many projects suggested throughout this sourcebook. See also Philip Goldstein, *How to Do an Experiment,* Harcourt, Brace, 1957.

As suggestions for preparing models or laboratory apparatus. There are many models and apparatus to use in class in addition to charts and commercial devices. Many such are suggested throughout this book.

A MODEL OF THE SOLAR SYSTEM: A model can be made from a Tinkertoy set, using an electric socket and bulb to represent the sun, and spheres of different sizes (rubber balls or balloons) to represent the planets (Fig. 5-23). Slip seventeen Tinkertoy hubs over a length of Tinkertoy stick mounted in a hole in the center of a wooden baseboard. (Nine of these are for the planets, and eight serve as spacers between each pair of planet hubs.) Then mount the socket on the top of this stick. An aluminum or other light metal rod is inserted into every other hub, and carries a sphere representing the planet. Each rod is bent in such a way that they can bypass one another. (The relative sizes of the spheres, approximately proportional to the planet, are given in Table 5-1.)

As a project for a class. This may be done by groups outside of class time. You will find other projects that are especially applicable to groups suggested throughout this book.

TAKING STROBOSCOPIC PICTURES: Students can begin with an erector set (Fig. 20-67) and use a rubber band for the belt; as an upper pulley on the shaft, roll on masking tape tightly to form a shaft of ¼″ diameter. For the large bottom pulley, students can use two small paint can covers or a 2″ pulley.

On the upper shaft place a 3″ heavy cardboard disk with four equally spaced ½″ openings. To calibrate the instrument find out the number of turns made by the disk for one revolution of the crank. Multiplying this by the number of ½″ openings gives you the total number of openings per revolution of the crank. Operate the crank for 15 seconds; during this interval count the number of revolutions. Multiply this by four to equate the motions to revolutions per minute; then multiply the number of revolutions by the calibration previously made to find the speed per minute.

The photographic process makes it possible to "freeze" various positions of the object as seen through the disk stroboscope. (See Fig. 20-68).

The remainder of this technique is described on p. 492.

Example of techniques and procedures in extending the lesson

Homework. Sometimes students raise questions, or the teacher finds it desirable to extend the lesson into the home. Several kinds of procedures have been found useful. Usually the student does not have the apparatus at home to carry on experimentation or self-demonstration. Procedures for which apparatus is readily available—e.g., collecting rock specimens, building from electrical parts available at home or from supply stores—will of course be used. However, there are paper and pencil procedures which stress various aspects of investigative techniques in science. Here is one example. You will find other similar types throughout the book.

MEASURING BOY POWER: As an assignment, one student or a small committee might compute a student's horsepower. Students will need instructions as a guide. These may be elicited in planning the assignment. One student who owns a bicycle might lend it to the group for this activity. The students will need to measure the diameter of the circle through which the pedals revolve, and also measure the push of each foot (by having a seated student press alternately with each foot on a bathroom-type scale). Average the two forces. Then the same student will need to ride the bicycle at full speed for 10 seconds, counting the number of revolutions of the pedals. Students need to be reminded to multiply by six to convert this into rpm; then multiply together the force measured earlier, the circumference of the pedals, and the rpm of the pedals. What is the final conversion needed to find the horsepower developed by a student? (See p. 381.)

Simple projects. Apparatus may be devised from materials at hand.

A CLASSROOM WIND TUNNEL: A committee of students working in a club, or on a project out of school, can build a model wind tunnel for demonstrating principles of aerodynamics. The students will need an electric fan, a square carton, some manila folders, and a platform balance. In Fig. 24-12 the apparatus is shown as a guide for student construction.

Students can measure forces on the model wings that are to be tested by using a balance. Cover each pan of the balance with a layer of wood about 2″ thick; drill a hole in the center of the wood cover for the left-hand pan and insert a wood dowel. The wings to be tested can be attached to the dowel by means of a thumb screw (Fig. 24-13). (See pp. 581–82).

Building apparatus. One procedure is given below. Other types are suggested throughout the book.

MAKING A SIREN DISK: Sometimes students may build a piece of equipment that can become a fine demonstration piece, and that can give students a chance to test their learnings. As an example, if a student is interested in building a siren disk, you may want to offer these directions as a guide.

Cut a perfect circle with a radius of about 7″ from a piece of stiff, straight cardboard. Using the center of the disk as the center of concentric circles, draw 4 circles with radii of exactly 1½″, 3″, 4½″, and 6″, respectively. Using a good protractor, measure off successive 60° angles around the center so that you can divide the disk into 6 equal "pie" segments.

Working first with the innermost (1½″ radius) circle, place a sharp pencil dot at each intersection of the circle with the segment lines (Fig. 19-26). This gives 6 equally spaced points. With a protractor and dividers or a compass, mark off 3 equally spaced dots between each segment dot. This will give you 24 equally spaced holes.

Repeat the procedure on the next circle outward, except that you must mark 4 equally spaced dots between each segment dot to yield 30 dots altogether.

Specifications for the next circles are given on p. 444.

Inventory-type projects. There are many projects which do not require ap-

paratus. Individual field trip investigations wherein students make a study of all the devices at home that use an electromagnet, or a trip to a garage to study the ignition system, cooling system, or lubrication of a car are some examples. Other projects are collecting several soil samples to be tested with indicators in the laboratory; testing the pH of vinegar, of aquarium water; cleaning silverware at home; applying the technique of paper chromatography to food dyes.

Examples of techniques and procedures for long-term projects

Clearly we have not exhausted even the most common patterns involving the use of laboratory techniques and procedures as employed by teachers. But we cannot ignore patterns which involve long-term investigations. The example below is included here to show the nature of an investigation which takes two to three years and which is "original" in the high school meaning of the term. The reader will not fail to note that the student began with a simple technique (which helped resolve a relatively simple problem), then evolved the problem into a full-scale investigation.

One abstract follows, of the type of project that many students find challenging to their creative abilities and that has been accomplished through persistence.

BIOCHEMISTRY OF VINEGAR[12]

I undertook vinegar-making as a project because of its biochemical aspect. It can be studied for both its enzymatic and bacterial reaction with a possibility of producing a large variety of acceptable vinegars. The possibility of vinegar

[12] Report by Ronald Gates (age 17), Columbus High School, Marshfield, Wisc. This paper was abstracted by Science Service, Washington, D.C., from the Westinghouse Science Talent Search entries.

varieties became an additional interest to me due to the increasing popularity in many Wisconsin areas of serving vinegar with special cheese menus.

The main methods used in the vinegar industry today are the Quick Vinegar Process and the much older Orleans Method. I used both methods with some modifications of my own, introduced because of the limited quantity of vinegar produced in each of my yields and also because of the kind of generating material I used. With the Orleans Method the yields were maintained at approximately one quart, but in the Quick Process the yields were reduced by one half mainly to increase the number of runs per day.

I made 22 different kinds of vinegar: six with the Quick Vinegar Process (Table 1); fifteen with the Orleans Method modified, and one original variety from cattail roots according to a formula I arranged (Table 2). All vinegar samples in this project were obtained from the following substances either fresh or dried:

1. Fruits and vegetables:
   a. Plums, elderberries, high bush cranberry, grapes, apples (as cider), pineapple, sumac berries, beets;
   b. Carob pods with raisins and alcohol as well as plums and alcohol
2. Grain: malt
3. Flowers: dandelion flowers with oranges and lemons
4. Sugar: honey and brown sugar
5. Root: cattail rhizomes

Since the Quick Vinegar Process depends on the circulation of an alcoholic feed during the time of its oxidation to acetic acid, I had to provide a suitable apparatus for it (Figure 1). Consequently, I built an all glass generator modeled after the glass experimental vinegar generators described in the *Vinegar News Letter* by F. M. Hildebrandt but with considerable innovations of my own . . .

I was unable to follow the Orleans Method as it is usually practiced. So I reduced its rather laborous procedure to a few simple steps by which it was possible to prepare the generating material from crushed fruit, dissolved sugar and yeast in quantities small enough to be allowed to ferment in quart fruit jars (Figure 1) over a

period of six to eight weeks at 70–75° F. When it was evident that fermentation action was completed, vinegar bacteria was added as a starter for the acidification step. Clarifying of the mixture indicated when the acid conversion was finished, at which point the filtered vinegar sample was pasteurized at 140° F. The length of time for both the fermentation and acidification varied from sample to sample. However, in spite of the fact that the Orleans Method is slow, I obtained some of my most aromatic samples with it . . .

The last part of the project provided a series of interesting observations of the bacteria and enzymes occurring in vinegar-making. I observed that the *Acetobacter xylinum* grown in the Orleans samples appeared similar to that taken from a pure culture of *xylinum* (Figures 3, 4) appearing as small thin rods occurring in groups. The shorter and somewhat thicker rod bacteria found in samples from both processes I identified as possible *Acetobacter pasterianum* (Figure 5). Bacteria from the top and bottom of the Quick Vinegar generator showed some difference in shape. Cultures made from the bacteria grown on the beechwood shavings of the generator were found to be non-motile and arranged in pairs or singly in large numbers. Their negative response to iodine staining identifies them with the *Acetobacter schützenbachii* bacteria common to generators . . .

Titles of other papers that have been submitted in a country-wide science talent search (Westinghouse):

1. "New Positive Qualitative Differentiation of the Sodium and Potassium Ions by the Application of F-centers," Donald Fox, West High School, Phoenix, Ariz.
2. "A Point-emitter Colliding-Beam Proton Accelerator," John Wheeler, Idaho Falls High School, Idaho Falls, Id.
3. "Enzyme-substrate Complex," Thomas McGivern, Highland Park High School, Highland Park, Ill.
4. "Gas Chromatographic Determination of Free Energy in 1-Chloro-1-propene," Roger Peters, Central High School, South Bend, Ind.
5. "Determining Index of Refraction of a Solid from Its Solution by Means of the Michel-

son Interferometer," Bernard Barisas, Southwest High School, Kansas City, Mo.

6. "Design and Construction of Two Computers: The Quadraticator and Geometron," William Rothman, Erasmus High School, Brooklyn, N.Y.

7. "The Extraction and Chromatographic Separation of Plant Pigments," Karen Wurstlin, Columbia High School, East Greenbush, N.Y.

8. "Effects of Gamma Radiation on Deformed Sapphire Crystals," Michael Steinitz, Harrison High School, Harrison, N.Y.

9. "Hydrogen-oxygen Fuel Cell," Charles Hora, Bedford Sr. High School, Bedford, Ohio.

10. "A Transistorized pH Meter," Robert Peterson, Abington Sr. High School, Abington, Pa.

A word in closing

What we have been trying to indicate is that while science does mean "doing one's damnedest with one's mind, no holds barred,"[13] the fruits of science are developed in the deed. Brain and muscle, mind and hand are in constant collaboration.

Science is not "chalk-talk"; it is *experience in search of meaning*. In this section we have tried to indicate how certain techniques can be fitted into some patterns which are characteristic of the science teacher's approach to teaching science. As we have said, the entire text is given over to a description of activities which encompass a vast range of experience which serves this search for meaning.

[13] P. W. Bridgman, *Yale Review,* XXXIV, 444–61, 1945.

Section One PHYSICAL SCIENCE

CHAPTER 1

Molecular motions and forces

The concept of moving molecules, of molecules acting on each other, is basic to the student's understanding of matter. Most students have already developed some notions concerning molecules before meeting these concepts formally in class. Since their ideas may be inaccurate, you may need several lessons to present evidence of molecular motion and forces. The demonstration of one substance intermingling with another by means of diffusion can be an excellent introduction to molecular motion.

1.1 Diffusion

Have a student open a bottle of ammonia or perfume and then ask the students to raise their hands when they can smell the substance. Why don't all students raise their hands at the same time? Also

streak down the blackboard with a wet sponge. What becomes of the water as the board dries? Have the students explain water evaporation in terms of separate molecules. What happens to the crystals of paradichlorobenzene that are packed with stored woolens? Students can also explain what becomes of dry ice exposed to air. Elicit from this that the movement of particles is not visible because individual molecules are many times smaller than the smallest thing that can be seen under the optical microscope.

1.1a Diffusion in air

Place a few crystals of iodine in a large, stoppered Pyrex test tube and heat gently in a flame. Students should be able to see the purple vapor and the re-formation of crystals on the sides of the test tube. Molecules have moved.

Heat makes molecules move faster. This may be the time to lead into a discussion of the three states of matter: gas, liquid, and solid. Make a comparison of the relative molecular velocities in solids, liquids, and gases, then have students review the comparison so as to emphasize the concept that kinetic energy increases with increasing temperature.

Some teachers prefer the following demonstration because the whole class can see it. With a forceps place one gram of iodine in a 100-cc dry beaker supported by wire gauze on a ring stand. (If iodine touches the skin, wash off with ethyl alcohol.) Place an evaporating dish containing some water on the top of the beaker. Gently heat. Does any iodine melt? What is the purple gas? Examine the crystals on the underside of the evaporating dish. Students should be ready to use the kinetic theory to explain these changes.

Bring the wet stopper of a bottle of concentrated hydrochloric acid near the wet stopper of a bottle of concentrated ammonium hydroxide. As the two stoppers are brought near, but not touching, students should see a "white cloud" as ammonium chloride is formed. Again, molecules have moved (or diffused) from place to place, and the ammonium hydroxide and hydrochloric acid have reacted to form ammonium chloride and water. The white "smoke" is ammonium chloride.

This same reaction can be shown in another dramatic manner using a glass tube approximately ½" in diameter and open at both ends. Dampen two wads of cotton, one with hydrochloric acid and the other with ammonium hydroxide leaving enough surplus cotton to protect the fingers and then simultaneously plug each end of the tube with the dampened wads. The fumes of each substance will travel along the tube and where they meet a white ring of ammonium chloride will be formed. This might be an excellent time to ask the students to judge from the position of the white ring which moved more rapidly, the molecules of hydrochloric acid or of ammonium hydroxide.

You may also want to show the action of paradichlorobenzene crystals. Place a thin layer of these crystals in a Pyrex beaker and cover with a watchglass containing some cold water. Heat the crystals gently. Students can explain that the crystals turned to a gas, and then condensed on the bottom of the watchglass as new crystals. Molecules have moved from place to place.

1.1b Diffusion in a liquid

Place a piece of copper sulfate into a tall jar of water and let it stand in a conspicuous place in the classroom for several days. Have students observe the slow dispersion of the color throughout the container. In a similar demonstration, students may use a long pipette to place a drop of red dye (or a few drops of potassium permanganate solution) at the bottom of a tall jar of water leaving the water undisturbed. Students may think of many variations for further demonstration.

1.1c "A chemist's garden"

You may want to show the way silicates form from seed crystals. First cover the bottom of a 600-cc beaker, or its rough equivalent such as a fruit jar, with a ⅛" to ¼" layer of sand. Over this pour a solution made up of 100 cc of sodium silicate (water glass) in 400 cc of water. The specific gravity of this solution should be approximately 1.1. Sprinkle into this solution a small quantity of iron and copper chlorides, nitrates, and sulfates. These particles should be no larger than the head of a pin. Have the students watch the growth of the colorful "flowers" which should start forming within a half hour. As the crystals spread they become covered with a semipermeable metal silicate layer which permits the diffusion of water into the mass but prevents the diffusion of salt molecules outward. Very rapidly the crystals rupture because of internal pressure and so build upward layer on layer. In a few days the crystals of silicate will have grown into a multicolored "garden" which can be preserved by carefully siphoning off the water glass solution and replacing it with clear water. Students should be ready to explain the "garden's" growth in terms of molecular movement. (For another type of demonstration of molecular movement see 14.6 on paper chromatography.)

1.1d Using indicators to show diffusion

First demonstrate the action of ammonium hydroxide. Add 5 cc of water to test tube containing a drop of phenolphthalein solution. Soak a strip of filter paper in the phenolphthalein water and make it adhere to the inside of a long, carefully rinsed test tube. Invert this tube over an open bottle of ammonium hydroxide. Students should observe within a few minutes the reddening of the filter paper. Molecules have moved from the bottle up into the inverted test tube.

As a variation students can substitute a strip of wet red litmus paper for the filter paper. Why does the litmus paper turn blue when the tube is inverted over the ammonium hydroxide?

Here is a colorful demonstration that can be left undisturbed for a few days so that students can observe and be ready to explain what happens. Dissolve a small quantity of blue litmus powder in water, add a few drops of ammonium hydroxide, and half fill a tall cylinder. Now turn the rest of the litmus solution red by adding a few cc of acid. Introduce this acidulated water into the bottom of the tall cylinder by pouring it through a thistle tube that reaches to the bottom. In the beginning students should see a sharp line separating the red and blue solutions. What has happened after a few days?

1.1e Diffusion through a membrane

Fill a large test tube with water and add a few drops of alcoholic phenolphthalein (preparation, 8.4f); stretch a wet goldbeater's membrane or very thin cellophane over the mouth of the tube and fasten in place with a rubber band. (If cellophane is plastic-coated, remove film with 90% alcohol.) Stand this tube inverted over an open bottle of 5 to 10 per cent ammonium hydroxide (Fig. 1–1). Within seconds students should observe the reddish cloud which rises quickly through the length of the test tube. As molecules of ammonia gas diffuse through

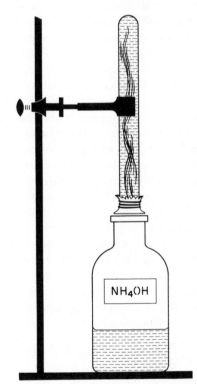

Fig. 1–1 Diffusion of ammonium hydroxide through a membrane into water containing phenolphthalein solution.

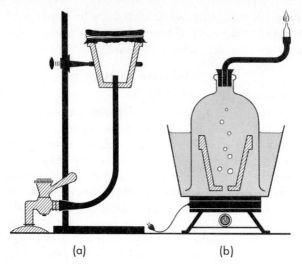

Fig. 1-2 Gas is first absorbed by the porous clay pot (a) and then, when this clay pot is immersed in boiling water (b), it gives up the gas.

(a)   (b)

the membrane, the phenolphthalein indicator in the solution changes from colorless to red.

Students may also show that, under some circumstances, certain molecules will pass through a membrane while others will not pass through. Prepare a dilute starch suspension (1 per cent); to this add a teaspoon of table salt. Fill several large test tubes with this mixture, stretch a wet membrane across the mouth of each tube, and secure each with a rubber band. Now insert each tube into a beaker containing a small quantity of water. After fifteen minutes test samples of water for the presence of starch with dilute iodine or Lugol's solution. Test another water sample with a drop of silver nitrate for the presence of salt. There is no positive reaction with the starch test but a white precipitate forms in the test for the salt. From this students should deduce that salt has diffused through the membrane and starch has not and so should observe that substances can diffuse independently.

1.1f *Diffusion of a gas through a solid*

Repeat the demonstration which used a strip of filter paper soaked in phenol-phthalein (1.1d), but cover the mouth of the bottle of ammonium hydroxide with a sheet of filter paper. Students should notice that ammonia molecules pass through the filter paper. Next substitute a sheet of wet membrane in place of the filter paper.

Another demonstration designed to show diffusion through a solid utilizes carbon disulfide and a balloon. Suspend an inflated balloon over a battery jar containing a shallow layer of carbon disulfide. (*Caution: Carbon disulfide is inflammable.*) After a half hour, remove the balloon and cut it open or turn it inside out. Students should smell the strong onionlike odor of the carbon disulfide which has diffused into the balloon. The vapor has passed by diffusion through the spaces between the large rubber molecules.

You may want to show diffusion of a gas through a solid such as a porous flower pot. Seal off the top of a red clay flower pot with a secured rubber sheet and then through its drainage hole connect the flower pot to an outlet of natural or illuminating gas (Fig. 1-2A). (*Caution: Be sure there are no sparks or flames in the room.*) After a few minutes shut off the gas, remove the pot, and immerse it, without its rubber sheet cover, in a container of hot water under a bell jar fitted with a delivery tube. Gas molecules that have diffused into the clay are now released and are displaced by the heavier water molecules. The molecules rise to the top of the bell jar and thence up the delivery tube and out the glass jet where the gas can be ignited (Fig. 1–2B).

Other demonstrations of diffusion, particularly those related to diffusion through animal or plant cell membranes, can be prepared by students. For example, they may core a raw carrot, fill it with molasses, and cork it with a stopper through which a foot-length of glass tubing has been inserted. Now place the carrot upright in a container of water and clamp in place. Within a few hours students should observe the rise of fluid in the glass tube. Mark the level, and an hour later record the distance the fluid has risen. Students may substitute a thistle tube containing molasses for the cored carrot. Stretch a wet membrane across the mouth of the tube and fasten with rubber bands and then clamp in place so that the bulb of the tube is under water. Other demonstrations of the osmosis of water molecules through membranes may be found in the companion volume.[1]

1.2   Brownian motion

Although molecular motion cannot be observed directly, a number of its effects can be observed. Students can see the result of collisions between molecules and microscopic particles.

1.2a   In liquids

Students may repeat Robert Brown's demonstration in which he suspended spores or pollen grains in water and then

[1] *Teaching High School Science: A Sourcebook for the Biological Sciences*, Morholt, Brandwein, Joseph (Harcourt, Brace, 1958).

examined their motion under the microscope. Mushroom and moss spores and pollen can be gotten from biological supply houses of which many are listed in the appendix. A small amount of carmine red powder or India ink added to a drop of water can be examined microscopically by students as another demonstration of this phenomenon. Although Brown thought that the moving specks he saw were molecules, we know today that what he saw were microscopic particles (spores) set in random motion by collisions with the invisible molecules of water.

1.2b   In gases

Evacuated tubes made of heat-resistant glass, containing a small quantity of mercury and covered with a thin layer of small, lightweight blue glass chips, are available from supply houses. Gently heat such a tube. As the mercury evaporates, its heavy fast-moving molecules leaving the liquid surface strike against the glass chips thus propelling them into the empty space above (Fig. 1–3A). The faster-moving molecules project some of the glass chips to the top of the tube; other chips are driven by slower molecules only a short distance. Plotting the heights of the glass particles against the number at each height, will produce a normal curve of distribution. With this evidence before them this might be a good time to elicit from students the notion that heat increases the kinetic energy of molecules.

A similar tube may be prepared readily in class. Put about a half inch of mercury into a 12″ Pyrex test tube and add a layer of minute colored glass chips, beads, or bits of balsa wood as in Fig. 1–3B. (Do not use plastic beads; they will melt.) To keep the poisonous mercury vapor out of the classroom atmosphere close up this tube with a one-hole stopper. From this stopper run a long piece of glass tubing to a large test

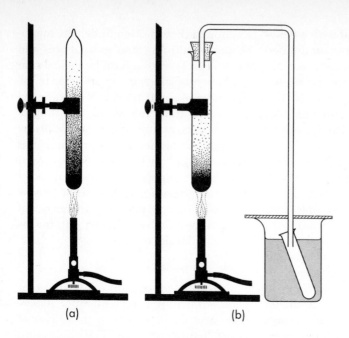

(a)   (b)

Fig. 1–3 Heating mercury to show the effects of rapidly moving molecules striking tiny glass chips.

tube standing in a beaker of cold water. This will condense any escaping mercury vapor. Cover the condensing test tube with a loosely fitted sheet of cardboard making a small hole in it for the glass tubing which leads from the apparatus containing the mercury.

Since the tube containing mercury is not evacuated as the commercial model is, slightly more heat will be needed to get the molecules into motion, but the final results are the same. It is possible to evacuate the air in the tube with a vacuum pump as the mercury is gently heated, but students may think that the evacuation causes the motion of the chips.

1.2c A smoke box

A small smoke box may be used by individuals for microscope observation of Brownian motion of carbon particles in smoke. Smoke boxes are available from supply houses or can be made by students. In the commercial box, focus a beam of light through a side window while cigarette smoke or smoke from touch paper is sucked into the box by a syringe tube (Fig. 1–4). A pen-type flashlight is ideal as a light source because its bulb has a small lens at the tip. Move the flashlight back and forth to focus it and then tape it to the microscope stage or other nearby support. It may be necessary to try several concentrations of smoke; if it is too dense, too much light will be scattered.

As a substitute for the commercial model you may use a small match box. Cut a hole in the top for the microscope, taping cellophane over this hole. Cut a hole in one side of the box to admit a beam of light from the pen-type flashlight. Cover this hole, too, with cellophane. Now make another hole in the opposite side of the box, and attach to it a small rubber tube (Fig. 1–5A). Smoke is blown in through this tube. On the side opposite the rubber tube make a small hole and lead-out tube for the escape of the smoke.

Students can make a more durable smoke box out of a small block of Lucite plastic about 2″ by ½″ in size (Fig. 1–5B). First drill two holes: one centered in the top approximately ½″ in diameter and in depth about three quarters of the way through the block's thickness, and the other hole in one end just large enough to admit a rubber tube snugly and drilled deep enough to be connected with the first hole. Polish the large center hole with a fine grit of the type used to finish telescope mirrors. Follow this with jeweler's rouge until the inside of the hole is optically clear. Drill a third hole 90° to the right or left of the small hole drilled in one end of the block. This will act as an escape vent and should connect with the center chamber. Its diameter should be about ⅛″. This done, coat all the outside surfaces of the plastic block with black lacquer except two circles: one at the bottom, to admit light to the microscope lens, and one opposite the smoke hole, to admit light from a pen-type flashlight. Cement a thin sheet of clear plastic over the large center hole. Finally fit a small rubber tube to the smoke hole. The box is used in the same way as the commercial model.

Plastic spheres of extreme fineness called microballoons are sold by the Bakelite Company.[2] A pinch dusted into the smoke box through a 2-mm hole in the top center of the smoke box,[3] these spheres will appear

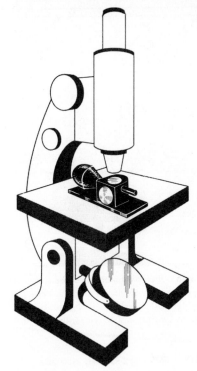

Fig. 1–4 Commercial smoke box mounted on microscope stage.

as individual particles when viewed through a microscope. Once they are made visible by the beam of light flashed from one side of the box, they can be seen to jiggle in place from the Brownian movement of the air molecules.

Similar observations can be made using very fine arrowroot starch powder.

[2] Bakelite Company, Division of Union Carbide Corporation, 30 E. 42, New York, N.Y.
[3] Demonstrations developed with Prof. A. Beiser of New York University Physics Dept. and Dr. A. Joseph of Physics Dept., Bronx Community College.

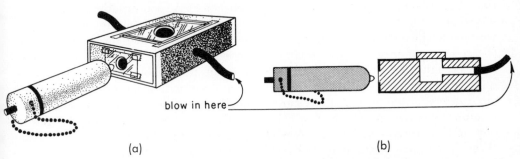

blow in here

(a)   (b)

Fig. 1–5 Two kinds of smoke box: (a) from a match box, (b) from a block of clear plastic.

Fig. 1–6 Brownian motion can be represented by ping-pong balls moving in an air stream. (Adapted from "chaos" machines designed by M.I.T. and PSSC of Educational Services, Inc.)

1.2d A large-scale model

For an assembly program or other group meeting, students can make a large-scale model of molecules in motion. Use a covered square wooden box at least 2 feet on each edge. Mount a heavy-duty fan (at least ½ hp) at the bottom so that the blades will rotate horizontally (Fig. 1–6). Just above the fan blades attach a sheet of ½" wire mesh horizontally, thus dividing the box into two compartments. Now replace one side of the box with a pane of glass or clear plastic sheeting so that the action inside the box can be observed. Fill the box above the chicken wire-mesh with 50 to 100 ping-pong balls. (Since the roundness is not critical, the cheaper Japanese ping-pong balls are quite satisfactory.) When the fan is turned on, students can see the balls in a chaos of random collisions, varied speeds, and indeterminate directions of motion. A good three-dimensional animated model of Brownian motion can be shown by adding

a few dark-colored balls and noting their erratic movements.

1.3 Kinetic theory of gases

The demonstrations of diffusion and Brownian motion may serve to introduce students to the basic theory concerning molecular motion and heat. We assume that in a solid the molecules have insufficient kinetic energy to overcome the molecular forces that attract each to each.

1.3a "Chaos" machine[4]

A simply built "chaos" machine developed at Massachusetts Institute of Technology for elementary physics classes might be of interest to your students (Fig. 1–7). Marbles used to simulate molecules are set in motion so that they strike an irregularly shaped piece of flat viscose sponge causing it to move about with the random jerkiness characteristic of a particle in Brownian motion.

A flat board about 12" × 12" can serve as the base. The motor is attached at the lower left corner of the base with the shaft tightly inserted into the center of one end of a 10" × 1" × 1" length of hardwood. Support the other end of this length by means of a nail and brass angle so that the wooden length when rotated just clears the base. In series into the motor circuit place a rheostat for d.c. or a variable voltage transformer for a.c. (12 v or 6 v to match the motor). A good variable voltage transformer is provided with toy electric train sets. About the other three edges of the base place 1½" × 1½" wooden lengths. Drop in the marbles (or steel balls) and then cover with a sheet of ¼" or thicker of glass or plastic supported by the lengths of wood that border the base. Adjust the motor speed for the best analog of molecular motion.

[4] Developed by Albert Baez of PSSC.

To illustrate Brownian motion place a flat viscose sponge in the center. As the agitated balls which represent molecules in random motion strike the sponge, it will be jogged about more or less in the characteristic manner of particles in Brownian motion. This can also be observed through a stroboscope. If the sponge is coated with fluorescent paint and the demonstration is conducted under ultraviolet light in darkness, the sponge will appear to undergo movements similar to those seen through a microscope. (*Warning: Ultraviolet must not be permitted directly to enter the eyes as it may cause detachment of the retina.*)

In the liquid phase, the energy of motion rises and so the molecules are less rigidly held; in gases, the kinetic energy is strong enough virtually to overcome the forces binding the molecules together. You may also want to show that when in a gaseous state a given substance expands taking up more space (volume) than that substance as a solid or liquid, and that a gas increases its pressure as it is heated.

1.3b Introduction to Charles' law

Students will learn that the molecules themselves do not expand, but the space between them increases. For example, cover the mouth of a flask with a rubber balloon and gently heat the flask. Why does the balloon become inflated? (For other work on expansion see 16.3.) Students may compare this with the relative incompressibility of liquids and solids.

The following demonstration of Charles' law[5] can be carried out by groups within a class with apparatus largely built by the group. Prepare a scale marked in millimeters on a piece of cardboard. To this attach a closed-end "J" manometer which has been prepared as follows. Partially fill it with the oil used in a vacuum pump

[5] Adapted from a model developed by Charles L. Bickel at Phillips Exeter Academy.

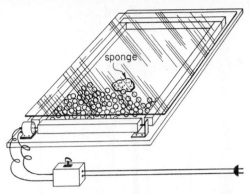

Fig. 1–7 "Chaos" machine in which marbles striking against each other simulate Brownian motion.

(available from scientific supply houses). Heat its closed end with a candle (a Bunsen burner is too hot) to drive the trapped air into the oil. Allow to cool. This may have to be repeated several times until the length of trapped air measures between 2½" and 3½" (See Fig. 1–8). Attach the inverted tube and a centigrade thermometer to the cardboard scale in such a manner that the mm scale lies along the column of trapped air. Thin copper wire can be used to make the attachment. Insert the cardboard and its tubes into 1½" diameter test tube which in turn is suspended from a ring stand into a beaker of water. The water level should be above the J-tube. Add ice to the water.

Now one student can read the volume change as indicated in mm and his partner can read the temperature in degrees centigrade. Record the data for every degree of change until the temperature drops down to about 5° C. This drop will occur in about 10 minutes. Then place the beaker over a source of heat and repeat the experiment with the temperature rising back to the original temperature of the water. Students can convert the centigrade readings to Kelvin by adding 273° and plot the graph down to 0° Kelvin. Do the same for the readings as the tem-

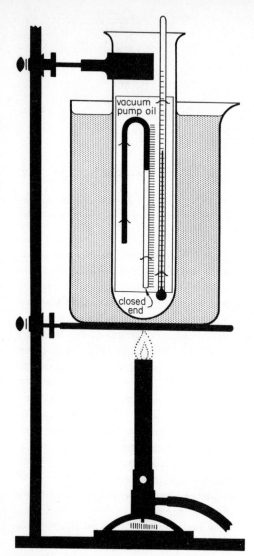

which can also verify this law. It can be done by groups, before the class as a whole, or as a special suggestion to one of your "science-prone" students. Take a capillary tube and trap some air in it by closing off one end completely and positioning a seal of mercury toward the other end, making sure to leave enough tubing for the mercury to move during temperature changes. The amount that the entrapped air expands or contracts can be read against a mm scale to which the capillary tube can be attached. Immerse the tube and scale in a beaker of water; insert a C° thermometer into the water and then by adding ice lower the temperature to about 0° C. Readings of temperature as against air volume can be taken at regular intervals. Then reverse the process by putting the beaker on a hot plate. Heat it until the water about the capillary tube reaches 100° C, again taking regular readings. Computation will show how closely the trapped air has acted in accordance with Charles' law. Allowance should be made for the error that will be caused by the vapor pressure of the mercury.

1.4 Intermolecular forces

1.4a Cohesion

Cohesion is the attraction between like molecules. Very apparent in solids it can also be clearly demonstrated in liquids. Mercury spilled on a tray tends to form "drops." Water, too, forms drops when spilled, and when pushed together these drops of mercury or water immediately combine into larger pools because of this cohesive attraction between molecules. Many of the students may have seen how a camel's-hair brush dipped in water is held to a point by the cohesion of the water molecules. The surface tension of water results from cohesion among its molecules.

Fig. 1-8 Apparatus for demonstrating Charles' law.

perature rises. The plot drawn through all the points should approximate a straight line as is predicted by Charles' law.

Charles' law states that for each degree centigrade or Kelvin that a gas rises in temperature it will expand 1/273 of the volume it would occupy at 0° C (273° Kelvin) provided the pressure remains the same throughout. Here is an experiment very similar to the one just described

1.4b *Surface tension*

Show the strong cohesive force of water molecules, which seem to form a tight "skin" on the surface of a glass of water, by having students carefully add bits of metal or other heavy substances to a "filled" glass of water until they can see the water's surface curve upward from the edge of the glass. Some teachers dramatize this effect by projecting a shadow picture of this "superfilled" glass onto the wall.

Floating a razor blade or needle. Students can carefully lower a thin, double-edged razor blade or needle flat onto the surface of water. If these objects are first made slightly oily by rubbing between the fingers, they will not be made wet by the water. Why do they float? Show that the reason is not due to density by lowering the razor blade end-first, or the needle pointed down. Have students show diagrammatically how the strong attractive force or cohesion of the surface molecules of water acts to form a film. Students should be ready to explain why the object sinks when they place a bit of soap near it.

Reducing surface tension. Students can show that soap reduces surface tension by making a loop out of 5″ of silk thread and then floating it in a low, wide container of water. Touch a bit of wet soap to the water inside of the silk loop and notice that it becomes a circle.

Students can also test the effect of alcohol on surface tension by substituting a drop of alcohol for the soap. What happens if a drop of alcohol is placed on the water between two floating toothpicks?

Wetting agents of the type used in detergents and in photography can be used in place of the materials mentioned here.

Surface tension and water drops. Attach a rubber tube equipped with a pinch clamp to a funnel, or else use a dropping funnel. Adjust the apparatus so that water flows drop by drop. Students should know that surface tension gives the drop its shape. A stroboscope (20.9) can be used to examine the drops closely. In fact, the speed of the stroboscope can be so adjusted as to make the drops appear to stand still.

Surface tension boat. A hollow "boat" made of a 2″ by 1″ piece of aluminum foil, partly filled with a few drops of alcohol and with a ½″ length of lightweight cotton wick (such as is used in a cigarette lighter) over the stern, will skim over water. The alcohol moves down the wick by capillary action; when it reaches the water, it reduces the cohesive force of water molecules and thus breaks the surface tension. As a result, there is less horizontal force behind the boat than in front, and the boat is pushed about. A piece of camphor about the size of a pencil eraser fastened to the stern of a boat made from a 2″ piece of balsa or other soft wood will act the same way. Tiny bits of camphor left to themselves on the water will also be propelled by the imbalance of surface tension.

Surface tension turbine. A surface tension turbine can be made by using a thin 3″ (approx.) aluminum propeller that is pivoted on a pin set on a piece of lead or wax (Fig. 1–9). Cut two notches in the blades, near the tip, but off center, to hold bits of camphor. Students can watch how the propeller is set with the blades and camphor just touching the surface of the water. The breaking of the surface tension by camphor will cause the blades to spin.

Surface tension "defying gravity." Fill a wide mouthed jar with water, cover the mouth with cheesecloth, and fasten securely. Now invert the jar quickly. Why does the water remain in the jar? If you punch a small hole in the cheesecloth with a pointed pencil, water runs out for an instant, but surface tension with the aid of atmospheric pressure "seals" the hole.

Water "sticks" to itself. Here is a quick demonstration of the "stickiness" of water.

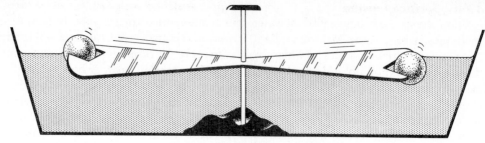

Fig. 1–9 Surface tension turbine.

All that is needed is a tin can. Close to the bottom punch a row of five holes with a nail point or ice pick a little less than ¼″ (5 mm) apart. When the can is filled with water, there will be five separate streams of water which can be made to "stick" together by pinching them into a single stream. They can then be broken apart from one end of the row to the other by interrupting their flow individually.

Surface tension of soap bubbles. You may also want to have students explain the shape of soap bubbles. There are inexpensive toy bubble kits on the market which are excellent for class use. As a bubble forms on a bubble pipe, students may observe that it has a tail. As soon as the bubble is released from the pipe, it becomes spherical and may shrink because there is greater tension on the outer than on the inner surface. Actually, the tension per *unit* of surface is the same inside and out, but since the outer surface is slightly greater in area its total tension is greater. You may want to point out to the class that the sphere is the most "economical" bounding surface there is since it encloses more volume for its area than any other form, just as a circle encloses more area than a square of the same perimeter. Thus the bubble becomes a sphere, with its size determined by the pressure inside and out.

Plateau's liquid. For laboratory activities, Plateau's liquid can be prepared for making soap films and bubbles. Sutton[6]

[6] Sutton, p. 92.

suggests this preparation. Combine 1 part of oleate of soda, 40 parts of water, and 13 parts of glycerin. When free oleic acid is used, the recipe calls for: 28.2 g oleic acid, 100 cc normal caustic soda solution, 300 cc glycerin, 1200 cc water. To this add 3 drops of concentrated ammonia and the result is a solution which will produce unusually tough bubbles, so tough in fact they can be rolled over table tops and even on the floor.

If large soap bubbles are wanted, prepare a pint or so of dilute soap solution and add to it about 1 g of table sugar and 5 cc of glycerin. Increasing the sugar content will increase the size of the bubbles that can be made.

Comparing specific gravities. At some time you may want to compare the specific gravity of several substances. The following is one preparation among many that can be made. Into a flat-sided jar mix together about 15 parts of 95 per cent alcohol and 9 parts of water. Using a pipette carefully add to the center of this mixture a little olive oil that has been colored with Sudan III for contrast.

Students can watch how these drops remain in the center of the fluid. Should the oil drops rise, add more alcohol to lower the specific gravity of the fluid, and should the drops sink, add a small amount of water to raise the specific gravity.

Aniline drop. Aniline has the same density at about 25° C as water. Being only slightly soluble in water, it maintains a distinct boundary when the two are brought together. Add from 75 to 100 cc of aniline oil to a beaker of cool water (approx. 15° C). Students can watch the aniline sink. Now gently heat the beaker and watch the aniline rise to the surface. As the water cools, drops of aniline detach themselves, form spheres, and again sink to the bottom. During this students can repeatedly watch the process of drop formation.

Additional soap films. When there is time, as in club and project activities, students may move from simple examples of contraction of soap films to complex catenoid figures and also beautiful designs due to minimal surfaces.

Students can first show the contraction of soap films by inverting a funnel which has a soap film across the mouth. The film will rise toward the funnel's narrow end. A wire frame with a sliding cross wire can be purchased from one of the supply houses. When this is dipped into a soap solution, a film is formed across the U-shaped frame; as the film contracts, the thin cross wire is pulled down to close the open end of the U-shaped frame.

A thin wire ring may be prepared easily; attach a loop of thin white thread to the ring. If this is dipped into soap solution, a film is formed containing limp thread. Now puncture the film with a needle *within* the thread loop. Why does the outer film contract so that the loop of thread forms a circle? What is a minimal surface?

Large circles can be made from wire coat hangers to form larger bubbles. This thin soap film, generally 12 to 15 molecules in thickness, forms beautiful colors due to diffraction (20.5b).

An adjustable frame for making thinner and thinner films can be made by shaping wire to form a two-prong fork. A movable wire looped around the two fork-like sections can slide at right angles to stretch the soap film. Students can observe the changes in color as the film is thinned out by moving the cross-piece.

1.4c Adhesion

Adhesion is the attraction between unlike substances. Water adhering to the tip of a pencil after it has been dipped into water is a simple example of adhesion. You may elicit examples such as glue sticking to wood, graphite to paper, chalk to a blackboard, chewing gum to a shoe, or the new high-strength contact cements.

Wet several glass microscope slides and stack them. Then have students try to pull them apart without sliding them. Air pressure may be neglected since it acts against the edges of the water film as well as against the surface of the slides. Also the force of air pressure acts equally in all directions.

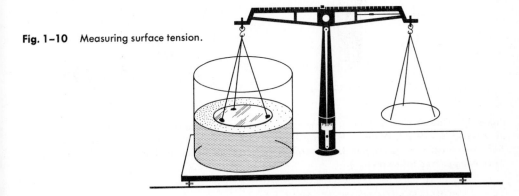

Fig. 1–10 Measuring surface tension.

Adhesive forces between glass and a liquid such as mercury or water can be measured. With sealing wax anchor a thin string to the center of a glass disk about 2″ in diameter. Attach a low-range spring balance to the free end of the string, or suspend the disk from one arm of a balance (Fig. 1–10). Note the weight of the disk as indicated on the balance. Now lower the disk onto the liquid until it just touches the surface. Read the force required to lift the disk off the surface of the water or mercury. Repeat this several times and average the readings. Then subtract the measured weight of the disk from this average. If the area of the disk in square centimeters is divided into the average adhesive force in grams, the result is the adhesive force in grams per square centimeter. You may want to have students try the experiment with both water and mercury and compare the values obtained.

1.4d Capillarity

Students have seen water or ink rise along a blotter or move up the end of a Turkish towel; many of them have dipped a sugar cube into tea or coffee; some may know that water moves up from the roots to the leaves of a plant through conduction tubes as a result of several forces of which capillarity is one of the most important. How does fuel rise up the wick of an alcohol lamp? How does water rise in the soil?

Wetness of water and mercury. Have students pour 10 cc of water into one graduated cylinder and 10 cc of mercury into another (Fig. 1–11A). When students compare the two, lead them to observe that the water "wets" the glass which is another way of saying that the adhesive force between water and glass molecules is greater than the cohesive force between water molecules. This being the case, the water's surface film adheres to the glass so that the edges seem to "climb" the cylinder walls, forming a concave meniscus.

Mercury, on the other hand, does not "wet" the glass, that is, the cohesive force between its molecules is greater than the adhesive force between them and glass. Students can see that the meniscus in this

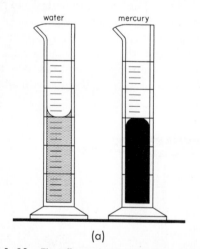
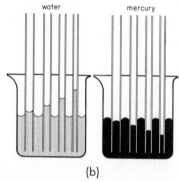

(a)   (b)

Fig. 1–11 The effects of adhesion: The meniscus of water curves upward at the edges while that of mercury curves downward. Water rises in capillary tubes, mercury is pushed down. Water has a greater adhesive attraction for glass than does mercury. (The curve of meniscus and bore of capillary tubes have been exaggerated for emphasis.)

case is convex, that it turns down at the sides of the cylinder.

Capillary tubes. Another way to demonstrate the "wetness" of liquids is to see to what degree they rise in capillary tubes. If students draw out tubing (25.2b) so that lengths of different bore are produced, they may use these to show that the elevation or depression of any liquid is inversely proportional to the diameter of the capillary tubes. A modified test tube rack or window screening can be made to support the capillary tubes in the fluid. Place the series of tubes into water stained with a drop of red ink (Fig. 1–11B). Students can measure the height of the water columns that will rise in the capillary tubes. They should be ready to explain why the level of water in the tubes will be above the level outside the tubes. Why is the greatest effect seen in the thinnest tube? Now repeat using mercury, making sure the level in the container is the same as was used for water. Why is the mercury below the level outside the tubes? How is the amount of depression related to the size of the tube? In which tube is the depression greatest?

Capillarity between glass plates. Stack two lantern slides so that they make contact. At one side tape the edges together, but, at the opposite side, insert thin splints or microscope coverslips to separate the two plates a fraction of an inch (Fig. 1–12).

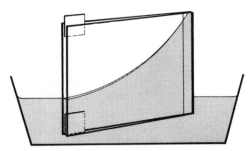

Fig. 1–12   Capillarity between glass plates.

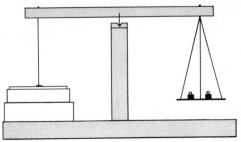

Fig. 1–13   Measuring adhesion between lead and glass.

Now stand the two lantern slides on end in colored water. Students will see a curved (parabolic) line of liquid rise between the plates. Notice that the liquid rises highest on the side where the plates are in closest contact.

It is also possible to measure adhesion between two solids. Attach one side of a simple beam balance to a flat disk of lead which has been polished to as near a perfect plane as possible. Place this polished surface against a very smooth well-cleaned plate glass. Add small weights to the opposite side of the balance to measure the adhesive force (Fig. 1–13). Divide the force by the area of the lead disk to get the force per unit area.

1.5   Molecular dimensions using Langmuir's technique[7]

Here is a demonstration by which students can deduce the order of size of a molecule. A drop of oleic acid is allowed to spread out until it is monomolecular in thickness, then computation based on area and density leads to an approximation of molecular size.

Oleic acid is a fatty molecule, $C_{17}H_{33}COOH$. The acid end of this

[7] Originally reported by Dr. Irving Langmuir, *J. Chem. Soc.*, 1848 (1917). Some of this material was adapted from a demonstration prepared by Clifford C. Little of the Hill School, Pottstown, Pa.

Fig. 1-14 Monomolecular layer. (Alexander Joseph.)

long hydrocarbon chain, COOH, is attracted to water whereas the $C_{17}H_{33}$ end is very weakly attracted. Under the right circumstances this substance will range itself over the surface of water with the COOH in the water and the more weakly attracted end above. Under these circumstances the most stable arrangement is only one molecule in thickness.

First prepare a cookie or lunchroom tray by painting it with flat black paint. If you wish to protect the tray, line it with aluminum foil and blacken the foil. Whatever you use be sure first to wash the tray thoroughly and then rinse with alcohol. Allow the paint to dry a day.

Prepare a very dilute solution (1%, 0.5%) of oleic acid in ethyl alcohol. This can be done by a druggist. You can make up your own in the following manner. Shake together 5 cc of oleic acid and 95 cc of alcohol. Measure out 5 cc of this solution and mix with 45 cc of alcohol. Using a medicine dropper count the number of drops to a cc. Knowing the density of oleic acid, 0.898 g/cc, the weight of acid per drop can be calculated.

First find the weight of acid per cc (cm^3) of dilute solution.

$$\frac{5 \text{ cm}^3}{100 \text{ cm}^3} \times 0.898 \text{ g/cm}^3$$
$$= 0.0449 \text{ g/cm}^3$$
$$\frac{5 \text{ cm}^3}{50 \text{ cm}^3} \times 0.0449 \text{ g/cm}^3$$
$$= 4.49 \times 10^{-3} \text{ g/cm}^3$$

Let us say that it takes 50 drops to make a cm^3.

$$\frac{4.49 \times 10^{-3} \text{ g/cm}^3}{50 \text{ drops/cm}^3} = 8.98 \times 10^{-5} \text{ g/drop}$$

With this information at hand the experiment can be run. Pour distilled water into the tray. For best results it should be warm, about 40° C. Lay a metric ruler across the tray. When all is still, place one drop of old SAE #30 engine oil onto the surface. In the center of this oil slick put one drop of the dilute oleic acid solution. A circle forms almost instantly whose diameter is measured by the ruler (Fig. 1–14). For the sake of example let us say it is 32 cm. Now the molecular size can be calculated. (The solvent, in this case alcohol, can be disregarded since it dissipates leaving only oleic acid to form the circle.)

$$\text{Density } (d) = \frac{\text{Mass } (m)}{\text{Volume } (Ah)}$$

Solving for h

$$h = \frac{m}{Ad}$$

The mass is 8.98×10^{-5} g/drop as previously calculated.

The radius of the monomolecular layer is 16 cm. The density of oleic acid is 0.898 g/cm^3.

$$h = \frac{8.98 \times 10^{-5} \text{ g}}{\pi(16)^2 \text{ cm}^2(0.898 \text{ g/cm}^3)}$$
$$= 1.25 \times 10^{-7} \text{ cm}$$

Here are some general suggestions and alternatives. Absolute cleanlines is extremely important. For instance, a minute trace of protein can cause the circle to develop star patterns at its edge. Be sure to rinse the dropper and tray in water and then in alcohol before each trial. Do not touch the inside surface of the tray.

Instead of engine oil, lycopodium or talcum powder or chalk from blackboard erasers can be used on the water's surface as background.

When putting the drop of oleic acid on the background there must not be a splash. The experiment can be disturbed by any vibration.

The larger the percentage of oleic acid concentration the larger the circle that results. A 1% solution can be made by mixing one drop of acid with 99 drops of alcohol. Doubling the amount of alcohol will give you a 0.5% solution.

Stearic acid, $C_{17}H_{35}COOH$, can be used in place of the oleic acid. If it is used benzene is the solvent. Oil cannot be used as a background since it reacts with benzene. Use lycopodium, talc, or chalk in its place. For stearic acid the water in the tray must be near boiling.

When Dr. Langmuir first drew up his report in 1917, he gave the following results.

Oleic acid	1.12×10^{-7} cm
Stearic acid	2.5×10^{-7} cm

These are measurements of the molecular length only. From these figures one can get a rough approximation of atomic size by dividing the length by 56, the number of atoms in the molecule. This makes the atomic size in the 10^{-9} cm range.

Further extrapolations can be made. Using Avogadro's number, the cross section of a molecule can be estimated.

The molecular weight of oleic acid is 282.46. Dividing this by Avogadro's number

$$\frac{282.46}{6.02 \times 10^{23}}$$
$$= 46.9 \times 10^{-23} \text{ grams per molecule}$$

Knowing the weight per molecule, one can find out how many oleic acid molecules are in 1 drop of dilute solution using the example cited above.

$$\frac{8.98 \times 10^{-5} \text{ g/drop}}{46.9 \times 10^{-23} \text{ g/molecule}}$$
$$= .192 \times 10^{18} \text{ molecules in a drop}$$

Dividing this into the area of the circle made by one drop of dilute oleic acid

$$\frac{\pi(16)^2 \text{ cm}^2}{.192 \times 10^{18}} = 42.3 \times 10^{-16} \text{ cm}^2$$

(the cross section of one molecule)

In his 1917 report Dr. Langmuir listed his calculation for this as 46×10^{-16} cm^2. What really is being estimated here is not the cross-sectional size of the molecule but rather the cross-sectional space per molecule.

In summary here is what can be deduced from this demonstration. The length of an oleic acid molecule is roughly 1.25×10^{-7} cm, its width is roughly 6.5×10^{-8} cm (derived by taking the square root of the cross section, 42.3×10^{-16} cm^2).

CAPSULE LESSONS
Ways to get started in class

1-1. Begin by showing these "silent" demonstrations, that is, offering no explanations at the time. Ask students to watch and be ready to explain what they see. Streak a blackboard with alcohol. Wet several students' hands with rubbing alcohol. Prepare the demonstration given in 1.1d in which ammonium hydroxide diffuses through a membrane into water containing alcoholic phenolphthalein. Now ask students what happened to the alcohol on the blackboard; why did the hands feel cold? Once the term "molecules" has been elicited, ask students to list all the statements and questions they can about molecules. Someone might list them on the board. They may say: Molecules are invisible; they move very rapidly in the "gas" state; the more rapidly they move the "hotter" a substance is. What is evaporation? Why do we feel cooler when our perspiration dries? Connect the notion of heat with molecular motion. As a result of student discussion, some statements on the blackboard may well need modification, some may have to be discarded, and others will stand the test of being put up against known facts.

1-2. Or you may want to begin by opening a bottle of ammonium hydroxide in one corner of the room, noticing how long it takes to diffuse and be sensed by students at the opposite side of the room. Develop a concept of "molecule" and "atom" in this first lesson.

1-3. Use a ping-pong ball demonstration box (1.3a) to show "molecular" motion. From here students may move into diffusion (1.1), Brownian motion (1.2), and, possibly, change of state (2.2a).

1-4. If you want to show to the whole class at once direct evidence of molecular motion, begin by using a microprojector to cast on a wall Brownian motion in smoke. Have students attempt to explain the erratic motions of the carbon particles. This can lead to the elucidation of the main facts about molecules.

1-5. At some other time, you may want to show the absorption of illuminating gas by charcoal of a porous clay or porous ceramic pot (1.1f). At this point, students may be ready to discuss diffusion, change of state, and the kinetic theory of molecules.

1-6. As a project a group of students can show the diffusion of minerals and water through a membrane (1.1d), or through a hollowed-out carrot. Elicit explanations of how fluids rise in tubes.

1-7. Show examples of forces exerted by molecules: surface tension, adhesion, and cohesion. Use several of the demonstrations described in this chapter as laboratory activities for small groups of students.

1-8. You may want to use a film such as *Molecular Theory of Matter* (Encyclopaedia Britannica) or the filmstrip *How Heat Travels* (Popular Science) or similar films and filmstrips. Such films might be used as introduction, or as summary lessons.

1-9. Look into some laboratory workbooks for additional suggestions. There are many in general science, chemistry, and physics. Keep a log of successful lessons with ideas for projects for students who want to go further along in the topic, or who can progress faster than the rest of the class.

PEOPLE, PLACES, AND THINGS

If your school is handicapped by a shortage of demonstration aids, you may be able to borrow films, filmstrips, or equipment for standard demonstrations from a nearby school or college. Ideas for assembly programs and for school exhibits can be exchanged among schools. In fact, in some schools, student clubs from two or more schools can hold joint meetings or plan a science fair, a debate, or a series of seminars. Often graduate students from a college in the community will take on a share of responsibility by sponsoring a student club, or procuring judges for a fair, or giving a talk on a specialized topic in science, or acting as a consultant for a small group of students of high-level ability in science.

Frequently students' parents can be invited to speak to the class on some chemical process, the use of an instrument in the laboratory, a new plastic and how it is made, or some other specialized technique. These talks can be very effective in relating classwork to industry. They also offer opportunities for students to see scientists of many kinds talk about their own work. They learn what scientists do, what they look like, how they think. (Be advised of the administrative policies in your school before you invite outside speakers into the classroom.) Plan to interest your parents' association and invite their participation.

BOOKS AND PAMPHLETS

These are only a few of the books which are pertinent to the work discussed in this chapter. These and many other references classified by subject and with complete bibliographical data are given in the bibliography at the end of the book.

Asimov, I., *Inside the Atom,* Abelard-Schuman, 1958.

Beeler, N, and F. Branley, *Experiments in Science,* Crowell, 1955.

Bonner, F. T., and M. Phillips, *Principles of Physical Science,* Addison-Wesley, 1957.

Boys, C. V., *Soap Bubbles,* Doubleday, Anchor Books, Garden City, N.Y., 1959.

Brinckerhoff, R., F. Watson, B. Cross, and P. Brandwein, *The Physical World,* Harcourt, Brace, 1958.

Cheronis, N., J. Parsons, and C. Ronneberg, *The Study of the Physical World,* Houghton Mifflin, 1957.

Gilreath, E., *Fundamental Concepts of Inorganic Chemistry,* McGraw-Hill, 1958.

Hausman, E., and E. Slack, *Physics,* 4th ed., Van Nostrand, 1957.

Lemon, H., *Galileo to Cosmic Rays,* U. of Chicago Press, 1934.

New York State Education Department, *General Science Handbook,* Part III, *Physics Handbook,* Albany, 1956.

Read, J., *Through Alchemy to Chemistry: A Procession of Ideas and Personalities,* Macmillan, 1957.

Richardson, J., and G. Cahoon, *Methods and Materials for Teaching General and Physical Science,* McGraw-Hill, 1951.

Scientific American, "Atoms Visualized," June, 1957; "Diffusion in Metals," May, 1957; "How Giant Molecules are Made," September, 1957; "How Giant Molecules are Measured," September, 1957.

Sutton, R., *Demonstration Experiments in Physics,* McGraw-Hill, 1938.

Swezey, K., *Chemistry Magic,* McGraw-Hill, 1956.

Vergara, W., *Science in Everyday Things,* Harper, 1958.

Weber, R., M. White, and K. Manning, *Physics for Science and Engineering,* McGraw-Hill, 1957.

FILMS AND FILMSTRIPS

This partial list is intended only as a guide toward film and filmstrip selection. Refer to the more complete listing at the end of the book where films are classified by subject and where a key to abbreviations and the addresses of distributors are given. The cost of film rental, of course, may be subject to change. Films are sound and black and white unless otherwise specified.

Behavior of Gases (f, s), PSSC, Modern Talking Pictures, inquire rental.

Chemistry Series (f, fs) (kinetic molecular theory, atomic theory, chemical formulas), McGraw-Hill, inquire rental.

Kinetic Theory (f, s), PSSC, Modern Talking Pictures, inquire rental.

Molecular Forces in Matter (fs), Jam Handy, $4.50.

Molecular Theory of Matter (f, s), Indiana U., $2.00.

Properties of Matter (f, s), 15 lessons in introductory physics, EBF, inquire rental.

FREE AND INEXPENSIVE MATERIALS

This is only a partial listing of free and inexpensive materials available to the teacher at this time. A more complete listing, including addresses, is given at the end of the book. Many of these materials are distributed to teachers without charge. Where there is a small fee, the cost is indicated, although the prices are subject to change. While we recommend the material for use in the classroom, we do not necessarily sponsor the products advertised.

An Outline of the History of Chemistry (wall chart), Mallinckrodt Chemical Works.

Periodic Chart of the Elements (11″ × 14″), General Electric Co.

Chemicals from the Atmosphere, Chemicals from Farm and Forest Products, Manufacturing Chemists Assoc.

CHAPTER 2

Matter: properties,

changes, and conservation

Many of our demonstrations and laboratory activities in general science, physics, and chemistry are concerned with properties, physical and chemical changes, units of measurement, and the concept of conservation of matter and energy.

While much that is developed in this chapter is introductory, applying to areas usually studied in general science, cross-references are indicated for extensions of these activities into more advanced work in chemistry and physics. For a more detailed cross-reference see the index.

2.1 Properties of matter

2.1a General properties

The following demonstrations have been selected out of many on the basis of their simplicity and their success in clarifying the general characteristics of all matter.

Impenetrability and its effects. In their work in elementary science, students have probably stuffed a piece of cloth into a tumbler, and then, inverting the glass, pushed it down into a basin of water. Why did the cloth remain dry?

Students may also set up the demonstration materials shown in Fig. 2–1A, B, C. When students pour water into the fun-nel in A and B, why doesn't water enter the bottle? Students should be able to explain the need for the opening in C to allow air to escape before water can enter the bottle. Students readily develop the notion that no two substances can occupy exactly the same space at the same time. As one application of this, students may demonstrate how the displacement of water is one way to calculate the unknown volume of a solid body. What is the volume of a given small brass weight? Students can tie a string to the weight and suspend it submerged in a graduated cylinder filled with water to the 50-cc level. Note the change in the water level? (See also 2.1c for further work on measurement.)

At this point students can be shown an apparent contradiction of the law that no two substances can occupy the same space at the same time by mixing equal volumes of alcohol and water. Mixed, the total volume is about 4 per cent less than the combined volumes when separate. Here the concept of intermolecular spaces can be introduced to show that there is no contradiction. The molecules of each liquid have intermingled, taking up intermolecular space previously empty. This also occurs with sugar in water. In other words, when one material can dissolve in

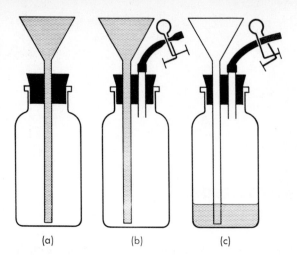

(a) (b) (c)

another and fill intermolecular spaces, the combined volume is less than the sum of the two original volumes.

Comparing mass and weight. Students often find it difficult to distinguish between mass and weight. Some teachers have found this approach successful. Prepare cubes of cardboard or plywood. Each face can be lettered to show the mass (in selected units) of one cubic foot of lead, balsa wood, water, and other substances.

Students should recognize that mass remains the same any place for any object as long as the number of that object's atoms remains the same. On the other hand weight can vary at different locations: at the poles, at the equator, down a mine, on a mountain top—since weight is the result of the force of gravity which varies from place to place. On the moon a student's mass is the same as on the earth but his weight is one sixth of his earth weight because the moon's gravity is one sixth that of the earth. Put another way, on the moon it would take just as much energy to accelerate a car from rest to 50 mph on level ground as on earth but it would take only one sixth as much energy to climb identical inclines. Mass is related to the amount of force needed to accel-erate an object, to overcome an object's inertia, and is the same for a given object wherever it might be, but weight varies as the amount of gravity varies. If a student weighed 150 pounds on earth he would weigh 25½ lb on the moon, 4200 lb on the sun, 60 lb on Mars, 0 lb in a satellite orbiting about the earth, but in every instance his mass would be the same. Would the number of atoms in an object weighing 100 lb decrease if it were transported to the moon where it would only weigh 17 lb? To take away part of an object's mass it is necessary to take away some of its substance, to reduce the number of its atoms. Weight is always proportional to mass. If two objects are weighed in the same place and their weights are equal, then their masses are equal and the relationship between the two objects will remain the same wherever they are weighed. For instance, if the 150-lb student carried a 50-lb bag and went some place where he weighed only 3 lb, then his bag would weigh but 1 lb—the relationship (3 to 1) would be the same in both places. Here the prepared cubes can be used for further illustration. For instance, a cubic foot of lead on earth weighs 705 lb, a cubic foot of water 62.4 lb, their ratio being 11.1. On Mars the lead would weigh 282 lb, the water about 25 lb, and the ratio between them would be 11.1 just as on earth.

Inertia. Center a coin on a 3″ × 5″ card placed over the mouth of an empty tumbler. If the card is quickly flicked away, the coin does not fly off with it but falls into the tumbler (Fig. 2–2A). You may demonstrate the same action with a commercial device (Fig. 2–2B) available from supply houses which consists of a small metal cup with a lever and a marble. Place a small card over the depression in the metal cup and top this with the marble. When the metal lever is flipped, the card flies off and the marble falls into the cup. (For further material on inertia see Chapter 17. Action-reaction is described in Chapters 17 and 24.)

Or a student can tie a string to a sheet of cardboard, and pile wooden blocks on the cardboard. When the board is pulled slowly, the blocks are not upset; a sudden jerk knocks them down.

Suspend an iron inertia ball (Fig. 2–3) or a bundle of books by a string that is just strong enough to support the weight and attach another piece of the same string below the ball or the books. When the lower string is pulled suddenly it breaks. Now replace it with a new string and pull slowly. Why is it that the upper rather than the lower string breaks when this slow pull is exerted?

Volume. How does the volume of a pound of feathers compare with that of a pound of mercury? Have students weigh out 10-gram portions of mercury, water, clay (kaolin), table sugar, and similar materials. Place each 10-gram sample in a separate bottle, all of equal size. Have students compare the volumes the different substances occupy.

2.1b Specific properties

Certain properties distinguish one substance from another; these can be summarized by students after they have had some of the following laboratory experiences in the demonstration of specific properties.

Malleability. Show silver and gold leaf, and tin foil. If possible, pound out some lead on an anvil (or similar surface) with a hammer. Indicate the use of malleable iron in automobiles, in rivets for steel construction, and aluminum rivets for aircraft, and so on. (See also 10.1c.)

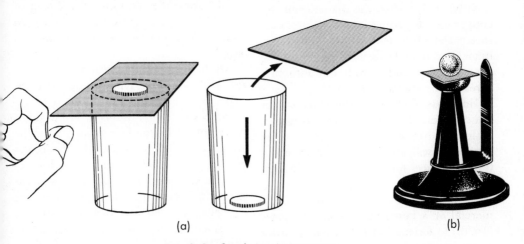

(a)　　　　　　　　　　　　　　　(b)

Fig. 2–2 Simple inertia apparatus.

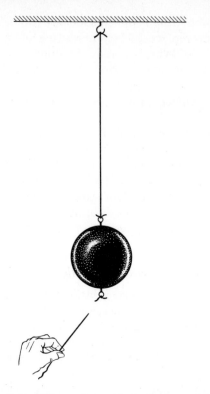

Fig. 2–3 When pulled suddenly, the lower string breaks. A slow pull causes the system to swing.

Ductility. Show spools of wire from the supply room. Take apart a length of insulated electric wire to show the thin copper strands. Pull a thin wire through a hole slightly smaller than the diameter of the copper wire to reduce it to a smaller diameter. Demonstrate the thin tungsten filament in a light bulb. Heat glass tubing over a flame and pull it out into fine thread. (See also 10.1c.)

Hardness. Cut a pane of glass with a glass cutter. If possible, demonstrate a scale-of-hardness kit (see appendix for supply houses), and have students learn to test substances for hardness using Mohs' scale (4.5b).

It may also be possible to use a commercial or a homemade hydraulic press (16.5b) to force a hard steel ball bearing down into blocks or thick sheets of differ-ent metals. The harder the metal, the shallower the depression will be. You may want to have students test brass, cast iron, cold-rolled steel, steel from a file, tool steel, and hardened tool steel. (Harden by first heating to a cherry red, then dipping in water.) Different samples of stainless steel can also be examined, pure aluminum can be compared with aluminum alloys.

2.1c Measurement

You will want to have students compare the English and metric units of measurement. In laboratory work, students can measure with rulers, yardsticks, meter-sticks, a vernier caliper, and a micrometer. Problems can be devised in which students are challenged to find first the surface area and then the volume of a block or a section of a dowel stick (cylinder).[1] (Students should, of course, repeat all measurements several times and average the results for accuracy.)

They can also find the volume of an irregular-shaped rock by water displacement. (Further work on Archimedes' principle may be found in 16.6a.)

Units. For a treatment on mass and weight units and their interrelationships see the appendix. This includes a description of the mks system wherein there is an exact discrimination between mass and weight.

Optical micrometer. You may want to use a "black box" type of apparatus for experiments in the measurement of extremely small dimensions where students have not yet learned the principles of the reflection of light on which this device depends. (You might refer to the laws of reflection, using this apparatus as an example. See 20.1b.) Students can follow the procedures given and observe that it is

[1] The text and laboratory guides prepared by PSSC offer many original approaches in developing concepts of units of measurement.

possible to calibrate and use an instrument even though they do not fully understand it.

They will need to fasten a microscope slide to a block of wood (about 2 x 5 x 10 cm) with strips of tape (Fig. 2–4). Cover the entire surface of this slide with black tape. Toward one end cut a narrow slot just wide enough to receive a needle. (See Fig. 2–4C.) Notice that the end of the block has been cut away to allow clear passage for the rubber bands. Using the needle as a fulcrum, pivot a second, clear slide above the black-covered slide and secure in place by means of a rubber band.

The block can be nailed or glued to a board. To one side as in Fig. 2–4A, B, place a pin or nail. Sighting down a ruler or a thread align the pin's reflection with the needle. Mark this on a piece of paper that has been taped to the board. Now insert a hair or thickness of paper or other thin material between the ends of the slides. (See Fig. 2–4C.) Again align the pin's reflection with the needle and mark this on the piece of paper. You may want to use this as an arbitrary unit of measurement. Or you may want to have the students think of ways to calibrate this optical micrometer.

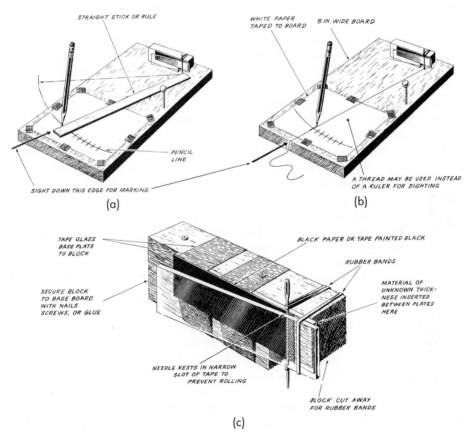

Fig. 2–4 Optical micrometer made from needles, rubber bands, and microscopic slides. (PSSC of Educational Services, Inc.)

For instance, a rough calibration can be made by measuring a tablet of paper and dividing by the number of sheets to get the thickness of each sheet. Then insert one thickness at a time into the optical micrometer making a mark with each addition. Another means of calibration uses the cellophane wrapping from a package of cigarettes, a single thickness of which is .001".

Although the optical micrometer that is finally built is crude, it measures much smaller distances than could be measured directly with a centimeter rule. Could it measure the diameter of a hair? Is a single hair the same diameter all along its length? Do brunettes and red-heads have the same size hair?

Can students improve the design of the micrometer? What factors influence its accuracy? How many significant figures can be justified in the results?

Parallax measurement of distance with the cross-staff. Parallax, the apparent displacement of an object when seen from two different points, has been observed by students. For example, when traveling along a highway in a car, they have certainly noticed the apparent shift in position of a church tower or smoke stack with relation to the background scene. Often parallax makes problems in using a camera viewfinder. How often has one found later that a photograph shows a subject's head missing? The lens of the camera and the lens of the viewfinder did not have exactly the same point of view. In other cases, parallax is useful for the measurement of long distances, the interocular distance being used as the base line. The cross-staff, using a longer base line, permits more accurate measurement.

As a special project, a student may want to make a cross-staff consisting of a long, straight rod and a short cross-piece which can slide on it (Fig. 2–5A). A schematic of the cross-piece is shown in Fig. 2–5B. Dimensions are not critical, but much trial and error can be avoided if the straight rod has the dimensions of a meterstick; in fact, a meterstick makes an excellent rod. The two arms that extend down from the cross-piece are guides to hold it in position on the rod. They may be brads or strips of wood. The two brads, B_1 and B_2 (size 18), on top of the cross-piece are for sighting. Set the brads one centimeter apart as accurately as possible for the range of distances which are to be measured. (Two- or three-centimeter distances can also be used, but one-cm distances make the arithmetic simpler.)

Now the cross-staff is ready for use. Find the distance of some selected object located about 100 to 500 meters away. Be sure that it stands in front of a well-defined background such as a building, or trees, against which parallax can be measured as one moves from one point to another. Visualize an imaginary line from this object to the point where the viewer stands. This is the line OD shown in Fig. 2–5B. Also visualize a base line, AC, perpendicular to OD. Move to point C and locate point C'. Move to point A, and sight past the object O and find point A' in the background. Then move to D and hold up the cross-staff with one end about 1 cm from the eye and sight along the rod toward object O. Slide the cross-piece back and forth on the rod until B_1 just covers C' and B_2 covers A'. Measure the distance S from the eyepoint to the cross-piece, the distance between B_1 and B_2, and the length of the base line, AC. With some practice, students will find it more convenient to set S at some fixed value and then choose a base line to go with it.

If your students have studied radian measure, they will recognize that

$$\theta = \frac{AC}{OD} = \frac{A'C'}{OE}$$

$$\phi = \frac{A'C'}{DE} = \frac{B_1B_2}{S}$$

Now the ratio $OD/A'C'$ is very small and may be dropped in these approximations so that

$$OD = \frac{AC \times S}{B_1B_2}$$

since

$$\frac{S}{B_1B_2} = \frac{OD}{AC}$$

Considering the approximations, the errors in measurement, and the errors of sighting, how accurate are the results? Over what range of distances could this device be used? Could a base line of 15 cm be used to measure a distance of 50 km? What is the longest base line that could be used?

Some teachers prefer to develop these measurements of distance at this time; other teachers use these activities in studies of star distances (Chapter 5) or in studies of lenses (Chapter 20).

Simple micro balance. Students often find it difficult to gain a concept of weights as small as milligrams and micrograms. A very sensitive balance can be made from a soda straw, match book, balancing screw, and a tongue depressor held upright by a clothespin. The needle is pushed through the soda straw to act as a pivot. Calibrations are marked on the tongue depressor (Fig. 2–6).

When an analytical balance is not available, students can build a single-arm version of Zehnder's balance.[2] This balance, which will weigh micrograms, can be made from the following materials: a block of wood 3″ x 1″ x 1″, two halves of a microscope slide (or other small pieces of smooth

[2]Modified from *UNESCO Source Book for Science Teaching*, UNESCO, 1956, p. 33.

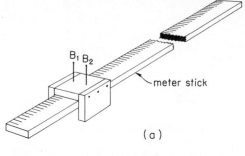

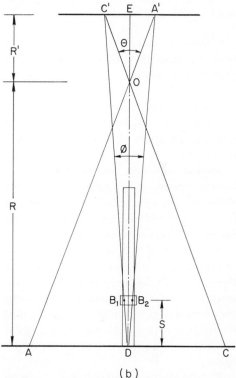

Fig. 2–5 Apparatus for parallax measurement of distance. (Redrawn from M. Tom Thomas, Brown University.)

glass), two very fine sewing needles, a drinking straw, a one-inch wood screw, and a piece of Styrofoam available from a hobby shop or a florist shop.

Cut the Styrofoam with a knife to the shape shown in Fig. 2–7 and insert the fine sewing needles in place with a drop of model airplane cement. Cut out the block

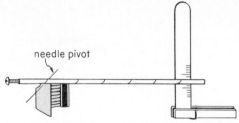

needle pivot

Fig. 2–6 Microbalance made from a soda straw with a needle fulcrum, a book of matches, a screw, and a short piece of wood. (Redrawn from PSSC of Educational Services, Inc.)

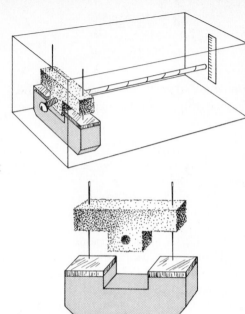

Fig. 2–7 Microbalance of great sensitivity that can be made by students. (Alexander Joseph, courtesy of *Science World*.)

of wood to form a letter "U." With a nail make a hole to insert the drinking straw in the lower center of one face of the Styrofoam and insert the straw.

On the other side of the Styrofoam, just below the straw, insert the 1″ wood screw at an angle of 30 to 45° from the horizontal. On top of the legs of the U-shaped wood block, cement the pieces of broken microscope slide as shown in the diagram. Finally, place the Styrofoam balance assembly on the U-block so that the needles rest on the glass.

Now build a cabinet for the balance out of glass, cellophane, or plastic as shown. Adjust the screw in the Styrofoam until the device is in balance. Then slip the parts into the "house." At one end of the cabinet, attach a door of glass. Cement a paper scale on the outside center of the door.

Finally, calibrate the balance. Cut #40 copper wire with a razor blade into ½-cm lengths. Insert these weights by means of tweezers, one at a time, into the end of the drinking straw. When a weight is added to the balance, close the glass door with cellulose tape to prevent air currents from moving the balance. Mark the position of the straw on the scale after each piece of wire is inserted. Each piece of wire will weigh 225 micrograms, or 225 millionths of a gram. The weight of 4½ pieces of wire will be about one milligram. The sensi-

tivity of this balance is about 45 micrograms per centimeter.

After the balance has been calibrated, students can weigh tiny pieces of paper, ½-cm lengths of human hair (red, blond, brunette), and ½-cm lengths of insect wings.

At this point you may also want to develop the concepts of density and specific gravity in relation to examples of measurement independent of specific properties of substances. See the index for further activities related to these concepts.

2.2 Changes in matter
2.2a *Physical change*

You may want to elicit several examples of changes that are only physical. Students usually mention paper or cloth being torn or cut, wood being rendered into sawdust, ice melting, evaporation from a wet blackboard. They can demonstrate several of the following for the class.

Dissolving.[3] Dissolve salt or sugar in water. Taste the water; the properties of clarity and homogeneity of the substance have not been changed even though its flavor has been altered. Point out that the taste is the same throughout, showing the degree of mixing. Evaporate the water either by letting the container stand for a few days or by heating some of the liquid in an evaporating dish. Now taste the crystals which remain. This demonstrates one important characteristic of some solutions—that the solute and the solvent do not chemically combine to form a new substance even though they mix very thoroughly.

Distillation. Some teachers set up either a homemade Liebig condenser (Fig. 2–8A), a less elaborate system of flask and delivery tube leading to an iced test tube (Fig. 2–8B), or a simple still made from three cake pans of the kind with a cone in the center (Fig. 2–8C). The cones in the center are kept a small distance apart by using match sticks as separators. In this demonstration, students can see two of the states of matter as a substance changes from liquid to gas and back again to liquid. If a few crystals of potassium permanganate are added to the water to be distilled, students can begin to recognize that distillation is one way to separate a "mixture" of chemicals.

To show a liquid changing to a solid, imbed a small container such as a metal toothbrush tube or cigar tube in dry ice and put some water in it. If the container

[3] Note that the classification of the process of solution as a physical or a chemical change is rather arbitrary; we follow present usage of most school texts on the matter. True chemical solutions are those in which one material, the solute, is so thoroughly dispersed in another, the solvent, that the resulting substance is homogeneous throughout and is optically void even when examined under an ultra-microscope. Nonordinary true solutions are distinguished from the ordinary in that the solute dissociates in the solvent into positive and negative ions. (See Chapter 8.)

is small enough, the water will freeze very quickly; if it is filled to the brim, you can also show that water expands when it freezes. Ice melting into water exemplifies another change of state, solid to liquid. If you boil and distill the resulting liquid, you will have shown all three phases.

Change of phase of dry ice. Place dry ice into a container and pour the CO_2 from the container (as if pouring water) into limewater or bromthymol blue to show the presence of gaseous carbon dioxide.

2.2b Chemical change

Burn paper or wood splints. Is this a chemical or physical change? Into a 250-cc beaker that is resting on a metal tray place four tablespoons of granulated sugar. To this add just enough concentrated sulfuric acid to wet the sugar. Students should observe the mass of carbon that rises over the beaker and note the heat that is produced in this chemical change. (Chapters 6 through 15 deal with chemical reactions.)

Mixtures and compounds of iron and sulfur. Have students sprinkle iron filings on filter paper and then pass a magnet over the filings. Spill powdered sulfur on another filter paper, and pass a magnet over this chemical. Now mix the two elements. Have students dip a magnet into this mixture and notice that the iron filings are removed from the mixture.

You may prefer to demonstrate the next activity rather than plan for student work because carbon disulfide vapors are explosive and should therefore be kept away from flame or spark. Add a little sulfur to a fourth of a test tube of carbon disulfide to show that it dissolves. In another test tube add iron filings, instead of sulfur, to the carbon disulfide. The students now know one property of sulfur, its solubility in carbon disulfide. Can any of them suggest a way to remove the sulfur from the

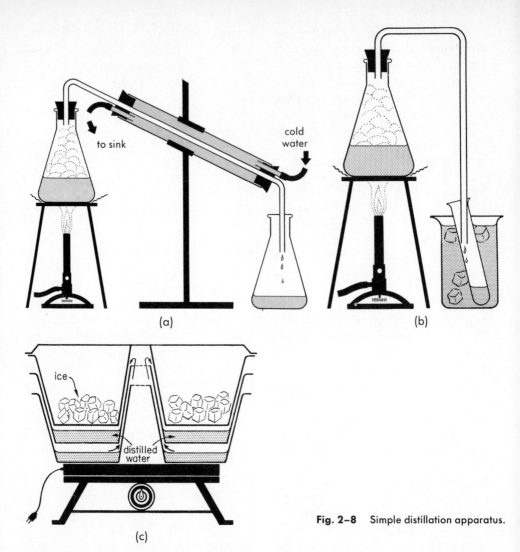

cold water

to sink

(a)

(b)

ice

distilled water

(c)

Fig. 2–8   Simple distillation apparatus.

solution? How would one remove the iron filings from the other test tube? (*Caution: If you do evaporate the carbon disulfide and sulfur solution, the operation should be carried out under a hood or on the roof. Carbon disulfide is explosive.*)

Next mix 4 grams of sulfur into about 6 grams of iron filings. Heat this mixture in a Pyrex test tube clamped in a ring stand. Heat until the contents glow. Then remove the flame and break the tube by immersion in cold water or by covering it with toweling and striking it against a stone-topped table or with a hammer. What is the appearance of the substance? How does this compare with the mixture before heating? What tests can be used to discover whether this is a new compound or still a mixture of iron filings and sulfur? Try the effect of a magnet; of carbon disulfide.

Physical and chemical properties of antimony and iodine. You may also want to have students identify the properties of the individual elements antimony and iodine. For example, they may identify the crystalline form, color, and odor. Then they may attempt to dissolve each element in water and in carbon tetrachloride. What is the color of each solution?

Gently heat a small quantity of each solution in a test tube. After the carbon tetrachloride evaporates, what is left as a residue in each case? (*Caution: Work in a hood.*) Is this a physical or chemical change?

Next grind two iodine crystals in a mortar until a fine powder is produced. (Avoid touching iodine crystals.) To this add a pinch of powdered antimony and gently mix with a wood splint. (*Caution: Do not grind—this mixture can explode from friction.*) Then divide the quantity between two large (10″ x 1″) test tubes. To one tube add 4 cc of the solvent carbon tetrachloride. Equip the test tube with a one-hole stopper through which a thistle tube has been inserted. Have the thistle tube extend just a little below the stopper into the tube. Support by clamping to a ring stand. Heat the test tube for almost 20 minutes so gently that less than half of the liquid is found in the upper part of the apparatus. Remove from heat if necessary during the operation.[4] (*Caution: Do all heating under a hood.*)

After the precipitation settles, decant the hot supernatant liquid into a dry tube. What happens when the liquid cools? Then have students heat the liquid again until it evaporates to half its volume, and cool again. Watch for crystal formation.

While the solution is gently heating, students can use the second portion of the mixture for this test. Add 2 cc of carbon tetrachloride and filter into a test tube; wash the filter paper with about 15 drops of carbon tetrachloride. After the paper dries is the residue the same as the original mixture or is it a different substance?

Now heat the tube containing the fil-

[4] Modified from *Basic Laboratory Studies in College Chemistry*, W. Hered and W. Nebergall, D. C. Heath, Boston, 1957.

trate so that the liquid evaporates. What is formed?

Rusting of iron. Students may also demonstrate the rusting of iron as a chemical change. First clean some steel wool by dipping it into dilute nitric acid and then rinsing in water followed by a final dip in dilute acetic acid. Insert this cleaned steel wool into a long test tube or cylinder and invert it into a beaker of water placed where students may observe changes from day to day. This is an example of slow oxidation.

A more carefully designed demonstration may be prepared by supporting the tube or cylinder in the water so that students can see that a gas from the enclosed air in the tube has "disappeared" since water has risen approximately one fifth of the way up the tube (Fig. 2–9). When inserting the tube, let its end be about ½″ below the water surface. Prepare a control setup without the steel wool to show that there is no rise in the water level within that tube.

To show the small temperature rise during the slow oxidation of iron start with a vacuum bottle which has a one-hole stopper. Through the stopper insert a laboratory thermometer which has a small-

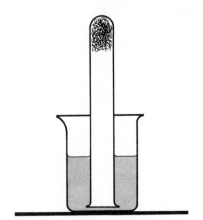

Fig. 2–9 Slow oxidation of iron uses oxygen from trapped air.

range calibration. Add a few cc of water to the bottle and place a portion of new, washed (in detergent) steel wool inside. Stopper and set out of the sun and away from heat. Have students keep a record of temperatures over several days and compare with room temperature at the same times.

Making a blueprint. Students can show another example of a chemical change, this time effected by sunlight. Lay a key or other opaque object on a sheet of blueprint paper (either purchased or prepared).

Here is one way to prepare the blueprint paper.[5] Dissolve 10 g of ferric ammonium citrate in 50 cc of water. In another container, dissolve 10 g of potassium ferricyanide in 50 cc of water. In a room darkened as if for movie projection, mix the two solutions and pour into a long, shallow pan. Dip single sheets of stiff paper into the solution and dry them in the darkened room.

Expose the blueprint paper and object to the sunlight for about 5 minutes; then wash the paper in running water. Why is the change chemical?

Making a photographic print. Show the effect of light upon chemicals by mixing in a test tube 4 cc of 2 per cent silver nitrate solution with 4 cc of 5 per cent sodium chloride solution. A white precipitate will form. Wrap a clear, sharp photographic negative around the tube and expose to sunlight for a class period. When you remove the negative, the image will be visible on the walls of the test tube because the light has caused reduction of the silver in the silver chloride to free silver (black).

Fermentation. Students may show the fermentation of molasses to alcohol and carbon dioxide effected through chemical reactions of the enzymes of yeast plant cells. Prepare a dilute (5 to 10%) molasses solution to which a few dry green peas are

added. To this preparation, add one quarter of a package of dry yeast (or the enzyme zymase). Keep this in a warm place. Within a few days, depending on the room temperature, students can smell the odor of alcohol. They can also devise a way to collect the gas given off and test it with limewater.

2.2c   Compounds into elements

In the demonstrations already described, substances were changed chemically; in some cases elements combined or recombined to form new compounds. At this point, you may want to show that compounds can be separated into elements.

Decomposition of water (electrolysis). Prepare and operate a Hoffman electrolysis apparatus as presented in 7.1b, or use the simplified apparatus that is also described there. Collect the gases and test for the characteristic properties of oxygen and hydrogen. To test for oxygen insert a glowing splint halfway up the tube making sure the mouth of the tube is held downward. If there is sufficient oxygen, the splint will burst into flame. To test for hydrogen, bring a glowing splint to the tip of the downward held test tube. If there is hydrogen, there will be a "pop" often followed by a pale blue flame.

Decomposition of mercuric oxide (heat). Carefully pour mercuric oxide into a dry Pyrex test tube in such a way that it does not stick to the sides of the tube. Heat the bottom of the tube in a flame, directing the students' attention to the appearance of shiny drops along the cool, upper walls of the test tube. Students may introduce a glowing splint into the tube to show the presence of oxygen.

Release of oxygen from hydrogen peroxide.[6] For approximately three minutes gently heat a test tube of hydrogen per-

---

[5] *Handbook of General Science*, Part III, N.Y. State.

[6] *Handbook of General Science*, Part III, N.Y. State.

oxide in a water bath; then introduce a glowing splint. Students should notice that no oxygen is released. Now add a pinch of manganese dioxide. With a glowing splint show that oxygen has been released in the presence of a catalyst. You may also use iron oxide (rusty nails) as a catalyst.

Release of oxygen from potassium chlorate. This is a striking demonstration. Gently heat a large (1½″ x 16″) Pyrex test tube with about 1″ of potassium chlorate supported by a clamp on a ring stand (Fig. 2–10). As the salt at white heat liquefies, with tongs gingerly insert long strips of wood about ¼″ x ¼″ x 2′ such as might be whittled from a wooden crate, making sure the ends of the sticks go into the molten salt. Keep students at a distance. The wood strips should not be burning when inserted. The reaction is self-igniting. Notice the brilliant light and tall flames which leap several feet out of the test tube. This is a good demonstration of the role of oxygen in supporting combustion.

2.3 Conservation of matter in chemical changes

Students may demonstrate and explain why ashes are lighter than the original wood, what happens when a candle burns down, why iron when rusted weighs more than before rusting.

You may set up an experiment by weighing out at least 2 ounces of iron filings which are then spread out and allowed to rust. Upon reweighing have students explain why the rusted filings weigh more than before rusting.

A more exact variation of this demonstration can be carried out through the use of a micro balance. (See 2.1c.) Cut a strip of pure tin foil approximately 1 milligram in weight. Weigh the strip and then transfer to a porcelain crucible and heat until the tin is completely oxidized

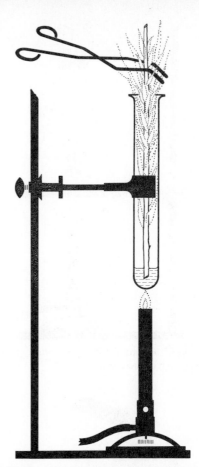

Fig. 2–10 Wood bursts into flame when inserted into molten potassium chlorate. (Be sure to heat gently.)

to a white powder. Transfer the powder to the micro balance and weigh again. The gain should be about 25 per cent.

When a ton of coal is burned, only a small amount of ash is formed. Why? Does the weight of the ash of a cigar compare with that of the original tobacco?

Chemical reaction in solution. Here the law of conservation can be demonstrated with a visible change which takes place immediately. Suspend on a thread an unstoppered vial containing sodium chromate solution in a flask containing a small amount of silver nitrate. (Or substitute

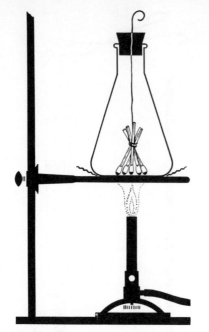

Fig. 2–11 Conservation of mass: burning matches in a closed flask.

solutions of potassium iodide and lead nitrate.) Cork the flask and carefully weigh it on a balance. Then invert the flask so that a chemical reaction occurs. Although there has obviously been a chemical change, the weight of the materials remains unchanged.

Burning matches in a closed pressure flask. In this demonstration students can weigh materials before and after burning. Tie a small heap of matches together with wire and suspend them from the stopper of a flask as in Fig. 2–11. After weighing wrap the flask in metal window screening as a safety cover. Be sure that the heads of the matches touch the bottom of the flask. Now heat the bottom of the container so that the matches ignite. Weigh the tube again. Explain the results.

Ammonium dichromate volcano. For a dramatic demonstration of a decrease in weight during chemical change, fill a small (size 000—about 1″ in diameter) porcelain

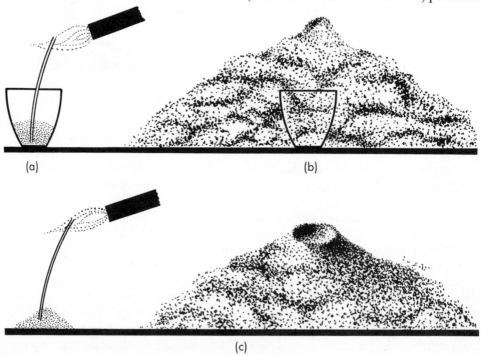

(a)   (b)

(c)

Fig. 2–12 Ammonium dichromate volcano: (a) igniting magnesium fuse, (b) resulting "moss" after burning, (c) ammonium dichromate burned on a flat surface.

crucible with ammonium dichromate and insert a 3″ magnesium fuse so that it touches the crucible's bottom. Record the weight of the crucible alone and then of it and its contents. After placing the crucible on an inverted metal tray, ignite the magnesium fuse with a Bunsen or other hot flame (Fig. 2–12A). Stand aside as the flame shoots upward and a tremendous quantity of green moss-like cinder spouts out of the crucible (Fig. 2–12B). The resulting "moss" may measure 10″ in diameter and be 4″ to 5″ high. Collect this and weigh it with the crucible. When the weight of the crucible is subtracted, the cinder material (chromic oxide) should weigh almost 40 per cent less than the original ammonium dichromate and magnesium. The gases that were given off are ammonia and oxygen. Done in a darkened room, this demonstration can be very spectacular.

If you omit the crucible, and simply ignite a magnesium fuse in 1 ounce of ammonium dichromate formed into a conical pile, the crater that forms makes a graphic model of a volcano cinder cone (Fig. 2–12C).

Many of the demonstrations described in this chapter are introductory to many lessons in chemistry, atomic energy, expansion due to heat, or other topics. Whatever your frame of reference, you may find it helpful to consult the index.

CAPSULE LESSONS
Ways to get started in class

2-1. Begin with an introduction to the properties of matter. Students may demonstrate and ask questions as they use the illustrative materials that you have made available (see suggestions in this chapter). Identify general and specific properties of matter.

2-2. Make a cardboard model of a cubic foot (or cubic centimeter). On each face print the name and mass of that volume of many different substances: air, fresh water, salt water, mercury, lead, gold, and the like. Show the different faces of the cube to the class. Develop the distinction between volume, mass, and weight. Also clarify the meaning of weight. Plan laboratory lessons on measurement: length, area, volume, weight. Use two- and three-dimensional objects such as paper cylinders, spheres, boxes, prisms, and so on. Use centimeter and foot rulers. Provide practice with calipers and micrometers.

2-3. You may want to begin by asking a student to pour water into a bottle through a funnel inserted into a one-hole stopper (Fig. 2–1). Elicit suggestions from the class. Develop the properties of matter through demonstrations and applications to daily living.

2-4. Or start with physical and chemical changes. Develop the notion of molecules and atoms. Continue into a development of the conservation of matter, or move into diffusion, or the properties of matter.

2-5. Begin one lesson with the ammonium dichromate volcano (2.3). Scoop up all the mass of green material which spouts out of the crucible. Ask students to predict whether this weighs more than, less than, or the same as the original material. Then have a student weigh the material. Explain the loss of weight. How can you reconcile this with the notion of conservation of matter?

2-6. Look into several of the laboratory workbooks in general science, chemistry, or physics for additional suggestions for ways to begin specific topics. There are many of these; examine *Laboratory Experiments in Physics* by Dull and Metcalfe (Holt), *Experiences in Science* by Blackwood (Harcourt, Brace), *Laboratory Experiments in Physics* by Marcus (Prentice Hall), *Laboratory Experiments in General Chemistry* by Campbell and Steiner (Macmillan), *Laboratory Manual for Introductory Chemistry* by Meyer (Macmillan).

2-7. In one lesson you may well want to show a film or filmstrip, either as introductory to the new work at hand or as a summary of work of the week. *Basic Principles of the Analytical Balance* is a film offered free of charge from the Communicable Disease Center of the U.S. Public Health Service; *Characteristics of Gases, Liquids, Solids* compose three films available for rental from Institutional Cinema Service. Have you seen *Precisely So* (General Motors)?

2-8. Keep a log of successful lessons. As these are revised from year to year, in the light of variations in classes and students, you will have a valuable piece of action research. See the companion volume, *Teaching High School Science: A Book of Methods,* P. F. Brandwein, F. Watson, and P. Blackwood (Harcourt, Brace, 1958).

PEOPLE, PLACES, AND THINGS

There are times when a teacher needs help: equipment, a special chemical for an experiment, an idea for a project for a special youngster with a high interest in science. Scientists in a college, university, industry, or research institution nearby may be of considerable help. A graduate student of a local college can often suggest ideas for a special demonstration or a project. In fact, many high school students have been sponsored in their project work as a result of this cooperation, and they have often been encouraged to continue in science.

You may also get help from a college librarian in tracking down a special reference. An instrument supply house in the community, or students' parents may have equipment that can be borrowed on occasion.

BOOKS AND PAMPHLETS

These are only a few of the books which are pertinent to the work discussed in this chapter. These and many other references classified by subject and with complete bibliographical data are given in the bibliography at the end of the book.

Asimov, I., *Inside the Atom,* Abelard-Schuman, 1956.
Avery, M., *Household Physics,* 3rd ed., Macmillan, 1955.
Bischof, G., *Atoms at Work,* Harcourt, Brace, 1951.
Daniels, F., and R. Alberty, *Physical Chemistry,* Wiley, 1955.
Farber, E., *The Evolution of Chemistry,* Ronald, 1952.
Hazel, J., *A Basic Laboratory Course in College Chemistry,* 2nd ed., Wiley, 1957.
Hodgman, C. C., et al., *Handbook of Chemistry and Physics,* Chemical Rubber, 1960.
Jaworski, I., and A. Joseph, *Atomic Energy,* Harcourt, Brace and World, 1961.
Scientific American, "Fresh Water From Salt," March, 1957.
Smith, A., and J. Cooper, *Elements of Physics,* 6th ed., McGraw-Hill, 1957.
Van Nostrand, *Scientific Encyclopedia,* 1956.

FILMS AND FILMSTRIPS

This partial list is intended only as a guide toward film and filmstrip selection. Refer to the more complete listing at the end of the book where films are classified by subject, and where a key to abbreviations and addresses of distributors are given. The cost of film rental, of course, may be subject to change. Films are sound and black and white unless otherwise specified.

Atoms into Molecules (f, s), Indiana U., $4.75.
Atom: How Big is an Atom? (f, s), Indiana U., $4.75.
Basic Principles of Analytical Balance (f, s), Communicable Disease Center, U.S. Public Health, free.
Characteristics of Gases, Characteristics of Liquids, Characteristics of Solids (f, s), Institutional Cinema Service, $2.00 each.
Electron Theory (fs, 2 in series), Visual Sciences, $2.00 each.
Eye to the Unknown (mass spectrometry), (f, s, c), Modern Talking Picture Service, free.
History of the Atomic Concept (fs, 2 in series), Visual Sciences, $5.00 set.
Matter and Energy (f, s), Indiana U., $2.00.
Precisely So (measurement of time, space, weight), (f, s), General Motors, free.
Simple Changes in Matter (f, s), Indiana U., $2.00.
The Turning Point (measurement, ball bearings), (f, s, c), General Motors, free.
Unlocking the Atom (f, s), U.S. Atomic Energy Comm., free.
Weighing with the Analytical Balance (f, s), EBF, inquire rental.

FREE AND INEXPENSIVE MATERIALS

This is only a partial listing of free and inexpensive materials available to the teacher at this time. A more complete listing, including addresses, is given at the end of the book. Many of these materials are distributed to teachers without charge. Where there is a small fee, the cost is indicated, although the prices are subject to change. While we recommend the material for use in the classroom, we do not necessarily endorse the products advertised.

ABC's of Hand Tools, General Motors; ask for additional materials for class use.

The Amazing Story of Measurement, Lufkin Rule Co.

Chemistry: The Conquest of Materials, K. Hutton (Pelican, 1957), $0.85.

A Dictionary of Science, E. Uvarov and D. Chapman (Penguin, 1951), $0.65.

History of Measurement, Poster Illustrations, Educational Services, Ford Motor Co.; ask for booklets too.

Manual of Carpentry, U. S. Steel Corp.; useful for students who plan to do project work.

Precision: A Measure of Progress, General Motors; includes reading of micrometer.

Superstition to Supersonics (teacher's manual free with class orders of students' books), Holt, $0.66.

Universe and Dr. Einstein, L. Barnett, Mentor, 1952, $0.35.

CHAPTER 3

Weather and the atmosphere

Although meteorology as a science had its beginning nearly a century ago, the greatest strides in forecasting weather have been made in the past 25 years. At first the great improvements in forecasting grew out of the formulation of new theories. Today increasing accuracy in weather forecasting more and more is due to the massive use of electronic devices. These can correlate in minutes, data that formerly took days and even months. Some devices can be sent into the upper atmosphere where so much of our surface weather is determined; from a distance they can track and trace violent storms such as hurricanes and tornadoes.

Radar, radio, computers, automatic recorders—a host of devices—with new ones being developed each year, are raising weather forecasting to an accuracy believed impossible a few years ago. Yet whatever the device there is a relatively small list of questions which they seek to answer over and over again, day in and day out, every minute of the day at thousands of locations.

What is the air's temperature? How wet is the air? How much rain or snow is falling? Of what is the air composed? How much pressure is the air exerting? How fast is the air moving and in what direction?

Simple instruments to answer these questions and thereby demonstrate the principles of meteorology can be made and used in the classroom. There are some 4000 amateur weather stations reporting data to the Weather Bureau. In fact the students and teachers in many schools have successfully established such weather stations.

3.1 Temperature of the air

(You may also want to refer at this time to Chapter 18, Heat and Heat Engines.)

3.1a Thermometers

Air thermometer. The fact that heat causes expansion of air can be applied to make an air thermometer (Fig. 3–1).

Insert one end of an 18″ length of glass tubing through a one-holed rubber stopper; then fit the stopper into a flask. Invert the flask so that the glass tubing can be inserted into a beaker of water; clamp the flask to a ring stand. Now have a student warm the flask with his hands. How does he know that warm air expands? What happens to the column of liquid? Can he predict what should happen when he removes his hands? What happens to the column of liquid when the air in the flask cools and therefore contracts once he does remove his hands? What are the limitations in using an air thermometer?

Liquid thermometer. This is a basic instrument and students should learn to use it well; when inexpensive thermometers are used, they should be calibrated against an accurate laboratory thermometer. Thermometers, liquid or otherwise, for out-of-doors reading should be mounted away from buildings so that the readings are not affected by heat radiated from the buildings. They should be placed in the shade. If a thermometer is mounted on a post at a distance from classroom windows, it can be read from the classroom with binoculars or a low-power telescope.

Thermometer scales. The relation between centigrade (Celsius) and Fahrenheit scales can be derived by groups of students working together. Each group can insert two thermometers, one centigrade and the other Fahrenheit, into a beaker containing ice and water. As they gradually heat the water, they take five or more readings recording in tabular form and in degrees the simultaneous levels of each thermometer. All the groups can now compare their two sets of readings. One degree on the centigrade scale is 1.8 degrees on the Fahrenheit scale. One Fahrenheit degree is equal to 5/9 of a centigrade degree. To convert °F to °C, $°F = (°C \times 9/5) + 32°$; to convert °C to °F, $°C = 5/9 (°F - 32°)$.

Students may check their results against a temperature equivalent scale. They may also prepare graphs of the results and thus have a ready means for translating one system into the other. On graph paper they can represent Fahrenheit degrees on the ordinate from 0° to 220° F; on the abscissa show centigrade degrees from −20° to 104° C. Locate the point where 32° F equals 0° C. Also mark the point where 212° F equals 100° C. Draw a straight line through these two points. If drawn correctly, such straight-line correlation can be used as a way of changing readings from one scale to another.

Maximum-minimum thermometer. Commercial maximum-minimum thermometers are available; these can be reset

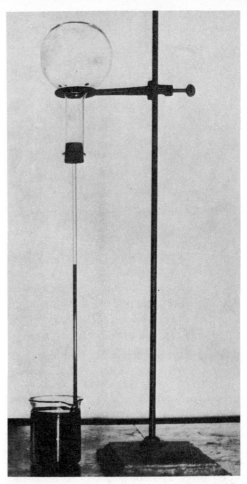

Fig. 3–1 Air thermometer. (Brookline Public Schools, Brookline, Mass.)

by means of a small magnet supplied with the instrument. Or simple ones can be made from inexpensive dial-type thermometers as follows (Fig. 3–2). Remove the glass face, and bend down the point of the needle so that it just grazes the surface of the dial. Now soot the dial scale with candle flame and set the thermometer in a convenient place for 24 hours. As the temperature changes, the needle moves along the dial, and traces a curve in the soot, with the maximum and minimum temperatures for the day at the ends of the line. Determine these temperatures by re-

Fig. 3–2 Maximum-minimum thermometer made from a dial-type thermometer.

moving the soot with a camel's-hair brush and reading the dial. Students may use the thermometer for further readings by recoating the scale with soot. They should keep readings for several days and check them against those found in the newspaper, or those made with a commercial model.

Thermograph. Commercial thermographs consist of a coiled compound bar or a bellows thermometer unit moving a tiny inked pen over a clock-driven drum covered with graph paper. The paper is marked off in hours (most thermographs cover seven 24-hour periods). As the drum turns under the power of an 8-day clock mechanism, the pen trails a graph of temperature against time. Some thermographs use a rotating disk instead of the drum.

Students can easily make a 12-hour thermograph from a spring-wound alarm clock that is in running order (Fig. 3–3). Remove the minute hand and cement a stiff cardboard or thin aluminum disk to the hour hand. Soot the disk with a candle flame, but be careful not to ignite the cardboard. Next set up a dial-type thermometer with the glass face removed. Bend the needle so that it just grazes the disk's sooty layer without touching the cardboard itself. Allow the instrument to run for twelve hours to provide a circular graph of the temperature changes. By measuring the radial distance of any point along the graph from the starting temperature position of the needle, it is possible to determine the temperature at any time during the preceding twelve-hour period.

3.2 Moisture in the air

3.2a Relative humidity

Relative humidity is the amount of water vapor present in the air compared with the maximum amount of moisture that the air can hold at that temperature. As indicated in Table 3–1, the higher the temperature the greater the amount of water the air can hold. Thus the same weight of water in the air results in a higher relative humidity at 40° F than at 80° F.

Fig. 3–3 A 12-hour thermograph.

TABLE 3-1
Relative humidity values

temperature °F	grams of water vapor per cubic meter					
	4.85	7.27	9.41	13.65	17.31	30.4
86	16%	24%	31%	45%	57%	100%
68	28%	42%	54%	79%	100%	
61	36%	53%	69%	100%		
50	52%	77%	100%			
43	67%	100%				
32	100%					

Moisture in the air. Students can demonstrate the presence of moisture in the air by weighing anhydrous copper sulfate (greyish white in color) or sodium hydroxide pellets before and after 4 hours of exposure to the atmosphere. The absorption of water by each substance will increase its weight. You can then heat the materials to drive off the moisture and reweigh them to show their original dry weight. (You may find it wise to heat the materials before you expose them to the air at the beginning of the test, since they have probably picked up some moisture in storage. Often sodium hydroxide requires much less than 4 hours to gain weight measurably.)

Making a chart of relative humidity. One of the major skills a student can develop in his science classes is to relate concepts to data. If one of your students likes to draw, he might turn Table 3–1 into a large illustrated chart. He might, for instance, show beakers filled in proportion to the relative humidity, with different-sized beakers used for each temperature to represent the capacity of the air at that temperature. As students understand the chart, they will be able to relate temperature to relative humidity.

3.2b Hygrometers

Students can gain experience using two kinds of hygrometers to measure relative humidity of air.

Wet- and dry-bulb thermometer. This type of thermometer, available commercially, consists of two identical thermometers, but with the bulb of one covered with a cotton wick resting in a small vial of water. Or you may prefer to have students make a wet- and dry-bulb thermometer from any two identical thermometers as shown in Fig. 3–4.

The difference between the readings of the two thermometers is determined, and then students can calculate the relative humidity by reading a psychrometric chart as shown in Table 3–2. At the top of the chart, students first find the difference between wet- and dry-bulb readings, then move straight down until they reach the number that is directly opposite the dry-bulb temperature. This number is the percentage of relative humidity.

Psychrometer. A sling psychrometer is a type of wet- and dry-bulb thermometer mounted so that it can be spun on a handle. This instrument gives a more accurate reading than the simple wet- and

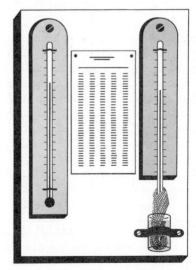

Fig. 3–4 Wet- and dry-bulb thermometer mounted with humidity chart.

TABLE 3-2
Relative humidity chart

TEMPERATURE OF DRY BULB

	61	62	63	64	65	66	67	68	69	70	71	72	73	74	75	76	77	78	79	80	
41	7	4	2																		41
42	10	8	6	4	2																42
43	14	12	10	7	5	3	2														43
44	18	16	13	11	9	7	5	3	1												44
45	22	20	17	15	12	10	8	6	5	3	1										45
46	27	24	21	18	16	14	12	10	8	6	4	3	1								46
47	31	28	25	22	20	17	15	13	11	9	7	6	4	3	1						47
48	35	32	29	26	24	21	19	16	14	12	10	9	7	5	4	3	1				48
49	40	36	33	30	27	25	22	20	18	15	13	12	10	8	7	5	4	3	1		49
50	44	41	37	34	31	29	26	23	21	19	17	15	13	11	9	8	6	5	4	3	50
51	49	45	42	38	35	32	30	25	24	22	20	18	16	14	12	11	9	8	6	5	51
52	54	50	46	43	39	36	33	31	28	25	23	21	19	17	15	13	12	10	9	7	52
53	58	54	50	47	44	40	37	34	32	29	27	24	22	20	18	16	14	13	11	10	53
54	63	59	55	51	48	44	41	38	35	33	30	28	25	23	21	19	17	16	14	12	54
55	68	64	60	56	52	48	45	42	39	36	33	31	29	26	24	22	20	18	17	15	55
56	73	69	64	60	56	53	49	46	43	40	37	34	32	29	27	25	23	21	19	18	56
57	78	74	69	65	61	57	53	50	47	44	41	38	35	33	30	28	26	24	22	20	57
58	84	79	74	70	66	61	58	54	51	48	45	42	39	36	34	31	29	27	25	23	58
59	89	84	79	74	70	66	62	58	55	51	48	45	42	39	37	34	32	30	28	26	59
60	94	89	84	79	75	71	66	62	59	55	52	49	46	43	40	38	35	33	31	29	60
61	100	94	89	84	80	75	71	67	63	59	56	53	50	47	44	41	39	36	34	32	61
62		100	95	90	85	80	75	71	67	64	60	57	53	50	47	44	42	39	37	35	62
63			100	95	90	85	80	76	72	68	64	61	57	54	51	48	45	43	40	38	63
64				100	95	90	85	80	76	72	68	65	61	58	54	51	48	46	43	41	64
65					100	95	90	85	81	77	72	69	65	61	58	55	52	49	46	44	65
66						100	95	90	85	81	77	73	69	65	62	59	56	53	50	47	66
67							100	95	90	86	81	77	73	69	66	62	59	56	53	50	67
68								100	95	90	86	82	78	74	70	66	63	60	57	54	68
69									100	95	90	86	82	78	74	70	67	63	60	57	69
70										100	95	91	86	82	78	74	71	67	64	61	70
71											100	95	91	86	82	78	74	71	68	64	71
72												100	95	91	86	82	79	75	71	68	72
73													100	95	91	87	83	79	75	72	73
74														100	96	91	87	83	79	75	74
75															100	96	91	87	83	79	75
76																100	96	91	87	83	76
77																	100	96	91	87	77
78																		100	96	91	78
79																			100	96	79
80																				100	80
	61	62	63	64	65	66	67	68	69	70	71	72	73	74	75	76	77	78	79	80	

TEMPERATURE OF WET BULB

To use the chart, match up the wet- and dry-bulb temperatures. The figure in the square where these intersect is the relative humidity. For example, suppose the dry-bulb thermometer reads 72° F, and the wet-bulb thermometer reads 63° F. Then the relative humidity would be 61% (circled in the table above). (From P. F. Brandwein et al., *You and Science*, Harcourt, Brace, 1960.)

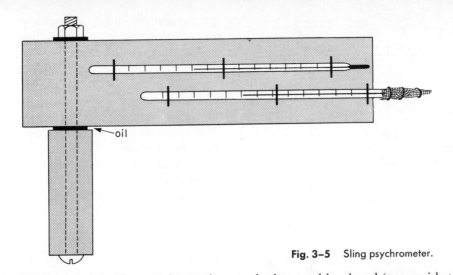

Fig. 3–5 Sling psychrometer.

oil

dry-bulb thermometer, because it permits more complete evaporation of the water from the wick in relation to the air's level of dryness. Weather stations use the psychrometer for determining relative humidity and dew point. A psychrometer may be purchased from a supply house (see listings in the appendix), or students can readily make one (Fig. 3–5). They will need to mount two identical liquid thermometers with fine copper or brass wire onto a 2″ board, with the bulb of one extending below the end of the board. This bulb is covered with cotton gauze or a wick held in place by a rubber band. Attach a handle to the other end of the board. A strong cord may serve as a handle. Now wet the gauze wick and twirl the psychrometer as in Fig. 3–6. Students can read the wet- and the dry-bulb temperatures and find the relative humidity by consulting the psychrometric chart (Table 3–2).

Two direct-reading hygrometers. A very simple direct-reading hygrometer can be made (Fig. 3–7) by suspending from a clamp on a ring stand or a piece of wood a gut string of the type used in violins or ukeleles. The top of the string is fastened securely, but the bottom is at-

tached to a rubber band (to provide tension) which is thumbtacked to the base. A toothpick passed through the string serves as an indicator on a cardboard scale fastened to the base. Calibrate the scale by marking the position of the pointer every day for several weeks, and ascertain the humidity as reported by radio or from a

Fig. 3–6 Swinging psychrometer about to ready it for a reading. Notice the use of a loop of rope as a handle.

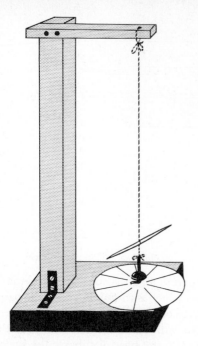

Fig. 3–7 Direct-reading hygrometer made from a gut string.

wet- and dry-bulb thermometer for the same day and hour.

As a special project, students can also make a hygrometer by attaching a small weight such as a washer to one end of a human hair, and using a toothpick as pointer (Fig. 3–8). Wash the hair in a detergent and allow to dry. Then pass the hair over a glass rod and fasten the other end of the hair with cellophane tape. Since the length of the hair will vary with humidity, the weight will move up or down. Have students place a small index card behind the toothpick and calibrate the hygrometer by marking the humidity daily as indicated by radio or psychrometric readings.

3.2c Dew point

The dew point, that is, the temperature reading at which moisture from the air condenses to form droplets, is an impor-

tant factor in forecasting the probability of rain or snow. You may want to begin by showing the condensation of water on the outside of a pitcher or tall beaker of cold water. (When air of a classroom is exceedingly dry as a result of steam heating, it may be difficult to reach the dew point.) Next nearly fill a tall metal tumbler or a shiny tall tin can with tap water, and stand in the water an accurate easy-to-read thermometer such as the dial-type (used in photographic developing) which is dependable down to one half of a degree. Now add one or two ice cubes and have one student observe the outside surface of the container for condensation droplets while a second student observes the thermometer scale. As the ice melts, the temperature of the water drops. What is the temperature when drops of condensed atmospheric water vapor appear on the outside surface of the container? This is the classroom's dew point. In the same manner when air outdoors reaches

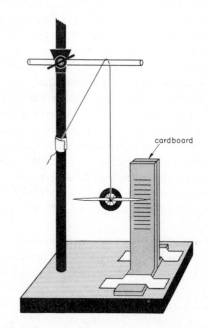

Fig. 3–8 Hygrometer using a length of hair.

the dew point, clouds form, and when during the night the surface of the ground cools the air to the dew point, dew forms.

(*Note:* For more precise measurements you may want to use a sensitive thermocouple and galvanometer or other precision electrical thermometer.)

For a more rapid demonstration, you can use dry ice in the water to speed the cooling. (*Caution: Always handle dry ice with gloves or tongs.*) Another method employs a small quantity of ether inside the container. Place the container on the window sill with the window open, and be sure that there are no flames in the room. The ether's rapid evaporation will probably cool the container to the dew point. Less flammable alcohol can be used in the same way though it evaporates more slowly.

If students add common salt to the water-ice mixture, it may reach a temperature low enough to deposit frost instead of dew on the outside of the container. A thick layer of frost can be created very rapidly by placing only dry ice inside the metal container. Snow crystals instead of droplets form from atmospheric water vapor whenever the air temperature is at freezing or below. You may want to have students examine snow crystals under the microscope. Use dry ice to chill the stage of the microscope and a slide.

3.2d Clouds

Artificial clouds in a flask. A cloud can be formed in a flask rather easily (Fig. 3–9). Fit a pressure-type flask with a two-hole stopper in which two short glass tubes are inserted. Connect one tube to a rubber tube fitted with an aspirator bulb (these are sold by supply houses and drugstores, or you can take one from an atomizer). Fit the other glass tube with rubber tubing and a pinch clamp. Aim the light beam of a projector through the flask and perform the demonstration in a darkened or dimly illuminated room. Place black velvet or black paper behind the flask to provide contrast.

Add about 30 cc of water to the flask. Close the flask, squeeze the bulb to increase the pressure in the flask, and then release the pinch clamp. No cloud will form, because condensation nuclei are not present. Now hold a smoldering match for a moment inside the flask leaving behind a wisp of smoke, close the flask, and repeat the same procedure. The smoke particles act as condensation nuclei, and when the pinch clamp is released a cloud forms. If dry ice is packed around the flask, some of the cloud will fall as snow. The cloud forms, because the sudden expansion that follows opening of the pinch clamp cools

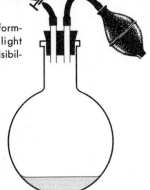

Fig. 3–9 Flask fitted for forming a cloud. A beam of light can be used for greater visibility.

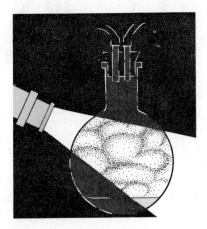

the flask. Show the change in pressure by connecting a mercury barometer or a mercury manometer U-tube to a third hole in the stopper (Fig. 3–10).

Cloud in a bottle. Many teachers use this approach to show how smoke particles act as condensation nuclei for water vapor in the air. Then if the volume of air is cooled by reducing the pressure, fog forms. A student can perform this preparation. Add an inch of water to a quart bottle that can be corked. Insert a burning match into the bottle so that smoke is produced. With a vacuum pump reduce the pressure in the bottle so that fog forms when the air is cooled. If the air pressure is alternately increased and decreased, students will find that clouds disappear and reappear.

Sutton[1] suggests that if a small amount

[1] R. Sutton, "Simplicity in Demonstrating Physics," *Science Teacher,* April 1948.

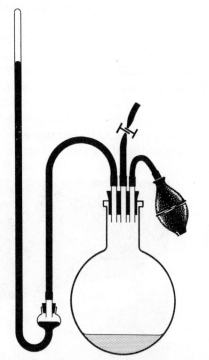

Fig. 3–10 Change of pressure and cloud formation.

of ether or alcohol is poured into a flask and stoppered quickly, then allowed to reach thermal equilibrium, a cloud forms when the stopper is removed. Notice what happens when the stopper is replaced and then removed again.

If a top-opening deep-freeze chest is available, you can introduce water in the bottom and seed the water vapor in the box with small fragments of dry ice (made by scraping dry ice) to cause the water vapor to precipitate. (Adding alcohol to the water will prevent it from freezing.)

3.2e   Water cycle

Students can demonstrate the water cycle by holding a chilled mirror above an open pan of water that is being heated electrically or by the sun's rays. (To increase the rate of heating by the sun use a black pan or place black paper in the bottom of the pan.) If dry ice is placed against a chromium-plated metal mirror of the type made for camping, "snow" or frost will develop directly from the water vapor in very much the same manner as snow forms directly from water vapor in clouds. (Further studies of low temperature with dry ice and acetone or alcohol are described in 4.6d.)

A complete closed water cycle can be set up in a length of ½″ glass tubing bent to form a large 8″ x 10″ square and joined at the top by a wide T-tube (Fig. 3–11). A small amount of water is heated at the bottom. Vapor will rise up one side, condense in the upper cross arm, and descend the other side. If the return section is cooled by ice cubes (as shown), the water cycle is accelerated. If the bottom tube is blackened, it can be heated by the sun or by the rays from an electric heater unit or an infrared bulb.

Rain gauge. Commercial rain gauges are available and easy to use, but students can devise one from any deep tin can and

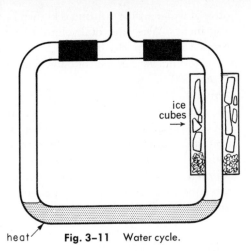

Fig. 3–11 Water cycle.

heat

an ordinary ruler (Fig. 3–12). Students can get accurate readings if they measure the water level immediately after rain stops falling. If this is not feasible, keep a thin layer of oil in the can. Floating on the water's surface, oil keeps the level fairly accurate by impeding evaporation.

Snow into rain. Pack ten or twelve inches of snow into a test tube. How much water will form from it? Generally ten inches of hard-packed snow will yield one inch of water.

3.3 Composition of the air

A rough estimate of the composition of air (oxygen, 20 per cent, and nitrogen plus the other gases, about 80 per cent) may be shown in several ways.

3.3a *Oxygen and nitrogen*

Students can invert a graduated cylinder over a burning candle secured to a cork floating in water. Oxygen is consumed and carbon dioxide is formed. The carbon dioxide being soluble is absorbed by the water which rises to occupy part of the volume of the cylinder.

Red phosphorus can be used instead of the candle. Prepare a thin float of cork

about 1¼" in diameter; on this place about 2 g of red phosphorus. Float the cork in a container of water. Plan to use a large cylinder, one about 2" in diameter and about 20" tall. Ignite the red phosphorus with a hot wire previously heated in a Bunsen burner, and immediately invert the cylinder over the float so that the mouth of the cylinder is below the water level. Watch the clouds of white "smoke," phosphorus pentoxide, inside the cylinder. When the reaction stops, the white cloud quickly clears since it, like SO_2, is very soluble in water. The water level rises inside the cylinder to take the place of the oxygen. Measure the water level with the mouth of the cylinder just under the surface of the water and compare the water level with the full length of the cylinder. What is the approximate volume of nitrogen?

As a project, some students can use an example of slow oxidation such as the rusting of steel wool or iron filings to show

Fig. 3–12 Simple rain gauge.

the proportion of oxygen to the other gases in air. Clean the steel wool by dipping it in a 2 M acetic acid solution, leaving it in until hydrogen bubbles rapidly stream off the steel wool. Rinse the steel wool in distilled water; shake off the water and insert the wool in the bottom of a 100-cc graduated cylinder so that it occupies about a quarter of the volume of the cylinder. Then support the cylinder, mouth downward, in a beaker of water so that the water levels inside and outside of the cylinder stand at the 95-cc mark (or some other specific mark). Students can disregard the volume of the steel wool since it is negligible. How high does water rise in the cylinder when the steel wool is permitted to rust over a period of a few days.

3.3b   Carbon dioxide in the air

To show that a very small quantity of carbon dioxide exists in air, bubble air through a quantity of limewater or bromthymol blue by using a hand pump. It will take several minutes of pumping for even a slight reaction to occur since the amount of carbon dioxide in air is normally about 0.04 of 1 per cent by volume.

Quantitative results may be obtained by using chips of sodium hydroxide (*Caution: Solid or conc. NaOH must not come in contact with skin*). Weigh the chips of hydroxide on a sensitive balance. Support them on a wire screen in a vertical tube fitted with a one-hole stopper at each end. Leaving one open for air to escape, connect the other opening to a hand pump. After long pumping by hand or by means of an electrically driven pump, weigh the chips of sodium hydroxide again. The increase in weight is due to the absorption of carbon dioxide. (At times there will be some error from absorption of water vapor.) Calculate the volume of air in cubic inches the pump delivers in a given time. Measure this by forcing water out of an inverted

bottle of water whose volume is known in cubic inches. When the total volume of air pumped is known, divide by 1728 cubic inches to find the number of cubic feet of air pumped.

Air weighs about 1¼ ounces per cubic foot at 32° F (1.29 grams per liter at 0° C). Multiply this by the number of cubic feet pumped and then divide the product into the gain in weight of the sodium hydroxide chips to get the approximate amount of carbon dioxide per cubic foot.

3.4   Atmospheric pressure
3.4a   Barometers

Several types of mercury barometers are sold by scientific supply houses; of these the Fortin cistern type is the most accurate. Each time this instrument is read, the meter scale must be adjusted to the level of the mercury in the bottom before reading the height of the mercury column. Also correct for expansion or contraction of the mercury that accompanies temperature changes using the correction scale that usually comes with the barometer. Avoid shaking or jarring a mercury barometer; the mercury column may break the sealed end of the barometer tube.

After making a Torricelli barometer in class, students may want to make a homemade J-tube type of barometer. For details on making mercury barometers see 16.1c.

Aneroid barometer. Clock- or wall-type dial barometers are usually of the aneroid type. They are inexpensive and fairly accurate, but they must be checked periodically against a mercury barometer and adjusted by turning the correction knob or screw.

Homemade aneroid barometer. Students can make a barometer from a milk bottle or a pint- to quart-size jar, rubber sheeting, and a soda straw (see 16.1d). The thin rubber sheeting is stretched across the mouth of a small glass bottle and held securely with thread and household cement. Next glue a soda straw (or straw from a whisk broom) on a very thin disk of cork which in turn is glued to the center of the rubber sheeting. Students can support the straw on a pointed piece of matchstick that has been glued to the side of the bottle. Then prepare a scale on cardboard and place this behind the tip of the straw. Calibrate the scale by checking with another barometer and number the scale from that point up and down. Students can record the daily changes they find during a month's time. This crude barometer is susceptible to temperature changes which introduce errors in the reading of pressure. For other details on making aneroid barometers see 16.1d.

Barograph. A barograph is an instrument which continuously records air pressure over a period of time, just as the thermograph does for temperature. Students would be especially interested in reading barometric changes that occur during the passage of a storm.

A 12-hour barograph can be constructed from an old alarm clock by following the directions given for the homemade thermograph (3.1a) but with an aneroid unit replacing the dial-type thermometer. Aircraft altimeters can also be used as aneroid barometers by means of a conversion scale to change altitude readings into barometric readings in inches or millimeters of mercury. Some altimeters contain a barometer scale and their readings need no conversion.

3.5   Winds

Some of the factors underlying the origin of winds can be demonstrated by students: Air expands when heated, warm air rises, volume-for-volume warm air is lighter than cold air, heat absorption varies with color and texture of a surface. Activities to demonstrate air pressure are described in Chapter 16. See also Chapter 18, particularly thermal expansion of gases, 18.2c.

3.5a   Wind direction

Ferrel's law. Students can demonstrate the effect of the earth's rotation upon wind direction by using a slate globe that rotates easily on its axis. For this demonstration hold the axis vertically. Pour a small amount of water on the north pole of the stationary globe. Watch how the water runs in the paths of the meridians to the opposite pole. Dry the globe; spin it in the same rotation as the earth's, west to east, and pour a little water on the top end of the rotating globe. When the globe comes to rest, trace the path of the water. Students will notice that it no longer follows the path of the meridians. Does the path of water curve to the right or to the left in the northern hemisphere? Is the path the same in the southern hemisphere? What effect does this rotation of the earth have on the direction of winds? Can a study of a successive series of weather maps show this?

Simple weather vane. A simple weather vane can be made as shown in Fig. 3–13. Have students place a triangular piece of aluminum as a pointer and a wide aluminum tail at the ends of a 16″ length of 1″ x 1″ wood. A hole is drilled in the stick at its balance point and the wood oiled. The stick is then mounted on a length of 2″ x 4″ wood stock by means of a screw and washers. (A roller-skate wheel makes an excellent bearing. Oil the bearing to prevent rusting.) The vane can be mounted at any high point where the direction of the wind is not deflected by surrounding buildings or hills. In what

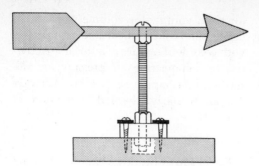

Fig. 3–13 Weather vane mounted on a roller-skate wheel.

attitude does the pointer face—toward or away from the wind?

Remote-indicating weather vane. The weather vane just described can be modified so that, though mounted on the roof, the wind direction can be read in the classroom (Fig. 3–14). In this case, the vane is mounted on the shaft of a 2000-ohm radio volume control from which the stops that prevent the arms from moving a full 360° have been broken off. The volume control is then mounted on a metal frame. Next connect the center terminal and one side terminal of the volume control in series with a low-range milliammeter, a switch, and a 3-volt battery. As the vane turns, the current through the volume control changes, and these changes are indicated on the milliammeter dial, which can be

calibrated by marking the needle position for each of the points and subordinate points of the compass. Then the vane may be mounted on the roof with two wires leading to the classroom where the battery, milliammeter, and switch are located. To conserve the battery, the current is turned on only when the wind direction is to be read.

3.5b   Wind speed

Anemometers show the wind speed on a scale located either on the instrument or at a remote position. Commercial models are expensive, but students can make small demonstration anemometers (without a scale) to show the principle. There are also several types of simple instruments that can be calibrated whose construction makes excellent student projects.

Vane-type anemometer. Attach a sheet of aluminum to a flat stick by metal rings and use a sideboard as a scale (Fig. 3–15). To calibrate select a windless day and hold the device outside a car window. When the car attains a speed of 5 mph, mark the position the edge of the aluminum sheet takes in relation to the scale. Repeat at intervals of 5 mph up to 40 mph. If the device is now mounted on a weather vane

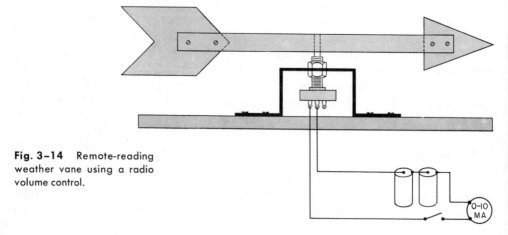

Fig. 3–14   Remote-reading weather vane using a radio volume control.

(Fig. 3–16), students can read the wind speed.

Centrifugal anemometer. This cup-type anemometer uses a ball in a curved glass tube as indicator. For cups, use four aluminum soup ladles bolted to a 6″ sheet aluminum disk by means of aluminum strips (Fig. 3–17). Attach the disk to a ¼″ bolt set in a ball-bearing skate wheel and clamp the wheel to a board which is mounted on a small wooden pedestal. (One good way to fasten down a roller-skate wheel is with 4 washers and 4 screws: the washers rest on the outer edge of the wheel and the screws go through them, down along the side of the wheel, and into the baseboard. This makes it unnecessary to drill holes in the skate wheel.) On top of the disk attach a curved glass tube that contains a small metal ball. Seal both ends of the tube with small corks or tape; hold the tube in place by bolting a metal strap to the aluminum disk. Wind speed is indicated by the height of the ball in the tube. Place a white card marked with evenly spaced parallel black lines so that it acts as a scale for reading the position of the ball in the tube. This instrument may be calibrated in the same way as the vane-type anemometer above.

Remote-reading electrical anemometer. This kind of anemometer is similar to the centrifugal model described above in that the same cup, disk, and ball-bearing arrangement is used, but the bolt that

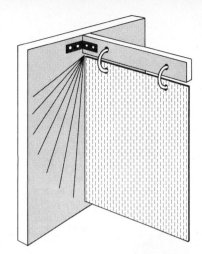

Fig. 3–15 A hanging sheet of aluminum used as a vane anemometer.

holds the aluminum disk to the skate wheel is made long enough to extend above and below the wheel (Fig. 3–18). It is held in position by a nut at the top and bottom, as shown. Attach a small (2″ long) alnico bar magnet to the bottom of the bolt by means of an aluminum strap to the bolt head. Then support the skate wheel by an aluminum frame bent as shown. On each side of the magnet mount one 100-turn coil of insulated magnet wire (gauge 30 to 36). Then connect the ends of the coils to a galvanometer or a low-range milliammeter in series with a small radio selenium rectifier or crystal diode 1N16 or 1N34 and a switch. Place the anemometer in the wind or in the air stream of an electric fan. As the magnet

Fig. 3–16 A vane anemometer mounted on a wind direction indicator.

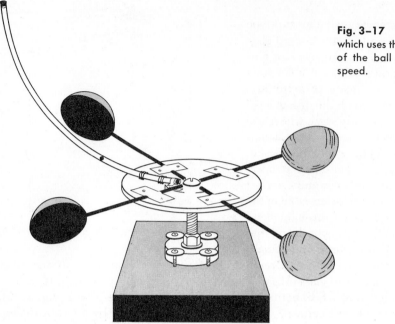

turns past the coils of wire, it induces an a.c. in the coils. The rectifier converts a.c. to d.c. for the meter. The higher the speed of the wind, the faster the rotation of the magnet and the greater the current that is generated. This instrument can be calibrated in a moving automobile as described above. Once calibrated, the anemometer can be placed on the roof, with two insulated wires connecting it to the meter and switch in the classroom.

3.6　Weather maps

After students have learned some of the factors that affect the daily weather, and they know how to use instruments to measure air pressure, temperature, wind direction, velocity, and relative humidity, they can put their knowledge to practical use. On a prearranged day have each student bring to class a weather map from the previous day's newspaper. After some practice in learning the symbols, have

students indicate their forecast of the daily weather for the rest of the week. Compare the forecasts with the actual conditions by having students collect weather maps for the entire week. What conditions may radically alter the forecast of the day's weather?

3.6a　Interpreting weather maps

Secure a set of 40 identical, large U.S. weather maps so that each student has a map to interpret. Students can study the explanations of symbols on the back of each map.

Isotherms. Students may use maps and data from a newspaper (or older data from an almanac) to prepare isothermal charts. To do this, they mark the average temperature for July at several places that they can locate, then draw a line connecting the points whose average temperature is 50° F. The same is done for places having an average temperature of 60° F and 70° F, etc. Students can explain why the iso-

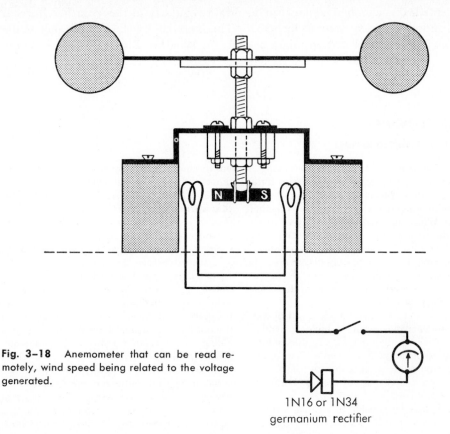

Fig. 3–18 Anemometer that can be read remotely, wind speed being related to the voltage generated.

1N16 or 1N34
germanium rectifier

therms nearly correspond in their direction to the parallels of latitude. How does the temperature of land compare with that of water in the same latitude? How does the heat equator differ from an isotherm?

Three-dimensional model of a weather front. As a project, a group of students can make a large model of a cold front or a warm front (see any text on meteorology). They will need to secure six transparent squares of plastic and mount them in slots in a heavy wooden base. (Glass may be used but it is hazardous.) To show the advancing position of the front, cover each square with a layer of black paper or, better, dark blue cellophane, starting at the base of the first square and rising from each to each. Represent rain by thin

dashed lines of blue ink or paint lines and clouds by Bon Ami, soap, or white water paint. If the spacings between the sheets are made to represent 100-mile distances, it will be easier to place the clouds, rain, and position of the front in correct proportion. When done, the model is viewed from front or back with a light source positioned in accordance.

3.6b Setting up a weather station

A class committee or student club may plan an outdoor instrument shelter in which they can keep a maximum-minimum thermometer, psychrometer, and barometer; the weather vane and anemometer can be mounted as described in this chapter. A mercury barometer (either a homemade or a commercial one) can be set up indoors in a convenient location. Such a school weather station might become an amateur station that contributes data regularly to the Weather Bureau. This is accomplished by application to the U. S. Weather Bureau in Washington, D. C.

CAPSULE LESSONS
Ways to get started in class

3-1. You may want to begin by having a committee of students collect local weather data. They can attempt to make forecasts and compare their predictions with those of the Weather Bureau. What factors affect the daily weather? From the weather map students can read the terms "pressure," "temperature," "humidity," and "precipitation." Then students are ready to explore what these terms mean and the instruments that are used to measure these characteristics of the air around us.

3-2. As a club activity leading out of class work, students may want to build a weather station. Refer to the directions in this chapter for ways to make the instruments. Or you may prefer to purchase some accurate commercial instruments (see listing of supply houses in appendix).

3-3. It may be possible to arrange a trip to a local weather station, an airport weather station, or one at an Air Force base. These trips must be planned well in advance, for some stations have a busy schedule of such visits. Also obtain and file parental permission notes if this is the custom in your school system.

3-4. You may want to display the Weather Bureau cloud chart. For a minute each day, have students identify the clouds present in the sky. A committee of students may want to check the clouds at three-hour intervals during the day.

3-5. Students can help you to prepare a Torricelli barometer (16.1c). Why is mercury used in the barometer? Compare the mercury system with the aneroid. If possible place an altimeter under a bell jar and use a vacuum pump to remove some of the air from the bell jar. What change is produced in the altimeter? What happens when air is returned to the bell jar?

3-6. At some other time connect a U-tube manometer containing water dyed with red ink or eosin to a small funnel by means of a tube. Across the funnel fasten a thin sheet of rubber. Gently press on the rubber sheeting. What effect has this increase in pressure on the height of the liquid in the U-tube manometer?

3-7. Devise several demonstrations to show that warm air rises. A simple but effective illustration is to hold a cartwheel or thin paper streamers attached to a rod in the warm air currents high above a Bunsen flame. (*Caution: Do not allow streamers to reach flames.*) Also show convection currents as described in 18.3b.

3-8. Have a committee of students canvass several adults in different occupations to learn the many superstitions concerning weather and the individual means used for predicting a change in the weather. How much of the statements is folklore? Are there correct working hypotheses in any of the predictions? How much is based on trial and error, pure chance, the wrong identification of causes? Point out that even if two events are connected in time that does not mean the events are causally connected. Red sun followed by a storm does not mean the red sun caused the rain. Crickets may chirp and rain may fall but crickets have no rain-making powers. From this discussion students can begin to summarize the true causal factors that determine the daily weather pattern.

3-9. Begin one lesson with a shiny metal container, ice water, and a thermometer. Why does water condense on the outer surface? Where does the water come from? From here students may trace the entire water cycle. What happens to water streaked down a blackboard, or the moisture that is breathed onto a mirror? Introduce the terms "evaporation" and "condensation"; later lead into humidity and relative humidity. Introduce the chart of relative humidity percentages; have a student explain how to calculate relative humidity. How much moisture can cold air hold?—warm air?

3-10. On occasion have a lesson using a film as a summary of the main concepts developed in this work. Show a film or strip such as *Air Masses and Fronts* (Indiana U.), *Canopy of Air* (Life),

Clouds (N.Y.S. Dept. Commerce), or others dealing with weather and climate. What kind of weather is found on the leeward side of a mountain range?

3-11. Students may bring from home several examples of barometers and thermometers. Also ask them to bring in those attractive figures dressed in cobalt chloride paper and which are turned by a gut string so they move in and out of the house with changes in humidity. Have students explain how these devices work. Also explain how a weather vane works. Some students may make an anemometer as described in this chapter.

PEOPLE, PLACES, AND THINGS

It may be possible to turn for assistance to your local weather bureau or to state and federal agencies. There may be an instrument supply house from which you may borrow instruments for short periods. Better still, a guest speaker may talk to the class on some aspect of weather forecasting; there may be an ex-serviceman who was trained in meteorology.

Some teachers plan field trips to airports to study the methods used to check weather conditions 24 hours a day. Arrangements must be made in advance; students, too, must plan together on the expected outcomes of the field trip.

There are several weather kits available from supply houses (see appendix) which enable young people to set up their own weather stations.

Books and pamphlets

These are only a few of the books which are pertinent to the work discussed in this chapter. These and many other references classified by subject and with complete bibliographical data are given in the bibliography at the end of the book.

Cheronis, N., J. Parsons, and C. Ronneberg, *The Study of the Physical World,* Houghton, Mifflin, 1957.

Eddington, A., *The Nature of the Physical World,* Cambridge U. Press, 1953.

Fisher, R., *How to Know and Predict the Weather,* New American Library, 1953, $.50.

Haltiner, G., and F. Martin, *Dynamical and Physical Meteorology,* McGraw-Hill, 1957.

Kimble, G., *Our American Weather,* McGraw-Hill, 1955.

Krick, I., and R. Fleming, *Sun, Sea and Sky,* Lippincott, 1954.

Pettersen, S., *Weather Analysis and Forecasting,* McGraw-Hill, 1956.

Scientific American, "Circulation of the Atmosphere," December, 1956; "Origin of Hurricanes," August, 1957; "Sun Clouds and Rain Clouds," April, 1957; "Tornadoes," May, 1958.

Scientific Encyclopedia, Van Nostrand, 1956.

Shapley, H., ed., *Climatic Change: Evidence, Causes and Effects,* Harvard U. Press, 1953.

Swenson, H., and J. Woods, *Physical Science for Liberal Arts Students,* Wiley, 1957.

Films and filmstrips

This partial list is intended only as a guide toward film and filmstrip selection. Refer to the more complete listing at the end of the book where films are classified by subject and a key to abbreviations and the addresses of distributors are given. The cost of film rental, of course, may be subject to change. Films are sound and black and white unless otherwise specified.

Air in Action (f, s), Audio Film Center, $2.00.

Air Masses and Fronts (f, s, c), Indiana U., $6.00.

Atmosphere and its Circulation (f, s), EBF, $2.50.

Atom and the Weather (f, s), U.S.A.E.C. and field offices, free.

Basic Weather (fs, 2 in series), Society for Visual Education; $3.25 each.

Big Winds (fs, c), Popular Science through McGraw-Hill, $6.00.

Birth of a Volcano—Paricutin (f, s), Institutional Cinema, $2.00.

Birthplace of Icebergs (Father Hubbard's series), (f, s), Teaching Film Custodians, free.

Canopy of Air (fs, c), Life, $6.00.

Clouds (f, s), Almanac, $2.00.

Clouds (f, s), N.Y. State Dept. Commerce, free.

Cold Front (f, s, c), Indiana U., $4.25.

Earth, Latitude and Longitude (f, s), Institutional Cinema, $2.00.

Earth and Sky Series: Seasons, Stars, Rocks, Weather, Constellations, Earth Satellite, Solar Energy, etc. (11 fs in series), Popular Science through McGraw-Hill, $3.50 each.

Earth, Rotation and Revolution (f, s), Institutional Cinema, $2.00.

Everybody Talks About It (U.S. Weather Bur.) (f, s), Teaching Film Custodians, free.

Expedition to Antarctica (MGM film) (f, s, c, 2 rls), Teaching Film Custodians, free.

Face of the Earth (f, s, c), EBF, $4.00.

Geological Work of Ice (f, s), EBF, $2.50.

Great Lakes, How They were Formed (f, s, c), N.Y. State Dept. Commerce, free.

Great Winds (2 fs), United World, $4.50.

Ground Water (f, s), EBF, $2.50.

Hurricane Hunters (f, s), Dept. Navy, free.

Ice Cap II (testing clothes and equipment) (f, s), Dept. of Army, free.

It's in the Air (air conditioning) (f, s, c), Modern Talking Pictures, free.

Men, Steel, and Earthquakes (f, s, c), Modern Talking Pictures, free.

Minerals and Rocks (f, s, c), EBF, $4.50.

Modern Weather (storm, atmospheric waves) (f, s, 2 rls), Almanac, $3.50.

Mountain Building (f, s), Institutional Cinema, $2.00.

Mt. Rainier (glaciers) (f, s, c), EBF, $4.00.

Occluded Fronts (f, s, c), Indiana U., $4.50.

Operation Hurricane (f, s), Indiana U., $1.00.

Pipeline to the Clouds (f, s, c), General Electric, free.

Prophet without Honor (MGM) (Admiral Maury and ocean currents, f, s), Teaching Film Custodians, free.

Report on Smog (f, s, c), Stanford Research Institute, free.

The River (f, s), U.S. Department of Agriculture or N.Y. State Dept. Commerce, free.

River of Ice (alpine valley glacier) (f, s), N.Y. State College of Agriculture, Cornell, $1.00.

The Seasons (2 fs, c, 2 in series), United World, $4.50 each.

The Seasons (f, s, c, 2 rls), Teaching Film Custodians, free.

Seasons and Their Cause (f, s), Audio Film Center, $2.00.

Seasons of the Year (f, s), Coronet, inquire film library.

Thundering Water (f, s, c), N.Y. State Dept. of Commerce or N.Y. Central System, free.

Tides (f, s), Almanac, $2.00.

Tornadoes, What They Are and What To Do About Them (fs), VEC, $3.50.

The Unchained Goddess (f, s, c), Bell, free.

Volcanoes in Action (f, s), EBF, $2.50.

Warm Front (f, s, c), Indiana U., $4.50.

The Weather (f, s), EBF, $2.50.

Weather (fs, c), Harcourt, Brace, $6.00.

Weather Fronts and Forecasting (fs, c), Popular Science through McGraw-Hill, $6.00.

Weather Instruments (f, s), Indiana U., $2.00.

Weather Research (f, s) (*Search* series filmed at U. of Chicago), Young America, inquire film library.

Winds and Their Causes (f, s), Indiana U., $2.00.

Wonder Trail (erosion) (f, s), Teaching Film Custodians, free.

Work of the Atmosphere (f, s), EBF, $2.50.

Work of Rivers (f, s), EBF, $2.50.

Work of Running Water (f, s), Ideal, $2.00.

You and the Weather (f, s, c), Texas Company, regional office.

FREE AND INEXPENSIVE MATERIALS

This is only a partial listing of free and inexpensive materials available to the teacher at this time. A more complete listing, including addresses, is given at the end of the book. Many of these materials are distributed to teachers without charge. Where there is a small fee, the cost is indicated, although the prices are subject to change. While we recommend the material for use in the classroom, we do not necessarily endorse the products advertised.

Daily Weather Maps, United States, with map codes and symbols, Supt. Documents, $0.02 each, $.60 month.

Instructions for Climatological Observers, Supt. Documents, $0.50.

Hobby Publications, #25, Supt. Documents, free.

How to Work with Tools and Wood, Pocket Books, $0.25.

Meteorology: Careers and Education, American Meteorological Society, free.

Project Cirrus (cloud seeding), General Electric, free.

Rainmaking, A Study of Experiments, Dept. Public Information, United Nations, $0.15.

Smog, Standard Oil, free.

Stanley Tool Guide, Educational Dept., Stanley Tools, $0.25.

The Weather, How and Why, New York *Times,* $0.25.

Weather Almanac, The New Information Bur., $0.15.

Weather Bureau Publications (list of publications and prices), Supt. Documents, free.

Weather Forecasting, Supt. Documents, $0.25.

Weather and You (for current science and aviation), W. Leeds, American Education Publications, inquire cost.

CHAPTER 4

The earth's surface: land and water

Many students collect rocks: some are fascinated by their form and color; others are interested in crystal structure, or are curious about fossils; some see rocks primarily as chemistry; still others see in rocks a handwritten history of the earth itself. These hobbies can lead into lifetime interests and work.

Every part of the country has at least some rock cover. This cover not only offers a geological history of a region but also determines its type of vegetation. Although the professional geologist has special tools, many of his more common tools can be duplicated by students. Much help can be obtained from supply houses which specialize in geological materials (see directory in appendix). Geology is also a rich field for the student interested in making models.

4.1 The earth's surface

There are many aspects of land study—from field trips planned for the study of living things and rocks and minerals to excavations and speleology. Some aspects of the work which yield easily to classroom study follow. Suggestions for more intensive study will be found in the references at the end of this chapter.

4.1a Major land forms

The United States can be divided into broad physiographic units which exem-plify the main land forms. Land formation comprises the building up and the wearing away of areas of the earth. Students can describe new land formations such as the upheavals that produce "young" mountains, deposition of soil by water or wind, eroded mountain areas that have been worn down to plateaus and plains. Other examples are the uplifted regions and the results of former glaciation, lava flows, and volcanic eruption.

Excellent maps of these physiographic regions are available from the United States Geological Survey. A study of these land forms will help students develop understanding of the climatic and topographic influences affecting the development of the land and its uses. Some of the land forms which may be studied with profit: a flood plain and delta (Mississippi Flood Plain); a glacial lake plain (Fargo Quadrangle); a coastal plain (Wicomico Quadrangle); plains that have been uplifted and eroded (Great Plains as shown in the Caldwell Sheet); a high plain or plateau that has been long exposed to factors of erosion in a humid climate (Appalachian Plateau as shown in the Pittsburgh Quadrangle); an old mountain region (Appalachian Piedmont as shown in the Milledgeville Quadrangle); Appalachian Mountains (Harrisburg Quadrangle); plains cities (Cleveland, St. Louis, or Denver Quadrangle); Rocky Mountains (Chief Mountain, Montana); Columbia

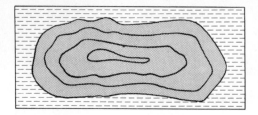

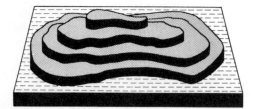

Fig. 4–1 Three-dimensional models of terrain to show the nature of contour lines on a map.

Lava Plateau in the Spokane area in the Washington-Idaho Sheet; Colorado Canyon and Plateau in the Arizona Sheet; coast ranges; Sierra Nevada Range; Cascade Range; a region of mature drainage (Charleston Quadrangle); a glaciated valley (Watkins Quadrangle).

4.1b Contour maps and scale models

Many teachers find that students learn to interpret contour maps more rapidly if a three-dimensional contour model is prepared (Fig. 4–1). Geodetic Survey maps for your local area (a hilly region if possible) may be purchased from your state geological department or from the Geodetic Survey Office in Washington, D. C., or from large map stores in many cities. For large-area contours you may find a convenient aid in the Flight Charts obtainable from the Geodetic Survey Office or at most airports that service private aircraft.

Students can build a contour model using a baseboard of plywood or pressed wood. A large sheet of tracing paper is used to outline the first or lowest contour on the map. Transfer this outline to another layer of plywood or pressed wood and cut it to the shape of the contour; add this to the base. Repeat this procedure for the second and subsequent contours until all are finished and layered. These layers can be assembled with glue and nails. Some teachers have students cut out the original contour portion of the map which they then paste on the proper contour layer. (When contour models are made of a tall mountain, students may want to use contour intervals of 500 or 1000 feet.) Once built, the layers can be smoothed off with plaster. Students can then, if they wish, mark the contour edges with India ink or paint the surface to match the ground cover. For a simpler, though less effective, model, cardboard can be used instead of wood.

Lines of light can also be used to demonstrate what the contour lines on a map represent.[1] Rule parallel scratches 1/16″ apart in the surface of a 2″ × 2″ glass slide that has been opaqued either with emulsion or a thin coat of black tempera. When placed in a projector and focused on an irregular surface such as a bunched up piece of cloth, the lines of light will flow in and out marking the contour levels (Fig. 4–2).

With practice in making and reading contour maps, students will soon recognize the meaning of contour lines crowded together in one area and widely separated in another part of the map. They can quickly recognize the terrain and can learn to measure distances with close accuracy as well as visualize an area from a contour map.

[1] Adapted from an article in *Teaching Tools Magazine* by John P. Vergis, Associate Professor, Arizona State University, Tempe, Arizona.

4.1c Changes in the earth's surface

A sand table (below) or a sand tray, a large pan with sand in it, or even an aquarium with sand in it, can be used by students as a modeling medium to develop concepts of land structure and change. Other devices are suggested below.

Uplifting of land: mountain formation. Several of the movements of the earth's crust can be demonstrated in class. Some teachers use a roll of cotton to show folding of the land due to lateral pressure. Even better, you may want to use several thin layers of sponge rubber, each a different color. Apply lateral pressure by pressing from opposite ends of the sponge layers (Fig. 4–3). This pressure is normally due to the weight of oceans and land masses. Students will notice how the layers bend and form a mountain. They can identify synclines and anticlines.

Faulting. Models of faulted mountains can be built out of layers of wood varying in thickness and painted different colors. If the models are made so that they slide apart, students can demonstrate the short, steep slope on one side and the shift in levels of the rock strata as one section or block slips over the other.

To show faulting that results from the loss of elasticity during the folding of strata, use differently colored layers of modeling clay, in place of sponge rubber. If the clay is sufficiently stiff and lateral pressure is applied (as described above for folded mountains), the layers or folds break and a fault develops. It may be possible to show that a fault may result in an earthquake if one mass shifts and sets up vibrational waves. Try to float the clay model on very soft, wet, "water soluble" clay and move one mass on the side of the fault. Does the entire mass go into vibration? You may want to use a map of Cali-

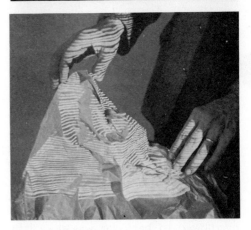

Fig. 4–2 Light passing through an opaque slide on which parallel lines have been scratched provides a graphic means of showing contour lines. (John P. Vergis, Arizona State University.)

fornia to trace the San Andreas fault.

Volcanic action. You can show the formation of a volcanic mountain by using ammonium dichromate as described in 2.3. The material erupts like a volcano and throws up "cinders" which build up the typical volcanic cinder cone.

Delta formation. Many students already know that a fast-moving stream can

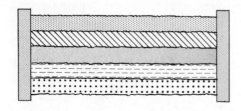

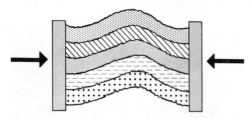

Fig. 4–3 Sponges of various colors to represent folding of strata.

carry large rocks and other suspended materials. What happens to the suspended particles when the velocity of the stream is reduced by some barrier or when they reach the mouth of a river? It may be possible to take students out-of-doors to examine regions in your locality where streams are slowed down with a subsequent deposition of soil particles. Or use the sedimentation jar containing different-sized particles. Fill with water, shake, then allow to settle, noting the size of particles and their order of settling out. If a stream overflowed its banks or was slowed by some barrier, how would the particles deposit themselves? Why are strata of sedimentary rock found in a succession, from bottom to top, of conglomerate, sandstone, shale, and limestone? (See also 4.2a.)

It may also be possible to make a delta in a sand table, a sand tray, or a large plastic wading pool. As in Fig. 4–4, use soil to set up a river channel with a large bay at the bottom. Pour in muddy water at a high speed at the upper end. Watch how the suspended mud or silt drops out in the "gulf" water and not in the river channel. Keep the bay water fairly shallow to speed the building of deltas, but not so shallow that the water simply piles its debris against the bottom wall.

Meanders and oxbow lakes. New rivers usually run deep and straight. Old rivers, on land that has been leveled by erosion, meander lazily across the flat land. Students can show how these slow-moving rivers may deposit silt on one side of the river so that a loop is cut off as an oxbow lake. In a sand table use clay as a base to model several meanders and allow sand and water to flow into these slowly (Fig. 4–5). As the "river" course changes, students can demonstrate how the sand will be dropped on the inner or slower side of a curve in the "river," and erode the outer edge. The river will then gradually build up a new channel. Demonstrate how an oxbow lake results from a cutoff.

Ground water and cave formation. You may want to have students show how underground caves are formed. Bubble some CO_2 into water (or use soda water from a bottle) to duplicate the way that CO_2 from the air is absorbed in rainwater. Then set up a device (say a funnel with rubber tubing and a screw clamp) to keep dropping the carbonated water on a piece of limestone ($CaCO_3$). Eventually a tiny dent will form. Compare this with the action of dilute hydrochloric acid which will etch a dent in a few minutes. While the action of CO_2 is slower, it is continuous, as ground water comes in contact with limestone deposits. Geologically there is more than enough time for huge caverns to be formed.

The equation for the reaction

$$H_2CO_3 + CaCO_3 \rightarrow Ca^{++} + 2\,HCO_3^-$$

explains how we get hard water (Ca^{++} ions

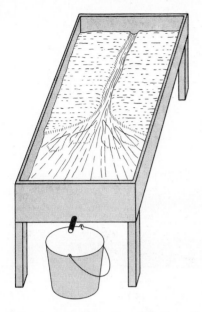

Fig. 4-4 A sand table to show delta formation.

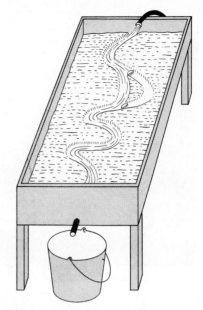

Fig. 4-5 A sand table to show meander and ox-bow lake.

in solution). Although the $CaCO_3$ is virtually insoluble in pure water, the bicarbonate formed by this process is very soluble. For a discussion of hard water and water-softening agents, see 4.7b.

As students study how ground water can form caverns and sink holes, can build new rock formations such as stalagmites and stalactites, they can be led toward the phenomenon of ground water trapped between layers of impervious rock, thus making possible the artesian well.

Wells and springs. You may want to have students demonstrate a working model that will show ground water, the water table, an artesian well, and a spring (Fig. 4–6). Students can build a watertight layer of modeling clay at one end of a large aquarium tank to represent an impervious rock layer. Then add a layer of gravel or small pebbles to act as the aquifer (water-holding bed). Over these

place another layer of modeling clay to represent the upper impervious rock layer, and lastly lay in a covering of soil. Students should explain that in their model the permeable layer is open at the top of the hill. Then they can drill a hole with a pencil in the flat area of the model and insert a medicine dropper stem without its bulb. Pour in water to represent rain on the hilltop; if the layers of clay are watertight, water will trickle through the soil to the top layer of clay. If a student digs a shallow well in the upper soil layer, he will strike the ground water (water table level). Water trapped between the two impervious layers will squirt out of the dropper stem to represent an artesian well. A wire may be used to drill a small hole in the side of the hill to show how a spring flows.

As a project, some students may want to study geological maps of their local area to determine the origin of

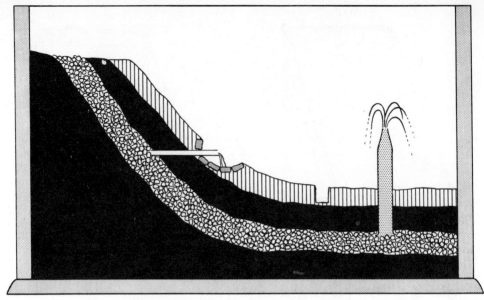

Fig. 4–6 Model of an artesian well and spring.

springs, artesian wells, and other sources of water.

Weathering. On a short field trip around the school lawn or the neighborhood, students will come upon several examples of physical weathering: exfoliated rocks where layers have peeled away as a result of cracking due to alternate hot and freezing temperatures; cracks in boulders which widen each year as water fills the cracks, freezes, and expands; roots of trees which grow into such a crack and thus cause fragmentation. Students can demonstrate the effect of freezing water on rocks such as schist by freezing rocks in a mixture of dry ice and acetone.

Students can examine concrete and brick to see the effects of weathering by rain and winds. Determine the origin, too, of the rock debris (talus) found at the bottom of a hillside. Students can examine with a hand lens fine sand and coarse gravel from a beach. How have the sand particles become rounded?

Chemical weathering has already been described in the action of carbonic acid on rocks. But it can also be observed in a walk through the neighborhood. What is the texture of rocks where lichens grow? Also examine the bottom of several rocks and see the effect of decay microorganisms. Students may try to find out what causes the "rust" that streaks some kinds of marble exposed to rain and air.

Most chemical weathering is the result of solution, carbonation, oxidation, or hydration. Some oxides are soluble in water. Many aluminum compounds combine with water; some mineral aluminum silicates (feldspars) are broken down in hydration into the hydrous aluminum silicate, kaolin. Feldspar, by the way, is estimated to make up perhaps 60 per cent of the earth's crust.

Erosion. The transport by wind, water, or ice of soil or products of weathering is erosion. On a trip around the school grounds or on the way to school, students may notice soil washed down into the roads or street from a lawn or pasture. In some sections of the country the unfortunate effects of winds carrying soil are seen as dust storms.

Students may discuss, in a special report, the way in which erosion by water wears down land in one region of the country and builds up new land, at times, thousands of miles away. (Students can demonstrate delta formation or oxbow lakes as described earlier in this section.)

Raindrop erosion can be explored in many ways. Set outdoors a large sheet of white cardboard supported against a wood post. After a rainstorm note the amount of soil splattered up on the cardboard. Or set out large wooden disks, such as are used in shuffleboard, on bare soil. After several months, examine them and explain why soil under the disks is slightly higher than the surrounding soil level.

Some students may want to demonstrate the amount of soil contained in the runoff from a hillside that is contour-plowed, as compared with one that is furrow-plowed or bare (Fig. 4–7). What are some soil conservation methods in use in your neighborhood?

Erosion and loess. Loess is simply fine wind-blown soil or silt. A film of loess gathers on window panes almost everywhere. Its presence and also a "micro demonstration" of erosion can be shown in this manner. Flick a few drops of water on a "dirty" window. The runlet of water will carry (erode) the loess.

The chalkboard is a particularly good tool for demonstrations in earth science. For instance, the demonstration of erosion of loess on the window may be done on the chalkboard with chalk dust representing loess.

We have presented here only an introduction as a guide to discussion, for a full treatment of physiography is beyond the scope of this book. There are excellent films, filmstrips, and color slides as resources in this area of conservation of soil. These may be found in film catalogs (see directory of distributors in the appendix). The companion volume, *Teaching High School Science: A Sourcebook for the Biological Sciences,* describes many studies of erosion as it relates to conservation and farming.

"Old" and "young" landscapes. The ledge of the chalkboard can be used to show the difference between young and old landscapes, particularly mountains. As a mountain erodes, its sharp V-shaped structure rounds out and finally flattens.

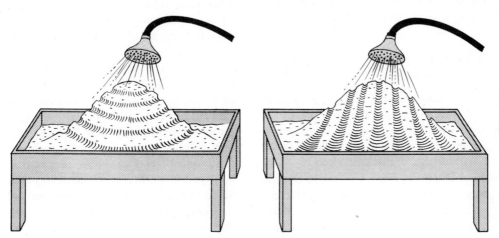

Fig. 4–7 Comparing soil erosion: contour plowing and straight plowing.

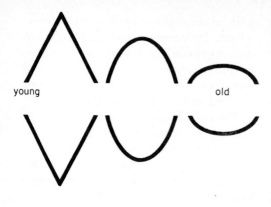

young   old

Fig. 4–8   Outlines of "old" and "young" valleys and mountains.

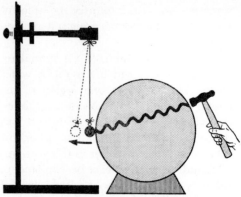

Fig. 4–9   A water-filled flask used to show the transmission of shock waves.

Students can build a young mountain out of clay on the ledge of the chalkboard, and then build other models to show the sequence of transition to an old mountain (Fig. 4–8). They can then trace the outlines of these shapes on the chalkboard. At this point, a student may recognize that these diagrams, upside down, describe young and old rivers.

With discussion, the concept that the aging of mountains and rivers is connected may be developed. As young landscapes become old, through erosion, peaks are rounded off and their soil coursing along the beds of rivers rounds them off, too, by filling them in and by abrasive action.

4.1d   Demonstrating a seismic wave

A hollow metal or plastic globe filled with water can be used to represent the earth with the container itself representing the crust, and the water, the liquid core.

At one side of this globe and in contact with it (as in Fig. 4–9) hang a small metal ball on a pendulum string from a ring stand. Now hit the side of the sphere opposite the pendulum bob with a hammer. Students can explain that the wave will travel through the water to the other side, and kick the bob, making the pendulum bob a recorder of the seismic wave. You may want to use an empty globe as a control.

4.2   Types of rocks

4.2a   Sedimentary rock

Students can demonstrate in class the formation of sedimentary rock.

They can collect fine clay, colored sand and gravel, and rocks of varying sizes along with twigs, leaves, shells, or small toy animals; pour these materials into a large battery jar of water and stir vigorously to simulate the action of a fast-moving stream. What will happen when the speed of water is slowed? Within the class period, students can see how the heavier particles settle quickly to the bottom of the battery jar while fine particles such as clay remain suspended. Let the jar stand undisturbed for several days so that students can see that even the finest particles finally settle out. Recall the complete cycle of erosion: rock is worn down in one place and new rock is formed in another. This new rock is sedimentary, the kind

TABLE 4-1
The sources of sedimentary and metamorphic rocks

source	sedimentary rock	metamorphic rock
clay	shale	slate-schist-mica
sand	sandstone	quartzite
gravel	conglomerate	quartzite, etc.
marl shell beds	limestone	marble
peat	bituminous coal	anthracite coal (graphite)
granite		gneiss

often seen profiled in a building excavation or "cut" along a highway right-of-way in the mountains.

Several realistic demonstrations can be done to show how rocks are formed. Prepare hardened sedimentary rock by mixing plaster of Paris with an excess of water so that the plaster settles as a sediment to the bottom, where it will harden. If the same process is demonstrated with powdered calcium carbonate mixed with Portland cement, synthetic limestone will form at the bottom. Students can also make a "shale" by mixing clay and Portland cement with water. Allow this mixture to settle and the water to evaporate. Or use self-hardening pottery clay in the same way.

Fossils in sedimentary rock. Students should be able to use the preceding demonstrations to explain the formation of a fossil within sedimentary rock. They may also show how imprints have been formed. Make up a thin paste of plaster of Paris and pour it into boxes or tin forms which have previously been coated with petroleum jelly. On the surface of the plaster lay several shells or leaves of trees, or have a student touch his hand to the plaster. After the plaster hardens, students have an imprint of the shell, leaf, or hand.

4.2b   Metamorphic rock

Mix some cement, place it in a covered mold, and subject this to pressure in a strength-of-materials machine of the kind illustrated in 16.5b or between the jaws of a vise. Students may compare how much harder this cement is than cement that has hardened merely on standing (see hardness test 4.5b).

4.2c   Igneous rock

By using the thermite process (10.2c), you can create the extremely high temperatures necessary for the formation of igneous rocks. Often a glassy slag is formed in a way that is similar to the change from limestone into marble when hot magma enters fissures in limestone. (See Table 4–1, forms of rock.)

4.3   Identification of minerals

Hardness. The hardness scales (Tables 4–2 and 4–3) can be used as preliminary means for identification of minerals. (For details see 4.5b.)

TABLE 4-2
Hardness scale

Mohs' scale	working scale
1. talc	1. very easily scratched by fingernail; soft greasy feel
2. gypsum or rock salt	2. just scratched by fingernail
3. calcite	3. scratched by brass pin or copper coin
4. fluorite	4. easily scratched by knife but will not scratch glass
5. apatite	5. scratched with difficulty with knife and just scratches glass
6. feldspar	6. not scratched by knife, easily scratched by file, scratches glass
7. quartz	7. little affected by file, will scratch hard glass
8. topaz	
9. corundum	
10. diamond	10. will scratch anything

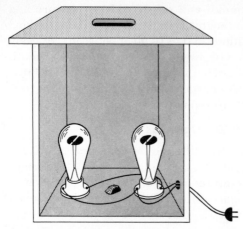

Fig. 4–10 Mineral identification using ultraviolet box.

4.3a   Chemical identification

Chemical tests for various elements that make up rocks are described in several sections of those chapters devoted to chemistry. For more elaborate analyses, stu-dents may want to refer to a qualitative analysis text (see bibliography in appen-dix).

4.3b   Ultraviolet identification

Ultraviolet light provides a rapid method for identification of minerals in rocks (Table 4–4). Students can build a simple identification box (Fig. 4–10) from a wooden box about 12″ x 6″ x 10″ (the dimensions are not critical). Fasten two porcelain-base sockets to the inside of the bottom of the box and wire them to an electric cord and plug. Seal the seams of the box on the inside with black masking tape to make it lightproof. Then equip the cover with an overhanging edge as shown to form a light trap. Cut an oval hole about 1″ by 3″ in the center of the cover. Two 2-watt argon bulbs, which can be obtained from a scientific supply house (see appendix) or a large electrical

TABLE 4-3
Hardness of certain minerals (Mohs')*

agate	6–7	cadmium	2.0	iridium	6–7	pumice	6
alabaster	1.7	calamine	4.5–5	iridosmine	6–7	pyrite	6–6.5
alum	2–2.5	calcium	1.5	iron	4–5	rock salt	2
aluminum	2–2.9	carborundum	9–10	kaolin	2.0–2.5	Ross' metal	2.5–3
alundum	9+	cesium	0.2	lead	1.5	rubidium	0.3
amber	2–2.5	chromium	9.0	lignite	1.1–1.3	ruthenium	6.5
andalusite	7.5	copper	2.5–3	lithium	0.6	selenium	2.0
anthracite	2.25	diatomaceous		loess (0° C)	0.3	serpentine	2.5–4.5
antimony	3.0–3.5	earth	1–1.5	magnesium	2.0	silicon	7
aragonite	3.5–4	dolomite	3.5–4	magnetite	5.5–6.5	silver	2.5–3
arsenic	3.5	emery	7–9	manganese	5.0	silver chloride	1.3
asbestos	5	feldspar	6–6.5	marble	3–4	sodium	0.4
asphalt	1–2	flint	7	meerschaum	2–3	steel	5–8.5
augite	6	galena	2.5–2.7	mica	2.5–4	stibnite	2
barite	2.5–3.5	gallium	1.5	opal	5.5–6.5	strontium	1.8
bell-metal	4	garnet	6.5–7.5	osmium	7	sulfur	1.5–2.5
beryl	7.5–8	glass	4.5–6.5	palladium	4.5–5	tellurium	2–2.5
bismuth	2–2.5	gold	2.5–3	phosphorus	0.5	tin	2
bituminous coal	1–1.4	graphite	1–2	phosphor bronze	4	tourmaline	7–7.5
boric acid	3	hematite	5.5–6.5	platinum	4–4.5	wax (0° C)	0.2
boron	9.5	hornblende	5.5	plat-iridium	6.5	Wood's metal	3
brass	3–4	indium	1.2	potassium	0.5	zinc	2

* Values compiled from Smithsonian Series.

supply company, are screwed into the sockets and serve as the ultraviolet source. Place a mineral specimen in the box, turn on the lamps, and look into the box in a darkened room. Every mineral will glow differently. (*Warning: Arrange the argon lamps in such a position that no direct rays of ultraviolet light enter the eyes. An overdose can cause detachment of the retina.*)

Some students may want to make a portable ultraviolet box using dry cell batteries and a model TT Fordson tractor or model T Ford ignition cell (stocked by Montgomery Ward or Sears Roebuck) as shown in Fig. 4–11. Connect the primary to a switch and batteries. Then connect

TABLE 4-4
*Fluorescent minerals**

| | | color of fluorescence | |
name, description, and locality	Raymaster (approx. ultraviolet 3600–3650 angstrom units)	Argon mixed gas lamp (approx. ultraviolet, 3300–3700 angstrom units)	Mineralight (approx. ultraviolet 2537 angstrom units)
autunite, xl scales on rock, N.H., N.C.	bright yellowish green	bright yellowish green	bright yellowish green
calcite, oxline. Tex. I	cream	none	pale cream
calcite, oxline. Tex. II	rose-pink, weak blue phosphorescence	none	bright blue, strong
calcite, oxline. Franklin, N.J.	pale rose-red	none	blue phosphorescence, brilliant rose-red
calcite and willemite. Franklin, N.J.	pale rose-red and bright green	bright green	brilliant rose-red and green
curtsite, Cal.	brilliant yellowish blue	bright yellowish blue	bright yellowish blue
fluorite, cleavage, England	brilliant blue	bright blue	dull blue
fluorite, oxline. Ohio	yellowish green	yellowish green	yellowish green
hackmanite. Canada	bright orange	none	none
opal, hyalite. N.C.	bright green	bright green	bright green
opal, massive. Nev.	green	green	green
petroleum, in bottle	bright green	bright green	bright green
scapolite (wernerite). Quebec	brilliant golden apricot	bright golden apricot	dull yellow
scheelite in quartz. Idaho, etc.	none	none	blue
sodalite, in syenite. N. H.	orange	none	none
[1] sphalerite with wurtzite. Utah	bright golden-brown, green, etc. Variegated colors	none	none
[1] sphalerite. S.W. Africa	bright golden-brown	golden brown	golden brown
tremolite, oxline. N. Y.	bright orange to pink	none	pink
willemite with franklinite. Franklin, N.J.	bright green	bright green	brilliant green
willemite and calcite. Franklin, N.J.	bright green and pale pink	green	brilliant green and rose-red

* From Ward's *Natural Science Catalog,* No. 578, Ward's Natural Science Establishment Inc., Rochester 9, New York.

[1] Strongly phosphorescent and triboluminescent.

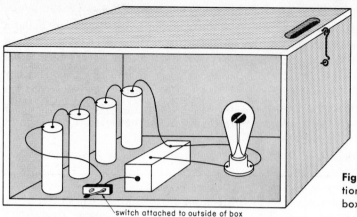

switch attached to outside of box

Fig. 4–11 Mineral identification using portable ultraviolet box (battery operated).

the secondary to an argon bulb or to a small ultraviolet lamp of the type used for illuminating instrument panels of airplanes. (These may be purchased from aircraft supply companies or the nearest airport repair shop.) Install the entire equipment into a box, making sure everything is well anchored, and use in the same manner as the classroom model already described. (*Caution: If you obtain larger and more powerful ultraviolet-ray sources, avoid looking into them directly. These rays can cause permanent damage to the retina of the eye.*)

4.3c Crystal study

Students may study small individual crystals on a slide under the low power of a microscope. Illuminate the crystals from above by means of a narrow, sharp beam of light. Many rocks and crystalline minerals and compounds may be identified by their crystalline structure. (References are suggested at the end of this chapter.)

4.4 Oil and ore formations

4.4a Oil and oil pockets

These pockets generally occur in rock formation under limestone layers. You may want to set up a working model of an oil pump as shown in Fig. 4–12. Plaster of Paris can be used to represent the lime-

stone dome usually found over the oil pocket. A small two-way hand pump can be operated by a pumping rig; the large baby carriage wheel is friction-driven by the shaft of a small electric motor against the rubber tire. The well pipe is a length of glass tubing connected to the intake of the pump; the outlet of the pump delivers its oil through a rubber or plastic tube to a "storage tank," which may be a battery jar or tin can.

Students can also use this same model to show how old wells are rejuvenated by water or air pressure. Drill a hole into the well and pump in water to lift the oil, or pump in air *very gently* to force oil out of the surrounding porous rock. Students can simulate porous rock in the model by using vermiculite instead of plaster for the dome.

4.4b Ores

You may want to refer now to the section on metallurgy for a discussion of ores. See 10.2 for preparation of metals from their ores and 10.3 for tests for various metals.

4.5 Study of rocks

4.5a Rock collections

It may be possible to plan a collecting trip to an area under excavation if the school is located near a quarry or mining region, or near the excavations for a highway or a building, or near a section known for fossil remains.[2]

Displaying collections. The best kind of box for displaying rock collections is one divided into small square or rectangular compartments. Some students use egg boxes for temporary storage and shallow cigar boxes with cardboard or thin plywood partitions for permanent collections. Plastic boxes with built-in compartments are excellent for storage since specimens are visible yet protected from dust. The compartments can be lined with a thin layer of cotton to prevent fragmentation of specimens.

Rock classification. The tendency toward indiscriminate collecting is avoided when students use separate boxes for each

[2] See the companion volume by P. F. Brandwein, F. Watson, and P. Blackwood, *Teaching High School Science: A Book of Methods,* Harcourt, Brace, 1958.

particular group of rocks. At the beginning, many students collect rocks belonging to the three major categories: igneous, sedimentary, and metamorphic. As the students become more specialized, they classify rocks into varieties within a group: kinds of granite, types of gneiss, fossils, minerals, semiprecious stones, and others.

Fossil collections. Information concerning fruitful places to collect rocks containing fossils can be obtained from many sources: the local museum of natural history, the state museum, the state department of mines, or a college geologist. The U. S. Geological Survey Office sells maps of almost all counties in the United States showing the kinds of rocks present. Some regions of the country are especially rich in fossil remains in sedimentary rock.

Mineral collections. Mineral ores are among the most colorful of rocks in a collection. Students may include in their collection a specimen of the ore and a

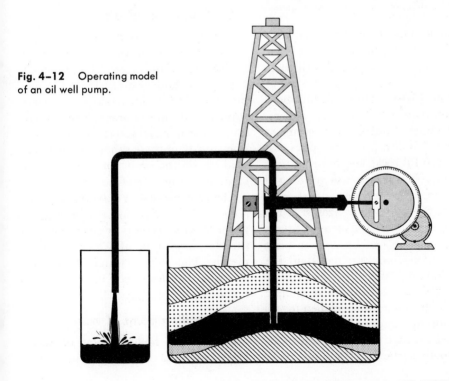

Fig. 4–12 Operating model of an oil well pump.

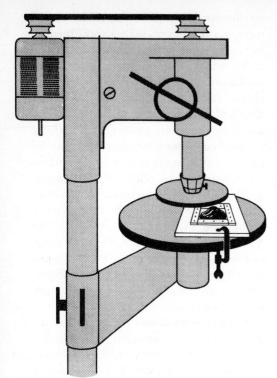

Fig. 4–13 A drill press used as a rock polisher.

small sample of the metal that is extracted from it. Methods for extracting some metals from their ores are described in 10.2

Polishing rocks. Some students have found a satisfying hobby in collecting semi-precious stones. Students may want to learn how to polish precious stones and pieces of colorful rocks and ores.

For the preliminary coarse grinding of the rocks use emery powder or carborundum (No. 60) and water against a flat metal wheel. A metal disk on a drill-press chuck (Fig. 4–13) can be used to press down against the stone or mineral with the grinding mixture. After the flat surface or bevel desired has been obtained, change to No. 120 grinding powder, then to still finer grinding material, and finally to jeweler's rouge to make an optically smooth surface. Crystalline rocks

display beautiful patterns when polished flat.

4.5b Hardness and compressibility of rocks and ores

Scratch test. Small kits may be purchased which students can use for testing the hardness of rocks. The hardness scale (Mohs'), beginning with talc as number 1 and ending with the diamond as number 10, is shown in Table 4–2. These rock specimens are graded in a comparison of which sample can scratch other rocks or be scratched by them. Some students, particularly collectors, may want to refer to Table 4–3 for hardness values of some common minerals.

Compressibility. The strength-of-materials machine described in 16.5b can be used to compare the compressibility of various rocks. Use specimens of the same size for comparison.

4.6 Properties of water

Many of the properties of water, especially its physical properties, effect changes in the crust of the earth. Changes due to expansion and contraction of water, methods of producing a safe potable water supply, and some characteristics of hard and soft water are described in this section. Many of these same properties are studied in the unit on weather and climatic changes (see Chapter 3).

Chemical properties of water. You may refer to 7.1b, 7.2c for the splitting of water into its elements by electrolysis and the decomposition of water by active metals. The role of water in chemical reactions is described in Chapter 8, Solutions.

4.6a Boiling point of water

Finding the boiling point of water. Have students boil water in a flask equipped with a two-hole stopper carrying a laboratory thermometer in one hole. The thermometer bulb should be set just above the water's surface in its steam. At the same time the other hole in the stopper must be left open so that pressure does not build up in the flask. Students can read both the centigrade and Fahrenheit boiling temperatures. Some teachers have students use several kinds of thermometers to check the accuracy both of the thermometers and of the individual taking the reading.

The reading will be correct (a barometric reading of 760 = 76 cm) only at sea level when the atmospheric pressure is normal. You may want to have students use the table in the appendix, which shows the relationship between altitude, barometer reading, and boiling point.

4.6b Raising the boiling point

Can the boiling point be changed? You will want to demonstrate either the *raised boiling point* of a solution such as sugar and water, or an alcohol-water mixture, or the effect on the boiling point of *raising the pressure.*

Dissolved salts in water. Use the apparatus described for boiling water (with a two-hole stopper) to demonstrate that the molal boiling-point elevation for aqueous sugar solutions is 0.52° C. Show that the temperature of a boiling molal solution[3] of sugar is raised 0.52° C. A molal solution is one wherein one mole of a substance, an amount in grams equal to the substance's molecular weight, is dissolved in a kilogram of water. (See 8.3b.) To avoid the use of tables and other calculations to correct temperature readings in relation to current barometric readings, first measure the temperature of boiling distilled water. This can be your control

[3] See 8.3b and 8.3c for making up solutions—molal, molar, and others.

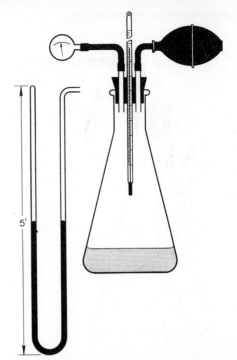

Fig. 4–14 Effect of increasing pressure on the boiling point of water. The device for indicating the pressure can either be a gauge or a closed end U-tube.

to which can be compared the raised boiling points of various solutions. The general rule is that the boiling point is elevated 0.52° C for each mole (Avogadro's number) of solute particles added to 1000 g of water. You may want to point out that in the case of NaCl there is ionization, and therefore twice as many solute particles per formula unit as in the case of a molecular substance such as sugar. Also interionic attraction affects boiling and freezing points. See 8.2.

Raising the pressure. Equip a Pyrex pressure flask with a three-hole stopper. One hole carries a pressure gauge; another connects to a small pump or aspirator; the third carries a thermometer. Boil water in the flask; keep heating after the water boils. By squeezing the aspirator, the pressure on the surface of the water is

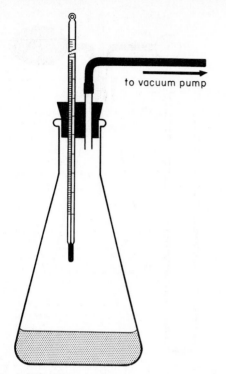

to vacuum pump

Fig. 4–15 Effect of reducing pressure on the boil-point of water.

increased. Students should observe that the temperature rises higher than the normal boiling point. As a safety measure, do not permit the temperature to rise more than a few degrees. See Fig. 4–14.

4.6c   Lowering the boiling point

The boiling point may be lowered by reducing the pressure of the air above the water in either of two ways. One method (Fig. 4–15) uses a hand vacuum pump connected to a two-hole stopper fitted to a flask of boiled water that has been removed from the heat and allowed to cool slightly. In the other hole insert a thermometer so that students can see how much the boiling point has been lowered. As the vacuum pump is used to lower the pressure, the water will resume boiling.

The second method is more striking; water is made to boil by apparently *cooling* it (Fig. 4–16). Boil water in an open flask, then allow the water to cool for one minute. Seal the flask tightly with a solid stopper, and invert it under running cold water, or rest a piece of ice on the upended base. The cooling of the air (and condensation of water vapor) in the flask will lower the pressure and water will boil below the boiling point. You can show this more clearly by using a two-hole stopper, with a thermometer in one hole and a vacuum gauge connected through the other to show the temperature and the pressure. (A mercury vacuum gauge can be made from the J-tube type of mercury barometer as described in 16.1c.)

4.6d   Freezing point

Have students insert a laboratory thermometer into a beaker of chipped ice and measure the temperature of the melt. Students should observe the freezing point on both the Fahrenheit and centigrade scales.

Methods of freezing water. For classroom use there are three simple methods, in addition to refrigeration and the use of liquid air, that may be used to produce rapid freezing. In the simplest method students can place a mixture of rock salt and ice around a beaker or test tube of water. (This is in itself a demonstration of the effect of impurities on the freezing point.) Or small quantities of water may be frozen by means of a spray tube of ethyl chloride, which can be purchased in a drug store. (*Caution: This is a mild anesthetic and must not be inhaled.*) For much lower freezing temperatures, use a mixture of dry ice in acetone or denatured alcohol. (*Caution: Handle dry ice with tongs or rubber gloves.*) This mixture is sufficiently cold to condense sulfur dioxide and ammonia into liquid form. It can be used to perform most of the demonstrations normally done with liquid air.

Expansion of water on freezing. Show that many substances including water expand on freezing by using a mixture of rock salt and ice as the freezing medium. Into this place a sealed bottle of water which, for safety, is inside a closed canvas sack. If you use an open test tube, mark the water level and compare it with the later ice level. In a rural area, students may have noticed the popping off of milk bottle caps in winter. Have them explain what happened.

4.6e   Density

You may want to have students discuss the advantage of ice being less dense than water in relation to life in a lake or pond.

Density of water at room temperature is less than its maximum density. To show the temperature at maximum density, fill a thin-walled flask with distilled water and fit it with a two-hole stopper containing a long straight capillary tube and a thermometer. Then place the flask into a jar filled with ice and water. Have students watch for the point of maximum lowering of the column of water in the capillary tube, and read the temperature (about 4° C).

Surface tension. In some classes you may want students to study phenomena of surface tension in relation to water (see 1.4b).

Hydrostatic pressure. See 16.5.

Heat capacity. See 18.4a.

4.7   Purifying water

4.7a   Physical purification methods

Distillation. Any type of condenser can be used to show that impurities such as salts, dyes, or ink added to the water in a flask will remain in the flask; the dis-tilled water can be tested for the presence of salt or acid or other materials.

Students on the chemistry laboratory squad may prepare a salt solution using sodium chloride to simulate sea water. Have students taste this in class. Then fill a third of a Pyrex test tube or small flask with the salt water and plug with a stopper through which a delivery tube extends as in Fig. 2–6B in Chapter 2. Students may taste the distilled water and explain what has happened in distillation.

You may also want them to heat equal volumes of sea water and the distilled water in separate evaporating dishes to look for salt deposits in each.

Commercial stills made of noncorrosive metals are obtainable from scientific supply houses, but this purchase requires a license from the Bureau of Internal Revenue of the Treasury Department.

"Cake-tin still." A simple condensing device for producing distilled water for laboratory use can be made from three aluminum or tin cake-baking pans of the type that have a "core," a hollow center section (see Fig. 2–6C in Chapter 2).

Commercial Liebig condenser. The standard apparatus for the distillation of water in the classroom is the well-known

Fig. 4–16   Boiling water by "cooling" it.

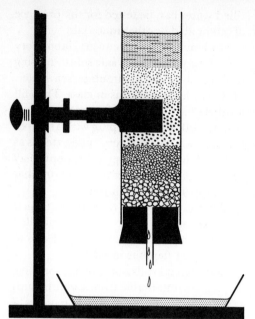

Fig. 4-17 Filtering water through sand and gravel.

Liebig condenser. The top of the center tube is connected to a stoppered Pyrex flask in which water is heated to the boiling point. Cold running water from the tap enters the bottom connection of the water jacket and returns to the drain through the upper connection. Distilled water drips out of the bottom end of the center condensing tube.

Homemade Liebig condenser. A simple adaptation of a Liebig condenser can be assembled in a few minutes by using a lamp chimney or glass cylinder fitted with two-hole stoppers at both ends. (See Fig. 2-6A in Chapter 2.) Run a length of glass tubing completely through the cylinder and through each stopper so that it extends out some three inches at each end. Then fit a short glass tube into the second hole of each stopper; these tubes serve as the "water jacket" connections. One end of the long tube is connected to a stoppered flask of boiling water; distilled water drips out the other end.

Filtration. To show the principle of water purification by filtration, first set up a simple sand filter in a glass funnel. Place a piece of cotton or filter paper at the neck of the funnel to retain the sand. Then students may pour in muddy water and collect the clear water below. For finer filtration add a layer of charcoal under the sand.

Filtration as practiced in large-scale water purification generally makes use of filtration towers or beds. Students can make a model filtration tower by fitting the bottom of a 2"-diameter open-end glass cylinder or a lamp chimney with a one-hole stopper and a glass tube. Set the cylinder in a vertical position, in a clamp attached to a ring stand, with a beaker underneath. Pour into the cylinder a layer of coarse gravel and then cover with a layer of fine gravel and finally with a layer of sand (Fig. 4-17). Students may add a layer of charcoal under the sand. Pour in muddy water and collect the clear water in the beaker.

A filtration bed may also be made as a student demonstration in class. Drill or punch a dozen ¼" holes in the bottom of a tin plate or aluminum baking pan. Line the bottom with a paper towel and add a layer of gravel, then a layer of sand. Now pour muddy water into this and collect the clear water that drips out the holes (Fig. 4-18).

Coagulation or flocculation. Alum is frequently used to remove colloidal suspensions of fine clays from drinking water. Students may see this action by pouring a water suspension of fine powdered clay into two tall glass cylinders. The clay particles, which are colloidal, show little in-

Fig. 4-18 Filtration bed.

clination to settle. Now add to one cylinder alum which has been made alkaline by the addition of ammonium hydroxide solution. Within a few minutes students should observe the colloidal clay particles settle to the bottom as a light, loose precipitate, forming a floc. This method of inducing flocculation is used to remove solids from water-supply systems and some indoor swimming pools.

Sedimentation. Students can readily show that particles larger than colloidal size will simply fall to the bottom of still water. Shake mud in water in a tall bottle and let it stand; the water will be clear the next day.

Aeration. Have students boil tap water for 20 minutes before class time. This will expel almost all gases, including air. Let this cool and set half of it aside. Have students taste this. How does it compare with water from the tap? Elicit a means for improving the taste of boiled water. Pour some of the boiled water back and forth from one glass to another about 40 times. Then have the same students make comparison tastes of the boiled and the re-aerated water.

You can also make a simple aerator from a clean glass-model force pump.

Connect it to a glass nozzle over a wide jar to collect the water. Students should be able to see how the pump sucks up the cooled boiled water and sprays it into the air to aerate it.

4.7b *Chemical purification methods*

Chlorination. Chlorination is the method most commonly used to destroy disease organisms in drinking water. Students can demonstrate the effectiveness of this process. Place a Petri dish or other shallow dish of a mixed culture of protozoans on the stage of a microscope or microprojector; observe the motile organisms. Then set aside half of the culture as a control. Next set up a simple chlorine generator consisting of a Pyrex test tube and a delivery tube drawn out to a fine tip, as shown in Fig. 4–19. In the test tube place a pinch of manganese dioxide and 0.25 cc of concentrated hydrochloric acid. Place the delivery tube into the culture; gently heat the test tube. After 2 minutes, remove the delivery tube (before turning off the heat) and place it in a solution of hypo (sodium thiosulfate) to neutralize any excess chlorine. Have students observe the organisms again and find that

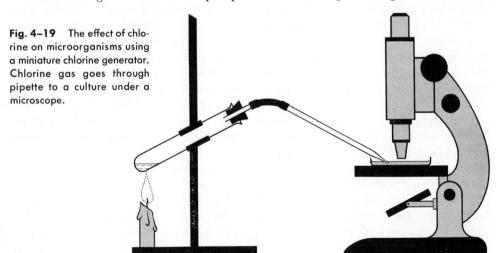

Fig. 4–19 The effect of chlorine on microorganisms using a miniature chlorine generator. Chlorine gas goes through pipette to a culture under a microscope.

they are now dead. Place the control sample back on the microscope to show that the control organisms are still alive. The demonstration can be set up with the microprojector so that the whole class can watch the process.

In some swimming pools and in water-supply systems sodium hypochlorite, in solution or in solid form, is the source of the chlorine used as disinfectant. Show the action of sodium hypochlorite on protozoans by using the same demonstration substituting Clorox or a similar commercial bleach solution in place of the gaseous chlorine. Home laundry bleaches are 5 per cent sodium hypochlorite solutions. You may also use a few grains of solid sodium hypochlorite.

Ozonation. Ozone also can be used to destroy microorganisms in water. Use the ozone generator described in 7.1b to supply ozone gas. Use the procedure described for chlorination to introduce the gas into the protozoan culture. A steri-lamp used in some home refrigerators or bactericidal ultraviolet lamp (which produce small quantities of ozone) may be placed over the culture. Have students observe the protozoans under a microscope before and after the irradiation treatment.

Softening water. If local water is not hard, you can readily prepare some for demonstration. "Temporary" hardness is due to calcium and magnesium ions, present as bicarbonates, dissolved in the water to make a solution of calcium bicarbonate. To make your own "temporary" hard water bubble carbon dioxide through water containing limestone or marble chips. "Permanent" hard water is produced by calcium or magnesium ions, present as sulfates which are not as easy to precipitate out. To prepare "permanent" hard water shake water with flakes of gypsum. Some teachers like to prepare a solution with both types of hardness (tempor-

ary and permanent), since this is the usual condition of hard water.

Temporary hard water. The simplest way to soften temporary hard water is by boiling it. The bicarbonates are then changed to insoluble carbonates according to this reaction

$$[Ca^{++} + 2\,HCO_3^-] \to$$
$$CaCO_3\downarrow + CO_2\uparrow + H_2O$$

The precipitated salt, $CaCO_3$, will gather on the walls of the container, removing water-hardening calcium ion from the solution.

Permanent hard water. Washing soda (sodium carbonate) will soften permanent hard water, according to the reaction

$$[Ca^{++} + SO_4^=] + [2\,Na^+ + CO_3^=] \to$$
$$CaCO_3\downarrow + [2\,Na^+ + SO_4^=]$$

More commonly used, however, are zeolites which are silicates of sodium and aluminum. Zeolites are characterized by an ionic structure in which the sodium cations (positively charged ions) are bound loosely and thus are readily replaced by magnesium or calcium ions. One among many zeolites that you may use in class is a sodium aluminosilicate sold under the trade name Permutit. This can be purchased in a glass tube for classroom demonstration from the Permutit Corporation or from a scientific supply house (see appendix). When hard water is run through it, calcium (or magnesium) ions in the water take the place of the sodium in the lattice, removing the "hardness." Salt water must be run through this zeolite to "regenerate" it with sodium ions.

The effect of hard water. Have students use ordinary soap to test the hard water before and after softening. Have them wash their hands in each kind of water, or add a soap solution with a medicine dropper into test tubes of hard water and of treated hard water. (*Note:* Use pure soap, not detergents, for most detergents form suds even in hard water.) Compare the suds formed in each case. Show that the hard water forms curds instead of suds.

Ion-exchange resins and chelating agents. Have a student demonstrate how ion-exchange resins are used as a more inexpensive way to soften water and to remove all traces of minerals, thus producing water as free from ionic substances as distilled water. Scientific supply houses sell ion-exchange resins for purifying water.

Chelating agents combine with the metallic ions in hard water, such as magnesium, calcium, and iron. The metal ions are then no longer free to react with the soap, making the water soft. A typical chelating agent that you may want to try in class is Versene (the tetra-sodium salt of ethylene-diamine tetra-acetic acid). This softens water almost immediately and will even work on hard water that contains much iron. (These chelating compounds are available from chemical supply houses in powdered form and in solution.)

Wetting agents. A wetting agent, by reducing surface tension (see 1.4b), causes water to spread over a solid such as thread in cloth and can be, therefore, more readily absorbed by the solid. These can be purchased from scientific supply houses or chemical supply companies. Almost any of the modern household detergents for clothes washing will be found to contain wetting agents which account for the greater solubility of this soap substitute. (Sodium lauryl sulfate is a common wetting agent used in detergents.) The effectiveness of most of the modern synthetic detergents can be demonstrated with almost any kind of hard water; suds form easily.

4.8   Water of crystallization

Many inorganic compounds form crystals in which water plays a part in the crystal lattice.[4] The effect of the removal of the water upon the crystalline structure is readily demonstrated. Heat a copper sulfate crystal or a piece of hardened plaster in a crucible or test tube. They will give off their water of crystallization, leaving a powder. In fact, if the test tube in which these substances are heated is held at an angle, students may notice drops of water form on the inner surface of the tube. Introduce cobalt chloride paper as a test for water. Now transfer the anhydrous copper sulfate to another test tube and add a drop of water. Can students see the blue hydrated salt form? Some teachers provide a series of salts such as alum, barium chloride, sodium chloride, and sodium nitrate and have students test them all for water of crystallization.

4.8a   *Efflorescence*

Many crystals effloresce, or give off water of crystallization to the atmosphere without heating. The most common example is washing soda (sodium carbonate). Open a fresh box; have students weigh out a given quantity and place this in an evaporating dish. Results are evident within 20 minutes as white powder forms on the clear crystals. In a week they should find remaining a heap of white powdered sodium carbonate. Have students weigh the powder and compare this with the weight of the crystals to show the quantity of water given off.

4.8b   *Deliquescence*

Have students devise a demonstration to show how some substances absorb water and become moist. Use drying agents such as $NaOH$ or $CaCl_2$.

[4] Further studies on growing crystals are described in 8.2f.

CAPSULE LESSONS
Ways to get started in class

4-1. Take the class on a geological field trip in the neighborhood. If natural outcroppings are not available, perhaps a visit to an excavation for a building may be in order. Students should come equipped with proper clothes for a field trip, a knapsack or box for samples, and pad and pencil for notes.

4-2. Using the U. S. Geological Survey charts, develop a cross-section chart of the rocks underlying the region surrounding the school. This information may also be obtained from the state geological office or state department of mines.

4-3. Have students prepare a demonstration of the formation of sedimentary rock and its importance to man. Lead into a discussion of factors which cause erosion and the need for conservation of land, or into a study of fossil formation and the history of the earth.

4-4. Show students some excellent fossil and rock collections made by other students who have become "expert." Develop several laboratory periods in which students gain an introductory knowledge of the difference between igneous, sedimentary, and metamorphic rocks.

4-5. Students may exhibit samples of important ores and show minerals under fluorescent light. This may be part of a laboratory period or a special hall case exhibit.

4-6. Have students identify fossil specimens and explain how they came to be found in the rock—usually sedimentary. Students may follow this with a discussion of ways to estimate the age of the rocks.

4-7. You may want to show films of the action of wind, water, glaciers, and so forth, as an introduction, or as a summary of this study.

4-8. In a class in general science or earth science or chemistry, you may want to show how universal a solvent water is. This may come out of a study of leaching of minerals from soil and rocks, or a study of the composition of the ocean. Have students test the solubility of different common materials in water, using the demonstrations given in this chapter.

4-9. Show a working model of a water purification system including sedimentation, filtration, coagulation, and aeration. Have students trace the local drinking water back to its source.

4-10. Can boiling points or freezing points be used to test the adulteration of products? Students may want to compare the boiling points and freezing points of cane sugar syrup, maple syrup, and glucose syrup at the same concentrations. In this way they can tell whether a product marked "pure maple syrup" really is pure.

4-11. As a laboratory activity have students devise ways to test degrees of hardness of water, using a pure soap solution. What are some ways to soften water? You may want to have students use the activities described here or refer to laboratory manuals in general science, earth science, and chemistry.

4-12. Provide the class with several chemical substances and have them determine whether they are efflorescent or deliquescent. Which substances can be used as drying agents?

4-13. Students may demonstrate the preparation of different solutions: dilute, saturated, supersaturated. They may also show the formation of crystals if hypo or similar substances are used.

4-14. Collect samples of water, for example, pond water or runoff after a heavy rain. In class, test these for acidity and for impurities such as chlorides (add 1% $AgNO_3$) and carbonates (add HCl). (See the index and the chemistry chapters for tests.)

4-15 If possible, plan a field trip to a water purification plant, or to some industrial plant that uses large quantities of water softeners. What kinds of water pipes are used? What problems need to be solved in the plant?

4-16. Show a textile stained with a syrup solution and another stained with grease. How can the stain be removed? Test solubility by soaking the cloths in water, alcohol, kerosene, and carbon tetrachloride (where permitted). Lead into a discussion revealing that a given solute varies widely in its solubility in various solvents.

PEOPLE, PLACES, AND THINGS

It may be possible in your community to visit places of geological interest. Or students may examine a profile of land formation where excavation is going on for building construction. Some teachers often invite a geologist from a local college or the parent of a student to speak to the class on the geological formations of the area. A field trip may also be planned to visit a museum of natural history.

Students can study geological maps of their area. These can be purchased from the Geological Survey through the Superintendent of Documents, Washington, D. C.

For practical applications of this work in class, you may be able to invite a mining or petroleum engineer from the community or from a college school of engineering to speak about ways to search for gems, ores, and petroleum.

BOOKS AND PAMPHLETS

These are only a few of the books which are pertinent to the work discussed in this chapter. These and many other references classified by subject and with complete bibliographical data are given in the bibliography at the end of the book.

Beeler, N., and F. Branley, *Experiments in Chemistry,* Crowell, 1952.

Callison, C., ed., *America's Natural Resources,* Ronald, 1957.

Cavelti, H., *Introductory General Chemistry,* Blakiston, 1952.

Deming, H., *General Chemistry,* Wiley, 1954.

Douglas, J., *The Story of Oceans,* Dodd, Mead, 1952.

Dull, C., *Modern Chemistry,* Holt, 1956.

Eiby, G., *About Earthquakes,* Harper, 1957.

Farber, E., *Nobel Prize Winners in Chemistry,* Abelard-Schuman, 1953.

Harker, A., 8th ed. revised by C. Tilley, S. Nockolds, and M. Black, *Petrology for Students,* Cambridge U. Press, 1954.

Hodgman, C., et al., *Handbook of Chemistry and Physics,* Chemical Rubber, 1954.

Loomis, F., *Fieldbook of Common Rocks and Minerals,* Putnam, 1948.

Namowitz, S., and W. Stone, *Earth Science,* Van Nostrand, 1955.

Pearl, R., *How to Know the Minerals and Rocks,* McGraw-Hill, 1955.

Pough, F., *Field Guide to Rocks and Minerals,* Houghton Mifflin, 1955.

Rapport, S., and H. Wright, *The Crust of the Earth,* Signet, 1955.

Shimer, J., *This Sculptured Earth,* Columbia U. Press, 1959.

Snell, C., and F. Snell, *Chemistry Made Easy,* Chemical Pub. Co., 1959.

Stovall, J., and H. Brown, *Principles of Historic Geology,* Ginn, 1954.

Van Engeln, O., and K. Castor, *Geology,* McGraw-Hill, 1952.

Weaver, E., and L. Foster, *Chemistry for Our Times,* McGraw-Hill, 1954.

FILMS AND FILMSTRIPS

This partial list is intended only as a guide toward film and filmstrip selection. Refer to the more complete listing at the end of the book where films are classified by subject and where a key to abbreviations and the addresses of distributors are given. The cost of film rental, of course, may be subject to change. Films are sound and black and white unless otherwise specified.

Ausable Chasm (f, s, c), Association Films, inquire branch offices.

Birth of The Soil (f, s, c), Indiana U., $3.25.

Birthplace of Icebergs (f, s), Indiana U., $1.75.

CaCO₃ (f, s, c), Gardner-Denver Co., free.

Changing Earth's Surface (fs), Popular Science through McGraw-Hill, $6.00.

Crystal Gazing (f, s, c), Indiana U., $3.25.

Earthquakes (part of series, *The Search*) (f, s), Young America, inquire local film library.

Electro Chemistry (f, s), EBF, $2.50.

Electrolysis (fs), Popular Science through McGraw-Hill, $6.00.

Geology (fs, c), Ohio State University Teaching Aids Lab., $4.00.

Geophysical Year (fs), Current Affairs Films, inquire cost.

Great Lakes: How They Were Formed (f, s, c), Indiana U., $3.25.

Mountain Building (f, s), Indiana U., $2.00.

New Worlds of Marble (f, s, c), Vermont Marble Co., free.

Petrified River (f, s, c), U.S.A.E.C., free.

Properties of Water (f, s), Coronet, inquire local film library.

Rocks and Minerals (f, s, c), Indiana U., $3.25.

Volcanoes in Action (f, s), EBF, $2.50.

Work of the Atmosphere (f, s), Indiana U., $2.00.

Work of Ice (f, s), EBF, $2.50.

Relief Maps (plastic), Ward's Natural Science, $41.50.

Ward's Color Slides for Geology (color slides in selected sets), Ward's Natural Science, $35 each set of 50.

Ward's Shaler-Davis Geomorphological Models, Ward's Natural Science, 6 sets, $24 to $72.

FREE AND INEXPENSIVE MATERIALS

This is only a partial listing of free and inexpensive materials available to the teacher at this time. A more complete listing, including addresses, is given at the end of the book. Many of these materials are distributed to teachers without charge. Where there is a small fee, the cost is indicated, although the prices are subject to change. While we recommend the materials for use in the classroom, we do not necessarily endorse the products advertised.

Field Trip Guide, Educational Service Bur., American Gas Association, free.

Rock Detective Kit (produced by Gemological Institute of America), available from Cenco Supply House, $9.95.

Elementary Mineral and Rock Collection, Ward's Natural Science, $10.50.

Mineral Collector's Guide, D. Jensen, Ward's Natural Science, $1.00.

Prospecting for Uranium, U. S. Gov't. Printing Office, 1955, $0.30.

Reprints from *Life Magazine,* "World We Live In" series: "Earth is Born," Dec. 8, 1952; "Miracle of the Sea," Feb. 9, 1953; "The Face of the Land," April 13, 1953; "The Canopy of Air," June 8, 1953. $0.20 each.

Rocks and Minerals: A Guide to the Most Familiar Species, H. Zim and P. Shaffer, Simon and Schuster, $1.00.

Also write to oil companies for free pamphlets and films dealing with oil geology.

CHAPTER 5

Planets, stars, and other bodies

Many students are interested in astronomy, and this interest can help build a lifetime hobby. Work in astronomy can range from identification of the stars to the very complex study of their composition. In studying the heavens, the student will learn many of the principles of physical science. This is a rich field for student projects. Students can build operational reflecting telescopes with photographic attachments, planetariums, and spectroscopes. They can observe the motions of the planets, map the stellar relationships, and study the composition of brighter stars.

5.1   Earth and its motions

5.1a   Introductory demonstrations of rotation and revolution

A basketball and a team of students may be pressed into use as working models of the earth's motions. The following "exercises" may help graphically to show the relationship of the earth to the sun. You and your students may think of other exercises.

1. Assume the sun to be in the center of a circle of students. Have students pass a basketball around the circle from left to right (west to east), then right to left (east to west). These questions can be raised: Which way does the earth move around the sun? Have students pass the ball around to show the correct motion. Is this motion a rotation or a revolution? (One student may twirl the ball around on a finger, or twirl it in the air to show a rotation. It might be pointed out that we know the direction the earth travels about the sun by the direction of the earth's shadow on the moon during a lunar eclipse.)

2. Have one student toss the ball directly across to another. Why doesn't the earth move in this manner? Why does it move in an orbit?

3. Assume now that each student is standing in a specific place in the earth's orbit. What is the inclination of the earth's axis on or near the dates September 23, March 21, December 22, June 22? Where do the sun's direct rays strike on these dates? What has the earth's tilt in the plane of the sun to do with the seasons?

4. What is the real path of the earth through space when the fact that the solar system as a whole is moving is considered?

A simple yet graphic way to demonstrate the rotation and revolution of the earth (Fig. 5–1) is to have a student carrying a globe walk in a circle around a bright lamp (the sun). Have the student slowly spin the globe on its axis as he carries the "earth" around in its orbit. As he moves around the darkened room, students will see on the globe the lighted portions or areas of daylight and the darkened portions or areas of night. If possible, arrange to have the globe spin approximately once for every degree of movement around the

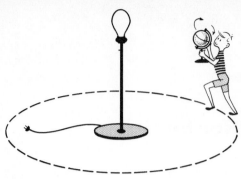

Fig. 5-1 Relationship of earth to sun.

circle. The wider the circle, the more nearly accurate the representation.

A student may want to set up a toy electric train on a circular track with a strong electric bulb in the center of the circle to represent the sun. A small geography globe can be mounted on a flat car. If a low-speed, worm-gear-drive, low-voltage motor is available, it can be used to spin the globe on its axis as the train moves around the circle. (Current for the motor may be obtained from the toy locomotive circuit.)

Charting the length of day and night. Students may use slate globes to explore the factors that determine the variations in length of day: the earth's revolution about the sun, the inclination of the earth's axis, and the fact that the earth's axis maintains a fixed angle. Use colored chalk to mark the equator and the Tropics of Cancer and Capricorn. Mark your location on the globe and identify your relation to the sun's rays and the lengths of day and night at the time of the summer solstice (June 22); autumnal equinox (September 23); winter solstice (December 22); and vernal equinox (March 21).

Students will need to prepare graph paper to tabulate their data. On the abscissa of each graph they should indicate the first days of each of the twelve months;

on the ordinate axis, the even hours of the day from midnight to midnight.

From an almanac, students can find the time of sunrise and sunset for the first day of each month; these should be marked on the graph. Shade the portion which represents night. What conclusions can be drawn from this chart? Why is there a change in the hours of sunlight and darkness?

Angles of sunlight on the earth's surface. At approximately 41° latitude during the summer the sun's rays fall on the earth at an angle of 72° to 49° at noon depending upon the date, and during the winter, at an angle of 26° to 49° at noon depending upon the date. Small blocks of wood about 1″ square and 6″ long can be cut so that one end has an angle of 60°, and the other end, an angle of 30°. Students can place each slanted end on graph paper and trace the area that is covered by each. How much larger is one area than the other? If a beam of light 1″ square falls at an angle of 30° and a similar beam at an angle of 70°, which beam will have the greater heating effect on the square inch of surface? Use a photoelectric exposure meter at each position to measure differences in light intensity. Students can relate this to an explanation of seasonal changes in temperature at the same latitude. Of course, any pair of widely different angles can be used in this demonstration.

Position of the sun from day to day. A small group of students might complete this activity over several days. Securely fasten in the upper half of a south window a piece of cardboard about 1′ square with a hole near its center about ⅜″ wide. At the *same* hour each day for a week, students should locate the spot of sunlight that falls on the floor or a desk. Make several tracings of the spot at 5-minute intervals. On successive days at the same hour is the spot the same distance from the window as on the first day? What statement can be made about the elevation of the sun in the sky?

Foucault's proof of rotation. There are several varieties of Foucault's classical demonstration of the earth's rotation, all of which require a room with a very high ceiling, such as a gymnasium. Attach a strong, thin fishing line or piano wire (or #14 steel wire) to the ceiling with some type of universal joint, such as a fishing-line swivel or a ball-type electric socket pull chain. To this line attach near the floor a canvas sack filled with fine dry sand (25 to 35 lb) to act as the pendulum weight (Fig. 5–2). The longer the line the better the results. The sack should have a small hole (approx. ¼″ in diameter) at the bottom to allow sand to trickle out in a fine stream. (For a given size hole dry sand trickles out at a constant rate regardless of the amount of sand in the container.) The floor should be covered with paper to protect it against the sand. No drafts should be present in the room.

The pendulum is set into motion. Instead of the straight trace of sand that might be expected to form under the swinging pendulum, a specially curved pattern will form, as the earth rotates under the pendulum, which always points toward the center of the earth. If the pendulum is permitted to swing for 24 hours, the trickling sand will form a rough circle. However, decreasing amplitude produces an ellipse. This apparent rotation of the pendulum is clockwise in the Northern Hemisphere. It will take about one hour of swing to detect the effect of the rotation clearly.

To show how the pendulum works take a table or television stand or any framework mounted on wheels and hang a pendulum underneath. While it is swinging, move the table about a given point

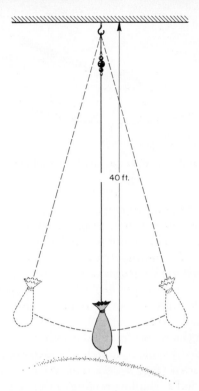

Fig. 5–2 Foucault pendulum.

so that one end is toward this point at all times. This point represents the North Pole, the moving table the earth's surface as it rotates, the table the ceiling from which the pendulum is suspended. It can be pointed out to students that direction as we commonly think of it is relative to the earth's surface only, a surface that is moving and so changing our relation to space. For instance, assume someone faces north and keeps facing that direction for 12 hours. He would still be facing north in relation to the earth's surface but in those 12 hours he would have completely about-faced in regard to space.

The sundial as evidence of rotation. An excellent device for showing the rotation of the earth about the sun is the sundial. Students can construct the simplest form of sundial by setting a pencil into a lump of modeling clay (Fig. 5–3A). The pencil

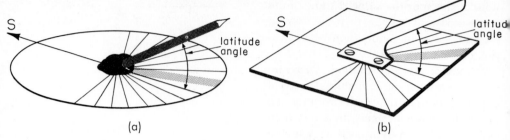

Fig. 5–3 Sundials: (a) pencil inserted in modeling clay, (b) sheet metal attached to wood or metal base.

should point to true north-south and be set at the latitude angle for your community. This puts it parallel to the earth's axis. The latitude can be readily determined from a geographic map or by using the device explained in 5.1b. A paper circle with a scale is used to mark the shadow every hour.

A more professional sundial can be made by students from heavy sheet copper or brass (Fig. 5–3B). The gnomon, the sundial's shadow-casting indicator, is riveted or bolted to sheet metal plate. The angle of the gnomon is that of the latitude. The positions of the shadow are tentatively traced in white pencil each hour, and finally inscribed into the metal with a sharp pick or scribing tool. The metal is then polished with steel wool and coated with clear lacquer or varnish to protect it against tarnishing.

Shape of the earth. Students can demonstrate how the earth's shape came to be an oblate spheroid, that is, slightly flattened at the poles. Whirl two flexible steel hoops set at 90° to each other on a hand-operated rotator so that students can see how the equatorial region bulges out and the poles flatten slightly.

5.1b *Latitude and longitude*

Time zone meridian. Using a sundial and simple arithmetic, students can locate the north-south line or meridian on which local time is based. The earth is divided into time zones 15° longitude wide, the distance the earth rotates in one hour. Within each of these bands all clocks are set to one standard time. Standardization became necessary in the last half of the nineteenth century with the advent of rapid transport and communication. Before that each locality had its local time based on sun time. For any particular observer whenever the sun reaches its highest point above him—i.e., is directly above a line which passes beneath the observer straight north and south—it is noon sun time for that particular place. A sundial tells sun time. Whenever the shadow of the sundial's indicator is directly north and south, it is noon sun time. This will almost always be at variance from standard time, in some places by several degrees. When it is noon by the clock, that is, by your standard time, measure the angle the sundial's indicator makes with its noon line, that is, the line directly north and south. For every degree this angle is to the left, you are four minutes before noon sun time; for every degree the shadow is to the right, you are four minutes after noon sun time. When the shadow is to the left at noon standard time, it means your time zone meridian is to the east of you, and vice versa.

Students can approximate how far away this meridian line of longitude is. The distance between degrees longitude at the equator is about 70 miles. For every 5° latitude this distance decreases about 4⅓ miles. For instance, if you are at 35° latitude and at noon standard time the shadow on your sundial reads 4 degrees to the left of its noon line, you are approximately 160 miles east of your time zone's meridian. At 35° latitude the distance between degrees longitude is about 40 miles. If it takes the earth 4 minutes to rotate one degree, how fast is the surface of the earth moving in your locality? To make all this clearer you may want to mount a small sundial, made from a pin or toothpick whose point is stuck in modeling clay or wax, on the surface of a globe. Rotate this globe near a single source of light and demonstrate noon sun time.

Finding latitude at night by the North Star. Since the North Star is directly over the North Pole, its elevation from any point is the latitude of that point. Students can make a simple "sextant" (Fig. 5–4) to determine the latitude of their locality. They can tape a drinking straw to a protractor and suspend a small plumb bob made from several paper clips, from the center of the protractor. Sight the North Star in the evening sky (use the Big Dipper as guide) through the straw. When the plumb bob hangs freely, at what angle does the thread cross the protractor? Take several readings of the angle and get an average. This angle of elevation subtracted from 90° is the latitude of your locality.

If a sextant is available, its use can be demonstrated to the class. Inexpensive plastic sextants are available from supply houses (see appendix). Surplus Air Force sextants, called octants, may be purchased at a very low price from concerns that sell surplus military goods. With a chronometer, navigation tables for longitude, and a sextant, the teacher can demonstrate the

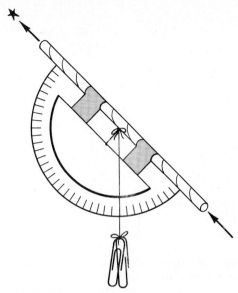

Fig. 5–4 Sextant made from a drinking straw, paper clip, and protractor.

use of the lower limb of the sun for measuring the longitude. Perhaps you can arrange to have a military or airline navigator or a Navy or Merchant Marine officer demonstrate the use of the sextant to the class.

Finding latitude during the days of the equinox. Students can use a short stick at noon on September 23 or March 21 to determine their latitude, as follows. Hold the stick vertical, resting on the ground; measure the length of its shadow. Measure the stick and make a diagram (Fig. 5–5). Use trigonometry or a protractor to measure angle A. This angle is the latitude of your location. This procedure works *only* during the equinoxes, when the sun is directly over the equator. On the summer solstice, June 22, add 23° 27', the latitude distance in degrees from the Tropic of Cancer to the equator; and on December 22, the winter solstice, subtract 23° 27' since on that date at noon the sun is directly over the Tropic of Capricorn south of the equator.

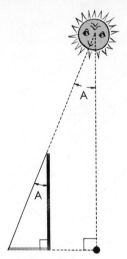

Fig. 5–5 Length of shadow at equinox can be used to calculate latitude.

5.1c The moon

Phases of the moon. Small groups of students may work together with a small light bulb, a slate globe, and a smaller sphere, such as a marble or jack ball, to represent the moon. First indicate the orbits of the earth and moon by moving the earth around the sun (lamp), and the moon (ball) around the globe; then stand the objects in relation to each other and show the new moon, full moon, and the first and last quarters. When would eclipses occur?

5.2 Eclipses

5.2a Model eclipse

Set up a lamp as the sun, a ball on a ring stand as the moon, and a globe as the earth. Move the moon around the earth in a circular orbit. Then move the moon between the sun and earth so that the students can see the shadow of the moon upon the earth. If students rotate the globe and carry it around the lamp at the same time, they will be able to see the path

of the "eclipse" across the earth. Then you may want to display maps that show the path of recent eclipses across the earth's surface.

5.2b Projection eclipse

Demonstrate a synthetic eclipse of the sun on a motion picture screen (Fig. 5–6) by removing the slide carrier from a large lantern-slide projector made for 3¼″ x 4″ slides. Cut a piece of cardboard to fit in the slide carrier compartment of the projector, and make a circular hole in it. Next take a clear glass slide of the same size, and paste on it a circle of black paper or aluminum foil slightly smaller than the hole in the cardboard. Insert the cardboard in the slide carrier compartment, turn on the projector, and focus on the screen. Then slowly slide the glass slide past the cardboard. As the black circle (the moon) passes the circle of light (the sun), an eclipse will slowly appear. Continue moving the slide until a full eclipse forms. The last half of the eclipse phase takes place as the "moon" continues its motion.

The effect is very realistic. The rough edges of the cardboard circle will look like the edges of the corona. Cracks can be cut in the cardboard to simulate solar flares.

If possible distribute photographs and magazine illustrations of total and partial eclipses.

5.2c Pinhole-camera coronagraph[1]

Here is how this coronagraph works. The sunlight enters through a pinhole at one end of a box, casting an image of the sun onto a screen of frosted glass or tracing paper. On this screen there is a black disk

[1] Adapted from *Planet Earth*, a book of experiments, by A. Joseph, published by the I.G.Y. Committee of the National Academy of Sciences, Washington, D. C.

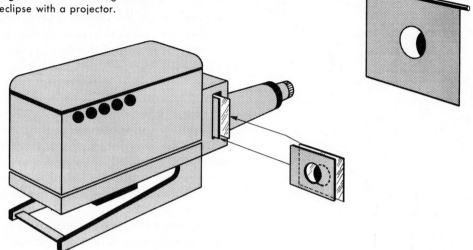

Fig. 5-6 Simulating an eclipse with a projector.

which cuts out all of the sun's image, leaving only its corona. Another shield slightly larger cuts out other light sources. Through a fogged negative, essential to protect the eyes, the student can view and study this image. Since the image's screen is movable, he can position it for sharpest focus.

(*Warning: Students should not look directly at the sun with the naked eye, through a telescope, or through the pinhole of the camera. Serious damage to the eye may be incurred if this warning is ignored.*)

The first step in making the pinhole camera is to obtain two or three shoe boxes. Knock out the ends and glue the boxes together to form one long box. The longer the box the better. In the center of one end of the construction, as in Fig. 5-7A, cut out a 1″ square hole. Over this, mount a slightly larger square of aluminum foil fastened with tape. Make a hole in the center of the foil with the point of a very fine sewing needle. The hole must be smaller than 1/100″ in diameter in order to work. Carefully cut away most of the opposite end of the box, leaving a ¼″ frame all around.

To construct a movable viewing screen: Cut two pieces of cardboard to fit the inside cross section of the box; cut a rectangle from each piece to form a window about 3″ x 4″. Sandwich between these two pieces of cardboard a slide of ground glass (obtainable from a photography shop), or a sheet of tracing paper, so that it is framed as a window (Fig. 5-7B). Glue or staple the edges of the cardboard frames together.

To construct a focusing stick for the movable screen: Cut a thin slot along the bottom edge of one side of the box as shown in Fig. 5-7A. Fit a thin strip of wood into this slot at right angles to the box. Glue the base of the movable screen to the flat surface of the stick, as in Fig. 5-7A. (Use model-airplane, quick-drying cement for this work.) Allow to dry.

Hold the pinhole toward some distant lighted object (not the sun), place your eye at the opposite end of the box, and move the window back and forth until you see an inverted image of the scene on which you are focusing. At night, try this on a full moon.

To use this camera to observe the sun's

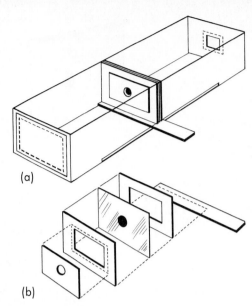

(a)

(b)

Fig. 5–7 Pinhole camera coronograph. The cutaway shows the parts that make up the center piece.

corona, the eyes must be protected as follows. Make a fogged negative by simply exposing plain uncovered film to light, then develop it. Tape the fogged negative to the back of the box. Looking through this film, estimate the size of the image of the sun that appears on the screen. Cut a circle of black paper slightly smaller than the image of the sun and paste it on the ground glass or tracing paper. Superimpose on the ground glass a cardboard square with a hole 1/16″ larger than the black circle. This will cut out the rest of the light and allow you to see the corona on the screen. (*Warning: Do not look at the sun or its image with the naked eye; blindness may result. Look only through the fogged negative.*)

5.3 The sky: observations, maps, and models

5.3a Mapping the sky

Horizon silhouette chart. The first step in mapping the sky in a particular area

is to make a horizon silhouette chart (Fig. 5–8). A Geodetic Survey map, aeronautical chart, or local surveyor's map (or, usually, a city map) will show true north.

Homemade transit. For use with the sky map, a simple transit for "shooting" the position of the stars can be prepared (Fig. 5–9). On a heavy wood base place a 360° protractor (or two 180° protractors). Then take an 8″ length of broomstick and cut a notch in the top by making two vertical saw cuts 1″ deep and removing the wood between them with a chisel. Two 1/8″ holes are drilled to hold a long thin nail which serves as a pivot for a metal tube. Mount a protractor on the tube for measuring its angle of elevation. A thin nail set vertically in the top of the broomstick serves as an indicator. The broomstick carrying the tube is set in a hole at the center of the 360° protractor, and held loosely with a woodscrew so that it can rotate freely. A nail in the side of the stick near the bottom acts as a pointer for the relative position along the horizon. When in use make sure the base is level. Here a carpenter's level can be helpful. By sighting a star through the tube, students can measure its altitude. As the stars move, their position may

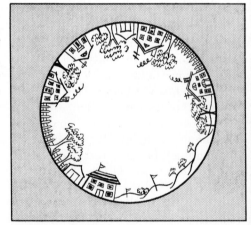

Fig. 5–8 Silhouette chart of horizon used to locate the relative position of the stars.

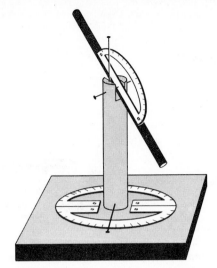

Fig. 5-9 A simple transit for shooting the position of stars.

a planetarium projector (Fig. 5–10). Split the globe into its two halves at the seam, and mount several small lenses in holes cut in the globe. In the center of the lower half of the globe install a standard porcelain socket and fit it with wire and a plug. A 100-watt bulb provides a light source. Prepare star slides for use with the lenses, one for each lens, by tracing the desired constellations on paper, and transferring with carbon paper to sheet copper slides, about 2″ x 2″. Drill a small hole for each star; the brighter the star, the larger the hole. Then attach the slides behind the lenses with cellophane tape. The slides are inserted under the lenses through appropriate slits in the globe's surface. Aim one lens at the ceiling and focus by turning the lens in its mount. Several sets of slides can be made and alternated. Small table-top planetarium projectors which make use of the classroom ceiling as the "sky" are available from scientific supply houses and some large toy shops.

Two globes, with lenses for constellations in each, can be used, mounted at the

be checked against tables of hourly positions of stars for your latitude. (Navigator's tables, U. S. Hydrographic Office, Washington, D. C.) By aiming at the North Star, students may find latitude. You can then add the stars in their proper positions to the horizon silhouette chart (Fig. 5–8). You stand the homemade transit (Fig. 5–9) on the horizon silhouette chart for orientation.

Photographic star trails. Any camera that can make time exposures can be aimed at the North Star and used to photograph star trails. Use a finder or set a drinking straw over the top center of the camera as an aiming tube. Moonless nights when stars are bright are best for taking star trails. At nightfall when the last trace of twilight is gone, open the shutter; remember to close it before dawn breaks.

5.3b Projection planetariums[2]

Globe planetarium. A geography globe removed from its stand can be altered into

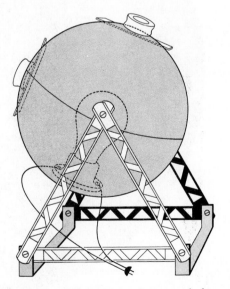

Fig. 5-10 Planetarium projector made from a globe, erector set parts, and lenses.

[2] If enough space is available, you may want to inquire about installing a Spitz Planetarium. (Send for the *Ann Arbor Story* from Spitz Laboratories, Inc., Yorklyn, Delaware.)

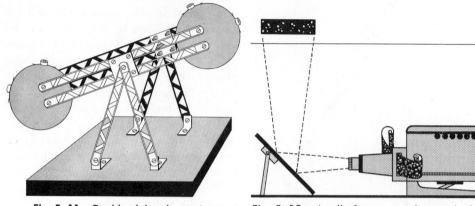

Fig. 5–11   Double globe planetarium.

Fig. 5–12   A roll of paper can be punched or exposed film scraped to show the constellations.

SUMMER SKY

Fig. 5–13a   Simplified star chart. Stars and constellations in the summer sky. (From R. Brinckerhoff, B. Cross, et al., *The Physical World*, Harcourt, Brace, 1958.)

Fig. 5–14 15° wedges of circular star chart applied to globe.

Fig. 5–15 Star globe.

WINTER SKY

Fig. 5–13b Stars and constellations in the winter sky.

ends of an Erector set framework that pivots in the middle (Fig. 5–11). Moving the framework causes the "constellations" to move across the ceiling "sky."

Paper-roll planetarium. Another projection planetarium can be made from a lantern-slide projector (Fig. 5–12). For "slides," use black paper made in a roll about 3½″ wide. First copy the constellations from a star chart (see bibliography at end of this chapter) onto the paper with chalk or white crayon; then punch holes according to the brightness of the stars. A standard size (3¼″ x 4″) lantern-slide projector with the slide carrier removed will carry the paper roll. Put one end of the strip into the slide compartment, use a mirror to throw the beam from the projector onto the ceiling, and focus. Then slowly pull the black strip through the projector. If you use a star map of the Northern Hemisphere, students can rotate the projector to show the apparent rotation of the stars about the North Star. Instead of a roll of black paper you can use a roll of film which has been exposed to daylight and then developed. Punch holes with needles to represent the stars.

Tin-can planetarium. To make a simple tin-can planetarium students need a #2½ or larger-sized empty tin can. On the bottom of the can trace the position of stars of one or more constellations and punch holes with a nail and hammer for each star. Nails of different thickness can be used to indicate relative magnitude of stars. Then a strong flashlight can be placed inside of the can. When the room is darkened, the image of "stars" can be projected on the wall or ceiling. Or students may prefer to mount a socket containing a 100-watt light bulb on a board. Connect a lamp cord and plug to the socket and tape the socket connections to prevent shock.

Students can project a large number of constellations at one time if they prepare a group of these "tin-can" planetariums. Use a star chart for the positions of the stars and the distances between stars, or refer to the simplified star chart in Fig. 5–13.

5.3c Astronomical globes and charts

Commercial star globes are available from scientific supply houses, or students can build one from a large geography or slate globe. The best results are obtained by mounting circular star charts on a metal globe (Fig. 5–14). These should be cut into 15° wedges, transferred one at a time to the globe, and fastened with rubber cement. Next take seven drill bits of increasing size from 1/16″ upward, and drill a hole for each star according to which of the six magnitude (brightness) classifications it falls into. After the holes are drilled for the important stars that make up constellations, split the globe at the seam or equator and place a socket with a 100-watt bulb inside the globe (Fig. 5–15). Notice that the wire connected to the socket passes out through a hole near the South Pole. Reseal the equator with masking tape and give the entire globe a coat of dull black paint. If the paint should fill in any of the star holes, clean them out with a toothpick or a pin. When the paint is dry, plug in the lamp; the stars will glow. It is important to point out to students that a star globe depicts the heavens inside out as if the earth were a mirror and we were looking down upon the reflection of the universe.

Illuminated star chart. It is easy to make a very effective chart in which the stars glow (Fig. 5–16). Simply take a large star chart and glue it to thin plywood or Masonite. Then drill a hole for each star, using a drill size proportional to the brightness of each star, as in the preceding

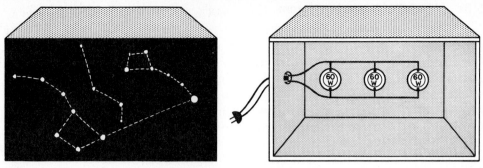

Fig. 5–16 Illuminated star chart.

project. Place the chart over a box that is fitted with several electric light bulbs to illuminate the "stars" from the rear. If a circular chart is used with the pole star as the center, the entire chart can be rotated to demonstrate the apparent motion of the stars. A photograph taken of the rotating illuminated chart will look exactly like star trails.

Florence flask celestial globe. A large round-bottom Florence flask makes an excellent and simple celestial globe (Fig. 5–17). On the outside use quick-drying white lacquer to represent the stars of the constellations. Then prepare some black dye and water, or India ink in distilled water. Add enough of this mixture to half fill the flask; the water level acts as the celestial horizon. Then cork the flask. Students can now turn the flask from the North to the South Pole while looking up at the "stars" against the black background of the liquid. Or rotate the stars about the pole star while holding the pole star in the correct position to represent your latitude.

Umbrella celestial dome. The inside of an open black umbrella may be marked with white chalk to represent the stars, with the center of the umbrella top acting as the pole star (Fig. 5–18). If the umbrella is turned, the illusion of star trails is apparent.

Fig. 5–17 Florence flask used as a celestial sphere.

Fig. 5–18 The inside of a black umbrella can be marked to represent the position of the stars.

5.3d Model of the solar system

A Tinkertoy set makes an excellent source of parts for assembling a model of the solar system, using an electric socket and bulb to represent the sun, and spheres of different sizes (rubber balls or balloons) to represent the planets (Fig. 5–19). First slip seventeen Tinkertoy hubs over a length of Tinkertoy stick mounted in a hole in the center of a wooden baseboard. (Nine of these are for the planets, and eight serve as spacers between each pair of planet hubs.) Then mount the socket on the top of this stick. An aluminum or other light metal rod is inserted into every other hub, and carries a sphere representing the planet. Each rod is bent in such a way that they can bypass one another. The relative sizes of the spheres, approximately proportional to the planet, are given in Table 5–1.

5.3e Telescopes

For telescopes that can be made by students, see section 20.3a. The following telescopes are simple ones, which serve mainly to teach the principles involved.

Refracting telescope. Some students may want to build a refracting telescope. Two convex lenses are used: an eyepiece lens with a focal length of 1″ or less and an objective lens with a focal length of 8″ or more. A very simple type consists of these two lenses mounted in lens holders on a meterstick (Fig. 5–20). The magnifying power will be the product of the focal lengths of the two lenses. The image will be inverted, but this is of no consequence in a telescope for use in astronomy. If students set up a permanent telescope, an eyepiece lens to set the image upright may be purchased from a supply company (see listings in appendix).

Another version of a refracting telescope, made from two convex lenses, uses an objective lens with a focal length of 20″ to 30″ and an eyepiece lens with a focal length of about 1″.

Students will need to make two cardboard tubes that fit snugly, one inside the other, and which can be slipped in and out for focusing; these tubes will carry the lenses. Mount the lenses by making a pair of cardboard rings for each lens that just fit inside the proper tube. Notice that the objective lens is to go into the larger of the tubes. Note, too, that the center hole in each ring should be ½″ smaller in diameter than the lens it will carry. Mount the objective lens in one end of the larger tube.

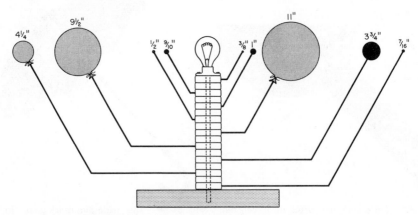

Fig. 5–19 Model of the solar system made from Tinkertoy parts, balloons, wire, and a light bulb.

TABLE 5-1

Sphere size to represent planets

Mercury	3⁄8″
Venus	1″
Earth	1″
Mars	1⁄2″
Jupiter*	11″
Saturn*	9½″
Uranus*	4″
Neptune*	4″
Pluto	7/16″

* Planets to be represented by balloons.

Cement one ring in position. After the cement has dried, place the lens in position, slide the second ring until it holds the lens against the first, and then cement the second ring in place. Repeat the same procedure at the outer end of the narrower tube for the eyepiece lens.

When the cement is completely dry, the telescope is ready for testing. Students can focus the telescope by sliding the tubes until they can focus a distant object. It is sometimes necessary to shorten the narrower tube by cutting it at the end away from the lens. The magnification will be the product of the focal lengths of the lenses, that is, about 20 to 30 power.

If there is fuzziness or too many colored rings in the image, make a diaphragm, that is, a disk with a ¼″ hole to place over the eyepiece lens.

A more professional telescope can be made by using aluminum or brass tubing in place of cardboard, and spring wire in place of the cardboard rings to hold the lenses in the tubes.

The telescope produces an inverted image. This is no handicap when observing the moon, planets, or stars. An additional eyepiece lens can be added to erect the image if the need arises.

Galilean telescope. The Galilean telescope, like the opera glass, provides an erect image by using a convex objective lens and a concave eyepiece lens (Fig. 5–20C). Use two short tubes that fit together snugly with the mounting system shown in Fig. 5–20C. Mount the convex lens in the larger tube, and at the opposite end of the smaller tube mount the concave lens. Slide the smaller tube to focus the telescope. The magnifications will depend upon the focal length of the two lenses. For longer focal length lenses, the tubes need be increased in length only slightly.

Reflecting telescopes. The principle of the reflecting telescope may be demonstrated with a concave shaving mirror, a section of a pocket mirror, and a short-focus lens as in Fig. 5–21. They can be supported by clamps in a ring stand, or mounted in a cardboard tube. If a beam of light is directed at the concave mirror from a distance of a few feet, and chalk dust is blown into the area in front of the lens, the path of the beam of light from the concave mirror, to the small mirror (held at a 45° angle), and into the eyepiece lens can be seen.

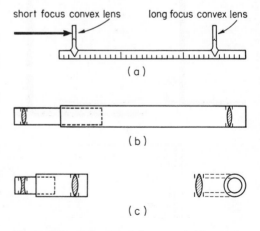

short focus convex lens   long focus convex lens

(a)

(b)

(c)

Fig. 5–20 Refracting telescope: (a) lens relationship set up on a meterstick, (b) lenses position in an adjustable tube, (c) details of mounting lenses in tubes. The short assembly in the lower left is a Galilean telescope.

Photographing through a telescope. A telescope can be used with a ground-glass-back camera (Fig. 5–22). Remove the camera lens and focus the telescope eyepiece until the star images are clearly seen in the ground glass. Inserting the film holder which has been loaded with Royal Pan or the newer high-speed Royal X Pan, or similar high-speed film, expose for the duration necessary. For the full moon, a one-second exposure is generally sufficient. To photograph stars, the telescope must be mounted on an equatorial mount.[3] (You may be able to borrow one from an amateur astronomer.) You must be able to follow stellar motion which is 15° an hour. Naturally best results are obtained when the exposure is taken away from a city's sky glow, the flash of headlights, and

[3] See the *Amateur Astronomer's Handbook,* J. B. Sidgwick (Macmillan); the *Amateur Astronomer,* Patrick Moore (Norton); and many articles in *Scientific American.*

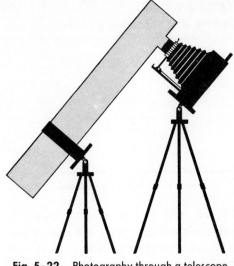

Fig. 5–22 Photography through a telescope.

so forth. Develop the film in high-contrast developer. More information can be found in *Astrophotography with Your Camera* (#C-20) published by the Eastman Kodak Co., Rochester, N.Y.

5.3f *Spectroscopes*

If a prism or grating spectroscope is available, it may be used to demonstrate the spectral lines of elements such as sodium or strontium by adding a salt of these metals to a Bunsen flame. For the spectral lines of metals you can also set up an electric arc using about 34 volts d.c. Or use a carbon arc for the same purpose by drilling out the center of the carbon

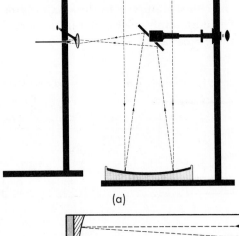

(a)

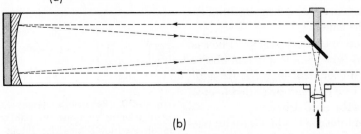

(b)

Fig. 5–21 Reflecting telescope: (a) principle can be shown with a shaving mirror, a pocket mirror, and a lens; (b) section of single reflecting telescope.

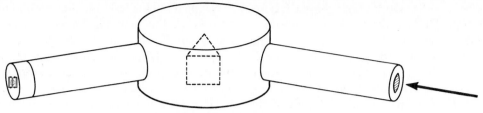

Fig. 5–23   Tin-can spectroscope using a prism.

rods and packing them with powdered metal or metallic salts. The spectrum lines can be compared to a standard spectrum scale.

Students may want to make a spectroscope (Fig. 5–23). They can mount two safety razor blades on a drilled-out pipe cap to produce a slit through which a fine line of light will travel; the pipe is inserted into the side of a tin can that contains a triangular prism. Another pipe is inserted in the can, and it holds an eyepiece lens through which the spectrum is viewed. Laboratory clamps hold the pipes in place. The image may also be projected against a wall. The position of the prism must be carefully adjusted.

One simple grating spectroscope can be made from a rectangular box (Fig. 5–24). At one end of the box cut a hole, and provide a slit by placing over the hole a piece of aluminum foil in which you cut a slit with a thin, sharp knife. At the other end, opposite the slit, cut out a 1″ hole, and tape a piece of plastic spectrum[4] grating across the hole. To use the spectroscope, aim the slit at the light source that is being examined—the sun, an unfrosted bulb, sodium light, or the color produced in gas flames or in an electric arc by metals. Notice that the spectrum will be shifted to one side. This is essentially the way the elements in the stars or other heavenly bodies are detected. Many other details on

the making and using of spectroscopes can be found in 20.3b and 20.5a.

5.4   Satellites

Many of the principles behind orbiting satellites (and space travel in general) are of such a nature that they cannot be easily demonstrated in the classroom, yet in some instances analogies can be drawn.

5.4a   Trajectories

While working out his law of gravity, Newton wondered why the moon did not fall into the earth. On the other hand he knew the moon was moving—why didn't it simply fly off into space? After careful observation and calculation he learned that the moon moves about two thirds of a mile each second. During this time it falls toward the earth 1/20 of an inch. Putting these two facts together, he saw that the two motions are such that a

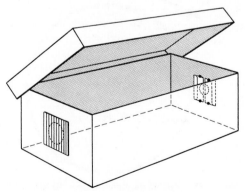

Fig. 5–24   Grating spectroscope.

---

[4] Available from Edmund Scientific Co., Barrington, N. J. Enough gratings for the entire class are available for a few cents each.

nearly perfect circle about the earth is the result. The answer to both questions is "yes"—the moon is falling toward the earth and it is also flying out into space.

Two factors control the motion of satellites, natural or man-made: forward (angular) momentum and the pull of the earth's gravity (Fig. 5–25). It is the pull of gravity that makes the satellite travel not in a straight line but in a curve. When the curve of a falling object is such that it does not strike the earth and yet comes back on itself, that object is in orbit; that is, the object perpetually "falls" toward the earth without ever hitting it.

If someone tosses a baseball straight away from him, what line does the baseball's path describe? A curve. Why? If one could throw the ball hard enough, this curve would eventually equal the curve of the earth's surface and the baseball would be in orbit.

Twirl a weight horizontally from a string. (If the string is fed through the center hole of a spool, the whirling and the length of the string can be more exactly controlled.) Suddenly shorten the line. What happens? The closer a satellite is to the earth's surface, the faster it must travel in relation to that surface to keep it in orbit.

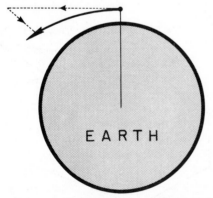

Fig. 5–25 Two factors control the motion of all satellites—gravity and angular momentum.

Swing a bucket half full of water about your head. The centrifugal force balances the gravitational pull on the water and keeps it from falling out. At the same time the pull you exert on the bucket keeps it and the water orbiting about you.

Here are some general facts about the trajectories (the orbits) of satellites.

A satellite's orbit is elliptical. The closer the satellite's approach to the earth, the faster it moves. As it goes out on the further reaches of its elliptical orbit, it slows in accordance with Kepler's second law: that the radius from the moving body to the body about which it revolves will sweep equal areas in equal times. A rough analogy to this can be made by rolling a marble about the inside of a bowl or up an incline in a curve. The higher the marble rolls the more slowly it moves.

A satellite's mass has nothing to do with its position or distance above the earth and its speed in orbit. A hydrogen atom and a five-ton satellite must travel the same speed a given distance about the earth in order to stay in orbit. What will vary according to mass is the amount of energy needed to lift the material to a given speed and distance.

Launching a satellite. See Chapter 24 for greater detail on rocket motors. Fig. 5–26 shows essentially how rockets stacked one on another raise the satellite to its orbital speed and position.

Perhaps students will want to calculate escape velocity; some texts which will help them are listed at the end of the chapter.

5.4b Charting a satellite

Perhaps a student knows someone who was part of Operation Moonwatch. Have him report to the class on the nature of the operation.

An observer in Operation Moonwatch was expected to report this information:

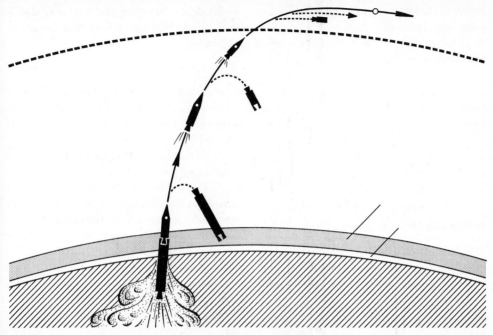

Fig. 5–26 A multistage rocket boosts a satellite into orbit. Each stage provides greater thrust, the third (final) stage imparting to the satellite the velocity required for orbit at a given altitude.

his location, the time, and the direction of the satellite (which requires two measurements—the location of the moon around the horizon and its position above the horizon). These directions are given in angular measurements. Thus, with 360° in a full circle, and 90° in a right angle, the direction around the horizon starts with 0° at north, goes eastward with 90° at east, 180° at south, 270° at west. The po-

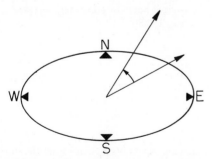

Fig. 5–27 Two dimensions locate a satellite—angle above the horizon and angle on the horizon in relation to north.

sition above the horizon is developed from the base that there are 90° between the horizon and the point directly overhead. A useful exercise is developed in Fig. 5–27.

5.4c The period of a satellite

Some students may wish to calculate the period of a satellite. For this purpose, Kepler's third law (known also as the *harmonic law*) is applied. This law states that the square of the period of revolution of a satellite is equal to the cube of its mean distance (from the primary, in this case, the earth). The law may be written more compactly in equation form, $P^2 \backsim d^3$. Now, employing the equation to determine the period, the following simplification of a more complex calculation is offered.

We know that the moon revolves around the earth once in about 660 hours at a distance of 240,000 miles. We also know that the period P (the time for one complete circle) of a satellite changes with its average distance d from the center of the earth according to:

$$P^2 \sim d^3$$

By comparing a satellite to the moon, we have

$$\frac{P_s^{\,2}}{P_m^{\,2}} = \frac{d_s^{\,3}}{d_m^{\,3}}$$

$$P_s^{\,2} = d_s^{\,3} \left(\frac{P_m^{\,2}}{d_m^{\,3}} \right)$$

Substituting known values,

$$P_s = 5.6 \times 10^{-6} \times d_s \sqrt{d_s}$$

Students can then find the period of a satellite 10,000 miles from the center of the earth:

$$P_s = 5.6 \times 10^{-6} \times 10^4 \times 10^2 = 5.6 \text{ hours}$$

Students can then try these problems:

1. Find the period of a satellite 1000 miles high (5000 miles from the center of the earth).

2. Find the period of a satellite 40,000 miles from the earth's center.

3. From the results above, make a graph of the relation between period in hours and distance from the earth's center. At what distance would the period of a satellite be just 24 hours?

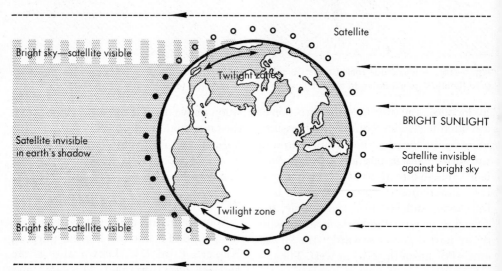

Fig. 5–28 A satellite is visible to an observer during the twilight hours of early morning. (Redrawn from R. Brinckerhoff et al., *The Physical World*, Harcourt, Brace, 1958.)

CAPSULE LESSONS

Ways to get started in class

5-1. You may want to begin by arranging a trip to a local planetarium to observe the motions of the heavenly bodies. Then lead into a discussion of planets, constellations, a notion of galaxies, and distances in space from the sun.

5-2. Some teachers begin with a discussion of the theories accounting for the origin of the universe, the earth, and other planets.

5-3. You may want students to use a miniature planetarium projector of the kind described in this chapter to project stars on the ceiling. Develop notions concerning planets, stars, and galaxies.

5-4. In a study of telescopes, a student might assemble the complete parts of a reflecting telescope as a class demonstration. Have him use a concave shaving mirror, a small hand mirror, and a short-focus lens. Arrange these to duplicate the telescope described in 5.3e.

5-5. Some students may observe constellations out-of-doors at night as special individual projects. It may be possible to plan a field trip for the entire class. (In your community, it may be necessary to have parental consent notes on file.) At such a time, students may observe stars and some of the planets with the naked eye and with the aid of a telescope. If a star chart is being referred to, it is a good idea to cover a flashlight with red cellophane. Red light does not affect the eyes' night adaptation.

5-6. Films can be used effectively to introduce notions of the planets, satellites, and their interrelationships. Have you used the film *Solar Family* (EBF) or the filmstrip *Our Neighbors in Space* (Harcourt, Brace)?

5-7. As a special project, a committee of students might prepare a script for an assembly or club program tracing the historical development of knowledge of outer space.

PEOPLE, PLACES, AND THINGS

If possible, plan a visit to a planetarium, or to see museum exhibits of astronomical instruments. Where field trips are not feasible, use the resources of your own community such as veterans in your PTA. An Air Force navigator or a Navy or Merchant Marine officer might be invited to demonstrate astral navigation.

A nearby college may have an astronomer on its staff who could speak to classes on new developments such as radio astronomy. He might also volunteer to act as consultant to a few youngsters engaged either in building models for class demonstrations or in studying meteors, or other work, as long-range projects.

BOOKS AND PAMPHLETS

These are only a few of the books which are pertinent to the work discussed in this chapter. These and many other references classified by subject and with complete biographical data are given in the bibliography at the end of the book.

Baker, R., *Astronomy*, Van Nostrand, 1950.

Bates, D. R., ed., *The Planet Earth*, Pergamon Press, 1957.

Bernhard, H., D. Bennet, and H. Rice, *New Handbook of the Heavens*, Mentor, 1954.

Bonner, F., and M. Phillips, *Principles of Physical Science*, Addison-Wesley, 1957.

Branley, F., *Experiments in the Principles of Space Travel*, Crowell, 1955.

de Vaucouleurs, G., *Discovery of the Universe: An outline of the History of Astronomy from the Origins to 1956*, Macmillan, 1957.

Gamow, G., *The Creation of the Universe*, Viking, 1956.

Holton, G., and D. Roller, *Foundations of Modern Physical Science*, Addison-Wesley, 1957.

Hoyle, F., *Frontiers of Astronomy*, New American Library, 1957.

Ingalls, A., *The Amateur Telescope Maker*, Scientific American, 1956.

Kruse, W., and W. Dieckvoss, *The Stars*, U. Michigan Press, 1957.

Olcott, W., 4th ed. by R. Mayall and M. Mayall, *Field Book of the Skies*, Putnam, 1954.

Payne-Gaposchkin, C., *Stars in the Making*, Harvard U. Press, 1952.

Scientific American, "The Universe," "Origin of Elements," "Evolution of Galaxies," entire issue, Sept., 1956; "Chemistry of Jupiter," June, 1956; "Radio Sky," July, 1956; "Clouds of Magellan," April, 1956; "Observations of Satellite I," Dec., 1957; "A Rocket Around the Moon," June, 1957; "Age of the Solar System," April, 1957.

Row, Peterson, *Beyond the Solar System*, Basic Science Education Series, Evanston, Ill.

Texereau, J., *How to Make a Telescope*, Interscience, 1957.

Watson, F., *Between the Planets*, Harvard U. Press, 1956.

Zinner, E., *The Stars Above Us: The Conquest of Superstition*, Scribner, 1957.

FILMS AND FILMSTRIPS

This partial list is intended only as a guide toward film and filmstrip selection. Refer to the more complete listing at the end of the book where films are classified by subject and where a key to abbreviations and the addresses of distributors are given. The cost of film rental, of course, may be subject to change. Films are sound and black and white unless otherwise specified.

Airplane Changes Our World Map (f, s), EBF, $2.50.

Animals in Subgravity Conditions (f, s), Indiana U., $3.00.

Constellations (fs, c), Popular Science through McGraw-Hill, $6.00.

Earth and Its Seasons (f, s), Indiana U., $1.75.

Earth & the Sky Series (3 fs, c), Popular Science, $6.00 each.

Earth & Universe Series (7 fs), Society for Visual Education, $3.50 each.

Earth in Motion (f, s), EBF, $2.50.

Earth: Our Planet (cosmic theory of creation) (f, s), Indiana U., $4.00.

Eclipse (f, s), Almanac, $2.00.

Exploring Space (f, s), Teaching Film Custodians, inquire rental.

Exploring the Universe (f, s), EBF, $2.50.

How Earth was Born (tidal theory) (f, s), Almanac, $2.00.

How Many Stars? (f, s, c), Indiana U., $3.25.

Infinite Universe (f, s), Almanac, $2.00.

Latitude by Polaris (f, s), TF 1545 Civil Aeronautics Admin., free.

Looking at the Stars (fs), McGraw-Hill, $3.50.

Mars (f, s), Indiana U., $3.00.

Moon (f, s), EBF, $2.50.

Movements of the Earth and Science (fs), United World, $3.00.

Nautical Astronomy (f, s), Indiana U., $2.50.

Neighbors in Space (fs, c), Harcourt, Brace, $5.50.

Operation Hour Glass (f, s, c), Association Films Inc., free.

Our Mr. Sun (f, s, c), Bell Telephone, free.

The Planets (fs), United World, $3.00.

Principles of Celestial Navigation (position finding on earth) (f, s, 2 rls), Almanac, $3.50.

Solar Family (f, s), EBF, $2.50

Solar System (f, s), PSSC, Talking Pictures, Inc., $6.00.

Star Gazers (Galileo and his trial) (f, s), Indiana U., $1.50.

Star Identification (f, s), MN 83F, Civil Aeronautics Admin., inquire rental.

Starry Universe (fs, c), Life Magazine, $6.00.

The Stars (fs), United World, $3.00.

Story of the Telescope (f, s), Institutional Cinema, $2.00.

The Story of Time (f, s, c), Almanac, $4.00.

The Strange Case of the Cosmic Rays (f, s, c), Bell Telephone, free.

The Sun (f, s), Indiana U., $3.00.

Sun's Family (fs, c), Pop. Sci. through McGraw Hill, $6.00.

This is the Moon (f, s), Institutional Cinema, $2.00.

Time, the Servant of Man (f, s), Modern Talking, free.

Trips Through Space (f, s), Institutional Cinema, $2.00.

The Universe (the elements) (f, s), Indiana U., $4.75.

Upper Atmosphere Studies (f, s), Indiana U., $3.00.

A World is Born (from Disney's *Fantasia*) (f, s, c, 3 rls), Institutional Cinema, $8.00.

FREE AND INEXPENSIVE MATERIALS

This is only a partial listing of free and inexpensive materials available to the teacher at this time. A more complete listing, including addresses, is given at the end of the book. Many of these materials are distributed to teachers without charge. Where there is a small fee, the cost is indicated, although the prices are subject to change. While we recommend the material for use in the classroom, we do not necessarily endorse the products advertised.

Astral Navigation, wall charts, General Dynamic Corp., inquire price.

Planet Earth, pamphlets, charts, and kit, Publication Office, National Academy of Sciences, Washington, D.C., inquire price.

Star Charts, available from Planetarium, map companies, and Museum of Natural History.

Research Progress Report, National Aeronautics and Space Administration, Ames Research Center, Moffet Field, California, free.

Smashing the Sound Barrier, Brinckerhoff, R., Science Research Assoc. 57 West Grand Ave., Chicago 10., $.60.

Exploring Outer Space, New York Herald Tribune, 230 W. 41 St., N.Y. 36, inquire cost of class set of booklets.

Hammond's Guide to the Exploration of Space, wall chart, Hammond, inquire cost.

Research Progress, National Advisory Committee for Aeronautics, Lewis Flight Propulsion Laboratory, 21000 Brookpark Road, Cleveland Ohio, inquire cost for class set.

The Story of I. G. Y., picture book and explanatory text, Esso, free.

Earth Satellite, Volume 57, No. 4 issue of *Oil Power,* Socony Mobil Oil, free.

Rockets into Space, Joseph, A., Science Research Associates, $.60.

The Birth and Death of the Sun, Gamow, G., Mentor, $0.50.

A Guide to the Stars, American Oil Co., free.

Astronomy Pamphlets, 20 in set, Adler Planetarium and Astronomical Museum, Chicago, $0.15 each.

The Gyroscope Through the Ages, Sperry Gyroscope Co., free.

How to Use Your Bulletin Boards, Johnson, D. & Olander, C., National Council of Teachers of Mathematics, Washington, $0.50.

The Origin of the Earth, Smart, W., Pelican, $0.65

Pan American World Airways Teacher, Pan American World Airways, free.

The Science Book of Space Travel, Goodwin, H., Cardinal, $0.35.

Stars: A Guide to the Constellations, Sun, Moon, Planets, Zim, H. & Baker, R. H., Simon & Schuster, $1.00.

Current reports on satellite and astronomy research can be found in *Life, Time, Scientific American,* and *Sky and Telescope.*

Section Two CHEMISTRY

CHAPTER 6

Elements and compounds—

their nature and reactions

Basically this chapter deals with demonstrations and teaching aids for the presentation of the first principles of chemistry. Beginning with a short account of symbols and atomic diagrams, it enters into that area where chemistry and physics meet—electron configuration. This leads into bonding.

Of interest to teachers of physics as well as of chemistry will be the section given over to models—atomic, molecular, and crystal. In the section on chemical reactions attention is given to the relationship by property of elements in the same group. Oxidation-reduction is discussed, and the chapter ends with the types of molecular reactions.

6.1 Alphabet of chemistry

6.1a Symbols and names

The introductory unit in high school chemistry frequently includes the study of oxygen and hydrogen, which many teachers use to introduce students in a nonrigorous fashion to simple symbols, formulas, and equations. The teacher may write out a sentence, then a word equation, and finally the chemical equations for a reaction. For instance, the decomposition of mercuric oxide can be taught as follows.

Mercuric oxide decomposes into mercury and oxygen.

(sentence)

mercuric oxide → mercury + oxygen
(word equation)

$$HgO \rightarrow Hg + O$$
(symbol and formula equation)

$$2\,HgO \rightarrow 2\,Hg + O_2$$
(balanced chemical equation)

Names. Many students learn the chemical symbols readily once they learn the derivation of the symbols. It is interesting and helpful to give the original Latin name of the elements (e.g., sodium—*natrium*; silver—*argentum*) if only to caution students against trying to derive symbols from English equivalents. Table 6–1 furnishes the names for which the "unusual" symbols are abbreviations.

Self-testing device. A simple device for learning symbols is an electric question-and-answer game. Each student can make his own tester on a sheet of stiff cardboard, using pairs of push-through paper fasteners connected in back by bell wire, as shown in Fig. 6–1. (Note that the wire from one of a pair of fasteners goes, not to its mate, but to one of another pair.) On the front of the cardboard attach a flashlight cell in series with a miniature socket and two long flexible wires, and place a

1.2-volt bulb in the socket. Trace the wires on the back, and for each wire write (on the front of the cardboard) the name of an element or a compound next to the fastener at one end and its symbol next to the fastener at the other end. When students touch one of the long wires to a name and bring the other wire to the corresponding symbol, the bulb will light. This sort of device can also be used for matching other paired sets such as compounds and their names, elements and their valences, atoms and their electron configuration.

6.1b Atomic diagrams

This area of "dry" chemistry poses unique instructional problems because many of its concepts are based on the submicroscopic behavior of atomic particles. One cannot catch and tame a single electron and so demonstrate its mass or orbital as one can rig a set of pulleys and demonstrate the concept of "mechanical advantage." In atomic models, an atom is pictured as a particle composed of a number of protons, electrons, and neutrons organized in a specific pattern. Much of the experimental data on which the "probable" structure is based may be

Fig. 6–1 Self-testing device for student drill on chemical formulae and other routine material.

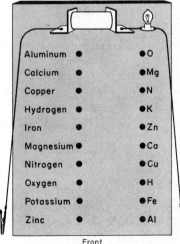

Aluminum ●   ● O
Calcium ●   ● Mg
Copper ●   ● N
Hydrogen ●   ● K
Iron ●   ● Zn
Magnesium ●   ● Ca
Nitrogen ●   ● Cu
Oxygen ●   ● H
Potassium ●   ● Fe
Zinc ●   ● Al

Front

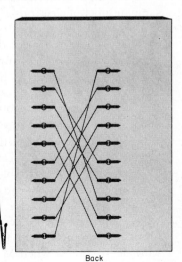

Back

TABLE 6-1

Original names, from which symbols were derived, of some common elements*

present name	early name	symbol
antimony	stibium	Sb
gold	aurum	Au
iron	ferrum	Fe
lead	plumbum	Pb
mercury	hydrargyrum	Hg
potassium	kalium	K
silver	argentum	Ag
sodium	natrium	Na
tin	stannum	Sn

*All these early names are Latin.

presented in tabular or graphic form included later in this chapter. Although students are happiest with and frequently demand "reality," some teachers point out that models are just that—models only.

In building up representative atomic diagrams, students should learn the following main principles.

1. An atom contains electrons, protons, and neutrons (except protium—the most common isotope of hydrogen).

2. Electrons are negatively charged particles, protons are positively charged, and neutrons have no electrical charge.

3. The atom of an element contains the same number of electrons as protons and therefore is electrically neutral.

4. The atom consists of a dense nucleus surrounded by electrons arranged in various energy levels known as shells or orbits.

5. The nucleus of the atom contains the "heavier" particles: protons and neutrons.

6. The atomic number is the number of protons in the nucleus of an atom.

7. There is a specifiable maximum number of electrons that can be contained in each electron shell: for the K shell, which is nearest the nucleus, this maximum is 2; for the L shell, 8; and for the M shell, 18, except when M is the outermost shell of an atom it may contain no

more than 8 (the octet rule). See Table 6-2, for the electron numbers in the other shells. Electrons go successively to fill the lowest energy levels (shells) as their number increases.

8. An outermost shell in an element of atomic number greater than 2 never has more than 8 electrons in it (a stable octet).

9. The atomic weight (actually mass number), rounded off to the nearest whole number, is numerically equal to the sum of the protons and neutrons in the nucleus of the atom. Isotopes of a given element have the same number of protons but different numbers of neutrons. Many teachers prefer to present this rule after the principles of chemical behavior of elements, variation in properties (periodic and intragroup), and bonding have been taught largely on the basis of atomic number and electron arrangements.

Schematic atomic models. A variety of schemes is used to represent atomic models. Fig. 6-2 shows the various schemes for representing the lithium atom.

In a circle which represents the nucleus, place the atomic number followed by a p or a plus sign. Draw large circles representing the required orbits and place the correct number of small circles representing the electrons. The small circles may or may not include a minus sign to designate the electron. After the atomic weight concept is established or coincidentally with the use of atomic number, the number of neutrons is written in the nuclear circle followed by the symbol for the neutron, n.

Another scheme uses a rectangle to represent the nucleus for purposes of demarcation with the atomic number represented by a number followed by a p or +, the appropriate number of neutrons (n) in the lower part of the rectangle, and a number representing the number of electrons (e or −) on each circle representing electron orbits. Sometimes the circles

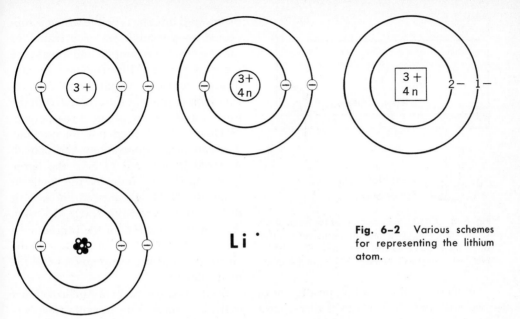

Li ·

Fig. 6-2 Various schemes for representing the lithium atom.

designating electron orbits are replaced by the electron numbers suitably spaced from the nucleus. It is good practice to have the electron numbers for each shell placed on the same horizontal line as the number of protons in the nucleus to show that the total number of electrons equals the total number of protons.

Electron-dot diagrams (sometimes called electronic symbols) are very convenient devices, particularly for focusing attention on valence electrons. The chemical symbol represents the kernel of the atom, that is, everything in the atom except the valence electrons. A dot (·) represents a valence electron. The dots are often symmetrically arranged about the kernel symbol. Students can associate the name of the element with the symbol and use the symbol with the atomic number Z represented as a left hand subscript and the mass number A represented as a right hand superscript. Some teachers prefer to use A as a left hand superscript. Thus lithium is represented as $_Z\text{Li}^A$, that is, $_3\text{Li}^7$ (American form) or as $_Z^A\text{Li}$, that is, $_3^7\text{Li}$ (international form).

6.2 The presence of electrons in matter

The electrical nature of matter can be established by experiments from electrostatics, electrochemistry, and electricity. Charged rods, electrification by friction, use of electroscopes, electron flow from a battery, and repulsion and attraction can all be shown. Several sections of this book, especially Chapter 21, Currents and Fields, and Chapter 13, Electrochemistry, will be useful here. See also the index and the table of contents.

Experiments which show that the electron possesses mass make use of the cathode-ray tube. Details on the use of the tube can be found in Chapter 21.

6.3 Bonding

6.3a Ionic bonding

Conductivity of fused NaCl. Mount a standard porcelain lamp base on a block of wood 6″ x 3″ x ½″ (Fig. 6–3). Connect one binding post to one lead from 110-volt a.c. source and include a knife switch.

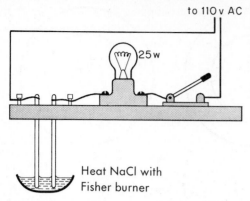

to 110 v AC

25 w

Heat NaCl with
Fisher burner

Fig. 6-3 Conductivity apparatus for fused NaCl. Other salts with lower melting points whose conductivity in the fused state may be tested include NaCl with some KCl, $NaNO_3$, KNO_3, and $AgNO_3$.

Connect the other binding post to one of two stiff and thick (1/16″) metal electrodes. These electrodes may be made of copper wire or from deflagrating-spoon handles and should be at least 4″ long. They fit into a metal sleeve through the wood and are connected to binding posts on the top of the board. They are positioned so that they are no more than ½″ apart since they will have to fit into the material (NaCl) which will be placed into a small porcelain crucible (00 or 01). The other binding post is connected to the second lead. The assembly is attached to a ring stand with a utility clamp. A 25-watt lamp is inserted into the socket.

Turn on the current, close the switch, and have students observe that the lamp does not light. Short circuit the electrodes with the blade of a wooden-handled knife or spatula. Have them observe results and explain that the circuit is now complete and that the metal is a conductor. Repeat with the wooden handle and have students explain that wood is a nonconductor. In sequence use the halite block and the crucible containing granulated NaCl (to a depth of ½″). The NaCl may be melted over a Fisher burner in approximately 3 minutes. The conductivity assembly may

be lowered into the crucible which is supported on a triangle set on a tripod, or may be lifted into position underneath the lamp by grasping the crucible with laboratory tongs. A variation that works rapidly is to preheat the crucible with the burner and drop in about ½ teaspoon of NaCl into the heated red-hot crucible. The salt melts immediately and enough material is provided to light the lamp. Have pupils explain why the lamp lit when the NaCl was melted and why it did not light when the NaCl was solid. A dramatic variation of the procedure is to keep the NaCl in contact with the electrode until the lamp goes out as the melt solidifies.

Students can explain failure to conduct in the solid state on the basis of strong electrostatic attraction of oppositely charged particles (ions). Conversely, they can explain the conductivity of the melt in terms of the increased kinetic energy of the ions which permits them freedom of motion to conduct the current. Lead students to see that the strong electrostatic attraction between ions constitutes a "binding" force, in other words, an *ionic bond*. Have them recognize that the resulting electrovalent (ionic) compounds have a rigid structure composed of ions arranged in a crystal lattice—a regular pattern of oppositely charged particles which, in turn, results in a regular macroscopic structure. The extent to which the subject of crystals is dealt with depends on the entire teaching situation but the following characteristics of ionic compounds are significant: quite hard and brittle, fairly high melting points, insulators in solid form, nonmolecular, that is, no particular anion belonging to or bound to a particular cation.

6.3b Covalent bonds

Nature of covalent substances. Covalent substances are generally gases or liquids at ordinary temperatures, are nonconductors as liquids or solids, and solidify into molecular crystals. Such crystals are very soft, have a low melting point, are volatile, and are nonconductors. The differences between covalent substances and ionic substances may be shown by duplicating the NaCl demonstration with liquid CCl_4. A solid such as naphthalene may be used and tested in a manner analogous to fused NaCl. (*Caution: Naphthalene vapor is readily inflammable.*) Such crystals may result from dipole-dipole attraction between polar ends of adjacent molecules or from weak molecular forces of attraction between molecules. These forces are much weaker than the covalent bonds which bind atoms into molecules. The characteristic properties of such substances are the result.

Certain elements such as carbon and certain compounds form crystals which are bound together by covalent bonds. Examples are the diamond (carbon) and silicon carbide (SiC). In the diamond, each carbon atom is joined by four pairs of covalent bonds to four other carbon atoms. This results in a massive 3-dimensional lattice which is bound by these strong covalent bonds. Such solid substances are consequently extremely hard, have very high melting points, and are nonconductors.

Polar. Draw atoms of H and Cl and explain how these may be bonded. Ask students why this bond is different in degree from the bond in the H_2 molecule, why, also, it is much stronger than the relatively loose ionic bond. Have them attempt to explain why experimental data indicate that the electron pair spends more time under the influence of the Cl atom than under the H atom. Students easily get the idea that Cl has a greater attraction because of its greater nuclear charge (actually greater electronegativity). The electron-dot diagram may also be used to show the displacement of the electron pair.

Have them explain why such a bond is called a *polar covalent* bond. Analogy to magnetic poles can help get the idea across. They may reason that the H end (the proton) is more positive and the Cl end is more negative. Have them define a dipole as a molecule having separate centers of + and − charge.

Such polar molecules result from the unequal sharing of one or more pairs of electrons. Indicate to the class that there are experimental methods capable of identifying and measuring polarity of such bonds (dipole moment, dielectric constant). Have them explain why 1. the bonds in water between the hydrogen and oxygen are polar bonds, 2. why the water molecule is not a linear molecule, not

H:O̤:H, but rather is H:O̤: .
                             H

Polar-nonpolar. You might have students draw atom model and electron-dot diagrams for CH_4 (methane) and CCl_4 (carbon tetrachloride) and have them explain why these substances have polar bonds, and yet are nonpolar. Explain, if necessary, that the symmetrical arrangement of the electron pairs (polar bonds) results in the molecule having common negative and positive centers of charge, for instance:

	H	Cl
:O::C::O:	H:C:H	Cl:C:Cl
	H	Cl
carbon dioxide	methane	carbon tetrachloride

Saturated-unsaturated. Covalent bonds occur particularly in carbon compounds such as ethane, ethylene, and acetylene. Ethane has single bonds only, ethylene has a double bond, and acetylene has a triple bond. Structural formulas which utilize a dash (—) to represent a pair of electrons are frequently used to represent bonds in organic chemistry and to some extent in inorganic chemistry. Compounds which contain only single bonds are saturated; those which have a double or triple bond are unsaturated. This implies that atoms can be added to the unsaturated compound. Thus the addition of two hydrogen atoms to a molecule of ethylene or four hydrogen atoms to a molecule of acetylene converts these unsaturated substances to the same saturated compound, ethane.

Here is a demonstration of the difference between the behavior of saturated and unsaturated compounds and hence between single and double or triple bonds. Prepare a dilute solution of bromine water. Bubble natural gas (almost exclusively methane) into the bromine water for 2 minutes. Prepare acetylene according to the procedure described in 14.2c; bubble the gas through the bromine water as in Fig. 6–4. The bromine water is readily decolorized by the acetylene due to addition of the bromine atoms to the triple bond of acetylene. (*Caution: Teacher demonstration only; bromine water is highly caustic.*)

6.3c Coordinate-covalent

In NH_3 and H_2O, there appear pairs of electrons which are unbound to other

atoms. If a chemical situation arises in which another atom which has room for an additional pair of electrons is present, then the unbound pair of electrons are shared with the particle or structure which has room for it. The result is a coordinate covalent bond. Both water and ammonia contain unbound pairs of electrons. In liquid ammonia or water a substance such as HCl gives up its proton to the unbound electron pair in ammonia, resulting in a chemical change which produces the ammonium ion (NH_4^+) and the hydronium ion (H_3O^+), respectively. These two substances will help provide the background for understandings of acid behavior (reaction of a polar molecule with water), the behavior of such weak basic substances as ammonia water ($NH_3 + H_2O$; or NH_4OH), and complex ions as, for example, the hydrated cupric ion, $Cu(H_2O)_4^{++}$, or the cupric tetrammine complex, $Cu(NH_3)_4^{++}$, in which the unbound electron pairs fit into the unoccupied orbitals of the cupric ion.

Formation of a coordinate covalent bond. Pass HCl gas (11.2c) into water and test with conductivity apparatus (8.4d). To 5 ml of cupric sulfate solution add an aqueous solution of ammonia until the pale blue precipitate of $Cu(OH)_2$ forms. Add ammonia solution until a deep blue solution of the complex $Cu(NH_3)_4SO_4 \cdot H_2O$ forms. Evaporate slowly to dryness with the formation of the intensely blue crystals of the complex. Compare the color of the solution and these crystals with that of the original cupric sulfate crystals and solution. To verify demonstration, again produce the $Cu(OH)_2$ ppt. Test one half of the solution by addition of NaOH solution; no deep blue color results. Repeat with the other half, adding 5 ml of concentrated NH_4Cl (NH_4^+ ion); the negative result shows that the addition of the NH_3—not the presence of the NH_4^+ ion—

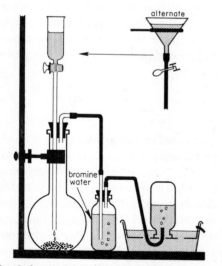

alternate

bromine water

Fig. 6–4 Acetylene is bubbled through bromine water. (*Warning—caustic*). Any residual gases are collected for safety.

was responsible for the formation of the blue color.

6.3d   Metallic bonds

Metals are the only solids which as a group conduct electricity in the solid state. The atoms of the metals are arranged in geometric patterns forming a gross crystal structure (see 6.4d on constructing crystal models). To account for such properties as electrical conductivity, malleability, and ductility the metallic lattice is presumed to consist of points representative of the positive metallic ions. The space between the lattice points (metallic ions) is filled with a cloud of valence electrons which holds the positive ions together. The valence electrons are relatively free to move, thus accounting for electrical conductivity. Ductility and malleability are explained as being due to the ease with which the nuclei can slip past one another without having the crystal pull apart.

Temperature and metallic conductivity. Suspend an iron wire spiral (about 2″ diameter) from a rubber stopper in a ring stand. The spiral is made from about two feet of 12-gauge black iron wire and is wound with its spirals well apart to prevent a short circuit. Connect both ends to a source of low voltage (6 v d.c.) and read the ammeter which is connected in series (Fig. 6–5). Then flick a Bunsen burner flame over the wire spiral with a resultant drop in the observed current. Using almost any standard lamp enclosed in an insulating box (Transite is good) as a heat source results in a perceptible change after some time has elapsed. Another device is to use a 550- or 600-watt heater element. Students note the instantaneous current when the connection is first made and then a perceptible drop before the heater element develops a stabilized current. A typical set of readings are 5.8 amperes (instantaneous) and 5.4 amperes (stabilized).

Heat and electrolyte conductivity. Prepare a saturated solution of NaCl which is then filtered. Place in a 400-ml beaker positioned on a tripod and containing long graphite electrodes about 2″ apart dipping into the solution almost to the bottom of the beaker. Connect to a 10-volt a.c. source. Then heat the contents of the beaker and note the rise in current. A typical reading has been 5.4 amperes at room temperature and 6.4 almost at boiling, with a steady rise as the temperature increased.

6.3e   Hydrogen bonding

A hydrogen bond consists of a proton shared between two atoms. This is possible because the proton's very small size permits it to be attracted by the electrons of two different atoms. This sort of hydrogen bridge can exist only between small atoms of high electronegativity and is evident in the peculiar properties of such substances as H_2O, HF, and NH_3. For example, H_2O has an abnormally high boiling point compared with the boiling points of its

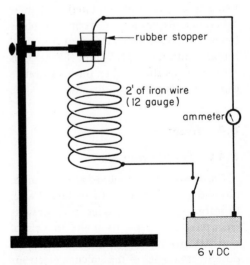

Fig. 6–5   The relationship between temperature and metallic conductivity can be shown when the wire spiral is heated with a Bunsen burner.

analogues—H_2Te, H_2Se, and H_2S—whose boiling points decrease in this order. It might be expected that if this pattern were followed, the boiling point of H_2O would be lower than that of H_2S. Actually it is much higher than that of H_2Te. The same patterns emerge when the boiling points of the hydrogen halides are considered. Apparently the hydrogen bonds make it very difficult for the particular molecules to detach themselves from the liquid phase. Molecules of such substances as H_2O, HF, and NH_3 are bound together by hydrogen bonds. Among the peculiar properties of water which may be explained in part by means of the hydrogen bond idea are its high boiling point and its very high specific heat.

Hydrogen bonding in liquids.[1] Place 100 ml of the following liquids in separate 300-ml bottles: glycerin, $18M$ H_2SO_4, glycol, water, ethanol, ether, and benzene. Swirl each bottle equally and note relative time until the disappearance of each vortex. The viscosities here are different primarily because of more or less intense hydrogen bonding, although ether and benzene can be differentiated and their difference explained in terms of polar forces. One can also show that an equal molal solution of $CHCl_3$ and $(C_2H_5)_2O$ is more viscous than either pure substance due to hydrogen bond formation.

6.4 Models

6.4a Simple models

Cardboard and thumbtacks. Show large, circular models made of cardboard with thumbtacks near the edge to represent electrons (Fig. 6–6), or make models of clay and wire (Fig. 6–7). Students may observe analogies of the valence electrons

[1] J. Arthur Campbell, *J. Chem. Educ.*, 34, A 105 (1957)—a Chem Ed tested demonstration.

for each of the important elements. See Table 6–2 which gives the information for constructing these models for other common elements. Have students make their own small-scale models at their desks. Develop the idea that the valence electrons are usually found in the outer orbit. Ask students to form compounds with the models. They may begin with atoms of hydrogen and oxygen. Have them show that oxygen has 6 outer electrons with two spaces for the electrons needed to complete the orbit of 8 electrons. Then ask students to hold a model of hydrogen on each side of a model of oxygen so that the single electron of each hydrogen fills the space of the electrons missing in the oxygen atom (Fig. 6–8); at the same time show that one electron from the oxygen is shared with hydrogen. At this point, students should recognize that the electrons now belong to both atoms at the same time (sharing, 6.3b). You may also wish to distinguish among the various kinds of bonding (6.3). Thumbtacks of various colors may also be used to make models of entire atoms with one color for neutrons, another for protons, and a third for electrons. The electrons can be positioned to accord roughly with their orbits while the neutrons and protons are clustered in the center of the cardboard circle.

Tinkertoy and plywood. A more complicated, but more useful model can be made by students with a Tinkertoy set. In large circles of plywood, about 2′ in diameter, drill eight ¼″ holes equidistant around a circle drawn just inside the edge of the disk; then drill another ¼″ hole in the center (Fig. 6–9). Now get some Tinkertoy or similar knobs with a ¼″ hole in the center. Have students paint or draw the symbol of each element they intend to represent on a 3″ cardboard circle, and paste each of these on a knob. Into the

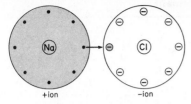

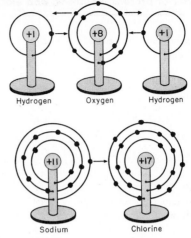

Fig. 6–6 Simple atomic models made from cardboard and thumbtacks. You may want to point out that for NaCl there is a transfer of the one outer (M shell) electron from Na to Cl, thereby ionizing both particles while at the same time giving each particle an outer ring of eight electrons.

Fig. 6–7 Atomic models made from wire mounted on wooden stands with colored lumps of clay to represent the nucleus and electrons. The sets of arrows in the H₂O model emphasize that covalent sharing is two-way. In water each H shares its one electron with O and, in turn, O shares one of its electrons with each H. The one arrow between Na and Cl points up the one-way transfer of an electron.

center of each knob place one of the small ¼″ dowels that come with the Tinkertoy set. Then place these in the center of the plywood circle to identify the element under construction. Next take Tinkertoy knobs and paint a negative sign on each one to represent the outer, or valence, electrons. Then fit a small Tinkertoy stick (long enough to go through two plywood circles) into each; these then can be placed into any number of the holes on the rim of the plywood circles to represent the desired structure.

You may demonstrate these models on the blackboard if you attach rubber vacuum cups to the backs; or suspend them with wire from the blackboard molding. After showing various atoms, have students show the three different kinds of bonding.

6.4b Constructing atomic models

It might be well to point out to students that whatever model of atomic structure is used, such a model is not reality. It is used only because it helps explain the gross behavior of substances in terms that are easily understandable. Even the best models are labeled "probable" or "possible." In addition to the restrictions imposed by the difficulties of quantum and wave mechanics, students should realize that much of the acceptable theory is based on spectral rather than chemical data; that atoms do

not therefore necessarily behave, chemically, the way spectral data would indicate that they should behave. Also, once atoms have combined, the electrons belong to an entirely new structure. See Table 6–2 which gives the number of particles by type for each element.

References. Probably the most suitable material for making three-dimensional models is Styrofoam. This material may be purchased from the Star Band Company Inc., Broad and Commerce Streets, Portsmouth, Va., in the form of white balls of various dimensions (¾″ to 6″ diameter), colored balls (yellow, black, red, green, blue: 1″ to 3″ by ½″ increases), white eggs (from 1½″ x 2½″ to 3″ x 4¼″), and columns, boards, blocks, and discs in a large variety of sizes. Local sources such as florist supply houses may also carry materials of this sort. Vegetable and other dyes may be used to color the white Styrofoam. These include tempera, water colors,

TABLE 6-2
Number of protons, neutrons, and electrons by element

name	symbol	protons*	neutrons	K	L	M	N	O	P	Q
						electrons				
hydrogen	H	1	0	1	0	0	0	0	0	0
helium	He	2	2	2	0	0	0	0	0	0
lithium	Li	3	4	2	1	0	0	0	0	0
beryllium	Be	4	5	2	2	0	0	0	0	0
boron	B	5	6	2	3	0	0	0	0	0
carbon	C	6	6	2	4	0	0	0	0	0
nitrogen	N	7	7	2	5	0	0	0	0	0
oxygen	O	8	8	2	6	0	0	0	0	0
fluorine	F	9	10	2	7	0	0	0	0	0
neon	Ne	10	10	2	8	0	0	0	0	0
sodium	Na	11	12	2	8	1	0	0	0	0
magnesium	Mg	12	12	2	8	2	0	0	0	0
aluminum	Al	13	14	2	8	3	0	0	0	0
silicon	Si	14	14	2	8	6	0	0	0	0
phosphorus	P	15	16	2	8	5	0	0	0	0
sulfur	S	16	16	2	8	6	0	0	0	0
chlorine	Cl	17	18	2	8	7	0	0	0	0
argon	A	18	22	2	8	8	0	0	0	0
potassium	K	19	20	2	8	1	0	0	0	0
calcium	Ca	20	20	2	8	2	0	0	0	0
scandium	Sc	21	24	2	8	9	2	0	0	0
titanium	Ti	22	26	2	8	10	2	0	0	0
vanadium	V	23	28	2	8	11	2	0	0	0
chromium	Cr	24	28	2	8	13	1	0	0	0
manganese	Mn	25	30	2	8	13	2	0	0	0
iron	Fe	26	30	2	8	14	2	0	0	0
cobalt	Co	27	32	2	8	15	2	0	0	0
nickel	Ni	28	31	2	8	16	2	0	0	0
copper	Cu	29	35	2	8	18	1	0	0	0
zinc	Zn	30	35	2	8	18	2	0	0	0
gallium	Ga	31	38	2	8	18	3	0	0	0
germanium	Ge	32	40	2	8	18	4	0	0	0
arsenic	As	33	42	2	8	18	5	0	0	0
selenium	Se	34	45	2	8	18	6	0	0	0
bromine	Br	35	45	2	8	18	7	0	0	0
krypton	Kr	36	48	2	8	18	8	0	0	0
rubidium	Rb	37	48	2	8	18	8	1	0	0
strontium	Sr	38	50	2	8	18	8	2	0	0
yttrium	Y	39	50	2	8	18	9	2	0	0
zirconium	Zr	40	51	2	8	18	10	2	0	0
niobium	Nb	41	52	2	8	18	12	1	0	0
molybdenum	Mo	42	54	2	8	18	13	1	0	0
technetium	Tc	43	56	2	8	18	14	1	0	0
ruthenium	Ru	44	57	2	8	18	15	1	0	0
rhodium	Rh	45	58	2	8	18	16	1	0	0
palladium	Pd	46	61	2	8	18	18	0	0	0
silver	Ag	47	61	2	8	18	18	1	0	0
cadmium	Cd	48	64	2	8	18	18	2	0	0
indium	In	49	66	2	8	18	18	3	0	0
tin	Sn	50	69	2	8	18	18	4	0	0
antimony	Sb	51	70	2	8	18	18	5	0	0

*The number of protons and the atomic number are the same for each element.

name	symbol	protons*	neutrons	K	L	M	N	O	P	Q
							electrons			
tellurium	Te	52	76	2	8	18	18	6	0	0
iodine	I	53	74	2	8	18	18	7	0	0
xenon	Xe	54	77	2	8	18	18	8	0	0
cesium	Cs	55	78	2	8	18	18	8	1	0
barium	Ba	56	81	2	8	18	18	8	2	0
lanthanum	La	57	82	2	8	18	18	9	2	0
cerium	Ce	58	82	2	8	18	20	8	2	0
praseodymium	Pr	59	82	2	8	18	21	8	2	0
neodymium	Nd	60	84	2	8	18	22	8	2	0
promethium	Pm	61	84	2	8	18	23	8	2	0
samarium	Sm	62	88	2	8	18	24	8	2	0
europium	Eu	63	89	2	8	18	25	8	2	0
gadolinium	Gd	64	93	2	8	18	25	9	2	0
terbium	Tb	65	94	2	8	18	27	8	2	0
dysprosium	Dy	66	96	2	8	18	28	8	2	0
holmium	Ho	67	98	2	8	18	29	8	2	0
erbium	Er	68	99	2	8	18	30	8	2	0
thulium	Tm	69	100	2	8	18	31	8	2	0
ytterbium	Yb	70	103	2	8	18	32	8	2	0
lutetium	Lu	71	104	2	8	18	32	9	2	0
hafnium	Hf	72	107	2	8	18	32	10	2	0
tantalum	Ta	73	108	2	8	18	32	11	2	0
tungsten	W	74	110	2	8	18	32	12	2	0
rhenium	Re	75	111	2	8	18	32	13	2	0
osmium	Os	76	114	2	8	18	32	14	2	0
iridium	Ir	77	116	2	8	18	32	17	0	0
platinum	Pt	78	117	2	8	18	32	17	1	0
gold	Au	79	118	2	8	18	32	18	1	0
mercury	Hg	80	121	2	8	18	32	18	2	0
thallium	Tl	81	123	2	8	18	32	18	3	0
lead	Pb	82	125	2	8	18	32	18	4	0
bismuth	Bi	83	126	2	8	18	32	18	5	0
polonium	Po	84	126	2	8	18	32	18	6	0
astatine	At	85	126	2	8	18	32	18	7	0
radon	Rn	86	136	2	8	18	32	18	8	0
francium	Fr	87	136	2	8	18	32	18	8	1?
radium	Ra	88	138	2	8	18	32	18	8	2
actinium	Ac	89	138	2	8	18	32	18	9	2?
thorium	Th	90	142	2	8	18	32	18	10	2
protactinium	Pa	91	140	2	8	18	32	20	9	2?
uranium	U	92	146	2	8	18	32	21	9	2
neptunium	Np	93	144	2	8	18	32	23	8	2
plutonium	Pu	94	148	2	8	18	32	24	8	2
americium	Am	95	148	2	8	18	32	25	8	2
curium	Cm	96	149	2	8	18	32	25	9	2
berkelium	Bk	97	152	2	8	18	32	26	9	2
californium	Cf	98	151	2	8	18	32	28	8	2
einsteinium	E	99	155	2	8	18	32	29	8	2
fermium	Fm	100	152	2	8	18	32	30	8	2
mendelevium	Mv	101	155	2	8	18	32	31	8	2
nobelium	No	102	?	2	8	18	32	32	8	2

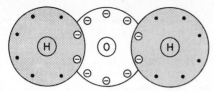

Fig. 6-8 A model of H₂O made of cardboard and colored thumbtacks. Emphasize that one shared electron comes from H and the other comes from O in each bond.

enamels formulated with aliphatic solvents, siliconized enamels, floral dyes, rubber-based paints, etc. Spray techniques are effective. Be sure to use care when pushing the wire through the Styrofoam. Knitting needles or any other wire of similar thickness may be used for axes of models.

A new technique for the projection of simple orbitals utilizes models constructed of cellulose acetate sheet (0.003″) which are superimposed upon each other according to definite patterns for 1s, 2s, and 2p orbitals. These are used with an overhead projector, and the images are made fuzzy by using the projector out of focus. Two Polaroid sheets are used in conjunction with the models and the projector, making possible various orbital combinations.[2]

Various scientific supply houses manufacture teaching models. One among many is "A Three Dimensional Atom Model" by Standard Scientific Co., Chicago, which uses colored magnets to represent fundamental particles and several

shells which rotate around the nucleus. The model permits construction of a variety of atomic models.

Selected references on two-dimensional, three-dimensional, and giant models follow. All of these are selected from Demonstration Abstracts, *Journal of Chemical Education*, November 1959 (36, A 689).

Two-dimensional models. Concentric circles on board into which pegs representing electrons are placed. (Wellings, R. E., 10, 179 [1933].) Board painted with rings (orbitals), electrons shown by golf tees inserted, or key tags hung on hooks. (Bondoc N. R., 19, 395 [1942].) Symbols, drawings, etc. backed with zig-zag strips of sandpaper stick to a black wool-covered board. (Joyner, A., 25, 375 [1948].) Colored beads on pegs. (Herron, F. Y., 28, 473 [1951].)

Three-dimensional models. Balls and wire molecules. (Evans, W. L., and Day, J. E., 1, 100 [1924].) Rubber balls, dowels, arranged in cubic lattice; 4″ x 4″ x 3″ metal box with glass windows with symbol and atomic number of elements inside on winding ribbon. (Higley, G. O., 2, 499 [1925].) Tinkertoy blocks and wire. (Dye, W. B., 8, 140 [1931].) Detachable plaster-of-Paris balls (electrons), molded on frame of spot-welded brass wire. (Scott, E. C., 8, 1845 [1931].) Wooden balls, wire frame, wooden beads (electrons), tetrahedra made of sheet tin for organic structure. (Pouleur, A. L., 9, 301 [1932].) Rubber balls, wire. (French, S. J., 10, 564 [1933].) Colored modeling clay and wire for student use. (Weaver, E. C., 17, 148 [1940].) Paper-maché, colored or painted with

[2] H. Bradford Thompson, "Dynamic Projection Display for Atomic Orbitals and the Covalent Bond," *J. Chem. Educ.*, 37, 118 (1960).

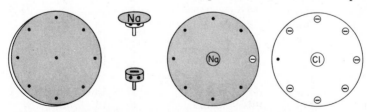

Fig. 6-9 The parts from a Tinkertoy set can be used for atomic models.

rings (orbitals), fastened with welding rod bent at proper angles to show orbitals; photographs in article. (Fowles, G. W. A., 32, 260 [1955].) Atomic models for a beginning course in College Chemistry. (Dodson, Vance H., 33, 528 [1956].)

Giant models. Oxygen: 1.5″ wooden balls on 3.16″ wire bent into orbits up to 4′ in diameter. (Brooks, W. G., 24, 245 [1947].) Sodium atom: tadpole-shaped brass pieces (electrons) on wires (3-ft. orbits) in three dimensions. (Hall, G. A., 24, 564 [1947].)

Dynamic models. Painted ping-pong balls spinning in rotating air jets going in circular and elliptical orbits. (Black, J., 7, 450 [1930] from *J. Optical Soc. Amer.*, 19, 317 [1929]; also Van Dam, T. W., et al, 29, 75 [1952], Sister M. Liguori, 29, 529 [1952].)

6.4c Molecular models

Sets from which molecular models may be constructed are available in considerable variety. One type consists of color-coded spheres representing such atoms as O, H, C, Cl, C, Br, etc. These are all of the same size and contain varying numbers of holes so that the atoms may be joined together. Wooden pegs and metal springs are used to join the atoms to represent bonding. Snap fasteners, metal wedges, and hook and eye connectors are in use in Fisher-Hirschfelder and Fisher-Hirschfelder-Taylor models, Fisher Scientific Co. A set sold by Griffin and Tatlock, Kemble Street, Kingsway, London W. C. 2, has considerable versatility since a large number of holes is drilled in the atom balls. The Brode-Hurd-Boord models (Tinkertoy) are sold by E. H. Sargent and Co., Chicago 30, Ill.

The high cost of commercial sets combined with the great need for models has produced a great variety of techniques and devices for model building. Often a choice of technique depends upon the material available. Over the next few pages some of the more recent approaches are summarized. The references at the end of each summary are to the *Journal of Chemical Education.*

Polystyrene foam spheres. A section of 25 students was given a list of bond angles, covalent radii, and van der Waals radii for a number of simple structures. A sufficient number of foamed polystyrene spheres (1½″ diameter) was provided for each student to build a model of one molecule or ion. The following suggestions were made: (1) for assembly of atoms use water-based glue or pipe cleaners; (2) for coloring agent use water color or enamels formulated with aliphatic solvents; (3) use Kenney's method (sanding balls which are just slightly oversize and then reducing to exact size by rotating them against a hole of the proper diameter in a piece of plastic sheet until they will just pass through) for reducing the spheres to the desired size. The students were left to their own method for locating bond axes and "covalent faces." (James B. Pierce, "Molecular Models: A General Chemistry Exercise," 36, 595 [1959].)

Scale models color coded. Foamed polystyrene balls are used on the scale 1.5″ per angstrom (1″ represents H, the smallest, and 7″ represents Cs, the largest). These balls are painted with tempera with a modern dishwashing detergent added to water as a wetting agent; upon drying, they are sprayed with clear plastics. Color scale may use up to 25 hues from red through oranges and yellow and greens to blue. Red has lowest negativity and blue the highest. The balls may be suspended or connected by stiff wire pushed through washer and ball center, one end being made into a loop and the other into a hook. Half-inch diameter spheres are glued to the atom sphere to represent outermost electrons (white) and electron vacancies (black). These may be placed in pairs at locations showing valence structure. Three-dimensional models can be constructed from the same material, fastened together by glue and wooden connectors. Suggested color scale: yellows for zero charge, red for high positive, blue for high negative, with varying hues in between. Models for teaching general chemistry include H_2O, H_3O^+, NH_3, NH_4^+, HNO_3, NO_3^-, and NaF. (R. T. Sanderson, "Models for Demonstrating Electronegativity and Partial Charge," 36, 507 [1959]. This author has written a 36-page booklet, *Principles and Construction of New Chemistry Teaching Aids,* available at low cost from the Bureau of Audio-Visual Instruction, Extension Division, State University of Iowa, Iowa City, Iowa. This booklet furnishes a wealth of detail on model building such as scale sizes, paint recipes, repairing, methods, and materials.)

"Pop-It" beads. Colored plastic "Pop-It" beads can be used for construction of complicated organic structures such as polypeptides. Such beads usually have only one hole but other holes may be introduced easily in the side of the regular bead with a heated metal rod. Heavy nichrome wire can be used as a bonding connector. (R. Quentin Blackwell, "Schematic Models of Biochemical Polymers," 34, 500 [1957].)

Sponge rubber. Atom spheres are made from sponge rubber balls of various sizes and colors available at retail stores. Bonds are made of ⅜″ wooden dowels and pieces of ⅜″ screen door retaining spring. Pliobond rubber cement is used. A plaster cast made of the rubber balls serves as a jig to retain the rubber balls and as a template to mark the location of the bonds. The position of the holes for locating tetrahedral positions in carbon atoms is marked on the cast by placing a card-board equilateral triangle (length of side given by the formula, $l = 0.817 \times d$, where l = length of side of triangle and d = diameter of the rubber sphere) in a horizontal position in the spherical hollow of the cast and marking the points where the apices touch the wall. The cast is then clamped by its top and bottom surfaces into an adjustable drill press vise and is aligned for drilling by placing a drop of mercury or small bead in the hollow and adjusting the position of the cast so that the mercury or bead comes to rest on one of the marks. A hole is then drilled vertically through the cast at the mark. Point markings before drilling the rubber ball holes are made by inserting a ball point refill through the openings in the cast. The plaster cast template is used to drill similar holes in differently colored rubber spheres representing different elements such as N and O. Larger spheres and a corresponding larger jig are used for atoms from Si to Br. Separate sets of holes are used for varying bond angles. Glycerol is used as a lubricant to aid insertion of dowels and springs. Models retain the necessary rigidity for demonstration purposes. Recommended diameters and bond materials: C atom—2½″, single bond—dowel 2½″ long, double bond—2½″ spring, triple bond—3½″ spring. (Rudolph M. Anker, "Construction of Molecular Models," 36, 138 [1959].)

Colored rubber balls. Models can be made from colored balls of hard rubber with specially designed bond holes and a variety of turned aluminum rod connectors. A special bond-restraining clip makes possible the construction of strained ring molecules where the bond angles vary from the normal bond angles of unrestrained molecules. The angles between bond holes in the molded rubber balls correspond to the values normally used; that is, $109°28'$ for carbon, $111°$ for oxy-

gen, 109° for nitrogen, etc. (Lee A. Su-
bleskey, "Molecular Models with Variable Bond Angles," 35, 26 [1958].)

For a general listing of molecular models see 24–80s, static models, 24–81s, scale
models, and 24–82s, isomer models; Demonstration Abstracts, prepared from the *J.
Chem. Educ.* by H. N. Alyea, p. A 689,
Nov. 1959.

6.4d   Crystal models

Cardboard. Cardboard cutouts may be
folded into shapes representative of the six
main crystal systems (cubic, tetragonal,
orthorhombic, hexagonal, monoclinic, and
triclinic). Tabs may be left on the cutout
for gluing. Fold lines may be scored with a
dull knife to permit easy folding. Perfor-
ated tape of the type used in sealing
cracks in plasterboard walls is a good con-
structional material as is rubber or contact
cement. Adhesive tape of various sorts
may be used either as a supplement to
tabs or with cutouts in which no tabs are
used. Fig. 6–10 shows diagrams of the six
crystal systems, and positioned with them
are the cutouts which may be folded
to produce a model. By the use of similar
cutouts with pencil or crayon striations
placed according to correct designs, the
models of 32 crystal classes representative
of the various symmetries of the six systems may be constructed.[3]

Shadow models. Slides are made by en-
closing a layer of steel bearing balls in a
hollow 3½″ by 4″ lantern slide which is
then projected. The slides are made from
1/16″ acetate sheet. One slide contains
about 900 1/16″ steel balls and is used to
show random versus ordered positioning,
closest packing of spheres, slip planes, and
holes in crystal lattices. A second slide
contains about 300 ⅛″ balls and a few

3/32″ balls to show how impurities (the
smaller balls) occupy regular lattice sites
and thus create points of potential strain.
(Malcolm E. Kenney and Selby M. Skin-
ner, "Hollow Lantern Slides Illustrating
Crystal Structure," 36, 495 [1959].)

Bubble model. Air is blown at uniform
pressure through a capillary tube dipped
beneath the surface of a pool of soapy
water. A two-dimensional crystal model
can be seen growing as the little bubbles
rise to the surface, attract one another,
and come together to form "bubble rafts,"
each bubble touching six others.[4]

6.5   Chemical reactions

6.5a   Relative activities of
elements

By reference to individual members of
each group in the periodic table starting
with Group I, students might answer such
questions as: How may Li, Na, and K
(each considered separately) attain a complete outer shell? (By losing one electron.)
Then deal with Be, Mg, and Ca in the
same vein. Then consider Al in Group III.
Exhibit samples of aluminum, magnesium, and sodium and have students
identify them as metals on the basis of
their chemical experience. Proceed in a
similar way with elements of Group VII
and then those of Groups VI and V. Have
students identify samples of nonmetals.
Metals might be defined as elements containing a few electrons (1, 2, or 3) in their
outermost shells, which they tend to lose
in chemical reacton with other elements.
Have students frame a parallel definition
for nonmetals. Label the Groups by Ro-
man numerals.

Group I. Place a small piece of dried
sodium on water in a small basin. Repeat
with a similar piece of potassium. The po-

[3] Alan Holden and Phyllis Singer, *Crystals and Crystal Growing,* Doubleday and Co., Garden City, N.Y.,
pp. 151, 284–88.

[4] Holden and Singer, *Crystals and Crystal Growing.*

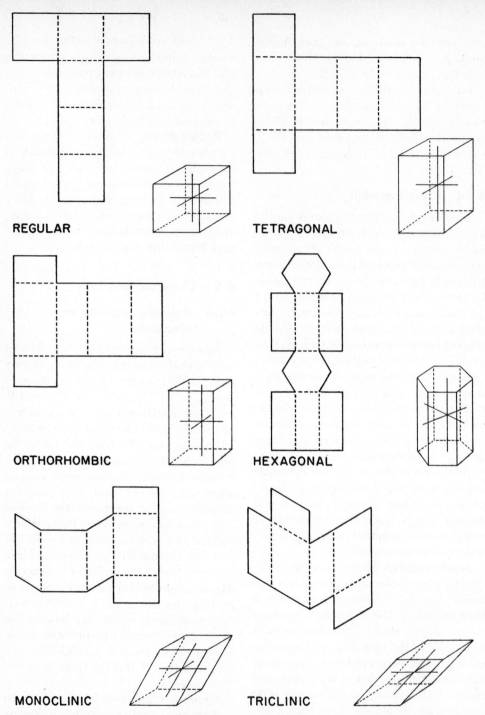

REGULAR

TETRAGONAL

ORTHORHOMBIC

HEXAGONAL

MONOCLINIC

TRICLINIC

Fig. 6-10 The six crystal systems. Paper model patterns are shown to the left of the structural forms. (From H. H. Sisler et al., *General Chemistry,* Macmillan, 1949, and A. Holden and P. Singer, *Crystals and Crystal Growing,* Doubleday, 1960. Copyright 1960 by Educational Services, Inc. Used by permission of Doubleday & Co., Inc.)

tassium will catch fire while the sodium does not. Place a piece of potassium on an ice cube. Place a piece of calcium in water and compare its relative activity with the action of potassium in water. This shows relative activity in elements in Groups I and II in the same period. (When handling sodium and potassium, use tongs.)

Group II. Place a piece of Mg ribbon and then a piece of Ca in cold water in a 6″ test tube. Test for hydrogen with a burning splint. Have students observe results and attempt explanation on the basis of atom diagrams. Have them reach conclusions similar to those regarding relative activity of K and Na in Group I. Demonstrate action of a small piece of dried Na in a 6″ test tube containing 2″ of water. Test for hydrogen. Show that a burning Mg ribbon will continue to burn in steam. Hold a 6″ length of Mg with tongs, ignite, and place into steam produced by water boiling vigorously in a small beaker (250 ml). A 250-ml Erlenmeyer flask may also be used as a steam generator. Have students arrive at the generalization that in a given period, progress from left to right in the periodic system results in a decrease in metallic properties.

Groups VI and VII. You may want to contrast metals and nonmetals in terms of valence electrons. Point out that whereas metals tend to lose electrons until they have a complete outermost orbit, nonmetals gain electrons to achieve the same result. Establish the decrease in nonmetallic activity with increasing atomic number and increasing ionic radius in these groups. The relative activity of the halogens can be shown by shaking antimony powder into cold chlorine water, warmed bromine water (highly caustic), and hot tincture of iodine (highly inflammable), respectively. The elements of Groups I and II generally tend to lose electrons to elements of Groups VI and VII.

Group V. Students can deal with Group V elements in the same fashion. They will see that this group which starts out with nonmetals becomes progressively more metallic, ending with Bi. Exhibit samples of these elements, particularly P, Sb, and Bi. Crush Sb in a mortar and pestle and attempt the same with Bi. Have the pupils note such properties as luster and brittleness.

Group IV and electron sharing. Based on the study of the sequence Na, Mg, and Al, students may realize the increasing difficulty with which atoms lose an increasing number of electrons. Students can now consider Group IV and realize that carbon would have to lose 4 electrons or gain 4 electrons to attain a complete outer orbit. Is there some other way in which carbon could react with another element without losing or gaining electrons? Students often propose the idea of sharing electrons as requiring less energy. Attention is now drawn to the line in the periodic table (see appendix) which demarcates nonmetals from metals. Students might ask questions about B which is labeled a nonmetal. Point out that B behaves as a nonmetal because its small size causes it to hold on to its valence electrons more strongly than the rest of the elements of the group which are progressively more metallic. Boron therefore tends to act like its neighbor carbon by sharing electrons. In order to provide extension of the idea of sharing, the teacher may raise such questions as how two nonmetals such as sulfur and oxygen can combine to form an oxide. Hydrogen is treated in the light of carbon, that is, as an element which contains about one half the electron capacity of its outer shell. Therefore it, like carbon, tends to share electrons. Elements just preceding or following an inert gas (Group 0) tend to gain or lose electrons, forming ions and ionic bonds. Virtually all other types of combinations involve sharing electrons.

6.5b *Oxidation-reduction*

Oxidation is defined as a chemical change in which electrons are lost. Thus oxidation results in an increase in the oxidation state (number) of the element oxidized. Reduction (deoxidation) is defined as a chemical change in which electrons are gained. Thus reduction results in a decrease in the oxidation state of the element reduced. The types of molecular chemical equations which are considered oxidation-reduction reactions include: combination, synthesis of binary compound from its element; decomposition, analysis of a binary compound into its elements; and single replacement.

Oxidation state rules

1. The oxidation state of an atom as an element is zero. Even though the element exists in diatomic or more complicated molecular form, its oxidation state is zero. Thus just as the oxidation state of the element Mg is 0 so also the oxidation state of O in O_2 or of H in H_2 is zero.

2. Positive ions have a positive oxidation state so that the oxidation states of Na^+, Mg^{++}, and Al^{+++} ions are respectively $+1$, $+2$, $+3$. Negative ions have a negative oxidation state so that the oxidation states of Cl^- and $O^=$ are, respectively, -1 and -2.

3. In virtually all compounds (except hydrides) hydrogen is assigned an oxidation state of $+1$.

4. In virtually all compounds (except peroxides) oxygen is assigned an oxidation state of -2.

5. For neutral molecules of compounds the sum of the oxidation states of all the atoms must add up to zero. For example, in H_2O for which the oxidation states are evident from rules 2 and 3, the sum of the oxidation state of all the hydrogen atoms is equal to that of the single oxygen atom.

Where more than a single atom of an element is present in a compound, the sum of the oxidation states of each atom will be referred to as the oxidation number. Thus in H_2O, H has an oxidation state of $+1$ but the oxidation number of hydrogen is $2(+1)$ or $+2$. For the single oxygen atom, the oxidation state is -2. This may be represented schematically as

Oxidation states	$+1$	-2
	H_2	O
Oxidation numbers	$+2$	-2

The positive oxidation number in a compound must be equal to the negative oxidation number. Application of the rules makes it possible to determine the oxidation numbers in a binary compound and from these oxidation numbers, the oxidation state is apparent. For example, in SO_3

Oxidation state		-2
	S	O_3
Oxidation number	?	-6

Thus the single S atom has an oxidation number of $+6$ and therefore an oxidation state of $+6$.

In ternary molecules, the use of the fundamental rules permits the determination of the oxidation state of the desired element; the oxygen is treated as the only negative part of the formula and everything else is treated as if it were positive. For example, to determine the oxidation state of S in H_2SO_4, one schematic is

Net charge			0	0
Oxidation states (known)	$+1$		-2	
	H_2	S	O_4	
Oxidation numbers (known)	$+2$		-8	
Solution	$+2+x$		$-8=0$	
	x		$=+6$	

Here again the single S atom has an oxidation number of $+6$ and therefore an oxidation state of $+6$.

6. For a complex ion, the oxidation numbers of all the atoms add up to the charge on the ion. For example, to deter-

mine the oxidation state of S in the sulfate ion, $SO_4^=$, the sum of the positive and negative oxidation numbers must be equal to minus 2 (-2), that is, the negative oxidation number must exceed the positive oxidation number numerically by 2. A schematic that may be used is

Net charge			-2
Oxidation state (known)		-2	
	S	$O_4^=$	
Oxidation number (known)		-8	
Solution	$x + (-8) =$	-2	
	$x =$	$+6$	

The oxidation state of the single S is $+6$ since only 1 S is present. When an ion has more than one atom of the element whose oxidation state is to be determined, the result obtained (oxidation number) as in the case of $SO_4^=$, is divided by the number of atoms present to obtain the oxidation state of the element. For example: to determine the oxidation state of Cr in $Cr_2O_7^=$, the schematic solution is

Net charge			-2
Oxidation state (known)		-2	
	Cr_2	O_7	
Oxidation number (known)	$x - 14$		
	$x + (-14)$	$= -2$	
	$x =$	$+12$	

Since $x = 2$ Cr, then 2 Cr $= +12$, Cr $= +6$.

It must be noted that oxidation state is not the same thing as valence. Valence is represented by a number (unsigned) which indicates the number of hydrogen atoms with which the atom may combine or the number of single bonds which it may form. Oxidation state as defined is a signed number. The valence and oxidation state need not necessarily be identical. For example, in methyl alcohol the valence of C in CH_3OH is 4 according to the number of single bonds present. The oxidation number of C, calculated according to the rules, is -2. Even more peculiarly, the oxidation state of an element in a compound may be 0. For example in CH_2O,

according to the rule, the oxidation state of C is 0.

Redox reactions. Simple demonstrations include all examples of oxidation such as the rusting of iron, combustion of methane, burning of wood, etc. In the following chapters on chemistry, 7 through 15, you will find many examples which might be useful in the demonstration of oxidation-reduction.

Nearly instantaneous oxidation-reduction.[5] Prepare a dilute solution of $KMnO_4$ (0.01 M). Acidify a portion with sulfuric acid and add a solution of $FeSO_4$ while stirring. The reduction of permanganate is almost instantaneous. Add an equal volume of oxalic acid of the same approximate concentration as the $FeSO_4$ to another sample of the acidified $KMnO_4$; no color change occurs. However, on the addition of a crystal of a manganous salt ($MnSO_4$, $Mn(NO_3)_2$, or $MnCl_2$) the reaction is autocatalyzed and the permanganate color disappears. (Concentrations are not too critical for a "rough" experiment.)

Electrolysis of aqueous Na_2SO_4.[5] Electrolyze a solution of Na_2SO_4 in a U-tube apparatus (Fig. 6–11), using inert graphite electrodes and at least 30 volts d.c. Put a few drops of litmus into the solution around each electrode. Test for hydrogen at cathode and oxygen at anode. The litmus at the cathode turns blue and that at the anode turns red.

Cathode	$2 H_2O + 2e \rightarrow H_2 + 2 OH^-$
Anode	$2 H_2O \rightarrow O_2 + 4 H^+ + 4e$
Net equation	$2 H_2O \rightarrow 2 H_2 + O_2$

Electrolysis of H_2SO_4 solution with Pb electrodes.[6] Place two Pb plates into a 400-ml beaker containing H_2SO_4(2:1). Connect to a 6-volt d.c. source. PbO_2 is

[5] Suggested by a procedure described in *Chemistry*, M. J. Sienko and R. A. Plane, McGraw-Hill Book Co., N. Y., 1957.

[6] Adapted from *Chemistry*, Sienko and Plane.

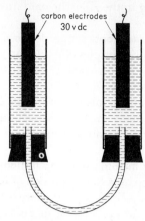

carbon electrodes
30 v dc

Fig. 6–11 Apparatus for the electrolysis of aqueous sodium sulfate.

deposited on the positive electrode and H_2 is liberated at the negative electrode. After 5 minutes have passed, disconnect and permit the cell to discharge through an electric bell.

Electrolysis in nonaqueous solvent.[7] Prepare a saturated solution of KI in acetone. Position Pt electrodes about one inch apart and pass at least 60 volts d.c. through the solution. A brown substance deposits on the positive electrode. When the negative electrode is placed into water, a gas—presumably H_2 (from deposited K)—is liberated and the solution formed turns litmus blue.

Electricity by chemical reaction.[8] "Connect one terminal of an electrical socket holding an ordinary small photoflash bulb to a 1' length of #16 copper wire with its lower half wound into a spiral. Connect the other terminal to a battery alligator clip, and insert in the clip a 12" length of magnesium ribbon wound into a spiral. Prepare 200 ml of 6 N H_2SO_4.

"Drop a 12" length of magnesium ribbon into a test tube one quarter full of 6 N

[7] From a demonstration by Joseph Castka, Martin Van Buren High School, New York City.
[8] From a demonstration submitted to the *J. of Chem. Ed.* by Fidel Villarreul G., Institute Tecnologico de Monterrey, Mexico.

H_2SO_4; hydrogen gas is evolved. Hold a lighted match at the mouth of the test tube; the hydrogen-air mixture explodes with a pop. Lower the magnesium ribbon and copper spiral simultaneously into the 150-ml beaker containing 100 ml of 6 N H_2SO_4; electricity is generated, setting off the photoflash bulb.''

6.5c   Types of molecular reactions

Combination. Such reactions involve the direct combination of two substances, $A + B \rightarrow AB$.

two elements
$$2\,Na + Cl_2 \rightarrow 2\,NaCl$$
$$4\,Al + 3\,O_2 \rightarrow 2\,Al_2O_3$$
two compounds
$$CaO + H_2O \rightarrow Ca(OH)_2$$
$$H_2O + SO_2 \rightarrow H_2SO_3$$
$$CaO + CO_2 \rightarrow CaCO_3$$

A simple demonstration is burning a length of magnesium. (*Caution: Hold with tongs.*)

Lighting and explosion of a "hydrogen gun." The apparatus consists of a cylindrical tin can which has a small perforation in the side near the bottom of the can. The can has a long metal handle attached (a piece of thin sheet metal may be bent and secured around the can with a bolt) and is completely filled with hydrogen by downward displacement of air. The hydrogen emerging from the small hole is ignited. It continues to burn until the explosion limit is reached, resulting in an explosion.

Decomposition. Decomposition is the breaking down of a compound (by heat, electricity, or light) into simpler substances, $AB \rightarrow A + B$. It may be considered as the reverse of combination.

1. Decomposition of a binary compound.

Heat $2\,HgO \overset{\triangle}{\rightarrow} 2\,Hg + O_2 \uparrow$
Electrolysis $2\,NaCl \rightarrow 2\,Na + Cl_2 \uparrow$

2. Decomposition of ternary compounds (special examples).

Most carbonates except those of Group I decompose to yield CO_2 and a metallic oxide.

$$CaCO_3 \xrightarrow{\triangle} CaO + CO_2 \uparrow$$

Metallic hydroxides (except Group I) decompose to yield H_2O and a metallic oxide (anhydride).

$$Ca(OH)_2 \xrightarrow{\triangle} CaO + H_2O \uparrow$$

Certain ternary acids decompose more or less readily to yield H_2O and a nonmetallic oxide.

$$H_2SO_4 \xrightarrow{\triangle} H_2O + SO_3 \uparrow$$

Chlorates may decompose to yield O_2 and a chloride.

$$2\,NaClO_3 \xrightarrow{\triangle} 2\,NaCl + 3\,O_2 \uparrow$$

For an excellent and quite spectacular demonstration of decomposition see the ammonium dichromate volcano, 2.3.

Single replacement. Single replacement occurs when an element reacts with a compound to produce a different element and a different compound. Students may "predict" the occurrence or failure of a particular reaction of this type by using concepts implicit in the correct use of the electromotive (activity) series (see appendix).

1. Metallic replacement: $C + AB \rightarrow CB + A$

The very active metals replace hydrogen in water, producing a hydroxide (base). At elevated temperatures for the less active of these metals, an oxide may result.

$$2\,Na + 2\,H_2O \rightarrow 2\,NaOH + H_2 \uparrow$$
$$3\,Fe + 4\,H_2O \rightarrow Fe_3O_4 + 4\,H_2 \uparrow$$

Metals above hydrogen replace hydrogen in acids.

$$Zn + 2\,HCl \rightarrow ZnCl_2 + H_2 \uparrow$$
$$Cu + HCl \text{ (no reaction)}$$

A more active metal replaces a less active one from its compounds (salt solution).

$$Zn + CuSO_4 \rightarrow ZnSO_4 + Cu \downarrow$$
$$Cu + ZnSO_4 \text{ (no reaction)}$$

The very active metals and flourine will react with the water in the solution.

2. Nonmetallic replacement: $D + AB \rightarrow AD + B$.

A more active halogen replaces a less active one in its compounds (solution).

$$Cl_2 + 2\,KBr \rightarrow 2\,KCl + Br_2$$

Single replacement trees. Any of the metal replacement combinations, particularly with some little arrangement of the replacing metal into a "tree" form, are good. Placing a triangular file or spatula into $CuSO_4$ solution produces quick results. A tree made of Cu wire or foil and placed into $AgNO_3$ solution also is effective.

Double replacement. In double replacement reactions two compounds (often but not necessarily in solution) react to form two different compounds. The mechanism of this type of reaction involves an exchange or switching of the compounds in the generalized pattern of

$$\underline{A\ \overset{\frown}{B}} + \underline{\overset{\frown}{C}\ D} \rightarrow AD + CB$$

This type of reaction frequently involves the process of ion exchange so that the positive ion of one compound combines with the negative ion of the other compound.

$$\underline{A^+\ \overset{\frown}{B^-}} + \underline{\overset{\frown}{C^+}\ D^-} \rightarrow A^+\ D^- + C^+\ B^-$$

This process is often described as the combination of the extremes and the means. Theoretically many reactions which do not actually occur may be "predicted." Reactions do occur if one of the following conditions is fulfilled.

1. When a gas is one of the possible products and the conditions are such that the gas does escape.

$$2 \text{ Na Cl} + \text{H}_2\text{SO}_4 \rightarrow \text{Na}_2\text{SO}_4 + 2 \text{ HCl}\uparrow$$

$$\text{NaCl} + \text{H}_2\text{SO}_4 \rightarrow \text{NaHSO}_4 + \text{HCl}\uparrow$$

These salt and sulfuric acid reactions take place only when concentrated sulphuric acid is reacted with solid NaCl and go to completion when heated. The presence of water prevents the reactions from becoming complete since the HCl will dissolve in the water. It is possible to reverse the reactions by forcing hydrogen chloride into the saturated sulfate or bisulfate solutions.

2. The formation of a slightly ionized substance as in neutralization reactions going virtually to completion.

$$\text{Na OH} + \text{H Cl} \rightarrow \text{NaCl} + \text{H}_2\text{O}$$

(Some teachers permit the notation HOH for water to aid pupils in balancing equations.)

3. Precipitation, the formation of an insoluble substance from solution. Students may "predict" the occurrence of this type of reaction by checking on the solubility of the possible products.

$$\text{Na Cl} + \text{Ag NO}_3 \rightarrow \text{NaNO}_3 + \text{AgCl}\downarrow$$

If the reaction does not fulfill either of the two previously mentioned conditions and neither of the possible products is insoluble, then the reaction may be considered as not occurring (not going to completion) but rather as reaching equilibrium. For instance,

$$\text{NaCl} + \text{CuSO}_4$$

(No reaction takes place since both possible products Na_2SO_4 and CuCl_2 are soluble.)

Almost any reaction producing a precipitate, particularly a colored precipitate, is effective in demonstrating double replacement. For example, solutions of lead nitrate and potassium dichromate yield a copious yellow precipitate. For other possible demonstrations see Chapter 8, Solutions.

Catalysis. One of the best known demonstrations of a catalyst is the release of oxygen from potassium chlorate in the presence of manganese dioxide. For this see preparing oxygen from an oxidizing agent in 7.1b.

Autocatalysis.[8] You will need two 250-ml beakers. Mix two solutions as follows: 6 g of oxalic acid in 300 ml of water, and 100 ml of $0.001M$ KMnO$_4$ solution. Pour 150 ml of the oxalic acid solution in each of the beakers; then add 5 ml of concentrated H_2SO_4 to each. To each of these add 50 ml of the KMnO$_4$ solution.

Into one beaker drop a small crystal of MnCl$_2$ about the size of a pin head. Stir both solutions. In a few seconds the solution containing the crystal of MnCl$_2$ will start to lose color, becoming colorless in about a minute.

The other solution will not change in color for two or three minutes but when sufficient Mn^{++} ions are present it, too, will start to become colorless. The Mn^{++} autocatalysizes the solution as follows

$$2 \text{ MnO}_4^- + 5 \text{ C}_2\text{O}_4^= + 16 \text{ H}_3\text{O}^+$$
$$= 2 \text{ Mn}^{++} + 10 \text{ CO}_2 + 24 \text{ H}_2\text{O}$$

[8] Adapted from a demonstration designed by D. A. Dreisbach, Hiram College, Hiram, Ohio.

CAPSULE LESSONS

Ways to get started in class

6-1. Begin by developing the structure of atoms with their orbits of electrons. Have students use models to show atomic structure and valence of atoms as they lose or gain electrons. What is the difference between an atom and an ion?

Have students use commercial models or Tinkertoy kit materials as they explain the day's work. Some students in committee may build the electric quiz game (6.1a), or you may want all students to make some sort of self-testing device as a review to show valence and different kinds of bonding among compounds.

6-2. Develop the notion of the combination of elements by definite proportion through the use of models of atoms and diagrams on the blackboard. Illustrate by demonstration (or by individual laboratory work).

6-3. After students know some of the basic properties of some gases, metals, and nonmetals, bring to class a large chart of the periodic table. Ask students to interpret the chart. Why are elements listed as they are read across the table and also vertically? Select certain elements at random and ask what characteristics students would predict for them. Develop concepts of degrees of activity, kinds of reactions which might be possible, and similar relationships among the elements in the table.

Some students may report on the history of the development of finding relationships among the elements.

6-4. At some time you may want to show filmstrips such as *Atoms into Molecules: Periodic Table* (Indiana U.), *Velocity of Chemical Reactions* (EBF), or *What are Elements and Compounds?* (Popular Science through McGraw-Hill).

6-5. In some classes or some year, you may want to introduce several reactions in sequence and have students observe results. Then elicit from students some basic similarities or differences that they notice in the many demonstrations. In this way students begin to classify the kinds of reactions that they are working with over the year.

6-6. Other times, teachers often summarize over several days many kinds of reactions that have already been studied. They review to give a new view, in the sense that they use different chemicals from those that students used in laboratory work. Thus they build up, or reconstruct, a classification of the kinds of reactions that students observed.

6-7. Show demonstrations (or charts) of common chemical reactions found in everyday life: oxidation-reduction in a storage battery during charging; acid-soda fire extinguisher; reactions that go on to an end, such as reduction of HgO.

PEOPLE, PLACES, AND THINGS

Have you the responsibility for staging science assembly programs? Or do you need ideas for projects for students? Graduate students at a nearby college or university often help students with a special technique; at times gifted students are privileged to learn specialized techniques or work with apparatus in a university laboratory.

It may be possible to plan field trips to study the chemical processes involved in papermaking, dyeing, rubber manufacturing, preparation of an antibiotic, or metal refining.

BOOKS AND PAMPHLETS

These are only a few of the books which are pertinent to the work discussed in this chapter. These and many other references classified by subject and with complete bibliographical data are given in the bibliography at the end of the book.

Berry, A. J., *From Classical to Modern Chemistry,* Cambridge U. Press, 1954.

Deming, Horace G., *General Chemistry,* Wiley, N. Y., 1955.

Dull, Charles, *Modern Chemistry,* Holt, 1955.

Feigl, F., *Chemistry of Specific Selected and Sensitive Reactions,* Academic, 1949.

Friess, S., and A. Weissberger, *Investigation of Rates and Mechanisms of Reactions,* Interscience, 1953.

Holden, A., and P. Singer, *Crystals and Crystal Growing,* Doubleday, 1960.

Jacobson, C. A., *Encyclopedia of Chemical Reactions,* Reinhold, 1958.

Nebergall, W. H., and F. C. Schmidt, *General Chemistry,* Heath, 1959.

Sienko, M. J., and R. A. Plane, *Chemistry,* McGraw-Hill, 1957.

Pauling, Linus, *General Chemistry,* Freeman, 1954.

Weaver, Elbert C., and Laurence S. Foster, *Chemistry For Our Times*, McGraw-Hill, 1954.

FILMS AND FILMSTRIPS

This partial list is intended only as a guide toward film and filmstrip selection. Refer to the more complete listing at the end of the book where films are classified by subject and where a key to abbreviations and addresses of distributors are given. The cost of film rental, of course, is subject to change. Films are sound and black and white unless otherwise specified.

Atoms Into Molecules (periodic table) (fs), Indiana U., $4.75.

Chemical Reactions (f, s, 2 rls), Institutional Cinema, $3.00.

Chemistry Series (set of 5 fs) (structure of atom, periodic table, ionization, electrolysis, acids), McGraw-Hill, $6.00 each.

Foundations of Chemistry (series of 8 fs), Society for Visual Education, $3.25 each.

From Alchemy to Chemistry (f, s), Indiana U., $4.75.

Modern Alchemy (Seaborg, Lawrence, Segré) (f, s), Indiana U., $5.25.

The Missing Elements (f, s), Indiana U., $4.75.

Velocity of Chemical Reactions (f, s), EBF, inquire rental.

What are Elements and Compounds (fs, c), Popular Science through McGraw-Hill, $6.00.

FREE AND INEXPENSIVE MATERIALS

This is only a partial listing of free and inexpensive materials available to the teacher at this time. A directory of addresses is given at the end of the book. Many of these materials are distributed to teachers without charge. Where there is a small fee, the cost is indicated, although the prices are subject to change. While we recommend the material for use in the classroom, we do not necessarily endorse the products advertised.

Manufacturing Chemists' Associations and industrial or pharmaceutical companies offer free films and pamphlet material. Write to such companies as Shell Oil, Esso, Union Carbon and Carbide, DuPont, and U. S. Steel for samples of their free materials. (See directory in the appendix for addresses.)

CHAPTER 7

Oxygen and hydrogen

Our understanding of the nature of combustion and of the role of oxygen in burning had its beginning in the classic experiments of Joseph Priestley and Antoine Lavoisier. Lavoisier's discovery of the percentage of oxygen in air and his formulation of the law of conservation of matter are additional landmarks in the birth of modern chemistry. In this chapter, demonstrations simulating these classic experiments are described. Though time-consuming, Lavoisier's experiment has been characterized as "a fascinating marathon."

The widely used demonstrations on the preparation and properties of oxygen and hydrogen are supplemented by a variety of additional material which may prove useful as enrichment. Related demonstrations dealing with ozone and hydrogen peroxide are included.

7.1 Oxygen: its preparation and properties

7.1a Classic experiments on the nature of combustion

Simulating Priestley's experiment. Heat 3 g of mercuric oxide in a #6 heavy-wall ignition (or Pyrex) test tube until decomposition occurs as evidenced by the beginning of the formation of a Hg mirror on the cooler upper portion of the test tube. Insert a glowing splint into the test tube

while continuing to heat. Have students note the results as well as the formation of the mirror of mercury droplets. Follow either by teacher demonstration or student experiment in which two test tubes of water are inverted into a basin (pneumatic trough). The end of the delivery tube is placed into the first test tube. It is advisable to start with a fresh 3-g sample of HgO in a test tube generator and immediately collect ⅔ of a test tube of the first gas sample produced (Fig. 7–1). Then collect the same volume of gas in the second test tube. Test the contents of each test tube with a glowing splint. Have students note the difference in the behavior of the splint in each tube; the splint will merely continue to glow in the first test tube of gas while it flames up in the second. This experience helps students real-

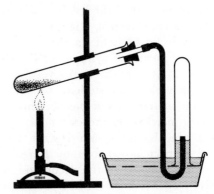

Fig. 7–1 Heating mercuric oxide to produce oxygen.

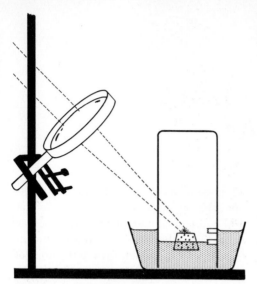

Fig. 7–2 Simulating Priestley's experiment by heating mercuric oxide with a lens.

ize the necessity for providing for escape of generator-enclosed air in future gas generation experiments.

If you wish to duplicate Priestley's experiment more closely, you can set up as follows. Place a small flat cork in a dish of mercury or water (make certain that the cork is dry). Then place one gram of mercuric oxide on the cork, invert a cylinder over the float, and remove some of the cylinder's air by means of a rubber tube and small exhaust pump. Mark the level of the liquid in the cylinder. Now use sunlight or an arc lamp as a light source and focus a beam of light on the mercuric oxide by means of a large convex lens (Fig. 7–2). Repeat this over several days. After a week or so, students should see that the mercuric oxide has decomposed, leaving mercury on the cork float. They should be able to explain that the liquid level has been forced down by the oxygen that was released in the decomposition. Have students mark the new level of the liquid in the cylinder. Then, by slipping a sheet of glass under the mouth of the

cylinder, remove the cylinder from the dish of liquid. Invert it and remove the glass cover; quickly lower a small, burning candle into the cylinder. Notice that the candle burns brilliantly in the oxygen-enriched air. As a control, have a student lower the candle into a similar cylinder of ordinary air.

Simulating Lavoisier's experiment. Students may simulate Lavoisier's work in which mercury is heated to form mercuric oxide. Use a Florence flask fitted with a one-hole cork which carries a ¼″ diameter delivery tube bent to the shape shown in Fig. 7–3A. Place a weighed quantity (1 to 5 grams) of mercury in the flask. Arrange the delivery tube in a basin of mercury or water, and place a glass cylinder over the end of the tube as shown. Now remove some air from the cylinder by means of a small rubber tube and exhaust pump. (A rubber tube and mouth suction can also do the job.) Mark the level of the liquid which has risen into the cylinder. Heat the Florence flask on an electric heating device or a Bunsen burner arranged so that the flask is heated slowly and continuously. After several days of slow heating, students should see that some mercury has disappeared and that some red mercuric oxide has formed. The volume of gas in the cylinder will decrease, indicating the removal of a gas.

Now students can remove the mercuric oxide and weigh it to show that it weighs more than did the original mercury. Elicit the notion that the weight gained is due to the oxygen that has combined with mercury to form mercuric oxide. If about 1 cc of mercury is used for every 4 cubic inches of air trapped in the Florence flask and reservoir and the reaction goes until all oxygen is consumed, you should find approximately one fifth of the original air space of the cylinder filled with liquid. A burning taper placed in this remaining

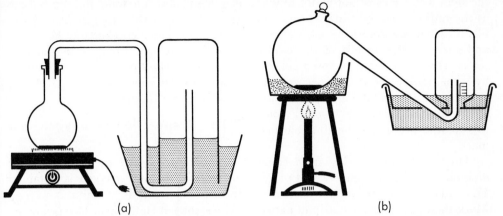

Fig. 7–3 Simulating Lavoisier's experiment: (a) using a Florence flask and hot plate, (b) using a retort with dimensions which approximate those of Lavoisier's.

de-oxygenated air will be quickly extinguished. Or you may want to reverse the process by rapidly heating the mercuric oxide. Within ten minutes students should observe the oxide reduced back to mercury. During this time the volume of gas in the cylinder should increase to its original volume, once the mercury has returned to its original state. The air in the jar should briefly support combustion of a burning splint or taper.

When Lavoisier originally did his experiment he found that 9 cc of mercury consumed somewhere between 7 and 8 cubic inches of air out of a total volume of 50 cubic inches of air. You may roughly duplicate his experiment (Fig. 7–3B).

"The bulb of the retort should have a capacity of 600-700 cc, and the tapering neck, 14-16″ long, should be ½″ in diameter at the lower end. The glass air reservoir approximately 6″ by 3″ (a 1-lb-size glass jam jar will serve) makes a bell jar of the required size. A glass pneumatic trough should be used; 8″ by 4″ is a convenient size. Support the improvised bell jar on a shelf made of thin sheet lead. In the interest of historical accuracy it is desirable that the volume of enclosed air should be approximately 50 cubic inches

(50 old French cubic inches = 990 cc). If the apparatus has the dimensions given above, the enclosed volume should approximate this volume. However, for the sake of simplicity and effectiveness it is advisable to find the total enclosed volume and divide this into 50 equal parts, each approximately 1 cubic inch. Provision must be made for the expansion of air in the early stages. Accordingly, make a graduation mark on the bell jar at least 1″ up from the rim and call this the 50-unit mark. When setting up the apparatus, arrange for this mark to coincide with the level of the water in the trough. Thus, the total enclosed space will be the volume of the bell jar to the 50-mark plus the volume of the retort diminished by that portion of the neck of the retort protruding into the bell jar and the space (9 cc) occupied by the mercury. It is sufficiently accurate to find the volume of the bell jar by filling it with water, and using a measuring cylinder. Find the volume of the retort by weighing the water which fills it. If the neck of the retort is half an inch wide, the retort is quite easily filled by pouring in water and tilting to expel entrapped air. Otherwise, add some water to the retort and boil it for 10 minutes, then immerse

the stem in a vessel of hot water so that as the retort cools the water enters and fills it. When the retort is cool, weigh it and subtract the weight of the empty retort. Divide the total enclosed volume by 5; the result is the volume between the graduations 40 and 50. Find what section of the bell jar above the 50-mark holds this volume, and make the 40-cubic inch mark.

"Divide the space 40-50 into 4 equal divisions and label them 42.5, 45, and 47.5; smaller divisions are not necessary. Mark these divisions on a strip of paper, paste it in position, and coat it with molten wax. Dry the retort and pour in 4 oz of mercury (4 oz = 9.0 cc). (It is extraordinary how the diagram in many textbooks exaggerates this volume.) Place the retort in a sand bath, the bell jar in position, and then add water to the trough. By means of a bent tube suck out air if necessary until the water levels are equal in the trough and the bell jar and are exactly on the 50-mark. Heat the retort, using a small Bunsen flame. Adjust the flame so that that the mercury is just short of boiling. Turn off the flame for about an hour each day so that the class may see how the volume of air diminishes. The red oxide becomes visible at the end of the 2nd day."[1] Wheatley has found that on cooling at the end of the 12th day, after allowing for changes of temperature and pressure, the water always reaches the 42.5-mark—that is, 7.5 cubic inches of air have been absorbed. (Lavoisier found a loss of 7-8 cubic inches.) After 12 days, further heating does not seem to decrease the volume of the air. If the retort is cleaned with dilute nitric acid, it can be used over and over again with a minimum of trouble.

An electric hot-plate, set at low heat,

[1] Adapted from an experiment described by W. Wheatley on p. 67 of *Lecture Experiments in Chemistry*, ed. by G. Fowles, 4th ed., G. Bell & Sons, Ltd., 1957.

is a good substitute for a Bunsen burner since it permits the experiment to go on without too much checking on the operation of the heater. It may be desirable to remove the HgO produced and demonstrate that it yields oxygen on being heated with a burner.

7.1b Preparation of oxygen and ozone

Preparing oxygen by electrolysis of water. Nearly pure oxygen is obtained from the electrolysis of water. You may use a standard Hoffman or H-type apparatus (Fig. 7–4), or else build your own apparatus. The usual demonstration with the Hoffman apparatus can be done in different ways using different currents and acid concentrations.

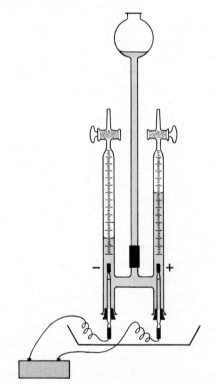

Fig. 7–4 Standard H-type (Hoffman) apparatus for the electrolysis of water.

Sources of current. The sources of direct current which may be used include

1. four dry cells connected in series with a knife switch

2. a lead storage cell (6 or 12 volts), or Edison cells.

3. the charging output of a battery charger or a power supply unit (Cenco 79561 supplies 6.5 volts d.c.)

4. a 110-volt d.c. source in series with a lamp and a knife switch: a 25-watt lamp may be used; larger wattage lamps provide a bigger voltage and cut down on the time needed for collection of a usable gas volume (this may be as little as 20 ml of O_2 and 40 ml of H_2)

5. a centralized school d.c. power supply (variable)

Acid concentration. This is highly variable. Some typical concentrations used are: 5 ml of concentrated sulfuric acid to 150 ml of water; and 10 ml of concentrated sulfuric acid to 600 ml of water. Higher concentrations are a matter of choice. Some prefer first to fill the apparatus with distilled water to show its virtual nonconductivity, then to drain and refill with an acid-water mixture which is prepared in front of the class. For individual student work a 90 per cent sodium sulfate solution and a 6-volt d.c. current eliminate the dangers of using an acid solution.

Gas collection. The gases may be collected as shown in Fig. 7–5. Time must be allowed, for the escape of air in the delivery tube is an important factor. Good results may be obtained with relatively small volumes of gases by using #1 or #2 test tubes in which gases are collected by air displacement. Hydrogen may be collected by placing the test tube mouth downward above the stopcock and opening the stopcock. This gas is tested with a burning splint. A short length of rubber tubing (no more than 6″) is used to col-

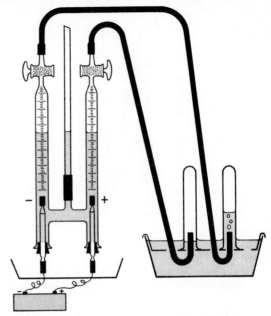

Fig. 7–5 Collecting the gas products of water electrolysis.

lect the oxygen by upward displacement of air. The oxygen is identified by the glowing splint test. Of course, a similar length of rubber tubing may be used in the hydrogen collection to "balance" the picture seen by the students. You may want to direct student attention to such experimental details as where the gases are being liberated and how they are being collected inside the apparatus: note the proportionate volumes of hydrogen and oxygen.

A variation of the H-type apparatus is the "Brownlee" form of electrolysis apparatus (Fig. 7–6A). Its Cenco catalog number is 81185.

A simplified apparatus. You or your students can construct a simplified apparatus suitable for individual laboratory work.[2] A polyethylene or clear plastic dish serves as the base. Two holes are melted

[2] Louis Teichman, "A Simplified Electrolysis Apparatus," *J. Chem. Educ.*, 34, 291 (1957).

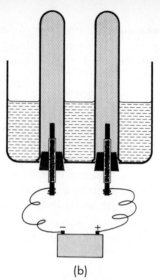

(a)   (b)

Fig. 7–6 Two versions of the Brownlee type of gas apparatus: (a) as supplied by a scientific house (Central Scientific Co.); (b) simplified version which can be made in the laboratory.

through the bottom of the dish by applying the heated mouth of a 4″ test tube. If a sufficient supply of platinum electrodes is not available, graphite electrodes such as the filament supports of a photoflood lamp or of a high-wattage projection lamp may be used. The electrodes, fused into glass tubing, are inserted in rubber stoppers which are placed in these holes (Fig. 7–6B). The dish is mounted on a tripod, filled with acidulated water to just above the level of the electrodes, and the filled test tubes inverted over the electrodes.

If acid is to be used, students should be trained in techniques of quickly inserting the test tube below the surface of the acidulated water and then positioning it by handling the portion above the water-acid. (*Caution: Students should wash hands immediately with water and then with dilute bicarbonate of soda. Students with any sort of skin sores or cuts should not be permitted to do this part of the experiment.*) The acid should be very dilute (10 ml of concentrated acid to 600 ml of water). A saturated solution of Na_2SO_4 can be used instead.

Preparing oxygen from an oxidizing agent. Potassium chlorate with manganese dioxide is the standard source of oxygen in teacher demonstration as well as student laboratory work. The standard mixture is made with two parts by weight of C.P. potassium chlorate and 1 part by weight of C.P. manganese dioxide. Teacher demonstrations generally require about 15 g of this mixture in a 200-mm (8″) Pyrex test tube generator. Potassium chlorate supplies oxygen at a slower rate without the catalyst, as demonstrated in 2.2c. This experiment is an example of the breakdown of compounds into simpler constituents—in this case an element, O_2, and a compound KCl. (*Caution: Potassium chlorate should not be mixed with any material except manganese dioxide. The presence of organic materials, powdered metals, or other impurities may cause a violent explosion with even a small amount of friction.*) When adding manganese dioxide, mix it *gently* together with potassium chlorate on a glass dish or crucible. (*Warning: Do not grind potassium chlorate.*) Do not mix on filter paper since organic materials may form an explosive mixture. Before heating the materials, test a small sample of the $KClO_3$ and MnO_2 in a Pyrex test tube. Heat in a flame; discard any material that begins to sparkle. Do not fill the generator test tube to a depth of more than an inch and a half. Attach a one-hole stopper and delivery tube and heat the test tube. Allow the bubbles of gas to escape for a minute or so until all the air in the system has been swept out, and then collect the oxygen in gas bottles (usually 6 or 8 oz when for demonstration purposes).

Test the oxygen in one of these bottles with a glowing splint. Insert the splint to a distance of one inch, remove, and blow out. Repeat this several times and finally pour the last remaining sample of oxygen over the glowing splint. To show that the oxygen comes from the potassium chlorate and not from the manganese dioxide, heat samples of each in separate test tubes, the manganese dioxide preferably first. Have students note the relatively long time needed to heat the potassium chlorate before an inserted glowing splint burns. Allow the potassium chlorate to cool somewhat; then drop in a pinch of manganese dioxide (a little bit on a splint) and have students observe renewed gas evolution; follow with the glowing splint test to confirm the production of oxygen at a lower temperature and faster rate. A spectacular, supplementary demonstration consists of dropping an unlighted wooden splint into molten potassium chlorate after having removed the heat. The splint is quickly burned, producing a long violet flame which flares upward from the test tube mouth. (*Caution: Keep your face at a safe distance from the mouth of the test tube. Melt the potassium chlorate in a large, heavy Pyrex test tube. See 2.2c for other precautions.*)

Other catalysts may be employed with potassium chlorate. A small crystal of potassium dichromate, dropped into

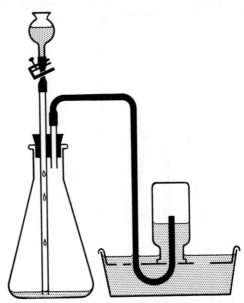

Fig. 7–7 Oxygen can be prepared without heat by reacting sodium peroxide with water.

molten $KClO_3$, produces oxygen very rapidly. Ferric oxide (Fe_2O_3), fine sand, and powdered glass can also be used. Oxygen may be produced by the thermal decomposition of potassium nitrate. (*Warning: Explosive.*) Heating 1 g of $KMnO_4$ produces copious amounts of oxygen. Other sources include silver oxide, lead dioxide, and red lead.

Sodium peroxide. You may prefer, at times, to use a simple method that does not require heat. Oxygen can be prepared from the reaction of sodium peroxide with water (Fig. 7–7). Make a generator from a Pyrex Erlenmeyer flask by fitting it with a two-hole stopper carrying a dropping funnel and a delivery tube. (Instead of a dropping funnel, a straight tube connected to a small funnel by a short length of rubber tubing, with a screw-type pinch clamp, as shown, may be used.) Place about 15 g of sodium peroxide in the flask, connect the delivery tube, and prepare to collect oxygen by water displacement. (*Caution: Do not handle Na_2O_2 with bare*

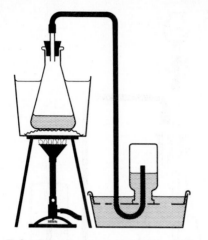

Fig. 7–8 Preparing oxygen by heating hydrogen peroxide solution plus catalyst.

hands since it reacts with water exothermically, yielding caustic NaOH. If handled accidentally, shake off any residue and wash liberally with water.) Adjusting the stopcock or pinch clamp, add water drop by drop. After air has escaped from delivery tube, oxygen is collected. Note that the temperature of the flask rises, indicating an exothermic reaction

$$2\,Na_2O_2 + 2\,H_2O \rightarrow 4\,NaOH + O_2$$

The presence of NaOH as a product may be shown by the addition of two drops of phenolphthalein to the generator contents, which should then be poured down the sink drain with a copious flow of water.

Hydrogen peroxide. Hydrogen peroxide may also serve as a source of oxygen and has been used in student laboratory experiments where the teacher does not choose to use potassium chlorate. The decomposition of H_2O_2 is catalyzed by MnO_2. A pinch of MnO_2 dropped into 5 ml of the 3% H_2O_2 commonly used as an antiseptic gives a splint test for oxygen. The generator shown in Fig. 7–8 may be used. Collection bottles may be small scale

(2-oz or 4-oz bottles). Pelleted MnO_2 may be substituted for the powder where frothing proves troublesome, although this is generally unnecessary. Pelleted activated charcoal is also an effective catalyst. It has the added merit of clearly establishing the H_2O_2 as the only possible source of the oxygen liberated. The same type of generator may be used as for the H_2O_2 and MnO_2 combination. Oxygen may be evolved from hydrogen peroxide in test tube experiments which use a living yeast culture, or dried yeast, or ferric ion (a crystal of a ferric salt) as catalysts. The speed of decomposition and consequently the amount of oxygen produced in such demonstrations depend on the concentration of the H_2O_2 used. The 30% solution available in most laboratories may be diluted to such concentrations as 6% which gives fast reactions with most catalysts. The 30% solution of peroxide must be handled carefully. Contact with skin results in "burned," whitened tissue. On accidental contact with such solution, flush copiously with water. H_2O_2 may also be decomposed by heat alone. The 3% solution may be heated in a water bath and decomposition occurs at varying temperatures (60°–80°C) depending on the concentration. Test tubes of oxygen may be collected by water displacement. For hydrogen peroxide's role in oxidation-reduction, see 7.3.

Hypochlorites. Oxygen may also be prepared from hypochlorites.[3] Half a teaspoon of bleaching powder is mixed with about an inch of water in a large test tube. Addition of 10 drops of 5% cobalt nitrate solution and subsequent heating result in the evolution of oxygen. A pinch of black cobalt oxide, sometimes used in borax bead tests, also gives positive results. Solu-

[3] Joseph Castka, "Oxygen from Hypochlorites," *The Teaching Scientist*, 8, 28 (1951–52), The Federation of Science Teachers Associations of New York.

tions of $CuSO_4$ or $FeSO_4$ or crystals of these substances also work. Common household hypochlorite ($NaOCl$—5.25%) solutions such as Clorox, Rosex, etc. give good results with all catalysts except $FeSO_4$.

Sodium perborate. A solution composed of 5 g of sodium perborate and 150 ml of water yields oxygen upon heating. This may be done in a test tube demonstration; the method may also be used to produce laboratory quantities of oxygen.

Generating ozone. In this demonstration a high-voltage source is needed (Fig. 7–9A,B). Use a standard induction coil or a model T Ford or TT Fordson tractor ignition coil. Connect the primary to a 6-volt battery and a single-throw switch. Next take a Liebig condenser and use the water-jacket connections to furnish air and remove ozone (Fig. 7–9A). If a Liebig condenser is not available, use a 12″-long glass cylinder about 2″ in diameter, with a two-hole stopper at each end, through which a glass tube passes that runs the length of the cylinder (Fig. 7–9B). Run a wire through the middle of the center tube of either the Liebig or the homemade condenser. The other holes of the stoppers in the homemade condenser are each fitted with a short glass tube connected to a rubber tube, to serve as the jacket connection. Air will be pumped into one tube and ozone removed from the other.

Now wrap a layer of aluminum foil around the outside of the glass cylinder or Liebig condenser. Wrap a bare copper wire around the foil to act as a connection. Then connect the foil wire and the inner wire to the secondary (high-voltage) connections of the induction coil. Close the switch, pump in air, and collect the ozone. (*Caution: Do not touch the foil-wrapped cylinder while the switch is closed; do not inhale ozone.*)

You can obtain ozone by using small ultraviolet bulbs called "sterilamps" used in electric deodorizers and in some refrigerators. Never look directly at these lamps. Most of them work on the secondary circuit of a toy electric train transformer set at 14 volts. If such a lamp is placed in a wide-mouth jar as in Fig. 7–9C, air can be pumped in and air rich in ozone produced.

Ozone may be bubbled into a culture of protozoa. Show its sterilizing effect by examining a drop of protozoa culture under a microscope before and after ozonization. Ozone may also be used to destroy the smell of onions. Students can also show a test for ozone by placing moist starch-potassium-iodide paper near the gas; it will turn blue.

7.1c *Factors affecting oxidation*

Concentration of oxygen. The usual demonstrations performed with the bottles of collected oxygen include burning of sulfur, phosphorus, or iron (steel wool). The burning of iron is performed in the bottle which contains about one inch of water since the heat may cause a hot pellet of oxidized material to fall to the bottom of the bottle and crack it unless the water layer is present. A rather thin wad of steel wool (2–3″ long) is held by tongs or forceps, the tip ignited in the Bunsen flame, and the whole then slowly inserted into the oxygen. Deflagrating spoons used for burning S or P should be lined with a thin sheet of asbestos. This prevents the clogging of the spoon by unburned, melted sulfur which generally has to be burned off before the spoon is reusable. The spoon is heated in the Bunsen flame until the S or P catches fire. Have pupils observe the intensity of the burning in the pure oxygen and contrast with rate of burning in air. Other similar demonstrations use a glowing stick of charcoal, or a glowing cigarette, which is inserted into the oxygen.

Effect of particle size on oxidation reactions. In oxidation of solids, the size of the particles determines the total surface available for reaction with the oxygen or oxidizing agent. The smaller the particles, the faster the reaction.

Slow oxidation of iron. Students can demonstrate the slow oxidation of iron and also the effect of surface area on the speed of the reaction by placing iron filings or steel wool on a float in a jar of water and inverting a graduated cylinder over it (Fig. 7–10). (Since steel wool is usually coated with oil at the factory,

wash it in a detergent and then rinse it in water before using it.) Usually the moistened steel wool is pushed into the curved bottom section of a suitable device (a 100-ml graduate or a 50-ml eudiometer tube). When iron filings are used, it is necessary first to moisten the bottom of the cylinder so that the filings adhere to the side and bottom. Let the setup stand for a week and have students record the water level inside the cylinder daily. Eventually all the oxygen will combine with the iron to produce rust (iron oxide) and about 20 per cent of the air originally in the cylinder will be replaced by water, showing that the oxygen was removed. If

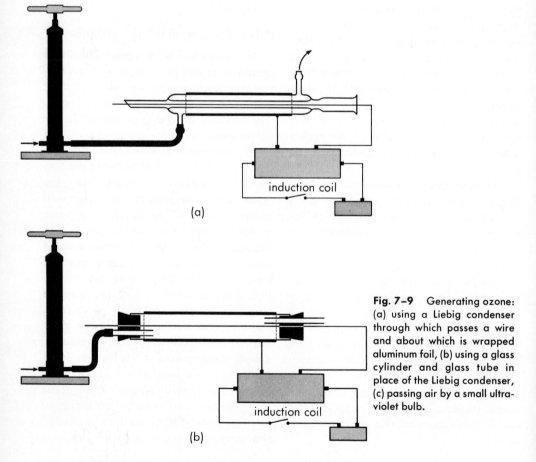

induction coil

(a)

induction coil

(b)

Fig. 7–9 Generating ozone: (a) using a Liebig condenser through which passes a wire and about which is wrapped aluminum foil, (b) using a glass cylinder and glass tube in place of the Liebig condenser, (c) passing air by a small ultraviolet bulb.

students set up separate, simultaneous demonstrations with iron filings, steel wool, and a solid piece of iron all of the same weight, they should be able to deduce the effect of increased surface (small particle size) on the speed of the reaction.

Where quantitative results are sought, the air pressure inside the cylinder is adjusted to atmospheric by the temporary insertion of a bent glass tube into the air inside the cylinder. A 100-ml graduate is very convenient for this type of operation since the volume of air is readily read off. At the end of the experiment, the water levels inside and outside are again adjusted so that internal pressure equals atmospheric. This is done by lowering the graduate into a battery jar. Therefore if this type of experiment is desired, a deep battery jar should be used as the base of the assembly. To show that the oxygen has been removed place a cover or stopper over the mouth of the graduate, withdraw it from the jar, invert, and insert a burning splint. The splint is extinguished by the oxygen-depleted air (nitrogen). To show that slow oxidation does produce some heat, moisten the inside of a half-pint thermos bottle, shake in iron filings, and stopper with a one-hole rubber stopper through which a thermometer has

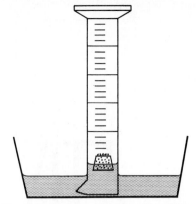

Fig. 7-10   Slow oxidation of iron filings.

been inserted. After several hours, enough heat will be released inside the thermos bottle to cause a perceptible rise in the thermometer reading.

Dust explosions. You can demonstrate a dust explosion in a tin can (1 gal size) with a friction cover. Drill or punch out a hole in the bottom of the tin can to receive a small-stem funnel (Fig. 7–11), and connect the stem of the funnel to a rubber tube at least 5 to 8 feet long. Place a candle in the bottom of the can to serve as a future source of ignition. Then place a small piece of paper in the bottom of the funnel and add about 15 cc of lycopodium powder or very fine cornstarch or a very small amount of powdered aluminum. Now stand the can on a wide tripod as shown. Have the class stand back about 15 feet, and remove any inflammable materials that may be near or above the can. Light the candle and put on the cover. Standing well away from the can, blow into the rubber tube or use a hand pump or syringe bulb so that the "dust" is raised. The dust inside ignites instantaneously in the presence of the candle flame. Watch the cover fly off and a huge flame shoot upward into the air. Show that a compact pile of the lycopodium or starch will not explode when ignited since it is,

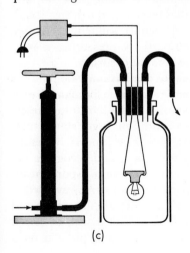

(c)

Fig. 7–11 Can prepared to demonstrate dust explosions. The squeeze bulb has an extension of 15 feet of rubber tubing.

essentially, a solid mass rather than a powder. This demonstrates the effect of particle size on sudden explosive combustion.

Also show that lumps of iron, aluminum, or sulfur will not ignite easily. However if aluminum powder, sulfur powder, or iron filings are placed into the end of a long glass tube and blown into a Bunsen flame, they ignite rapidly and brilliantly.

Kindling temperature. Students know that ordinary combustion requires a fuel and a source of oxygen. Show students that heat is needed to ignite the fuel.

Students should recognize that a certain temperature (kindling temperature) must be reached before a substance takes fire and begins to burn. However, the size of the particle or particles of a particular substance, the bulk of the substance to be set on fire, the conductivity of the substance (particularly of metals), all play a part in the rapidity with which the given sample will take fire. A piece of Mg ribbon is not easily ignited by a match. How-

ever, if one end is frayed into several narrow strips, a match will ignite it. Students may know that Mg plates may be placed on the operating burners of a gas stove and used as a griddle for cooking pancakes, eggs, etc. It may be demonstrated that it is almost impossible to ignite one end of a piece of Dowmetal (Mg alloy) strip (1/16–⅛″ in thickness) with a Bunsen burner flame. The conductivity of the metal prevents the heated section from reaching the kindling temperature. A pile of Mg shavings placed on an asbestos sheet, however, is easily ignited with a Bunsen burner and makes a spectacular display. (Extinguish with salt, sand, or bisulfite powder.) A match flame will not ignite the kerosene in an evaporating dish. However, dropping in a piece of cotton, which serves as a wick, makes it possible to ignite the surface of the wick with a match. The kerosene in the dish, without a cotton wick, may be ignited with a Bunsen burner. Obviously, the temperature of the flame, the continuous availability of large quantities of heat, make it possible to ignite the kerosene. The burning kerosene may be extinguished by placing an asbestos sheet over the evaporating dish. Kerosene vapor, sprayed from an atomizer into a match flame (the burning match should be clamped to a ring stand, not held in the hand), will ignite. Here we have small particles presenting a relatively large amount of surface to air.

Spontaneous combustion. Spontaneous combustion is responsible for many fires in homes, granaries, and other storage reservoirs where conditions favor slow oxidation and prevent the escape of the resulting heat. Students should recognize the conditions that promote spontaneous combustion so that they can be avoided.

Mix equal parts of pure turpentine and pure Japan drier. Soak a wad of cotton waste in the mixture and place it on a metal tray. After some time the wad will burst into flame. Relate this to the spontaneous combustion of oily rags. (The drier speeds the process.)

In another demonstration, dissolve a small piece of white phosphorus about the size of a pea in 5 ml of carbon disulfide, and soak a piece of filter paper in the solution. (*Caution: Carbon disulfide is highly combustible and must not be used near open flames or sparks. Handle phosphorus with tongs.*) Hang the filter paper on a ring stand or place it on a fireproof surface; when the carbon disulfide has evaporated, the phosphorus will burst into flames. For a more striking demonstration, paint the word FIRE on a large sheet of paper with a brush dipped in the solution and suspend it on wire between two ring stands. After a few minutes the lettered portion will burn brightly. (*Caution: This solution must not be stored. It must be disposed of in a safe place, and the brush must be destroyed immediately by burning. White phosphorus may only be cut to size safely when immersed in water. In air the heat produced by cutting is sufficient to cause its kindling temperature to be exceeded. Excess P-CS$_2$ solution may be burned outside. Shaking with CuSO$_4$ solution causes a reaction in which P particles are covered with a copper deposit. This may be used with the solution until it is disposed of by burning. Burns from P-CS$_2$ solution are severe; in case of accident keep the burned member soaked with 3% aqueous solution of CuSO$_4$ until treated by a physician.*)

7.1d Kinds of flames

Flame zones. Place a 3×5 card downward on the top of a Bunsen flame into the light blue zone. As soon as charring occurs, remove and flick with the wrist to extinguish card flame. Repeat by placing a card at a slight slant vertically into the flame. The flame pictures indicate that the interior of the flame consists of unburned gas.

Insert an ordinary pin or needle through the wood immediately below the head of a "strike-anywhere" or safety match and position, stick downward, in the barrel. Light the burner, have pupils observe that the match does not burn. Then raise slowly by using two splints as supports for each end of the pin, until the match catches fire. Another variation of this procedure is shown in Fig. 7–12.

Place a one-foot piece of glass tubing inside the inner blue cone of a Bunsen flame. Ignite the gas issuing from the exposed end. Slowly raise the end in the inner cone until it is extinguished. Place a platinum or nichrome wire, mounted in a glass handle, on the top of the barrel of the burner. Have pupils note the two hot spots which become one as the wire is raised into the point immediately above the inner cone.

Flame and conductivity. Use a large portion ($8'' \times 8''$) copper wire mesh to show the Davy safety lamp principle.

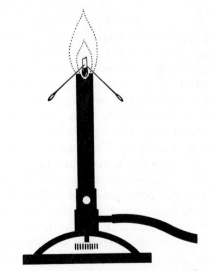

Fig. 7–12 A match head suspended within the cooler interior of a flame will not ignite at once.

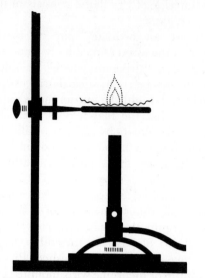

Fig. 7–13 Heat is conducted away so rapidly by the gauze that the gas below the cut-off flame does not ignite.

Light the gas above the gauze (mesh) (Fig. 7–13). Pass your hand under the gauze through the space separating the top of the burner from the gauze to extinguish the flame. Now light the gas under the mesh and show that it burns only below the wire mesh. Have students explain on the basis of metallic heat conductivity. A related demonstration using a candle flame utilizes a loosely wound copper wire helix (about ½" diameter and 1" long when coiled) to extinguish a candle flame. The coil is lowered over and into the flame, causing it to be extinguished since the temperature falls below kindling.

Luminous flame. Close the collar of a Bunsen burner so that a luminous flame results. This is not always easy. It may be necessary to cover the collar holes tightly with the finger tips. Permit the unburned carbon to accumulate on the bottom or side of a test tube placed in the luminous flame. Placing a test tube in a similar manner into a candle flame results in a carbon deposit. Relate the yellow flame to

the presence of an incandescent material (solid) by dusting some finely powdered charcoal into or by dropping or blowing iron filings through a blue Bunsen flame.

Oxidizing and reducing flames. Holding a piece of copper sheet (a ½" strip) in tongs, insert into the oxidizing portion (tip of inner cone) of the Bunsen flame. Note the production of black cupric oxide. Lower the copper strip into the middle of the inner (reducing flame) and note reduction of the oxide to the metallic state.

Davy safety lamp. Use a commercial Davy safety lamp or make one from copper screening and two corks (Fig. 7–14). Use thumbtacks to hold the gauze to the upper cork. In this way the lower cork is removable and can support a small candle. With the candle burning in the "safety lamp" and with the room well ventilated, aim a flow of gas from an unlighted Bunsen burner against the gauze. Students should be ready to explain that the gas does not ignite outside the gauze because the gauze conducts the candle's heat away from the gas so that its kindling temperature is not reached.

Blast lamp. Demonstrate a blast lamp which uses a mixture of compressed air and gas. Show that this will melt Pyrex glass tubing easily whereas the ordinary Bunsen flame will not. (The flame is hotter because the additional oxygen makes more of the fuel burn.)

Water from a flame. Use a length of rubber tubing of sufficient length to permit bringing a Bunsen burner to the blackboard. Use a small flame, and write in condensed water some suitable word or phrase such as the class designation (Fig. 7–15). This may also be done with the hydrogen flame from a laboratory hydrogen generator.

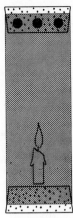

Fig. 7-14 Principle of the Davy safety lamp—flame enclosed by wire screening.

7.2 Hydrogen: its preparation and properties

7.2a Testing for hydrogen

The usual test for hydrogen consists of igniting the sample with a burning splint immediately after the hydrogen container is turned upward. The slight admixture with oxygen results in the characteristic "pop." Under ordinary circumstances it is definitely dangerous to attempt to light the hydrogen jet coming from a hydrogen generator. A safe way for doing this is the "sample" method. A test tube sample, collected by downward displacement of air, is ignited, mouth downward, at the Bunsen burner. If the sample contains air or oxygen, this small sample explodes safely. If the sample contains hydrogen only, the hydrogen ignites and burns with a blue flame at the mouth of the test tube. This burning hydrogen sample is then carried back to the end of the delivery tube of the hydrogen generator which can now be safely ignited since by evidence of the sample no air is mixed with the generator contents. Successive samples are tested and brought back to the end of the

Fig. 7-15 Water, a product of combustion, condenses from the flame onto the blackboard.

hydrogen generator delivery tube without danger until one burns long enough to be brought to the jet. If a given sample does contain air, the generator delivery tube cannot be ignited since the small explosion results in instantaneous and complete combustion. A safety tube can also be used which is described below.

Safety tube.[4] A tube which employs the principles of the Davy safety lamp (see Fig. 7-14) to prevent flashback into a gas generator may be inserted into a delivery tube. A metal tube of the same size as glass tubing is fitted at both ends with 80 mesh Monel metal gauze.[5] One way of doing this is shown in Fig. 7-16B where caps are made and screwed or soldered to the ends of the metal tube to hold the gauze in place. The device is inserted into the delivery tube by means of rubber tubing joints at each end as indicated in Fig. 7-16A.

7.2b Replacement from a dilute acid

Replacement (displacement) of hydrogen from a dilute acid by a metal is the

[4] This tube was developed by Samuel H. Liebowitz, Chairman, Science Department, Charles Evans Hughes High School, New York City.
[5] One source of the Monel screening is Industrial Wire Cloth Company, 323 Broadway, New York 7, New York.

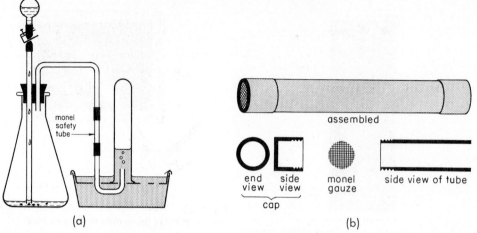

Fig. 7-16 Preparing hydrogen: (a) displacement from an acid by a metal—note the safety tube of Monel mesh that has been inserted into the delivery tube, (b) Monel mesh safety tube which prevents flashback into the generator when inserted into the delivery tube. (Adapted from *Journal of Chemical Education*, Vol. 11, No. 5, May, 1934.)

most common method for preparing hydrogen in the laboratory. It involves the action of fairly active metals such as zinc or iron (5 g) upon a dilute acid (generally 20–25 ml of dilute HCl, 1 to 3, or dilute H_2SO_4, 1 to 6). The amounts of metal and acid concentration to be used can vary within wide limits. The generator may be a wide-mouth 6″ bottle, an Erlenmeyer flask, or a Florence flask equipped with a thistle tube, the bottom of which extends into the liquid to just above the bottom of the flask. A clamp may be attached below the thistle as in Fig. 7–16A or a dropping funnel may be used. The delivery tube assembly is fitted tightly to prevent leaks. You will notice that a metal cylinder with Monel metal mesh at each end has been inserted into the delivery tube to prevent flashback. This, of course, is optional. (For details see Fig. 7–16B and above.) A preliminary demonstration sequence may involve test tube demonstrations of various metals. In addition to Zn and Fe, Al, Mg, and Cu may be used with various acids. This gives students some experience with the electromotive series and the relative

activities of the metals, establishing that metals below hydrogen, such as Cu, do not replace hydrogen in dilute acids. A 1″ piece of Mg ribbon gives a good hydrogen test and establishes Mg as being relatively more active than Zn or Fe. Aluminum with HCl gives a disappointing reaction at first until, after the oxide coating is dissolved, the reaction frequently is so active that it overflows the test tube. The test tubes series is set up in a test tube rack. Dilute acetic acid (1 to 3 or 1 to 4) may be tried so that pupils can evaluate the relative activities of acids. Several bottles of hydrogen are collected after permitting the air in the generator to escape. This may usually be effected by rejecting the first bottle collected. You may want one displacement bottle only half filled with water and thus later be able to show the explosive nature of the hydrogen-air mixture.

7.2c *Hydrogen from water*

By electrolysis. The electrolytic preparation of hydrogen has been described in the electrolysis of water, 7.1b.

By active metals. A small pellet of sodium, about ¼ the size of a pea, dried on filter paper (kerosene removed), and cut with a small knife from a larger portion is dropped into a 6″ test tube containing about 2″ of water. Students can observe the evolution of gas, the motion of the metal pellet which melts to a round ball, and the final disappearance of the metallic ball. The gas issuing from the test tube mouth is tested with a burning splint. Red litmus or phenolphthalein (two drops) is added to the remaining material in the test tube, establishing the other product as a base—in this case NaOH. You may want to establish the indicator reaction as a test for bases by performing it in advance with dilute solutions of NaOH, $Ca(OH)_2$, NH_4OH, etc. The Na demonstration is repeated with a single small piece of Ca metal. Student attention may be directed to the fact that the Ca is not kept under kerosene and does have (generally) a white powdery coating.

By less active metals. Samples of Mg and Al placed in cold water do not produce hydrogen, thus confirming previous experiences regarding relative metallic activity (electromotive series), and establishing by example the relative ease with which metals of Groups IA and IIA replace hydrogen from water. Methods for demonstrating that Mg replaces hydrogen from steam were described in 6.5a under Group II elements. Less active iron will replace hydrogen when the iron is heated by steam passed through a Pyrex ignition tube containing rust-free iron filings or steel wool (Fig. 7–17). Filings may be held in place by loose plugs of glass or steel wool. The hydrogen is collected as indicated in the diagram. This reaction represents one of the commercial methods for producing hydrogen

$$3\,Fe + 4\,H_2O \rightarrow Fe_3O_4 + 4\,H_2$$

Using steam. A convenient variation of the above procedure uses a 6″ Pyrex, ignition, or silica test tube positioned horizontally in a ring stand clamp. A small piece of asbestos paper moistened with water is placed in the bottom of the test tube. A small heap of iron filings (3 g) is placed in approximately the middle of the tube (Fig. 7–18). Small quantities of glass wool may have to be inserted to keep the filings in position. A one-hole rubber stopper with a delivery tube is used to collect small quantities of the hydrogen produced (a 2-oz collecting bottle is

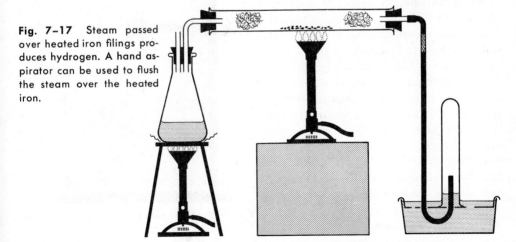

Fig. 7–17 Steam passed over heated iron filings produces hydrogen. A hand aspirator can be used to flush the steam over the heated iron.

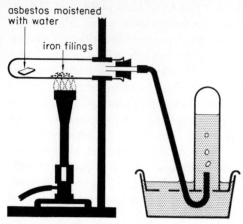

asbestos moistened with water

iron filings

Fig. 7–18 Steam is produced by heating the water-soaked asbestos sheet. This steam passing over the hot iron filings produces hydrogen.

good). First the iron filings are heated vigorously with a large Fisher burner, then the burner is flicked toward the asbestos paper to generate steam. With adequate practice a bottle of hydrogen is collected within a minute. It may be necessary to repeat the sequence several times. The same setup is used to demonstrate the production of water gas by substituting several pieces of coke, or a pile of powdered charcoal for the iron filings. Hydrogen may also be produced using steam and silicon in this setup.

By immersion. A piece of sodium, about ¼ to ½ the size of a pea, is placed in a sodium spoon, which is then inserted under an inverted test tube bottle or cylinder which is filled with water (Fig. 7–19). At all times the spoon must be held completely under the water to prevent ignition of hydrogen. If a sodium spoon is not available, make a wire gauze container shaped like a ball, and hold it with tongs in order to keep it under the collecting cylinder. A small metal tea egg can also be used in the same manner. The sodium hydroxide produced is tested for by using red litmus paper or phenol-

phthalein. A somewhat similar procedure is used with calcium. Invert a test tube filled with water in a beaker of water. Drop a shaving of Ca about 1 cm square into the beaker. The Ca is then covered with the test tube to collect the evolved gas.

7.2d Properties and reactions of hydrogen

Density of hydrogen. To show the density of hydrogen, the bottles of hydrogen collected in laboratory preparation may be lifted mouth downward without using a glass cover plate and placed on a plate. Light a wax taper or a birthday cake candle attached to a long piece of stiff wire and slowly bring the flame to the mouth of the bottle, continuing its insertion until the tip of the candle is halfway into the bottle. The candle flame goes out showing that hydrogen does not support combustion. Withdraw the candle slowly and note that it reignites on the way out of the bottle at the mouth of which the hydrogen is burning with an almost imperceptible blue flame. This operation may be repeated several times. A way of showing the lightness of hydrogen is to open simul-

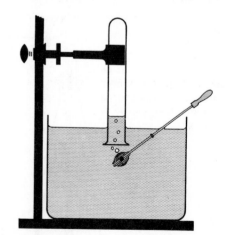

Fig. 7-19 Immersing sodium under a test tube to collect the resulting hydrogen.

taneously two bottles of hydrogen to the air, one mouth downward, the other mouth upward for one minute. Then bring the mouth of each bottle to the Bunsen flame. The result shows that the hydrogen has escaped from the bottle which was mouth upward.

Reaction with oxygen. A balloon may be inflated from a tank of hydrogen or from the sidearm of a suction flask fitted as a hydrogen generator. The balloon is tied to a long cord so that it floats near the ceiling of the room and may be ignited by a burning candle attached to the window pole. Students are greatly impressed with this demonstration, particularly if the balloon is floating near the ceiling as the class enters and is then ignited later. If the balloon contains a hydrogen-air mixture, its ignition will produce a loud explosion. Another way of igniting such a balloon is to attach a fuse which is made by soaking a piece of string in a dilute solution of potassium nitrate. This is prepared in advance and permitted to dry. To show that hydrogen and air (oxygen) produce an explosive mixture, ignite a collecting bottle with a half air-half hydrogen mixture. When the bottle is brought to the Bunsen flame there is a noise, perceptibly louder than the characteristic "pop" of pure hydrogen. A follow-up uses a bottle of air placed mouth downward on a covered bottle of hydrogen. The cover plate separating the bottles is withdrawn. Some of the hydrogen passes into the upper bottle so that each bottle contains a hydrogen-air mixture. When the mouth of each bottle is brought to a flame, a loud explosion results.

Making H₂O. Hold the burning hydrogen jet from a generator, which has been properly lighted as in 7.2c, inside a bell jar or large beaker. The water vapor forms almost instantaneously and may be identified by adding a pinch of white anhydrous copper sulfate which turns blue in the presence of water.

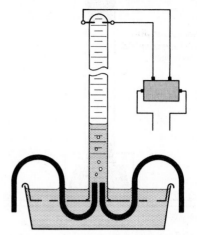

Fig. 7–20 Eudiometer used to ignite hydrogen and oxygen in definite proportions.

An electrolytic eudiometer may be employed for a more extensive study of the synthesis of water by combination of oxygen and hydrogen (Fig. 7–20). The eudiometer is filled with exact volumes in the ratio of 2 of hydrogen to 1 of oxygen, which volumes are collected by water displacement. A spark is passed through the mixture by connecting the electrodes to the secondary terminals of an induction coil. The induction coil primary circuit is connected with a switch in series to a 6-volt battery or some equivalent device such as to 12 volts a.c. from a toy electric train transformer. A Tesla coil may also be used to produce the spark across the eudiometer terminals. Useful demonstrations may be performed where ratios of hydrogen to oxygen other than the 2:1 are used. The uncombined gas may then be identified by inverting the eudiometer tube and using the tests for hydrogen or oxygen. Another procedure is to add more of either gas to the residue and again spark the new mixture. If the residual gas is the same as the added gas, no explosion

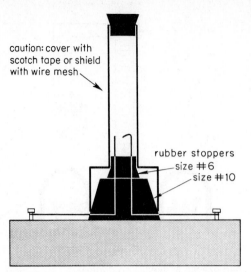

caution: cover with scotch tape or shield with wire mesh

rubber stoppers
size #6
size #10

Fig. 7–21 Eudiometer made from glass chimney, rubber stopper, and nichrome electrodes.

results. If it is different, another explosion results. (*Caution: The eudiometer assembly and the battery jar in which it is generally inserted should be surrounded by a cylinder of mesh wire to protect the observer if a defect in the tube should develop.*)

Explosive mixtures. A device for studying explosive mixtures can be made from a 10½″ glass chimney (Cent. Scientific Co. #14390). The larger end of the chimney is mounted firmly on a cork or rubber stopper (No. 10) which is nailed to the wooden base of the assembly. Previously a smaller rubber stopper (No. 6), fitted with two pieces of nichrome wire which will serve as electrodes, is fitted tightly into the tube constriction where the larger circumference meets the smaller. These electrodes are forced through this rubber stopper and shaped to simulate a spark plug (Fig. 7–21). The ends of these electrodes pass through the rubber stopper which serves as a mount and are connected to binding posts. The upper, longer portion of the chimney may be filled, as is the manufactured eudiometer, with selected volumes of hydrogen and oxygen. The capacity of

this portion is approximately 100 ml. A cork stopper is then inserted into the top opening. The apparatus is then covered with the cylinder of wire mesh and a spark is passed through the gases by means of the same devices described previously. The cork stopper is shot into the air as a result of the explosion.

The eudiometer is used to study other explosive mixtures. A drop or two of gasoline may be placed into the cylinder portion, thus producing a gasoline-air mixture. A procedure which relates Bunsen burner operations with this eudiometer is to fill the chimney with a mixture of gas and air by opening the Bunsen burner collar, then use the burner as a delivery tube to fill the chimney by downward displacement of the air. This gas-air mixture explodes readily when sparked. An adroit teacher may then close the collar unobtrusively and attempt to repeat the operation. This time, the cylinder being filled only with fuel gas, there is no explosion. This challenges student curiosity and tests observational powers. The teacher may remove the stopper to take a look, then replace the stopper, and spark again. Timing is important in this demonstration. If not enough gas escapes during the first removal of the stopper, it may be necessary to repeat. The rewarding final "bang" generally helps establish the meaning and importance of explosive mixtures. The hydrogen gun, described in 6.5c, also may be used to demonstrate the action of an explosive mixture.

Burning hydrogen in chlorine. Collect a bottle of chlorine gas according to procedures for preparation and collection of chlorine (see 11.2a). Use the conventional 6-oz gas-collecting bottle with a wide mouth. Bend the lower end of a metal blowpipe into a small J-tube which can easily fit into the gas-collecting bottle. A similar glass J-tube is easily prepared and

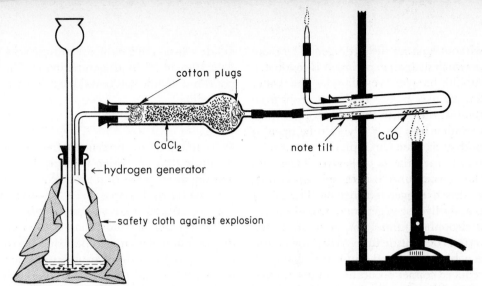

Fig. 7-22 A typical arrangement of apparatus for reducing metallic oxides. (Redrawn from L. Malm and H. Frantz, *College Chemistry in the Laboratory*, Freeman, 1950.)

should have a tapered end. Connect this J-shaped burning tube to a hydrogen generator and light the hydrogen emerging from the jet by the usual "sample" method (see 7.2a). Lower the burning hydrogen flame into the chlorine. Have students note that the light blue hydrogen flame changes to a grey in the chlorine and that the yellow color of the chlorine apparently disappears with the formation of colorless hydrogen chloride. Remove the hydrogen flame. Bending or pinching the rubber tubing connecting the J-tube to the generator causes the flame to go out. Blow the breath across the mouth of the bottle and note the formation of vapor characteristic of hydrogen chloride in moist air. A piece of blue litmus paper will turn red in this vapor. Compare this with the bleaching action of chlorine previously in the bottle on moist litmus paper.

Reducing metallic oxides. This demonstration may be performed in many ways. One typical arrangement of apparatus is shown in Fig. 7-22. The hydrogen generator contains about 15 g of Zn to which 10 ml of water are added plus a few drops

of $CuSO_4$ solution as a catalyst. Fill the drying tube with $CaCl_2$ grains, plugging each end with loose cotton. Place from 2 to 4 g of the wire form of cupric oxide in the test tube in which it is to be heated. In its two-hole stopper place a tapered delivery tube and a connection to the drying tube. Add 20 ml of sulfuric acid to the generator and after 15 seconds take a sample of the hydrogen and attempt to ignite the delivery tube using the "sample" method (see 7.2a). Bring the collection bottle with the burning hydrogen flame to the delivery tube leading from the test tube of cupric oxide in order to ignite the escaping hydrogen. Now heat the cupric oxide for 3-5 minutes until evidence of reduction appears. Remove the burner and continue to allow the hydrogen to flow over the cooling oxide in order to prevent reoxidation. Have students note the accumulation of water in the lower portion of the test tube. Add a pinch of anhydrous $CuSO_4$ to this water and note the change in color to blue. Another typical arrangement is to keep the mouth of the test tube, in which the CuO is being heated, open to the air without igniting the hydrogen. The room in which such an experiment is conducted should be well ventilated. The water formed may be observed as it drops from the test tube onto the table top. A third variation uses an 8″ Pyrex tube open at both ends. The CuO, placed about midway in the tube, is preheated. Then with the burner underneath still operating, air-free hydrogen is turned on. This means that the hydrogen generator would employ a dropping funnel for acid admission instead of a thistle tube. When the hydrogen hits the heated CuO, the change to reduced copper occurs almost instantaneously. When a collecting bottle is placed with mouth open, some two inches from the other end of the heated tube, water condenses immediately inside the bottle. Turning off the hydrogen results in immediate reoxidation (darkening) of the copper. This process may be carried on intermittently to indicate the reason why hydrogen must be permitted to play over the heated metal as it cools.

7.3 Hydrogen peroxide

Hydrogen peroxide is an oxidizing agent and is much less stable than water. In this compound and the related peroxides, the two oxygen atoms are bonded together. In such compounds oxygen is considered to have an oxidation state of minus 1.

Oxygen is liberated easily from 3% hydrogen peroxide by using the various catalysts mentioned in 7.1b. Amounts are not critical and a pinch of catalyst generally assures suitable results.

7.3a *Oxidizing action of hydrogen peroxide*

Show the oxidizing action of hydrogen peroxide by adding 5 cc of 1 N potassium iodide solution to 5 cc of 6 N sulfuric acid. Add 10 cc of 3% hydrogen peroxide. The potassium iodide will be oxidized, liberating iodine

$$H_2O_2 + 2\,I^- + 2\,H^+ = I_2 + 2\,H_2O$$

You can test for the presence of free iodine by adding starch, which will turn black. The equation shows that the sulfuric acid is necessary as a source of H^+ (hydrogen ion). Soluble K_2SO_4 is also produced.

For another demonstration of the oxidizing action of hydrogen peroxide, add a few drops of potassium chromate solution to 25 cc of water in a tall test tube. Then add about 1 cc of 6 N sulfuric acid. On top add enough diethyl ether to make a layer 5 cm deep. Then add one drop of 3% hydrogen peroxide and shake. After this comes to rest, perchromic acid (which is blue) forms in the ether layer. This is one of the best tests for hydrogen peroxide.

Another oxidation reaction can be produced by adding 5 cc of 3% hydrogen peroxide to 40 cc of water and 5 ml of 1 M lead nitrate solution; stir continuously. Then add 5 cc concentrated ammonium hydroxide. A heavy precipitate of brown lead peroxide will fall to the bottom. Here the ability of hydrogen peroxide to cause oxidation in an alkaline medium is demonstrated.

For another oxidation that serves as a test for H_2O_2, soak a piece of 4″ x 4″ filter paper in lead acetate solution. Once it is thoroughly wet, pass hydrogen sulfide gas (preparation, 9.2b) from a delivery tube connected to a small generator into the acetate solution. The paper will turn black. Place it on the inside walls of a beaker and add ordinary household 3% hydrogen peroxide. The black lead sulfide will be oxidized to white lead sulfate. The result will be a shade of grey, depending on the degree of reaction. This reaction may be used in an auditorium program to show that "black is white." Amounts and concentrations are not critical. A precipitate of black lead sulfide may be made by mixing ammonium sulfide and lead nitrate solutions. Then upon continuous addition of H_2O_2 (the 20% hair-bleaching solution sold in drug stores is good), the white sulfate is produced. (*Caution: Handle 20% H_2O_2 solution with care.*)

$$(NH_3)_2S + Pb(NO_3)_2 \rightarrow$$
$$PbS + 2\,NH_3^+ + 2\,NO_3^-$$

$$PbS + 4\,H_2O_2 \rightarrow PbSO_4 + 4\,H_2O$$

7.3b *Reducing action of hydrogen peroxide*

In some classes you may want to show that hydrogen peroxide can also act as a reducing agent. Prepare 200 cc of 0.1 M potassium permanganate and add 12.5 cc of 6 N sulfuric acid. Slowly add 25 cc of 3% hydrogen peroxide. Note the disappearance of the purple color of the permanganate ion as it is reduced:

$$2\,MnO_4^- + 5\,H_2O_2 + 6\,H^+$$
$$\rightarrow 5\,O_2 + 2\,Mn^{++} + 8\,H_2O$$

CAPSULE LESSONS
Ways to get started in class

7-1. As a demonstration, prepare oxygen and test for its presence in a way that students will long remember. Heat a large Pyrex test tube containing potassium chlorate, using a large burner as a source of heat. After the chlorate has begun to melt, use tongs to lower a long stick into it. Move out of the way as the entire stick bursts into brilliant flames. (*Caution: See 2.2c and 7.1b before performing this demonstration.*)

Then develop the equations for the preparation of oxygen and for other methods of releasing oxygen from compounds.

7-2. You may want to begin with a historical approach to the study of oxygen. Show the film *Historical Introduction to Chemistry* (Encyclopaedia Britannica). Have students summarize the main points they have learned from the dramatization of the famous experiments of Priestley and Lavoisier.

7-3. Show the relation between particle size and combustion by preparing the dust explosion with lycopodium powder as described in this chapter. Develop the notion of kindling temperature and combustion, and slow oxidation and spontaneous combustion.

7-4. Show the relation between conductivity of heat and kindling temperature. Demonstrate models of a miner's Davy safety lamp (7.1d). What are the three conditions that are needed for combustion?

7-5. Sometimes you may want to begin a lesson on kindling temperature by showing the low temperature at which phosphorus burns.

Use the phosphorus-carbon disulfide mixture painted on a large sheet of thin paper placed on a fireproof demonstration table. When the carbon disulfide evaporates, students should be able to explain why the phosphorus bursts into flame. (See spontaneous combustion, 7.1c.) (Discard the excess solution; make only enough for the demonstration since the mixture cannot be stored.) Develop through questioning the meaning of kindling temperature.

7-6. In one of the first laboratory periods have students examine the nature of the Bunsen burner and its flame. Use the demonstration with a safety match head to show the inner cone is cool in comparison with the outer cone's heat (7.1d). Also use a 3 x 5 card (7.1d). Have students adjust the air inlet and compare what happens to an evaporating dish or test tube held in a luminous flame and in a blue flame.

Demonstrate techniques for heating test tubes in a flame.

7-7. Have a student summarize the work by showing a filmstrip such as *Oxidation* (Popular Science). If the student has previewed the filmstrip first, he can develop the lesson by asking students questions as he shows it.

7-8. A committee of students or a class project may be formed around a case history approach to the discovery of oxygen. What methods in science were used to disprove the phlogiston theory? Students might use the booklet called *The Overthrow of the Phlogiston Theory,* edited by J. B. Conant, Harvard Case

History Studies (Harvard Univ. Press, 1956).

7-9. Plan a laboratory lesson in which students can prepare hydrogen and test its properties. Compare these properties with those of oxygen.

7-10. Compare the weight of hydrogen with air by weighing a balloon of air and one containing hydrogen.

7-11. Use a eudiometer tube to show the reaction of hydrogen and oxygen (see 7.2d).

7-12. Demonstrate the displacement of hydrogen from water by sodium or other active metals. Place the metal, in a sodium spoon as described in the chapter, under an inverted glass cylinder of water.

7-13. In one period, some teachers may wish to burn hydrogen in chlorine. Or burn natural gas to show the water produced during combustion. (Wave a Bunsen flame across the blackboard.)

7-14. As a summary, a group of students may present a film or a filmstrip on the role of hydrogen and/or oxygen in industry and prepare questions based on the film for class discussion.

PEOPLE, PLACES, AND THINGS

There probably are many people in your community to draw upon for help in developing a technique, in presenting a lecture, or in planning a field trip. Have your students watched oxyacetylene welding done at a local garage? If you are near a military base, it may be possible to invite someone to talk about LOX, liquid oxygen used in rockets.

In connection with this chapter's content you may want to have certain students investigate or perform the following.

a. *Scientific Experiments in Chemistry,* Henry Holt & Co., Inc., in cooperation with the Manufacturing Chemists Association Inc., N.Y., 1959

1. Experiment 17: Concentration of Hydrogen Peroxide and Its Decomposition Rate
2. Experiment 19: A Study of Catalysis
3. Experiment 20: Effect of Weight of Catalyst on Reaction Rate
4. Experiment 28: Heating Metallic Oxides
5. Experiment 5: Reaction Between Oxides and Water

b. *Journal of Chemical Education:* A Chem Ed Tested Demonstration

1. Flame Speed Demonstrations, W. E. Thrun, checked by R. Wheaton, p. A 91, Feb., 1959
2. Oxidation of PbO, Jean M. Saurer, checked by J. J. Hamerski, p. A 620, Oct., 1959
3. Kindling Temperatures of Substances, Kenneth G. Melgaard, checked by C. N. McCarty, p. A 93, Feb., 1960

c. *Journal of Chemical Education:* Demonstration Abstracts 2.s Oxygen and 3.s Hydrogen appearing in Feb., March, and April issues of 1957. For example, 3.s contains directions for experiments on hydrogenation of oils, and a variety of details regarding containers for H_2 and O_2 explosions as well as various explosive mixtures.

BOOKS AND PAMPHLETS

These are only a few of the books which are pertinent to the work discussed in this chapter. These and many other references classified by subject and with complete bibliographical data are given in the bibliography at the end of the book.

Conant, J., *Overthrow of the Phlogiston Theory,* Harvard Case History in Experimental Science, Harvard U. Press, 1956.

Farber, E., *The Evolution of Chemistry,* Ronald, 1952.

Hazel, J., *A Basic Laboratory Course in College Chemistry,* 2nd ed., Wiley, 1957.

Hodgman, C., et al., *Handbook of Chemistry and Physics,* latest ed., Chemical Rubber.

Hopkins, B. S., and J. Blair, Jr., *General Chemistry for Colleges,* 5th ed., Heath, 1956.

Kendall, J., *Great Discoveries by Young Chemists,* Crowell, 1953.

Kynch, G., *Mathematics for the Chemist,* Academic, 1955.

Lange, N., *Handbook of Chemistry,* 9th ed., Handbook Publishers, 1956.

Langford, O., *Using Chemistry,* McGraw-Hill, 1954.

Laubengayer, A., *General Chemistry,* Rinehart, 1957.

Margenau, H., and G. Murphy, *The Mathematics of Physics and Chemistry,* 2nd ed., Van Nostrand, 1956.

Markham, E., and S. Smith, *General Chemistry,* Houghton Mifflin, 1957.

Partington, J., *A Short History of Chemistry,* Macmillan, 1951.

Pauling, L., *College Chemistry,* 2nd ed., Freeman, 1955.

Pauling, L., R. Corey, R. Hayward, "The Structure of Protein Molecules," *Scientific American,* July, 1954.

Routh, J., *Routh's 20th Century Chemistry,* 2nd ed., Saunders, 1958.

Scientific American, "Lavoisier," May, 1956.

Steiner, L., and J. Campbell, *General Chemistry,* Macmillan, 1955.

Wald, George, "The Origin of Life," *Scientific American,* August, 1954.

Weeks, M., *Discovery of the Elements,* 6th ed., Journal of Chemical Educ., 1956.

FILMS AND FILMSTRIPS

This partial list is intended only as a guide toward film and filmstrip selection. Refer to the more complete listing at the end of the book where films are classified by subject and where a key to abbreviations and addresses of distributors are given. The cost of film rental, of course, is subject to change. Films are sound and black and white unless otherwise specified.

Chemistry of Combustion (f, s), Institutional Cinema, $2.00.

Chemistry of Fire (f, s), Ideal, $2.00.

Fire Magic (f, s, c), Modern Talking Pictures, free.

Oxidation (f, s), EBF, $2.50.

Oxy-acetylene Flame (f, s, c), N. Y. State Dept. of Commerce; inquire about rental.

Preventing Fire (fs), Popular Science through McGraw-Hill, $6.00.

FREE AND INEXPENSIVE MATERIALS

This is only a partial listing of free and inexpensive materials available to the teacher at this time. A more complete listing, including addresses, is given at the end of the book. Many of these materials are distributed to teachers without charge. Where there is a small fee, the cost is indicated, although the prices are subject to change. While we recommend the material for use in the classroom, we do not necessarily endorse the products advertised.

Handbook for Chemistry Assistants, also *Manual of Laboratory Safety,* Fisher Scientific Co., free.

CHAPTER 8

Solutions

Demonstrations and experiments on the subject of solutions could easily make a book in itself. In this chapter the broad general concepts and procedures that are frequently taught in high schools have been emphasized. For the student who wishes to go beyond the usual high school level on some special project, college texts and specialist's monographs, many of which are listed in the bibliography, will be helpful.

Various teachers will deal with the topics in quite a different order from that presented here. Different courses require different approaches. Teaching, in the long run, remains and must remain a personal invention. It should be noted that discussion of those substances which display both acidic and basic characteristics such as amphoteric hydroxides is included in Chapter 10.

8.1 Water

8.1a *Properties of water*

Water—the most common solvent—has a number of significant properties which are dependent on its characteristic dipole structure and the ease with which it forms hydrogen bonds. The water molecule is nonlinear. The bond angle between the hydrogen atoms is $104.5°$. The abnormally high boiling point may be explained by the association of water molecules through hydrogen bonds.

Water is one of the few substances which expands upon freezing. In addition it reaches its maximum density at $3.98°$ C. X-ray studies of ice indicate that four oxygen atoms are placed symmetrically about a single oxygen atom and that hydrogen atoms occur at the corners of a regular tetrahedron, the center of which is the oxygen atom. Ice has a highly organized structure in which these tetrahedra cause the formation of hexagonal channels throughout the structure. The low density of ice may be explained on the basis of this relatively open structure. When ice melts, the tetrahedra structures remain but a breakdown in the regular pattern takes place with a rise in density due to closer packing and the rupturing of some of the hydrogen bonds. Increasing the temperature still further causes this breakdown to continue but there is an opposing effect, namely, the greater kinetic motion of the molecules which causes the molecules to spread further apart. From the freezing point to about $4°$ C, the continuing collapse of the regular pattern of tetrahedra predominates and the density continues to increase. Above $4°$ C, more hydrogen bonds continue to be broken but the increase in kinetic motion predominates and the density decreases above $4°$ C. The high boiling point is due to the need for energy which must be expended in breaking existent hydrogen bonds so that the single molecules may enter the vapor phase.

8.1b *Water as a solvent*

The solution process, far from being completely understood, involves at least three energy processes: 1. Energy must be expended in overcoming solute-solute attraction (whatever the type of lattice). 2. Energy must be expended in overcoming the solvent-solvent attraction 3. Energy must be furnished by the solute-solvent interaction, the solvation process. Other factors playing a part in the process are temperature and pressure. The similarities in the structure of solute and solvent are prime determinants, and the overall generalization which is applicable is the "like dissolves like." In molecular solutions, similarity in electrical properties (dipole moment, dielectric constant) result in the solubility of alcohol in water (polar substances) and in the formation of mutual solutions of various hydrocarbons such as in petroleum or the solubility of waxes and fats in benzene and ether (nonpolar substances). Ionic solutes, because of their electrical nature, dissolve most readily in liquids which are highly polar such as water.

Solubility of sugar and sodium chloride in water. This demonstration is best performed after students have learned the meaning of molarity. Make saturated solutions (100 ml) of sucrose (131 g) and NaCl (31 g) at room temperature. Weigh out amounts first and then prepare the saturated solutions. Add just enough additional solute in each instance to show saturation. You may want students to calculate the molarity of the respective solutions (3.8 M for sucrose, 5.3 M for NaCl) and arrive at the conclusion that the molar solubility of NaCl is greater than that of

sucrose. They can thereby appreciate the greater attraction of the water molecules for the sodium and chloride ions as compared with that of the water molecules for sucrose molecules. The demonstration may include showing that ethyl alcohol and water are completely miscible but that the solubility of NaCl in the alcohol is slight (approximately ½ g of NaCl per liter of ethyl alcohol). Show the relative insolubility of gasoline in water, indicating that water is generally a poor solvent for substances which exist in solution as molecules. The great solubility of NH_3 and ethyl alcohol (molecular substances) in water may be explained on the basis of the breaking of the hydrogen bonds in water and the formation of new hydrogen bonds during the solution process.

Increasing temperature increases solubility. Increasing the temperature increases the solubility of most nonvolatile solutes (Fig. 8–1). The decomposition of $Na_2SO_4 \cdot 10H_2O$ at approximately 35° C results in the formation of Na_2SO_4 whose solubility then starts to decrease. Chemistry teachers generally use such solubility graphs to train students in their use and interpretation so that students may follow the changes in solubility with changes in temperature. Simple mathematical problems may deal with the additional amounts of solute needed to produce a saturated solution with a change in temperature, the amount of solute which should be deposited when a hot solution at a stated temperature is cooled suddenly to a lower temperature (supersaturation neglected), and the quantity of solute needed to produce a saturated solution in a different quantity of solute.

A qualitative demonstration of temperature effect generally involves the use of a substance such as NH_4Cl or KNO_3 which undergoes marked increase in solubility with temperature. Amounts used are non-

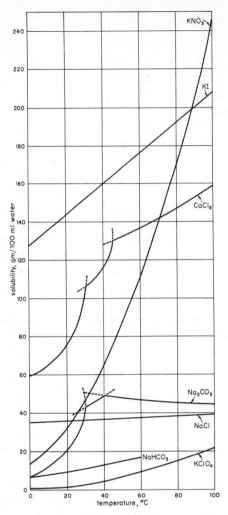

Fig. 8–1 Solubility graph.

critical. A pinch of the solute is added to approximately 20 ml of water at room temperature in an 8″ Pyrex test tube, then another small amount which fits on a wooden splint is added, then half a teaspoonful, then a full teaspoonful until a saturated solution is produced with some ¼″ of solute undissolved. Shaking, of course, follows each successive addition. The test tube is heated and another teaspoonful is added after students note the solution of the previous excess. After this additional amount has dissolved, the tube contents are cooled under the water tap as the test tube is shaken. The excess solute then reappears and in rather startling amount. This demonstration may involve development of such concepts as dilute, concentrated, saturated, and unsaturated solutions.

Temperature and a volatile solute. The effect of temperature on a volatile solute such as ethyl alcohol may be demonstrated by noting the temperature at which alcohol starts to distill from an alcohol-water mixture (80° C). This demonstration may be performed with the standard distillation setup or a less elaborate one using a glass tube air condenser. The first portion of the distillate is identified by odor and may be set on fire to identify the alcohol. This demonstration also illustrates fractional distillation. Permitting a 500-ml tall cylinder of tap water to stand over the radiator or in the sunlight for 20-30 minutes results in the escape of air bubbles which accumulate next to the glass walls. This shows the effect of increased temperature on gas solubility. Gentle, progressive heating of 5-10 ml of tap water over a Bunsen flame produces similar results much more rapidly. The same experiment may be performed with a sample of carbonated water. Such samples may then be boiled and upon cooling tasted to note the taste of water without the gas.

Pressure and gas solubility. Remove the cap from a sealed bottle of carbonated water. This reduction of pressure results in the escape of excess gas. A hand vacuum pump may be attached to the bottle after gas evolution has stopped to show the increased release of the dissolved carbon dioxide with the further reduction in pressure.

Rate of solution. The rate of solution of solids is generally increased by stirring, powdering, and increasing the temperature.

Powdering. Weigh out two samples of hydrated $CuSO_4$. Grind one sample in a mortar and pestle. Place the ground and unground samples in separate test tubes half filled with water. Cork and shake both tubes and note the larger portion of undissolved solute remaining in the test tube containing the unground sample.

Stirring. Select two copper sulfate crystals each about ¼ size of a pea and place in a test tube half filled with water. Cork and shake one test tube, leaving the other undisturbed in the test tube rack. Note that the crystal which was shaken is more completely dissolved.

Temperature. Prepare two, ground 1-g samples of the copper sulfate. Place one in a test tube one third filled with cold water and the other in the same amount of water which has been heated almost to boiling. Stopper and shake both samples and note that almost all of the sample dissolves in the hot water. This demonstration has many variations. An interesting one uses cube sugar, granulated sugar, and ground or powdered sugar in identical quantities with temperature and stirring as variants.

8.1c *Purification of water*

Distillation. In a large beaker prepare a half-liter sample solution of impure water containing an insoluble solid (clay), a soluble solid (chromic sulfate, green for visibility), a soluble gas (H_2S—2-5 ml of saturated solution). The amount of the material used is not critical. These substances are selected because the first 5-6 test tube samples of the distillate show progressively less evidence of H_2S when tested with a lead nitrate or acetate solution (dilute, not critical). Bumping is avoided by the use of boiling stones or several small pieces of glass rod in the distilling flask. The standard distillation setup is used and some 300-400 ml of the synthetic impure water are poured carefully into the distilling flask, using a glass rod to direct the flow of the material from the beaker into the flask.

Aeration. Under the hood, bubble compressed air through 300-500 ml of a dilute solution of H_2S for 5-10 minutes. Test 5-ml samples at two-minute intervals with a solution of a lead salt (nitrate or acetate) to show decrease in concentration of H_2S.

Coagulation. To each of two 500-ml cylinders add one teaspoon of clay and fill ¾ full of water and shake. To one add 25 ml of saturated aluminum sulfate and 5 ml of dilute NH_4OH. Stopper both cylinders, shake vigorously again, put aside, and observe periodically. After fifteen minutes have students observe the greater clarity of the layer of water above the coagulum settling in the cylinder to which aluminum sulfate and ammonium hydroxide were added.

8.2   Properties of solutions

The freezing and boiling points and vapor pressure of solutions differ from those of the pure solvent. The vapor pressure is decreased, the freezing point is decreased, and the boiling point is increased by amounts which are directly proportional to the *molal (m)* concentration of the solute. These properties of solutions are known as colligative properties since they depend quantitatively on the number of particles (molecules or ions) present in the solution. A molal (*m*) solution contains the Avogadro number, 6.02×10^{23}, of molecules (of a nonionic solute) in 1000 g of solvent. Thus a one molal aqueous solution of sucrose contains 342 g of sucrose dissolved in 1000 g of water. The freezing point of such a solution is $-1.86°$ C and the boiling point (at 1 atmosphere pressure) is 100.52° C. Doubling the quantity of solute particles in the same quantity of solvent would double the effect so that the freezing point for a 2 molal (2 m) solution would be $-3.72°$ C and its boiling point would be 101.04° C. Thus the molal freezing-point lowering constant for water is $-1.86°$ for the Avogadro number of solute particles per 1000 g of water. The molal boiling-point elevation constant is 0.52° C per Avogadro number of solute particles per 1000 g of water. These effects are due to the lowering of the vapor pressure.

The freezing-point depression also results with volatile solutes but the boiling-point elevation does not. For ionic solutes, the measurable effect is complicated by the *number* of particles present and interionic attraction phenomena. In the case of NaCl which should yield two ions (Na^+ and Cl^-) for each formula unit, we might expect that a 1 molal solution (58.5 g) in 1000 g of water would result in a freezing point of $-3.72°$ C. Actually this numerical effect, freezing-point lowering per mole NaCl, is exactly 3.72 only at dilutions such as 0.0001 m. At higher concentrations the interionic attractions are larger and the ions act less independently of each other. Thus for a 0.1 m solution of NaCl the freezing-point lowering, °C per mole NaCl, is 3.47. Different substances have different molal freezing-point and boiling-point constants. For example, the K_B (boiling-point constant) for benzene (normal boiling point: 80.15° C) is 2.53° C and its K_F (freezing point constant) is 5.12° C (normal freezing point: 5.48° C). The calculation of exact molecular weights is often based on experimental value of freezing-point depression.

Also see heat and electrolyte conductivity, 6.3d; electrolysis 6.5b and at greater length in 7.1b and 7.2c; conductivity of pure water and solutions, 8.4d; acids, bases, and salts, 8.3; pH and indicators in 8.4e and 8.4f.

8.2a Suspensions, solutions, colloidal dispersions

Some selected, representative, and fairly common demonstrations and experiments are described below. The number and variety of such available demonstrations are so great that they could easily make a book by themselves. The brief outline in Table 8–1 presents the important concepts representative of particles as they can exist in the three states of dispersion, and of the type of phenomena which may be more or less easily demonstrated. While there are terms for each main class of dispersions, you many want to point out that there is a continuum among dispersions and that boundaries between one type of dispersion and another cannot be sharply drawn.

Comparative demonstrations of dispersions. Clay, powdered chalk, MgO, and other solids (¼-½ teaspoon) are shaken with 10 ml or more of water in a test tube. Attention is directed to some of the visible particles at the top of the water layer. A sample is filtered; another is set aside for settling. Similar qualitative demonstrations or student experiments are repeated with NaCl or some colored salt such as $CuSO_4$ or $KMnO_4$. Some teachers deal with colloidal dispersions as a separate phenomena. Others at this time may perform a demonstration such as the following. A pinch of cornstarch is placed in 10 ml of water, then shaken, observed, permitted to settle, filtered (filtrate may be tested with iodine solution), and identified as a coarse suspension. The suspension is heated (attention is drawn to increased

TABLE 8-1

Characteristics of the various classes of dispersions

	coarse suspension	colloidal dispersions	solutions
number of phases	2 (heterogeneous) dispersed phase and dispersing medium	2 (heterogeneous) dispersed phase (internal phase) and dispersing medium (external phase)	1 (homogeneous) solute and solvent
size of particle	larger than 1000 Å $(1 \times 10^{-5}$ cm)	between 1000 Å and 10 Å $(1 \times 10^{-5} \ldots 1 \times 10^{-7}$ cm)	molecular dimensions: 1 Å (ordinary molecules or ions) $(1 \times 10^{-8}$ cm)
appearance	cloudy, display Tyndall cone	opalescent (relatively clear), display Tyndall cone	clear, no Tyndall cone
settling	settle out, larger particles first, at most within hours	rate of settling imperceptible ordinarily due to Brownian movement, convection currents, electrostatic repulsions; settle with ultracentrifuge	do not settle
visibility of particle	visible by microscope or unaided eye	cannot be seen by microscope; light scattered visible with ultramicroscope	cannot be seen by microscope
filtration	removable by ordinary filtration	pass through ordinary filter paper	pass through filter paper
electrical charge	uncharged	present particularly on lyophobic sol particles (electrophoresis, electrolytic coagulation)	electrolytes as ions
Brownian movement	possible for smaller particles	displayed: smaller the size, the more violent the motion	none
adsorption		adsorption of charges (ions), surface adsorption	

clarity and opalescence), filtered, and the starch in the filtrate shown by iodine test.

The various kinds of solutions can be demonstrated by the use of a quite soluble substance and the effects of temperature and pressure shown (8.1b).

Supersaturation. Supersaturation may be demonstrated with sodium thiosulfate. Dissolve 1 lb of "hypo" in each of two 1-liter Florence flasks, stopper the mouths of the flasks with cotton wads, and permit them to cool. Drop a crystal of NaCl into the contents of one and a crystal of "hypo" into the other. Crystallization results in the one into which the "hypo" crystal has been added. Filtration of the hot solution in a heated funnel (if available) into a thoroughly clean flask helps prevent crystallization on cooling before the addition of the seed crystal.

The general rules for the solubility of common salts and bases are given in Table 8-2.

8.2b   Gas solubility

A table showing the comparative solubility of gases in cold water at 760 mm as well as their densities in gram/liter at $0°$ C and 760 mm is given in Table 8–3. Such gases as ammonia, hydrogen chloride, sulfur dioxide, and nitrogen dioxide (either extremely or very soluble) may be used. Details as to how certain of these gases may be prepared are given in subsequent chapters. Any of these may be used in the two following "quickie" demonstrations. 1. One ml of water is placed into a 6-oz bottle sample of the dry gas. The palm of the hand is moistened with water, placed over the open mouth of the bottle, and the bottle shaken. The gas bottle then sticks to the outstretched palm without falling. 2. Invert a test tube full of the dry gas, stoppered by the thumb into a basin of water. The water rises quickly into the test tube, almost instantaneously in some instances, as the gas dissolves.

NH_3 or HCl fountain. A relatively dry sample of NH_3 is prepared by dropping concentrated NH_4OH from a dropping funnel onto 20 g of NaOH pellets in a bottle or flask generator. A 1-liter round-

TABLE 8-2
Solubility of common salts and bases*

NO_3^-	All *nitrates* are soluble.
$C_2H_3O_2^-$	All *acetates* are soluble ($AgC_2H_3O_2$ only moderately).
Cl^-	All *chlorides* are soluble, except AgCl, Hg_2Cl_2, and $PbCl_2$. ($PbCl_2$ is slightly soluble in cold water, moderately soluble in hot water.)
$SO_4^=$	All *sulfates* are soluble, except $BaSO_4$ and $PbSO_4$. ($CaSO_4$, Hg_2SO_4, and Ag_2SO_4 are slightly soluble; the corresponding bisulfates are more soluble.)
$CO_3^=$, $PO_4^≡$	All *carbonates* and *phosphates* are insoluble, except those of Na^+, K^+, and NH_4^+. (Many acid phosphates are soluble, as $Mg(H_2PO_4)_2$, and $Ca(H_2PO_4)_2$.)
OH^-	All *hydroxides* are insoluble, except NaOH, KOH, NH_4OH, and $Ba(OH)_2$. ($Ca(OH)_2$ is slightly soluble.)
$S^=$	All *sulfides* are insoluble, except those of Na^+, K^+, and NH_4^+, and those of the alkaline earths: Mg^{++}, Ca^{++}, and Ba^{++}. (Sulfides of Al^{+++} and Cr^{+++} hydrolyze and precipitate the corresponding hydroxides.)
Na^+, K^+, NH_4^+	All salts of *sodium*, *potassium*, and *ammonium* are soluble, except several uncommon ones, as $Na_4Sb_2O_7$, $K_2NaCo(NO_2)_6$, $(NH_4)_2NaCo(NO_2)_6$, K_2PtCl_6, $(NH_4)_2PtCl_6$.
Ag^+	All *silver* salts are insoluble, except $AgNO_3$ and $AgClO_4$. ($AgC_2H_3O_2$ and Ag_2SO_4 are only moderately soluble.)

* From L. Malm and H. Frantz, *College Chemistry in the Laboratory*, Freeman, 1950.

TABLE 8-3
Density and solubility of some common gases

name	density (gram/liter 0° C 760 mm)	solubility[1] (in cold water 760 mm)
air	1.29	ss
ammonia	0.77	es
carbon dioxide	1.98	ms
carbon monoxide	1.25	ss
chlorine	3.21	ms
helium	0.18	ss
hydrogen	0.09	ss
hydrogen chloride	1.64	es
hydrogen sulfide	1.54	ms
nitrogen	1.25	ss
oxygen	1.43	ss
sulfur dioxide	2.93	vs

[1] ss = slightly soluble; ms = moderately soluble; vs = very soluble; es = extremely soluble.

bottom Florence flask is filled with the dry gas (collection under the hood) by downward displacement of air. Before collection, permit the air in the generator flask to escape (a 250-ml Erlenmeyer flask is a good generator). (*Caution: Do not inhale the ammonia*). See Fig. 8–2 for the fountain apparatus details. The stopper assembly consists of a dropper containing a small amount of water and a long glass tube whose slightly tapered end will reach at least two thirds of the way up the bulb of the flask. This assembly is inserted into the bottle. The open end of the long glass tube is placed into a battery jar or beaker which holds approximately 1½-2 liters of water by positioning the inverted Florence flask in the ring attached to a ring stand. Squeeze some of the water out of the medicine dropper to start the fountain operating. Using an indicator such as 5 drops of phenolphthalein or a red litmus solution in the battery jar water before operating the fountain results in color changes indicating the formation of NH_4OH. Dry HCl may be prepared by

gently heating 15 g of NaCl with 20 ml of concentrated sulfuric acid in a 500-ml Florence flask fitted either with a dropping funnel or the conventional thistle tube. With the HCl fountain, a blue litmus solution or slightly alkaline (pink) phenolphthalein solution may be used as an indicator. The HCl gas is collected by upward displacement of air.

8.2c Heat of solution

Most solids dissolve in water by an *endothermic* process. This is readily demonstrated qualitatively by having a student note the decrease in temperature which results when ammonium chloride is dissolved in water. The amounts used may vary. Use a thermometer to read temperatures before and after the salt has been dissolved in the water sample.

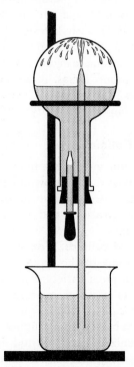

Fig. 8–2 Ammonia fountain.

Dissolving solid NaOH is an *exothermic* process since the hydration energy exceeds the lattice energy. Call students' attention to the precautions for preparing a solution which are printed on a can of commercial lye. When dissolving lye, 10 g of the solid are added slowly with stirring to 50–100 ml of water in a 250-ml beaker and the temperature rise noted.

8.2d Miscible and nonmiscible liquids

Place 10 ml of water in 1 test tube and 10 ml of carbon tetrachloride in another. Add 5 drops of vegetable oil (olive oil) or mineral oil (kerosene) to each test tube. Stopper and shake and note the solubility of the oil in the carbon tetrachloride. Repeat with similar quantities of water and carbon tetrachloride and drop in 5 drops of glycerine. Students may note the formation of a temporary emulsion when a large 8″ test tube is filled approximately ⅔ with water and ⅓ with kerosene, stoppered, and shaken. Now add about ½ ml of soap solution and shake again. A more permanent emulsion forms. A few ml of blue $CuSO_4$ solution may be used with the water to improve visibility.

8.2e Colloids

Brownian movement may be demonstrated by using the Brownian movement apparatus with cigarette smoke. See 1.2 for demonstrations and ways to make smoke boxes.

Types of colloids. You may want to refer to some of the types of colloids to show their great variety. For instance, gas in a liquid (fire-fighting foam), gas in a solid (Ivory soap cake), liquid in gas (visible steam from a kettle), liquid in a liquid (homogenized milk), liquid in a solid (Jello dessert), and solid in solid (colored glass).

Tyndall effect. Light may be used as a test for a colloidal suspension. Prepare a thin starch suspension (boiled) in a flat-walled glass jar; use a slide projector to focus a beam of light through it to show the Tyndall cone (Fig. 8–3). Compare this with lack of a cone when the light is shown through a solution. You may want to show a suspension of a solid in air such as chalk dust. Skim milk in water can be used to show the colloidal nature of milk, and diluted homogenized milk will show the colloidal suspension of butterfat.

Metals in suspension. Metallic colloids in which the metal is very finely divided can be formed by an electric arc under distilled water. Attach 2 pieces of the metal to be divided to wooden rods and connect to a 34-volt power source. (*Note:* A heater resistance unit, whether for a.c. or d.c., must be used to lower the voltage.) Assemble the arc as shown in Fig. 8–4. Touch the pieces of metal together and then separate them to form an electric arc under water. A metallic colloid in water will form since the electric arc produces extremely small metallic particles.

Sulfur in suspension. Make a colloidal suspension of sulfur by gradually adding 5 N hydrochloric acid to concentrated hypo (sodium thiosulfate) until the suspension is visible. Students should be able to see the yellow sulfur colloid. Or bubble chlorine into sodium thiosulfate solution. You can show that this is a colloidal suspension by demonstrating that it does not settle and that it is not a solution because it shows the Tyndall cone.

Coagulation. India ink is diluted 10-1 and a small amount filtered with passage of the ink through a filter paper. A few drops of dilute acetic acid are added to another sample, resulting in coagulation. Subsequent filtration removes the coagulate.

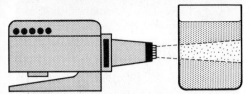

Fig. 8-3 Tyndall cone created by light striking particles in a colloidal suspension.

A sample of natural or synthetic rubber latex is diluted about 5:1. One sample is coagulated in a beaker by addition of acetic acid. The other is coagulated by the addition of enough salt to saturate the water. The coagulated material may be squeezed into a ball which, after being sufficiently compressed by hand, may be bounced on the floor.

Electrodeposition. Two copper strip electrodes are placed 10 cm apart in a beaker containing Neoprene (or natural) latex, and connected to a direct-current source, 110 volts d.c. if available. The latex is deposited on the anode within 15 minutes. Lower voltages take longer to produce a deposit.

Adsorption. A bottle of a colored gas, NO_2, or bromine vapor is shaken with a teaspoon of pelleted activated charcoal. The color disappears, indicating the adsorption of the gas. Heating the charcoal releases the adsorbed gas.

Making an emulsion. Fill a test tube one third full of water and add one inch of mineral or olive oil. Shake vigorously and note that the two substances rapidly separate. Now add one teaspoon of liquid soap and shake again. An emulsion of oil in water results.

8.2f   Crystals

A group of students may want to learn the factors underlying crystallization of salts and size of crystals. For the building of crystal models see 6.4d.

Copper sulfate. Compare the size of crystals of copper sulfate formed under these conditions.[1] Into three separate evaporating dishes pour 10 cc of copper sulfate solution. Let one solution evaporate at room temperature until crystals form. Heat the second dish in a water bath. To the third dish add a half teaspoon of gelatin (previously soaked in 5 cc of cold water) and heat to dissolve the gelatin. Let these stand for the next two days. Students should be able to compare the size of crystals formed and hypothesize on how crystals form. Finally, repeat this process using alum, nickel sulfate, Epsom salts, and almost any other soluble salt. You may also want to refer at this point to other activities related to crystallization described in 4.3c.

Potassium bromate. One of the simplest and finest crystals to grow without special laboratory controls is a large crystal of potassium bromate. There are two steps. First you need seed crystal. For this make a solution of potassium bromate in distilled water and place in a dish. Allow the water to evaporate in an atmosphere of about 70° F. (This is not critical.) Small crystals or seeds will form in the bottom of

[1] L. Meyer, *Laboratory Manual for Introductory Chemistry,* Macmillan, 1952.

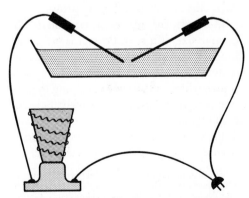

Fig. 8-4 Forming a metallic colloid in water by means of an electric arc.

Fig. 8–5 Crystal growing: (a) by evaporation—note cheesecloth covering, (b) in a sealed jar. (From A. Holden and P. Singer, *Crystals and Crystal Growing*. Copyright 1960 by Educational Services, Inc. Used by permission of Doubleday & Company, Inc.)

the dish when all the water has evaporated. Remove one small "seed crystal" and tie some very fine white cotton thread around it. Attach the loose end of the thread to a support over the growing solution. Lower the seed crystal suspended from the thread into the saturated solution of potassium bromate and allow to evaporate at room temperature. It can be done at a slower rate and at a more constant temperature in an electric refrigerator. When the crystal is ready, it is lifted up by the string. A crystal 1½″ long is easy to grow.

Methods for growing crystals.[2] The proper size of a seed crystal is ⅛″ to ¼″ long. To prepare such crystals place an ounce of saturated solution of the substance whose crystal you are going to grow into a glass and evaporate slowly. Selected seed crystals are dried and then tied with a slip knot using common white thread. It is wise to keep in mind that the slightest

contamination can affect the size and shape of a crystal. Hands should be thoroughly washed before handling a seed crystal.

The seed can be hung from a wire form bent into a cobra shape. The base is the wire bent into a sufficiently large circle to prevent tipping. When placed into a slightly unsaturated solution for growing, the seed should hang an inch or so from the bottom of the growing bottle. The end of the wire cobra should be below the solution surface. As a covering for the jar a piece of cloth through which the wire extends is held in place with a rubber band. Time and slow evaporation will do the rest of the job. (See Fig. 8–5A, 8–5B.)

Another method of suspending the seed crystal in its growing solution also provides a permanent mounting. Take a 5″ length of ¼″ glass tubing and slightly constrict one opening by holding in a Bunsen flame and squeezing with tweezers or forceps. When the tube is cool, drop in seed crystals until one catches in the constriction. This may be anchored into place by dropping

[2] Some of the following material was suggested by techniques described in *Crystals and Crystal Growing* by Alan Holden and Phyllis Singer (Doubleday, Garden City, N. Y., 1960). This book is an excellent and detailed guide to its subject.

several additional crystals down the tube. Clamp or attach the tube to a ring stand or other support in such a manner that the seed crystal is well immersed in its growing solution. Once grown, the crystal can be mounted by inserting the tube into a cork which in turn is inserted into the mouth of a bottle.

If, when growing crystals in a jar, your seed crystal becomes malformed or too many other crystals form, screw the cover on the jar for a while. The smaller crystals will tend to disappear and the seed will grow. If you are not suspending your seed crystal, it is a good idea to turn the crystal every so often so that growth on all faces is equal.

If you are growing your crystals in a crystallizing dish, rubbing vaseline around the upper inside rim will inhibit creeping. A tin can with a 5-watt bulb can cover the evaporating solution, or the solution can be set on the can to increase the rate of evaporation. Air-cooling with a fan will also hasten crystal growth.

Virtually any substance which crystallizes upon evaporation can be used for growing crystals. When grown, they can be preserved by being put in benzene, carbon tetrachloride, or some other liquid. The choice depends upon whether the crystals in question do or do not dissolve in the particular liquid. Crystals can also be protected with clear varnish.

Crystal blossoms. Cover pieces of coal, red brick, cinder, or unglazed porcelain in a crystallizing dish with a saturated solution of NaCl. Add more solution every few days for two weeks so that the level is maintained. At the end of two weeks add more saturated NaCl solution to which some Prussian blue has been added. Now allow to evaporate to dryness. Blossoms will form rather than the usual crystals. Other dyes can be added for other colors. Ferric chloride in place of the NaCl with-out a dye will produce yellow blossoms.

A crystal crown.[3] Cut a crown from a strip of tin, fastening it together with copper wire. Wrap it with strips of cotton cloth. Dip it into a solution of $K_2Cr_2O_7$ and allow to dry so that seed crystals are formed. Make a saturated solution of the $K_2Cr_2O_7$ at 80° C and immerse the crown. Allow it to remain overnight. Beautiful red crystals should cover the crown.

Crystal cloud. Heat a mixture of naphthalene and charcoal on a watchglass covered with a funnel. Notice the formation of crystals on the funnel by sublimation. Suddenly remove the funnel. The cooler outside air condenses the naphthalene vapor into a cloud of sparkling crystals.

Crystal shrub. Twist two pipe cleaners together at their middles and arrange the four ends as the branches of a shrub. Suspend this form into a hot saturated solution of $K_2Cr_2O_7$ containing some K_2SO_4. The red and white crystals that form have the appearance of red stems and white blossoms.

Crystal shapes. Here are some substances with the crystal shapes that they produce: Cubic, NaCl, KCl; tetragonal, KH_2PO_4, $NiSO_4$, SnO_2; rhombic, I_2, $MgSO_4$, KNO_3, K_2SO_4, $ZnSO_4$; monoclinic, $BaCl_2$, $KClO_3$, Na_2CO_3, Na_2SO_4; triclinic, $CuSO_4$, CaS_2O_3; hexagonal, SrI_2. Octahedrons are formed when NaCl crystallizes from alkaline, urea, or NH_4OH solutions. Funnel-shaped crystals result from a mixture of NaCl and alum.

8.3 Concentrations of solutions

In some of the previously discussed activities many kinds of solutions have been described. This section will deal with the preparation of these solutions as well

[3] Suggested by C. H. Stone, *J. of Chem. Ed.*, 7, 2170 (1930) and abstracted in Demonstration Abstracts, July, 1957.

as the preparation of more or less standard solutions commonly used in the laboratory or on the demonstration table.

8.3a Concentrations in physical units

Weight percentage. The number of grams of solute per 100 grams of solution is the weight percentage. A 10% solution of NaCl contains 10 grams of NaCl dissolved in 90 grams (or 90 milliliters) of water.

Volume percentage. This is used primarily with liquids. A 50% solution of alcohol by volume contains 50 ml of alcohol and 50 ml of water. The conversion of a solution of higher concentration (volume percentage) on this basis to a lower concentration may be performed by the following procedure.[4] Measure out the number of ml of the higher-percentage solution equal to the percentage needed for the new solution. For example, when you have 70 per cent alcohol on hand and want to prepare 50 per cent alcohol, measure out 50 ml of the 70% alcohol. Then add enough distilled water to bring the volume up to the number of ml equal to the percentage of the original solution, in this example to 70 ml.

The weight of solute per weight of solvent. Solubility curves and references in handbooks generally state the solubility as x grams of solute per 100 g of solvent (generally water) at a given temperature. Thus the solubilities in Fig. 8–1 are expressed as grams per 100 grams of water for a saturated solution for various temperatures.

The weight of solute per volume or unit volume of solvent. Some solubility curves use the scale of x grams solute per 100 ml of solvent (water) which is almost

[4] From *A Sourcebook for the Biological Sciences*, Morholt, Brandwein, Joseph (Harcourt, Brace, 1958).

identical with the relationship discussed in the paragraph above. A concentration could be expressed as 10 grams of NaCl per liter of solvent or as 10 grams of NaCl per liter of solution.

8.3b Concentrations in chemical units

Molarity. The molarity of a solution is equal to the number of moles of solute per liter of solution. A mole is one gram-molecular weight for molecular substance or one gram-formula weight for an ionic substance. Thus one mole of H_2SO_4 is 98 grams and one mole of NaCl is 58.5 grams. A capital M is used to designate the molarity of a solution. A 1 M solution of sulfuric acid contains 98 grams of sulfuric acid in one liter of solution. A 0.5 M solution of this acid would therefore contain $\frac{98}{2} = 49$ grams of acid per liter of solution. A 2.0 M solution of NaCl contains $2 \times 58.5 = 117$ grams per liter of solution.

$$\text{Molarity} = \frac{\text{no. of moles of solute}}{\text{no. of liters of solution}}$$

Sometimes the term formality, represented as F, is used in place of molarity particularly for ionic solutes. Thus a two formal solution ($2\ F$) of NaCl contains 2 formula weights of NaCl, that is, 2×58.5 g per liter of solution. This solution, of course, is also $2\ M$.

Molality. The molality of a solution is the number of moles of solute per 1000 grams of solvent (generally water). It may be wise to contrast this with molarity. A lower-case m is used to designate the molality of a solution. A 1 m solution of H_2SO_4 contains 98 grams of sulfuric acid dissolved in 1000 grams of water. A 0.5 m solution of this acid contains 49 grams per 1000 grams of water. A 0.1 m solution of NaCl contains 5.85 grams of NaCl dissolved in 1000 grams of water.

$$\text{Molality} = \frac{\text{no. of moles of solute}}{\text{no. of kilograms of solvent}}$$

Normality. The normality of a solution is the number of gram-equivalents of solute per liter of solution. One gram-equivalent of an element is defined as that weight of the element which will replace or combine with 1 gram of hydrogen. The expression, gram-equivalent or gram-equivalent weight, is used in the following contexts.

Gram-equivalent weight of an element equals the gram-atomic weight of the element divided by the valence of the element. Gram-equivalent of a compound in double decomposition and replacement reactions equals the gram-formula weight divided by the total valence of its positive or negative ions. The gram-equivalent of an acid is that weight of acid which contains one mole (1.008 grams) of hydrogen ion. The gram-equivalent of a base is that weight of a base which contains 17.008 grams of hydroxyl ion.

In the example below, 1 gram-equivalent of several substances is calculated.

Elements

$$\text{Na} = \frac{23\text{ g}}{1} = 23\text{ g}$$

$$\text{Ca} = \frac{40\text{ g}}{2} = 20\text{ g}$$

$$\text{Al} = \frac{27\text{ g}}{3} = 9\text{ g}$$

Acids

$$\text{HCl} = \frac{36.5\text{ g}}{1} = 36.5\text{ g }(36.46)$$

$$\text{H}_2\text{SO}_4 = \frac{98.0\text{ g}}{2} = 49.0\text{ g }(49.04)$$

$$\text{H}_3\text{PO}_4 = \frac{98.0\text{ g}}{3} = 32.7\text{ g }(32.67)$$

Bases

$$\text{NaOH} = \frac{40.0\text{ g}}{1} = 40.0\text{ g}$$

$$\text{Ca(OH)}_2 = \frac{74.1\text{ g}}{2} = 37.1\text{ g }(37.05)$$

$$\text{Al(OH)}_3 = \frac{78.0\text{ g}}{3} = 26.0\text{ g}$$

Salts

$$\text{NaCl} = \frac{58.5\text{ g}}{1} = 58.5\text{ g }(58.45)$$

$$\text{Na}_2\text{SO}_4 = \frac{142.0\text{ g}}{2} = 71.0\text{ g }(71.02)$$

$$\text{Ca}_3\text{(PO}_4\text{)}_2 = \frac{310.2\text{ g}}{6} = 51.7\text{ g }(51.70)$$

Gram-equivalent weight of compounds in oxidation-reduction reactions equals the formula weight divided by the change in oxidation state of the element oxidized or reduced. The change in the oxidation state is the number of electrons (lost or gained) per formula unit of the oxidizing agent or reducing agent.

A particular substance may have one gram-equivalent weight in one particular reaction and the same substance may have a different gram-equivalent weight in another specific reaction.

In the following reactions, the gram-equivalent weight of HNO_3 is calculated.

$$\text{Cu} + 4\,\text{HNO}_3 \rightarrow$$
$$\text{Cu(NO}_3)_2 + 2\,\text{H}_2\text{O} + 2\,\text{NO}_2$$
$$\text{Cu}^0 - 2\text{e} \rightarrow \text{Cu}^{++}$$
(oxidation)
$$\text{N}^{+5} + 1\,\text{e} \rightarrow \text{N}^{+4}$$
(reduction)

$$\text{Equivalent weight} = \frac{63.0\text{ g}}{1} = 63.0\text{ g}$$

$$3\,\text{Cu} + 8\,\text{HNO}_3 \rightarrow$$
$$3\,\text{Cu (NO}_3)_2 + 4\,\text{H}_2\text{O} + 2\,\text{NO}$$
$$\text{Cu}^0 - 2\,\text{e} \rightarrow \text{Cu}^{++}$$
(oxidation)
$$\text{N}^{+5} + 3\,\text{e} \rightarrow \text{N}^{+2}$$
(reduction)

$$\text{Equivalent weight} = \frac{63.0\text{ g}}{3} = 21.0\text{ g}$$

The changes in oxidation states may be calculated by the rules listed in 6.5b. Complete molecular or even net equations need not be solved since it is only necessary to calculate the number of electrons gained or lost per formula unit.

The equivalent weight of the oxidizing agent and the reducing agent in the change taking place in acid solution as in

$$NO_2^- + Cr_2O_7^= \rightarrow NO_3^- + Cr^{+3}$$

is calculated as follows.

$N^{+3} - 2e \rightarrow N^{+5}$
(oxidation)

Equivalent wt. $NO_2^- = \dfrac{46 \text{ g}}{2} = 23$ g

$Cr^{+6} + 3e \rightarrow Cr^{+3}$

Since the formula unit given is Cr_2O_7

$2\,Cr^{+6} + 6e \rightarrow 2\,Cr^{+3}$
(reduction)

Equivalent wt. $Cr_2O_7^= = \dfrac{216 \text{ g}}{6} = 36$ g

The balanced net equation for this reaction is

$$3\,NO_2^- + Cr_2O_7^= + 8\,H^+ \rightarrow$$
$$3\,NO_3^- + 2\,Cr^{+3} + 4\,H_2O$$

The total quantity of NO_2^- required is 3×46 g $= 138$ g and the total quantity of $Cr_2O_7^=$ required is 1×216 g. The ratio of reducing agent to oxidizing agent is

$$\frac{NO_2^-}{Cr_2O_7^=} = \frac{138 \text{ g}}{216 \text{ g}}$$

which is equal to the ratio of the equivalent weights, $\dfrac{23 \text{ g}}{36 \text{ g}}$.

Such an example may be used so that students realize that 1 gram-equivalent of the reducing agent = 1 gram-equivalent of the oxidizing agent in a chemical reaction of this type. Therefore, for this particular reaction, according to the fundamental definition of normality, a 1 N solution of nitrite ion (NO_2^-) contains 23 g of nitrite ion per liter of solution, and a 1 N solution of dichromate ion ($Cr_2O_7^=$) con-

tains 36 g of dichromate ion per liter of solution.

To calculate the number of gram-equivalents of a reactant present in a given volume of the solution of the reactant of a particular normality merely involves a restatement of the fundamental definition of normality:

$$N \text{ (normality)} = \frac{\text{no. of gram-equivalents}}{\text{no. of liters of solution}}$$

in the form: no. of gram-equivalents = $N \times V$ (volume of solution in liters). Since the number of gram-equivalents of reducing agent equals the number of gram-equivalents of oxidizing agent, the emergent principle is:

$$\underset{\text{(reducing agent)}}{N \times V} = \underset{\text{(oxidizing agent)}}{N \times V}$$

Dilution. The dilution formulas for solutions whose concentrations are expressed in M (moles/liter) or in N (gram-equivalents/liter) are, respectively,

$$M_1 \times V_1 = M_2 \times V_2$$

no. of moles$_1$ = no. of moles$_2$—that is, there is no change in the total number of moles, and

$$N_1 \times V_1 = N_2 \times V_2$$

the no. of gram-equivalents$_1$ = number of gram equivalents$_2$—that is, there is no change in the total number of gram-equivalents.

In practice, the volumes may be stated in milliliters (ml) instead of liters if this smaller unit (1 ml = 0.001 liter) is used consistently on both sides of the dilution formula.

The same principle obtains for other volumetric scales of concentration in which physical units involving weight of solute per volume of solution are used. Examples of the latter are grams per liter of solution or grams per 100 ml of solution. Here, as for molar and normal solutions, the relationships obtaining are

$$\text{Volume}_1 \times \text{Concentration}_1 =$$
$$\text{Volume}_2 \times \text{Concentration}_2$$

A tenfold molar dilution. To prepare 50 ml of 0.1 M HCl from a stock 1 M solution it is common practice to start with one tenth of the desired volume of the more concentrated solution and then add enough distilled water to bring this volume up to the final volume sought. Thus, take 5 ml of 1.0 M HCl and add enough distilled water to make the final volume of the solution 50 ml. Thus

$$V_1 \times M_1 = V_2 \times M_2$$
$$5 \text{ ml} \times 1.0 \, M = 50 \text{ ml} \times M_2$$
$$M_2 = \frac{5 \text{ ml} \times 1.0 \, M}{50 \text{ ml}} = 0.1 \, M$$

Taking 5 ml of the 0.1 M solution and diluting it to a final 50 ml would then produce 50 ml of a 0.01 M solution.

This same process may be followed through to produce solutions of a desired normality N from a given stock solution.

Dilution in physical units. To dilute a sample of AgNO$_3$ containing 20 grams per liter to a solution containing 4 grams per liter, the principle employed is

$$V_1 \times C_1 \text{ (concentration)} = V_2 \times C_2$$

Assume that you wish to dilute one liter of the stock solution:

$$1 \text{ liter} \times 20 \text{ g/liter} = V_2 \times 4 \text{ g/liter}$$
$$V_2 = \frac{1 \text{ liter} \times 20 \text{ g/liter}}{4 \text{ g/liter}} = 5 \text{ liters}$$

Therefore dilute the 1 liter of solution to 5 liters. This means that any given quantity of the stock solution would have to be diluted to a volume which is 5 times as great as the volume of the sample taken.

Thus if 20 ml of the original solution is to be diluted, the final volume must be 5 × 20 ml = 100 ml of final solution whose concentration is 4 grams/liter. This same type of operation may be carried through with such physical units as milligrams per milliliter.

Commercial concentrations. The common acids and ammonium hydroxide are generally purchased in large bottles having the weights as listed in Table 8–4. The labels on such bottles give the ranges for specific gravity and per cent solute acceptable according to American Chemical Society standards. The quantities used in *common laboratory practice* for the specific gravity and the per cent solute are also listed in the table. These quantities may not exactly represent the actual specific gravity or per cent solute but are close enough to be used without too great an error.

The molarity of the acid or base, as purchased, may be calculated from the specific gravity and the percentage of solute (by weight). Density in metric units is numerically equal to the specific gravity. Therefore to calculate the weight of sulfuric acid (H$_2$SO$_4$) in 1 ml of the purchased sample the following calculations are performed.

Weight of H$_2$SO$_4$ in 1 ml = density × weight per cent
$$= \frac{1.84 \text{ g}}{\text{ml}} \times 0.96$$
$$= \frac{1.77 \text{ g}}{\text{ml}}$$

Therefore 1 liter of solution would contain

$$\frac{1.77 \text{ g}}{\text{ml}} \times \frac{1000 \text{ ml}}{1} = \frac{1770 \text{ g}}{1}$$

Since one mole of H$_2$SO$_4$ = 98 g, to find the molarity of the solution divide the weight dissolved in 1 liter of solution by the weight of 1 mole.

TABLE 8-4

Commercial concentrations of desk acid and base solutions

quantity of solution in usual container	reagent	formula	molarity (formality)	normality	specific gravity	per cent solute
5 lb	acetic acid, glacial	$HC_2H_3O_2$	17 M	17 N	1.05	99.5%
	acetic acid, dilute		6 M	6 N	1.04	34
6 lb	hydrochloric acid, conc.	HCl	12 M	12 N	1.18	36
	hydrochloric acid, dil.		6 M	6 N	1.10	20
7 lb	nitric acid, conc.	HNO_3	16 M	16 N	1.42	72
	nitric acid, dil.		6 M	6 N	1.19	32
9 lb	sulfuric acid, conc.	H_2SO_4	18 M	36 N	1.84	96
	sulfuric acid, dil.		3 M	6 N	1.18	25
4 lb	ammonium hydroxide, conc.	NH_4OH	15 M	15 N	0.90	58 (28% NH_3)
	ammonium hydroxide, conc.		6 M	6N	0.96	23
solid	sodium hydroxide, dil.	NaOH	6 M	6 N	1.22	20

$$M \text{ (of solution)} = \frac{1770 \text{ g}}{1} \times \frac{\text{mole}}{98 \text{ g}} =$$

$$\frac{18 \text{ mole}}{1} = 18 \ M$$

Since the weight of a gram-equivalent of H_2SO_4 is 49 g $\left(\frac{98 \text{ g}}{2}\right)$, the normality of the purchased solution is calculated in the same manner as the molarity except that the weight of H_2SO_4 per liter of solution is divided by the equivalent weight of the acid:

$$N \text{ (of solution)} = \frac{1770 \text{ g}}{1} \times$$

$$\frac{\text{gram-equiv.}}{49 \text{ g}} = \frac{36 \text{ gram equiv.}}{1} = 36 \ N$$

In the case of NH_4OH, similar calculations may be made. Here it should be noted that the per cent of solute is 58% as NH_4OH or 28% as NH_3.

8.3c Standard laboratory reagents

The following alphabetic tabulation[5] of reagents and supplies indicates the concentrations most commonly used for most

[5] Adapted from *College Chemistry in the Laboratory*, No. 2, teacher's edition with instruction manual, Malm and Frantz (W. H. Freeman, San Francisco, Cal., 1958).

of the chemical solutions employed in demonstrations and experiments. It also gives brief directions how such solutions may be prepared.

Common acids and bases

Ammonium hydroxide: 15 M, use concentrated C.P. NH_4OH. 6 M, dilute 400 ml of 15 M to 1000 ml of solution. 1 M, dilute 167 ml of 6 M NH_4OH to one liter. 0.1 M, dilute 100 ml of 1 M NH_4OH to 1 liter.

Hydrochloric acid: 12 M, use concentrated C.P. HCl. 6 M, mix equal volumes of 12 M HCl and water, e.g. 500 ml (acid: 12 M) + 500 ml H_2O. 0.1 M, dilute 16.7 ml of 6 M HCl to 1 liter.

Nitric acid: 16 M, use concentrated C.P. HNO_3. 6 M, mix 375 ml of 16 M acid with 625 ml H_2O.

Sulfuric acid: 18 M, use concentrated C.P. H_2SO_4. 3 M (6 N), slowly with stirring add 167 ml of 18 M acid to approximately 500 ml of H_2O, then dilute to one liter. (*Caution: Stir constantly in a large Pyrex beaker since large quantities of heat are liberated.*) 0.1 M (0.2 N), dilute 33 ml of 3 M H_2SO_4 to 1 liter.

Acetic acid: 17 M, use glacial $HC_2H_3O_2$ (99.5%). 6 M, dilute 353 ml of 17 M $HC_2H_3O_2$ to 1 liter. 1 M, dilute 59 ml of 17 M $HC_2H_3O_2$ to 1 liter.

Sodium hydroxide: 6M, dissolve 255 g USP NaOH in water with stirring and dilute to 1 liter. (*Caution: Here large quantities of heat are liberated.*)

Other solutions

Ammonium acetate: 3 F, dissolve 231 g of $NH_4C_2H_3O_2$ per liter. Adjust the pH to pH 7 by neutralizing with NH_4OH until a test sample is green with bromthymol blue since the salt solution is usually acid because of the evaporation of ammonia. 1 F, dilute 77.1 g of the solid salt to 1 liter.

Ammonium chloride: 1 F, dissolve 53.5 g of NH_4Cl to make 1 liter of solution.

Antimony chloride: 0.1 F, dissolve 22.8 g of $SbCl_3$ and 250 ml of 12 M HCl per liter.

Barium chloride: 0.1 F, dissolve 24.4 g of $BaCl_2 \cdot 2H_2O$ per liter.

Barium hydroxide: 0.1 F, dissolve 35 g of $Ba(OH)_2 \cdot 8H_2O$ by heating the reagent with 1 liter of water in an Erlenmeyer flask. Mix well to complete the solution. Considerable solid $BaCO_3$ will remain. Avoid undue exposure to air, as CO_2 will be absorbed. Filter through a large filter paper directly into a stock bottle.

Bromine water, saturated: Keep from 10 to 20 g of liquid bromine in the stock bottle; refill with water and shake to dissolve as needed.

Cadmium nitrate: 0.1 F, dissolve 30.8 g of $Cd(NO_3)_2 \cdot 4H_2O$ per liter.

Calcium hydroxide: 0.02 F (saturated), keep an excess of solid $Ca(OH)_2$ in a large bottle fitted with a siphon. Fill with water, agitate the mixture, let it settle, and siphon off clear liquid as needed. Add water as necessary to replenish.

Chlorine water: Bubble Cl_2 from a cylinder of compressed Cl_2 gas or from a standard type of laboratory generator in which the Cl_2 is produced from MnO_2 and 12 M HCl or from $KMnO_4$ and 12 M HCl. An alternate procedure to 250 ml of 3% NaClO, or 150 ml of 5% NaClO (commercial bleaching solutions), add water and 35 ml of 6 M HCl. Add additional HCl as needed to give the greenish yellow color of chlorine and dilute to one liter.

Cobalt nitrate: 0.17 F, dissolve 49.5 g of $Co(NO_3)_2 \cdot 6H_2O$ per liter.

Cupric nitrate: 0.1 F, dissolve 24.2 g of $Cu(NO_3)_2 \cdot 3H_2O$ per liter.

Cupric sulfate: 0.5 F, dissolve 125 g of $CuSO_4 \cdot 5H_2O$ (finely crushed) per liter. 0.1 F, dissolve proportionate amount, 25 g of the hydrate in liter.

Ferric chloride: 0.1 F, dissolve 27 g of $FeCl_3 \cdot 6H_2O$ in 1 liter.

Hydrogen chloride in benzene, saturated: Pass dry HCl gas generated from NaCl and 18 M H_2SO_4 into dry benzene (dry the benzene by shaking with 50 g of anhydrous 4-mesh $CaCl_2$ per liter. Stopper and let mixture stand overnight, then filter or decant into stock bottle). Dry the HCl gas by passing it through a $CaCl_2$ tube.

Iodine: 0.1 F (0.2 F in KI), dissolve 12.7 g of I_2 and 53 g of KI in 200 to 300 ml of water. After complete solution, dilute to one liter.

Lead acetate: 0.1 F, dissolve 37.9 g of $Pb(C_2H_3O_2)_2 \cdot 3H_2O$ per liter.

Lead nitrate: 0.5 F, dissolve 33.1 g of $Pb(NO_3)_2$ per liter.

Litmus solution: dissolve 10 g of litmus powder per liter.

Magnesium nitrate: 0.1 F, dissolve 25.6 g of $Mg(NO_3)_2 \cdot 6H_2O$ per liter.

Manganous nitrate: 0.1 F, dissolve 28.7 g of $Mn(NO_3)_2 \cdot 6H_2O$ per liter.

Mercuric chloride: 0.1 F, dissolve 27.2 g of $HgCl_2$ per liter.

Mercuric nitrate: 0.1 F, dissolve 33.4 g of $Hg(NO_3)_2 \cdot \frac{1}{2}H_2O$ by warming this with 5 ml of 6 M HNO_3 to reverse any hydrolysis; then add water to make 1 liter.

Mercurous nitrate: 0.05 F, dissolve 28.1 g of $Hg_2(NO_3)_2 \cdot 2H_2O$ in 100 ml of 6 F HNO_3 plus enough water to make 1 liter. Do not warm the mixture to dissolve the salt. Keep some free mercury in the bottle to prevent oxidation to Hg^{++}.

Oxalic acid: 0.5 F, dissolve 63 g of $H_2C_2O_4 \cdot 2H_2O$ per liter.

Potassium bromide: 0.1 F, dissolve 11.9 g of KBr per liter.

Potassium chloride: 0.1 F, dissolve 17.4 g of KCl per liter.

Potassium chromate: 1 F, dissolve 194 g of K_2CrO_4 per liter. Dilute to lower concentrations as needed.

Potassium ferricyanide: 0.1 F, dissolve 32.9 g of $K_3Fe(CN)_6$ per liter.

Potassium ferrocyanide: 0.1 F, dissolve 42.2 g of $K_4Fe(CN)_6 \cdot 3H_2O$ per liter.

Potassium hydroxide: 1 F, dissolve 56.1 g of KOH per liter.

Potassium iodide: 0.1 F, dissolve 16.6 g of KI per liter.

Potassium nitrate: 0.1 F, dissolve 10.1 g of KNO_3 per liter.

Potassium thiocyanate: 0.1 F, dissolve 9.7 g of KCNS per liter.

Silver nitrate: 0.1 F, dissolve 17.0 g of $AgNO_3$ per liter. Store in brown bottle.

Sodium acetate: 1 F, dissolve 136 g of $NaC_2H_3O_2 \cdot 3H_2O$ per liter.

Sodium carbonate: 1 F, dissolve 106 g of Na_2CO_3 per liter.

Sodium chloride: saturated (5.4 F), use a purified grade, but not C.P.; do not use table salt which contains $MgCO_3$. Shake about 400 g of this NaCl per liter of water, at intervals for a long period of time, to saturate the solution thoroughly. Filter mixture until clear and decant it into stock bottle.

Sodium chloride: 1 F, dissolve 58.5 g of NaCl per liter. This may be used for studying pH of solutions; therefore test the solution for pH 7 with bromthymol blue (green color), and if necessary adjust pH by addition of NaOH or HCl drop by drop.

Sodium chloride: For Solvay process demonstration, saturate 100 ml of 15 M NH_4OH with sufficient NaCl to produce excess on bottom. Use the clear solution for the demonstration.

Sodium hydrogen carbonate: 1 F, freshly prepared, dissolve 84 g of $NaHCO_3$ per liter.

Sodium sulfate: 1 F, dissolve 322 g of $Na_2SO_4 \cdot 10H_2O$ per liter.

Sodium hydrogen sulfate: 1 F, dissolve 120 g of $NaHSO_4$ per liter.

Sodium sulfide: 2 F, dissolve 240 g of $Na_2S \cdot 9H_2O$ per liter.

Sodium thiosulfate: 1 F, dissolve 248 g of $Na_2S_2O_3 \cdot 5H_2O$ per liter.

Stannic chloride: 0.1 F, (2 F in HCl), dissolve 35.1 g of $SnCl_4 \cdot 5H_2O$ in 167 ml of 12 M HCl, warming a little to reverse any hydrolysis before diluting the solution to one liter.

Stannous chloride: 0.5 F (1.5 F in HCl), dissolve 113 g of $SnCl_2 \cdot 2H_2O$ in 125 ml of 12 M HCl by warming the mixture gently until solution is complete; then dilute to one liter. Add some tin metal to the bottle to prevent oxidation to stannic ion.

Zinc nitrate: 0.1 F, dissolve 29.7 g of $Zn(NO_3)_2 \cdot 6H_2O$ per liter.

Zinc sulfate: 0.5 F, dissolve 144 g of $ZnSO_4 \cdot 7H_2O$ per liter.

8.4 Acids, bases, and salts

8.4a Acids

Properties of acids. Students should be warned that tasting substances or solutions is very dangerous since certain substances are poisonous or very harmful even in minute quantities. They may be permitted to taste a very dilute solution of the weak NH_4OH. Have them rub a drop of the diluted hydroxides between the fingers but insist that they thoroughly wash their hands with water immediately after each test. Warn them that frequent and thorough washing is a necessity in the laboratory since certain bases are caustic substances and that even very small quantities brought accidentally in contact with the eye may have dangerous and harmful effects. Have them read the labels on a bottle of household ammonia and on a can of lye and note the treatment for accidental external contact and internal consumption. Have them read the label on a bottle of commercial "milk of magnesia" and note its antacid use and properties. Demonstrate how baking soda solid and solution may be used in dealing with accidents with acids. A few drops of concentrated acid may be spilled on the demonstration table, sponged with large quantities of water, and then sponged with a solution of $NaHCO_3$. The reading of such labels as mentioned before can have valuable impact as motivation for the study of neutralization. Students can insert strips of blue and red litmus paper into the samples; test with colorless and red phenolphthalein and perhaps other indicators (see 8.4f). Students should keep a record of their observations. You may also want to have students test acid substances (vinegar, lemon juice, soda pop, etc.) at home. Acid reaction with bases to form salts and water is covered later in this chapter.

General preparation of acids. Show that nonmetallic oxides combine with water to form acids. Place a pinch of sulfur in a deflagrating spoon (lined with asbestos) and heat in a Bunsen burner. When the sulfur ignites, lower the spoon into a wide-mouth bottle containing 25 cc of water. Be sure that the spoon does not touch the water. Cover the bottle with a square of glass as completely as possible. After the sulfur has burned, remove the spoon and stopper the bottle so that you can shake it to dissolve as much of the sulfur dioxide as possible. Test the water with red and blue litmus paper and with colorless and red phenolphthalein.

You may want to repeat this demonstration using a very small piece of red phosphorus.

8.4b Bases

Properties of bases. Prepare dilute solutions of several bases such as ammonium, calcium, potassium, and sodium hydroxide by adding a few drops of a concentrated solution of each to individual test tubes containing about 15 cc of distilled water. What is the feel of a hydroxide when rubbed between the fingers?

Test with indicators: red and blue litmus paper, red and colorless phenolphthalein, and others (Table 8–5). Reaction with acids to form salts is covered later in this chapter in 8.4c.

General preparation of bases. Students should understand that active metals and their oxides give basic water solutions (hydroxides). To 15 cc of water add a lump of calcium oxide (not powdered). Test the resulting solution with litmus and phenolphthalein.

Carefully add a very small piece of metallic sodium (size of a small pea) to a beaker half full of water. Use a sodium spoon to place the sodium under water.

(*Caution: The reaction between sodium and water is very vigorous, even explosive.*) With a test tube holder invert a test tube over the sodium to try to catch some of the evolving gas, and test the gas with a lighted splint. Also test the water with litmus and phenolphthalein. See 7.2c for related procedures.

You may also want to hold a strip of magnesium ribbon with a forceps, ignite it, and dissolve the white solid in a small amount of water. Heat the water to dissolve the solid and test with litmus and phenolphthalein.

Students will want to test various basic substances (ammonia water, strong and weak soap, washing soda, etc.) at home.

8.4c   Salts

Properties of salts in solution. Have students add a pinch of table salt to a

TABLE 8-5
pH range and colors of standard indicators*

name of indicator	pH interval	color change	solvent
methyl violet	0.2 — 3.0	yellow, blue, violet	water
thymol blue	1.2 — 2.8	red to yellow	water (+ NaOH)
benzopurpurin 4B	1.2 — 4.0	violet to red	20% alcohol
methyl orange	3.1 — 4.4	red to orange yellow	water
bromphenol blue	3.0 — 4.6	yellow to blue violet	water (+ NaOH)
congo red	3.0 — 5.0	blue to red	70% alcohol
bromcresol green	3.8 — 5.4	yellow to blue	water (+ NaOH)
methyl red	4.4 — 6.2	red to yellow	water (+ NaOH)
chlorphenol red	4.8 — 6.8	yellow to red	water (+ NaOH)
bromcresol purple	5.2 — 6.8	yellow to purple	water (+ NaOH)
litmus	4.5 — 8.3	red to blue	water
bromthymol blue	6.0 — 7.6	yellow to blue	water (+ NaOH)
phenol red	6.8 — 8.2	yellow to red	water (+ NaOH)
thymol blue	8.0 — 9.6	yellow to blue	water (+ NaOH)
phenolphthalein	8.3 — 10.0	colorless to red	70% alcohol
thymolphthalein	9.3 — 10.5	yellow to blue	70% alcohol
alizarin yellow R	10.0 — 12.0	yellow to red	95% alcohol
indigo carmine	11.4 — 13.0	blue to yellow	50% alcohol
trinitrobenzene	12.0 — 14.0	colorless to orange	70% alcohol

* From Malm and Frantz, *Teacher's Manual for College Chemistry,* 1958.

clean evaporating dish, stir the salt solution, and test with litmus and phenolphthalein. Have them taste this neutral solution. Then evaporate the sample to dryness; let them taste the crystals.

Have students find out whether all salts react the same way to litmus and phenolphthalein. Before class a laboratory squad might prepare dilute solutions of many salts for the class to test: sodium chloride, sodium carbonate, sodium nitrate, potassium bromide, ferric chloride, copper sulfate are examples. This might lead to a study of hydrolysis (see below).

General preparation of salts. The following general reactions yield salts.

1. the direct union of their elements, e.g., sodium and chlorine

$$2\,Na + Cl_2 \rightarrow 2\,NaCl$$

2. an acid and a metal, e.g., zinc and dilute HCl

$$Zn + 2[H^+ + Cl^-] \rightarrow H_2 + [Zn^{++} + 2Cl^-]$$

3. an acid and a hydroxide, e.g., sodium hydroxide and dilute HCl

$$[Na^+ + OH^-] + [H^+ + Cl^-] \rightarrow H_2O + [Na^+ + Cl^-]$$

4. an acid and a metallic oxide, e.g., copper oxide and sulfuric acid

$$CuO + [2H^+ + SO_4^=] \rightarrow H_2O + [Cu^{++} + SO_4^=]$$

5. an acid and a salt, e.g., sodium carbonate and hydrochloric acid

$$[2\,Na^+ + CO_3^=] + 2\,[H^+ + Cl^-] \rightarrow H_2O + CO_2 + 2\,[Na^+ + Cl^-]$$

6. a salt and another salt, e.g., silver nitrate and sodium chloride

$$[Ag^+ + NO_3^-] + [Na^+ + Cl^-] \rightarrow AgCl\downarrow + [Na^+ + NO_3^-]$$

7. a metallic oxide and a nonmetallic oxide, e.g., calcium oxide and carbon dioxide

$$CaO + CO_2 \rightarrow CaCO_3$$

Hydrolysis of salts. Hydrolysis of a salt to form a *base* can be demonstrated by adding sodium carbonate to water; test with litmus or other indicator.

$$Na_2CO_3 + H_2O = 2\,Na^+ + OH^- + HCO_3^-$$

Hydrolysis of a salt to form an *acid* can be demonstrated by adding ammonium chloride to water; test with a blue litmus solution or other indicator.

$$NH_4Cl + H_2O = NH_4OH + H^+ + Cl^-$$

8.4d   *Properties of ionic solutions*

Conductivity of pure water and solutions. You may want to illustrate conductivity of a solution at this time. Use a standard electrical conduction apparatus or prepare the one shown in Fig. 8–6. Take two carbon rods from flashlight cells and heat to drive out the wax used in sealing the cell. Mount them in a $2'' \times 3''$ wood or plastic block supported in a clamp on a ring stand. Connect the rods with small battery or alligator clips in series with a porcelain socket containing a 10 or 15 watt bulb and a 110-volt a.c. or d.c. source. Prepare a series of containers filled with: distilled water; tap water; sodium chloride $(0.1\ \mathcal{N})$[6]; sugar $(0.1\ \mathcal{N})$; copper sulfate $(0.1\ \mathcal{N})$; hydroxides such as $(0.1\ \mathcal{N})$ ammonium potassium, and sodium hydroxide; acetic acid $(0.1\ \mathcal{N})$; and glacial acetic acid.

Test the conductivity of various solutions by lowering the rods into small glass jars containing the solutions (be sure to rinse off the rods after each test). Com-

[6] For preparation, see 8.3b and 8.3c of this chapter.

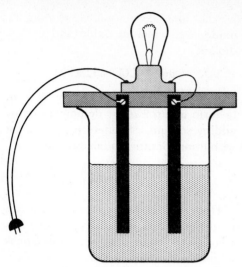

Fig. 8–6 Conductivity apparatus.

ml of 0.1 *N* sodium hydroxide; the other is filled with 50 ml of 0.1 *N* hydrochloric acid. (See 8.3b and 8.3c for a discussion of molar and normal solutions and their preparation.)

You may want to demonstrate the use of an indicator such as phenolphthalein by adding a drop or two to a 10-ml sample of the dilute acid in a beaker. Stand the beaker on white filter paper under the burette containing NaOH. Demonstrate to students how to add a drop at a time of the NaOH from the burette and stir the acid solution with a stirring rod. Students should notice that the color change which occurs where the base strikes the acid disappears when the solution is stirred. Approximately 10 ml of the alkaline are added to the 10 ml of hydrochloric acid in the beaker. Stop adding the alkali when the color change becomes permanent. Test with red and blue litmus paper, too. Have students explain what is meant by a neutral solution and what is meant by end point.

Students may now pour 5 cc of the neutralized solution into an evaporating dish and heat to dryness after adding 1 extra drop of HCl since some is lost in boiling. Examine and taste the residue.

As a special project, a student might want to learn the extent to which grape juice, red cabbage juice, or raspberry juice might be used as indicators.

If there is a shortage of burettes, you may prefer the following procedure. Prepare a dilute solution of hydrochloric acid by adding 5 cc of the 0.1 *N* acid to 20 cc of water; stir with a glass rod. In a watch-glass place 5 cc of limewater, $Ca(OH)_2$. To this add a drop of phenolphthalein and note the red color. Students can use a medicine dropper to add the dilute acid a drop at a time to the base, stirring the solution as they do so. Point out that this technique is called *titration*. How many

pare the results with tap water, distilled water, and solutions of sugar, salts, acids, and bases. The degree of brightness of the bulb is a measure of the conductivity of the solution. Fairly accurate measurements of conduction in very poor or extremely dilute conductors can be made by substituting a milliammeter (or a galvanometer in series with a selenium rectifier if a.c. is used) in place of the bulb.

It is important to have students keep a record of the solutions which are good, fair, or poor conductors, as well as nonconductors. (Be sure to rinse the electrodes as they are transferred from one solution to the other.)

Students can also use this simple apparatus to show the effect of *concentration* upon conduction of current. Use several different concentrations of salts, bases, and acids. Also show that pure (undiluted) acids are not good conductors. Test conductivity of glacial acetic acid and then add progressively larger amounts of water.

8.4e Neutralization

Students working in small groups may prepare two burettes. One is filled with 50 drops are needed to decolorize the phenolphthalein? If this neutralized solution is heated over a water bath, students can examine the texture and taste of the residue.

Students can practice writing simple neutralization equations, using acids and bases, of the types below.

$$H_2SO_4 + 2\ NaOH \rightarrow Na_2SO_4 + 2\ H_2O$$
$$HCl + KOH \rightarrow KCl + H_2O$$
$$NaOH + HCl \rightarrow NaCl + H_2O$$
$$HNO_3 + KOH \rightarrow KNO_3 + H_2O$$

Chemically equivalent quantities. Some teachers treat neutralization (and titration) from the qualitative viewpoint, so that students get the idea that at neutralization (end point) chemically equivalent quantities of acid and base have reacted. A supplementary demonstration may take the form of neutralizing (titrating) 10 ml of acid of a different concentration such as 0.2 N HCl with the same standard 0.1 N NaOH. Students will intuitively decide that since twice the volume of the standard base was used, the acid concentration must be twice that of the previous acid (0.1 N) used. In effect they learn that

$$\text{Volume}_{(Acid)} \times \text{Concentration}_{(Acid)} =$$
$$\text{Volume}_{(Base)} \times \text{Concentration}_{(Base)}$$

since the total quantity (weight) of the acid substance is *chemically equivalent* to the total quantity (weight) of the basic substance.

A more rigorous mathematical treatment requires that students know the meaning of a chemical-equivalent (gram-equivalent weight) and can use concentration expressed in normality (and molarity) with some degree of comprehension. These concepts were treated in 8.3b. The writing of molecular neutralization equations may serve as the basis for the development of deeper comprehension of such concepts. After the initial demonstrations

or experiments on neutralization, students can write such equations as

$$NaOH + HCl \rightarrow NaCl + H_2O$$
$$2\ NaOH + H_2SO_4 \rightarrow Na_2SO_4 + 2\ H_2O$$
$$3\ NaOH + H_3PO_4 \rightarrow Na_3PO_4 + 3\ H_2O$$

They may be asked to interpret the meanings of these equations in terms of the number of moles of base reacting with the number of moles of acid, finding that 1 mole of NaOH will neutralize 1 mole of HCl but that 2 and 3 moles, respectively, are required for complete neutralization of 1 mole each of H_2SO_4 and H_3PO_4. Volume for volume, a 1 M solution of H_2SO_4 has twice the base-neutralizing ability of a 1 M solution of HCl. This may be demonstrated by a titration using 0.1 M solutions of H_2SO_4 and NaOH.

In neutralization, the net reaction is $H^+ + OH^- \rightarrow H_2O$; 1.008 grams of H^+ is chemically equivalent to and will react with 17.008 grams of OH^-. This may lead to the concept of equivalent weights of acids and bases and consequently to the definitions of normal solutions. Volume for volume, a solution of any acid of a given normality is chemically equivalent to a solution of any base of the same normality. This leads to the principles developed in 8.3b, dealing with normal solutions.

Titration is the process of determining the concentration and, if necessary, the total quantity of the acid or base in an unknown. This process is carried out volumetrically, using a standard solution of known concentration and an indicator. The end point may be determined by means other than indicators; one such procedure, based on the electrical measurement of conductivity, is known as electrolytic titration. The process of titration may also be used to study oxidation-reduction reactions colorimetrically using indicators or by making electrical measurements. Details of such procedures are described in advanced texts on qualitative and quantitative analysis (see appendix).

Electrolytic titration. Take two platinum wire or sheet electrodes (or pieces of stainless steel cut from an old knife blade) and hang each of them from a piece of glass tubing inserted in each of the holes of a two-hole stopper. Solder wires to the electrodes; paint the soldered joint with asphaltum or molten paraffin. Connect the electrodes in series with a milliammeter, a rheostat, and a low-voltage battery. The stopper containing the electrodes is held in a clamp so that the electrodes can be dipped into various solutions.

One test that may be used involves dipping the electrodes into a concentrated solution of $Ba(OH)_2$ with a few drops of phenolphthalein. (The solution will be pink.) At 6 volts, the meter will read about 10 milliamperes. With the electrodes still in solution, add 3 N H_2SO_4 slowly until the meter reads zero: this is the point of neutralization. Note that the phenolphthalein turned colorless *before* the neutralization point was reached. This indicates that the point at which phenolphthalein changes color is not the neutral point, pH 7, but rather on the basic side of neutral (actually, it is pH 8–10).

You may also want to have students practice using this apparatus in other neutralization reactions. Start with a base and add acid, or vice versa. Students should observe the meter reading of various acids and bases; they should be able to explain the observations. The neutralization point is the point at which the meter reads zero. You may also want to have students try testing various acid-base indicators such as litmus, methyl red, congo red, bromthymol blue, and so forth to see if they indicate true neutral (pH 7) or have a more acid or more basic end point. (For indicators see 8.4f and 8.4g.) Students should recognize that an indicator that does not show pH 7 end point is still useful.

8.4f Indicators

An indicator is usually a weak acid. Its general formula may be represented as H*In*. This weak acid dissociates slightly to form a hydrogen ion and the indicator anion, *In*⁻. In the case of phenolphthalein, the molecular form of the acid, H*In*, is colorless while the anion is colored red. The addition of hydrogen ions represses the ionization of the indicator acid with the formation of the colorless molecular species. The addition of base (OH^- ion) causes more acid to dissociate, thereby increasing the concentration of the colored anion.

Marked color changes in indicator solutions occur when the strategic change in the hydrogen ion concentration takes place. The table of indicators (Table 8–5) states the pH range during which the marked change in color takes place and gives the colors marking the transition in concentration.

Indicator behavior and common ion effect. Where teachers choose to present an explanation of indicator action, the following demonstration may be made the basis of the explanation. The demonstration shows the effect of a common ion (anion) on the concentration of the hydrogen ion concentration of a weak acid and hence a change in indicator color.

Add a drop of methyl orange to 10 ml of 1 M acetic acid, resulting in a red (pink) color. Add a few crystals of sodium acetate, stir, and note that the color changes to orange-yellow (pH interval is 3.1, red, to 4.4, orange-yellow).

The preparation of indicator solutions[7]

Methyl violet, 0.05%: Dissolve 0.5 g of the dye in one liter of water.

[7] Adapted from L. E. Malm and H. W. Frantz, *College Chemistry in the Laboratory*, No. 2, teacher's edition with instruction manual, Freeman, 1958.

Methyl orange, 0.1%: Dissolve 1.0 g of the dye in one liter of water.

Methyl red, 0.1%: Grind 1.0 g of the dye with 37 ml of 0.1 F NaOH in a mortar to dissolve it; add water to dilute this to one liter.

Bromcresol purple, 0.1%: Grind 1.0 g of the dye, dibromo-o-cresol-sulfonphthalein, with 18.5 ml of 0.1 F NaOH in a mortar to dissolve it; add water to dilute this to one liter.

Bromthymol blue, 0.1%: Grind 1.0 g of the dye, dibromothymolsulfonphthalein, with 16.0 ml of 0.1 F NaOH in a mortar to dissolve it; add water to dilute this to one liter.

Phenol red, 0.1%: Grind 1.0 g of the dye, phenolsulfonphthalein, with 28.2 ml of 0.1 F NaOH in a mortar to dissolve it; add water to dilute this to one liter.

Phenolphthalein, 0.1%: Dissolve 1.0 g of the dye in 700 ml of 95% ethyl alcohol and dilute to one liter with water.

Alizarin yellow R, 0.1%: Dissolve 1.0 g of the dye, sodium nitrobenzeneazosalicylate, in 200 ml of 95% ethyl alcohol; add water to dilute this to one liter.

Indigo carmine, 0.1%: Dissolve 1.0 g of the dye, sodium indigo-disulfonate, in 500 ml of 95% ethyl alcohol; add water to dilute this to one liter. (While this dye is readily soluble in water alone, such a water solution does not keep well.)

The meaning of pH. Pure water has an extremely small conductivity and therefore is very slightly ionized. This slight conductivity may be demonstrated by using a conductivity apparatus with neon tube in place of the regular bulb. Only one molecule in every 555,000,000 ionizes. The equilibrium constant may be expressed most simply by the expression

$$K = \frac{[H^+] \times [OH^-]}{[H_2O]} =$$
$$1.8 \times 10^{-16} \text{ moles of ionized water per mole of water}$$

The units represented by the square brackets are moles per liter.

Since the concentration of the hydrogen (hydronium ion) and the hydroxide is so very small, it may be disregarded when computing the amount of ionized water in a liter. There are 55.5 moles of water in a liter. The ion-product constant for water, $K_w = |H^+| \times |OH^-| = 1 \times 10^{-14}$, is obtained by multiplying the equilibrium constant, 1.8×10^{-16}, by the molar concentration of water, 55.5 moles.

Since the hydroxyl ion concentration is the same as the hydrogen ion concentration, the ion-product constant for water may be written as

$$X \times X = 1 \times 10^{-14}$$
$$X^2 = 1 \times 10^{-14}$$
$$X = 1 \times 10^{-7}$$

Therefore the concentration of each ion (hydrogen and hydroxyl) in pure water is 1×10^{-7} moles per liter. This is the situation in a neutral solution. If the concentration of the hydrogen ion in solution is increased, the concentration of the hydroxyl ion decreases. For example, if the hydrogen ion concentration is increased tenfold to 1×10^{-6}, the concentration of the hydroxyl ion decreases correspondingly to 1×10^{-8}, since the ion-product of water remains constant at 1×10^{-14}.

The acidity or alkalinity of a solution may therefore be represented by such an expression as $[H^+] = 1 \times 10^{-4}$. However, such a system is inconvenient and has been replaced by the pH system, which was suggested by Sorenson. By definition, the pH of a solution is the logarithm of the reciprocal of the concentration of the hydrogen ion $[H^+]$.

$$pH = \log \frac{1}{[H^+]} \text{ or } pH = -\log [H^+]$$

Thus, if $[H^+] = 1 \times 10^{-4}$, then the pH of the solution is 4.

$$pH = \log \frac{1}{1 \times 10^{-4}} = \log 10^4 = 4$$

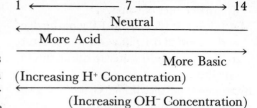

The pH of a neutral solution is 7. This means that the quantity of hydrogen (hydronium) ion is 1×10^{-7} mole or 0.0000001 gram per liter and that the quantity of hydroxyl ions is 1×10^{-7} mole or 0.0000017 gram per liter. In 10 million liters of water there is one mole of H^+ ions (1.008 gram) and one mole of OH^- ions (17.008 gram). These weights of the respective ions represent the weight of the Avogadro number (6.02×10^{23}) of each type of ion. This is a natural property of water. Divided down this means that in

one liter of water (which is $\frac{1}{10,000,000}$ of

10 million liters) there would be $\frac{1}{10,000,000}$

of a gram of hydrogen (H^+) ion. This fraction is expressed exponentially as 1×10^{-7} which is the number of grams per liter (moles per liter) of hydrogen ion present in neutral water. The pH of an acid solution is less than 7 and that of an alkaline solution is more than 7.

A decrease in the numerical value of pH indicates an increase in H^+ ions. If the pH of water is neutral, pH 7, then a tenfold increase in H^+ ion content would give a 10^{-6} concentration of hydrogen ions (pH 6). If the pH were 3, it would indicate that the hydrogen ion concentration was 10,000 times that of a neutral solution, that is, a fairly strong acid. Notice that the changes in pH are logarithmic, that is, increase in multiples of 10.

In a practical sense students easily learn to use pH values as an index of hydrogen ion concentration and hence as a measure of the acidity or alkalinity of a solution. The simple schematic device, represented as follows,

is readily developed by a series of demonstrations.

Use the usual conductivity apparatus with a lamp to show differences, if any, between solutions of the strong acids (HCl, H_2SO_4, HNO_3) and acetic acid; and between solutions of strong bases ($NaOH$ and KOH) and NH_4OH. Solutions of the same normality (0.1 N is one possible concentration) should be used. Other substances which may be tested include boric acid, barium hydroxide, and calcium hydroxide (0.04 N is the limiting concentration for $Ca(OH)_2$ because of its relative insolubility).

Test the same solutions with an ammeter replacing the lamp. Test solutions with litmus and with hydrion paper or with a universal indicator (Gramercy is one such).

Start with glacial acetic acid and test with conductivity apparatus and show effects of progressive dilutions. Use conductivity apparatus with argon and neon bulbs. Test conductivity of tap water, distilled water, or ion-exchange processed water with neon bulbs.

These demonstrations establish the fact that different acids and bases have varying degrees of ionization. The results are interpreted in the light of the series of tables (Table 8–6). The pH of various substances shown in Table 8–6 C may be demonstrated by using hydrion paper, a universal indicator, or selected indicators listed in the table of indicators (Table 8–5). These results are used to demon-

TABLE 8-6
Degrees of ionization and pH values for common substances

A   Degree of ionization (solution at 18° C)

acid		base	
nitric	0.82	potassium hydroxide	0.77
hydrofluoric	0.784	sodium hydroxide	0.73
sulfuric	0.51	barium hydroxide	0.69
hydrofluoric	0.07	lithium hydroxide	0.63
acetic	0.004	ammonium hydroxide	0.004

B   Relative degree of ionization of some acids and bases

ACIDS			BASES	
completely or nearly completely ionized	*moderately ionized*	*slightly ionized*	*completely or nearly completely ionized*	*slightly ionized*
nitric	oxalic	hydrofluoric	potassium hydroxide	ammonium hydroxide
hydrochloric	phosphoric	acetic	sodium hydroxide	all others
sulfuric	sulfurous	carbonic	barium hydroxide	
hydriodic		hydrosulfuric	strontium hydroxide	
hydrobromic		all others	calcium hydroxide	

C   pH values for equivalent (0.1 N) solutions

hydrochloric acid	1.1	alum	3.2	ammonia	11.1
sulfuric acid	1.2	boric acid	5.2	sodium carbonate	11.6
orthophosphoric acid	1.5	pure water	7.0	trisodium phosphate	12.0
citric acid	2.2	sodium bicarbonate	8.4	sodium hydroxide	13.0
acetic acid	2.9	borax	9.2	potassium hydroxide	13.0

D   pH values of some acids and bases (0.1 N)

acid	pH	base	pH
hydrochloric	1.1	sodium bicarbonate	8.4
sulfuric	1.2	ammonia	11.1
acetic	2.9	sodium carbonate	11.6
boric	5.2	sodium hydroxide	13.0

E   Approximate pH values of some common substances

apples	3.0	maple syrup	6.7
cabbage	5.3	saliva (human)	7.0
carrots	5.0	sauerkraut	3.5
ginger ale	2–5	shrimp	7.0
cow's milk	6.5	tomatoes	4.2
lemons	2.3	cherries	3.6
milk of magnesia	10.5	human urine	4.8–8.4

strate hydrolysis, and the molecular and ionic equations representing the process are developed. Litmus is commonly used as the indicator but in many cases fails to show many of the pH differences. One simple demonstration using litmus consists of rapidly dipping large strips of red litmus paper into solutions of sodium bicarbonate and sodium carbonate. The concentrations are not critical. The immediate removal of the dipped litmus paper results in pale blue for the bicarbonate and the usual deeper blue for the carbonate.

8.4g   Preparation of buffer solutions[8]

Sometimes when teaching the use of indicators and the general subject of pH you will need solutions whose pH is known beforehand. Students can then take samples and seek to determine their pH by whatever methods are currently being studied.

Clark and Lubs stock solutions. You will need to prepare the following five solutions. These mixed with each other in the varying proportions listed in Table 8–7 will make up solutions from pH 4 through pH 10. In each case you add enough water to make up a liter. It should be noted that none of these buffer solutions need preservatives to prevent mold formation. Naturally you will want to check the solutions with a pH meter if one is available.

Solution 1. Sodium hydroxide, 0.1 N, prepared carbonate-free and standardized according to the usual volumetric procedure, 4 g to the liter.

Solution 2. Potassium acid phthalate, 0.1 M, prepared by dissolving 20.42 g of $KHC_8H_4O_4$ per liter.

Solution 3. Monopotassium phosphate, 0.1 M, prepared by dissolving 13.62 g of KH_2PO_4 per liter.

Solution 4. Potassium chloride, 0.1 M, prepared by dissolving 7.46 g of KCl per liter.

Solution 5. Boric acid, 0.1 M, prepared by dissolving 6.2 g of H_3BO_3 in the 0.1 M KCl (Solution 4) to make a liter.

McIlvaine's stock solutions. These four solutions each require 3 to 5 ml of toluene as an additive to inhibit the growth of mold. With these solutions you can make up mixtures whose pH varies from 4 through 11. Table 8–8 lists the proportions for each pH level. In each case the final solution will equal 1000 ml so that water does not need to be added.

Solution A. Citric acid, 0.1 F: Dissolve 21.0 g of $H_3C_6H_5O_7 \cdot H_2O$ in distilled water and dilute to one liter. Add 3 to 5 ml of toluene to the solution to prevent the growth of mold.

Solution B. Disodium phosphate, 0.2 F: Dissolve 71.6 g of $Na_2HPO_4 \cdot 12H_2O$ in distilled water and dilute to one liter.

Solution C. Borax, 0.05 F: Dissolve 19.07 g of $Na_2B_4O_7 \cdot 10H_2O$ in distilled water and dilute to one liter.

Solution D. Sodium carbonate, 0.05 F: Dissolve 5.30 g of Na_2CO_3 in distilled water and dilute to one liter.

8.4h   Specific gravity determinations

A typical way of quickly determining the strength of a solution is the specific gravity method using a hydrometer. A storage battery and a battery hydrometer

TABLE 8-7
Clark and Lubs solutions—mixing proportions for varying pH

pH	solution 1	solution 2	solution 3	solution 5
4	4.0 ml	500 ml		
5	238.5	500		
6	57.0		500 ml	
7	296.3		500	
8	39.7			500 ml
9	213.0			500 ml
10	439			500 ml

[8] Adapted from the *Teacher's Manual for College Chemistry in the Laboratory*, No. 2, by Malm and Frantz (W. H. Freeman, San Francisco, Cal., 1958.)

TABLE 8-8
McIlvaine's solutions—mixing proportions for varying pH

pH	solution A	solution B	solution C	solution D
4	615 ml	385 ml		
5	485	515		
6	368	632		
7	176	824		
8	27	973		
9			1000 ml	
10			225	775 ml
11				1000

offer an example of this method. A fully charged acid storage battery contains about 20% sulfuric acid with a specific gravity of 1.270. In a discharged battery the solution has a specific gravity of about 1.100 with a concentration of sulfuric acid slightly above 10%. Since water has a specific gravity of 1, anything above 1 represents the relative ratio of the solute. From this you can determine the percentage of a solution with a specific gravity higher than 1.

8.4i Colorimetric analysis

Colorimetric determinations are not very accurate unless special and expensive equipment such as a colorimeter or spectrophotometer is available. But the principle of this type of analysis can be taught quite readily. A modified version of Beer's law is useful: the color of a solution containing a colored ion deepens with increasing concentration.

Students may want to make a series of reference standards of, say, copper sulfate in water. They might proceed as follows. Take about 5 g of $CuSO_4$ and dissolve it in about 10 cc of water in a test tube. Pour half of this solution into a second test tube (of the same size) and add 5 cc of water. Repeat, diluting each new solution half and half with water until almost no color is visible. Calculate the concentration of each solution and label the tubes.

If the students are now given an "unknown" solution of copper sulfate, they can compare it (against a sheet of white paper) with their "standards" and estimate its composition.

As a project, a student may want to set up a series of buffer solutions (see 8.4g) of known pH and add a specific quantity of a particular indicator to each, for use as reference standards in measuring pH. Quantitative analysis texts will provide the details.

8.4j Gravimetric analysis

Gravimetric analyses depend on the fact that many ionic reactions go essentially to completion if there is a slight excess of one reagent. The simple qualitative test for the presence of chloride ion can be turned into an appropriate analysis for high school work.

If students are given a dilute silver nitrate solution and a known quantity of an "unknown" chloride solution, they can proceed as for a volumetric titration. Dripping the silver nitrate solution into the chloride will produce a white precipitate of silver chloride. The process should be continued until no more precipitate will form. A slight excess of the silver nitrate should be added. The precipitate is then filtered out, dried by heating, and weighed. From this weight the percentage of chlorine in the sample can be calculated.

For example, if a sample weighing 2.0 grams yields a precipitate of silver chloride weighing 4.9 grams, the percentage of chlorine in the sample was

$$\frac{35.5 \times 4.9}{143.3 \times 2.0} = .606 = 60.6\%$$

CAPSULE LESSONS

Ways to get started in class

8-1. What kinds of oxides form bases? Acids? Weigh out 0.5 gram of calcium oxide, place in a dry test tube, and add 5 cc of water. Then test with red and blue litmus paper. Elicit from students the kind of ions present.

Repeat this procedure on other metallic oxides; also use nonmetallic oxides and have students draw conclusions. For example, add 3 cc of water to a very small quantity of phosphorus pentoxide. (*Caution: Do not touch.*) Test with blue and red litmus paper. What ions are present?

8-2. Develop the notion of pH by a titration to determine the percentage of acid in vinegar. This may be a demonstration or a laboratory activity. Test for the presence of acids in vegetables.

8-3. You may want to have a group of students prepare a standard set of tubes at different levels of pH. Then students may use an indicator to determine the pH of aquarium water, drinking water, saliva, milk, samples of soil from different regions or from different layers in one region. To test soil mix about half a jar of soil with a quarter jar of water, shake, and filter the water. The water is then tested with an indicator. What is the effect of pH on the uptake of chemicals from the soil?

You may want to demonstrate the effect of an acidic environment on the digestion of proteins by pepsin (use an alkaline as a control).

8-4. Demonstrate buffers by making up several solutions of known pH and then mixing these to produce neutrality. Or mix a series of known pH solutions, and add phenolphthalein or some other indicator to show how color changes with pH.

8-5. What is meant by neutralization? You may begin a lesson by having students combine equal quantities of equal-strength HCl and NaOH. Does the resulting solution show acidic properties? Basic? Can it be distinguished from an equal-strength solution of NaCl?

8-6. Show the ability of solutions to conduct electricity by using the apparatus described in this chapter in 8.4d.

8-7. Develop a lesson to show the need for indicators. Plan to have students use several indicators to test the pH range and usefulness of specific indicators for specific situations. For example, use indicators from both the acid and base ranges.

8-8. Have students establish a definition of hydrolysis in this way. They may prepare a few cc of salt solutions to which a few drops of universal indicator are added. These can be compared with a standard set of pH levels (8.4f) to find the approximate pH of the salt solutions. You may want to use several of these salts in solutions: ammonium chloride, ammonium sulfate, sodium carbonate (washing soda), potassium nitrate.

8-9. You may want students to devise ways to show whether size of materials (for example, powdered copper sulfate and an equal quantity of unground sulfate in water) affects the rate of solubility, or whether a rise in temperature affects the rate of solubility.

PEOPLE, PLACES, AND THINGS

If possible, plan a trip to an analytical chemical laboratory at a local plant or at a nearby college or university. Some teachers draw upon these sources to borrow equipment, books, or films for high school classes or club work.

Local hospital technicians or analytical chemists are generally eager to cooperate with bright students who wish to undertake a special project.

BOOKS AND PAMPHLETS

These are only a few of the books which are pertinent to the work discussed in this chapter. These and many other references classified by subject and with complete bibliographical data are given in the bibliography at the end of the book.

American Chem. Soc., *Physical Properties of Chemical Compounds,* Washington, D.C., 1955.

Arthur, P., *Analytical Chemistry,* McGraw-Hill, 1957.

Ayres, G. H., *Quantitative Chemical Analysis,* Harper, 1958.

Basolo, F., and R. Pearson, *Mechanisms of Inorganic Reactions: A Study of Metal Complexes in Solution,* Wiley, 1958.

Deming, H., *General Chemistry,* Wiley, 1955.

King, E. J., *Qualitative Analysis and Electrolytic Solutions,* Harcourt, Brace, 1959.

Lange, N., *Handbook of Chemistry,* 9th ed., Handbook Publishers, 1956.

Meyer, L., *Laboratory Manual for Introductory Chemistry,* Macmillan, 1952.

Robinson, R., and R. Stokes, *Electrolyte Solutions,* Academic, 1955.

Sarton, G., *A History of Science,* Harvard U. Press, 1959.

Swift, E., *Introductory Quantitative Analysis,* Prentice-Hall, 1954.

Wagner, W., C. Hull, and G. Markle, *Advanced Analytical Chemistry,* Reinhold, 1956.

FILMS AND FILMSTRIPS

This partial list is intended only as a guide toward film and filmstrip selection. Refer to the more complete listing at the end of the book where films are classified by subject and where a key to abbreviations and addresses of distributors are given. The cost of film rental, of course, is subject to change. Films are sound and black and white unless otherwise specified.

Colloids (f, s), Indiana, $2.00.

Colloids (f, s), EBF, $2.50.

Crystals Under The Microscope (f, s), Almanac, $2.00.

Electro Chemistry (f, s), Indiana, $2.00.

Ionization (f, s, c), Coronet, inquire local film library.

Solutions (f, s, c), Coronet, inquire local film library.

FREE AND INEXPENSIVE MATERIALS

This is only a partial listing of free and inexpensive materials available to the teacher at this time. A directory of addresses is given at the end of the book. Many of these materials are distributed to teachers without charge. Where there is a small fee, the cost is indicated, although the prices are subject to change. While we recommend the material for use in the classroom, we do not necessarily endorse the products advertised.

Chemicals from Minerals, Manufacturing Chemists Assoc., free.

Chemistry: The Conquest of Materials, K. Hutton, Pelican, 1957, $.85.

First Aid Manual, American Medical Assoc., Chicago, $.10.

Laboratory Emergency Chart; Handbook for Chemistry Assistants, Fisher Scientific Co., free.

Scientific Experiments in Chemistry, Manufacturing Chemists Assoc., inquire price.

CHAPTER 9

The chemistry of sulfur,

phosphorus, carbon, and silicon

Many minerals, other than metals and metallic ores, found in the earth's crust play an essential role in our everyday life. Among the most important is sulfur, which is used to manufacture sulfuric acid—fundamental in our industrial world. In fact, the consumption of sulfuric acid has been used as an index of our industrial development. A modern plant produces in one day more acid than the plant of 150 years ago could produce in a year.

In this chapter, techniques are developed for presenting the important nonmetallic products of the earth's crust—sulfur, phosphorus, carbon,[1] silicon, and some of their compounds.

9.1 The chemistry of sulfur

9.1a Forms of sulfur

You may want to have students observe the differences among the rhombic, monoclinic, and amorphous forms of sulfur. All these allotropic forms can be prepared in class.

Rhombic crystals. Powder about 1 g of rhombic (roll) sulfur and dissolve in 6 ml of carbon disulfide, CS_2. Pour into a watch

[1] In this chapter we shall present only the inorganic compounds and the element itself; for organic compounds, see Chapter 14.

glass and permit the liquid to evaporate in a hood or on the sill of an open window. To slow down evaporation and thereby produce larger crystals, cover the watch glass with a beaker (open end down), with one portion of the beaker lip resting on a pencil. (*Caution: Carbon disulfide is very inflammable and therefore no open flame should be present in the vicinity of the demonstration.*) The crystals may be examined with a magnifier hand lens. A few drops of the solution on a microscope slide may be viewed under low magnification as the process of evaporation occurs.

Monoclinic (prismatic) crystals. Prepare monoclinic sulfur by gently heating about 200 grams of powdered sulfur in a wide porcelain dish. As some of the sulfur changes to a liquid, add more powdered sulfur. The color should remain pale yellow. If it turns dark, it has been overheated and the procedure should be repeated with fresh sulfur and gentler heating. Let the material cool without lifting it off the ring stand. When a crust about 1/16 inch thick forms, carefully punch at least 2 holes through the crust with an ordinary iron nail. Then pour out the lower layer of hot sulfur through one of the holes. Now students can remove the crust from the crucible; they should observe the monoclinic sulfur crystals on the underside of the crust (Fig. 9–1).

Fill a test tube half full of small pieces of roll sulfur. Melt slowly and carefully. Have a student note that the solid initially melts to a lemon-yellow liquid (114.5° C). Do not let the liquid get much darker than this color. If spot overheating results in a darker color, cease heating briefly while gently shaking the test tube to permit better contact between the overheated and unheated or underheated portions of the contents. Pour into a folded filter paper. Have a student observe the formation of a crust on the surface. As soon as the crust forms, open the filter paper permitting excess liquid to run onto the table top. A mass of needle-like crystals remains on the filter paper; a sample may be observed with a hand lens.

Amorphous (plastic, elastic) sulfur. Fill a test tube half full of small pieces of roll sulfur (the same test tube used in the alternate procedure above may be used). Heat the test tube slowly and carefully, permitting students to observe successive changes from straw-yellow color at the melting point to a liquid form which becomes progressively redder. As this occurs, a point is finally reached at which the test tube may be inverted and held mouth downward with the red-brown material so viscous that it does not flow. Right the test tube and continue heating to a dark brown, almost black liquid. Continue to heat until the sulfur boils (445° C). Slowly pour the contents into a beaker of cold water, noting the formation of strands of amorphous sulfur. Permit this material to cool for about one minute. Remove the amorphous sulfur and show that the strands have slightly elastic properties. By the end of the period the mass has hardened, indicating the beginning of the process of returning to the rhombic—the most stable form of sulfur at room temperature. Be-

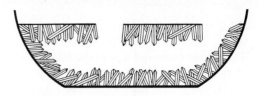

Fig. 9–1   Sulfur crystals in a crucible.

low 96° C all forms of sulfur revert to the rhombic form.

Both the rhombic and monoclinic forms of sulfur consist of crystals in which the fundamental building block is the sulfur molecule, an eight-membered puckered ring of sulfur atoms. The yellow liquid form known as λ (lambda sulfur), which forms just at the melting point, still consists of these eight-membered rings whose spherical shape permits them to roll over each other readily. The μ (mu sulfur) form of liquid sulfur forms at above 200° C. Apparently the eight-membered rings break open, thereby allowing the rings to join other broken rings to form long chains. The tangling of these chains results in increasing viscosity, and the increasing darkness of the material may be explained by the greater absorption of light by freed electrons. Then the chains break with decreasing viscosity and increasing darkness resulting before the boiling point. The sulfur vapor at 445° C again consists of S_8 molecules.

9.2   Chemical properties of sulfur

Place a piece of roll sulfur into an asbestos-sheet-lined deflagrating spoon. Ignite with the Bunsen burner flame and lower the burning sulfur into a 6-oz gas-collecting bottle. After approximately one minute remove the deflagrating spoon, cover the bottle with a cover plate, and extinguish the burning sulfur by plunging into a container of water. Have a student describe the odor of the sulfur dioxide formed. Pour

½″ of red or neutral litmus solution into the bottle, replace the cover, and shake. The litmus turns red due to the formation of the sulfurous acid solution. Alternatively, the bottle may be covered with a square of cardboard with a punched hole to accommodate the deflagrating spoon, and the SO_2 may be used to bleach a dilute solution of $KMnO_4$.

Heat some sulfur in a 6-inch test tube until it is boiling vigorously. Gradually insert a long thin strip of copper or copper foil, held with tongs, into the vapor with the formation of cupric sulfide (black). If some burning sulfur adheres when the strip is removed for inspection, extinguish the flame by plunging into water. Sulfur, like oxygen, supports the combustion of metals.

9.2a   Preparing zinc sulfide

Mix 1 g of zinc dust with an equal bulk (about ½ g) of flowers of sulfur in a mortar and pestle. Form a pointed cone of the mixture on an asbestos sheet. The instructor may ignite this tip with a Bunsen burner having a long piece of rubber connecting hose so that the instructor may retreat some five feet as soon as the mixture starts to fire. A safer procedure is to insert a magnesium ribbon fuse into the cone. The fuse (about 1½ inches long) may be ignited with a Bunsen flame. If the ends are frayed with a scissors, it may be ignited with a match flame. Students should stand across the room from the demonstration table since rapid combustion occurs with the formation of a large white cloud of ZnS which rises to the ceiling. On a larger scale, this demonstration makes a very dramatic replica of the mushroom A-bomb cloud and has been used on many occasions to simulate this effect. A demonstration on the formation of metallic sulfides by direct union consists of heating over a small Bun-

sen flame a bright silver quarter on which a small heap of flowers of sulfur has been placed. The silver blackens almost immediately. Bright silver coins may also be wrapped with rubber bands. Over a few days black Ag_2S will form due to the presence of sulfur in the rubber.

9.2b   Hydrogen sulfide

Preparation and properties. Since hydrogen sulfide is poisonous, it should be prepared in a hood (where possible) and the precautions to prevent unnecessary escape of the gas, indicated in Fig. 9–2, should be followed, including an end collecting bottle containing NaOH solution to absorb surplus H_2S. Three or four lumps of ferrous sulfide, FeS, are placed into the generator followed by enough dilute hydrochloric acid (6 M HCl) to cover the ferrous sulfide. Collect 1 bottle of the gas and replace the collecting bottle with a bottle containing about one inch of water to produce a saturated hydrosulfuric acid solution which may be used later in the production of metallic sulfides by precipitation (see below).

Insert a burning splint about two inches into a bottle of gas positioned mouth upward. Have students note that the flame goes out and that a yellow solid accumulates on the sides of the bottle toward the top. This demonstrates that sulfur is the product of the combustion of H_2S in a limited supply of air.

Replace the last two bottles in Fig. 9–2 with a jet tube and ignite the hydrogen sulfide. Permit the burning jet to impinge on the bottom of a small beaker which contains cold water and again note the formation of a sulfur deposit. Collect the products of combustion by holding the jet inside of a small beaker held in a semivertical position. After one minute identify the sulfur dioxide formed by careful odor

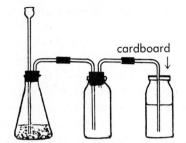

Fig. 9-2 Preparation of hydrogen sulfide gas.

test. Under these conditions, the more complete combustion of hydrogen sulfide yields sulfur dioxide among the products.

$$2 H_2S + O_2 \rightarrow 2 H_2O + 2 S$$
(limited air)
$$2 H_2S + 3 O_2 \rightarrow 2 H_2O + 2 SO_2$$
(unlimited air)

Extinguish the flame (it may be blown out or the jet may be removed). Fill the generator bottle with water, decant the liquid contents, flush down drain, and wash the FeS remaining in the generator with water to stop the action.

Metallic sulfides. To 5-ml portions of solutions of $AgNO_3$, $Cd(NO_3)_2$, $Pb(NO_3)_2$, $ZnSO_4$, $SbCl_3$, and $CuSO_4$ add 3–4 ml of the hydrosulfuric acid solution (see above). Note the production of colored sulfides which may be used to identify the metals in their salt solutions (Table 9–1). Prepare and collect bottles of H_2S and SO_2 (see 9.2c), cover with glass plates, and place the bottle of SO_2, mouth downward, on top of the bottle of H_2S. Remove the plates and note the coating of sulfur forming on the sides of the bottles.

TABLE 9-1
Sulfide precipitates

Sb	orange	Cu	black
As	yellow	Pb	black
Bi	brown	Ag	black
Cd	yellow	Zn	white

$$2 H_2S + SO_2 \rightarrow 2 H_2O + 3 S\downarrow$$

9.2c Sulfur dioxide

Although sulfur dioxide is poisonous, there is little likelihood that students will be poisoned by it, for even small quantities have a very sharp, choking odor.

Preparing sulfur dioxide by direct combination. The simplest method for preparing this dioxide, and the one that is used commercially, can be demonstrated by students. Burn sulfur in a large quantity of air or oxygen. In the classroom, you may want to use a little sulfur under a funnel as in Fig. 9–3.

$$S + O_2 \rightarrow SO_2$$

Laboratory preparation of sulfur dioxide. A common laboratory method uses the reaction of dilute sulfuric (or hydrochloric) acid upon sodium sulfite or sodium acid sulfite.

$$[Na_2^+ SO_3^=] + [H_2^+ SO_4^=] \rightarrow$$
$$[Na_2^+ SO_4^=] + H_2O + SO_2$$

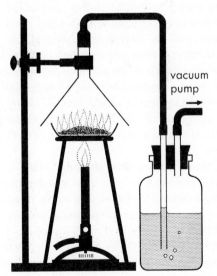

Fig. 9-3 Preparation of sulfur dioxide by burning sulfur.

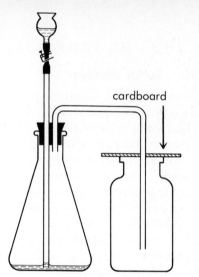

Fig. 9–4 Preparing sulfur dioxide by dropping hydrochloric or sulfuric acid into sodium sulfite.

$$[Na^+ HSO_3^-] + [H^+ Cl^-] \rightarrow$$
$$[Na^+ Cl^-] + H_2O + SO_2$$

Students may prepare a generator consisting of a dropping funnel of the commercial type, or the homemade apparatus in Fig. 9–4. Have them drop acid slowly and collect the gas in bottles by air displacement. Students should insert the delivery tube through a hole in a small square of cardboard to cover each bottle. After several bottles of gas have been collected, place the delivery tube into one inch of water in another bottle to prepare a water solution (sulfurous acid) which may be tested later with blue litmus paper and 1″ strip of magnesium ribbon in 5 ml of the solution which results in slow production of hydrogen.

Liquefying sulfur dioxide. This gas liquefies at −10° C. The low temperatures needed for liquefying sulfur dioxide can be obtained by preparing a mixture of 100 ml of acetone and small lumps (½–1″) of dry ice (Fig. 9–5). Stand a Pyrex test tube in the cooling mixture under a hood so that it receives sulfur dioxide from the delivery tube of the generator; arrange a small cardboard cover. You may prefer to use a tank of sulfur dioxide as the source of gas.

An alternate procedure is to use a small U-tube as a collector. The unliquefied gas is led into a concentrated solution of sodium hydroxide to prevent its escape into the room. This assembly also permits the delivery tube from the generator to be replaced by a stopper so that, when the liquid container is removed from the cooling mixture, it may be permitted to evaporate into the NaOH solution under the hood.

Some properties of sulfur dioxide

Forms an acid. Students can show that sulfur dioxide forms an acid when bubbled into or shaken with water.

$$SO_2 + H_2O \rightarrow [H_2SO_3] \leftrightarrows H^+ + HSO_3^-$$
$$H^+ + SO_3^=$$

Sulfurous acid (H_2SO_3) has not been isolated, but such a solution can yield sulfites and bisulfites on the addition of hydroxides. Whether the normal or the acid salt is produced depends to a large extent on the relative quantities of reagents used. For example, if a solution of sodium hydroxide is divided into two equal parts, and one part is saturated with SO_2, a solution of sodium acid sulfite will be produced. Test with litmus paper to show the acidity of the solution, due to the reaction

$$HSO_3^- \rightleftarrows SO_3^= + H^+$$

Hold a burning splint at the mouth of a bottle of the sulfur dioxide gas and then insert into the gas. This demonstrates that the gas neither burns nor supports combustion. Moisten the palm of the hand and pour about 2 ml of water into a second bottle. Cover the bottle mouth with your hand and shake. Show the students that the bottle now adheres, unsupported, to the palm. Relate the demonstration to the high solubility of the gas, sulfur dioxide.

Reducing agent. In some classes you may want to show the action of SO_2 as a reducing agent. Add 5 cc of each of $0.1N$ $KMnO_4$ and $6 N H_2SO_4$ to 100 cc of a solution of SO_2 in water. As the purple permanganate is poured in, its color will begin to disappear, and in a short time students should see that the solution becomes completely colorless. Have them develop the equation

$$2 KMnO_4 + 5 SO_2 + 2H_2O \rightarrow$$
$$K_2SO_4 + 2 MnSO_4 + 2 H_2SO_4$$

Bleaching action. Bleaching with SO_2 may be demonstrated in a variety of different ways; for example, the previous demonstration may be performed without acid. It is often labeled the "wine to water to milk" demonstration. A 500-ml cylinder is partially filled with about 400 ml of very dilute $KMnO_4$ solution. The concentration is not too critical ($0.02 N KMnO_4$ —$\frac{1}{2}$ to 1 g in a liter of water is used). Pour in, while stirring, sufficient saturated SO_2 solution to change the "wine to water." Then again stir in enough $BaCl_2$ solution ($0.5 N BaCl_2$—61 g of $BaCl_2 \cdot 2H_2O$ per liter) to change the "water to milk." Generally, if this is used as an introduction, the explanation dealing with bleaching by the reducing action of SO_2 (H_2SO_3) is deferred until later in the lesson after the test for a sulfate ion (see 9.3d).

Pieces of red apple skin, colored carnations, gladioli, a blade of grass, and a bean leaf can be bleached in the water solution of SO_2. Following this the color of a bleached flower, as, for example, a red carnation, may be regenerated by immersing in a solution of H_2O_2. If speed is desirable a 6% solution or even the hair bleaching 20% solution (commercially available) may be used to regenerate the color. Grass and plant leaves do not bleach completely

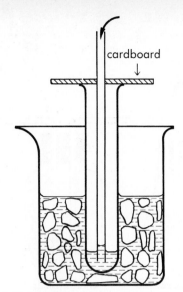

Fig. 9-5 Liquefying sulfur dioxide in acetone and dry ice mixture.

but rather fade to a pale green or brownish color. Placing the plant leaf into HNO_3 solution causes some degree of color regeneration. The fact that an oxidizing agent regenerates the color may be used as a teaching device to explain bleaching with SO_2 as a reducing agent. A variation of the permanganate bleaching consists of pouring the permanganate solution into a cylinder which contains 2 g of solid $NaHSO_3$ (which may be slightly acidified with a few drops of HCl). Bleaching may be carried on by the gas alone as in Fig. 9-6. Though this takes longer than immersion in a solution, the freshness and form of the flower are preserved.

9.3 Sulfuric acid

Several methods for preparing this most important compound of sulfur can be demonstrated in class.

9.3a Preparation from sulfurous acid

Show that sulfurous acid can become sulfuric acid by taking up oxygen. Let

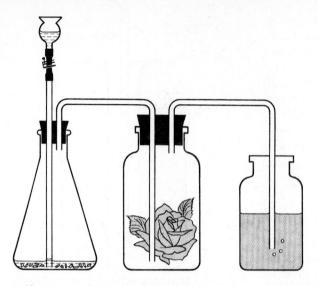

Fig. 9–6 Bleaching a rose in sulfur dioxide gas.

sulfurous acid stand open to the air or shake up with air in a test tube. A more rapid method is to add a few drops of hydrogen peroxide (as an oxidizing agent) to the sulfurous acid. The peroxide is reduced to water.

$$H_2SO_3 + H_2O_2 \rightarrow H_2SO_4 + H_2O$$

9.3b *Contact process*

You may demonstrate on a small scale the contact process for manufacturing sulfuric acid. In this process sulfuric acid is produced from sulfur, air, and water. A catalyst, such as platinized asbestos, vanadium oxide, or asbestos saturated with Fe_2O_3, is needed.

To reproduce the contact process on a laboratory scale you will need to assemble your apparatus in the relationship shown in Fig. 9–7. The funnel can be held in place over the burning sulfur by means of a burette clamp attached to a ring stand. You will note that the funnel is positioned in such a manner as to allow some air to mix with the SO_2. The SO_2-air mixture then goes to a U-tube for dust removal. The U-tube is filled with glass beads. From there the SO_2 is bubbled through

concentrated H_2SO_4. You may point out to students that one of the properties of sulfuric acid is its ability to absorb water, thus making it an excellent drying agent. On the industrial level the SO_2 is actually washed into water before going through dust removal. After being bubbled through the H_2SO_4, the dry SO_2 goes into the reaction chamber where it changes into SO_3. The chamber can be made of 1″ to 2″ diameter Pyrex tubing 18″ in length. At each end there is a one-hole stopper and a plug of glass wool. The catalyst itself is a 3″ to 4″ plug of platinized asbestos held in place by the glass wool. The SO_3 is now bubbled through water where some of it enters the solution. After 5 minutes this can be tested with blue litmus paper and with $BaCl_2$ solution to show the presence of sulfate. For this $BaCl_2$ test see 9.3d. See Fig. 9–8 for one type of aspirator that can be used to keep SO_2 flowing through the apparatus. The reaction chamber containing the catalytic platinized asbestos is heated with a Fisher or a wing top Bunsen burner. You may want to wrap the chamber with asbestos to prevent cracking.

You can point out that not all of the

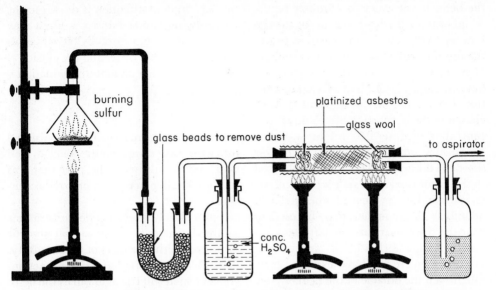

Fig. 9–7 Apparatus assembled to show the contact process of producing sulfuric acid.

SO₃ goes into solution. This waste is avoided on the industrial level by using sulfuric acid as the solvent. You can demonstrate this by placing a second bottle (not shown in Fig. 9–7) between the reaction chamber and the collecting bottle containing water. In this second bottle place about 2″ of concentrated H₂SO₄. It will be noted that no SO₃ clouds appear above the acid. Industrially the sulfuric acid collecting chamber is kept at a 98% concentration by adding water and drawing off acid.

This demonstration can be done without the dust remover or the bottle with sulfuric acid used to dry the SO₂ if you do not wish to approximate the industrial process.

To show the formation of sulfur trioxide place only 10 ml of a saturated solution of sulfur dioxide in a 2-liter flask. Shake the flask for a minute. Fasten a piece of platinum foil with a wire to a glass rod. Heat the foil to redness and then plunge it into the SO₂ solution. For the few seconds the

platinum remains red-hot, clouds of white fumes appear.

9.3c Properties of sulfuric acid

Physical properties. Student attention is drawn to the "oiliness" and high viscosity of sulfuric acid by gently swirling the contents of a bottle half filled with the concentrated 18 M acid. Contrast with

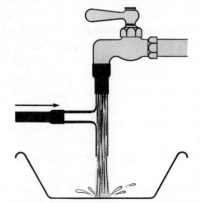

Fig. 9–8 One type of aspirator which can be used with such apparatus as that in Fig. 9–7 to keep a gas flowing.

the behavior of water in a similar bottle. A laboratory hydrometer or a storage battery hydrometer may be used to test the specific gravity of a given acid sample. Demonstrate the correct procedure for diluting sulfuric acid. Use selected quantities dependent on the amount of acid chosen in the proportion of 145 ml of concentrated acid to 870 ml of water to produce a sample of the more or less standard dilute acid (1:6) commonly used in the laboratory. *Always pour the acid into the water* and stir as the acid is being slowly added. A thermometer may be used to have the students realize the large temperature change although it is generally satisfactory merely to have a student carefully touch the outside of the beaker after the acid has been added. This may be explained on the basis of the heat liberated when such hydrates as $H_2SO_4 \cdot H_2O$ and $H_2SO_4 \cdot 2H_2O$ are formed during dilution.

Chemical properties. The teacher may decide to redemonstrate the action of metals with the dilute sulfuric acid, using Zn, Fe filings, Cu turnings, and Mg placed separately in 5-ml samples of the acid. The test for hydrogen is tried with each test tube. (See 7.2a.)

As a dehydrating agent. Immediately following the dilution demonstration, the teacher may show the dehydrating action of concentrated sulfuric acid on sugar, wooden splints, paper, and certain crystalline hydrates. A beaker of desired size (250 ml or 400 ml usually) is filled approximately ⅕ with granulated sugar. Enough sulfuric acid is added to cover the sugar and is stirred with a glass rod until a relatively viscous mass results. The glass rod is left in the beaker contents. As the sugar chars and the char rises, the embedded glass rod rises in the carbon mass. This quantity of sugar is generally sufficient to have the resultant mass rise some one to two times the height of the

beaker. Student attention is drawn to the steam being emitted and a student may be permitted to test carefully the temperature of the beaker by feeling the outside of the beaker. One representative equation is

$$C_{12}H_{22}O_{11} + 11 \ H_2SO_4 \rightarrow$$
$$12 \ C + 11 \ H_2SO_4 \cdot H_2O$$

A wooden splint may be rapidly inserted into a test tube sample of the concentrated acid and withdrawn. The part that was immersed will emerge in a charred condition.

Immediately after such demonstrations as these you may want to call student attention to the dangers of using sulfuric acid. Because of its dehydrating action, concentrated sulfuric acid burns the flesh. Even dilute acid may cause serious damage to flesh and clothing. Hot sulfuric acid (boiling point 338° C) produces extremely serious burns. If any acid gets on hands, immediately wash off with water. Neutralize any remaining acid with a thin paste of sodium bicarbonate (baking soda). Ammonium hydroxide or dilute sodium hydroxide may be used to neutralize any acid dropped on the demonstration table. The product is then washed away with water. The sodium bicarbonate may also be used for this purpose but larger quantities of water may be needed to clean up after the acid has been neutralized.

Reaction of the sodium bicarbonate with acid may be demonstrated in a beaker into which 5 ml of dilute acid have been poured. Add a teaspoon of the sodium bicarbonate and have the students observe the resultant effervescence. A burning splint may be lowered into the liberated gas to identify it as carbon dioxide. Students can write their names in dilute acid on a piece of white paper. After the acid has soaked in, the paper is warmed over a low Bunsen flame (the paper must not be permitted to catch fire) and the name appears due to charring action.

As an oxidizing agent. Place a few copper turnings into a test tube and add 3 ml of concentrated sulfuric acid. Have the students note that no perceptible reaction occurs. The test tube contents may then be warmed and the sulfur dioxide produced may be identified by a careful odor test and by using the burning splint test to show that the gas produced is not hydrogen. The test tube should be kept under the hood until the reaction stops. Careful dilution of the cooled contents produces the blue copper sulfate color. Hot, concentrated sulfuric acid will oxidize carbon and sulfur with the production of SO_2. With a more active metal than copper, such as zinc, slightly diluted hot acid may reduce to hydrogen sulfide although some sulfur dioxide may also be produced. Typical equations are

$$Cu + 2\,H_2SO_4 \rightarrow$$
$$CuSO_4 + 2\,H_2O + \quad SO_2$$
$$S + 2\,H_2SO_4 \rightarrow$$
$$2\,H_2O + 3\,SO_2$$
$$4\,Zn + 5\,H_2SO_4 \rightarrow$$
$$4\,ZnSO_4 + 4\,H_2O + \quad H_2S$$

9.3d   Test for sulfate ion

This test is done by adding $BaCl_2$ solution to a given sulfate solution such as Na_2SO_4 which produces a precipitate. You then show that the precipitate does not dissolve in concentrated HCl. A sulfite solution will also produce a white precipitate but this precipitate dissolves in concentrated HCl with the evolution of SO_2. However, there is often a small residue of white precipitate which remains undissolved due to the air-oxidation of the sulfite ion to sulfate. A solid sulfite is usually identified by adding concentrated HCl and permitting the SO_2 liberated to bleach a dilute $KMnO_4$ solution. Sulfites in solution may be acidified with a drop of the acid. Then drops of dilute $KMnO_4$ will decolorize upon addition to the solution.

9.3e   Thiosulfate in volumetric analysis

At some time you may want to show students the principle of iodimetry. Alyea[2] suggests the following technique for volumetric analysis. Pour 0.1 N sodium thiosulfate solution into a 50-cc burette. Titrate by running the thiosulfate into a beaker containing 200 cc of water to which a few drops of a starch suspension and 25 cc of iodine solution have been added.

The blue color of the iodine-starch complex disappears (serving as an indicator) as the iodine is converted to colorless iodide ions and the thiosulfate changes to tetrathionate.

$$2\,S_2O_3^= + I_2 \rightarrow S_4O_6^= + 2I^-$$
$$\text{thiosulfate} \qquad \text{tetrathionate}$$

The thiosulfate ("hypo"—sodium thiosulfate) also acts as a reducing agent in its action as an anti-chlorine agent to remove excess chlorine from textiles after bleaching them. See the demonstration on the laboratory preparation of chlorine, 11.2a; the chlorine safety trap may contain sodium thiosulfate.

9.4   The chemistry of phosphorus

Phosphorus is obtained from rock phosphate, $Ca_3(PO_4)_2$, by heating a mixture of the phosphate with sand and coke in an electric furnace. The most important use of phosphate rock is its conversion to superphosphate (a fertilizer) by reaction with sulfuric acid. The insoluble $Ca_3(PO_4)_2$ is partially converted to calcium

---

[2] H. Alyea, "Tested Demonstrations in General Chemistry," *J. Chem. Educ.* reprint, from 1955–56 volumes.

dihydrogen phosphate which is soluble in water and partially into the slightly soluble calcium sulfate. A simple demonstration of the relative solubilities of the two phosphates consists of placing half a teaspoonful of each of the powdered compounds into half a test tube full of water and shaking vigorously.

The various oxidation states of phosphorus compounds vary from -3 (as in phosphine PH_3) to $+5$ (as in phosphoric acid, H_3PO_4). Phosphorus frequently has the oxidation number of $+3$ (as in phosphorous acid, H_3PO_3).

Handling phosphorus. White (or yellow) phosphorus must be stored under water, cut under water when possible, and handled with tongs. Dry small cut portions by pressing them on blotting paper. In experiments where phosphorus deposits form on test tubes, be sure to dispose of these white phosphorus remains by adding an acidified solution of bleaching powder or bromine water. White phosphorus (and yellow also) produces white fumes (oxides) almost immediately on exposure to air. It ignites at $30°$ C. This may be initiated by touching the piece of phosphorus with a slightly heated glass rod. White phosphorus is therefore stored under water in a glass-stoppered bottle.

9.4a   Oxidation of phosphorus

Burn a bit of phosphorus on a cork float, in a tray or basin of water, or under a bell jar or inverted glass cylinder (Fig. 9–9). Students can see the thick phosphorus pentoxide smoke that forms. Since the smoke is soluble in water, forming phosphoric acid, the air is quickly cleared. Test the solution with litmus or other acid indicator. This demonstration is often used to show the percentage of oxygen in the air. Students notice that water rises one fifth of the way up the cylinder as the gas is absorbed by water. Roughly this represents the one-fifth oxygen content of the air.

Students may be shown some of the differences between red and white phosphorus. For example, white phosphorus dissolves in carbon disulfide while red phosphorus does not. Red phosphorus must be heated well above room temperature before it ignites. Have students report on the manufacture of friction kitchen matches containing nontoxic P_4S_3 and oxidizing materials, and on the use of red phosphorus in the friction section of a box of safety matches.

The "glow" of phosphorus. In a "cold flame" demonstration, a few small pieces of white phosphorus are placed in a dry flask which is then filled with glass wool. Heat the flask in a water bath and pass a stream of dry carbon dioxide through the flask. The phosphorus vapor carried along with the gas is oxidized on contact with the air and produces a green "flame" at the top of the exit tube. The "flame" is so cool that one may hold a finger in it. This activity should be carried out under a well-ventilated fume hood.[3]

9.4b   Phosphates

Sodium salts of phosphoric acid have a wide variety of uses in industry as fertilizer, as water-softening agent, in baking powder, in fireproofing, and in rustproofing of metals. You may want to show some of the actions of these phosphates at this time. The action of trisodium phosphate detergent and water softener is described in 4.7b.

Distinguishing reactions of phosphoric acids. In some classes you may want students to see that under certain conditions phosphorus pentoxide can react with water to form three different acids. A meta phosphoric acid forms first with cold

[3] Oscar E. Lanford, *Using Chemistry*, McGraw-Hill Book Co., N.Y., 1959.

water; then as the solution is heated, a pyro acid is formed; at the boiling temperature of the solution, the ortho acid is formed.

$$P_2O_5 + H_2O \rightarrow 2\ HPO_3 + H_2O \rightarrow$$
$$H_4P_2O_7 + H_2O \rightarrow 2\ H_3PO_4$$

The three acids can be distinguished in the following manner.[4] Gradually add a level saltspoonful of phosphorus pentoxide to 150 ml of cold distilled water (filter if necessary). Divide this solution among three flasks—I, II, III. Let flask I boil vigorously for 10 minutes; place flask II in a water bath just at the boiling point so that the solution in the flask is about 85° C, and let this remain for 30 minutes.

Prepare a solution of egg albumen by adding white of egg to 10 times its volume of water. To a small sample of the solution in flask III (cold), students can add a bit of the albumen solution and watch coagulation take place in the flask. To another cold sample, add excess 10 per cent solution of silver nitrate and look for the flocculent white precipitate. This reaction identifies the *meta acid*.

Cool the solution in flask I and add egg albumen; no coagulation results. (Should coagulation occur, continue to heat the solution until a sample shows no further coagulation.) This is the *ortho acid*, more strongly acidic than the others. To a small sample add ammoniacal silver nitrate;[5] a bright yellow precipitate results.

The *pyro acid* is formed in flask II which has been in a water bath for half an hour. Cool samples and test with the albumen solution until a sample no longer coagulates albumen. Cool a fresh sample and test with silver nitrate solution; a powdery

[4] G. Fowles, *Lecture Experiments in Chemistry*, 4th rev. ed., G. Bell and Sons Ltd., London, 1957 (Exp. 377, p. 295).

[5] Prepare by adding ammonium hydroxide to a silver nitrate solution to the point at which the silver hydroxide which has been precipitated just dissolves.

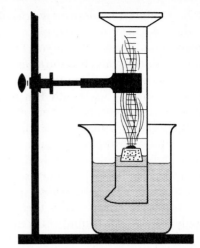

Fig. 9–9 Burning phosphorus on a cork float.

white precipitate forms different from the flocculent precipitate formed by the meta acid.

9.5 The chemistry of carbon

Inorganic carbon compounds will be described in this section; the organic compounds are discussed in Chapters 14 and 15.

9.5a Allotropic forms of carbon

Two crystalline forms of carbon exist: diamond and graphite. Students can examine chips of each form under the low power of the microscope by focusing light from a gooseneck lamp down on the stage. Each form has a crystalline structure. Note the differences—a study in contrasts: the diamond, the hardest substance, which scratches all others, and the soft black graphite used as a lubricant and writing material as well as an electric resistor and, in atomic reactors, as a neutron moderator.

Production of charcoal and coke by destructive distillation. The amorphous varieties of carbon are coke, charcoal, and carbon black (soot). Charcoal and coke may be produced by destructive distillation. Into a Pyrex test tube place some pieces of wood. Six wooden splints broken in half or an equivalent amount of sawdust will serve. Clamp the test tube to a ring stand so that its mouth tips down slightly. Stopper with a one-hole stopper and run a delivery tube to a bottle stoppered with a two-hole stopper. This delivery tube should extend well down into the bottle. From the other stopper hole extend a glass tube whose tip has been drawn to a jet. Heat the wood strongly, observe the liquid collecting in the bottle, and ignite the gas which eventually emerges from the jet tube. It may be necessary to relight continuously since the gas may contain considerable water vapor. Test the liquid in the collecting bottle with blue litmus paper which turns red because of the presence of acetic acid, one of the products. Remove the solid residue and ignite with the Bunsen flame. Have students note that the charcoal formed now glows virtually without a flame.

The same setup may be used for the production of coke. It is filled one half full with bituminous coal. This is heated strongly and the gas produced (coal gas) is ignited. The coal tar residue in the bottle is examined. Occasionally, but not always, since bituminous coal samples are variable, a test for ammonia gas in the volatile matter emerging from the heated tube may be made successfully by inserting a moist piece of red litmus paper between the stopper and the bottle side so that it hangs down into the gaseous contents of the bottle. A cannel coal sample almost always results in a positive test for NH_3. Permit the contents of the test tube to cool. Pour out on asbestos sheet. Then hold a small piece of the coke in the Bunsen flame and attempt to ignite it. Compare its combustion with that of a small piece of soft coal.

9.5b Properties of carbon

Carbon (charcoal) as a reducing agent. Place 5 g of the wire form of cupric oxide in a test tube with an equal amount of powdered charcoal. Clamp to a ring stand so that the test tube's mouth is tipped slightly upward and stopper with a one-hole stopper. Run a delivery tube down into a tube of limewater. Heat the charcoal and cupric oxide strongly for 4–5 minutes, observing the formation of the precipitate of $CaCO_3$ in the limewater. After this precipitate forms, remove the delivery tube from the limewater, remove the stopper from the reaction test tube, and pour the contents quickly into a beaker of cold water. The unused charcoal floats on top of the water and the copper formed (identified by its color) and the unreduced cupric oxide sink to the bottom.

Carbon as an adsorption agent. Drop 2 g of pelleted activated charcoal into a bottle of colored gas such as NO_2 or bromine vapor. Shake vigorously and note the removal of the color due to the adsorption by the charcoal.

Vigorously shake 50 ml of dark brown sugar solution with 1 g of powdered boneblack in a stoppered flask for a minute or more. Filter the mixture through a filter paper. The filtrate is then poured twice more through the contents of the filter paper. Note the removal of the brown color. The filtrate, however, will give a positive test for sugar when a drop is boiled with 5 ml of Benedict's or Fehling's solution.

Carbon black may be readily produced by permitting the yellow Bunsen burner flame to impinge on a cold test tube or on the bottom of a beaker. Switching to the oxidizing flame results in the complete removal of the deposited carbon black.

9.5c Inorganic compounds of carbon

Carbon monoxide. The demonstration

of the preparation of carbon monoxide (a poisonous gas) should be carried out under the hood. Assemble the apparatus as follows. Clamp a 250-ml flask to a ring stand and support it on a ring and gauze above a Bunsen burner. Into a three-hole stopper place a dropping funnel whose stem runs down close to the flask's bottom, a thermometer, and a delivery tube which runs to a trough for gas collection by water displacement. (See Fig. 7–16A.) Place 30 ml of concentrated sulfuric acid into the 250-ml flask. Gently heat the flask with a Bunsen flame until the temperature reaches 100° C. Admit formic acid a drop at a time from the dropping funnel and collect the CO by water displacement. The first bottle collected probably contains air and will result in an explosion when the gas-air mixture is ignited. Ignite the gas in the second bottle and after it starts to burn (with a blue flame) replace the glass plate. Add 10 ml of limewater, shake, and the precipitate shows that CO_2 was formed as a result of combustion. A third bottle may be tested with the same amount of limewater to show that the CO does not result in a precipitate.

Carbon dioxide. Have students trace the carbon dioxide cycle in nature. They may bubble exhaled air into a beaker containing bromthymol blue or limewater. If a dilute solution of bromthymol blue is used, bubble enough exhaled air into the solution so that it just turns yellow. To this add some elodea or other aquarium plants and place in the sunlight. Within the hour students should see that the carbon dioxide has been absorbed by the green plants in the process of photosynthesis. Recall the formation of wood and subsequent stages in coal formation.

Preparation of carbon dioxide. The usual laboratory method of preparing carbon dioxide involves the reaction of carbonates with a dilute acid (Fig. 9–10). Limestone or marble chips are broken down into a calcium compound and carbonic acid which decomposes.

$$CaCO_3 + 2\,HCl \rightarrow CaCl_2 + H_2CO_3$$

$$H_2CO_3 \rightarrow H_2O + CO_2$$

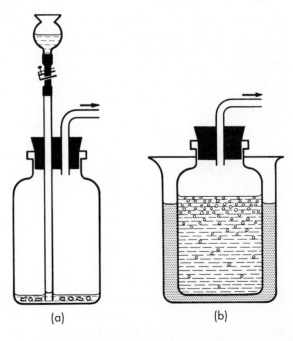

Fig. 9–10 Preparing carbon dioxide: (a) using a dropping funnel to deliver acid to carbonate, (b) heating soda water in a water bath.

(a)

(b)

Other methods of preparation described later are also shown in Fig. 9–10. The CO_2 may be collected by water displacement. For this see Fig. 7–16A.

Fermentation. Students may prepare a fermentation apparatus consisting simply of a bottle containing molasses or glucose solution and yeast. This is closed with a stopper connecting a delivery tube into a beaker of limewater (Fig. 9–11). Also have students refer to the use of carbon dioxide in breadmaking (see below). (*Caution: Do not plug the fermentation bottle with a solid stopper. An explosion may result.*)

As a result of these demonstrations students should be able to summarize some of the properties of carbon dioxide. The fact that the gas is heavier than air can be observed in its use as a fire extinguisher (see below).

Dry ice. Dry ice (solid CO_2) must be handled with gloves or tongs. Students can use it as a source of CO_2 or it can also be used with acetone or alcohol to produce low temperatures for liquefying SO_2 or NH_3 (see Fig. 9–5).

Soda water. Students may confirm some of the facts they find in their textbooks. For example, what is the gas in soda pop? Students may attach a one-hole stopper equipped with a glass bend and a rubber tube with a pinchcock to a small bottle, half filled with fresh soda (Fig. 9–11).

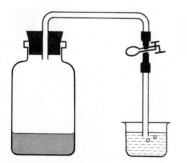

Fig. 9–11 Bubbling the carbon dioxide produced by fermentation through limewater.

Have the rubber tube carry the gas evolving from the soda into a small jar of limewater. It may be necessary to shake the bottle from time to time, or heat it gently in a water bath to release the gas more rapidly. The same bottle can be used a number of times if the pinchcock fits tightly.

Baking soda and baking powder. Students should understand that the function of baking powder or soda is to release the gas CO_2 as the product bakes, thus making tiny bubbles in it. They may already know that yeast cells do the same thing, though it takes longer. Baking soda, $NaHCO_3$, simply reacts with an acid (such as lactic acid from sour milk) to yield CO_2.

Baking powders contain a substance which hydrolyzes slightly acid, along with $NaHCO_3$; therefore they will produce the leavening effect with the addition of water alone.

Carbon dioxide fire extinguisher. Students may demonstrate the principle of operation of CO_2 fire extinguisher in several steps. First pour from a container of dry ice to extinguish a candle (Fig. 9–12A). Then stand several candles in a battery jar with half an inch of sodium bicarbonate at the bottom (Fig. 9–12B). Light the candles; then pour dilute acid (or ordinary vinegar) down the side of the jar. As carbon dioxide is released, students should notice that the candles are extinguished.

Then make a working CO_2 fire extinguisher using a quart milk bottle (Fig. 9–12C). Pour a half quart of 50 per cent sodium bicarbonate solution into the bottle, and hang an open vial containing 2 cc of concentrated sulfuric acid from the neck of the bottle, then stopper the bottle with a large one-hole cork fitted with a short glass tube and a long rubber tube that has a nozzle at the end. Wrap a towel

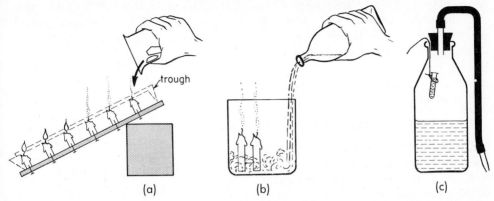

Fig. 9-12 Carbon dioxide as a fire extinguisher: (a) poured down a trough containing candles, (b) poured into jar, (c) a model carbon dioxide fire extinguisher.

tightly about the upper part of the extinguisher and the stopper to prevent the accidental wetting of the demonstrator. To demonstrate the action of fire extinguisher, prepare a small fire with paper in the sink or in a small basin on a stone-top laboratory table. Then extinguish the fire by inverting the bottle and directing the stream at the fire. (Make certain that no students are in the path of the stream, for it may spray them with some acid.) If you have a foamite extinguisher, you may want to show that it is effective in putting out burning benzene where the soda acid type often fails.

Students can also make their own CO_2 fire extinguishers, using a Skrip ink bottle, a length of drinking straw, candle wax, sodium bicarbonate powder, and vinegar (Fig. 9–13). To use, invert the bottle.

CO_2 supports combustion of Mg. To demonstrate that carbon dioxide, which extinguishes ordinary flames, will support the combustion of magnesium, ignite a 5-cm length of magnesium ribbon and thrust it into a bottle of CO_2 gas. A dramatic version of this procedure is first to show that carbon dioxide in either of the previous fire-extinguishing demonstrations after being used to extinguish a wood or candle flame *will* support the combustion

of magnesium. Students can identify the black deposit on the walls of the container as carbon and the white deposit as magnesium oxide.

Carbonic acid (CO_2 in water). Carbonic acid is a weak acid resulting from a reversible reaction between water and carbon dioxide. Show sample of ordinary club soda or Seltzer as an example of carbonic acid. Test with a sensitive indicator.

$$H_2O + CO_2 \rightleftarrows H_2CO_3$$

In some classes students may want to trace the effect of carbon dioxide from the air dissolved in rainwater, that is, the

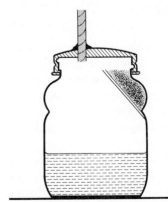

Fig. 9-13 A model fire extinguisher made from a Skrip ink bottle.

action of ground water (see section 4.1c).

Carbonates, normal and acid. If powdered calcium carbonate is heated in a rotating iron tube by a large Meker burner or a blast lamp (Fig. 9–14), the carbonate will be decomposed, liberating carbon dioxide.

$$CaCO_3 \rightarrow CaO + CO_2$$

Quicklime (calcium oxide) remains in the tube. When the oxide has cooled, add it to water to form calcium hydroxide. Slaking lime proceeds exothermically. A piece of quicklime may be slaked in an evaporating dish by the addition of water. This results in the formation of steam and the swelling of the mass of lime to a powdery texture. Mix 1 cc of the solid $Ca(OH)_2$ with 10 ml of H_2O and test this with an indicator to show that it is base. Allow to settle and pour off clear liquid. Bubble CO_2 into the clear $Ca(OH)_2$ solution to show how the solution serves as an indicator for CO_2.

$$Ca(OH)_2 + CO_2 \rightarrow CaCO_3 \downarrow + H_2O$$

Carbonate into bicarbonate. Students can bubble CO_2 gas from a carbon dioxide generator (Fig. 11–12) or tank through a solution of sodium carbonate to form the bicarbonate.

$$[2Na^+ + CO_3^=] + CO_2 + H_2O \rightarrow$$
$$2[Na^+ + HCO_3^-]$$

If dry sodium bicarbonate is heated, it will release water and carbon dioxide and change to the carbonate—the reverse of the above reaction. The solution of the resulting carbonate is tested with pH paper and shows a base in pH to about 11.5.

pH of carbonates and bicarbonates. Have students try to measure the pH of solutions of equal amounts of sodium carbonate and sodium bicarbonate. Establish the difference in pH (0.1 N

$NaHCO_3$: pH-8.4; 0.1 N Na_2CO_3: pH-11.6) by using pH paper (hydrion paper) or a universal indicator. (See 8.4f.)

$$Na_2CO_3 + H_2O \rightleftarrows 2\,Na^+ + HCO_3^- + OH^-$$
$$+$$
$$H_2O$$
$$\uparrow\downarrow$$
$$H_2CO_3 + OH^-$$
$$NaHCO_3 + H_2O \rightleftharpoons Na^+ + OH^- + H_2CO_3$$

9.6 The chemistry of silicon

Although silicon does not exist free in nature, silicon dioxide is prevalent in sand, sandstone, clay, and quartz—in fact, it is an ingredient of most rocks.

Silicon has a valence like that of carbon, but, unlike carbon, it forms only a few compounds in which silicon atoms are linked together. In the silicones, however, silicon atoms form long chains alternating with oxygen atoms. The chemistry of these organic linkages, mainly silicones, is a wide field for study, and a possible idea for project work. Students may be familiar with one of these compounds, "silly putty," a silicone rubber. A ball of this material will bounce like rubber. However, if the same ball is placed on an anvil and struck with a hammer or mallet it scatters into a large number of small bits. If the "putty" is pulled apart suddenly in the hands, a sharp break occurs with the formation of two large pieces. If, on the other hand, the piece of "putty" is slowly drawn apart, a continuous thread which may reach many feet may be formed.

9.6a Preparation of silicon[6]

Silicon may be produced from an intimate mixture of 3.2 g of dry, precipitated silica or dry, fine silver sand and 1 g of magnesium powder in a 5″ test tube (ordinary glass may be used). Clamp the

[6] Adapted from G. Fowles, *Lecture Experiments in Chemistry*, 4th rev. ed., G. Bell & Sons, Ltd., London, 1957 (Exp. 358).

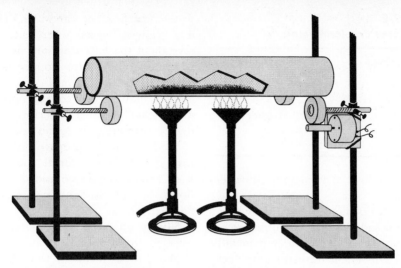

Fig. 9-14 Releasing carbon dioxide by heating calcium carbonate in an iron tube. The tube is turned slowly by means of a low-speed motor.

tube, with its mouth pointing in a safe direction, on a retort stand and place an iron tray under the tube. Heat the mixture with a hot Bunsen flame. In a few seconds fumes appear. The next moment reaction occurs with a dazzling flash of light. (*Caution: The instructor and any observers should wear protective glasses [blue glass goggles] and the demonstrator's hands should be protected with gloves.*) The tube frequently shatters and occasionally sparks are violently ejected, but the bulk of the product falls in the iron tray. When the mass is cool, the best pieces of silicon are removed and boiled in a small flask with concentrated hydrochloric acid to remove magnesium and magnesium silicide. The silicon is dried after being filtered off. It may be identified by heating strongly with Bunsen flames below and above the sample, with a sample on a piece of broken porcelain or on an iron spoon. The element glows and leaves a white deposit of silica.

9.6b Some compounds of silicon

Glass. In some classes you may want to

show that glass is more like a "supercooled liquid" than crystalline in structure by comparing its melting point with that of a crystalline substance (which has a sharp melting point).

Silicon glass. In a nichrome wire loop melt a bit of sodium carbonate, quickly dip it into powdered silica, and heat to form a transparent bead. Prepare several beads.

Making and staining glass. Students can make some glass in a small crucible heated by an electric arc furnace (25.3a) or a blast lamp, using small quantities of powdered limestone ($CaCO_3$) and fine sand (SiO_2) as the raw materials. Add traces of different metallic oxides to get glass of different color (see Table 9-2).

For ordinary glass, use 17 oz of clean fresh sand, 4 oz sodium carbonate, and 2 oz of borax. Heat until melted. A very small batch can be made in a metal crucible over a Meker burner. To color the glass, sprinkle into the batch a bit of one of the oxides listed in Table 9-2.

To make bottle glass use 6.3 oz of sand, 2.3 oz of sodium carbonate, and 1.1 oz of

TABLE 9-2
Oxides used in coloring glass

amethyst	manganese dioxide
blue	cobalt oxide
green	black copper oxide
purple	gold oxide
ruby	cupric (red) oxide
white	tin oxide
yellow	silver oxide

$CaCO_3$ and heat in a crucible with a very hot flame.

In another demonstration, slowly heat a solid glass rod or soft glass tubing to red heat. Dip into a dry powdered metallic oxide. Then reheat until the oxide fuses into the glass. Students may make rods of different colored glass by using different oxides (Table 9–2). The amount of the oxide that is used will determine the intensity of the color. Also try using several oxides to produce multicolored effects. (*Note:* Do not attempt to "stain" ordinary sheet glass; it will crack.)

Other kinds of glass. Have students report on the way Pyrex glass is made. Compare the rate of expansion of Pyrex with that of soft glass. Students can examine shatterproof plate glass of which one type is a glass-plastic-glass sandwich. This can be simulated by dipping a test tube in collodion. When dry, strike the tube a blow; it will crack, but not shatter.

Silicate gardens. Prepare a solution of one part of sodium silicate (Na_2SiO_3) to 4 parts of water in a large beaker to make water glass. Students can watch the chemical "flowers" grow when a few small crystals of the following salts are added: chlorides of cobalt, iron, copper, nickel, or lead; sulfates of aluminum, iron, copper, and nickel; nitrates of cobalt, copper, iron, and nickel. A fuller description of this demonstration can be found in 1.1c.

Students might prepare hall cabinet displays of these colorful chemicals. A fresh crystal should be added every few hours so that students can watch the "garden" grow.

Silicate ion exchange. You may want to refer to the alumino-silicate cation exchange tube (zeolite) that has been described in 4.7b.

Etching glass. There may be an occasion to demonstrate the action of hydrofluoric acid in etching glass (see 11.1a).

Water repellent property of silicones. Into a wide-mouth bottle (about 250-cc) place 20 cc of chlorosilane mixture. Cover the bottle for about 5 minutes until the vapor fills the bottle. Insert a piece of filter paper into the vapor for a minute. Add drops of water to this treated paper and also to untreated filter paper. On which paper does water remain as "drops" on the surface? (*Caution: The treating of the filter paper should be done under a hood.*) The chlorosilane comes in a glass ampule from which the tip is snapped when the chemical is to be used. An ampule can be used only once.

CAPSULE LESSONS

Ways to get started in class

9-1. You may want to select some of the demonstrations in this chapter to give a quick, general introduction to the properties of sulfur (and the other elements studied here). Burn sulfur and then shake water in the SO_2 to form an acid solution, etc.

9-2. Have students make the allotropic forms of sulfur and examine the different crystalline structures.

9-3. As one lesson in the topic, students may show the bleaching effect of sulfur dioxide on cloth, paper, flowers, or fruits.

9-4. In some classes you may want to demonstrate the use of hydrogen sulfide in qualitative analysis. This may be a technique that some students could use in a special long-term project.

9-5. Demonstrate the allotropic forms of carbon. Elicit the uses of carbon in industry. Develop some of the compounds of carbon in class and establish tests for their presence.

9-6. Trace the carbon dioxide cycle in nature; establish the sources of energy and the transformations of one form into another.

9-7. Compare the heat-resistant qualities of Pyrex and soft glass—and the index of refraction of each. Also show the properties of shatterproof glass. Students can prepare an exhibit of stained glass.

9-8. In some class or club, demonstrate the water-repellant qualities of silicones.

9-9. If possible, plan a field trip to an industrial chemical plant. Students should plan in advance what chemical reactions they might observe.

PEOPLE, PLACES, AND THINGS

If you have the responsibility for planning an assembly program or sponsoring a local science fair, you can get assistance from the chemistry department of a nearby college. Many suggestions are offered in such publications as *Advanced Experiments in Gas* (American Gas Assoc.) and *Demonstrations in Science* (Texaco Research Center).

Graduate students or practicing chemists or chemical engineers in your community might give assistance to a youngster who wants to do a special project in chemistry for the local science fair or for the Westinghouse Science Talent Search (Science Service, Washington, D. C.).

BOOKS AND PAMPHLETS

These are only a few of the books which are pertinent to the work discussed in this chapter. These and many other references classified by subject and with complete bibliographical data are given in the bibliography at the end of the book.

Berry, A., *From Classical to Modern Chemistry*, Cambridge U. Press, 1954.

Clements, R., *Modern Chemical Discoveries*, Routledge, London, 1954.

Deming, H., *General Chemistry*, Wiley, 1955.

Gould, E., *Inorganic Reactions and Structure*, Holt, 1955.

Graham, R., and L. Cragg, *The Essentials of Chemistry*, Rinehart, 1959.

Hutchinson, E., *Chemistry: The Elements and Their Reactions*, Saunders, 1959.

Iler, R., *The Colloid Chemistry of Silica and Silicates*, Cornell U. Press, 1955.

Lange, N., *Handbook of Chemistry*, 9th ed., Handbook Publishers, 1956.

Langford, G. B., *Out of the Earth*, U. of Toronto Press, 1954.

Rodd, E. H., *Carbon Compounds*, Elsevier, 1952.

FILMS AND FILMSTRIPS

This partial list is intended only as a guide toward film and filmstrip selection. Refer to the more complete listing at the end of the book where films are classified by subject and where a key to abbreviations and addresses of distributors is given. The cost of film rental, of course, is subject to change. Films are sound and black and white unless otherwise specified.

Black Diamonds (f, s, c), Sterling-Movies, USA., inquire rental.

Carbon and Its Compounds (f, s), Ideal, $2.00.

Chemistry Series (series 6 f, s, c), McGraw-Hill, $8.00 each.

Collecting and Preparing Soil Samples for Testing (f, s), Illinois University Voc. Ag., $1.00.

Glass and You (f, s, c), Association, free.

The Glass Center of Corning (f, s, c), Association, free.

Magic on a Stick (sulfur match) (f, s), Teaching Film Custodians, free.

Peat and Coal (f, s), Institutional Cinema, $2.00.

Pencil Points (f, s), Almanac, $2.00.

Putting Sulfur to Work (fs, c), Popular Science through McGraw-Hill, $6.00.

Sand and Flame (f, s), U.S. Bur. of Mines, free.

Silicones (f, s), General Electric, free.

Soil Testing for Lime Requirements (f, s, c), Cornell University Extension, $2.00.

Story of Coal (f, s), Indiana, $1.75.

Story of Sulfur (f, s), Institutional Cinema, $2.00.

Sulfur (f, s, c), U.S. Bur. of Mines, free.

Sulfur and Its Compounds (f, s, c), Coronet, inquire local film library.

Testing Soils for Available Phosphorus and Interpreting the Test (fs), Illinois University Voc. Agric., $1.00.

This is only a partial listing of free and inexpensive materials available to the teacher at this time. A directory of addresses is given at the end of the book. Many of these materials are distributed to teachers without charge. Where there is a small fee, the cost is indicated, although the prices are subject to change. While we recommend the material for use in the classroom, we do not necessarily endorse the products advertised.

Advanced Experiments with Gas, American Gas Assoc.

Art of Making Fine Glassware, Cambridge Glass Co.

Encouraging Future Scientists: Keys to Careers, National Science Teachers Assoc.

Handbook for Chemistry Assistants, Fisher Scientific Co.

Chemistry: The Conquest of Materials, K. Hutton, Pelican, 1957, $0.85.

How Heat Resistant Chemical Glassware Is Made, Corning Glass Works.

Laboratory Emergency Chart, Fisher Scientific Co.

Laboratory Glass Blowing, Sales Dept., Corning Glass.

Names of Chemicals, ed. by Elbert Weaver, W. M. Welch Scientific Co.

New Worlds of Modern Science, Dell, $0.35.

Occupational Outlook Handbook, Bull. 998, Supt. Documents, U.S. Govt. Printing Office, $3.25.

A Thousand Science Projects, Science Service, Washington, $0.25.

Superstition to Supersonics, Manufacturing Chemists' Assoc., sold in class sets.

Many companies provide a booklet and kit of samples of their products. For example, several Louisiana sulfur companies and the Coal Institute extend these courtesies.

CHAPTER 10

Metals and the alkali metals

Over seventy of the ninety-two natural elements are metals. Alkali metals are light, soft, and highly reactive whereas the heavier, relatively inert, copper, gold, and silver show a similarity to the alkali metals only in having a plus 1 oxidation state. Mercury is a liquid at room temperature; tungsten melts at 3370° C. Potassium and sodium are so reactive they are stored in kerosene; gold and platinum are unaffected by nitric acid.

We shall first consider in this chapter some of the physical and chemical properties of metals, the extraction of metals from their ores by various metallurgical processes, and some of the typical reactions of metals that can be described in the laboratory. In addition we shall consider the properties of the amphoteric hydroxides of some metals. Several of the tests for the identification of metals are described for the students' use in project work which they may undertake in more advanced explorations in chemistry.

Toward the end of the chapter we present a description of the alkali metals, mainly sodium and potassium.

10.1. Structure and properties of metals

10.1a Atomic structure

Many teachers have students make models of the atoms of metallic elements using clay and wood splints, wire and beads, or Tinkertoy parts. Some of these devices have been described in 6.4. They can be helpful in developing the concept of how metals differ from nonmetals.

10.1b Crystal structure

Students may also build models of the crystal structure of some metals by using beads and wire or Tinkertoy parts. (See 6.4d.) Many of these student-made models can become part of the department's audio-visual resources for class demonstrations. Students are often stimulated to build apparatus when they have seen the products of others and have seen the worth of the project. Of course, commercial kits are also available from supply houses.

10.1c Physical properties of metals

Metallic luster and opacity. These qualities may be explained in terms of the electron mobility within energy levels. The electrons may be set in motion by photons (light quanta) by absorbing all the frequencies in the visible spectrum and thereby moving to a higher level. They then drop back to a lower level, emitting energy. All the visible wave lengths may be absorbed and re-emitted. The only selectivity in the behavior toward visible light quanta occurs in such colored metals as copper and gold. The interception and extinguishing of light quanta by the mobile electrons explain opacity except in layers only a few atoms thick (thinner than 10^{-5} cm). Gold is yellow by reflected light. However, when thin, it transmits green light. This may be demonstrated by holding up gold leaf mounted between two glass sheets in sunlight and noting its green color.

Malleability and ductility. These properties make it possible to deform metals and thus are the basis of many metal fabrication operations. Most metals also have high tensile strengths. Macroscopically a piece of metal is regarded as a single crystal. However, when a polished or etched piece of such metal is examined under the microscope, it shows a large number of crystals often arranged in a fairly definite recognizable pattern. These are called grains and show grain boundaries which are separations of the grains in the crystal. Single pure crystals of metals, produced by special processes, are generally softer, and have a higher electrical conductivity because there are no crystal boundaries. Tensile strength of such crystals is greater than that of gross metal. A single crystal has a nearly ideal lattice structure with few empty spaces and irregularities.

Working metal makes it harder due to the formation of grains. Hardening may be easily demonstrated by hammering a piece of gross metal such as copper sheet. Bending a fairly thick copper wire (12 gauge) or a piece of iron wire also results in increased hardness. It is almost impossible to get the wire back to its original shape. In both cases, some of the glide planes have been destroyed and the metal is harder. Annealing metals results in a "healing" of the crystal structure with a realignment of crystalline structure and consequent resoftening. In demonstrating this annealing process a bobby pin is first shown to be elastic. It is heated to red heat in the hot tip of the Bunsen flame and then plunged into cold water (demonstration

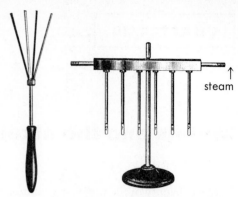

Fig. 10–1 Commercial conductometers. (Central Scientific Company.)

of tempering). The metal now may be easily broken into little pieces by the fingers. The heating and shock cooling are repeated. Then the metal is reheated and permitted to cool in air. The metal may now be bent on itself without breaking. The pliability of metals contrasts with the rigidity of ionic crystals.

Thermal conductivity. Students may hold two or more strips of metal and heat them. Heat conductometers consisting of metal rods of different metals heated from a central heating zone may be used to show the varying thermal conductivity of metals. Representative devices are shown in Fig. 10–1. For ways to build your own conductometer see 18.3a.

Electrical conductivity. Electrical conductivity may be tested by preparing a circuit with two dry cells in series with a small light bulb, with a gap in the circuit. Test the conductivity of various metal strips by inserting each into the circuit. An ammeter inserted in the circuit will provide more accurate readings than comparison of the brightness of the light bulb.

Metalloids. These elements fall on the borderline in physical and chemical properties between the metals and the nonmetals. This class of elements includes boron, silicon, germanium, arsenic, antimony, tellurium, and astatine. Silicon, for example, has the physical properties characteristic of metals, but its chemical properties are those of typical nonmetals. (Note that silicon and germanium are well-known semiconductors and that antimony is so brittle that its crystals are easily ground into powder.) Of the 101 elements (excluding nobelium), only 17 show primarily nonmetallic properties, 7 others are metalloids, and 77 may be classed as metals.[1]

TABLE 10-1
Activity series (electromotive series) of some metals

Displace hydrogen from cold water; react vigorously with acids	K Ba Sr Ca Na	React with oxygen giving oxides;
Displace hydrogen from steam and acids	Mg Al Mn Zn Cr	oxides not reduced by hydrogen or CO / Oxides reduced by C or Al (hot), not by H_2 or CO
Displace hydrogen from acids	S Cd Fe Co Ni Sn Pb H_2	React with oxygen giving oxides; oxides reduced by hydrogen
React with oxidizing acids such as HNO_3	Cu I_2 Hg Ag	
React with aqua regia ($HCl + HNO_3$)	Pt Cl_2 Au F_2	Oxides formed indirectly; lose oxygen when heated (incl. Hg)

10.1d Chemical properties of metals

Activity series. Several committees of students may discover for themselves some

[1] William H. Nebergall and Frederic C. Schmidt, *College Chemistry*, D. C. Heath and Company, Boston, 1957.

facts about the activity of metals by testing metals in salt solutions of other metals (see 6.5a). Many demonstrations may be prepared by students. For example, they may sandpaper an iron nail and let it stand in a solution of copper sulfate. Within the period they should observe the results. Which metal is more active? Then place a gold ring or a pin into copper sulfate. Which is the more active metal? Other students might place a strip of smooth zinc into a solution of lead nitrate. What changes occur within 15 minutes? They may also place a strip of copper in a mercuric nitrate or silver nitrate solution. Have students refer to a table of activity of metals, such as Table 10–1, or construct a simple one of their own on the basis of their observations of displacements.

Very often teachers develop broad generalizations related to the activity series. 1. The very active metals (Groups IA, IIA) replace hydrogen from water. 2. Metals which replace hydrogen from dilute acids are placed *above* hydrogen. 3. Metals which do not replace hydrogen from such acids are placed *below* hydrogen. 4. Such metals may be oxidized by oxidizing acids (HNO_3 and hot concentrated H_2SO_4). Gold and platinum do not react with such acids but do react with aqua regia. 5. A more active metal will replace a less active metal from its salt solutions. 6. The position of the metal in the activity series represents its relative ease of oxidation.

Activity of metals as reducing agents. At this point you may want to demonstrate examples of the activity of metals as reducing agents in displacing hydrogen from water and from acids.

Displacing hydrogen from water. Five test tubes are filled one third full with water. A piece of sodium one half the size of a small pea is dropped into one test tube. The tube is left unstoppered and after the sodium has completely reacted with the water, a burning splint is brought to the test tube mouth and the usual "pop" which identifies hydrogen results. The test tube contents are then tested with red and blue litmus paper and phenolphthalein; the indicator reactions show that a base has been formed. A small calcium turning is placed in the second test tube and the procedure repeated with the same results. Pieces of Mg ribbon, Al foil, and Cu foil or turnings may be placed in the rest of the tubes with negative results. Variations for using sodium and a procedure for potassium are described in 7.2c. This same section also describes procedures for showing that Mg will replace hydrogen in hot water.

A demonstration for comparing the activity of sodium with that of magnesium uses one-half gram of Mg powder which is added to 100 ml of water in a flask. The apparatus is stoppered with a one-hole stopper having a delivery tube leading to an inverted test tube in a beaker or basin of water. Heat the flask contents. When the water boils students should note the gas which is displacing the water in the inverted test tube. The hydrogen test is made with positive results.

The replacement of hydrogen in cold water by amalgamated Al foil is demonstrated in the following manner. A piece of foil is amalgamated by rubbing briskly with a piece of cotton soaked in a dilute solution of mercurous nitrate. Within 30 seconds students will be able to see the oxidation of the aluminum. A white incrustation (Al_2O_3) forms which may be shaken off as flakes. A student may test the temperature of the foil by placing a finger on the unamalgamated side. The foil is hot, indicating the speed with which Al oxidizes as fresh Al is brought to the surface of the amalgam and air penetrates the loosely adherent oxide. The piece of amalgamated Al is then placed into water in

a test tube, as before. The test tube is stoppered loosely and students may observe the evolution of gas. After 3–5 minutes a hydrogen test is made and gives positive results.

As a special project or demonstration, a student may show how hot iron (grease-free iron filings or steel wool washed with detergent) replaces hydrogen from steam (Fig. 10–2). Amounts are not critical but 15–20 grams of filings may be used and a 500-ml flask may serve as a steam generator. Some teachers use a steam trap, placed between the steam generator and the reaction tube. Others use an iron pipe instead of a Pyrex tube as the reaction chamber. The filings may be kept in position by small loose plugs of glass wool placed at both ends of the pile of filings.

Displacing hydrogen from dilute acids. Add 5–10 ml of dilute hydrochloric acid, 0.1 *M*, to each of a series of test tubes; into each tube place a strip of a variety of metals such as zinc, magnesium, tin, copper, and iron (sandpaper the surfaces first if necessary). Have the students compare the rate at which hydrogen evolves, make the test for hydrogen, and note the cases in which hydrogen is not released. Magnesium ribbon produces the hydrogen most rapidly, zinc and iron give good positive results, the tin yields a few bubbles but not enough to give a hydrogen test (set this tube aside, loosely stoppered, and test for hydrogen at the end of the period), and copper gives negative results—no hydrogen bubbles. Have students make their own activity series for these metals based on results obtained. Then have them check their observations by repeating with dilute sulfuric, 0.1 *M*, and with acetic acid, 0.1 *M*, to establish a valid generalization. Have them compare results with the activity series, Table 10–1, noting the slower production of hydrogen with the weak acetic acid. Strips of metals are not an ab-

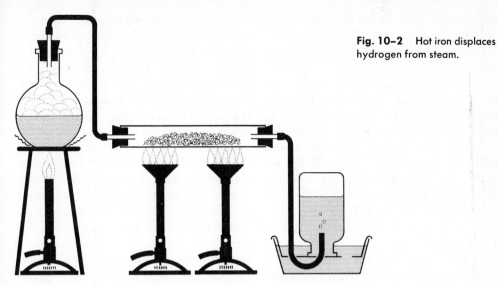

Fig. 10–2 Hot iron displaces hydrogen from steam.

solute necessity since mossy zinc, copper turnings, iron filings, etc., may be used but uniform strips, if available, constitute a good basis for comparison.

Students may be asked to predict on the basis of the activity series how rapidly the evolution of hydrogen would occur with aluminum sheet or foil. A piece of unpolished aluminum sheet or strip gives disappointing results at first with HCl but, with the gradual solution of the protective oxide coating, the reaction becomes increasingly active so that very often the test tube contents will run out of the test tube. Place the test tube rack near the sink, appoint a student observer, and test for hydrogen before the reaction runs away with itself. Then have students attempt an explanation.

Passivity.[2] Dip iron into concentrated HCl, then into fuming nitric acid for 2 minutes. Rinse with distilled water and place in dilute acid or in an aqueous solution of $CuSO_4$. The iron is passive and does not react. Hammer it or scratch it with a file, and now dip into dilute acid

or $CuSO_4$ solution. It reacts since its passivity has been destroyed.

Aqua regia. Pieces of gold leaf and Dutch metal leaf are placed into 2 ml of concentrated nitric acid. The pure gold leaf is unaffected while the Dutch metal dissolves almost immediately with some brown nitrogen dioxide being liberated. Then add 6 ml of concentrated HCl to the test tube containing the gold leaf which then dissolves in the aqua regia produced. Sisler[3] explains this reaction as being due to the increase in the reducing strength of the metal because of the availability of chloride ion for the formation of a very stable complexion.

$$Au + 4 H^+ + NO_3^- + 4 Cl^- \rightarrow$$
$$AuCl_4^- + NO + 2 H_2O$$

Replacement of metals from their salt solutions. Very often the demonstrations described below are carried out as individual student experiments or exercises. Strips of assorted metals—Zn, Cu, Al, Pb, Fe (sandpapered iron nails), etc.—are placed into about 10 ml of salt solutions of vary-

[2] H. N. Alyea, "Tested Demonstrations in General Chemistry," *J. Chem. Educ.,* 1959, p. 44.

[3] Harry H. Sisler, Calvin A. Vanderwerf, and Arthur W. Davidson, *General Chemistry,* The Macmillan Company, N.Y., 1949 (pp. 512–13).

ing concentrations (0.5 N is one such concentration) in test tubes. This means that many possible combinations of metals and salt solutions exist. Which ones are chosen depends on availability of materials, etc. Ideally, strips of the various metals should be placed into salt solutions of metals which they will replace, into solutions of their own salts, and into solutions (where possible) of metals that they will not replace. An illustrative table with one among many possible selections of metals and solutions is given in Table 10–2. Students may then be directed to arrange metals in order of decreasing activity on the basis of their findings.

Many teachers set up large-scale demonstrations using 10-oz bottles or 500-ml flasks with metal strips inserted in advance so that these may rest undisturbed for varying periods of time (30 minutes to several days) and be viewed as part of the class procedure. More concentrated solutions than those used for student experiments may be used (1 N or greater). A good simple set consists of Zn and Cu strips in $ZnSO_4$ and $CuSO_4$ solutions. Students observe that the Zn has no effect on the $ZnSO_4$ solution but has replaced the copper in $CuSO_4$, resulting in a copious red metal deposit (when a metal first replaces copper, the initial deposit, while thin, appears black). The Cu has no effect on either solution. After some time has elapsed the $Zn:CuSO_4$ setup, originally blue, is colorless because of the formation of zinc sulfate. The demonstration set may also include a semipermanent silver or lead "tree" exhibit in which Zn replaces Pb, and Zn or Cu replaces the Ag. A wide-mouth bottle permits the use of "trees" shaped from metal sheets by appropriate cutting and horizontal positioning of the connected strips to form the skeletal basis for the growth of the replaced metal crystals.

Quick demonstrations. A copper penny is placed into a solution of mercurous nitrate for at least one minute, removed, dried on a paper towel, and rubbed with

TABLE 10-2
Some common metals in solution[4]

Solution used		$AgNO_3$	$Pb(NO_3)_2$	$Zn(NO_3)_2$	$Cu(NO_3)_2$	$HgNO_3$
original color of solution		colorless	colorless	colorless	blue	colorless
Zinc	metal deposited	Ag	Pb	none	Cu	Hg
	color of resulting solution	colorless	colorless	colorless	colorless with time	colorless
Lead	metal deposited	Ag	none	none	Cu	Hg
	color of resulting solution	colorless	colorless	colorless	colorless with time	colorless
Copper	metal deposited	Ag	none	none	none	Hg
	color of resulting solution	blue with time	colorless	colorless	blue with time	blue with time

[4] A variation of a table appearing in T. E. Eckert, H. K. Lyons, and W. H. Strevell, *Discovery Problems in Chemistry,* College Entrance Book Co., N.Y., 1950.

the towel or a piece of cotton with the resultant amalgamation evident as a "dime." Place a degreased file (it may also have been previously dipped into dilute HCl) into $CuSO_4$ solution. Within one minute, remove and have a student identify the copper coating.

Amphoterism. A group of students can demonstrate how the hydroxides of some metals are amphoteric, acting as either an acid or a base. They may show that these hydroxides can be dissolved by a strong base and are thus called acid, and can also be dissolved by a strong acid, thus behaving traditionally like a base. Develop formulas and equations for reactions such as

$$Zn(OH)_2 + 2\,[H^+ + Cl^-] \rightarrow$$
$$2\,H_2O + [Zn^{++} + 2\,Cl^-]$$
$$Zn(OH)_2 + 2\,[Na^+ + OH^-] \rightarrow$$
$$2\,H_2O + [2\,Na^+ + ZnO_2^{=}]$$

In this case, zinc hydroxide forms both H^+ ions and OH^- ions in solution. In each case, salts are formed. Also use other common amphoteric hydroxides such as aluminum hydroxide, chromium hydroxide, lead hydroxide, and stannic (tin) hydroxide. (See also 10.3e for amphoterism of aluminum ions.)

10.1e Alloys

You may want to show students that alloys and amalgams can be considered solutions of one metal in another.

Making solder. A common alloy such as 50–50 solder used by tinsmiths and plumbers can be made in class by a group of students. Have the students weigh out equal amounts of tin and lead into an iron or porcelain crucible. Cover the surface with a half-inch layer of sodium carbonate to prevent oxidation and then heat. Carefully pour this 50–50 solder into small wooden blocks to cool and skim off any sodium carbonate on the surface. Students should

be ready to compare the properties of the original metals with those of the alloy. What is its advantage in use? Compare the melting point of this alloy (220° C) with those of tin (232° C) and lead (327° C). As advanced work, some students might want to study this phenomenon of melting-point lowering.

Students may also examine Wood's metal. The alloy can be melted by placing a small quantity in a test tube; insert this tube into a beaker of water and boil the water. Wood's metal melts at about 60° C which points up why it is used in automatic sprinklers.

Have students test for the elements that make up brass: copper and zinc. Dissolve a shot-size bit of brass in a small amount of nitric acid. Notice the blue-green color of copper. Add a drop of this solution to a drop of ammonia solution to get the deeper blue color due to formation of the complex $Cu(NH_3)_4^{++}$ ion that gives a more positive test for copper.

The presence of zinc can be tested for in the following way. Add 5 cc of concentrated sodium hydroxide to the dissolved brass in the test tube; filter and add to the filtrate 2 drops of sodium sulfide solution. A white precipitate of zinc sulfide will form.

Amalgams. Alloys with mercury are given the special name "amalgams." They have many interesting uses that students might report on.

In dentistry. A soft silver-mercury amalgam is used for fillings. The mercury is then squeezed out and the silver hardens in place. Students can prepare silver amalgam by "dissolving" silver filings in mercury. They can then pack the amalgam in a plaster mold and squeeze the mercury out through chamois; what remains in the mold will be solid silver.

In the electrolytic manufacture of sodium. In the electrolysis of salt, the sodium forms an amalgam with the mercury at the negative electrode.

In gold mining. The fine particles of gold are collected by mercury. Water containing gold and impurities flows over mercury in a pan. The mercury amalgamates the gold, separating it from the impurities. The gold is recovered by heating the amalgam; the mercury is driven off and condensed for future use.

Silver amalgam. This can be made by mixing a few ml of mercury with a small amount of silver nitrate solution in a mortar. The following reaction takes place.

$$Hg + AgNO_3 \rightarrow Ag + HgNO_3$$

As the metallic silver forms, it dissolves in the mercury left over from the reaction to form a solid amalgam. If it should happen that the amalgam does not solidify, add a few crystals of silver nitrate and grind. Wash the amalgam thoroughly with distilled water and press between pieces of filter paper to dry overnight.

If you put one-half gram of this amalgam in a test tube and heat gently, the mercury will deposit on the cooler surfaces of the tube.

Sodium amalgam. The method for making sodium amalgam consists of placing a small drop of mercury in a mortar and adding a still smaller amount of clean, dry sodium which has been cut into very small pieces. These small pieces are added to the mercury and pressed together with it by a pestle. Miniature explosions are heard as the amalgam forms. The amalgam reacts with water as does sodium itself.

Ammonium amalgam. If a small quantity of sodium amalgam is added to a concentrated solution of ammonium chloride and is slightly warmed, an ammonium amalgam is formed which then decomposes rapidly. The amalgam swells up and forms a porous mass which quickly disappears.

10.2 Preparation of metals from their ores

As might be expected from the activity series (Table 10–1), some metals are easily obtained from their ores while others are difficult to extract. Some of these more active metals are obtained commercially by processes that cannot be duplicated in the laboratory or classroom. The extractions are presented here in two groups, the second more difficult than the first. But as an introduction, we shall show how gold is extracted. This extraction process is unique because of the low chemical affinity of gold (it does react with strong chlorides).

10.2a Gold

Since gold is extremely inactive (hence a "noble metal"), it is usually found uncombined. The problem here is one of extraction of gold from a mixture rather than from a compound. Students can simulate such a mixture by filing a small piece of gold to make "gold dust" and mixing this with fine sand. Students may show how it is separated by "panning" in a pie plate. Or you may want to use the same mixture to show another process. Run the mixture in a wet loosely packed state over mercury (Fig. 10–3A). Students can observe how the mercury amalgamates the gold, separating it from the sand. Now heat the mercury-gold amalgam in a Pyrex test tube. Notice how the mercury vapor condenses in the cold receiving tube; the gold remains at the bottom of the heated tube (Fig. 10–3B).

10.2b Metals readily obtained from their ores

Metals fairly low in the activity series are readily extracted from their ores. Some common ores decompose readily on being heated; others require a reducing

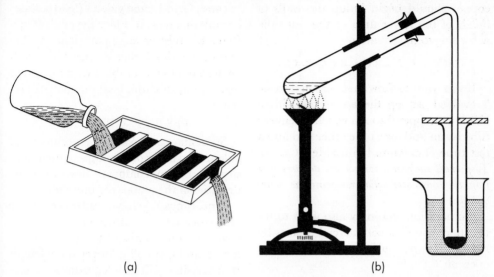

(a)   (b)

Fig. 10–3 Separating gold: (a) running gold-containing mixture over mercury, (b) then heating the gold-mercury amalgam to drive off the mercury.

agent, such as carbon. In some cases sulfide and carbonate compounds are changed to oxides, which are then reduced. In class several of these metallurgical operations can be demonstrated on a small scale.

Mercury. Heat cinnabar (mercuric sulfide) or mercuric oxide in a Pyrex test tube as in the setup shown in Fig. 10–4. (*Caution: Avoid mercury fumes.*) The ores will decompose according to the equations

$$2\,HgS + O_2 \rightarrow 2\,Hg + SO_2 + S$$
$$2\,HgO \rightarrow 2\,Hg + O_2$$

Students should notice how mercury collects in the cool upper portion of the tube. When cinnabar is used, sulfur and sulfur dioxide are formed. If the oxide is used, you may also want to test for oxygen.

Copper. Although reduction of copper oxide is not the commercial process for the production of copper, it is analagous to the reduction of copper sulfide. Place a mixture containing about 1 part of copper oxide powder to 3 parts of powdered carbon (the proportion is not critical since

this is a surface reaction) in a large Pyrex test tube. Clamp the test tube to a ring stand or hold it with a test tube holder and heat in the flame of a Meker burner (use the same setup as in Fig. 10–4). After some 10 minutes of heating, metallic

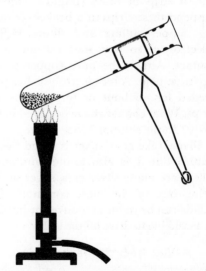

Fig. 10–4 Heating cinnabar or mercuric oxide will drive off fumes of mercury which condense on the cooler upper portion of the test tube.

copper should begin lining the walls of much of the lower area of the test tube according to the equation

$$3\,CuO + 2\,C \rightarrow 3\,Cu + CO + CO_2$$

If you want to show that carbon dioxide is evolved, set up the apparatus with a one-hole stopper through which a delivery tube is run and insert the other end into a test tube of calcium hydroxide. (*Caution: To prevent suckback, remove the delivery tube from the limewater before removing the source of heat.*)

On occasion, you may also want to try the more complex commercial process by roasting copper sulfide in a crucible in open air.

$$2\,CuS + O_2 \rightarrow 2\,Cu + SO_2 + S$$

(*Note:* The products of this reaction vary, but this is the usual equation given for it.)

The electrolytic purification of blister or raw copper can also be shown. Raw copper is cast in slabs which are used as anodes in the electrolysis. You may want to show this, using a strip of pure copper and a strip of brass (impure copper). Suspend these strips in a beaker containing copper sulfate and dilute H_2SO_4 (electrolyte) so that they do not make contact. Attach the pure copper to the negative pole. After electrolysis has proceeded for an hour or so, examine the strips. What changes have occurred in the strips? In the solution? (See 13.3a.)

Silver. Like gold, silver is found free in nature but it is also found combined. There are many silver ores, silver sulfide being one of the most common. The sulfide can be reduced to silver by heating in a crucible to drive off the sulfur.

$$2\,Ag_2S + O_2 \rightarrow 4\,Ag + S + SO_2$$

(*Note:* The proportions of S and SO_2 formed vary, but this is the usual equation given for the reaction.)

Lead. Grind some galena (lead sulfide) crystals in a mortar. Place the powder in a Pyrex test tube or small porcelain crucible and heat with a Fisher burner. Sulfur will be driven off and combine with oxygen to form sulfur dioxide; lead powder will remain.

$$PbS + O_2 \rightarrow Pb + SO_2$$

Students can examine specimens of galena and other ores, compute their density, and then compare these with the densities of the metals the ores yield.

Zinc. If possible have students examine zinc silicate under ultraviolet light to see that the mineral absorbs this short wave length and gives off a longer wave length that is visible. Ultraviolet radiation raises the energy levels of some electrons. As they return to the lower levels, they radiate visible light.

Just as lead sulfide can be roasted, so can zinc sulfide. Again use a large Pyrex test tube. In the roasting process both the sulfur and the zinc combine with oxygen in the air to form sulfur dioxide and zinc oxide. SO_2 goes off as a gas. The zinc oxide powder is reduced, usually by powdered carbon. The zinc vapor is carried by the delivery tube into a Pyrex tube to form zinc powder.

$$2\,ZnS + 3\,O_2 \rightarrow 2\,ZnO + 2\,SO_2$$
$$ZnO + C \rightarrow Zn + CO$$

10.2c Metals less readily obtained from their ores

Iron. Students may extract iron from hematite (Fe_2O_3). First have them pass a magnet over a small heap of the ore. The results of this test may be compared later with a similar test on the iron extracted from the hematite.

Mix equal amounts of powdered coke and ferric oxide; heat the mixture in a crucible in an electric arc furnace (25.3a). The mixture needs strong heat for 10 min-

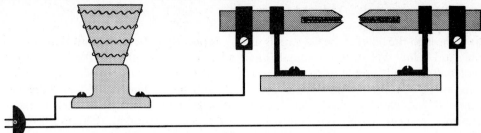

Fig. 10–5 Reducing iron oxide in an electric arc.

utes. After cooling for several minutes, spill the residue on filter paper and test with a magnet. How does this residue differ from the ore hematite?

Reducing iron oxide in an electric furnace. Although the operation of a blast furnace cannot be demonstrated in the classroom, it is possible to show the reduction of iron oxide in an electric furnace. Connect 2 carbon arc rods to a 1000-watt heating unit in a series circuit operating on the line current (Fig. 10–5). You may want to hollow the carbon rods and pack them with Fe_2O_3, as shown.

A mixture of carbon powder and Fe_2O_3 on a carbon block heated by a blast lamp or a welding torch will also yield iron.

Thermite process. Show the reduction of iron oxide on a large scale in the thermite process. The thermite mixture (sold under the trade name Thermit) and ignition powder can be purchased from a scientific supply house (see appendix). Or you can make the thermite mixture by mixing 3 parts of Fe_2O_3 with 1 part of aluminum powder. First insert three very small clay flowerpots one inside the other (Fig. 10–6) and place a piece of thin paper over the hole of the innermost flowerpot. (Be sure that each of the pots has a hole in the bottom.) Then support the nested pots in a ring stand and place a large basin filled with dry sand below.

Now place a teaspoonful of the thermite mixture in the inner flowerpot. Put a quarter teaspoonful of ignition powder or

potassium chlorate in a small hollow in the top of the thermite mixture. Into the ignition powder insert a 5″ magnesium ribbon to serve as a fuse so that 1½″ of the fuse is buried in the mixture. This leaves 3½″ standing vertically above the mixture. Have students move to the opposite side of the room. Ignite the fuse and stand back at least 8 feet. If the room is darkened, the reaction is more vivid. When the burning flame of the fuse reaches the ignition powder, it ignites and decomposes, giving off enough heat in the process to cause the aluminum in the thermite mixture to combine with oxygen in the iron oxide.

$$2\ Al + Fe_2O_3 \rightarrow Al_2O_3 + 2\ Fe$$

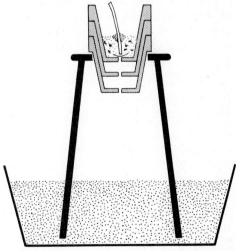

Fig. 10–6 Reducing a metal ore by the thermite process.

In this way iron oxide is reduced to iron, which will flow in a white-hot molten state through the holes of the flowerpots to the sand below. When the iron mass has cooled sufficiently, lift it with a pair of long tongs (it remains red hot for some time). If you have an anvil and heavy hammer, you can forge the iron into any shape. If two pieces of clean iron are placed on the sand before the fuse is lighted, the molten iron will flow over them and weld them together.

Some teachers place the charge in a few sheets of folded filter paper held in a ring on a ring stand so that it looks like a funnel without a stem. When the fuse is lit, the entire reaction is visible and the molten and fiery mass falls into a trough of sand placed under the paper funnel. A still more effective way is to have the fiery mass go through a tall beaker containing water placed on the sand in the trough. Students can see the water immediately boil vigorously (the beaker will most likely crack). Another method uses a crucible slightly imbedded in a 1" layer of sand. In place of the flowerpots a crucible with a hole in its bottom can be used.

(*Caution: Any thermite process experiment should be done with the greatest care. Stand back at least 8 feet, use a screen if available, and have students stand on opposite side of the room. Rehearsal without the presence of students is a must.*) However, for all the care necessary, the thermite process is an engrossing demonstration and well worth the extra precautions.

Tin. The usual tin ore consists of stannic sulfide mixed with arsenic compounds and some iron oxide. The ore is roasted and the iron oxide removed magnetically. Students can heat some SnS_2 in a Pyrex test tube or a crucible to get the oxide.

$$SnS_2 + 3\,O_2 \rightarrow SnO_2 + 2\,SO_2$$

The oxide is then reduced with powdered charcoal.

$$SnO_2 + 2\,C \rightarrow Sn + 2\,CO$$

Separation of ores by flotation.[5] Select a bowl and an eggbeater that can be used together. Put a mixture of 3 teaspoonfuls of sand and 4 teaspoonfuls of plumbers' litharge in the bowl. Add water to within an inch of the top and then pour in 25 to 55 ml of pine bath oil. (Be sure it is pine oil not pine essence.) Beat the mixture with the eggbeater, skimming the foam from the surface every so often. Add water to keep the bowl full. Pine oil can also be added as needed.

When the foam does not seem to pick up more litharge, carefully pour off the liquid in the bowl and inspect the residue. Note how much sand is left in the bowl. Spread some of the foam on a paper towel to dry. After the foam dries, see if the solid left on the towel resembles either the sand or litharge used in the beginning. The success of the process depends upon the frothing action of pine oil. The oil attaches itself to the ore but not to the earthy material. The plumbers' litharge represents an ore. The sand represents the earthy material from which the ore is to be separated. In place of litharge, ferric oxide or other powdered metals and metallic compounds may be used. Natural ores are not likely to be successful because of the difficulty of pulverization to a fine powder. Commercially it is profitable to use the flotation process even for concentrating ores that contain less than 1 per cent of the desired metal.

Some detergents or bubble bath oil capsules may be used in place of the pine oil.

If a small air blower is available, the froth may be obtained by blowing air into the ore, water, and oil mixture.

[5] Adapted from *Using Chemicals* published by the Bureau of Secondary Curriculum Development of the New York State Education Department, Albany, N.Y.

Reducing ores by electrolysis.[6] The principle of reducing ores by electrolysis can be illustrated by using copper sulfate to represent the ore.

Prepare a saturated copper sulfate solution by dissolving as much powdered copper sulfate as possible in 200 ml of water in a beaker. Set 15 ml of the solution aside in a test tube for later use.

Place two carbon rods in the solution in the beaker and connect them as electrodes in a series circuit with a 6-volt source. Allow the electrodes to remain in the solution for a few minutes and then inspect them to see if a deposit has formed on either one. Replace the electrodes and repeat the process several times until a deposit of copper can be clearly seen on the negative electrode. Then disconnect the battery.

Pour 15 ml of the copper sulfate solution from the beaker into a test tube. Compare the color of this solution with that of the original solution set aside at the beginning of the experiment.

There are many variations of this procedure. Some employ a strip of Cu as anode and a rod of graphite as cathode. Some use a thick Cu anode and a thin strip of Cu for the cathode. The graphite is preferable for a quick demonstration since it seldom requires more than 5 minutes. A good scheme is to reverse the electrodes (Cu-carbon) after copper has plated out and been observed by the class. This results in the removal of the deposited Cu from the graphite which now is the anode. A single good dry cell or two in series also gives good results.

10.3   Tests for various metals

Chemists need to be able to identify the composition of many unknown substances. In the laboratory, students may gain some understanding of how this is done by using

[6] Adapted from *Using Chemicals,* N.Y. State Bureau of Secondary Curriculum Development, Albany, N.Y.

TABLE 10-3
Color of various metallic sulfides

antimony	orange-red
arsenic	yellow
cadmium	yellow-orange (add alkali and heat)
chromium	black
copper	black
iron (FeS)	brown-black
iron (Fe_2S_3)	brassy
lead	black
mercury (HgS)	red or black
nickel (NiS)	black
silver	black or gray-black
stannous	gray-black
stannic	golden yellow
zinc (ZnS)	white

some of the routine checks that chemists use. Many practical applications are possible, for example, testing samples of soil in the community to determine which elements are found in the soils and which elements need to be added to deficient soil. As a long-range project, a student might become interested in an analysis of a mixed solution. Typical procedures for identifying an "unknown" are covered in qualitative analysis textbooks, several of which are listed at the end of this chapter and in the bibliography. For an introductory demonstration see metallic sulfides in 9.2b.

10.3a   Sulfide tests

Many metallic ions in solution can be identified by their reaction to form a sulfide when hydrogen sulfide is bubbled through. The characteristic color of the sulfide formed can often be used to identify the metal.

Students may use the table of color reactions (Table 10–3) to learn the identity of the specimen they have tested.

10.3b   Flame tests

Many salts will show the typical color of their metallic ions (see Table 10–4)

TABLE 10-4

potassium, rubidium, cesium	violet
copper	blue-green
lead, arsenic, selenium	light blue
calcium	orange-yellow
barium	yellow-green
sodium	bright yellow
lithium	deep red
strontium	red

when heated in a Bunsen flame. However, the yellow color produced by sodium is so much more intense than any of the other colors that the others are usually obscured. Only if the burner and the salts used are free of sodium can the other colors be seen when salts are introduced into a flame by means of a nichrome or platinum wire loop.

In common practice, the wire loop is cleaned by inserting it into hydrochloric acid and heated in a flame to incandescence until no color shows in the flame. Then dip the cooled wire successively in each of several salt solutions. Heat in a flame. When the flame is yellow, view through a square of cobalt glass so that the yellow sodium flame is filtered out.

In doing the flame tests, chemicals can be saved and solutions kept clean by having sets of test tubes made up in advance and labeled with the chemical to be tested, and then stoppered with a one-hole stopper through which a glass rod (into which a short length of nichrome wire has been sealed) is inserted. These tubes can be stored and used over and over again.

Another method that works with certainty for all metallic salts depends upon the absorption of fine particles of the salt in a gas. This method uses a Syracuse dish and a round-base Bunsen burner of the type shown in Fig. 10–7. Drill a ¼″ hole through the base into the stem as

shown. Into the Syracuse dish place some metallic zinc, the unknown salt to be tested, and dilute hydrochloric acid. The purpose of the zinc is to release hydrogen from the acid. The hydrogen then rises, carrying salt ions up into the flame. Zinc ions do not give a colored flame. If a carbonate of the metallic element is used in place of another salt of that metal, the carbon dioxide released as the result of the reaction with the HCl will do the work of the hydrogen gas. This eliminates the need for zinc in the setup. Now place a lighted Bunsen burner over the Syracuse dish. If the room is darkened, students should find the flame test color for the metal visible even for those ions that normally give a weak color. Another effective technique is to use polyethylene bottles of the sort used to spray cosmetics.

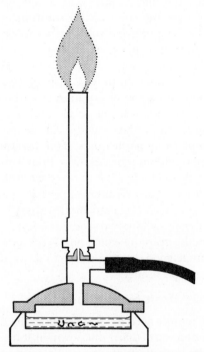

Fig. 10–7 The ions of a metallic salt carried upward by hydrogen will give their characteristic identifying color.

TABLE 10-5

Borax bead test colors for various metallic ions

	oxidizing flame	reducing flame
antimony	yellow-brown	
bismuth	yellow-brown	
chromium	green	green
cobalt	blue	blue
copper	blue	red
iron	yellow or brownish red	green
lead	yellow or brown	
manganese	violet	no color
nickel	brown-red	
uranium	yellow-brown	green

The solution can either be sprayed directly into the flame or into the collar opening of a Bunsen burner.

10.3c Borax bead tests

A borax bead is made to form on a platinum or nichrome wire loop (⅛″ diameter). Each student can seal the straight end of such a wire into a glass rod by heating the rod in the Bunsen flame to melt the glass, and inserting the wire. After it cools, students should fire-polish the other end of the tubing or rod to prevent cutting or scratching themselves.

Some teachers prefer to use glass rods for making large, bright borax beads. Use 10″ or 12″ lengths of ordinary ¼″ or slightly thicker soft glass rod. Students may make a number of borax bead glass holders and test many metallic salts in the following way. Heat the glass rod (or wire loop) to red heat; dip into dry borax (sodium tetraborate) and heat again. Watch how the borax melts into a bead on the wire loop; on the glass rod the bead will be larger and fuse into the glass. Once the bead is formed, students are ready to test the salts. Place the red-hot bead into a small quantity of powdered salt of the metal to be tested. Then reheat to red heat

and allow to cool, record the color, and compare with Table 10–5. A new glass rod should be used for each test; if the wire loop is used, the bead can be simply flicked off after reheating or crushed with a file.

10.3d Cobalt nitrate test

This test is used to identify some metallic ions which are not recognized by flame tests (Al^{+++}, Mg^{++}, Zn^{++}). Scoop out a shallow cavity in a small block of charcoal or a plaster block, and into this place a sample of the metallic salt to be tested. (Sulfates are generally used for student experiments.) Add a drop of water to the salt and heat strongly, directing the oxidizing part of the flame over the surface of the salt. (You may want to have students use a blowpipe to direct the flame over the salt.) What is the color of the substance when it cools? Now add 2 drops of dilute cobalt nitrate solution and heat again. On cooling, what is the color of the substance? Students can test several unknown substances set out for them in the laboratory. Aluminum compounds produce blue, magnesium compounds, pink, and zinc compounds, green.

10.3e Specific tests

Testing for iron. This element forms a number of strongly colored ions and compounds. There are specific tests for both ferrous and ferric ions. If a solution of potassium *ferro*cyanide is added to a *ferric* salt, a bright blue precipitate (Prussian blue) forms.

$$4\ Fe^{+3} + 3\ Fe(CN)_6^{-4} = Fe_4\left[Fe(CN)_6\right]_3$$

If potassium *ferri*cyanide is added to a solution of a *ferrous* compound, a dark blue precipitate (Turnbull's blue) forms.

$$3\ Fe^{+2} + 2\ Fe(CN)_6^{-3} = Fe_3\left[Fe(CN)_6\right]_2$$

In addition, *ferrous* ion gives no color

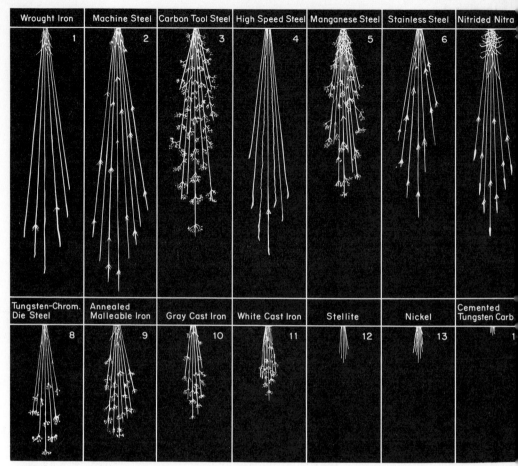

Wrought Iron	Machine Steel	Carbon Tool Steel	High Speed Steel	Manganese Steel	Stainless Steel	Nitrided Nitra
1	2	3	4	5	6	

Tungsten-Chrom. Die Steel	Annealed Malleable Iron	Gray Cast Iron	White Cast Iron	Stellite	Nickel	Cemented Tungsten Carb
8	9	10	11	12	13	1

Fig. 10–8 Spark patterns produced by various metals and alloys when held against a carborundum grinding wheel.

reaction with thiocyanate ion (SCN^-) but *ferric* ion produces a blood-red complex ion, probably $Fe(SCN)^{++}$.

Spark test for metals alloyed with iron. The other components of an iron alloy can be identified by means of the spark test, using a carborundum tool grinder. Both the color and the pattern of sparks provide the information about the alloy. Fig. 10–8 shows the spark patterns and Table 10–6 the corresponding compositions of these patterns for several substances alloyed with iron.

Colored ions of iron. Students can combine in a test tube 5 cc of ferrous sulfate solution ($FeSO_4$), 4 cc of dilute HCl, and 4 cc of $KClO_3$ solution. Then add together in another test tube 5 cc of ferric chloride ($FeCl_3$) solution and 4 cc of $Na_2S_2O_3$ (sodium thiosulfate) solution. In each case, students should be ready to explain the reasons for the changes as they occur.

Amphoterism of aluminum ions. Students can also examine the amphoteric property of several aluminum compounds. Mix together in a test tube about 10 ml of aluminum sulfate solution and a few drops of NaOH solution. Then divide the suspension into two parts by pouring half

TABLE 10-6
Characteristics of sparks generated by the grinding of metals*

metal	volume of stream	relative length of stream inches[1]	color of stream close to wheel	color of streaks near end of stream	quantity of spurts	nature of spurts
1. wrought iron	large	65	straw	white	very few	forked
2. machine steel	large	70	white	white	very few	forked
3. carbon tool steel	moderately large	55	white	white	very many	fine, repeating
4. high speed steel	small	60	red	straw	extremely few	forked
5. manganese steel	moderately large	45	white	white	many	fine, repeating
6. stainless steel	moderate	50	straw	white	moderate	forked
7. nitrided nitralloy	large (curved)	55	white	white	moderate	forked
8. tungsten-chromium die steel	small	35	red	straw [2]	many	fine, repeating
9. annealed malleable iron	moderate	32	red	straw	many	fine, repeating
10. gray cast iron	small	25	red	straw	many	fine, repeating
11. white cast iron	very small	20	red	straw	few	fine, repeating
12. stellite	very small	10	orange	orange	none	
13. nickel	very small	10	orange	orange	none	
14. cemented tungsten carbide	extremely small	2	light orange	light orange	none	
15. copper, brass, aluminum	none					

* Norton Company, Worcester 6, Mass.
[1] Figures obtained with 12″ wheel on bench stand are relative only. Actual length in each instance will vary with grinding wheel, pressure, etc.
[2] Blue-white spurts.

into another tube. To one tube add more sodium hydroxide solution; to the second, add hydrochloric acid. Students can observe that in each tube the precipitate clears. They can probably write the equations for the reactions.

$$Al_2(SO_4)_3 + 6\,NaOH \rightarrow$$
$$2\,Al(OH)_3 + 3\,Na_2SO_4$$

$$Al(OH)_3 + [Na^+ + OH^-] \rightarrow$$
$$[Na^+ + AlO_2^-] + 2\,H_2O$$

$$Al(OH)_3 + 3\,[H^+ + Cl^-] \rightarrow$$
$$[Al^{+++} + 3\,Cl^-] + 3\,H_2O$$

Perhaps some students will want to report on other compounds which exhibit amphoterism.

10.4   The alkali metals

The silvery alkali metals—lithium, sodium, potassium, rubidium, cesium—all have rather low densities and are often referred to as the light metals. They are soft enough to be cut with a knife. The alkali metals have one electron in the outer shell which is easily lost, forming positive ions. As a result, they are very reactive and correspondingly difficult to free from their compounds.

They are not found free in nature because of their reactivity. They react vigorously with water to liberate hydrogen, forming strong bases; they react readily with oxygen, hydrogen, the halogens, nitrogen, and sulfur. Almost all of their salts are extremely soluble in water. In fact the leaching effect of rain has resulted in the transportation of these salts to the ocean or inland seas.

In this section we have developed some procedures which have been found useful in showing the preparation and properties of sodium and potassium. We have also included a little of the metallurgy of these metals, showing how they are obtained from the electrolysis of their fused chlorides or hydroxides. The other alkali metals are not commonly found in the high school laboratory.

10.4a   The chemistry of sodium

Preparation of sodium metal. Sodium can be prepared in the classroom by the electrolysis of molten sodium chloride. A high-temperature refractory crucible heated by two large Meker burners is needed to melt the salt. Prepare two electrodes as follows: Take two Pyrex tubes about ¼″ outside diameter and fit an iron wire inside each tube snugly (the wire should not extend to the bottom of the tube). Connect one wire to the positive and the other to the negative terminal of a 6- to 12-volt storage battery or a d.c. rectifier or a battery charger as in Fig. 10–9. Perform under a hood. The ends of the tubes which stick into the molten sodium chloride are open. In place of the refractory crucible, you may use a small graphite crucible heated inside an asbestos-lined chimney.

When the salt is molten, lower the two glass tubes carrying the iron electrodes into it. It can be observed how the sodium

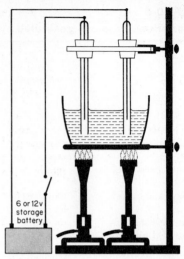

Fig. 10–9   Electrolysis of fused NaCl.

will collect inside the glass tube containing the negative electrode. Students can observe the silvery color as long as it is not in contact with air. If you break the tube and drop the pieces on which sodium has been deposited into a test tube of water, hydrogen will be evolved.

Reactions of sodium metal. Cut a small piece of sodium with a knife so that students can observe its color and softness. Drop a very small piece into water or use a sodium spoon to hold the sodium under the large inverted test tube; collect the hydrogen gas evolved (see 7.2c), and test the solution with litmus paper or other indicator. Students can establish the equation

$$2\,Na + 2\,H_2O \rightarrow H_2 + 2\,[Na^+ + OH^-]$$

You may want to show that sodium metal is commonly stored in kerosene to prevent a reaction with water, atmospheric vapor, or oxygen. (*Caution: Sodium should not be touched with bare hands as it will react with the moisture on the skin and cause a burn. Handle with tongs or forceps.*)

Sodium hydroxide. The production of sodium hydroxide is part of the electrolysis of brine with the formation of sodium hydroxide, hydrogen, and chlorine (see 11.2a). Another method, sometimes called the soda-lime process, uses limewater made by adding 1 g of calcium hydroxide to 10 cc of water in a test tube. In another tube prepare 10 cc of 1 N sodium carbonate solution. (See 8.3c for preparation.) Pour both into a 200-cc beaker; then heat at 95° C for 3 minutes. Sodium hydroxide is formed, according to the equation

$$[Ca^{++} + 2\ OH^-] + [2\ Na^+ + CO_3^=] \rightarrow$$
$$2\ [Na^+ + OH^-] + CaCO_3$$

To show that NaOH has formed, let the mixture cool and add a drop of malachite green solution. The green color vanishes immediately if the solution is at least 0.1 N in sodium hydroxide.

Sodium hydroxide is one of the strongest bases in common use. You may want to demonstrate the comparative strengths of several hydroxides by measuring their conductivity (8.4d).

The neutralization of HCl by NaOH is easily demonstrated (8.4e); the effect of NaOH on wool and cotton and its use in soap making may be described.

Sodium chloride. The properties of this common compound have been described in association with chlorine (Chapter 11) and with salts (Chapter 8).

Solvay process—making sodium bicarbonate. There are two ways to demonstrate this process depending upon your source of CO_2. If you are using dry ice take a wide-mouth bottle in which there is 250 ml of concentrated NH_4OH that has been saturated with solid NaCl. Drop in chunks of dry ice. The precipitate is $NaHCO_3$.

This demonstration may be performed using a regular CO_2 laboratory generator. The gas is bubbled through a wash bottle to remove acid vapors. The delivery tube leading from the wash bottle leads into a test tube containing 10 ml of concentrated NH_4OH which has been saturated with solid NaCl. Precipitation can be hurried if the test tube rests in a beaker of ice and water.

In each case the solid precipitate can be filtered out, blotted dry, and heated to produce carbon dioxide which is detected by bubbling the gas through limewater. The filtrate can be evaporated almost to dryness and then heated with solid $Ca(OH)_2$ or with 6 M NaOH. It then gives the positive litmus test for NH_3 showing that the other product was NH_4Cl.

Sodium peroxide. You may want to have students repeat the procedure for making oxygen from sodium peroxide (7.1b). Or add sodium peroxide to a very dilute solution of hydrochloric acid in a generator. The product will be sodium chloride and hydrogen peroxide.

$$Na_2O_2 + 2\ [H^+ + Cl^-] \rightarrow$$
$$2\ [Na^+ + Cl^-] + H_2O_2$$

You may also want to have students study hydrogen peroxide at this point. Add MnO_2 to release oxygen. (See 7.1b.) Then test its action as a bleach. (*Note:* Do not use it as an antiseptic as it is probably contaminated.) Students can also show its instability, particularly in light, and test it with indicators to show that it is a very weak acid. For further reactions of H_2O_2 see 7.3.

Migration of sodium ions through glass. A group of students may undertake an interesting and unusual project showing the migration of ions. They will need a vacuum lamp bulb. A 25-watt clear tubular showcase bulb, G.E., Westinghouse, or Sylvania, is essential. Do not use a standard clear light bulb.

Clamp a porcelain socket in an inverted position and connect it to a lamp cord and plug to fit a standard outlet. In a plain agate or enamel pan with a piece of clean iron (or a graphite rod) at the bottom, place a mixture of crystalline sodium nitrate (95 per cent C.P.) and sodium chloride (5 per cent). A wire should connect the iron or graphite rod to the positive side of a 45-, 67½-, or 90-volt "B" battery; the negative of the battery is connected to either side of the porcelain socket (Fig. 10–10). As an alternative you may use clean iron gauze in place of the graphite rod.

Heat the mixture with two Meker (or Fisher) burners until it is molten and adjust the heat so that the surface just stays liquid (about 350° C). Now lower the lighted bulb gently into the molten salts about an inch. After a time a grayish cloud will form inside the bulb. Disconnect the current and lift the hot bulb from the molten salt. Students can see that the

inside of the lamp is covered with a silvery layer of metallic sodium.

Students should establish that the sodium ions from the molten salts have replaced some of the sodium in the glass, causing free sodium ions to collect on the inside. These have a strong electron affinity, and will attract some of the electrons emitted by the filament of the bulb, forming sodium metal. To show that the silvery coating really is sodium, break the bulb carefully under water. The sodium will react with the water, forming hydrogen and sodium hydroxide. This experiment can be done under a funnel, and the hydrogen collected in a graduated pipette.

10.4b The chemistry of potassium

Preparation of potassium. Potassium can be produced with the same apparatus that was shown in Fig. 10–9 to prepare sodium, with molten KCl used in place of NaCl. The metal will collect inside the cathode, and it, too, will be silvery. When the reaction of potassium with water is to be shown, extremely small quantities should be used because potassium is even more active than sodium.

Compounds and reactions of potassium. Most of the compounds and reactions of potassium are similar to those of sodium. You may want to demonstrate some of the reactions presented for sodium earlier in this chapter, substituting potassium.

In addition, there are several tests for potassium. The definitive test uses 10 g of pure KCl, 13 g of solid $NaNO_3$, and 20 cc of water. Boil this mixture gently for 3 minutes; then cool it and decant as much liquid as possible. The precipitate is mainly KNO_3; dissolve it in as little boiling water as possible, cool, and filter. Test for potassium ion either in a flame test (10.3b) or, preferably, by adding

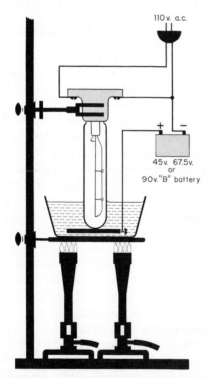

110 v. a.c.

+ −

45 v. 67.5 v.
or
90 v. "B" battery

Fig. 10–10 Arrangement of apparatus to show the migration of sodium ions through glass.

$Na_3Co(NO_2)_6$ solution. A yellow complex salt is formed.

$$2\,K^+ + Na^+ + Co(NO_2)_6^{\equiv} \longrightarrow K_2NaCo(NO_2)_6$$

For other tests for potassium, and sodium as well, you may want to refer students to a qualitative analysis text.

CAPSULE LESSONS
Ways to get started in class

10-1. Begin one lesson by showing bottles of white powdered substances—each an "unknown." How could a chemist discover their ingredients? Demonstrate how a flame test or borax bead test is done. Have students practice these techniques. Lead into a discussion of metals as a group of elements and their specific characteristics.

10-2. Introduce a lesson on metallurgy by showing examples of ores—galena, hematite, and bauxite. What are some possible ways that a metal can be extracted or won from its ore? Demonstrate a method by which the oxide is roasted, or a case of enrichment, or of flotation. Refer to those described here or in chemistry texts as specific laboratory methods. Students should be able to explain why a Bronze Age preceded an Iron Age.

10-3. At some time, have students as committees working together report to the class on the historical development in the metallurgy of iron, aluminum, copper, and other metals. Trace the changes from empirical methods toward processes that are less empirical.

10-4. In one lesson, show samples of strips of many metals. You may have to sandpaper some to bring out the luster. Elicit from students some of the physical properties of metals. Perform some of the demonstrations described here to show conductivity of heat, of electricity. How active are metals chemically? Show a few examples of the relative activity of some metals—sodium, potassium, iron, magnesium, or others. This demonstration may serve as an introduction to the reading of the text on the new topic.

10-5. You may want to show a film illustrating one or several metallurgical processes. Have you seen *Unfinished Rainbows* (Aluminum Co. of America), *This Is Magnesium* (Dow Chemical), *Metals and Non-Metals* (Indiana), or the filmstrip *Changing Ores Into Metals* (McGraw-Hill)?

A small booklet is also available for student reading describing the winning of aluminum from its ore, *ABC's of Aluminum* (Reynolds Metal Co.) or you will find use for such booklets as *Practical Data for Metallurgists* (Timken Roller Bearing Co.).

10-6. In some communities, it may be possible to make a field trip to an industrial plant concerned with the manufacture or processing of metals from their ores. (Be sure to get permission notes from parents if this is customary in your school.) Or you may find it more feasible to use a film such as *Iron—Product of the Blast Furnace* (Indiana) or *Art of Spark Testing* (Wyckoff Steel Co.).

10-7. As part of a series of lessons on metals and metallurgy, a group of students might prepare a display for a hall case, showing samples of basic ores that are important in the U.S. economy and the metals extracted from them. Also indicate the uses of the metals and the rate at which they are being consumed in the United States. What are the problems in the conservation of these materials?

Many teachers spend time discussing the opportunities for careers in fields of chemical engineering and sales with their classes. Several booklets are available for student use. In fact, a file of career booklets may be a part of the reference materials in the classroom or laboratory for student use.

10-8. Cut small pieces of sodium and potassium and show their reaction in water; also demonstrate their other chemical properties. Students should be able to observe some of the physical properties too. Establish the uses of sodium in industry.

10-9. In one lesson you may want to show some of the uses of sodium as a reducing agent. You may want to try one or more of the procedures described in this chapter. Have students develop equations for the reactions.

10-10. There may be an occasion when you want to show that sodium dissolves in mercury, forming an amalgam. Introduce the topic with a demonstration (several described here) and elicit the new properties of the amalgam; compare these with the original properties of the elements.

10-11. There are several films and filmstrips that may be used as a summary, or even as a vicarious field trip, to observe the metallurgy of sodium and potassium. Select from the list at the end of this chapter and in the more complete listing in the appendix. Other films and filmstrips, several of which are available as free loans, are listed at the end of the chapter and also at the end of the book.

PEOPLE, PLACES, AND THINGS

Many communities have rich resources for extending the activities of the classroom. There may be an industrial plant processing a metal or its compound; a chemical engineer may be available to speak to the class as an expert in some specific area or in guidance related to career information.

Are there sources of ores which students might collect on a field trip? Possibly parents or members of the geology department of a nearby college might suggest locales. You may borrow a collection of ores at times from students in your school. In fact, some students have hobbies which involve crystals and can easily give an illustrated lecture to the class.

BOOKS AND PAMPHLETS

These are only a few of the books which are pertinent to the work discussed in this chapter. These and many other references classified by subject and with complete bibliographical data are given in the bibliography at the end of the book.

Arthur, P., *Analytical Chemistry,* McGraw-Hill, 1957.

Basolo, F., and R. Pearson, *Mechanisms of Inorganic Reactions: A Study of Metal Complexes in Solution,* Wiley, 1958.

Bogert, L. J., *Fundamentals of Chemistry,* 8th ed., Saunders, 1958.

Darken, L., *Physical Chemistry of Metals,* McGraw-Hill, 1953.

Deming, H., *General Chemistry,* Wiley, 1955.

Fischer, R., *A Basic Course in Quantitative Chemical Analysis,* Saunders, 1956.

Jaffee, B., *Crucibles,* Simon and Shuster, 1948.

Luder, W., A. Vernon, and S. Zuffanti, *General Chemistry,* Saunders, 1953.

Nininger, R., *Minerals for Atomic Energy,* Van Nostrand, 1954.

FILMS AND FILMSTRIPS

This partial list is intended only as a guide toward film and filmstrip selection. Refer to the more complete listing at the end of the book where films are classified by subject and where a key to abbreviations and addresses of distributors are given. The cost of film rental, of course, is subject to change. Films are sound and black and white unless otherwise specified.

Aluminum on the March (f, s, c), Association, inquire rental.

Art of Spark Testing (steel) (f, s, c), Wyckoff Steel, free.

Atomic Metallurgy (f, s), U.S. Atomic Energy Comm., free.

Changing Ores into Metals (fs), Popular Science through McGraw-Hill, $6.00.

Chemistry of Steel, Chemistry of Iron (2 fs), American Iron and Steel Institute, free.

Copper (f, s, c), Anaconda, free.

Crystal Gazers (f, s), G.E., free.

Iron Making (fs), International, $4.00.

It's Asbestos (f, s, c), Canadian Consulate General, free.

Metallurgy Plus (f, s), Ideal, free.

The Petrified River (uranium) (f, s, c), U.S.A.E.C., free.

Romance of Radium (f, s), Teaching Films, free.

Story of Stainless Steel (f, s), Ideal, free.

This Is Magnesium (f, s, c), Dow, free.

Tin Plate (f, s, c), U.S. Bur. of Mines, free.

Uranium Prospecting (f, s, c) (one of series in *The Search,* filmed at Colorado School of Mines), Young America, inquire local film library.

FREE AND INEXPENSIVE MATERIALS

This is only a partial listing of free and inexpensive materials available to the teacher at this time. A directory of addresses is given at the end of the book. Many of these materials are distributed to teachers without charge. Where there is a small fee, the cost is indicated, although the prices are subject to change. While we recommend the material for use in the classroom, we do not necessarily endorse the products advertised.

Many steel companies have prepared booklets which can be read in advance of a trip to a mill, so that the trip can be made more profitable to students.

ABC's of Aluminum, booklet, Reynolds Metal Co.

Chemicals from Salt and the Sea; Chemicals from Minerals, booklets, Manufacturing Chemists' Association.

Copper: Oldest and Newest Metal, booklet, Copper and Brass Research Association.

Development of the Stainless Steels, booklet, Armco Steel Corporation.

How Steel Is Made, flow chart, U.S. Steel.

Iron and Steel, booklet, and *Reference and Audio-Visual Materials on Iron and Steel,* American Iron and Steel Institute.

Materials & Products Sample Kit (18 samples), Lone Star Steel Co.

Metallurgy and Wheels, booklet, General Motors.

Periodic Chart of the Elements, General Electric.

Practical Data For Metallurgists, booklet, Timken Roller Bearing Co.

Romance of Nickel, booklet, International Nickel Co.

Steel in the Making, booklet, Bethlehem Steel.

Wrought Iron, booklet, A. M. Byer Co.

Zinc in the World of Things, booklet, New Jersey Zinc Co.

CHAPTER 11

The halogens

The halogens (salt formers) constitute the members of Group VIIB: fluorine, chlorine, bromine, iodine, and astatine. The similarity in the chemical properties of the halogens is based on their typical electron configurations, their outer shells containing 7 electrons (2s, 5p), and thus they have a valence of minus one. As a group they are the most active nonmetals and have the highest electronegativities in each period. Fluorine has the highest assigned electronegativity, 4, and is the best oxidizing agent among the halogens. Variations in chemical activities and in physical properties are shown in Table 11–1. The elements exist as diatomic molecules having the representative structure, $:\ddot{X}:\ddot{X}:$ (X_2). The structure of the hydrogen halides may be represented as $H:\ddot{X}:(HX)$.

Fluorine occurs in the minerals fluorspar, CaF_2; apatite, $CaF_2 \cdot Ca_3(PO_4)_2$; and cryolite, Na_3AlF_6. Chlorine occurs in metallic chlorides, $NaCl$ being obtained from mines, wells, and the sea. Bromine occurs in metallic salts (Na, K, and Mg) and is extracted from sea water and brine wells. Iodine is recovered from California oil-well brine and from iodine salts present in Chile saltpeter.

11.1 The chemistry of fluorine

Fluorine, sometimes described as our most "vicious" element, is so active and so difficult to produce and store that related demonstrations are confined largely to hydrogen fluoride, HF.

11.1a Laboratory preparation of hydrogen fluoride

Hydrogen fluoride is generally produced in the laboratory in a shallow lead dish (Fisher 8-785) of 75-mm or 100-mm diameter. The dish is half filled with solid calcium fluoride (10 g) and 3–4 ml of concentrated sulfuric acid is added and stirred in with a splint (or iron nail) to make a paste. The stirrer is then washed with water and discarded. A glass plate covered with paraffin (by brushing or dipping into molten paraffin) has a design made in the paraffin by a file. The design (it may be as simple as a large X) is then exposed to the HF by covering the lead dish with the plate, with the design side down. Etching in this manner generally requires 20–30 minutes, the depth of the etch depending on the time of exposure. The paraffin is then removed in hot water. Students inspect the etched design visually and by using the finger nail to confirm the removal of glass by the etching process. (*Caution: With the lead dish completely covered, the demonstration need not be carried out under the hood. However, hydrofluoric acid, commercially available in wax and plastic bottles with a no-drip safety cap, may also be used for etching. The acid produces severe burns if contact with the skin is made. The usual treatment for acid burns, flushing with water fol-*

TABLE 11-1
Properties of the halogens

symbol	atomic no. and electron configuration	atomic weight	form and color	melting point °C	boiling point °C	ionization potential volts	oxidation potential volts (X^- to X_2)
F	9	2,7	19.00	pale yellow gas	−223	−187	17.42	−2.87
Cl	17	2,8,7	35.46	greenish-yellow gas	−101.6	− 34.6	13.01	−1.36
Br	35	2,8,18,7	79.92	reddish-brown liquid	− 7.3	58.7	11.84	−1.09
I	53	2,8,18,18,7	126.92	grayish-black, lustrous solid	113.5	184	10.44	−0.54
At	85	2,8,18,32,18,7	(211)					−0.2

lowed by use of $NaHCO_3$ paste, is used in the event of accidental contact. It is a good policy to have the teacher, only, used the bottled acid. This is a legal requirement in states such as New York.)

Hydrofluoric acid. Because hydrofluoric acid is one of the most dangerous chemicals found in high school chemistry laboratories extreme caution must be observed in handling it. It should be stored in paraffin bottles or bottles especially made for this purpose. When the acid comes in contact with the skin, extremely severe burns result. Ordinary glass allowed to stand in hydrofluoric acid reacts with it, releasing gaseous silicon fluoride which can be collected. At the end of the reaction the tray will contain water (some calcium fluoride may also be present if the glass contained lime).

$$CaSiO_3 + 6\,HF \rightarrow$$
$$CaF_2 + 3\,H_2O + SiF_4 \uparrow$$

This reaction is the basis for the etching of glass, which is simple to do in the laboratory.

Etching glass. Make a lead tray from a sheet of lead (Fig. 11–1) by folding up the sides and pinching the corners together. Or use a plastic tray completely covered with paraffin (which can be applied by dipping the tray in melted paraffin). Also dip the glass that is to be etched into melted paraffin until it is completely coated, front and back. Students may make simple designs in the hardened wax with a sharp nail by scraping off the paraffin wherever the glass is to be etched. Now place the glass in the lead or paraffined tray, and slowly pour in enough hydrofluoric acid to cover the glass. Let this stand for 20 minutes; then remove the etched glass, using plastic tongs. Carefully rinse the tongs and the glass with water; heat the glass slowly in hot water to melt

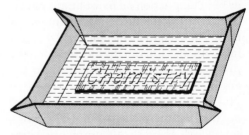

Fig. 11–1 Etching glass with hydrofluoric acid. The glass not to be etched is protected by paraffin.

off the paraffin. The etched design will stand out sharply against the protected clear glass.

11.1b Freon

You may want to refer at this point to the similarity between the structure of "freon" and CCl_4. Freon is the nontoxic, nonexplosive gas used as the refrigerant in modern refrigerators. It can be purchased in small containers and used to show the principle of refrigeration by spraying it on the outside of a test tube of water.

Since freon boils at approximately $-29°$ F, it can be boiled in a glass beaker resting on ice cubes. If you have students look up the basic formula, CCl_2F_2, they will learn that chlorine is also present in this gas. Newer freons use organic groups to replace the chlorine or fluorine atoms.

11.2 The chemistry of chlorine

11.2a Preparation of chlorine

Electrolytic preparation of chlorine. Chlorine is produced commercially by the electrolysis of fused chlorides or of brine. Its production in the laboratory by electrolysis of fused NaCl may be demonstrated by substituting a graphite electrode for the iron anode used in the demonstration for the production of sodium described in 10.4a. The chlorine may be identified by its odor (goggles should be worn by anyone testing for the odor) or by its bleaching action on moist litmus paper. The iron anode has the advantage of being changed to ferric chloride by reacting with the liberated chlorine, thereby preventing escape of chlorine into the air. The electrolysis of brine (saturated NaCl solution) or of 6 M HCl is carried out in a U-tube with graphite electrodes. A large-size U-tube (calcium chloride drying tube) with or without side arms may be used. The graphite electrodes may be mounted in a variety of ways. The simplest way is merely to have alligator or other clips attached to the graphite rods to permit them to dip into the solution a distance of 2 inches. This arrangement permits ready testing for the gases emitted. If the solution fills the tube to a distance of one inch from the opening, then a hydrogen test is obtained readily with a burning splint held to this space, after the apparatus has functioned for 1 to 2 minutes. Chlorine odor may be detected (*note caution below*), and pieces of litmus paper inserted into the liquid are bleached. In the electrolysis of brine, phenolphthalein solution or litmus solution or paper used to test the solution at anode for the NaOH produced is easily added or inserted.

(*Caution: Chlorine gas is poisonous. Experiments should be performed in a hood. Windows should be open. If chlorine gas is inhaled, it may be counteracted by inhaling the vapors of ammonia or alcohol.*)

In another possible arrangement, particularly if the U-tube is larger than the conventional 8″, a two-hole rubber stopper may be used to seat the electrode and to seat a glass delivery tube through which the gases produced may escape and be collected (generally by air displacement). A side-arm tube permits the use of a one-hole rubber stopper to seat the electrodes and collection of gases by rubber tubing delivery tubes connected to the side arms. Varying voltages may be used, the higher the voltage the greater the speed and intensity of the reactions. (30 volts gives good results, in 1–2 minutes, with an 8″ U-tube assembly.)

Laboratory preparation of chlorine. Because of the poisonous nature of chlorine, the laboratory preparation of chlorine is usually carried on as a teacher demonstration rather than as a student experiment.

A 500-ml Florence or Erlenmeyer flask is used as the generator. A chain of three bottles may be used for collection by air displacement with the last delivery tube leading into a bottle containing "hypo" (sodium thiosulfate) which acts as a chlorine trap. (See Fig. 11–3 for arrangement.) Some teachers prefer to use a more numerous set of collecting bottles in series so that enough bottles are collected for subsequent demonstration of the properties of chlorine. When only one or two bottles are included in the series, it is necessary to develop manual dexterity for removing one of the bottles, generally the second, covering it with a glass plate, and at the same time replacing it with an empty bottle. This process, repeated several times, provides the necessary supply of bottles of chlorine. A third alternative which works quite well uses a single gas-collecting bottle with the end of the delivery tube placed through a stiff cardboard to cover the bottle (Fig. 11–2). This affords ample protection to the demonstrator and, as one bottle of gas is collected, it is closed with a glass plate immediately after

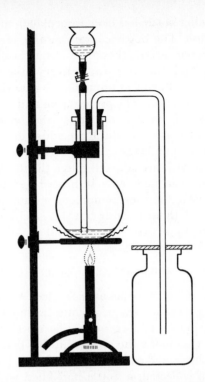

Fig. 11–2 Preparing chlorine from HCl and MnO$_2$. A chain of gas-collecting bottles may be used, with the last bottle containing hypo (sodium thiosulfate) as a trap for any excess gas. (See Fig. 11–3.)

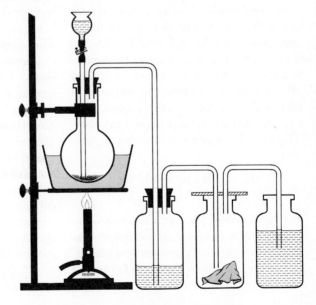

Fig. 11–3 Producing chlorine to bleach a piece of cloth. The first collecting bottle contains concentrated H$_2$SO$_4$ to dry the gas. The third bottle contains hypo (sodium thiosulfate) as an antichlorine agent. A water bath is not essential.

another bottle has been inserted for collection. The bottle containing the anti-chlorine agent (hypo) is kept available for insertion of the delivery tube at any time during or immediately after the gas collection. The preparation and collection is carried on under the hood. About 10–15 g of MnO_2 are added to the generator and then about 40 ml of concentrated HCl are added through the thistle tube. The generator is heated gently. (Some authorities recommend a water or sand bath for heating but this is seldom used in practice.) The chemical equation for this preparation is

$$4\ HCl + MnO_2 \rightarrow MnCl_2 + 2\ H_2O + Cl_2 \uparrow$$

Some 6 bottles of gas are collected. As the gas generation starts, a white cardboard held in back of the generator flask permits students to see the green chlorine being produced and collected. After the gas has been collected, a bottle half filled with water may be used to produce chlorine water. After this has been prepared, the delivery tube is again placed in the anti-chlorine (hypo) solution.

Alternate methods

HCl and KMnO₄. Use an unheated generator fitted with a dropping funnel and containing 5 g of solid $KMnO_4$. This has the advantage of better control by permitting the drop addition of the concentrated HCl and requiring no heat. Supplies of chlorine water for halogen replacement experiments are often prepared this way. The chemical equation for this preparation is

$$16\ HCl + 2\ KMnO_4 \rightarrow 2\ KCl +$$
$$2\ MnCl_2 + 8\ H_2O + 5\ Cl_2 \uparrow$$

From bleaching powder. To prepare single bottles of chlorine add about ½ teaspoonful of bleaching powder to a collecting bottle and add 2 ml of concentrated H_2SO_4 or HCl. Cover with glass cover plate. The equation for this reaction is

$$CaOCl_2 + H_2SO_4 \rightarrow$$
$$CaSO_4 + H_2O + Cl_2 \uparrow$$

Quick preparation of chlorine water. Acidify a solution of a common household bleach ($NaClO$) or add acid to a solid bleaching tablet (may be purchased in local grocery or chain stores).

11.2b   Chemical properties of chlorine

Combustion of antimony. Into one bottle of chlorine gas sift powdered antimony from a folded paper. Have students note the combustion of the powder as it reaches the chlorine and the formation of the white cloud of $SbCl_3$. Cover the bottle.

Combustion of steel wool. Ignite a long thin portion of steel wool held in tongs in a Bunsen flame and gradually insert into a bottle of chlorine gas. Have students note its vigorous combustion and the formation of a red cloud of $FeCl_3$. Cover bottle immediately after combustion is completed.

Combustion of copper. Heat a long strip of Cu foil in the Bunsen flame and insert into a third bottle of chlorine gas. The copper burns, forming $CuCl_2$.

Combustion of sodium to produce NaCl.[1] Properly prepared sodium burns spontaneously in an atmosphere of chlorine gas. For a result uncontaminated with metal oxides you will need one or more glass deflagrating spoons. These can be made by sealing 6-mm Pyrex glass rod to bottoms cut from 25-mm Pyrex test tubes. (See Chapter 25 for suggestions on handling of glass.) The rod is bent in a loop upward to form a spoon handle. Line the spoon with asbestos paper. The sodium is cut in 1-cm cubes under benzene, toluene,

[1] Adapted from a procedure originated by Robert N. Hammer, Michigan State University.

or other such hydrocarbon. Place a cube in the asbestos-lined spoon and heat gently until the sodium melts and displays a shiny, metallic surface whenever shaking of the spoon disturbs the oxide film on the surface. Immediately insert the spoon into a bottle of chlorine gas. It may be necessary to shake the spoon slightly to induce the sodium to burst into flame. (The oxide film acts as an inhibitor.) NaCl deposits on the inside of the bottle if the bottle has been kept covered as much as possible. Tasting the deposit will identify it. The presence of oxides may make the taste slightly bitter. If you use an iron deflagrating spoon, the NaCl deposit will be colored yellow by $FeCl_3$. If it should happen that the sodium bursts into flame while being melted, plunge the spoon immediately into the chlorine. After the demonstration is completed, allow the spoon to cool completely and then rinse it and the chlorine bottle with alcohol to remove any residual sodium. At this time you may want to refer to the electrolysis of fused salt as described in 10.4.

Burning H_2 in Cl_2. Lower a burning hydrogen jet (see 7.2a for safety procedure for igniting hydrogen) into a bottle of chlorine. Have students note the change in the color of the flame to gray and the disappearance of the chlorine color. The bottle is filled with colorless HCl. Blowing the breath across the top of the bottle causes this gas to fume in moist air. If the fumes impinge on a piece of blue litmus paper, the paper is turned red.

Decoloring litmus paper. Insert pieces of moist blue and red litmus paper into the last bottle. Both are bleached, with the blue developing some red color before being bleached.

Producing soot and HCl. Insert a burning paraffin taper into another bottle. It continues to burn, emitting black carbon (soot). Blowing the breath across the bottle mouth shows that HCl has been formed and that carbon in the taper did not burn.

Moisten a piece of filter paper with turpentine and drop into another bottle. The turpentine catches fire, producing soot and HCl. The equation for this reaction is

$$C_{10}H_{16} + 8\,Cl_2 \rightarrow 10\,C + 16\,HCl$$

Bleaching: the need for water. A sample of dry chlorine is prepared by inserting a bottle containing 1–1½ inches of concentrated H_2SO_4 into the series of bottles next to the generator (Fig. 11–3). The second bottle in the chain then contains dry chlorine. A piece of dry colored cloth (pretest this since not all dyes are bleached by chlorine) or a large dry piece of blue litmus paper is inserted into the bottle. No bleaching occurs. Then remove and wet the material and reinsert. Bleaching results. A variation of this procedure uses two bottles in the chain immediately after the sulfuric acid drying bottle. Into the first of these is placed the dry cloth or paper while the wet one is placed into the second.

Action of chlorine on microorganisms. There may be an opportunity to show the action of chlorine on protozoa and bacteria by using the chlorination demonstration described in 4.7b.

Burning methane in chlorine. To rubber tubing connected to a natural gas outlet attach a short length of glass tubing which has been pulled out to a tip. Now light the gas and adjust it to burn with a very small flame. Lower this into a bottle of chlorine gas.

$$CH_4 + Cl_2 \rightarrow HCl + CH_3Cl$$

Later shake the contents with water and test with litmus paper. For simplicity in writing the equation, we have assumed that the gas consists of pure methane. Note also that further reaction takes place, producing a mixture of CH_3Cl, CH_2Cl_2, and $CHCl_3$.

11.2c   Preparation and properties of hydrogen chloride

NaCl and H_2SO_4. Hydrogen chloride is prepared in the laboratory by reacting 2 teaspoons of solid NaCl with enough concentrated H_2SO_4 to cover the bottom of the thistle tube in the same type of generator used to prepare chlorine. (See Figs. 11–2, 11–3.) The gas is collected by upward displacement of air. To demonstrate the fact that the collecting bottle is filled (almost), blow across bottle mouth (a white cloud results) or hold a piece of moistened blue litmus paper at the bottle mouth. Collect two or three bottles of gas. Then position the end of the glass delivery tube about ¼″ above 1″ of water in another collection bottle. Have students observe the wavelike pattern of oily hydrochloric acid that forms on the water's surface and the convection-like pattern in the water as the acid sinks.

Tests. This solution may be tested later with blue litmus or by placing a 1″ strip of Mg ribbon into 10 ml of the acid in a test tube; or, for the chloride ion, see 11.2d.

Highly water soluble. One bottle of gas is covered and inverted into a basin of water. The water rapidly rises almost to the top of the bottle. (This helps students appreciate that collection by air displacement generally results in some residual air as an impurity.)

Does not support combustion. Hold a burning splint at the bottle mouth and then insert it into the bottle. The flame goes out, indicating the gas neither burns nor supports combustion.

Reacts with ammonia. A collecting bottle of similar size is filled either with NH_3 (for preparation see 12.3d) or with a few drops of concentrated NH_4OH, and the stoppered bottle shaken vigorously. A bottle of hydrogen chloride is placed stoppered with mouth downward on top of the bottle containing the NH_3. The covers are withdrawn and dense white fumes of NH_4Cl fill the bottle. This reaction may be related to the usual accumulation of a white solid on bottles of HCl and NH_4OH stored in too close proximity. Remove the wetted stoppers from a bottle of concentrated HCl and a bottle of concentrated NH_4OH. As the stoppers are brought close together (about 1″), the dense white fumes of NH_4Cl form. The same effect may be produced if a piece of cotton moistened with NH_4OH is brought close to the gas issuing from an HCl generator. (This is best done in a bell jar in which the moistened cotton is held on a long piece of glass tubing.) More concentrated hydrochloric acid than that which was used for the Mg test (see tests above) and chloride test (11.2d) may be produced by placing the delivery tube into 2 or more inches of water in a collecting bottle and then heating the generator vigorously so that a steady stream of the gas is produced. This acid, or the dilute desk acid, may be used to review the action of metals and dilute acids as described in 10.1e.

Action on metallic oxides. The action of the acid on metallic oxides may be demonstrated by soaking a piece of cotton or cloth in dilute acid and polishing brassware such as the sink gooseneck, door knobs, etc. (*Caution: Wear gloves although some teachers demonstrate the relative ineffectiveness of the acid on skin by "washing" their hands in the concentrated acid. Make sure you have no open cuts or sores.*) This demonstration may be related to the use of the acid in "pickling" metals. A similar demonstration uses the test tubes which may have been used in the thermal reduction of CuO by hydrogen (see 10.2b). Very often the insides of the test tubes are colored a copper-like red, probably by cuprous oxide. Such a test tube is "cleaned" by pouring in concentrated HCl. Show "cleaning" action of acid on marble, brick, etc. by pouring a few ml of the concentrated acid on a large piece of marble held over the sink.

11.2d   Test for chloride ion

To 5 ml of a dilute solution of NaCl add 5 drops of silver nitrate solution. Divide the resulting white precipitate, AgCl, and test tube contents into two portions in separate test tubes. Add concentrated nitric acid (2 ml at most) to one test tube. The precipitate does not dissolve. Add concentrated NH_4OH to the other tube and shake. If the precipitate does not completely dissolve, add more NH_4OH. If it results that a much greater volume of ammonium hydroxide was added than of nitric acid, confirm results by adding additional nitric acid to the first test tube. A good practice which demonstrates the need for the steps consequent to the initial precipitation of the AgCl is to add the silver nitrate solution to an "unknown" (sodium carbonate or oxalate may be used), producing a precipitate which is almost as white as the AgCl. Let students hazard a guess now as to what the unknown was. Then follow up with the addition of nitric acid and solution of the precipitates formed. Another related demonstration consists of adding the $AgNO_3$ solution to 10 ml of dilute $KClO_3$ solution. Students are generally surprised to learn that this (the chlorate) does not give a chloride ion test. This demonstration emphasizes the different behaviors of atoms in different oxidation states.

An HCl "fountain" similar to the ammonia fountain described in 8.2b may also be demonstrated.

11.3   The chemistry of bromine

11.3a   Commercial production

Chlorine is bubbled through a glass tower filled with glass beads or pebbles covered with magnesium bromide. Bromine is set free as is evidenced by its characteristic red-brown color. This represents the extraction of bromine from sea water.

Test for bromide ion. The simplest way of simulating the commercial production of bromine is to perform the test for the bromide ion. To 10 ml of a dilute solution of KBr or NaBr (0.5 N or dissolve two small crystals of KBr in 10 ml of water) add 1 ml of either CCl_4 or CS_2. Shake and show that two layers of colorless liquid result, the water solution being on top. Previously the solvent extraction test for free (elementary) bromine (in bromine water) is performed by mixing together 10 ml of bromine water and 1 ml of the CCl_4 or CS_2. After being shaken, this mixture resolves itself into two layers: the upper, colorless water layer, and the orange-red layer of the organic solvent which now contains virtually all of the bromine. These procedures also indicate that there is a marked difference in the color and chemical behavior of the bromine atom (in the molecule, Br_2) and of the ion (Br^-). Now add to the first test tube containing the ion 5 ml of chlorine water and again shake vigorously. As the chlorine is added to the water layer, a color change starts to occur (red-orange). After the test tube contents have settled, the orange-red color is concentrated in the lower layer of CCl_4 or CS_2.

$$2\ KBr + Cl_2 \rightarrow 2\ KCl + Br_2$$
or $\quad 2\ Br^- + Cl_2 \rightarrow 2\ Cl^- + Br_2$

This same reaction and demonstration may be used to explore or review oxidation-reduction in terms of electron trans-

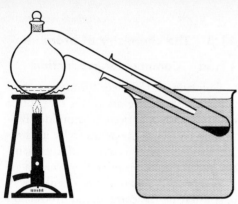

Fig. 11–4 Laboratory preparation of bromine in a retort, using KBr, MnO_2, and concentrated H_2SO_4.

fer, the greater oxidizing ability, and greater chemical activity of chlorine as compared with bromine.

11.3b Laboratory preparation

Bromine is usually prepared by the instructor under the hood since bromine vapor is poisonous. Accidental inhalation requires the same treatment as that for chlorine gas (see 11.2a). The apparatus is arranged as in Fig. 11–4. As an additional precaution to prevent the unnecessary escape of bromine vapor into the room pour some 20 ml of water into the 8″ collecting test tube to serve as a trap and dissolve any escaping bromine vapor. Mix 10 g of KBr and an equal amount of MnO_2 on a piece of paper and pour the mixture into the retort. If the retort is dry, the materials may be poured into it through the neck; otherwise pour into the opening in the retort top. Then concentrated sulfuric acid (10–15 ml) is poured into the retort through a funnel and the retort stoppered immediately. The reaction starts immediately without heating; bromine vapor fills the retort. The retort is then heated gently until liquid bromine (a heavy red-brown liquid) fills the lower portion of the collecting test tube. Very often just one large-sized globule is enough for experimental purposes although larger amounts may be prepared and collected by further heating. Some teachers prefer to use 2:1 sulfuric acid instead of the concentrated acid. The collecting test tube (filled with water if a water trap has not been used) is stoppered, shaken, and then poured into a gallon bottle which may serve as a stock source for bromine water, additional water being added as needed. When the collecting test tube is removed, replace it immediately with another test tube collector partially filled with water to prevent escape of bromine which may still be coming off.

Compared with other halogens. The equation for preparing bromine may be developed around the central principle represented by the preparation of other halogens. Chlorine, bromine, and iodine may be prepared in the laboratory by the oxidation of the binary halogen acids. Reasoning by analogy with the preparation of chlorine often results in students suggesting the oxidation of hydrobromic acid. It can be pointed out that HBr is much less stable than HCl and that the alternative is to prepare the HBr and simultaneously and deliberately oxidize it with an oxidizing agent such as MnO_2. One representative equation is

$$2\,KBr + 2\,H_2SO_4 + MnO_2 \rightarrow$$
$$K_2SO_4 + MnSO_4 + 2\,H_2O + Br_2 \uparrow$$

which is generalized into the form

$$2\,HX + 2\,H_2SO_4 + MnO_2 \rightarrow$$
$$K_2SO_4 + MnSO_4 + 2\,H_2O + X_2 \uparrow$$

This equation may be checked by preparing Cl_2 from its representative halide (NaCl), sulfuric acid, and manganese dioxide. Iodine is prepared later using the same general rule: halide + sulfuric acid + oxidizing agent (MnO_2).

11.3c Chemical properties of bromine

Generally, the demonstrations for which bromine is used are bleaching litmus paper with bromine water, and using bromine water to replace iodine from an iodide solution (described in 11.4).

The replacement experiments which are used to test for bromide (with Cl_2) and for iodide (with Br_2 or Cl_2) are generally sufficient to have students realize the relative order of activities of these halogens. The adsorption of bromine vapor by activated charcoal may be repeated if desired. A small drop of the liquid bromine is placed in a 500-ml flask, stoppered and shaken, or heated briefly and then stoppered. The activated charcoal (½–1 teaspoonful) is added and the flask is restoppered and shaken. The bromine color disappears with its adsorption.

11.3d Preparation of hydrogen bromide[2]

In a small flask fitted with a one-hole cork and delivery tube place 20 g of potassium bromide and cover the salt with moderately concentrated sulfuric acid (2 volumes of acid to one of water). On warming gently, the hydrogen bromide is evolved in abundance. The gas contains a little moisture and is sometimes very pale yellow but it is sufficiently pure for most experiments. If desired, add a collecting bottle charged with glass wool sprinkled with red phosphorus to remove the bromine. You may also add a drying tube charged with calcium chloride. Collect the gas as for chlorine (Figs. 11–2, 11–3). The collected gas may be used in the following demonstrations:

[2] Adapted from G. Fowles, *Lecture Experiments in Chemistry*, 4th rev. ed., G. Bell and Sons, Ltd., London, 1957.

1. Heat a loosely stoppered test tube full of the dry gas in a strong flame. Hold white paper in back of the test tube as the bromine appears.

2. Repeat the ammonia-chlorine experiment with a bottle of the HBr gas.

3. Place jars of the gas and of chlorine mouth to mouth and remove glass plates. Bromine is liberated.

A solution of the gas in water may be produced by bubbling the gas from the generator into water in a bottle or test tube. The entire apparatus setup for preparing the HBr in this manner is similar to that used for preparing and collecting HCl. (See 11.2c.)

11.4 The chemistry of iodine

11.4a Laboratory preparation and collection of iodine

On a piece of paper thoroughly mix one teaspoonful of potassium iodide with one teaspoonful of manganese dioxide. Transfer to the 250-ml beaker (as generator). Collect the product by using an evaporating dish which is two thirds full of water or a Florence flask almost filled with water. Some teachers report that using ice water in the bottle produces superior crystallization of the iodine. The bottom of the beaker or the flask should be dried. Add no more than 5 ml of concentrated sulfuric acid to the beaker and set the collection device in place. (*Note:* Too much acid seems to interfere with the formation of crystals, producing instead a brownish liquid. In place of H_2SO_4 you may add a few drops of concentrated H_3PO_4.) Heat gently for 3 minutes and remove the burner so that crystallization takes place.

Sublimation of solid iodine. Place ½ g of iodine crystals in an evaporating dish and cover with a watch glass partly filled with water. Place over a wire gauze and heat gently. Iodine crystals form on the bottom of the watch glass and may be exhibited and compared with the crystals formed from potassium iodide and H_2SO_4.

Solvents. Set up a series of test tubes containing 5–10 ml of H_2O, ethyl alcohol, and carbon tetrachloride (or carbon disulfide). Remove several crystals from the bottom of the evaporating dish with a splint and drop into the water. Shake and show that virtually no solution takes place. Repeat with another splint for the other two test tubes. Brown tincture of iodine forms in the alcohol and the characteristic purple color forms in the CCl_4. Now add a crystal of KI to the test tube containing the water and iodine and shake the tube. The iodine dissolves, giving a red-brown solution (formation of tri-iodide ion I_3^-). Add 5 ml of CCl_4 to this solution and shake vigorously. Virtually all the iodine is removed from the water layer, and a violet layer of CCl_4 results in the bottom of the tube. Add several drops of the tincture of iodine to starch paste or suspension. The typical blue-black color (starch I_2 complex) results. Add tincture of iodine to a white cloth. Let it dry and then place into a solution of hypo (1 teaspoon in a beaker of water). The iodine color is removed. This demonstration illustrates the use of the thiosulfate ion to determine the amount of iodine in a solution.

$$I_2 + 2 S_2O_3^{=} \rightarrow S_4O_6^{=} + 2 I^-$$

This demonstration can be related to the "magic cleaners" that are sometimes used by street peddlers.

11.4b   Test for iodide ion

To 10 ml of potassium iodide solution add 5 ml of CCl_4 and shake. Compare with the effect produced with the element. The ion gives no color reaction. Then add 5 ml of chlorine water, shake, and obtain the violet CCl_4 layer. Repeat procedure using bromine water instead of chlorine water and have students explain the relative activities of these three halogens on the basis of replacement reactions. For confirmatory tests use solution of KBr, I_2 solution, and CCl_4—violet color of iodine results; solution of KCl or NaCl, I_2 solution, and CCl_4—violet color of iodine results; repeat the second test, using bromine water instead of I_2 solution—red-brown color of bromine results.

CAPSULE LESSONS

Ways to get started in class

11-1. You may want to begin a study of halogens by extracting some chlorine from sea water which can be prepared from salt and tap or distilled water (see method suggestion in 11.2a). Demonstrate properties of chlorine as a representative of the halogens. Have students predict what the characteristics of the other members of the halogen family might be.

11-2. As a laboratory lesson students might bleach swatches of colored cotton. You may want to have them include chlorine water as well as bleaching powders (as suggested in this chapter). Relate this work to the use of Clorox (and similar preparations) as a disinfectant, showing the action of these substances on a wet mount of living microorganisms on a slide under the microscope.

11-3. Have students establish the relative reactivity of the halogens by demonstrations using bromine water, chlorine water, and iodine water added to halide solutions. Which displaces the other in series?

11-4. At some time you may want to show the burning of metals in bottles of chlorine gas. Develop a definition of oxidation. Students should develop the equations for the reactions.

11-5. Show the action of a fluorine compound, hydrofluoric acid, on glass. Students may demonstrate the etching of glass.

11-6. Students may plan a panel on the uses of halogens in medicine and industry: role of iodine in diet for normal thyroid functions and as an antiseptic; role of halides in cloud seeding; role in photography.

11-7. As a laboratory activity, students may be given "unknowns" and asked to identify the specific halide in "X."

11-8. Study properties and uses of radio-active iodine, I^{131}.

11-9. Study the pros and cons of the fluoridation of drinking water.

PEOPLE, PLACES, AND THINGS

If possible, take students to visit the local chlorination plant involved in purification of the water supply, or have them observe the chlorination system of the school's swimming pool or some local pool.

If there are any drug industries in your region, students may observe the use of several halogens. At some time a chemistry club can invite a chemist from a local college or university to give a talk on either the history of the halogens or their use in industry. A druggist may be urged to speak on the use of halogens in medicine, or a photographer to speak on bromine compounds in photography.

BOOKS AND PAMPHLETS

These are only a few of the books which are pertinent to the work discussed in this chapter. These and many other references classified by subject and with complete bibliographical data are given in the bibliography at the end of the book.

Arthur, P., *Analytical Chemistry,* McGraw-Hill, 1957.

Basolo, F., and R. Pearson, *Mechanisms of Inorganic Reactions: A Study of Metal Complexes in Solution,* Wiley, 1958.

Clements, R., *Modern Chemical Discoveries,* Routledge, London, 1954.

Dull, C., *Modern Chemistry,* Holt, 1955.

Hutchinson, E., *Chemistry: The Elements and Their Reactions,* Saunders, 1959.

Mellan, Ibert, *Halogenated Hydrocarbons: Sourcebook of Industrial Solvents,* Reinhold, 1957.

Weaver, E., and L. Foster, *Chemistry for Our Times,* McGraw-Hill, 1954.

FILMS AND FILMSTRIPS

This partial list is intended only as a guide toward film and filmstrip selection. Refer to the more complete listing at the end of the book where films are classified by subject and where a key to abbreviations and addresses of distributors are given. The cost of film rental, of course, is subject to change. Films are sound and black and white unless otherwise specified.

Electrochemistry (f, s), EBF, $2.50.

Electrolysis (fs), Popular Science through McGraw-Hill, $6.00.

Fluoridation Story (f, s, c), U.S. Public Health Service, free.

Halogens (fs), Popular Science through McGraw-Hill, $6.00.

Halogens (f, s), Coronet, inquire local film library.

Halogens (f, s, c), Indiana U., $3.25.

FREE AND INEXPENSIVE MATERIALS

This is only a partial listing of free and inexpensive materials available to the teacher at this time. A directory of addresses is given at the end of the book. Many of these materials are distributed to teachers without charge. Where there is a small fee, the cost is indicated, although the prices are subject to change. While we recommend the material for use in the classroom, we do not necessarily endorse the products advertised.

An Outline of the History of Chemistry (wall chart), Mallinckrodt Chemical Works, free.

Chemicals from Salt and the Sea, Manufacturing Chemists' Assoc., free.

Periodic Chart of the Elements ($11'' \times 14''$), General Electric, free.

CHAPTER 12

Nitrogen and its compounds

Nitrogen and its compounds are very important in our agricultural and industrial economy, and their study often forms an important part of high school chemistry courses. Demonstrations with phosphorus, a member of the nitrogen family, were described in Chapter 9; the other members of the nitrogen family—antimony, arsenic, and bismuth—are usually treated very briefly if at all in high school work. A short summary of the properties, oxidation states, and representative compounds of nitrogen is found in Table 12–1. The structural formulas of the nitrogen molecule and several nitrogen compounds are shown in Fig. 12–1.

12.1 Nitrogen gas

The fact that four fifths of the air is composed of uncombined nitrogen is evidence of how inactive a gas it is. (It does, of course, combine with some elements when strongly heated and in the presence of catalysts, and with oxygen in a high-temperature electric arc.)

12.1a Preparation of nitrogen

By burning phosphorus. In the classroom, nitrogen (actually oxygen-free air) may be produced by burning red phosphorus in a volume of air confined over water (see 9.4a). A burning splint is inserted into the residual gas and is extinguished. This indicates but does not really prove that nitrogen is present. This may be demonstrated by loosely filling a small porcelain crucible with Mg ribbon (2′). This is set on fire. While the white mass is still hot, a drop or two of water is added (*use caution*) and the odor of ammonia may be detected because of the hydrolysis of the small amount of Mg_3N_2 formed during the burning of the Mg. An alternate procedure is to place the contents of the crucible in a small beaker (100-ml) and cover the beaker with a watch glass to whose convex surface a piece of moistened red litmus paper is attached. A few drops of water are added to the beaker contents which are heated strongly. The red litmus turns blue due to the hydrolysis of the Mg_3N_2 and the liberation of ammonia. A sample of pure nitrogen taken from a cylinder of bottled gas is collected by water displacement. A burning splint is held at the bottle mouth and then inserted to show that the gas neither burns nor supports combustion. Moistened litmus paper may be placed into another bottle or test tube to show that the gas has no effect on the acid-base indicator.

From ammonium chloride and sodium nitrite. Nitrogen may be prepared from a gently heated solution of ammonium chloride and sodium nitrite. Four grams of ammonium chloride (NH_4Cl) and five grams of sodium nitrite ($NaNO_2$) are dissolved in 30 ml of water. The generator flask is warmed gently to start the reaction.

(*Caution: Since the reaction is an exothermic one, be prepared to immerse the generator in water in a pneumatic trough or basin to cool it if the reaction becomes too rapid.*) Warm the flask just enough to start the reaction. Permit the first gas sample (mixed with air) to escape and then start the collection. Collect the gas by water displacement. Test the gas collected with a burning splint.

12.2 Fixation of nitrogen

Nitrogen is such an inactive element that it was not possible for man to make it combine until fairly recently. Students might report on some of the early attempts to "fix" nitrogen. Although the Haber process for preparing ammonia from gaseous nitrogen and hydrogen is widely used commercially, it requires conditions that cannot be obtained in the high school laboratory.

12.2a Bacterial action

If it is possible to get clover plants or other legumes with the roots attached, students can see the nodules, or swellings, on the roots. These contain symbiotic nitrogen-fixing bacteria which change atmospheric nitrogen in the air spaces between

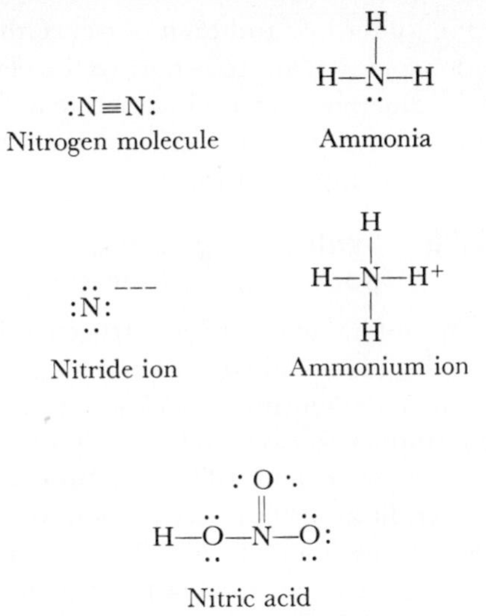

$:N\equiv N:$

Nitrogen molecule

$H-\overset{\overset{\displaystyle H}{|}}{\underset{\cdot\cdot}{N}}-H$

Ammonia

$:\overset{\cdot\cdot}{\underset{\cdot\cdot}{N}}:{}^{---}$

Nitride ion

$H-\overset{\overset{\displaystyle H}{|}}{\underset{\underset{\displaystyle H}{|}}{N}}-H^{+}$

Ammonium ion

$H-\overset{\cdot\cdot}{\underset{\cdot\cdot}{O}}-\overset{\overset{\displaystyle :O\cdot}{\parallel}}{\underset{\cdot\cdot}{N}}-\overset{\cdot\cdot}{\underset{\cdot\cdot}{O}}:$

Nitric acid

Fig. 12-1 Structural formulas of nitrogen and some of its compounds.

soil granules into nitrates, which increase the fertility of the soil.

Some students may want to examine these bacteria under a microscope. A nodule in a drop of water may be crushed between two microscope slides; then a small sample can be transferred with a medicine dropper to a clean slide. To this add a small drop of dilute methylene blue to stain the bacteria. Examine the prepa-

TABLE 12-1
Properties and compounds of nitrogen

atomic weight	electronic configuration	melting point °C	boiling point °C	ionization potential	oxidation potential
14	2, 5	−210.0	−195.8	e.v. 14.5	volts −1.25 to $NO_3{}^-$

oxidation states	compounds
+5	nitric acid, nitrates, nitrogen pentoxide (N_2O_5)
+4	nitrogen dioxide (NO_2) dinitrogen tetroxide (N_2O_4)
+3	nitrites such as $NaNO_2$, nitrous acid (HNO_2)
+2	nitric oxide (NO)
+1	nitrous oxide (N_2O)
−1	hydroxylamine (NH_2OH)
−2	hydrazine (N_2H_4)
−3	ammonia, ammonium salts, nitrides

ration under low and high power. Other students may want to report to the class on the different bacteria involved in nitrogen fixation and the role of bacteria in decay—the complete nitrogen cycle.

12.2b Synthesizing nitrogen compounds in the laboratory

The manufacture of a nitrogen compound from the nitrogen and oxygen in air can be demonstrated in class. Fit a two-hole stopper to each end of a Pyrex cylinder 2″ wide and 10″ long. Into each stopper, fit an electric arc carbon so that the ends just touch inside. Then insert a short glass tube in each of the remaining holes. Wire the carbon rods in series with a 1000-watt heating unit and connect to an electric outlet (Fig. 12–2). Wrap the protruding ends of the carbon rods with rubber or plastic tape to act as insulating handles. Attach the output of a small hand pump to one of the short glass tubes. Connect a rubber tube from the other short glass tube leading to an open bottle of water.

When you are ready to start the reaction, close the circuit and touch the ends of the carbon rods together. Then barely separate them to start an arc. In about 3 minutes, the nitrogen and oxygen in the air inside the tube will combine to form nitric oxide (NO), which is colorless; when the current is shut off and the gases cool, a brownish gas, nitrogen dioxide, will form in the cylinder.

$$N_2 + O_2 \rightleftarrows 2\,NO$$
$$2\,NO + O_2 \rightarrow 2\,NO_2$$

Push the handle of the pump down once or twice to wash the products into water and refill the reaction chamber with air.

Repeat the operation, collecting the gas each time. Use the pump to force the gas into *cold* water where it will dissolve, forming nitric and nitrous acids.

$$2\,NO_2 + H_2O \rightarrow HNO_2 + HNO_3$$

Another possible reaction with higher concentration of NO_2 is

$$3\,NO_2 + H_2O \rightarrow NO + 2\,HNO_3$$

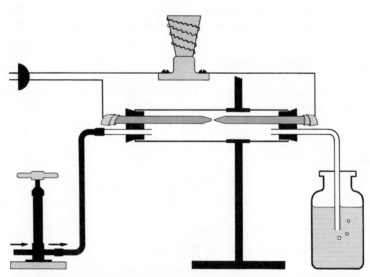

Fig. 12–2 Synthesizing nitrogen-oxygen compounds with an electric arc.

12.3 Common compounds of nitrogen

12.3a Oxides of nitrogen

Important aspects of nitrogen fixation are generally demonstrated by the study of the oxides of nitrogen, NO and NO_2. These gases are easily prepared and studied.

Nitrous oxide. Although the preparation of nitrous oxide by the *gentle* heating of ammonium nitrate is relatively dangerous (*Caution: It explodes when heated above 250° C*), the gas may be prepared by heating the ammonium nitrate until it *just melts and begins to decompose* (from 170° to 200° C, the decomposition range). The gas is collected by displacement of moderately hot water (60° C) or a saturated salt solution since it is somewhat soluble in cold water. Ten grams of ammonium nitrate are placed in the test tube generator and the apparatus is assembled as in Fig. 12–3. The ammonium nitrate is heated with a moving almost luminous flame until a steady evolution of the gas takes place. The flame should be regulated so that the froth produced by the escaping oxide is not more than ¼″ high.[1] Several bottles of the gas are collected, the first bottle being discarded. The equation for this reaction is

$$NH_4NO_3 \rightarrow N_2O \uparrow + 2\,H_2O$$

Possible demonstrations for which the bottles of gas may be used:

1. Insert a brightly glowing splint into one bottle; the splint bursts into flame. Consult the electronic structure for N_2O. The oxygen at the end of this linear molecule is easily given up, explaining why the gas supports combustion.

2. A piece of sulfur burning feebly at one corner in a deflagrating spoon is

[1] G. Fowles, *Lecture Experiments in Chemistry*, 4th ed., G. Bell and Sons, Ltd., London, 1957 (expt. 219).

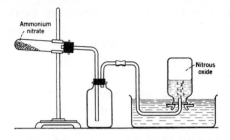

Fig. 12–3 Preparing nitrous oxide. The ammonium nitrate in the reaction chamber should not be heated much above 200° C (it explodes at 250° C). In place of the test tube, a 50- or 100-ml Florence flask may be used. (From C. Dull and W. Brooks, *Laboratory Experiments in Chemistry*, H. Holt & Co., 1954.)

inserted. The flame is extinguished (a test to distinguish between N_2O and oxygen).

3. A piece of steel wool held with tongs and ignited in air is inserted into the gas and burns as it does in oxygen.

Nitric oxide. A generator and water displacement apparatus assembly is set up similar to that used in the laboratory preparation and collection of hydrogen (see 7.1b). About 10 g of copper shot or turnings are put into the generator bottle, 10 ml of water are added through the thistle tube, and enough concentrated nitric acid is added to start the reaction and keep it going. (Acid diluted in proportions of 1 part of acid to 1 part of water by volume may be used directly. However, the addition of the concentrated acid, mentioned first, affords a measure of control since it may be added as needed to keep the reaction going.) A brown gas will fill the generator at first because some NO_2 may be produced and because the NO formed will react with the air in the generator. Start collecting the gases produced. Some NO_2 may wash into the collecting bottle through the water, but if it does the color disappears rapidly as it dissolves in the water in the bottle. Several bottles of the gas may be collected. Collect one bottle ⅔ full and leave this bottle in the basin or pneumatic trough. Fill the generator with water and decant. Some demonstrators prefer to keep the generator going and have an assistant collect an additional bottle or two. After the following demonstrations are completed, the generator bottle still contains colorless NO. When the stopper is removed, this changes to brown NO_2. The equations for this reaction are

$$3\,Cu + 8\,HNO_3 \rightarrow 3\,Cu\,(NO_3)_2 +$$
$$4\,H_2O + 2\,NO\uparrow$$
$$2\,NO + O_2 \rightarrow 2\,NO_2$$

Possible demonstrations for which bottles of the gas may be used:

1. Open one bottle to the air (under hood). Brown NO_2 fills the bottle, starting at the top and working downward. About 5 ml of water are then added to the bottle and the moistened palm of the hand is used to close the bottle. The bottle is shaken vigorously and adheres to the palm of the hand so that its weight is supported by air pressure. Remove the bottle from the hand; insert a piece of blue litmus paper and note that it turns red. (See the equations on the Ostwald process under Nitrogen dioxide, below.)

2. Into a second bottle insert a burning splint well into the bottle as rapidly as possible to prevent the formation of as much NO_2 as possible.

3. Ignite a small piece of red phosphorus (match head size) in a deflagrating spoon and insert into a bottle of gas. The phosphorus burns. (Yellow phosphorus gives better results. If the phosphorus fails to ignite, withdraw rapidly into air to reignite it.)

4. Insert the delivery tube from an oxygen generator into a bottle of gas which contains ⅔ NO and ⅓ water. The NO turns into dark brown NO_2 which dissolves in the water. The water rises to almost fill the bottle. This may be cited as a method of distinguishing between O_2 and N_2O. If bottles of NO and N_2O are covered with glass plates and positioned mouth to mouth one above the other, when the glass plates are withdrawn, no change in color results.

Nitrogen dioxide. The same type generator as that used for NO is employed. The gas, NO_2, is collected by upward displacement of air. The same amount of Cu (10 gm) is used and is reacted with concentrated HNO_3. Have two bottles of water at hand. One may be used as a trap into which the excess NO_2 is led. The other may have to be poured into the generator if the reaction becomes too vigorous since large quantities of NO_2 are readily produced. (*Caution: NO_2 is very poisonous. The reaction should be carried out under the hood and no gas should be inhaled.*) Collect two bottles of NO_2, after adding just enough concentrated acid (try to keep at 5 ml to cover the bottom of the thistle tube). A dropping funnel may be used instead of the thistle tube and affords a better degree of control. The equations for this reaction are

$$Cu + 4\,HNO_3 \rightarrow Cu(NO_3)_2 +$$
$$2\,H_2O + 2\,NO_2\uparrow$$
$$2\,NO_2 + H_2O \rightarrow HNO_2 + HNO_3$$
$$3\,NO_2 + H_2O \rightarrow 2\,HNO_3 + NO$$

Possible demonstrations for which bottles of gas may be used:

1. Repeat the solubility experiment (see 1. under NO demonstrations), using the moistened palm of the hand to close the bottle. After a lapse of one day, the experimenter may reveal the ring left on the palm of his hand by the reaction of the nitric acid with the body protein. Some students may recall this protein test from biology class; some may repeat it. A piece

of hard-boiled egg white is placed into nitric acid; it turns yellow after being heated gently. Pour off acid and add to the yellow egg white concentrated ammonium hydroxide which then turns it orange.

2. Place a bottle of gas mouth downward into a basin of water. Removing the cover plate results in rapid solution and the water rises in the bottle. This solution is then tested with litmus paper and the nitrate test (see later in this chapter) is performed, both yielding positive results.

12.3b Nitric acid

Preparation of nitric acid. Arrange the retort which serves as the acid generator and the large glass test tube which will serve as the condensing chamber. (See Fig. 11–4, preparation of bromine, for the basic arrangement of apparatus.) Place about ½ a small test tube full (10–15 g) of solid $NaNO_3$ into the retort by means of a paper funnel. Place the collecting test tube in position on the end of the retort and insert it in the water in the beaker. Add about 15 ml of concentrated sulfuric acid to the retort through a glass funnel. Do not permit any sulfuric acid to run down the neck of the retort or to wet the outside of the retort. Stopper the retort and wash the funnel with water to remove residual sulfuric acid. (*Caution: Both nitric and sulfuric acids produce bad skin and flesh burns. Avoid getting either acid on body or clothing. If either acid is spilled, wash off immediately with a large volume of water. Neutralize with bicarbonate of soda if necessary.*) Some authorities recommend the use of several cubes of ice in the cooling water bath, but this is really not needed if the test tube is about half immersed in the water. Heat the generator gently and collect about ½″ of the nitric acid. Although pure nitric acid is generally colorless, the acid produced in the laboratory preparation is generally yellow due to the presence of oxides of nitrogen from the decomposition of acid produced by heating. Have students examine the color of a bottle of commercial concentrated desk nitric acid. Shut off the burner. Remove the test tube containing the acid produced and replace it with a duplicate. This prevents the unnecessary escape of the vapors which may still be coming off the generator. The equation for this reaction is

$$NaNO_3 + H_2SO_4 \rightarrow NaHSO_4 + HNO_3$$

Properties of nitric acid. Dilute 1 ml of the acid prepared with 20 ml of water and test with litmus. Add 1 ml of the acid to a few copper turnings in a test tube. Have students note the brown gas produced and dilute with 10 ml of water to slow down the reaction. The teacher may want to demonstrate that nitric acid is an unusual acid since it produces no evidence of elementary hydrogen production when added to zinc, yet it does react with copper.

You can show that nitric acid is an oxidizing agent. The residual acid produced (2–3 ml) is placed into a 5″ Pyrex tube held by a test tube holder and heated gently. As the acid starts to boil, insert a glowing splint held with tongs into the vapor. Make sure that the vapors do not reach the hand. The splint bursts into flame, indicating the ease with which the acid liberates oxygen. Then permit the acid to cool and insert into the neck of the test tube a loose small wad of knitting wool or a loose plug of excelsior. Upon reheating the insert bursts into flame in the vapors of the acid. Pour the remaining contents of the test tube down the sink. Occasionally, when all the organic matter has not been consumed, the residual hot acid passing over the material near the test tube mouth will cause it to ignite.

Nitric acid solution can be prepared directly by gently heating solid sodium nitrate and concentrated sulfuric acid in an all glass retort, as shown in Fig. 12–4. Use a Pyrex test tube or beaker of water to dissolve the gaseous nitric acid that is given off. You may also collect the acid in a test tube inserted in water.

Reactions of nitric acid with metals. Students can show that the reaction of nitric acid with metals depends upon three factors: the concentration of the acid, the temperature, and the activity of the metal (see Chapter 10). For example, they may try the following reactions.

1. Copper, silver, or lead with dilute nitric acid

$$3 \, Cu + 8 \, HNO_3 \rightarrow$$
$$3 \, Cu(NO_3)_2 + 4 \, H_2O + 2 \, NO \uparrow$$
$$3 \, Ag + 4 \, HNO_3 \rightarrow$$
$$3 \, AgNO_3 + 2 \, H_2O + NO \uparrow$$

2. Copper, silver, or lead with concentrated nitric acid

$$Cu + 4 \, HNO_3 \rightarrow$$
$$Cu(NO_3)_2 + 2 \, H_2O + 2 \, NO_2 \uparrow$$

3. Zinc or iron with nitric acid

$$4 \, Zn + 10 \, HNO_3 \rightarrow$$
$$4 \, Zn(NO_3)_2 + NH_4NO_3 + 3 \, H_2O$$

4. Zinc or iron with very dilute, cold nitric acid

$$4 \, Zn + 10 \, HNO_3 \rightarrow$$
$$4 \, Zn(NO_3)_2 + NH_4NO_3 + 3 \, H_2O$$

Students should note that the action of nitric acid on a metal rarely produces appreciable quantities of hydrogen and that it is difficult to predict with certainty just what the reduction products will be. For instance, very dilute acid will produce hydrogen when reacted with magnesium.

Reaction of nitric acid with nonmetals. Students should be aware that concentrated nitric acid oxidizes nonmetals such as sulfur, carbon, iodine, and phosphorus to their oxides (or anhydrides). For exam-

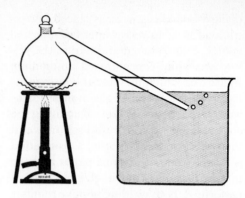

Fig. 12–4 Preparing nitric acid solution by gently heating sodium nitrate and concentrated acid.

ple, a piece of glowing charcoal will continue to burn under concentrated nitric acid.

$$C + 4 \, HNO_3 \rightarrow CO_2 + 4 \, NO_2 + 2 \, H_2O$$

(*Caution: This experiment is dangerous; the hot acid may spatter. Students should not be allowed to perform it; a teacher should do so only with elaborate precautions, including acidproof gloves and chemical eye shield.*)

Aqua regia. Perhaps some students will want to demonstrate that the 3:1 mixture of HCl and HNO_3 (aqua regia) will react with gold, whereas each of these acids separately will not. (*Caution: Aqua regia is an extremely strong reagent.*)

$$Au + HNO_3 + 3 \, HCl \rightarrow$$
$$AuCl_3 + 2 \, H_2O + NO \uparrow$$

Dutch metal leaf, which looks like gold leaf, dissolves in HNO_3; gold leaf does not. Add 3 volumes of HCl and the gold leaf dissolves instantaneously.

12.3c Nitrates

You will want to have students prepare nitrates by adding nitric acid to a metal or to a metallic hydroxide or carbonate.

Preparation of potassium nitrate. Saltpeter (potassium nitrate) may be produced by reacting solutions of Chile saltpeter ($NaNO_3$) and potassium chloride (KCl). The marked differences in the solubilities of the salts (reactants and products) at temperatures near boiling and near freezing make this preparation possible. Add 85 g of $NaNO_3$ and 74.5 g of KCl to 190 ml of water in a 600-ml beaker. Heat almost to boiling. The salts dissolve. Transfer to a smaller beaker and cool by placing the beaker in a large battery jar filled with chipped or broken ice cubes. Stir the salt solution as it cools. When the temperature of the solution reaches 5° C or lower, filter off some of the KNO_3 crystals. Remove some of the crystals of KNO_3 (10 g) to another filter paper and wash three times successively with 10–15 ml of cold distilled water. Dry the remaining crystals on filter paper. Dissolve in distilled water at room temperature. Test solution for chloride ion (see 11.2d) and for nitrate ion (see later in this section). Then run a flame test (see 10.3b) for potassium ion. The flame should be violet with no yellow sodium flame being present. If a yellow flame results, observe the violet potassium color through a blue cobalt glass.

Test for nitrate ion. To 5 ml of a solution of sodium or potassium nitrate add an equal volume of a freshly prepared solution of ferrous sulfate. The latter may be prepared immediately before its use and the saturated solution thus made is generally used. After these solutions are mixed, the tube is held in an inclined position and 1–2 ml of concentrated sulfuric acid is permitted to run down the side of the test tube. The characteristic "brown-ring"—$Fe(NO)SO_4$—results at the interface between the sulfuric acid and the mixed solutions.

Advanced students may want to read further about an ammonia test for nitrates. They can refer to a text in qualitative analysis (see bibliography at end of this chapter and in the appendix).

Testing for nitrates in soil. Students can bring to class samples of soil: rich garden soil, humus, sandy soil, and soil from the surface and from several feet below the surface (easily obtained where excavation is under way). Students will need to wash and filter these soil samples carefully, allowing the filtrates (which contain varying amounts of soluble nitrogen compounds) to stand until dry. The residues probably contain nitrates and ammonium salts. If these residues are each heated with NaOH, the ammonium salts will react with the hydroxide to release ammonia gas (easily recognized by its odor).

$$[NH_4^+ + Cl^-] + [Na^+ + OH^-] \rightarrow$$
$$NH_3 + H_2O + [Na^+ + Cl^-]$$

After ammonia has formed and is driven off by heating, students can test for nitrates by the brown ring test.

Test for a nitrate. When solid sodium or potassium nitrate is heated, a nitrite is formed and oxygen is evolved.

$$2\,NaNO_3 \rightarrow 2\,NaNO_2 + O_2$$

Students can test for oxygen with a glowing splint. They can also allow the residue to cool, dissolve it in hot water, and test for both nitrite and nitrate. (*Caution: Potassium nitrate is explosive.*)

Test for nitrite. The usual test for nitrite depends upon its oxidizing ability in acid solution.

$$NO_2^- + Fe^{++} + 2\,H^+ \rightarrow$$
$$Fe^{+++} + NO + H_2O$$

$$Fe^{++} + NO \rightarrow Fe(NO)^{++}$$

This occurs only in mildly acidic solutions, whereas the brown ring test for a nitrate takes place only with a very strong acid concentration (at the interface of concentrated acid and solution).

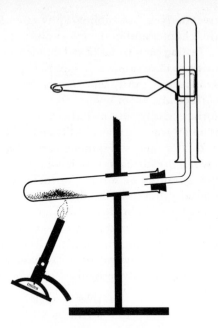

Fig. 12–5 Ammonia produced by heating NH_4Cl and $Ca(OH)_2$ is collected by downward displacement of air.

12.3d Ammonia

Ammonia is so common that we tend to forget that in appreciable amounts it is poisonous. All the following experiments should be performed in a well-ventilated room or under a hood.

Preparation. You may want to have each student prepare some ammonia in this striking demonstration. Have students mix a pinch (0.5 g) of calcium hydroxide with the same amount of ammonium chloride, in powdered form in the palm of the hand. Each of these separately is odorless. Then rub the palms together and bring the palms near the nose. Can students recognize the odor of ammonia? A piece of moist red litmus paper held above the mixture will turn blue. Have students wash their hands after this demonstration is completed. Mix 5 g of NH_4Cl and 4 g of $Ca(OH)_2$ on a piece of paper. Place in a test tube gen-

erator mouth downward, as shown in Fig. 12-5, since water is one of the products of the reaction. Test tubes or bottles are used to collect the ammonia gas by downward displacement of air. A piece of moistened red litmus paper is either stuck to or held near the mouth of the collecting container to show when it is almost filled with ammonia. Cover with a glass plate or use a rubber stopper.

Properties. Place the covered mouth of a bottle of ammonia gas under water and remove the cover. The water rises very rapidly, indicating the great solubility of ammonia. Test the water with litmus solution or two drops of phenophthalein. Into another bottle of the gas held mouth downward insert a glowing splint. Ammonia gas will not support combustion.

Take an empty bottle and place in it several drops of concentrated HCl. Cover with a glass plate and shake. Invert the bottle and place on the mouth of a covered bottle of ammonia gas. When the glass plates are withdrawn and the bottles left mouth to mouth the white fumes of NH_4Cl form.

For full details on the ammonia fountain see 8.2b.

Other combinations of ammonium salts and bases such as $(NH_4)_2SO_4$ and NaOH may be used to show the general principle that an ammonium salt reacts with a strong base to release ammonia. For example, 1 g of the solid ammonium sulfate is placed in a test tube and 3 ml of 6 M NaOH are added. The test tube is heated, and ammonia is identified by odor and moist red litmus paper.

A convenient way for preparing ammonia (relatively dry) consists of using a 500-ml Florence flask equipped with a dropping funnel and delivery tube. About 20 g of NaOH pellets are placed into the flask. Concentrated ammonium hydroxide is placed in the dropping funnel and permitted to drop on the NaOH pellets as needed. Of course, more NaOH may be used. A calcium chloride drying tube may be connected to the delivery tube to insure greater dryness.

Nessler's reagent—a test for ammonia. This reagent is an alkaline solution of potassium mercuric iodide, K_2HgI_4. To prepare dissolve 50 g of KI in 35 ml of cold water. Add a saturated solution of $HgCl_2$ (22 g in 350 ml of water) until a slight precipitate exists. Add 400 ml of 9 N NaOH and dilute to one liter. Allow to settle and decant the clear liquid. This reagent slowly forms a yellow to red-brown color when added to water containing small amounts of ammonia. The darker the color produced, the higher the concentration of ammonia. For instance, take a small quantity of the reagent and add dilute NH_4OH drop by drop, noting the increasing darkness. This reagent is used in the colorimetric quantitative determination of ammonia in water and sewage samples.

Liquefying ammonia. Collect gaseous ammonia in a Pyrex test tube (for preparation of ammonia see above). Cover the test tube with cardboard and put it in a beaker of dry ice and acetone (Fig. 12–6). This mixture produces a temperature low enough to liquefy the ammonia. When liquid ammonia (5 ml) has been produced in the test tube, stand the tube in a small beaker containing 20 ml of cold water.

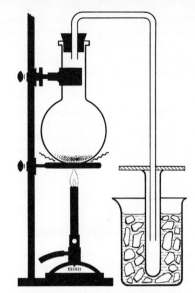

Fig. 12–6 Liquefying ammonia.

Place in hood. Students should notice that the ammonia absorbs heat from the cold water as it evaporates, freezing the water in the beaker. A more rapid freezing occurs if a test tube containing 2 ml of water is slipped inside the test tube containing the liquid ammonia. These properties of ammonia make it excellent as a commercial refrigerant.

Ammonia from urea. You may want to use synthetic urea to show its breakdown in warm water.

$$CO(NH_2)_2 + H_2O \rightarrow 2NH_3 + CO_2$$

Students will perhaps recall the barnyard (or baby) odor of ammonia.

CAPSULE LESSONS

Ways to get started in class

12-1. You may want to start a lesson by distributing a few grains of calcium hydroxide and ammonium chloride powder to each student. Have them rub these together between their palms and try to recognize the odor (described in 12.3d). Then elicit the equation for this reaction. Generate ammonia gas and have students examine its properties.

12-2. If possible, plan a laboratory period in which students test samples of soil for nitrates, using the brown ring test, a soil testing kit, and other tests (see 12.3c). What is the role of nitrates in the soil? How is the supply replenished?

12-3. Bring into the laboratory or classroom samples of soil fertilizers. What minerals do they share in common? What is the value of nitrates in the growth of plants? In the chemistry of animals and humans? Diagram the nitrogen cycle in nature: decay of plants and animals by bacteria of decay, the role of nitrogen-fixing bacteria in the soil and in roots of legumes, the conditions needed for the absorption of nitrates into plants.

Interested students of hydroponics may set up demonstrations of seedlings growing in solutions containing nitrates and other solutions in which nitrates have been omitted. Is there a difference in plant growth?

12-4. As a laboratory activity, groups of students can receive different metals and test the factors that determine the reaction of nitric acid with metals. Elicit the factors that influence the reactions such as activity of the metal, concentration of the acid, and the temperature.

12-5. Take a class on a vicarious field trip via a film such as *Plant Speaks, Soil Tests Tell Us Why,* (American Potash) or the *Nitrogen Cycle* (United World).

PEOPLE, PLACES, AND THINGS

It may be possible to call upon a county agent to talk with students about the cycle of nitrogen —nitrates necessary for good crop production. In fact, you may be able to take a class or club to visit a model farm or an experimental agricultural station to study farming practices that conserve the mineral content of the soil. There may be studies underway using radio-tracers to compare the uptake of nitrates and phosphates by different crops.

Where these resources are unavailable, films can be provided for a vicarious visit to a farm. Consult your local film library or a nearby school, college or industrial plant for assistance.

BOOKS AND PAMPHLETS

These are only a few of the books which are pertinent to the work discussed in this chapter. These and many other references classified by subject and with complete bibliographical data are given in the bibliography at the end of the book.

Bear, F. E., ed., *Chemistry of the Soil,* Reinhold, 1955.

Callison, E., ed., *America's Natural Resources,* Ronald, 1957.

Hyams, E., *Soil and Civilization,* Thames and Hudson, London, 1952.

Lyon, T. L., *Nature and Properties of Soil,* Macmillan, 1952.

Riegal, E., *Industrial Chemistry,* Reinhold, 1954.

U.S. Dept. Agriculture Yearbook 1957, *Soil,* U.S. Gov't Printing Office.

FILMS AND FILMSTRIPS

This partial list is intended only as a guide toward film and filmstrip selection. Refer to the more complete listing at the end of the book

where films are classified by subject and where a key to abbreviations and addresses of distributors are given. The cost of film rental, of course, is subject to change. Films are sound and black and white unless otherwise specified.

Chilean Nitrate: Gift of the Desert (f, s, c), Indiana, $3.25.

Feed the Soil and It Will Feed You (f, s, c), Beet Sugar Development, free.

Hunger Signs; Life of the Soil (2 f, s, c), Nat. Fertilizer Assoc., free.

Infinite Harvest (f, s, c), Spencer Chemical Co., free.

Nitrogen Cycle (f, s), United World Films, $3.00.

Plant Speaks, Soil Tests Tell Us Why; Plant Speaks Through Soil Analysis (2 f, s, c), American Potash, free.

What is Soil? (f, s), Popular Science through McGraw-Hill, $6.00.

FREE AND INEXPENSIVE MATERIALS

This is only a partial listing of free and inexpensive materials available to the teacher at this time. A directory of addresses is given at the end of this book. Many of these materials are distributed to teachers without charge. Where there is a small fee, the cost is indicated, although the prices are subject to change. While we recommend the material for use in the classroom, we do not necessarily endorse the products advertised.

Chemicals from the Atmosphere; Chemicals from Minerals; Chemicals from Farm and Forest Products, Manufacturing Chemists' Assoc., free.

Chemistry: the Conquest of Materials, K. Hutton, Pelican, $0.85.

CHAPTER 13

Electrochemistry

Electrochemistry deals with the relation between chemical energy and electrical energy—how chemical changes produce electrical energy and, conversely, how electrical energy brings about chemical changes. The many types of electrical cells originated in the discoveries of Galvani and Volta. The achievements of Sir Humphrey Davy and of Michael Faraday provided the foundations of present-day electrolytic processes.

Oxidation-reduction reactions produce thermal energy and with the appropriate apparatus—as in electrical cells—produce electrical energy. Electrical energy, used to bring about oxidation-reduction reactions, results in electrolysis and electrodeposition.

13.1 Electromotive series

Concepts related to the electromotive series have been discussed in connection with the chemical properties and behavior of metals (10.1e.) and of nonmetals, particularly the halogens in Chapter 9, and with oxidation-reduction rules (6.5b). For electrolyte conductivity see 8.4d, and for electrolytic titration see 8.4e.

Some teachers study oxidation-reduction phenomena from the viewpoint of half reactions. This treatment separates the over-all oxidation-reduction equation into two half-reactions, one representing the oxidation and the other the reduction.

Table 13–1 lists the electrode potentials for a selected number of half-reactions.

13.1a Electrode potentials and half-reactions

A simple galvanic cell. Add a few pieces of mossy zinc to 5–10 ml of dilute HCl, test for hydrogen, and also have students note that the test tube gets hot. Such "spontaneous" reactions can be used as a source of electrical energy. Now attach a strip of zinc (it may be amalgamated with Hg) and a strip of copper to the side of a beaker, connect each metal strip with wire to a 1.1-volt, low-current bulb, and pour the dilute acid into the beaker. Students note that the hydrogen bubbles are liberated at the copper strip and that the bulb lights. The chemical energy liberated as heat in the test tube reaction is now being liberated as electrical energy, and a simple galvanic cell has been produced. The equation for the test tube reaction is usually written in molecular form as

$$Zn + 2\,HCl \rightarrow ZnCl_2 + H_2 \uparrow$$

In terms of electron transfer (oxidation-reduction) this takes the form of the net reaction

$$Zn° + 2\,H^+ \rightarrow Zn^{++} + H_2$$

Considered in terms of half-reactions, the equations are

Oxidation: $Zn° - 2\,e \rightarrow Zn^{++}$
Reduction: $2\,H^+ + 2\,e \rightarrow H_2$

TABLE 13-1
Standard oxidation-reduction potentials

couple	half-reaction	potential volts
Li, L⁺	$Li \rightleftharpoons Li^+ + e$	+3.045
K, K⁺	$K \rightleftharpoons K^+ + e$	+2.925
Cs, Cs⁺⁺	$Cs \rightleftharpoons Cs^+ + e$	+2.923
Ba, Ba⁺⁺	$Ba \rightleftharpoons Ba^{++} + 2e$	+2.90
Ca, Ca⁺⁺	$Ca \rightleftharpoons Ca^{++} + 2e$	+2.87
Na, Na⁺	$Na \rightleftharpoons Na^+ + e$	+2.714
Mg, Mg⁺⁺	$Mg \rightleftharpoons Mg^{++} + 2e$	+2.37
Al, Al⁺⁺⁺	$Al \rightleftharpoons Al^{+++} + 3e$	+1.66
Mn, Mn⁺⁺	$Mn \rightleftharpoons Mn^{++} + 2e$	+1.18
Zn, Zn⁺⁺	$Zn \rightleftharpoons Zn^{++} + 2e$	+0.763
Cr, Cr⁺⁺⁺	$Cr \rightleftharpoons Cr^{+++} + 3e$	+0.74
Fe, Fe⁺⁺	$Fe \rightleftharpoons Fe^{++} + 2e$	+0.44
Cd, Cd⁺⁺	$Cd \rightleftharpoons Cd^{++} + 2e$	+0.403
Co, Co⁺⁺	$Co \rightleftharpoons Co^{++} + 2e$	+0.277
Ni, Ni⁺⁺	$Ni \rightleftharpoons Ni^{++} + 2e$	+0.250
Sn, Sn⁺⁺	$Sn \rightleftharpoons Sn^{++} + 2e$	+0.136
Pb, Pb⁺⁺	$Pb \rightleftharpoons Pb^{++} + 2e$	+0.126
H₂, H⁺(H₃O⁺)	$(½)H_2 \rightleftharpoons H^+ + e$	0.000
Cu⁺, Cu⁺⁺	$Cu^+ \rightleftharpoons Cu^{++} + e$	−0.153
Cu, Cu⁺⁺	$Cu \rightleftharpoons Cu^{++} + 2e$	−0.337
Cu, Cu⁺	$Cu \rightleftharpoons Cu^+ + e$	−0.521
I⁻, I₂	$I^- \rightleftharpoons (½)I_2 + e$	−0.536
Fe⁺⁺, Fe⁺⁺⁺	$Fe^{++} \rightleftharpoons Fe^{+++} + e$	−0.771
Hg, Hg₂⁺⁺	$2Hg \rightleftharpoons Hg_2^{++} + 2e$	−0.789
Br⁻, Br₂	$Br^- \rightleftharpoons ½ Br_2 + e$	−1.06
Cl⁻, Cl₂	$Cl^- \rightleftharpoons ½Cl_2 + e$	−1.36
Au, Au⁺⁺⁺	$Au \rightleftharpoons Au^{+++} + 3e$	−1.50
Mn⁺⁺, MnO₄⁻	$4H_2O + Mn^{++} \rightleftharpoons MnO_4 + 8H^+ + 5e$	−1.51
Pb⁺⁺, PbO₂	$2H_2O + Pb^{++} \rightleftharpoons PbO_2 + 4H^+ + 2e$	−1.455
H₂O, H₂O₂	$2H_2O \rightleftharpoons H_2O_2 + 2H^+ + 2e$	−1.77
F⁻, F₂	$F^- \rightleftharpoons (½)F_2 + e$	−2.85

* Selected from tables of oxidation potentials on pp. 1733, 1734, and 1735 of *Handbook of Chemistry and Physics*, 40th ed., Chemical Rubber Publishing Co.

[1] These values are in relation to the standard hydrogen-hydrogen ion couple which is assigned a value of zero. The concentration of the ions about each electrode is 1 *m* and the temperature at which readings are taken is 25° C. There is disagreement among observers for many of the values due to the difference of surface characteristics of electrodes.

The zinc is oxidized and the hydrogen ions are reduced. When this spontaneous chemical change occurs with the reactants in contact (as in the test tube), the electron transfer energy is liberated as heat. By separating the reactants physically, the electron transfer takes place through the conducting wire. The lamp serves as an indicator of the movement of electrons. A lecture table galvanometer used as a voltmeter (5-v range) may be substituted for

the lamp, and a reading of 1.0–1.1 volts results. (A graphite rod or a platinum electrode may be substituted for the copper strip.) Students should note the fall in voltage or extinguishing of the lamp as the Cu or C is polarized by the film of hydrogen bubbles which accumulates. Removing this electrode, washing it with water, wiping it dry, and then replacing it in the acid causes the bulb to relight. The chemical removal of the hydrogen may be shown by using dilute sulfuric acid as electrolyte, permitting the cell to polarize, and then stirring in a solution of potassium dichromate (oxidizing agent) which removes the hydrogen and restores the cell activity.

Simulated dry cell. Another demonstration simulates a dry cell by using zinc and graphite electrodes and a solution of ammonium chloride as electrolyte. Indirect evidence that electrons are leaving the zinc is provided by reversing the connections. This changes the direction of the galvanometer indicator. (Or use a 5-v d.c. voltmeter and show that the zinc must be connected to the negative terminal.)

Daniell cell. Standard apparatus sets consist of a glass jar, porous cup, porcelain mounting cap, and copper and zinc electrodes; the sets are available for individual students. The porous cup is filled with 1 *M* ZnSO₄ solution, the jar is filled with 1 *M* CuSO₄ solution, and the electrodes are inserted, the Zn into the zinc salt and the Cu into the copper salt. A voltmeter reading is taken (1.1 v). This demonstration establishes the concept that there are two competing reactions involved

$$Zn \rightleftharpoons Zn^{++} + 2e$$
$$Cu \rightleftharpoons Cu^{++} + 2e$$

and that since zinc is the more active metal, its electrons are liberated, the copper ions accepting these electrons and being changed to copper atoms.

Oxidation: $Zn \rightarrow Zn^{++} + 2e$
(zinc acts as reducing agent)
Reduction: $Cu^{++} + 2e \rightarrow Cu \downarrow$
(copper ions as oxidizing agent)

It may be pointed out that this is the same reaction as the one which proceeds spontaneously when a strip of zinc is placed into copper sulfate solution with the copper being plated out. Both experiments confirm the fact that a Zn atom is a stronger reducing agent (tends to lose electrons) than the copper atom. Thus the copper ions act as an oxidizing agent.

Comparison (standard) electrode. With one fixed electrode a series of demonstrations may be performed which establish relative positions. A flat tin rod or flat tin sheet may be used as a standard electrode. If the demonstration galvanic cell apparatus is not available, a beaker (400-ml) is used to contain the electrolyte (1.0 $M\, H_2SO_4$).

The electrodes are inserted one at a time and the voltage reading taken from the lecture table galvanometer equipped with the proper multiplier. (As each electrode is used, it is washed with water and placed on blotting paper or a paper towel.)

Readings fairly close to those expected from the table of standard values (Table 13–1) result. The two-way swing of the galvanometer makes it unnecessary to worry about making meter connections. Thus if the Zn-Sn couple gives a reading to the right, the Cu-Zn couple (where Cu gets the lead that went to Zn in the Zn-Sn couple) will give a reading to the left. Elements which may be coupled with tin include Al, Cu, Fe, Pb, Ni, Zn, and C.

According to the convention which is now almost universally accepted, the electrode at which electrons *leave* the solution is labeled the anode while the cathode is the electrode at which electrons enter the solution. This convention makes it easier to understand why the Zn plate in a dry cell is labeled negative (−). In the external circuit, the electrons travel from anode (Zn) to cathode (Cu). This is consistent with the usual identification of electrodes in electrolytic practice, where the electrode at which the electrons enter (−) is known as the cathode. In a conducting electrolyte, ions travel through the solution in both directions, the cations (+) moving toward the cathode and the anions (−) moving toward the anode.

Hydrogen electrode. In order to assign definite values for half-reactions (a measure of the tendency of electrons to flow) the potential of the hydrogen electrode is arbitrarily fixed at zero. Since few schools possess a hydrogen electrode, its use will only be briefly described here.

A platinum electrode sealed in a glass tube is immersed in a 1 molal solution of hydrochloric acid. The hydrogen pressure is one atmosphere. As the hydrogen is fed into the tube, its molecules are adsorbed on the surface of the inert platinum electrode. The reversible reaction (which may go in either direction depending on the nature of the other electrode) is written as

$$H_2 \rightleftarrows 2\,H^+ + 2e$$
or as $\quad \frac{1}{2}\,H_2 + H_2O \rightleftarrows H_3O^+ + e$

When the other electrode consists of Zn immersed in a 1 molal solution of a zinc salt, the voltmeter reads 0.76 v. When copper is used as the other electrode in a 1 molal solution of a copper salt (Cu^{++}), the voltmeter reads − 0.34 v (that is, it reads in the opposite direction indicating that the hydrogen is a better reducing agent than Cu). As noted above, the Daniell cell gives a potential of 1.10 v. This is the algebraic difference between the Zn and the Cu standard electrode potentials in relation to a hydrogen electrode (0.76 − (− 0.34) = 1.10 v).

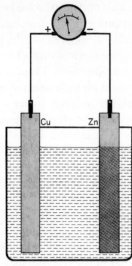

Fig. 13-1 Voltaic cell.

Generalizations. By convention the reducing agents which are more active than hydrogen (metals) are given a positive electrode potential and those below hydrogen are assigned a negative one. (See Table 13-1.) In a given galvanic cell, the electrode which has the higher positive potential is the anode.

The metals with the high positive electrode potentials at the top of the series are good reducing agents. They are the metals most easily oxidized by the removal of electrons. They have low electron affinities, low ionization potentials, and low electronegativities.

The elements with negative electrode potentials at the bottom of the series are good oxidizing agents when in the oxidized form, that is, when the metals are in the form of ions and the nonmetals are in the elementary state.

The reduced form of any element will reduce the oxidized form of any element below it in the series.

The strongest reducing agents are at the top of the series, decreasing in strength downward, while the strongest oxidizing agents are at the bottom of the series and decrease in strength going upward (Table 13-1). Thus any reducing agent (half-reaction) will react spontaneously with any oxidation agent (half-reaction) below it but not with one above it. Zn will reduce Cu ion but will not reduce Mg. Concomitantly, any oxidizing agent will react spontaneously with any reducing agent above it. Thus Br_2 will oxidize I^- but not Cl^-.

Variables and cell potential. The effect of concentration can be shown by the following. A tin rod mounted in a stopper is placed into a concentrated solution of $SnCl_2$ (saturated) and HCl. The bottle is about half filled with this solution. Then a dilute solution of stannous chloride (and HCl) fills the upper half of the bottle with as little mixing as possible. Almost immediately, crystals of Sn are deposited on the part of the rod in the more concentrated solution. The upper half of the Sn rod serves as anode and Sn^{++} ions go into solution. Electrons move to the lower half of the rod causing the more concentrated Sn^{++} ions to plate out there.

Gravity cells. The following methods may be used to keep mixing to a minimum in a gravity cell. 1. Weight the concentrated solution with sugar, put the dilute solution in first, and run the more concentrated solution in slowly through a dropping funnel reaching to the bottom of the bottle. 2. Fill the lower half of the bottle with the more concentrated solution and then cover it with a thin layer of molten paraffin. Permit this to harden and then insert the electrode and perforate the paraffin layer. Of course, such a concentration cell can be set up in the more usual patterns using two separate Sn electrodes. With this arrangement, a potential difference reading may be taken using a voltmeter.

Since cell reactions proceed with the evolution of energy (almost always some

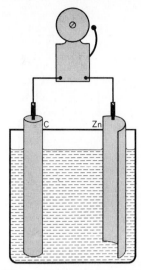

Fig. 13–2 Wet-type sal ammoniac cell.

of this is in the form of heat), increasing the temperature will lower the voltage since the higher temperature will repress the rate of reaction. By using different-sized electrodes it can be further shown by means of voltmeter readings that the potential of a galvanic cell is independent of the size of electrodes for a given set of half-reactions.

13.2 Batteries

Several electrical cells are described in the preceding section as demonstrations of the electromotive series.

13.2a Simple voltaic cell

Students may simulate the original voltaic cell by placing a copper penny and a silver dime on opposite sides of a piece of blotting paper (Volta used leather) soaked in dilute sulfuric acid. A 0–100 ma milli-ammeter will register the small current produced.

A larger cell (Fig. 13-1) may be made by a group of students. They should sand-

paper rods or sheets of copper and zinc. Then pickle the zinc in acid, wash in water, and dip into mercury to form a zinc amalgam. This will improve the action of the battery by preventing local electrolytic action between the zinc and the impurities it contains. Then stand the rods in a glass jar of dilute H_2SO_4 and connect them to a voltmeter to read the voltage. You may want to have students insert an ammeter as well. They can also prepare a similar cell using untreated zinc and note the lower voltage produced.

13.2b Sal ammoniac cells

Wet cell. Students can make a wet-type sal ammoniac cell by standing a carbon rod and a strip of zinc sheeting (or the zinc case of an old dry cell) in a jar of saturated ammonium chloride solution (Fig. 13-2). The zinc should be clean. A carbon rod from an old dry cell may be used; it should first be heated to red heat to drive out impurities and then cooled before using. This cell will provide current for several hours. In fact, students can renew the cell by reheating the carbon rod to depolarize it. They can also show how continuous depolarization can be established by placing a cloth bag of manganese dioxide powder around the carbon rod. Students may com-

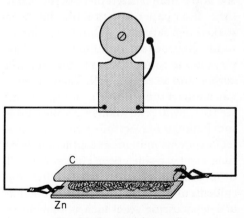

Fig. 13–3 Model dry cell.

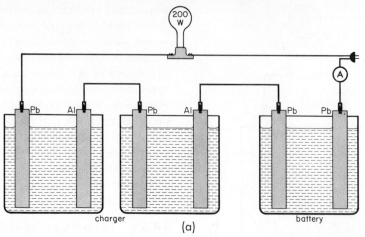

Fig. 13-4 Substitutes for a battery charger: (a) a rectifier can be made by connecting a 200-watt bulb in series with 2 cells containing saturated borax solution and lead and aluminum sheet electrodes, (b) an automobile generator driven by an electric motor.

pare the operating life of the cell with and without the depolarizer.

Dry cell. Students can also make a model of a dry cell by inserting a disc of filter paper soaked in sal ammoniac (ammonium chloride solution) between a penny and a dime. Touch the wires leading from a galvanometer to both coins to complete the circuit.

Students can prepare a larger dry cell (Fig. 13-3). Between a flattened carbon rod and a similar-sized piece of sheet zinc insert filter paper or cotton that has been soaked in a saturated solution of ammonium chloride (sal ammoniac). Use battery clips to connect wires to the zinc and carbon and an electric bell. Then students can connect the wires to a voltmeter and see that it will read about 1.5 volts (this is independent of electrode size). As a project, students may measure the length of time a cell can run a bell. The voltage will drop because of polarization. Then the students may further investigate the action of a depolarizing agent such as manganese dioxide as follows. Prepare a new layer of the sal ammoniac-soaked cotton, and in-

sert one layer of manganese dioxide between the cotton and the carbon rod and another layer between the cotton and the zinc. Now connect the new cell to operate the bell. Students should note how much longer the cell will operate. (Times vary, generally 20–30 minutes, which is substantially greater than the elapsed time without the MnO_2.)

13.2c   Lead storage battery

A simple lead storage battery can be made by hanging lead plates from opposite sides of a battery jar (400-600-ml) containing H_2SO_4 (1 part acid to 6 parts H_2O by volume). (Observe usual cautions for H_2SO_4. Use 6 volts d.c. for charging, no more. Insert electrodes and then turn on current.) Then charge with a battery charger; connect one plate to the plus lead of the charger and the other plate to the minus lead of the charger. If a battery charger is not available, a rectifier can be made by connecting a 200-watt bulb in series with 2 cells containing saturated borax solution with lead and pure aluminum sheet electrodes, as shown in Fig.

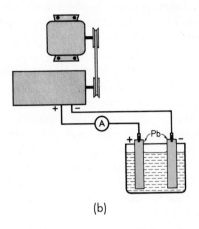

(b)

13-4A. Or use an automobile generator driven by an electric motor (Fig. 13–4B). An ammeter connected in series measures the charging rate. Regular storage batteries may also be charged with this equipment. In this demonstration, H_2 is liberated at one electrode ($-$) and the other ($+$) is covered with brown PbO_2. Three minutes charging produces a suit-

able deposit. The cell is then discharged by ringing a bell.

Note that commercial lead plates can also be used; the positive plate is a hollow grid filled with PbO_2, the negative plate is a grid filled with spongy porous lead produced electrically by plating out the lead too rapidly. This increases the surface area for electrolysis and increases the current output many times. The reactions for lead storage cells are as follows.

Discharge (electrical energy released)
Positive electrode

$$PbO_2 + 2 e^- + 4 H^+ \rightarrow Pb^{++} + 2 H_2O$$
$$Pb^{++} + SO_4^= \rightarrow PbSO_4$$

$$\overline{PbO_2 + 4 H^+ + SO_4^= + 2 e^- \rightarrow PbSO_4 + 2 H_2O}$$

Negative electrode

$$Pb \rightarrow Pb^{++} + 2 e^-$$
$$Pb^{++} + SO_4^= \rightarrow PbSO_4$$

$$\overline{Pb + SO_4^= \rightarrow PbSO_4 + 2 e^-}$$

Charge (chemical energy stored)
Positive electrode

$$PbSO_4 + 2 H_2O \rightarrow PbO_2 + 4 H^+ + SO_4^= + 2 e^-$$

Negative electrode (electrons entering,

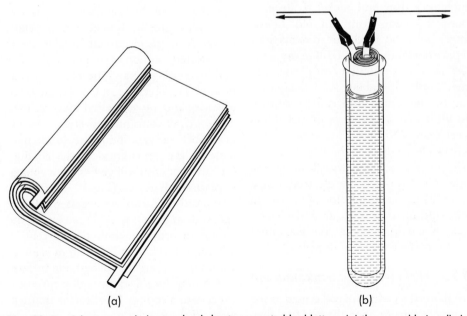

(a)   (b)

Fig. 13–5 A battery made by two lead sheets separated by blotters: (a) the assembly is rolled, (b) then inserted into a test tube containing 20% sulfuric acid and charged.

connection to negative [−] terminal of charging device)

$$PbSO_4 + 2 e^- \rightarrow Pb + SO_4^=$$

Total cell reaction

$$Pb + PbO_2 + 2\,[2\,H^+ + SO_4^=] \underset{charge}{\overset{discharge}{\rightleftarrows}} 2\,PbSO_4 + 2\,H_2O$$

Individual students may make batteries by using two sheets of lead foil separated by blotters (Fig. 13–5A) and rolled, placed in a test tube (Fig. 13–5B) containing 20 per cent H_2SO_4, and charged. There is one lead wire to each lead sheet.

Students may also prepare miniature lead storage batteries with 2 lead electrodes, using concentrated $NaHCO_3$ or Na_2SO_4 solution in place of sulfuric acid as the electrolyte. On charging, the positive plate forms lead dioxide as before. The voltage is about 1.7 volts, sufficient to ring a bell or light a 1.5-volt flashlight bulb.

13.2d *Edison alkaline cell*

You may want to have students compare the lead cell with the Edison cell, which uses iron and nickel oxide electrodes. Elements from an old Edison battery may be used, or students may prepare one in this way. Drill many small holes in a nickel-plated (*not* chromium-plated) iron tube about ¼″ in diameter. Plug the bottom with a rubber stopper, and fill it with small chips of nickel and nickel oxide (Ni_2O_3). This serves as the positive electrode. For the negative electrode use a tube filled with iron or iron oxide. Finally place the electrodes in a strong (21 per cent) solution of potassium hydroxide in a battery jar and charge. Students should find that the maximum voltage produced is 1.2 volts per cell.

13.2e *Nickel-cadmium alkaline cell*

In this cell a cadmium rod is used as the negative electrode. For the positive electrode use a stainless steel tube drilled with fine holes, plugged at the bottom with a rubber stopper, and filled with nickel hydroxide. The electrolyte is 21% potassium hydroxide in a battery jar. Then charge the cell; the maximum voltage developed should be about 1.2 volts.

If you have or can borrow a lead storage battery, an Edison battery, and a nickel-cadmium cell, you can test each for ampere-hour discharge and for voltage at low and high temperatures. The Edison battery should show the lowest ampere-hour life for its size. The nickel-cadmium and lead batteries are about equally effective but the lead storage battery is ⅕ to ¼ the price of a nickel-cadmium battery.

13.3 Electroplating
13.3a *Copper plating*

Use pure copper as the anode (positive) and the object to be plated as the cathode. Clean object to be plated by first placing it in dilute HCl. Upon removal wash thoroughly with water and then polish with a fine steel wool. For very fine plating you can follow the steel wool with jeweler's rouge. A simple electrolyte for class use is a saturated solution of copper sulfate. For careful work prepare the electrolyte as follows. Dissolve 70 g of $CuSO_4$ in 500 cc of water and 24 cc of ethyl alcohol; then add 14 cc of concentrated H_2SO_4. A few grains of clear gelatin in the solution may increase the smoothness of the coating. One fresh dry cell will give enough voltage to plate small objects (Fig. 13–6). If additional cells or a rectifier are used, place a rheostat and ammeter in series in the circuit in order to limit the current to 0.5 ampere. The plating current is about 1 amp per square foot of cathode surface, or 0.5 amp for 72 sq in. If this current is exceeded, a spongy layer forms that will wipe off the electrode.

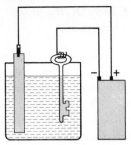

Fig. 13–6   In copper plating, small objects take one cell, whereas larger objects may require additional cells with a rheostat and ammeter.

13.3b   Nickel plating

In nickel plating use as the electrolyte a solution containing the following substances.

nickel ammonium sulfate	150 g
NaCl	25 g
boric acid	25 g
H_2O_2	7.5 g
water	1 liter

Use pure nickel as the anode and the object to be plated as the cathode. Copper is the easiest metal to plate with nickel. Use the circuits shown in Fig. 13–6, but with more current, about 12-15 amps per sq ft at 1.5 to 2 volts measured across the electrodes in the plating bath.

13.3c   Zinc plating

The electrolyte for zinc plating contains 10 per cent $ZnSO_4$, 2.5 per cent NH_4Cl, and 4 per cent ammonium citrate. Zinc is used as the anode and the object to be plated as the cathode. You will want to have students show one method of galvanizing; that is, plating an iron object with zinc (the other method is a dip into molten zinc). Once deposited, the zinc forms a coating of zinc oxide which stops further corrosion (oxidation by atmospheric oxygen). Use a voltage of 1.5-2 volts measured across the plating bath.

13.3d   Silver plating

The commercial method for silver plating is too dangerous for school use because silver cyanide, which is toxic, is involved. There are, however, safe modifications that students can perform.

Using old hypo. Use photographic hypo that has been used for some time; this used hypo contains silver salts from film or photographic paper, and it makes an excellent electrolyte for silver plating. Neutralize the acid in the old hypo by adding a dilute base until an indicator shows neutral. Use a piece of pure silver or a discarded pure silver object as the anode and a metal object to be plated as the cathode. About 2 volts, measured across the electrodes, is needed; the current needed is 1 amp per 18 sq in.

Using silver nitrate. Use silver nitrate as the electrolyte. Dissolve 10 g silver nitrate in 100 cc water; add to it a solution of gelatin made by dissolving 2.5 g in 50 cc water. Use the same apparatus as for copper plating. Connect a strip of old silver to the positive terminal, a carbon rod or copper strip to the negative terminal. (If copper is used, it must be free from grease and oxide. Dip it in concentrated nitric acid and rinse quickly in water.) Use three dry cells connected in series.

13.3e   Chromium plating

Chromium plating should be demonstrated by the teacher in a well ventilated room. (*Caution: Fumes of chromium compound are highly toxic.*) Chromium is easiest to plate on clean copper. For the electrolyte use a solution of 500 grams of chromic oxide (Cr_2O_3) in 2 liters of warm water to which 5 g of concentrated sulfuric acid has been added. Carefully stir to dissolve all the oxide. Arrange the apparatus so that the solution is kept hot (100-160° F), preferably on an electric hot plate. Use lead as the anode and the object to be plated as the cathode. For each square inch of object to be plated use 100 to 300 amps per sq ft, that is, 100-300 amps / 144 in². Temperatures and current densities vary over a wide range. A typical combination is a current density of 100-150 amps / sq ft at 110° F.

13.3f   Anodizing aluminum

A coating of desired thickness of aluminum oxide may be produced electrochemically by making the aluminum article the anode in an electrolytic bath containing an acid. One process uses a 3% solution of chromic acid at a temperature of about 100° F. The voltage is raised from zero to 40 v at the rate of about 8 v per minute and is maintained at full voltage for 30-60 minutes. The current density is 1 to 3 amps per sq ft. Electrolytic baths use sulfuric acid of varying concentrations from 15-25%. Anodic oxidation is a fertile area for student investigations since the oxide coating may then be dyed by a variety of procedures. Other metals such as magnesium may also be anodized. A solution contains 25% NaOH, 7% ethylene glycol, and 0.2% sodium oxalate. The coating is produced by applying either a.c. or d.c. to magnesium for 15 to 25 minutes at a current density of 10 to 25 amps per sq ft. Plating temperature is 75-80° C. The coating produced is essentially hard $Mg(OH)_2$.

13.4   Other electrochemical reactions

13.4a   Electrolysis

Electrolytic reduction of various materials has been discussed in the following areas of this book: electrolysis of water, 7.1b, 7.2c, 2.2c; electrolytic preparation of chlorine, 11.2a; migration of sodium ions through glass, 10.4a; redox reactions, 6.5b.

13.4b   Conductivity in an electrolyte

The current through an electrolyte consists of the motion of the negative and positive ions toward electrodes of opposite charge. (See the demonstrations on ion-migration in 13.4c and in 10.4a.) This current, of course, is different from current in a metallic conductor. The flow of electrons through a wire results in a magnetic field being produced about the conductor. The movement of ions through an electrolyte also results in a magnetic field. The field produced by the motion of cations moving in one direction reinforces the field produced by the anions moving in the opposite direction. A simple demonstration shows this magnetic effect. An 8″ length of glass tubing (½″ diameter) is placed over a demonstration compass positioned in a north-south direction. Each end of the glass tube contains a graphite electrode placed so that the length of path through the electrolyte is about 6″. One rubber stopper in which the electrodes are mounted has a small V-shaped slit made along its circumference lengthwise so that the gas generated by electrolysis may escape. The electrodes are connected through a knife switch to a 90-120-v d.c. source. The tube is filled with a saturated NaCl solution. When the switch is closed, the compass positioned beneath the glass tube is deflected sharply. When the polarity of the electrodes is reversed, closing the switch causes the compass to be deflected in the opposite direction. At this voltage and with the short length of path, the effect is almost instantaneous. The electrolyte gets hot very rapidly. The current range is between 1.5 and 2.0 amp. Therefore the switch should not be kept closed too long. An alternate arrangement of apparatus is shown in Fig. 13–7. The longer the glass tube, the higher the volt-

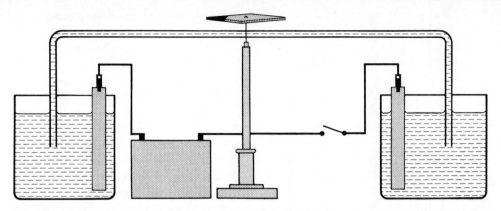

Fig. 13–7 When ions migrate through an electrolyte, a magnetic field is thereby produced. Keep the wires running from the electrodes to the battery as far away as possible from the ion bridge to prevent the magnetic field around the wire from affecting the results.

age required. Various electrodes and electrolytes may be used.

13.4c *Ion migration*

A striking demonstration of the migration of cupric ions may be performed in this way (Fig. 13–8).[1] Before the class begins prepare agar gels as follows:

Gel 1. Add 15 grams of powdered agar to enough cold 0.6 N KCl to make 1 liter when mixed; heat until the agar dissolves.

Gel 2. Combine 500 cc of 0.2 N KCl with 500 cc of 0.4 N $CuCl_2$; again add 15 grams of agar and dissolve by heating.

Pour the hot solution of gel 1 into a U-tube, turn the tube at an angle, and let the agar solidify so that it fills one arm only. When it has solidified in the U-tube, pour liquid gel 2 into the other arm and let it set. Insert platinum or stainless steel wires or small plates into the ends of the tube, not extending into the agar. On top of the first arm (the colorless one), add 3 N HCl; to the other arm (the blue one) add some saturated solution of copper chloride. Next connect the electrodes to a 110-volt d.c. source; a radio selenium

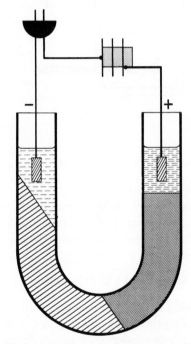

Fig. 13–8 Migration of cupric ions through agar gels.

rectifier can convert a.c. to d.c. with a small loss; or use a 90-volt radio "B" battery. The side of the U-tube containing the copper chloride is positive. Operate this for some 12 hours. Students should note that the blue color can be seen to

[1] Adapted from P. Arthur, *Demonstration Experiments in Chemistry*, McGraw-Hill, 1934.

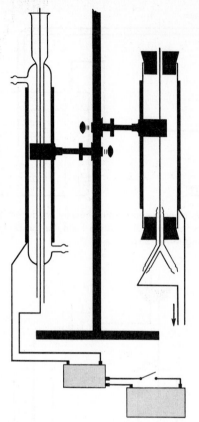

Fig. 13–9 Smoke precipitation apparatus.

move across the tube and up the opposite arm, indicating that the cupric ions are migrating from the positive to the negative electrode.

13.4d Smoke precipitation

Using a Liebig condenser. Run a wire through the center of a Liebig condenser or a glass cylinder (both are shown in Fig. 13–9). Then wrap foil or wire on the outside. Connect the outer foil or wire to one terminal of the secondary of an induction coil and the inner wire to the other terminal. Connect the primary in series with a switch and a battery as shown. Set the induction coil into operation by closing the switch. Blow smoke up through

the glass tube; no smoke will come out of the opposite end of the tube. Elicit from students that the smoke particles have become charged, causing them to coagulate and fall back down the tube.

Using a bell jar. A homemade Cottrell precipitator may be made from a large bell jar containing a 1-hole stopper through which an iron or copper wire about as thick as the handle of a deflagrating spoon is inserted (in practice this handle has been used). This wire reaches at least two thirds down the length of the bell jar. The bell jar is placed on a base on a metal plate (a sheet of copper) which is connected to ground. The bell jar is filled with cigarette smoke which may be blown in through the side tube. If such a jar is not available, the ordinary jar is merely lifted at the bottom and cigarette smoke is blown in. The device may be operated either with a Tesla coil or by means of an induction coil, operated by a 6-volt battery in series with a switch connected to the primary of the coil. One secondary lead is connected to the central wire and the other to the grounded base. If the Tesla coil is used, merely make contact with the central electrode. The smoke precipitates by electrical neutralization of the charged colloidal particles. After continuous operation, the deposit may be wiped from the sides of the bell jar with a cloth moistened with benzene.

13.4e Cleaning silverware at home

Students may use this electrolytic method for cleaning their own silverware. Fill an aluminum pan with boiling water or use a sheet of aluminum in an enamel or Pyrex basin. Add 2 tablespoons of sodium bicarbonate to the water and stir to dissolve the salt. Place the tarnished silver articles in the water so that they make contact with the aluminum for a few minutes. Finally wash the articles in warm water and dry with a soft cloth. (The procedure may have to be repeated if the silverware is heavily tarnished.)

CAPSULE LESSONS
Ways to get started in class

13-1. You may want to introduce this subject by electroplating small steel and iron objects that students bring to class. Use the copper plating solution and the method described in this chapter. Develop the chemical equation for the reaction and establish the basic principles.

13-2. If possible, arrange for a visit to an electroplating plant in your neighborhood. Have students find out the solutions used and the voltage needed to electroplate various metals.

13-3. A student may introduce the topic by reporting on the discovery of the Hall process for the electrolytic reduction of aluminum ore. What was the advantage of this new method? Establish the chemical equation and the principles of electrochemistry.

13-4. Students, in committee, may report to the class on the extraction of metals from their ores by electrochemical means. Perhaps they may show samples of the ores and the metal products as part of their talk.

13-5. Show the film *Electrochemistry* (EBF) or the free films *This is Aluminum* (Aluminum Company of America), *This is Magnesium* (Dow Chemical), or *Story of a Storage Battery* (Willard Storage Battery Company). Have students write a summary of the main facts revealed in the film.

13-6. Generate electricity by preparing a dry cell consisting of a penny and a dime with a disk of filter paper soaked in sal ammoniac between them. Connect wires from a galvanometer so that students see the needle move. How has electricity been produced here?

13-7. Have students describe the use of a storage battery in an automobile. What substances are used for the fluid? The plates? What is the reaction?

13-8. Have students report on the new silver dry cell and storage batteries; or visit a shop selling cadmium automobile batteries and report on these.

PEOPLE, PLACES, AND THINGS

Many people in your own community will answer students' queries about batteries: the local garage serviceman, the distributor of auto batteries or flashlight batteries, the chemists or electrical engineers to be found among the students' parents or on the staff of a nearby college.

It may be possible to arrange a field trip to a plant manufacturing batteries or an electroplating plant. Some companies distribute pamphlets which make profitable reading in advance of the trip. If electricity is not expensive in your region, there may be aluminum, copper, and alloy steel plants to visit.

BOOKS AND PAMPHLETS

These are only a few of the books which are pertinent to the work discussed in this chapter. These and many other references classified by subject and with complete bibliographical data are given in the bibliography at the end of the book.

Basolo, F., and R. Pearson, *Mechanisms of Inorganic Reactions: A Study of Metal Complexes in Solution,* Wiley, 1958.

Barken, L., *Physical Chemistry of Metals,* McGraw-Hill, 1953.

Hutchinson, E., *Chemistry; The Elements and Their Reactions,* Saunders, 1959.

Johnson, C., *Metallurgy,* American Technical Society, 1948.

Lange, N., *Handbook of Chemistry,* 9th ed., Handbook Publishers, 1956.

Riegel, E., *Industrial Chemistry,* 6th ed., Reinhold, 1954.

Sanders, H., *Electroplating,* International Textbook, 1950.

Scientific American, "Chemical Prospecting," July, 1957.

Sisler, H., et al., *General Chemistry: A Systematic Approach,* Macmillan, 1949.

Taylor, F. S., *A History of Industrial Chemistry,* Abelard-Schuman, 1957.

This partial list is intended only as a guide toward film and filmstrip selection. Refer to the more complete listing at the end of the book where films are classified by subject and where a key to abbreviations and addresses of distributors are given. The cost of film rental, of course, is subject to change. Films are sound and black and white unless otherwise specified.

Chemistry Series (series 5 fs) (ionization, acids, electrolysis), McGraw-Hill, $6.00 each.

Copper (f, s, c), Anaconda, free.

Electrochemistry (f, s), EBF, $2.50.

Electrochemistry (f, s), Indiana, $2.00.

How Batteries Work (fs), Popular Science through McGraw-Hill, $6.00.

Oxidation-Reduction (f, s), Ideal, $2.00.

Story of a Storage Battery (f, s), Willard Storage Battery Co., free.

This is Aluminum (f, s), Alcoa, free.

This is Magnesium (f, s), Dow, free.

This is only a partial listing of free and inexpensive materials available to the teacher at this time. A directory of addresses is given at the end of the book. Many of these materials are distributed to teachers without charge. Where there is a small fee, the cost is indicated, although the prices are subject to change. While we recommend the material for use in the classroom, we do not necessarily endorse the products advertised.

ABC's of Aluminum, Reynolds Metal Co.

Battery Charts, Electric Storage Battery Co.

Chemicals from Salt and the Sea, Manufacturing Chemists' Association.

Copper—Oldest and Newest Metal, Copper and Brass Research Assoc.

Edison Nickel-iron-alkaline Storage Cell, Edison Storage Battery Div., Thomas Edison, Inc.

Electrical Fundamentals (ammeters, and voltmeters), Educational Services, Chrysler Corp.

Electricity and Wheels, General Motors.

Inside Story of Dry Batteries, National Carbon Co., Div. Union Carbide and Carbon

Periodic Chart of the Elements (11″ x 14½″), Steinmetz, *Latter Day Vulcan, Electricity Around Us,* General Electric.

Romance of Nickel, International Nickel Co.

Short Stories of Science and Invention (C. Kettering), General Motors.

Zinc in the World of Things, New Jersey Zinc Co.

CHAPTER 14

Organic chemistry

The tremendous variety of organic compounds—approximately one million compounds have been identified and the number increases almost daily—makes organic chemistry a fascinating subject for students. They learn that they are not dealing with many elements and their compounds as in inorganic chemistry, but with compounds of carbon which almost always contain hydrogen and often oxygen as well. They will recognize other differences: many organic substances are not soluble in water, do not ionize or conduct electric current (although organic acids do), have large molecules whose pattern of side chains determines the properties of the compound.

In this chapter suggestions are offered for building models of possible variations (isomers) in the internal structure of organic compounds, and many typical reactions of characteristic organic groups are introduced. We have given space to the preparation of some fuels and also to one group of man-made compounds, the plastics. Finally, a few of the techniques of analysis are introduced.

14.1 Structural models of carbon compounds

In learning the structure of carbon compounds students can use commercial atom model building sets designed to show the internal structure of organic compounds; these sets are sold by supply houses (see appendix). Some students may want to devise models of Tinkertoy or similar sets (Fig. 14-1A, B). Students will want to try to build structural models of some of the compounds shown in Table 14-1. In 6.4 we have described various ways to prepare models which are just as applicable for organic as for inorganic compounds. If models are lacquered or painted, they can be kept as permanent teaching aids.

Students can also use gumdrops and toothpicks to make useful inexpensive models. Different-colored gumdrops can be used to represent the various elements, and single or double bonds can be made with one or two toothpicks. With these models students can show bond angles and spatial configurations.

Students can try to demonstrate the relationship between atomic structure and physical properties by building several models of isomers, for example, normal and isobutane:

$$
\begin{array}{ccccccc}
\text{H} & & \text{H} & & \text{H} & & \text{H} \\
| & & | & & | & & | \\
\text{H}-\text{C}-&\text{C}-&\text{C}-&\text{C}-\text{H} \\
| & & | & & | & & | \\
\text{H} & & \text{H} & & \text{H} & & \text{H}
\end{array}
\quad\text{(normal)}
$$

$$
\begin{array}{ccccc}
\text{H} & & \text{H} & & \text{H} \\
| & & | & & | \\
\text{H}-\text{C}-&\text{C}-&\text{C}-\text{H} \\
| & & | & & | \\
\text{H} & & | & & \text{H} \\
& & \text{H}-\text{C}-\text{H} \\
& & | \\
& & \text{H}
\end{array}
\quad\text{(iso)}
$$

You may want to establish the fact that the normal configuration "should" have a higher boiling point and melting point than the "iso" configuration (as indeed it does).

Branching of the chain *always* results in a lowering of the boiling point, the van der Waals force being smaller for a more compact molecule than for a longer molecule. Thus *n*-pentane boils at 36° C, isopentane at 28° C, and neopentane at 9.5° C. Unlike the variation in boiling points, there is no regularity in the change in melting point with branching because the effectiveness of the attractive forces depends on how well the molecule fits into the crystal lattice. Thus *n*-pentane melts at −129.7° C, isopentane at −160° C, and neopentane at − 160° C. In general, however, the more symmetrical and more compact the molecule, the higher its melting point.[1]

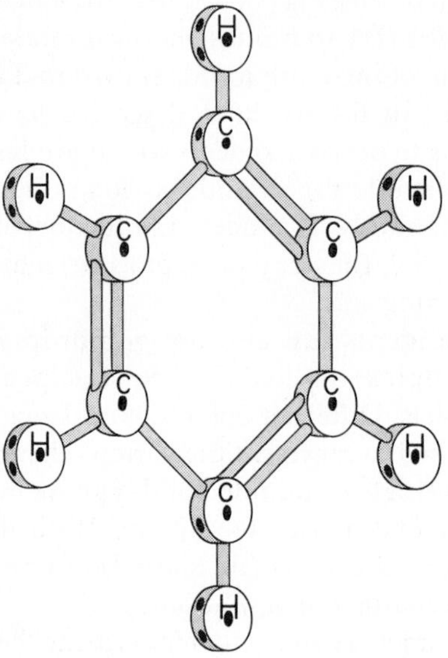

14.2 Properties and reactions of some hydrocarbons

14.2a Alkanes: methane series (paraffins—saturated hydrocarbons)

The compounds in this series have the general formula, C_nH_{2n+2}, and are not very reactive chemicals. Many are found in petroleum. The simplest hydrocarbon in the series is methane, CH_4.

Preparation of methane. Methane can be prepared in many ways; one method is suggested here (Fig. 14-2).

From sodium acetate and solid soda lime. Anhydrous sodium acetate must be used. It is prepared from the hydrate,

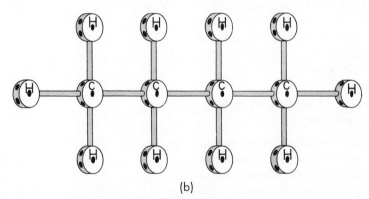

(a)

Fig. 14-1 Tinkertoy models of (a) C_6H_6, (b) C_4H_{10}.

[1] Carl R. Noller, *Chemistry of Organic Compounds*, 2nd ed., W. B. Saunders Company, Philadelphia, 1957, pp. 38, 40.

(b)

Fig. 14-1b

$NaC_2H_3O_2 \cdot 3H_2O$, by heating in an iron crucible or tray until no more water comes off. Mix one part of the fused sodium acetate with three parts of dry soda lime in a mortar. (*Caution: If the sodium acetate and soda lime are not thoroughly dry, the tube may crack.*) Place the mixture into an 8" Pyrex tube, spreading it evenly at the back of the test tube. Set up the apparatus for water collection of the gas (Fig. 14–2). Discard the first bottle collected. Collect the number of bottles of gas required and an additional bottle containing 1/10-1/5 of water (a mixture of methane and air is present in this bottle). Heat the generator gently at first and then more strongly. Fourteen grams of this mixture should produce one liter of methane.

$$NaOH + CH_3COONa \rightarrow CH_4 + Na_2CO_3$$

Properties of methane. Insert a burning splint into a bottle of the gas. The gas burns at the mouth of the bottle with a yellow flame but the splint is extinguished. Cover the bottle with a glass plate after the flame dies out. Then add 5 ml of limewater and shake the bottle. The limewater turns milky, indicating the formation of carbon dioxide as one of the combustion products. To another bottle of the gas add 5 ml of bromine water, cover, and shake the bottle. The bromine is not decolorized, showing that the methane is a saturated hydrocarbon. To another bottle of methane add 5 ml of a dilute solution of potassium permanganate (0.1 N), cover, and shake. The potassium permanganate is not decolorized, due again to the saturated nature of the hydrocarbon. Place the bottle containing the methane-air mixture inside a cylinder of wire mesh and bring a burning splint to its mouth. The mixture explodes. The lightness of methane may be demonstrated by pouring it upward into a bottle. The gas may also be

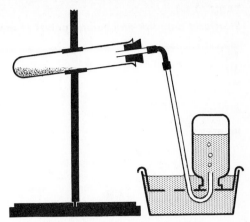

Fig. 14–2   Preparation of methane.

collected by downward displacement of air.

Additional demonstrations to show the nature of saturated hydrocarbons include: 1. Shake 3 ml of kerosene with 1 ml of a solution of bromine in CCl_4. The kerosene is miscible with the CCl_4 and since it usually does not contain unsaturated hydrocarbons, there is no removal of the bromine color. 2. Place a small piece of paraffin (size of a small pea) into 3 ml of the solution of bromine in CCl_4 and shake. The bromine is not decolorized.[2]

The various hydrocarbon mixtures such as kerosene, gasoline, and paraffin ignite with varying degrees of difficulty. A burning match dropped into 10 ml of gasoline in an evaporating dish causes the gasoline to catch fire (*Caution: An explosion may result from air admixture.*) However, repeating the experiment with kerosene causes no ignition, in fact, the match is extinguished in the kerosene. A few drops of kerosene on a watch glass may, however, be ignited with a small Bunsen flame. A cotton wick placed into the kerosene in an evaporating dish may also be ignited with a match.

[2] Lloyd E. Malm and Harper W. Frantz, *College Chemistry in the Laboratory*, No. 2., Freeman and Co., San Francisco, 1959, pp. 226, 227.

TABLE 14-1
Structural formulas and boiling points of some typical organic compounds

name	formula	structural formula	boiling point, °C
METHANE (ALKANES) SERIES	C_nH_{2n+2}	$H-\overset{\overset{\displaystyle H}{\vert}}{\underset{\underset{\displaystyle H}{\vert}}{C}}-\overset{\overset{\displaystyle H}{\vert}}{\underset{\underset{\displaystyle H}{\vert}}{C}}-\overset{\overset{\displaystyle H}{\vert}}{\underset{\underset{\displaystyle H}{\vert}}{C}}-\overset{\overset{\displaystyle H}{\vert}}{\underset{\underset{\displaystyle H}{\vert}}{C}}-$ etc.$-\overset{\overset{\displaystyle H\cdot}{}}{\underset{\underset{\displaystyle H}{\vert}}{C}}-H$	
methane	CH_4	$H-\overset{\overset{\displaystyle H}{\vert}}{\underset{\underset{\displaystyle H}{\vert}}{C}}-H$	−161.5
ethane	C_2H_6 or CH_3CH_3	$H-\overset{\overset{\displaystyle H}{\vert}}{\underset{\underset{\displaystyle H}{\vert}}{C}}-\overset{\overset{\displaystyle H}{\vert}}{\underset{\underset{\displaystyle H}{\vert}}{C}}-H$	− 88.3
propane	C_3H_8 or $CH_3CH_2CH_3$	$H-\overset{\overset{\displaystyle H}{\vert}}{\underset{\underset{\displaystyle H}{\vert}}{C}}-\overset{\overset{\displaystyle H}{\vert}}{\underset{\underset{\displaystyle H}{\vert}}{C}}-\overset{\overset{\displaystyle H}{\vert}}{\underset{\underset{\displaystyle H}{\vert}}{C}}-H$	− 42.17
butane	C_4H_{10} or $CH_3(CH_2)_2CH_3$	$H-\overset{H}{\underset{H}{C}}-\overset{H}{\underset{H}{C}}-\overset{H}{\underset{H}{C}}-\overset{H}{\underset{H}{C}}-H$	− 0.6 to − 0.3
pentane	C_5H_{12} or $CH_3(CH_2)_3CH_3$	$H-\overset{H}{\underset{H}{C}}-\overset{H}{\underset{H}{C}}-\overset{H}{\underset{H}{C}}-\overset{H}{\underset{H}{C}}-\overset{H}{\underset{H}{C}}-H$	36.2
hexane	C_6H_{14} or $CH_3(CH_2)_4CH_3$	$H-C-C-C-C-C-C-H$	69
heptane	C_7H_{16} or $CH_3(CH_2)_5CH_3$	$H-C-C-C-C-C-C-C-H$	98.4
octane	C_8H_{18} or $CH_3(CH_2)_6CH_3$	$H-C-C-C-C-C-C-C-C-H$	125.8

name	formula	structural formula	boiling point, °C
heptadecane	$C_{17}H_{36}$ or $CH_3(CH_2)_{15}CH_3$	H—C—C— etc. —C—H (with H atoms)	303
ETHYLENE (ALKENES) SERIES	C_nH_{2n}	...—C—C=C—C—...	
ethylene (ethene)	C_2H_4 or $CH_2:CH_2$	C=C (with H atoms)	−103.9
propene (propylene)	C_3H_6 or $CH_2:CHCH_3$	C=C—C—H	− 47.0
1-butene (α-butylene)	C_4H_8 or $CH_3CH_2CH:CH_2$	C=C—C—C—H	− 5
2-butene (cisisomer)	C_4H_8 or $CH_3CH:CHCH_3$	C=C	1
2-butene (trans-isomer)		C=C	2.5
ACETYLENE (ALKYNES) SERIES	C_nH_{2n-2}	...—C≡C—...	
ethyne (acetylene)	C_2H_2 or $CH:CH$	H—C≡C—H	− 83.6 (sublimes)
propyne (methyl acetylene)	C_3H_4 or $CH_3C:CH$	H—C—C≡C—H	− 23. 3

TABLE 14-1 (*continued*)

name	formula	structural formula	boiling point, °C
1-butyne (ethyl acetylene)	C_4H_6 or $CH\vdots CCH_2CH_3$		8.6
2-butyne (di-methyl-acetylene)	C_4H_6 or $CH_3C\vdots CCH_3$		27.2
BENZENE (AROMATICS) SERIES *	C_nH_{2n-6}	or	
benzene (benzol)	C_6H_6		80.1
toluene (methyl benzene)	C_7H_8 or $C_6H_5CH_3$	—CH_3	110.6
xylene (di-methyl-benzene)	C_8H_{10} or $C_6H_4(CH_3)_2$	ortho meta para	ortho = 144.4 meta = 139.1 para = 138.3
naphthalene	$C_{10}H_8$		217.9
anthracene	$C_{14}H_{10}$		340–42
SUBSTITUTED HYDROCARBONS chloromethane (methyl chloride)	CH_3Cl		− 24.2

* When the abbreviated symbol is used, it is understood that a hydrogen is bonded to each carbon except where another group is shown.

name	formula	structural formula	boiling point, °C
dichloromethane (methylene chloride)	CH_2Cl_2	Cl—C—Cl with H above and H below	40–41
trichloromethane (chloroform)	$CHCl_3$	Cl—C—Cl with Cl above and H below	61.2
tetrachloro-methane (carbon tetrachloride)	CCl_4	Cl—C—Cl with Cl above and Cl below	76.8
dichlorodifluoro-methane (freon-12)	CCl_2F_2	Cl—C—Cl with F above and F below	− 28
triiodomethane (iodoform)	CHI_3	I—C—I with I above and H below	none explodes at 210 (sublimes)
ALCOHOLS	$\ldots$—C—OH		
methanol (methyl alcohol)	CH_3OH	H—C—OH with H above and H below	64.6
ethanol (ethyl alcohol)	C_2H_5OH or CH_3CH_2OH	H—C—C—OH	78.5
n-propanol	C_3H_7OH or $CH_3CH_2CH_2OH$	H—C—C—C—OH	97.2
iso-propanol	$CH_3CHOHCH_3$	H—C—C—C—H with O H below middle	82.3
ALDEHYDES	R—C double bond O and H		

TABLE 14-1 (*continued*)

name	formula	structural formula	boiling point, °C
methanal (formaldehyde)	CH_2O or $HCHO$		-21
ethanol (acetaldehyde)	C_2H_4O or CH_3CHO		21
propanal (propionaldehyde)	C_3H_6O or CH_3CH_2CHO		48.8
n-butanal (n-butyraldehyde)	C_4H_8O or $CH_3(CH_2)_2CHO$		75.7
iso-butanal (iso-butyraldehyde)	C_4H_8O or $(CH_3)_2CHCHO$		61.5
KETONES 2-propanone (acetone) (dimethyl ketone)	$R-CO-R$ C_3H_6O or CH_3COCH_3		56.5
2-butanone (ethyl methyl ketone)	C_4H_8O or $CH_3COC_2H_5$		79.6
2-butanone-3 methyl (iso-propyl methyl ketone)	$C_5H_{10}O$ or $CH_3COCH(CH_3)_2$		93

name	formula	structural formula	boiling point, °C
ACIDS	$R—C\begin{smallmatrix}O\\OH\end{smallmatrix}$		
methanoic acid (formic acid)	HCOOH	$H—C\begin{smallmatrix}O\\OH\end{smallmatrix}$	100.7
ethanoic acid (acetic acid)	CH_3COOH		118.1
propanoic acid (propionic acid)	C_2H_5OOH or CH_3CH_2COOH		141.1
butanoic acid (n-butyric acid)	C_3H_7COOH or $CH_3CH_2CH_2COOH$		163.5 (at a pressure of 757 mm of Hg rather than 760 mm which is normal)
ESTERS	$R—C\begin{smallmatrix}O\\O–R\end{smallmatrix}$		
methyl acetate	$C_3H_6O_2$ or CH_3COOCH_3		57.1
methyl propanoate	$C_4H_8O_2$ or $CH_3CH_2COOCH_3$		79.9

TABLE 14-1 (*continued*)

name	formula	structural formula	boiling point, °C
isopropyl acetate	$C_5H_{10}O_2$ or $CH_3COOCH(CH_3)_2$	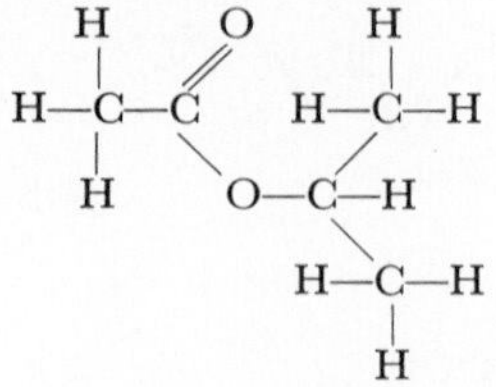 (structure shown)	89
ETHERS	R—O—R		
methyl ether	C_2H_6O or $(CH_3)_2O$	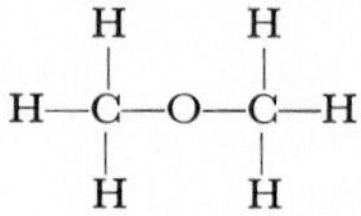 $H-\overset{H}{\underset{H}{C}}-O-\overset{H}{\underset{H}{C}}-H$	23.6
ethyl ether	$C_4H_{10}O$ or $C_2H_5OC_2H_5$	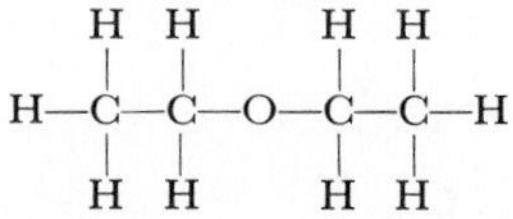 (structure shown)	34.6
ethyl methyl ether	C_3H_8O or $CH_3OC_2H_5$	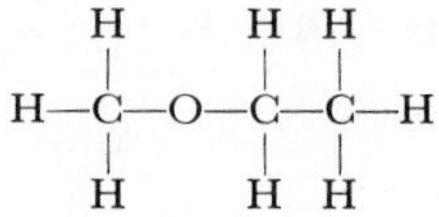 (structure shown)	7.9
ethyl isopropyl ether	$C_5H_{12}O$ or $C_2H_5OCH(CH_3)_2$	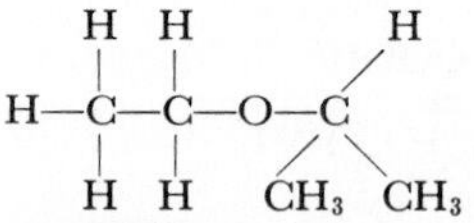 (structure shown)	54

Paraffin wax is not readily ignited with a Bunsen burner but a candle with a wick does ignite with a burning match.

Further studies of methane are described under fuels, 14.3. If the fuel gas in your laboratory is natural gas, it may be used for demonstration of the properties of methane of which it is largely composed. Merely collect your samples by water displacement.

14.2b Alkenes; ethylene series (olefins—unsaturated hydrocarbons)

These hydrocarbons are more reactive chemically because they have a double bond between two carbon atoms. Ethylene, C_2H_4, is the simplest in the series (see Table 14-1). The alkenes can be represented by the general formula C_nH_{2n}.

Ethylene: preparation and properties. Ethylene may be prepared as a demonstration by the dehydration of ethyl alcohol with sulfuric acid.[3]

Arrange the apparatus as in Fig. 14-3. Use a flask holding 400-500 cc. Remove the flask from the apparatus and place in it 25 cc of alcohol (industrial methylated spirit will serve); gradually add 80

[3] Adapted from G. Fowles, *Lecture Experiments in Chemistry,* 4th ed., G. Bell and Sons, Ltd., Lond., 1957, pp. 120, 121.

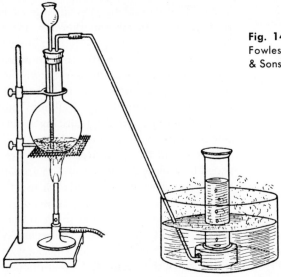

Fig. 14-3 Preparation of ethylene. (From G. Fowles, *Lecture Experiments in Chemistry*, G. Bell & Sons, Ltd., London, England, 5th ed.)

cc of concentrated sulfuric acid, cooling the flask between each addition of acid. Add a teaspoonful of silver sand to the mixture. The sand lessens the tendency of the heated liquid to froth. Place the flask back in its position and heat the liquid cautiously until it appears to boil (about 150° C). Regulate the flame so that the evolution of gas is steady and frothing is avoided as much as possible. Reject the first two jars of gas and collect the remainder. Ignite the contents of one bottle with a burning splint. A white luminous flame is produced. After combustion is complete, add 5 ml of limewater to the bottle, cover, and shake. The positive result indicates the production of CO_2 as a combustion product. Add 5 ml of bromine water to a second bottle, cover, and shake. The bromine color disappears due to the *addition* of bromine at the double bond. Oily droplets of ethylene dibromide may be formed. To another bottle add 5 ml of 0.1 N $KMnO_4$ solution (this may but need not necessarily be acidified with dilute H_2SO_4), cover, and shake. The solution of potassium permanganate is decol-

orized. This reaction is known as the Baeyer test for the double bond (see next below).

Baeyer test for the double bond. Students can show the comparative stability of paraffins (the alkanes) and olefins (the alkenes) with the Baeyer test. To a 5 per cent solution of ethylene, an olefin, add a few crystals of potassium permanganate. The reduction of the permanganate is shown by the fading of the violet color of the permanganate in the solution.

$$3 C_2H_4 + 2 KMnO_4 + 4 H_2O \rightarrow$$
$$2 MnO_2 + 2 KOH + 3 C_2H_4(OH)_2$$

With the paraffins this reduction is impossible; even oxidation is difficult. Thus $KMnO_4$ in a paraffin retains its violet color.

14.2c Alkynes: acetylene series (unsaturated hydrocarbons)

Acetylene, C_2H_2, is the first in this series of hydrocarbons containing triple bonds. The alkynes have the general formula C_nH_{2n-2}.

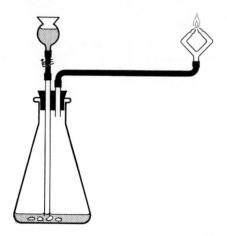

Fig. 14–4 Burning acetylene. A commercial air-acetylene mixer can be used in place of the bent Y-tube. For further details on generating acetylene see Fig. 6–4.

Preparation of acetylene. Acetylene can be generated in the reaction of water with calcium carbide (Fig. 14-4).

$$CaC_2 + 2 H_2O \rightarrow Ca(OH)_2 + C_2H_2$$

Place two grams of calcium carbide into a Pyrex flask. Since the reaction is very vigorous, the apparatus shown in Fig. 14-4 is recommended to control the slow dripping of water onto lumps of calcium carbide in the Pyrex flask generator. Use a dropping funnel, or make one from a funnel and a rubber tube with a screw-type pinch clamp. Slowly drop 15 cc. of water onto the carbide and collect several bottles of acetylene gas by water displacement (see Fig. 6-4). Discard the first bottle collected. Connect the delivery tube from the generator flask to a medicine dropper tube, bent Y-tube, or a special acetylene tip. Light the pure acetylene coming from the device available. (*Caution: Be sure all air has been swept from the generator. You may want to use a safety tube as described in 7.2 to prevent flashback.*) The ordinary pinched glass Y-tube produces a smoky yellow flame. The special tip, permitting some premixture with air and therefore more complete combustion, produces an intense white flame. (Before the incandescent light bulb this was often used for illumination.) Considerable carbon, of course, is still present in this luminous flame. This may be demonstrated by placing a portion of a cool test tube into the flame.

The use of the generator may be preceded by adding 3-5 ml of water to a small piece (pea size) of CaC_2 placed into a 6″ test tube. Acetylene gas is produced immediately and is ignited at the mouth of the test tube. It burns with a yellow smoky flame, and threads or particles of soot float in the air of the room. A drop of phenolphthalein, placed into the test tube after the reaction stops, turns red, indicating the formation of calcium hydroxide. (*Caution: Since acetylene-air mixtures are explosive, it is wise to wrap the test tube in a towel before igniting the gas and to keep open flames away from the larger acetylene generator used.*) Test bottles of acetylene with both bromine water and potassium permanganate solutions to show its unsaturated nature. (See properties of methane in 14.2a.) The results observed are the same as for the ethylene reaction. Bromine adds at the triple bond with the formation of $C_2H_2Br_4$.

Metal acetylides. Acetylene is a weak acid and may be used to produce metallic acetylides. These are dangerous explosives in the dry state but the precipitation of such acetylides is used as a characteristic test for acetylenic hydrogen (the single hydrogen attached to the terminal carbon having a triple bond). Pour a few cc of ammoniacal solution of cuprous chloride into a cylinder of acetylene. A copious precipitate of red cuprous acetylide (CuC–CCu) is produced at once. (*Caution: Do not leave the cuprous acetylide about; wash it away at once. It is explosive when dry.*)

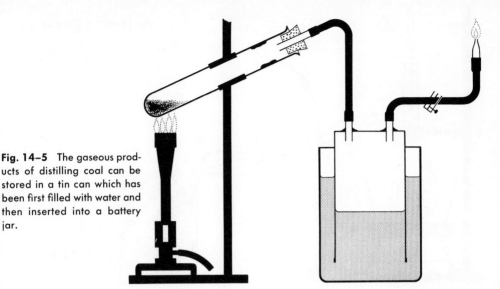

Fig. 14–5 The gaseous products of distilling coal can be stored in a tin can which has been first filled with water and then inserted into a battery jar.

14.2d *Aromatic hydrocarbons: benzene series*

The hydrocarbons just discussed are known as the *aliphatic* hydrocarbons. The *aromatic* hydrocarbons such as benzene, toluene, and xylene contain a six-membered ring having three carbon-to-carbon double bonds. The benzene series can be represented by the general formula C_nH_{2n-6}. Students may want to report on Kekulé's model of benzene. A sample of benzene can be examined to learn its physical properties. Add 5 ml of bromine water to 3 ml of benzene and shake the test tube. Benzene does not remove the color of bromine water. Repeat this experiment using 3 ml of benzene with 1 ml of a solution of bromine in CCl_4. Again no decolorization results. This indicates that the ring structure of benzene and its homologues more closely resembles that of the alkanes than that of the unsaturated hydrocarbons.

14.3 Fuels

In this section several suggestions for the study of fuels are offered, most of which are organic compounds of carbon. Some pertinent experiments were described in 9.5, which deals with carbon as an inorganic element. Some demonstrations using fuels are difficult for students to work with and might be better performed by the teacher. The work should be done under a hood in a well-ventilated room free from drafts.

14.3a *Destructive distillation of bituminous coal*

The distillation of coal, with the release of many industrial byproducts as well as harmful products which add to air pollution, makes a class demonstration that students find meaningful and provocative (Fig. 14-5). Grind some bituminous coal in a mortar with a pestle and place about 60 grams in a large Pyrex test tube. Fit the tube with a one-hole cork carrying a glass delivery tube. Students will need a storage tank made by first punching two holes in the bottom of a large tin can and then inserting a short glass or metal tube in each. Metal tubes should be soldered to the tin can; glass tubes can be sealed to the can

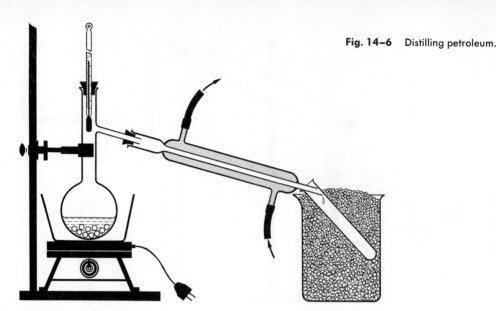

Fig. 14–6   Distilling petroleum.

with sealing wax or paraffin. Connect one of these short tubes by means of rubber tubing to the delivery tube; attach the other to a medicine dropper tube by rubber tubing with a screw-type pinch clamp. Finally fill the can with water, invert it in a battery jar of water, as shown, and hold it down with a small weight if necessary.

At this point, begin to distill the bituminous coal by heating the bottom of the test tube with a Meker or Fisher burner or a cone-shaped electric heating unit. After several minutes the coal breaks down into several substances. Gases leave the tube and fill the tin can, driving out the water. As the can fills with gas it will rise. Allow a short time for the air to be driven out of the can through the medicine dropper tube; then close the pinch clamp and collect the gas. To test the gas, open the pinch clamp and hold a match to the end of the dropper tube. Students will observe that the gas burns at the tip until the contents of the tin can are almost exhausted. Some of the volatile tar will be found floating on the water in the can. The remaining products of the destructive

distillation, including coke, will be found inside the test tube. See 9.5a for further information on destructive distillation.

14.3b   Composition of petroleum

Excellent demonstrations of the composition of petroleum-containing samples of most of the products are provided gratis to science teachers by several oil companies. Or students can make up a set of samples of natural petroleum, petroleum ether, kerosene, gasoline, fuel oil, lubricating oil, and asphalt, the principal products of the distillation of petroleum for an exhibit.

Distillation of petroleum. In some classes you may want to demonstrate the distillation of petroleum. (*Caution: This demonstration is hazardous. The room should be free of sparks or flames because the volatile products may escape into the air.*) Use a commercial sample of petroleum or prepare in class your own "petroleum" by mixing kerosene (20 ml), unleaded gasoline (10 ml), fuel oil (30 ml), lubricating oil (30 ml), and asphalt (10 ml). You may prefer to use a safer technique, starting with kero-

TABLE 14-2
Boiling-point ranges for petroleum fractions

boiling temperature	fraction
20°– 60° C	1 (petroleum ether)
60°–100° C	2 (light naphtha)
100°–205° C	3 (gasoline range 40–205°)
205°–275° C	4 (kerosene range 175–325°)
275° C	5 (residue: higher fractions)

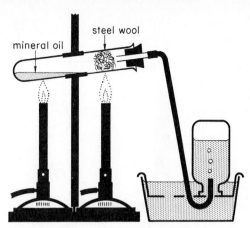

Fig. 14–7 Catalytic cracking of mineral oil in which heated steel wool acts as the catalyst.

sene and fuel oil. Prepare a distillation apparatus with a 360° C thermometer as shown in Fig. 14-6, placing 150 cc of petroleum into the flask. An electric heater is safer to use than an open flame, and the glassware should be Pyrex. Heat the mixture slowly (glass beads in the flask will prevent "bumping") and collect the successive fractions in the test tubes (cooled in ice-water bath) obtained over the temperature ranges shown above. It is not practical to try to separate the oils from the asphalt in class; vacuum distillation is needed for a successful separation.

A discussion of octane ratings may develop at this point, and students can refer to the models of branched and straight configurations of molecules (14.1). Additional work on octane ratings is included in the chapter on engines (Chapter 24).

14.3c Catalytic cracking of hydrocarbons

A 5-ml sample of colorless mineral oil (medicinal grade) is placed into an 8″ Pyrex test tube. A loose plug of steel wool is placed midway in the tube which is mounted slightly tipped so that both the oil and the steel wool may be heated either by separate burners or by changing the position of the single burner as needed from oil to catalyst to keep the reaction going (Fig. 14-7). An alternate arrangement consists of having the vapors of the boiling oil pass into a separate 8″ length

of Pyrex tubing which contains the steel wool. The first demonstration consists of merely heating the oil (but not the steel wool) and collecting whatever gaseous distillate is produced by water displacement. Samples may differ but when some gas is collected, it will neither decolorize bromine water nor a dilute potassium permanganate solution (see properties of methane, 14.2a). Sometimes, after the included air is permitted to escape, very little gas is produced and some of the vapor merely condenses as oily drops in the collecting bottle. To crack the oil, preheat the steel wool and then pass the vapors of the oil over the steel wool which when heated acts as a catalyst. The collected samples which have passed through heated steel wool decolorize bromine, indicating that unsaturated hydrocarbons are among the products of cracking hydrocarbons of the methane series.

14.3d Common fuels

Students can measure the temperature of different parts of a Bunsen burner flame with a thermocouple as shown in Fig. 14-8. (See also factors affecting oxidation, 7.1c, and flames, 7.1d.) At this point,

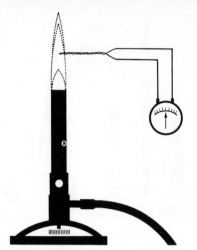

Fig. 14-8 Measuring the temperature of the different parts of a Bunsen burner flame with a thermocouple.

other common gaseous fuels such as manufactured, natural, and bottled gas can be studied.

Destructive distillation of wood. This is described in 9.5a.

Ethyl alcohol as a sootless fuel. Ethyl alcohol (grain alcohol and ethanol are synonyms) is used as rocket fuel and in some countries for combustion in engines. Unlike the fuels demonstrated above, it burns completely, leaving no residue and producing no soot.

This can be readily shown by burning it in an alcohol lamp or igniting a tiny quantity in a small open metal dish on the laboratory table top; no soot is produced when an evaporating dish is held over the flame. The equation for the combustion is

$$CH_3CH_2OH + 3 O_2 \rightarrow 2 CO_2 + 3 H_2O$$

Fuel gel. What are some advantages of having a fuel in the form of a gel? In a small beaker pour 45 cc of 95 per cent ethyl alcohol and 5 cc of saturated calcium acetate. In a few minutes the mixture will gel. Ignite a portion of this solid gel and cover with a glass plate to extin-

guish the flame. Some portable fuels such as Sterno are made this way.

Methane as a fuel. Methane, which makes up about 90 per cent of natural gas, can be prepared in the laboratory by heating sodium acetate and solid soda lime in a Pyrex test tube as described earlier (14.2a). Hold the tube horizontally with a delivery tube pointing upward. The gas can also be collected in an open, inverted test tube held over the delivery tube, as shown in Fig. 12-5.

Propane and butane as fuels. Butane and propane cylinders equipped with burner tops are sold by supply houses and hardware stores. Demonstrate the use of a propane cylinder as a substitute Bunsen burner in a room which is not equipped with gas. Students in some rural areas may be familiar with these gases, stored in tanks outside their homes for cooking and heating.

Acetylene. Demonstrate the combustibility of acetylene by igniting the gas at the point of the dropper (preparation, 14.2c). (*Caution: You will need to insert a safety tube, as described in 7.2, in the delivery tube to prevent flashback.*) Or collect the gas through a two-way pump and feed it into a basketball bladder as shown in Fig. 14-9. In fact, if the dropper tube, rubber tubing, and pinch clamp are then attached to the opening of the bladder, it serves as a

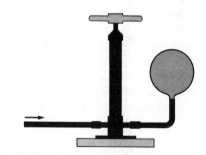

Fig. 14-9 Storing acetylene in a bladder by means of a two-way pump.

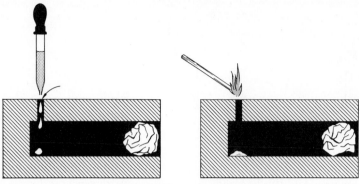

Fig. 14–10   A wooden cannon whose explosive is acetylene released by water dropped on calcium carbide.

source of gas and the jet of gas at the tip of the tube can be ignited.

Some teachers demonstrate the use of acetylene in propelling a "missile" (Fig. 14-10). They make a toy wooden cannon and insert calcium carbide and wadded paper; then drip water through a hole to form acetylene. When a lighted match is held to the "touch-hole," the paper is shot out. Or a tin can with the lid almost removed can be used (Fig. 14-11). (*Caution: Perform these demonstrations outdoors.*)

14.4   Hydrocarbon derivatives

Many of the classes of organic compounds included in high school chemistry are treated as *substitution* products of hydrocarbons. These include the halogen substitution products or organic halides, the alcohols, aldehydes, and organic acids among others. Such classes of compounds have characteristic functional groups which largely determine the properties of the class of compounds (see Table 14-3).

14.4a   Halogen substitution products: organic halides

Beilstein Test.[4] This test is used to show the presence of halogens in organic compounds. A heated spiral of copper wire with a cork serving as a handle is plunged into 5 ml of CCl_4. The wire is re-inserted in the flame and a green color results due to the formation of copper chloride.

Iodoform preparation.[4] This demonstration, also used to distinguish methyl alcohol from ethyl alcohol, represents the "haloform reaction" which can be employed for identification of methyl ketones and secondary methyl carbinols. A solution of iodine in potassium iodide water is prepared in the proportions of 25 g of iodine in a solution of 50 g of KI in 200 ml of water. Five drops of ethyl alcohol are dissolved in 2 ml of water. Two ml of 10% sodium hydroxide are added and then 3 ml of the iodine solution are added. The test tube is shaken and the brown iodine color vanishes. The yellow iodoform is produced in small crystals. Its characteristic odor is also evident.[5]

Preparing iodoform in quantity.[6] Place 10 g of iodine in a 500-cc conical flask and add 10 g of acetone. Make up a solution of 20 cc of 8 N sodium hydroxide solution

[4] Adapted from L. E. Malm and Harper W. Frantz, *College Chemistry in the Laboratory,* No. 2, Freeman and Co., 1959, p. 228.

[5] L. F. Fieser, *Experiments in Organic Chemistry,* 3rd ed., D. C. Heath and Co., 1955, p. 86.

[6] E. Wertheim, *Experiments in Organic Chemistry,* 3rd ed., McGraw-Hill Book Co., 1956, p.63.

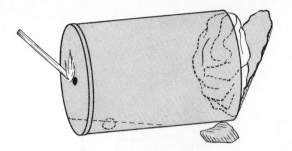

Fig. 14–11 Acetylene in a tin can will propel the wad of paper when ignited.

and 80 cc of water. Add this in small portions to the iodine, meanwhile shaking the flask continually. Keep the flask cool by periodically holding it in a stream of cold water. When all brown color has been removed from the liquid and *no scraps* of unattacked iodine are present on the bottom of the flask, filter the solid residue (iodoform) after decanting as much liquid as possible. Permit to dry on filter paper or desiccate. (*Caution: Iodoform is irritating to the skin. It may be removed by use of sodium thiosulfate solution.*)

Preparation of chloroform. Into a test tube containing 1 gram chloral hydrate add 2 cc strong sodium hydroxide solution. Gently shake the tube; students should note the odor of chloroform. (*Caution: Work in a well-ventilated room.*)

$$CCl_3CH(OH)_2 + NaOH \rightarrow$$
(chloral hydrate)
$$CHCl_3 + NaOOCH + H_2O$$
(sodium formate)

14.4b   *Alcohols*

Alcohols are regarded as being hydroxyl (OH) substitution products of the paraffin hydrocarbons. They are also regarded as the product from the primary oxidation of such hydrocarbons. Students can compare the properties of several alcohols as to viscosity, solubility in water, odor, reaction with litmus: methyl, ethyl,

isopropyl, glycerol, and others. (Alcohols are neutral to litmus.)

Solubility test. If you can obtain absolutely pure ethyl and methyl alcohol, add a few crystals of copper sulfate or of potassium permanganate to a small quantity of each alcohol. In pure ethyl alcohol they will not dissolve; in methyl alcohol they will dissolve. The lesser complexity of the methyl alcohol allows it to act very much like water. As you mix more and more complicated alcohols with water, the longer carbon chains decrease the miscibility.

Iodoform test for ethyl alcohol. The iodoform test for ethyl alcohol has been described in 14.4a., iodoform preparation. Acetone also gives a positive iodoform reaction. Methyl and butyl alcohols do not.

Formaldehyde test for methyl alcohol. A spiral of medium-gauge copper wire with a cork handle is heated in the Bunsen flame to red heat. It is then plunged into a test tube containing 5 ml of methyl alcohol. This procedure is repeated several times. Compare the odor of the vapors in the test tube with a sample of formaldehyde. The characteristic odor of formaldehyde is now present. The spiral of copper wire turns to a bright red when inserted into the methyl alcohol according to the equation

$$CH_3OH + CuO \rightarrow Cu + H_2O + H - C = O$$
$$\qquad\qquad\qquad\qquad\qquad\qquad\overset{||}{\underset{H}{}}$$

TABLE 14-3
Functional groups in organic chemistry

functional group	class name	general type formula	examples	
—X	halide	R—X	methyl chloride	CH_3Cl
—OH	alcohol	R—OH	methyl alcohol	CH_3OH
—O—R	ether	R—O—R	diethyl ether	$(C_2H_5)_2O$
$-\overset{H}{\underset{\diagdown}{C}}_{\diagdown O}$	aldehyde	R—$\overset{H}{\underset{\parallel}{C}}$=$O$	formaldehyde	$HCHO$
$-\overset{O}{\underset{\parallel}{C}}$—$R$	ketone	R—$\overset{O}{\underset{\parallel}{C}}$—$R$	acetone	$(CH_3)_2CO$
$-\overset{OH}{\underset{\diagdown}{C}}_{\diagdown O}$	acid	R—$\overset{O}{\underset{\parallel}{C}}$—$OH$	acetic acid	CH_3COOH
$-\overset{O-R}{\underset{\diagdown}{C}}_{\diagdown O}$	ester	R—$\overset{O}{\underset{\parallel}{C}}$—$OR$	ethyl acetate	$CH_3COOC_2H_5$
$-\overset{\vert}{\underset{\vert}{C}}$—$NH_2$	amine	R—NH_2	ethyl amine	$CH_3CH_2NH_2$
$-\overset{\vert}{\underset{\underset{H_2}{N}}{C}}$—$\overset{OH}{\underset{\diagdown O}{C}}$	amino acid	R—$\overset{H}{\underset{\underset{NH_2}{\vert}}{C}}$—$\overset{O}{\underset{\parallel}{C}}$—$OH$	glycine	$CH_2(NH_2)COOH$

Preparation of an alcohol. Methyl alcohol is a product of the destructive distillation of wood (see 9.5a). Ethyl alcohol is the only alcohol that can be readily prepared in the laboratory by fermentation of sugar.

Fermentation of sugar. Prepare a homogeneous suspension of yeast by stirring half a package of dried yeast into 50 cc of water. Place this in a flask containing 100 cc of 10 per cent sugar solution. Or dilute 25 cc molasses with 175 cc water and add a yeast suspension made from ⅛ package yeast mixed in 20 cc water. To either preparation add about 10 cc disodium phosphate solution (Na_2HPO_4). Close the bottle with a single-hole stopper and a delivery tube that ends in an open bottle of lime water; a thin layer of oil on the surface of the limewater will prevent evaporation. In 24 hours students can find that carbon dioxide has turned the limewater milky, and alcohol can be detected in the flask by its characteristic odor. As a project a student may want to set up a distillation apparatus and distill the filtered solution.

Filter the mixture (without disturbing the sediment of yeast cells) through glass wool into a distilling flask until the flask is about half filled. Distill (see 4.7a) the mixture; determine the alcohol content of the distillate, if possible, by using a hydrometer and table relating specific gravity to alcohol concentration.

14.4c   Ethers

These compounds are formed by condensation of alcohols with the elimination of water. For example, ordinary ether, diethyl ether, can be made by treating ethyl alcohol with a dehydrating agent such as concentrated sulfuric acid.

$$2C_2H_5OH \rightarrow C_2H_5-O-C_2H_5 + H_2O$$

You may want to demonstrate the reaction by adding about 1 cc of concentrated sulfuric acid, drop by drop, into a test tube of some 3 cc of pure ethyl alcohol. Test the odor at the mouth of the test tube and compare with ether.

Ether is distilled commercially at a temperature of 130° C. Great care must be used in distilling ether. Not only is the liquid readily inflammable, but its vapor forms with air a heavy and highly explosive mixture. This mixture is capable of drifting considerable distances and of exploding upon contact with an open flame. *This distillation is so hazardous it is not recommended for high schools.*

Inflammability of ether. Pour a few drops of ether into a watchglass and bring a flame slowly toward the ether from a point several inches above the liquid. Note that the flame flashes back to the ether when the flame is within ½″ to 1″ (ether vapor is heavy). It burns with a yellow flame.

14.4d   Aldehydes and ketones

The aldehydes and ketones are formed in the oxidation of hydrocarbons. The aldehydes contain a carbonyl group ($C=O$) with an alkyl group and hydrogen atom; the ketones have a carbonyl group with two hydrocarbon groups.

Formaldehyde can be prepared by passing air and methyl alcohol vapor over a heated metal catalyst. For example, heated copper changes to CuO and the heated CuO is reduced to Cu by the alcohol.

$$2\ Cu + O_2 \rightarrow 2\ CuO$$
$$CuO + CH_3OH \rightarrow Cu + H_2O + HCHO$$

This can be demonstrated by following the procedure for the formaldehyde test for alcohols, 14.4a.

Simple test for formaldehyde and acetaldehyde. Take a small coil of #20 copper wire and allow it to stand for some time until it is coated with black copper oxide. (A bit of copper wire that has been exposed out-of-doors will do.) Heat the wire to red heat in a Bunsen flame. Insert it three times into a 1 per cent formaldehyde solution in a test tube. Reheat the wire before each insertion. Then add Schiff's reagent.[7] A pink color results. Fehling's solution (see below) will show a yellow or orange precipitate in 1 cc of 40% formaldehyde.

Reactions which distinguish aldehydes from ketones. The hydrogen attached to the carbonyl group in aldehydes is oxi-

---

[7] Made by dissolving 0.5 g of fuchsin in 400 cc distilled water and adding drop by drop freshly made sulfurous acid until the color of the dye disappears. Store Schiff's reagent in a lightproof bottle in a cool, dark place.

dized by Fehling's solution or by ammoniacal silver nitrate. Ketones do not give the reactions described below.

Fehling's solution. Fehling's solution consists of two solutions which may be purchased separately or made up as follows.

Solution 1. 34.64 g of $CuSO_4 \cdot 5H_2O$ dissolved in water and diluted to 500 ml.

Solution 2. 173 g of sodium potassium tartrate (Rochelle salt) and 65 g of sodium hydroxide dissolved in water and diluted to 500 ml.

Equal volumes of these solutions are mixed before using and produce a deep blue solution containing a complex cupric tartrate ion. One ml of 40% formalin (formaldehyde) solution is added to 5 ml of the Fehling's solution and heated gently over the Bunsen flame or in a beaker of hot water. A red (sometimes described as orange-red) precipitate of cuprous oxide results. Other aldehydes may be used. Reducing sugars such as glucose also give a positive Fehling's reaction test.

14.4e   Organic acids

Properties. These acids contain the carboxyl group (COOH). The properties of these acids may be checked by experimental procedures including observation of the state of compound, solubility (tested by successive small additions of acid to 100 ml of water), litmus and indicator reactions, conductivity tests (see 8.4d), and heating. For example, tartaric acid decomposes upon heating while benzoic acid sublimes. Such demonstration series may be used to show that increase in molecular weight results in decrease in solubility and solidification (particularly for the fatty acids). You may also want to have students show that formic acid is a strong reducing agent. It will precipitate free silver from its oxide.

$$HCOOH + Ag_2O \rightarrow 2\,Ag + CO_2 + H_2O$$

Compare this with acetic and the higher acids in this group. The others are relatively difficult to oxidize; acetic acid, for example, is so difficult to oxidize that it is often used as a solvent in the oxidation of other organic compounds by relatively powerful oxidizing agents. You may want to have students titrate vinegar to determine its percentage of acid (see 8.4e).

Preparation of acetic acid. This acid may be produced by the reaction of sulfuric acid and sodium acetate (see 8.4a for the general method to produce an acid: salt of desired acid plus sulfuric acid). Place sodium acetate in a small Pyrex test tube, adding 1 ml of concentrated sulfuric acid and heating gently. Test the vapors with moist blue litmus which turns red. Cautiously smell the vapors and note the characteristic odor of the acid.

Preparation of oxalic acid. Oxalic acid is a simple organic dibasic acid composed of two carboxyl groups joined at the carbon atoms. You may want to have students observe that oxalic acid can be produced when sucrose molecules are broken down and oxidized while warmed in concentrated nitric acid. (*Caution: This should be done under a hood for a violent reaction results.*) Into a beaker pour 2.5 grams sucrose and add 20 cc concentrated nitric acid. Warm the mixture under the hood and slowly let it boil down. Finally cool the beaker in water and have students examine the crystals of oxalic acid.

14.4f   Esters

Esters are defined as the product, other than water, formed when an alcohol reacts with an acid. The esters whose formation is generally demonstrated in the laboratory include ethyl acetate, methyl salicylate, amyl acetate, and ethyl butyrate. A good introductory technique is to test solutions of the alcohols and acids separately with litmus (neutral or both red and blue) to demonstrate that alcohols do not ionize whereas organic acids do ionize to some extent in water solution. Samples of commercial esters including those mentioned above may be subjected to the conductivity test (8.4d) to show that they are also nonelectrolytes. This approach helps students appreciate the need for heating the reactants to speed the reversible reaction and the use of small quantities of sulfuric acid as a dehydrating agent (and catalyst). The dehydration serves to "couple" the other portions of the reactant alcohol and acid with the consequent formation of the ester. Representative general equations include

$$R-\overset{\overset{\displaystyle O}{\|}}{C}-OH + R'OH \rightleftarrows$$
(organic acid) (alcohol)

$$R-\overset{\overset{\displaystyle O}{\|}}{C}-O-R' + H_2O$$
(ester)

The accepted explanation of the mechanism involves the combination of the OH of the carboxyl group with the H from the alcohol to form water.

$$CH_3-\overset{\overset{\displaystyle O}{\|}}{C}-\boxed{OH + H}O-C_2H_5 \rightleftarrows$$
(acetic acid)   (ethyl alcohol)

$$CH_3-\overset{\overset{\displaystyle O}{\|}}{C}-OC_2H_5 + H_2O$$
(ethyl acetate)

The reaction is catalyzed by either acids or bases but such mineral acids as hydrochloric and sulfuric are usually used.

$$HOC_6H_4 CO\boxed{OH + H}O-CH_3 \rightleftarrows$$
(1, 2, salicylic acid)   (methyl alcohol)

$$HOC_6H_4COOCH_3 + H_2O$$
(1, 2, methyl salicylate)

$$CH_3CO OH + H O (CH_2)_4CH_3 \rightleftarrows$$
(acetic acid)   (n-amyl alcohol)

$$CH_3COO(CH_2)_4CH_3 + H_2O$$
(n-amyl acetate)

Ethyl acetate. Add 3 ml of acetic acid to 2 ml of ethyl alcohol in a test tube or an evaporating dish and then add 2–3 drops of concentrated sulfuric acid. Heat the test tube gently and by cautious sniffing note the odor of the product. Compare the odor with that of a commercial sample of ethyl acetate.

Methyl salicylate. Heat a mixture of 1 g of salicylic acid to which about 1 ml of methyl alcohol and 3 drops of sulfuric acid have previously been added. This may be done in a test tube but an evaporating dish prevents the possible formation of a plug of solid material. Testing the odor cautiously results in its identification as that of "oil of wintergreen."

Amyl acetate. Into a test tube add 5 ml of acetic acid, 3 ml of amyl alcohol, and about 1 ml of sulfuric acid. Heat gently and identify the odor as that of "banana oil."

Ethyl butyrate. Heat together in a test tube 2 ml each of butyric acid (note odor of rancid butter) and ethyl alcohol to which has been added 1 ml of concentrated sulfuric acid. Ethyl butyrate has the odor of pineapples.

14.4g Oils and fats

Oils and fats are glycerides, that is, they are esters of glycerine and fatty acids. The oils are liquids at room temperatures and the fats are solids. The oils generally contain larger percentages of the unsaturated fatty acids. Natural fats and oils are generally mixtures of a variety of glycerides.

Unsaturation.[8] The degree of unsatura-

---

[8] Adapted from C. R. Noller, *Chemistry of Organic Compounds*, 2nd ed., W. B. Saunders Co., 1957, p. 184.

tion of a solution is indicated by its iodine number. Standardized solutions of iodine monochloride (standardized by adding potassium iodide and titrating the liberated iodine with standard thiosulfate solution) are used. The amount of reagent remaining after reaction with a fat is determined by the same procedure (titration). The difference expressed in terms of grams of iodine (as if iodine had been added) per 100 grams of fat is known as the iodine number. This procedure may be simulated by using bromine dissolved in carbon tetrachloride. Shake 1 cc of olive oil with an equal volume of bromine solution in carbon tetrachloride. Repeat the procedure with cottonseed oil. The bromine color disappears due to addition. Repeat the test with 1 cc volume of lard. The bromine is now added, and the color of the solution remains.

How iodine is used to determine whether or not fats are saturated can be roughly approximated as follows. Into one test tube put a bit of stearic acid, into a second tube some oleic acid, and into a third a small piece of fat. Dissolve the fat in each tube by adding 4 cc of CCl_4. Then, drop by drop, add a dilute solution of iodine in carbon tetrachloride. Shake the solution after each drop and count the number of drops needed to change the solution to iodine color. Which contain quantities of unsaturated fatty acids?

Soap

Preparation. Soap can be made by melting 15 g of cocoanut oil in a 600-ml beaker and then adding 100 ml of 20% sodium hydroxide. This is gradually heated while stirring. Spattering may occur when the reaction starts. (*Caution: Wear goggles and gloves if hand stirring is employed. Sodium hydroxide is a caustic substance*). This subsides quickly, and gentle heating at the beginning keeps it to a minimum. As saponification proceeds, the amount of gelatinous

solid in the beaker steadily increases so that almost the entire beaker appears to be full of the solid substance. This takes place within 10 minutes. The solid product is then removed from the beaker, being pierced by the glass stirring rod. It is soaked in several washings of water in a large beaker. A small portion of the solid is cut from the main piece and used to produce a lather by brisk rubbing of water and soap between the hands. Since some sodium hydroxide is probably still present, it is advisable to wash the hands thoroughly with water after the lather or suds has been produced. It is possible to add more alkali to the soap produced and heat for additional time (10–20 minutes). However, for effective demonstration the material produced within the 10-minute period suffices.

Some of this solid may be shaken with 20 ml of water in a large test tube. The soap solution is then decanted. Solid salt (½–1 teaspoon) is added and shaken vigorously with the soap solution. This results in "salting out," the coagulated soap rising to the top of the solution. This "salting out" process may also be demonstrated with any sample of household soap or soap solution. A solution is made as described above and the addition of salt produces the effect (coagulation).

Properties. Place 2 ml of kerosene or cottonseed oil in a test tube. Add 10 ml of water, shake, and have students note that for a very brief time a cloudy emulsion results with the rapid separation of the mineral or vegetable oil to the top. Now add one ml of soap solution and shake, noting the emulsification of the oil(s). If emulsification is not complete, add more soap and shake again.

Add about 1 g of lampblack to 5 ml of water in each of two test tubes. Add 5 drops of soap solution to one test tube. Shake both vigorously and pour out contents. Note that although some lampblack does remain adherent to the test tube containing water only, none remains in the test tube containing soap.

Soap demonstrations with hard water (see 4.7b) may be repeated here. Samples of modern "soapless soap" detergents may be demonstrated. For example, one of these, Naconol, will lather in very salty water as well as in the presence of acids such as vinegar.

14.5 Plastics

There seems to be no end to the new plastics and other synthetic products that continuously become available commercially. Although the number of demonstrations that may be performed in the high school chemistry laboratory is limited, the few that can be carried on are extremely useful, for this area is one that has many applications in the daily lives of students. They ask about acrilan, about

TABLE 14-4
Trade names and composition of common plastics

trade name	chemical name and raw materials
Acrilan	polyacrilonitrile with vinyl acetate
Bakelite	phenol-formaldehyde: phenol and formaldehyde
Beetleware	urea-formaldehyde: urea and formaldehyde
Butanite	polyvinyl butyrate
Cellophane	cellulose (specially treated)
Celluloid	cellulose nitrate: cellulose + nitric acid
Dacron	polyester prepared from terephthalic acid + ethylene glycol
Durez (see Bakelite)	
Durite	polymer of phenol and furfural
Dynel	copolymer of acrylonitrile + vinyl chloride
Ethocel	polymer of ethyl cellulose, prepared from cellulose + ethyl chloride
Koroseal	polyvinyl chloride
Lucite (see Plexiglas)	
Lumarith (see Tenite)	
Lustron (see Styron)	
Melmac	melamine formaldehyde, prepared from cyanamide + diglycol
Neoprene	polychloroprene
Nylon	superpolymer of hexamethylenediamine + adipic acid
Orlon	polyacrilonitrile
Plexiglas	polymethyl methacrylate
Plaskon (see Beetleware)	
Polyethylene	polyethylene
Pyroxylin (see Celluloid)	
Resinox (see Bakelite)	
Saran	polyvinylidene chloride
Styrene	polyester of maleic anhydride + diglycol
Styron	polystyrene
Teflon	polytetrafluoroethylene
Tenite	polymer of cellulose acetate
Tenite II	polymer of cellulose acetate butyrate
Velon (see Saran)	
Vicara	complex polymer of zein (corn protein) + formaldehyde
Vinylite V	polyvinylchloride acetate
Vinyte X (see Nylon)	
Viscose rayon	cellulose (specially treated)

polyethylene, and the many other new names that appear on the labels of clothing and household aids; they are beginning to recognize these materials as "chemicals" which add utility or beauty to their lives. You may want to begin this work by compiling from their experience the trade names of many of these products along with their chemical composition (Table 14-4).

14.5a Structural models to demonstrate polymerization

As an introduction to plastics you may want to use commercial models or have students contrive homemade models (see 14.1, 6.4) to show the formation of polymers. For example, students may begin with a model of several ethylene molecules and build polyethylene $(-CH_2\ CH_2-)_n$. When the double bond in ethylene is converted to a single bond, an opening on each of the carbon atoms results.

$$\begin{array}{c} H \qquad\qquad H \\ \diagdown\qquad\diagup \\ C = C \\ \diagup\qquad\diagdown \\ H \qquad\qquad H \end{array}$$

When ethylene is the only substance present, each molecule can hook onto two others, forming a chain of indefinite length.

$$\text{etc.} -\underset{\underset{H}{\mid}}{\overset{\overset{H}{\mid}}{C}} -\underset{\underset{H}{\mid}}{\overset{\overset{H}{\mid}}{C}} -\underset{\underset{H}{\mid}}{\overset{\overset{H}{\mid}}{C}} -\underset{\underset{H}{\mid}}{\overset{\overset{H}{\mid}}{C}} \text{ etc.}$$

If any student wants to try to perform special demonstrations in this area, he will find good discussions of many polymerization reactions in Chapter 35 of Fieser and Fieser, *Organic Chemistry*, 3rd ed., Reinhold Publishing Corp., 1956.

Fig. 14–12 Bakelite, a phenol-formaldehyde resin, is prepared in a beaker sitting on wire mesh in a water bath.

14.5b Preparation of plastics

Bakelite. Developed by L. H. Baekeland in the first decade of this century, Bakelite is one of the oldest of the commercial phenolic plastics. It is easy to make a black plastic similar to Bakelite. Simultaneously pour 100 cc of a saturated solution of aniline hydrochloride and 100 cc of 40 per cent formaldehyde solution (commercial formalin) into a 300-cc or larger beaker; stir with a glass rod. At first students will find that a thick dark brown mass forms. When this is allowed to harden, a black plastic similar to Bakelite is formed. While it is still viscous, it can be poured into a child's sand mold.

True Bakelite, a phenol-formaldehyde resin, is somewhat more complicated to prepare (Fig. 14-12). Combine 50 grams of pure phenol (carbolic acid—*caution*) with 80 grams of formalin in a Pyrex or metal beaker. Heat in a water bath until the phenol crystals melt and the liquid turns clear. Then add half a gram of solid sodium hydroxide and continue heating slowly. After a time students should find that the mixture thickens. If the rate of thickening is too slow, add an additional small quantity of sodium hydroxide.

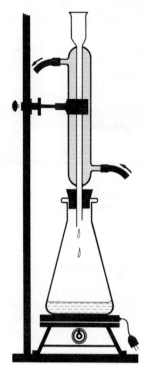

Fig. 14–13 Phenol-formaldehyde resin made from liquid phenol, formalin and ammonium hydroxide heated in a flask fitted with a reflux condenser.

When the substance becomes viscous, quickly pour it into a mold.

In some classes you may want students to prepare this variation. Into a dry beaker place 10 g resorcinol, 2 cc sodium hydroxide (10 per cent), and 10 cc 37 per cent formaldehyde. Set the beaker in a water bath (Fig. 14-12) at 50° C and stir until the crystals dissolve. Raise the temperature of the bath to 70° C (no higher) and keep the solution in the bath. After 10 minutes remove the beaker and let it cool. Remove the plastic disk from the beaker.

Note: Many plastics can be colored by the addition of an aniline dye to the still-liquid plastic. Students may also produce a marbled effect by mixing dyed batches of plastics.

Phenol-formaldehyde resin. Damerell [9] suggests this formula for preparing the resin. Combine 6 cc liquid phenol, 4 cc formalin, and 4 cc ammonium hydroxide (1–3) in a flask fitted with a reflux condenser as in Fig. 14-13. Heat for some 10 minutes until two layers separate out. Now pour into an evaporating dish and add 20 cc water. Pour off the water layer and heat the resin for a few minutes; the polymerized product is a phenol-formaldehyde resin.

Thiokol (a polysulfide elastomer). [10] Ethylene chloride and sodium polysulfide (technical grade, fused) may be purchased at scientific supply houses. It is first necessary to change the sodium polysulfide to sodium tetrasulfide. This is done by saturating a saturated solution of the polysulfide with sulfur. Filter or decant to remove excess sulfur. Add 100 ml of the tetrasulfide solution to 25 ml of ethylene chloride. A milk of magnesia pellet or a pinch of magnesium oxide is added as a catalyst. These materials are placed in a 500-ml flask to which an air or water condenser is attached vertically to serve as a reflux to prevent the escape of volatilized ethylene chloride. The mixture is then heated until the ethylene chloride starts to volatilize, after which heating is no longer necessary because the reaction is exothermic. Small particles of the Thiokol are formed at the interface between the tetrasulfide and ethylene chloride. These float to the top, agglomerate, and then sink to the bottom of the flask. The liquid is decanted and the solid washed several times with water. The water may then be squeezed out and the rubber-like qualities demonstrated.

[9] V. R. Damerell, *Laboratory Experiments in College Chemistry,* Macmillan, 1952.

[10] J. F. Castka, "Demonstrations on the Preparation and Molding of Plastics," *J. Chem. Educ.,* 20, 253 (1943).

Forceps or tongs should be used in handling the synthetic material. Since undesirable odors should not be permitted to escape into the room, the demonstration should be carried out under the hood particularly during the removal of the final product from the reaction vessel.

Urea-formaldehyde plastic. A common plastic used in inexpensive household materials such as Beetleware is made from urea and formaldehyde. Because the preparation of this plastic takes considerable time, it may be better suited for project work by a committee of students or as a club activity. The plastic can be made in the following way.[11] Place 177 grams of pure formaldehyde and 1.5 grams of calcium carbonate into a large beaker. Then add 55 grams of urea and 3 grams of ordinary granulated table sugar. Now boil this slowly for a full hour. Then pass this cloudy mixture through a pleated filter paper in a large funnel to collect the solids. Scrape the solids off the filter paper into a Pyrex Erlenmeyer flask and reflux for another 60 minutes with a Liebig condenser. Next put the contents into a flask connected to an aspirator, as in Fig. 14-14, and heat the flask gently until about 100 cc of water have been removed.

Now the material is ready for polymerization. First add 2.5 cc of acetic acid solution (50 per cent glacial acetic acid in water). (*Caution: Pour the acid down a stirring rod to avoid splattering when it is added to the contents of the flask.*) Use the aspirator to continue the evaporation for another 5 minutes. Now add 622 milligrams of acetic anhydride, and continue the evaporation with slow heating and the aspirator until another 50 cc of water has been

[11] Paul Arthur, *Lecture Demonstrations in General Chemistry*, McGraw-Hill, 1937.

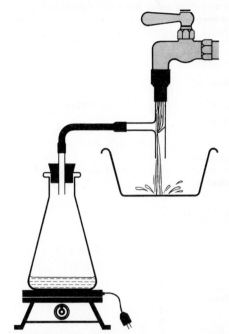

Fig. 14–14 Evaporation of the constituents of urea-formaldehyde plastic.

removed. Then pour the contents into a mold and allow to harden.

Acrylic plastics. The raw materials for making acrylic plastics can be purchased from Roehm and Haas (Philadelphia), or simpler kits can be obtained from such supply houses as Ward's Natural Science Establishment or General Biological (see appendix for addresses) in the form used to imbed biological and mineral specimens in clear plastic. The polymerizing agents are included in the kit along with complete instructions.

The raw materials usually consist of an uncatalyzed monomer with a catalyst. The materials are mixed and polymerization takes place. Sometimes heat is required.

Cellulose acetate. Cellulose acetate is a slow-burning, easy-to-handle plastic which can be prepared in this way. Place 6 cc of acetic anhydride and 2 drops of

TABLE 14-5
Flame and odor tests for plastics

plastic	trade name	type[1]	chief uses	flame and odor
phenolic	Bakelite, Plaskon Unilast Catalin	thermosetting	telephones cameras	smoulders, odor of carbolic acid
urea	Bakelite, Plaskin Beetleware	thermosetting	baking enamels, kitchen ware	smoulders, odor of formalin
melamines	Catalin, Melamine	thermosetting	ignition parts, buttons	smoulders, fishlike odor
cellulose	Acetate Rayon Lumarith Kodapak	thermoplastic	safety film lacquers	odor of vinegar, greenish flame
acetobutyrate	Tenite II	thermoplastic	instrument dials, radios	odor of rancid butter, white flame
nitrate	Colastic, Celluloid Nitron, Kodaloik	thermoplastic	watch crystals, tool handles	burns with fierce white flame
ethyl	Ethocol Lumarith EC	thermoplastic	electric app., airplane parts	sweet odor, burns well after start
cellulose	Cellophane Rayon	thermoplastic	wrapping, etc.	odor burnt paper, burns well
vinyl	Vinylite	thermoplastic	raincoats, phono records	acrid odor, greenish flame
styrene	Lustron, Styton	thermoplastic	dishes, radios	smokes, sweet odor
acrylic plastics	Lucite, Plexiglas	thermoplastic	lenses, goggles, musical inst.	floral odor, bluish flame
nylon		thermoplastic	hose, parachutes, tennis rackets	odor of burning leaves

[1] *Thermoplastic* means that the plastic may be melted and recast over and over again. *Thermosetting* means that the plastic will not melt and will retain its original shape.

concentrated sulfuric acid in 10 cc of 20 per cent acetic acid in a beaker. Then add ¼ gram of absorbent cotton, let this stand for 3 hours, filter, and discard the residue. The cellulose acetate will be found in the filtrate; dissolve this in ethyl acetate and allow foreign particles to settle. Then pour off the clear part and let the ethyl acetate evaporate until the clear cellulose acetate is left. (*Caution: Ethyl acetate is inflammable and toxic to breathe; have it evaporate under a hood. Handle with care.*)

14.5c Flame and odor tests for plastics

The simplest method of determining what type plastic a certain sample may be is to note its rate of burning, color of flame, and odor. To do this cut off a small piece of the sample and hold it in the blue Bunsen flame for not more than ten seconds. Note color of Bunsen flame. If sample burns, note color of its flame and then blow the flame out after another ten seconds, noting the odor carefully. Table

14-5 is a list of the twelve most common types of plastics along with their common trade names and characteristic results of flame and odor tests.

14.5d Working with plastics

Pressed plastics. Powdered plastic materials for molding under pressure can be obtained from any of the large chemical supply companies. A hot-molding press can be purchased from a scientific supply house (see directory in appendix) or can be made from a hydraulic jack or press (see 16.5b). A hot bed for the plastic can be made from a flat-top electric hot plate by removing the legs from the hot plate (so that they will not collapse) and placing the plate on the hydraulic press base. Two metal dishes that fit one within the other may be used as a mold. The outer mold is placed on the hot plate, powdered plastic is put in it, and the inner mold is set on top. The press piston forces the halves of the molds together.

Interested students may use the ordinary demonstration hydraulic press generally used in teaching physics. Homemade molds made in the school metal shop may be used. For demonstration purposes the mold may be heated directly by a laboratory burner and suitable pressure applied. Fast cooling is achieved with a wet bath towel, heavy sponges, etc. (Rapid cooling is particularly desirable with thermoplastics.) The use of the school hydraulic press does not permit careful controls but good judgment and some experience permit students to produce plastic disks of good quality.

Sheet plastic. Cellulose nitrate plastics can be drilled and cut with ordinary hand tools. To make joints, use acetone as a solvent to soften the edges that are to be joined; then clamp them together.

Cellulose acetate sheet plastic is most easily cemented into tanks and other shapes needed for use in the classroom and laboratory by standing the edges to be joined in ethyl acetate for 5 to 8 minutes. The edges are then held together with clamps until both pieces fuse. In a few minutes the parts begin to hold together; in a few hours permanent joints form. If properly made, the joint will be stronger than the stock. You may want to have students experiment with small pieces until they become skilled.

Cellulose acetate can be purchased in sheet form from hobby shops. Old safety film, which is cellulose acetate, can be dissolved in ethyl acetate and then used to make a thick plastic by letting the ethyl acetate evaporate. The plastic becomes very pliable and soft at moderately low temperatures. For this reason it can be easily shaped by hand or molded without heating.

Plexiglas and Lucite. These plastics may be cut with an ordinary band, circular, jig, or hack saw. In cutting thin sheets, use a saw which does not have much set. Routing tools may be used to carve designs and lettering. An end mill or ordinary metal drill may be used to make holes. Light pressure should be applied so as to avoid "grabbing." Techniques for machining soft metals on a lathe apply to machining Plexiglas and Lucite. Hand topping and threading, if done gently, can also be performed on these plastics. For holes 3/16" and larger a mild soap solution makes an excellent lubricant.

Plexiglas heated in an oven to 220° F (116° C) can be bent and formed easily. Lucite can be bent at temperatures 272° F to 284° F (120–140° C). At such temperatures these plastics can be pressed into forms and, upon cooling, will retain their new shapes. Allow them to cool somewhat before handling.

The techniques of cementing Plexiglas and Lucite are simple. The area to be

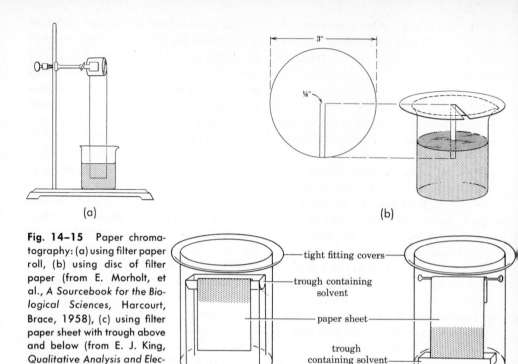

Fig. 14-15 Paper chromatography: (a) using filter paper roll, (b) using disc of filter paper (from E. Morholt, et al., *A Sourcebook for the Biological Sciences*, Harcourt, Brace, 1958), (c) using filter paper sheet with trough above and below (from E. J. King, *Qualitative Analysis and Electrolytic Solutions*, Harcourt, Brace, 1959).

(a)

(b)

3″

⅛″

tight fitting covers

trough containing solvent

paper sheet

trough containing solvent

descending

ascending

(c)

cemented is first softened by immersion in glacial acetic acid heated to 140° F (60° C). This softening takes from 2 to 5 minutes. (Dupont H94 cement requires no heating.) After softening mask the section to be cemented with 1″ cellophane adhesive tape. Press the pieces together lightly to press out excess cement; then use C-clamps to hold the pieces together. It is best to leave the pieces joined overnight to insure a complete and lasting bond. In place of the glacial acetic acid or Dupont H94, ethylene dichloride works well with Plexiglas while Dupont H78 prepares Lucite in 5 minutes when heated to 122° F (50° C). Glacial acetic acid and Dupont H94 can be thickened by dissolving chips and shavings of Lucite. These cements may also be applied with a brush.

To avoid scratching do not wipe Plexiglas or Lucite with dry cloth; use grit-free diaper cloth, chamois, or sponge moistened with soap and water, kerosene, naphtha, or wood alcohol. Do not use acetone, benzene, and lacquer thinners. Window-cleaning sprays should be avoided. Wiping these plastics with a dry cloth builds up an electrostatic charge which attracts dust. Application of automobile or furniture waxes is highly recommended to cover minor scratches and to protect against further scratching.

14.6 Analytical techniques in organic chemistry

Paper chromatography. The simplest demonstration techniques employ filter paper strips or such materials as paper handkerchiefs (Kleenex and other similar tissues). Long strips of filter paper (6″ or

8″) are cut from ordinary large-size filter paper. A paper handkerchief may be rolled together to produce a rather compact strip. The strips are suspended from a wooden strip clamped to a ring stand so that the ends reach ½″ into a developing solution (water will serve or the water may contain very dilute acetic acid or white vinegar). Colored materials such as ordinary vegetable dyes or various inks are used as the mixtures to be separated into colored bands. A small spot (no more than ⅛″ diameter) is made with each dye about 2″ from the bottom of each paper strip. The spot may be permitted to dry although this is not necessary. As the water or acid solution ascends the paper strip, the components of the colored mixture separate out into a variety of different-colored bands. The time needed for such a demonstration is variable but good results are generally obtained within one class period. Another method which may be employed consists of cutting a 1-cm wide paper strip to the middle of the filter paper. This strip may be folded downward into a vertical position. The spot is placed on the wick at the chosen distance, and the filter paper is then placed over a beaker which contains the developing solution. Bands develop on the wick. A variation of this technique places the colored spot on the horizontal filter paper near the top of the wick. The solvent which ascends the wick causes the spot to spread out into a series of colored rings. A green vegetable dye may produce rings or bands which indicate yellow, blue, and red components. Fig. 14-15 shows variations of these techniques, employing both strip and wick procedures. Another solution which may be used is a 10–30% solution of denatured alcohol. When alcohol is used, the paper strips may be suspended as described before but the solution on containers should be loosely covered to prevent evaporation of the alcohol.[12]

Adsorption chromatography. Students can prepare a demonstration to show this convenient method of separating compounds. They will need a 12″ length of ½″ bore glass tubing. Insert a plug of absorbent cotton at one end of the tube, and fill the tubing up to about ½″ from the other end with activated magnesium silicate. Fasten the tube in an upright position to a ring stand. Then combine portions of solid dyes in a container with 30 cc dilute ammonia solution. Students can add quantities equivalent to the head of a pin of solid bromthymol blue, fluorescein, methyl orange. Pour about 10 cc of the solution of mixed dyes into the column; then pour dilute ammonia solution through the column. Which dye moved the greatest distance? How could the individual substances be recovered?

[12] For an analysis of chlorophyll which uses the techniques of paper chromatography see pp. 14, 16, and 17 of *A Sourcebook for the Biological Sciences,* by E. Morholt, P. F. Brandwein, and A. Joseph (Harcourt, Brace, 1958).

CAPSULE LESSONS

Ways to get started in class

14-1. Have students use models of atoms to build simple organic substances such as methane. They may then predict how more complex molecules in the series might look. In how many positions can the carbon atoms be attached in a 3-carbon compound? A 5-carbon compound? What difference in properties might result? From this, develop graphic diagrams on the board so that students learn these configurations as two- and three-dimensional.

14-2. Introduce the topic of plastics by demonstrating the polymerization of a Bakelite plastic as described in this chapter. Establish the notion of polymerization by using models of molecules which can be linked together. Demonstrate the plastic filling material that dentists use for filling cavities.

14-3. Using a synthetic rubber kit from a rubber company, follow the instructions for extracting the synthetic rubber from the latex. Demonstrate vulcanization by heating the latex in water with flowers of sulfur.

14-4. Prepare several problems for the class to investigate: unknown fibers that students must identify by running through several tests; samples of different rayons that must be identified; several plastics to mold into small boxes for laboratory use.

Student committees can use a hall case to build a display of the many ways to identify fibers or show uses of different plastics.

14-5. You may want to begin or summarize a lesson with a film showing the manufacturing processes involved in preparing modern fuels or fashioning plastics. Have you shown your classes *Pattern For Chemicals* (Shell), *Powering America's Progress* (Modern Talking Pictures), *Origin and Synthesis of Plastic Materials* (Indiana U.), *Kingdom of Plastics* (General Electric)?

14-6. In some communities it may be possible to invite an expert to talk to the class on the refining of oil or on prospecting for oil. A geologist in the neighborhood may be asked to relate how oils are re-formed in the ground. What microorganisms are used as a "tracer" in prospecting for oil deposits?

14-7. Students will want to read some of the pamphlets available from many industrial companies. You may want to have students read *ABC of Modern Plastics,* (Bakelite) *Advanced Experiments with Gas* (American Gas), pamphlets from the American Petroleum Institute, and others.

Some students who wish to read advanced work can read with profit some chapters in a textbook of organic chemistry (see listings at end of this chapter).

14-8. You may want some classes to learn techniques needed to identify "unknowns." Begin the topic by showing one or more of the three films in a series called *Techniques of Organic Chemistry* (Young America). One deals with fractional distillation, melting points, and molecular weight, another with chromatography, and a third with solubility tests and crystallization. In a laboratory activity students can determine melting points or work through a distillation.

14-9. Plan a laboratory period in which students identify an unknown ester. Students can use the procedure of alkaline hydrolysis, followed by a qualitative identification of both the alcohol and acid fractions.

14-10. In a club activity or as a group project students can identify the aldehyde group on given sugars by the reducing reaction of silver reagents with copper.

14-11. In one class period you may want to introduce plastics by preparing one or more of those described in this chapter.

14-12. In a series of demonstrations, plan a flow sheet to show the results of progressive oxidations of methane or ethane alcohol to aldehyde. Also demonstrate the reactions of alcohols with acids to form esters.

14-13. Students can demonstrate techniques for distinguishing saturated and unsaturated fats. Develop the significance in reactivity, in general, and also in body metabolism.

14-14. To show the practicality of plastics you may want students to make simple objects out of Plexiglas or Lucite. In this manner they can gain a firm grasp of the wide uses and techniques which make plastics so valuable as a basic material.

14-15. You may want to set up a simple paper chromatographic demonstration as an indication of how organic unknowns can be separated.

PEOPLE, PLACES, AND THINGS

Where can a teacher turn for aids when students ask about the composition and manufacture of the plastics they bring to class? Often graduate students majoring in organic chemistry will sponsor a small number of students of high-level ability in planning small experiments.

It may also be possible to have students assigned to work in a college lab or a pharmaceutical house over the summer. New opportunities are open now in the National Science Foundation Summer Institutes for High School Students.

Industry has much to offer in providing subject matter, films, and answers to specific problems. Supply houses have kits available for preparing plastics in class. Perusal of the available chemicals listed in a catalog from a supply house or Eastman Kodak, among others, will stimulate new approaches and possibilities (see directory of supply houses in appendix).

BOOKS AND PAMPHLETS

These are only a few of the books which are pertinent to the work discussed in this chapter. These and many other references classified by subject and with complete bibliographical data are given in the bibliography at the end of the book.

American Chemical Society, *Physical Properties of Chemical Compounds; Advances in Chemistry,* Series 15., Washington, D.C., 1955.

Anderson, A., and G. Pritham, *Laboratory Experiments in Physiological Chemistry,* 2nd ed., Wiley, 1954.

Anfinsen, C., *The Molecular Basis of Evolution,* Wiley, 1960.

Arthur, P., *Analytical Chemistry,* McGraw-Hill, 1957.

Arthur, P., *Lecture Demonstrations in General Chemistry,* McGraw-Hill, 1937.

Baker, S. W., *Electronic Theories of Organic Chemistry,* Oxford U. Press, 1958.

Barnett, E. de B., *Mechanism of Organic Chemical Reactions,* Interscience, 1956.

Bates, R., *Electrometric pH Determinations,* Wiley, 1954.

Belcher, R., and C. Wilson, *New Methods in Analytical Chemistry,* Reinhold, 1955.

Bier, M., ed., *Electrophoresis: Theory, Methods and Applications,* Academic, 1959.

Braude, E., and Nachod, F., eds., *Determination of Organic Structures by Physical Methods,* Academic, 1955.

Brown, E., *An Introduction to Electronic Theories of Organic Chemistry,* Longmans, Green, 1958.

Chemical Rubber Co., *Handbook of Chemistry and Physics,* Cleveland.

Chiddix, J. C., *Chemistry Projects,* Science Publications, Normal, Ill., 1959.

Clapp, L., *Chemistry of the Covalent Bond,* Freeman, 1957.

Cowgill, R., and A. Pardee, *Experiments in Biochemical Research Techniques,* Wiley, 1957.

Cox, D., *Planning of Experiments,* Wiley, 1958.

Daggett, A., and W. Meldrum, *Quantitative Analysis,* Heath, 1955.

Dushman, S., and A. Joseph, *Chemistry of Petroleum,* American Institute of Petroleum, 1961.

English, J., Jr., and H. Cassidy, *Principles of*

Organic Chemistry, 2nd ed., McGraw-Hill, 1955.

Ferris, S. W., *Handbook of Hydrocarbons,* Academic, 1955.

Fieser, L., and M. Fieser, *Basic Organic Chemistry,* Heath, 1959.

Fieser, L., *Experiments in Organic Chemistry,* Heath, 1957.

Fritz, J., and F. Hammond, *Quantitative Organic Analysis,* Wiley, 1957.

Fruton, J., and S. Simmonds, *General Biochemistry,* 2nd ed., Wiley, 1958.

Hamilton, L., and S. Simpson, *Quantitative Chemical Analysis,* 11th ed., Macmillan, 1957.

Harrow, B., and A. Mazur, *Textbook of Biochemistry,* 7th ed., Saunders, 1958.

Hine, J., *Physical Organic Chemistry,* McGraw-Hill, 1954.

Joseph, A., *Physics and Petroleum,* American Institute of Petroleum, 1960.

Ketelaar, J., *Chemical Constitution,* 2nd ed., Van Nostrand, 1958.

Kharasch, M., and O. Reinmuth, *Grignard Reactions of Non-Metallic Substances,* Prentice-Hall, 1954.

King, E., *Qualitative Analysis and Electrolytic Solutions,* Harcourt, Brace, 1959.

Kitchener, J., *Ion-Exchange Resins,* Wiley, 1957.

Lange, N., *Handbook of Chemistry,* 9th ed., Handbook Publishers, 1956.

Malm, L. E., and H. W. Frantz, *College Chemistry in the Laboratory,* No. 2, Freeman, 1954.

Maw, G., *Aids to Organic Chemistry,* 5th ed., Williams and Wilkins, 1958.

Mellon, M., *Quantitative Analysis: Methods of Separation and Measurement,* Crowell, 1955.

Melville, Sir H., *Big Molecules,* Macmillan, 1958.

Meyer, L., *Laboratory Manual for Introductory Chemistry,* Macmillan, 1952.

Raphael, R., *Acetylenic Compounds in Organic Syntheses,* Academic, 1955.

Scientific American, "Giant Molecules," Sept., 1957; "Organic Chemical Reactions," Nov. 1957.

Semenov, N., *Some Problems of Chemical Kinetics and Reactivity,* trans. by J. Bradley, Pergamon, 1958.

Shriner, R., R. Ruson, D. Curtin, *The Systematic Identification of Organic Compounds* (lab manual), 4th ed., Wiley, 1956.

Surrey, A. R., *Name Reactions in Organic Chemistry,* Academic, 1954.

Wells, A. F., *The Third Dimension in Chemistry,* Oxford U. Press, 1956.

Wertheim, E., *Experiments in Organic Chemistry,* 3rd ed., McGraw-Hill, 1956.

Williams, E., and R. Johnson, *Stoichiometry for Chemical Engineers,* McGraw-Hill, 1958.

Yoe, J., and H. Koch, *Trace Analysis,* Wiley, 1957.

FILMS AND FILMSTRIPS

This partial list is intended only as a guide toward film and filmstrip selection. Refer to the more complete listing at the end of the book where films are classified by subject and where a key to abbreviations and addresses of distributors are given. The cost of film rental, of course, is subject to change. Films are sound and black and white unless otherwise specified.

Another Step Forward (f, s, c), Colorado Fuel and Iron Corp., free.

Atomization (f, s), Shell, free.

Crude Oil Distillation (f, s), Shell, free.

Fossil Story (f, s, c), Shell, free.

Gasoline's Amazing Molecules (f, s, c), Modern Talking Picture Films, free.

Kingdom of Plastics (f, s, c), General Electric, free.

Oil (f, s), Institutional Cinema, $2.00.

Oil for Aladdin's Lamp (f, s), Shell, free.

Men and Oil (f, s), Modern Talking Picture Service, free.

Miracle Flame (f, s, c), American Gas Assoc., free.

Molding Phenolics (f, s), Bakelite, free.

Of Men and Molecules (f, s, c), Goodrich, free.

Origin and Synthesis of Plastic Materials (f, s), Indiana U., $2.75.

Our Common Fuels (f, s), Indiana U., $2.00.

Pattern for Chemicals (cracking petroleum) (f, s), Shell, free.

Pipe Line (f, s, c), Shell, free.

Plastics (f, s), Young America, $3.00.

Powering America's Progress (bituminous coal) (f, s, c), Modern Talking Picture Service, free.

Refining Oil for Energy (f, s, c), Shell, free.

Rubber From Rock (silicone rubber) (f, s, c), Dow, free.

The Story of Charles Goodyear (f, s), Teaching Films Custodians, free.

Techniques of Organic Chemistry (f, s, c) (solubility tests, precipitates, supersaturation), Young America, inquire local film library.

Techniques of Organic Chemistry (f, s, c) (extraction, chromatography) Young America, inquire local film library.

Techniques of Organic Chemistry (f, s, c) (fractional distillation, molecular weight, melting points) Young America, inquire local film library.

This is Oil (5 f, s, c), Shell, free.

The Waiting Harvest (coal chemistry) (f, s, c), U.S. Steel Corp., free.

World that Nature Forgot (plastics) (f, s, c), Modern Talking Picture Service, free.

10,000 Feet Deep (f, s), Shell, free.

CHAPTER 15

Consumer chemistry

In this broad chapter we have compiled many demonstrations spanning varied fields of organic and inorganic chemistry —chemistry as it is meaningful in the daily lives of students. With this aim, we have included some of the simple tests for identifying fibers in the textiles used in clothes and several suggestions for dyeing fabrics and for making fibers by the viscose, cuprammonium, and nitrate processes. This is followed by tests for nutrients in foods, a study of personal products such as cosmetics that may be prepared in the laboratory, and a series of demonstrations using household chemicals. The over-all objective of this chapter is to show how chemistry brings beauty and utility to the home and enhances individual comfort and health. Plastics other than synthetic fibers are covered in 14.5; flavorings can be found in 14.4f under esters.

15.1 Clothing fibers

If students bring to class samples of cloth, both known and unknown kinds, they can test these samples by burning to discover whether acidic or basic fumes are given off; or they may add chemicals and observe the reactions. They can also inspect the fibers under the microscope.

15.1a *Microscopic inspection*

Students can shred the fibers of their sample textiles into individual threads for examination under the microscope. Students will notice, for example, that wool fibers are scaly, cotton fibers are flat and twisted and resemble a collapsed tube, silk resembles bamboo, and linen fibers are uneven with pointed sections extending sideways; synthetic rayon fibers are regular and transparent, viscose has stripes, and acetates are smooth. A committee of students may work up a table listing the various visible features of fibers.

15.1b *Burning tests*

Students can distinguish between animal and plant fibers by burning a few single fibers from each of several kinds of textiles.

Hold the fibers with tweezers and ignite them with a match. Compare the way the fibers burn. (Note the rate of burning and the amount of residue.) Natural plant fibers (cotton and linen) have the odor of burning paper. Natural animal fibers (silk and wool) have the odor of burning feathers. (Refer to Table 15–1.)

Heating the fiber in a test tube results in destructive distillation. Cotton, the cellulose plant fiber, produces acid fumes which turn blue litmus to red. Wool and silk which are animal fibers and contain nitrogen yield ammonia upon being heated, and this changes red litmus to blue. The vapors of wool change moist lead acetate paper to black or dark brown, indicating that wool contains sulfur. The

TABLE 15-1
Burning and solubility tests for some fibers*

	burning test	solubility tests
acetate	fiber shrinks from flame and forms irregular dark bead; when cool is hard but can be crumbled between fingers	soluble in acetone (5 min. at room temp.) soluble in 37 per cent HCl (10 min. at room temp.) soluble in 65 per cent H_2SO_4 (15 min. at room temp.) soluble in 90 per cent formic acid (5 min. at room temp.) soluble in metacresol (boil, 10 minutes) not soluble in sodium hypochlorite, ammonium thiocyanate
cotton	fiber does not shrink from flame, no bead formed; odor of burning paper	soluble in 65 per cent H_2SO_4 (15 min. at room temp.) not soluble in acetone, formic acid, HCl, sodium hypochlorite, ammonium thiocyanate, metacresol
Dacron (polyester)	fiber shrinks to form rounded bead which is hard to crush between the fingers (when cool); smoke is dark and sooty	soluble in metacresol (boil, 10 min.) not soluble in acetone, formic acid, HCl, H_2SO_4, sodium hypochlorite, ammonium thiocyanate
nylon	fiber shrinks to form round bead like Dacron, and difficult to crush between fingers; smoke is white and not sooty	soluble in 90 per cent formic acid (5 min. at room temp.) soluble in 37 per cent HCl (10 min. at room temp.) soluble in 65 per cent H_2SO_4 (15 min. at room temp.) soluble in metacresol (boil, 10 min.) not soluble in acetone, sodium hypochlorite, ammonium thiocyanate
orlon	burning test like acetate but characteristic odor	soluble in 70 per cent ammonium thiocyanate (boil, 10 min.) not soluble in acetone, HCl, H_2SO_4, sodium hypochlorite, metacresol
rayon (viscose)	burns like cotton, fiber does not shrink from flame; odor of burning paper, no bead formed	soluble in 37 per cent HCl (10 min. at room temp.) soluble in 65 per cent H_2SO_4 (15 min. at room temp.) not soluble in acetone, formic acid, sodium hypochlorite, ammonium thiocyanate, metacresol
silk	fiber does not shrink from flame, soft fluffy knob formed; odor of burning feathers like wool, another animal fiber but burns faster than wool	soluble in 37 per cent HCl (10 min. at room temp.) soluble in 65 per cent H_2SO_4 (15 min. at room temp.) soluble in 5.25 per cent sodium hypochlorite[1] (15 min. at room temp.) soluble in 70 per cent ammonium thiocyanate (boil, 10 min.) not soluble in acetone, formic acid, metacresol
wool	same as silk, but burns more slowly	soluble in 5.25 per cent sodium hypochlorite not soluble in acetone, formic acid, HCl, H_2SO_4, ammonium thiocyanate

* Modified from *Technical Information Bulletin* X-12, January, 1956, "Identification of Fibers," E. I. DuPont de Nemours & Company, Inc., Wilmington, Dela.

other two natural fibers do not give this test for sulfur. Wool is the only natural or synthetic fiber which contains sulfur. Such synthetics as nylon which contain nitrogen yield vapor which changes red litmus to blue. The vapor from heated rayon and acetate will change blue litmus to red.

15.1c Chemical tests

Distinguishing plant and animal fibers. Animal and vegetable fibers may not only be distinguished by testing the vapors released in decomposition (distillation) by heat but also by testing with KOH or NaOH (5% solution). In one method, insert fibers of wool into a Pyrex test tube; fill the tube one third full of 5 per cent sodium hydroxide. Gently boil this for 10 to 15 minutes so that students can see the wool fibers disintegrate and dissolve in the fluid. Silk and Aralac (made from casein —a milk product) dissolve as does Dacron. Cotton, rayon, linen, and nylon are not dissolved.

Since both silk and wool dissolve in NaOH, a further test to distinguish between them is necessary. Add 5 ml of dilute lead acetate solution to each. In the test tube containing the wool, the lead acetate solution turns black due to the presence of sulfur in the wool. The silk solution does not give this result.

Fiber test kit. You may want to introduce chemical tests by using a kit which may be purchased from Calco Chemical Company.[1] You may, however, prefer to prepare a kit for your own needs. The Calco test kit contains a chemical that reacts differently with each natural or synthetic fiber so that a different color change results. A test color chart and ample materials for hundreds of tests are included in the kit. Use white cloth which has first been boiled in water so that confusion in

[1] A division of American Cyanamid Company, Rahway, New Jersey.

color reactions do not result. (Or use a dye remover available from the drugstore when white cloth is not on hand.)

Should you plan to prepare your own fiber testing kit, you will need 10 per cent sodium hydroxide, sulfuric acid, acetone, and Elsner's reagent, the latter made by combining 250 grams of zinc chloride, 10 grams of zinc oxide, and 212.5 cc of water.

Laboratory activities may be devised to reveal the following characteristics of different fibers: wool and silk are both soluble in sodium hydroxide and also show the xanthoprotein test (see 15.3b); cotton will dissolve in sulfuric acid, but wool will not; both silk and rayon dissolve in hydrochloric acid, but only silk dissolves in Elsner's reagent; acetate dissolves in acetone (Table 15–1).

Color tests. Different kinds of rayon can be distinguished by a color test. Use white samples of acetate or celanese rayon, viscose rayon, and cuprammonium rayon. Place them in neocarmine dye. Follow with a water rinse and dip these into a 10 per cent sodium hydroxide solution. Students will find that the cuprammonium rayon will turn deep blue, celanese (or acetate) will be yellow-green, and the viscose will be violet.

Cotton can also be distinguished from linen by a color test. Samples of each fiber can be treated with 1 per cent fuchsin dye in alcohol and then washed in dilute (3 M) ammonium hydroxide (ammonium water). Linen will turn rose-colored while cotton remains white. For another test boil cotton and linen in water, then in dilute methylene blue, and wash in NaOH. Notice that cotton turns green whereas linen becomes dark blue.

In still another test boil samples of white linen and cotton in 50 cc of water to which 5 cc of HCl has been added; this removes the sizing on the fabric. Rinse and then dry. In the laboratory students should wet the samples in glycerin, blot off the excess, and then examine each sample against a dark background to note the difference between the cotton and linen fibers. Linen becomes translucent while cotton remains unchanged.

Distinguishing silk from wool. Insert a small sample of silk and one of wool into individual test tubes. To each tube add hot 10 per cent sodium hydroxide to cover each sample of cloth. Then add a dilute solution of copper sulfate (a few drops to a half test tube of water). What difference exists between the silk and wool that may be used to distinguish these two animal fibers?

Establishing the percentage of wool. Students will want to try to devise a laboratory activity for determining the percentage of wool in a wool-cotton or wool-Dacron fabric. The fiber test kit described earlier may be used, or the students can dissolve out the wool in concentrated NaOH after first weighing the dry fabric. If they rinse, dry, and weigh the remains of the fabric, they can calculate the percentage composition by weight.

15.1d Preparing textile fibers

Mercerizing cotton. A heavy cotton thread or a starch-free piece of cotton goods can be mercerized by students. Sodium hydroxide solutions (30% or 40%) are used to mercerize the cotton. The thread may be passed through the concentrated NaOH, rinsed, and then dried with the sequence of operations being repeated at least 5 times or until the thread is silky appearing (shiny). The cloth may be made starch-free by boiling in a beaker containing a taka diastase tablet for 5 minutes. One piece of the cloth is then removed and used as a control. The other is permitted to soak in 40% NaOH solution for at least 7 minutes. It is then rinsed for 2 minutes in water and then for one minute in dilute acetic acid (3 M). It is then rinsed again in water. A dye bath of Congo red is prepared from 300 ml of water, 0.1 g of Congo red dye, 0.1 g of sodium carbonate, and 0.2 g of sodium sulfate.[2] Two separate dye baths are used, one for the mercerized sample and the other for the control. The bath is kept at 90-100° C during the dyeing. The cloth samples should be kept in the dye bath for 10 minutes. One method of preserving uniformity of conditions is to have the test tubes containing the dye heated in a boiling water bath for the required time. The samples show that the dye has taken much more effectively on the mercerized sample since it develops a deeper color.

Preparing nylon. In some classes you may want students to prepare nylon using a procedure suggested by Damerell.[3] Heat a mixture of 6 grams adipic acid and 5 cc hexamethylenediamine in a Pyrex beaker at 200° C for 5 minutes, then at 225° C for another 5 minutes. After water has formed, cool the mixture and examine the solid nylon (solid polyamide). Reheat the polyamide until it is motile; then carefully pour from the beaker through a pipette so that a long thread forms.

Preparing a viscose fiber.[4] Viscose solution may be obtained from the Viscose Company, 350 Fifth Ave., N.Y.C. A glass cylinder, 60 cm $\times$ 7.5 cm (diameter), almost filled with 3 N H_2SO_4 is required. Above the cylinder, support a glass funnel capable of holding 200 to 250 ml viscose, and to its stem attach a capillary tip of about 0.5 to 1.0 mm bore. Fill the funnel with viscose and lower the capillary into the acid. A long thread will form and descend through the liquid to form a coil at

[2] E. Wertheim, *Experiments in Organic Chemistry*, 3rd ed., McGraw-Hill Book Co., N. Y., 1950, p. 157.
[3] V. R. Damerell, *Laboratory Experiments in College Chemistry*, Macmillan, 1952.
[4] Paul Arthur, *Lecture Demonstrations in General Chemistry*, McGraw-Hill Book Co., Inc., N. Y., 1939, p. 419.

the bottom of the cylinder. With a sufficiently fine capillary, the apparatus will continue to form a thread for 10 to 12 hours (Fig. 15–1).

Solutions of $ZnCl_2$ are used to produce a form of regenerated cellulose known as vulcanized fiber. This form of regenerated cellulose may be demonstrated by adding several tufts of cotton to a 200-ml test tube half full of Cross and Bevan's reagent (dissolve 240 g of $ZnCl_2$ in 400 ml of concentrated HCl). Stir until the cotton is disintegrated. Pour the viscous liquid into a beaker containing 200 ml of 3 N NaOH. Cotton-like fibers appear.[5]

Cuprammonium process. In brief, cotton is first dissolved in Schweitzer's reagent, and the solution is run into an HCl or sulfuric acid bath to produce coagulation into regenerated cellulose.

Schweitzer's reagent consists of a saturated solution of cupric hydroxide in a solution of 28% ammonium hydroxide. To prepare, precipitate cupric hydroxide from a copper sulfate solution by the addition of ammonia. The precipitate is washed thoroughly and then filtered through cotton cloth and again washed until the wash water is free of sulfate (until the addition of dilute barium chloride solution does not produce a precipitate). To the washed cupric hydroxide add only enough concentrated (28%) ammonium hydroxide to dissolve. (*Note:* Dissolving cupric hydroxide in 28% ammonium hydroxide is a slow process.)

Filter paper and absorbent cotton can then be dissolved in this solution. This is then fed through a capillary tube into a cylinder of 3 N sulfuric acid, as in Fig. 15–2, to produce a fiber of crude rayon.

Preparation of cellulose acetate. Prepare a solution of 10 cc of glacial acetic acid, 3 cc of acetic anhydride, and 2 drops

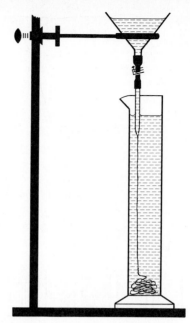

Fig. 15–1 Viscose sets into a fiber form when it runs from the capillary tip into the 3 N H_2SO_4.

of concentrated sulfuric acid (a catalyst). Immerse a small piece of absorbent cotton in the solution. Cover the solution and let it stand for at least a day to allow the cotton to dissolve. When a clear solution is produced, pour it in a thin stream into a large container of water. Cellulose acetate is precipitated, which is the basis for the production of celanese (acetate rayon).

Solutions of cellulose acetate may be produced from either commercial samples of cellulose acetate molding powder, molded articles such as combs or toothbrush handles (pretested by burning and decomposition tests described in Table 15–1), or from safety film (gelatin emulsion may be removed by boiling in water). Dissolve in either acetone or chloroform. Viscous solutions of various concentrations may be prepared depending on original cellulose acetate selected and quantity of solvent used. (*Caution: Keep away from flames.*) A thin film of this material may be brushed or poured on a glass plate

[5] Paul Arthur, *Lecture Demonstrations in General Chemistry*, McGraw-Hill Book Co., Inc., N. Y., 1939, p. 419.

Fig. 15–2 Tie (or scarf) dyeing.

and the solvent permitted to evaporate under the hood. Students may attempt to prepare filaments by allowing the solution to run through a fine capillary opening from a funnel or thistle tube (a pressure bulb may be necessary to force the solution through the aperture, or a hypodermic needle may be used). To simulate commercial production, the filament may be air dried. It also may be permitted to run into water.

15.2 Dyeing fabrics

15.2a Dye classification

Dyes may be classified according to their method of application.

Direct dyes. Direct dyes produce fast colors on textiles without the use of other chemicals. Being amphoteric proteins, wool and silk may be dyed directly by dyes containing acid or basic groups such as malachite green, crystal violet, methylene blue, and martius yellow. Cotton and other cellulosic fibers may be dyed directly by such substantive dyes as Congo red which become attached to the fibers by hydrogen bonding. Substantive dyes have high molecular weight, show colloidal properties, and are capable of hydrogen bonding.

Mordant (adjective) dyes. A mordant is a chemical substance which unites with a dye making it stick to the cloth (colorfast). Dyes which require use of a mordant are known as adjective dyes. Metallic oxides or hydroxides are deposited on the cloth fibers by soaking the cloth in a metallic salt such as aluminum chloride, which is then converted to the colloidal hydroxide (or oxide) by steaming or by treating with dilute base. The mordanted material is placed in the solution of the dye which combines with the metallic mordant to form an insoluble colored lake (a complex salt). Common mordants used with cotton include compounds of aluminum, tin, chromium, and iron. Turkey red is obtained by forming a lake from alizarin (a weak yellow color) with an aluminum mordant. Most acid azo dyes require a metallic mordant for use with cotton. The fastest azo wool dyes usually use chromium or copper as mordants. Basic dyes use an acidic mordant such as tannic acid. Basic dyes include methyl violet, methylene blue, malachite green, and fuchsin.

Chrome colors. Chrome colors are mordant dyes for dyeing wool with a mordant of sodium or potassium bichromate. They are applied in 3 ways.

1. Chrome-bottom. Wool is first mor-

danted with bichromate and then dyed in a separate bath.

2. After-chrome (or top-chrome). The wool is dyed in an acid bath and is passed into mordanting salt. Or the salt may be added to the bath after the dye is taken up.

3. Meta-chrome. Dye and mordant are applied in the same bath, the meta-chrome mordant consisting of one part potassium chromate and two parts ammonium sulfate.

Vat dyes. Vat dyes are insoluble compounds of the indigo or anthraquinone type which can be reduced to colorless compounds soluble in dilute alkali, and which can be reoxidized on exposure to air to form the insoluble dye. Indigo blue (insoluble) is reduced by sodium hydrosulfite $Na_2S_2O_4\cdot2H_2O$ (made by reducing sodium bisulfite, $NaHSO_3$) to the soluble indigo white. The fabric is immersed in the alkaline solution of the reduced dye (vat), this leuco (white) base being absorbed by hydrogen bonding. Exposure to air results in its reoxidation.

Sulfur dyes. These are second to the azo dyes in amount produced among the synthetic dyes. Their exact chemical compositions have not been established. They are prepared by heating derivatives of aromatic amines and phenols with sulfur and sodium sulfide to give a soluble vat dye. Sulfur black is the most important sulfur dye. It is produced from 2, 4 dinitrophenol by heating with sulfur and sodium sulfide. The fabric is immersed in the soluble vat dye, and air oxidation develops the final color.

Ingrain dyes. Ingrain dyes are produced in place on the fiber, that is, the dye is formed within and on the fiber. This method is used for applying azo dyes to cotton or rayon. The cotton is impregnated with an amine (an amino group) which is then diazotized and developed by immersion in a solution of a phenol. A general method of application is preliminary dyeing in the azo dye, then rinsing and diazotizing at a low temperature with sodium nitrite and an acid, and finally a "coupling" or developing with a phenol such as beta-naphthol. An example of ingrain dyeing is soaking the fabric in an alkaline solution of beta-naphthol and drying. The dry fabric is then passed through a cold solution of diazotized p-nitroaniline. The bright red precipitate, p-nitroaniline red, is insoluble and fast to washing.

Dispersion dyes. SRA dyes belong to the dispersion class of dyestuffs. They are made into fine dispersions by grinding with sulforicinoleic acid (SRA) so that dyeing is possible. They are applied to acetate rayons and to other hydrophobic fibers such as nylon.

15.2b Dyeing in the laboratory or at home

Before students attempt to dye fabric, they should remove all sizing and filler or dirt by boiling in water or in a solution of sodium carbonate followed by rinsing in clear water. Use glass or porcelain enamel containers (plastic ones will usually become permanently stained with the dye). Metal containers should not be used, as they often react with the dyes and thus ruin the batch.

15.2c Tie dyeing

An interesting home or laboratory project is tie dyeing. Use 4, 5, or 6 different colors of direct cotton dyes. Boil out the starch or sizing of a 4' square sheet of cotton, and let it dry. Pick up the square at the center as shown in Fig. 15–2, and allow it to drop. Then tie a length of cotton with string in knots every 5" or so as shown. Dip the cloth one section at a time

TABLE 15-2
Dyes for various fabrics

cotton	azo dyes and direct cotton dyes
linen	vat dyes and direct cotton dyes
viscose	vat dyes and direct cotton dyes
cuprammonium rayon	vat dyes and direct cotton dyes
cellulose acetate	SRA colors
silk	a few direct cotton dyes and acid dyes
wool	top-chrome mordant dyes and some vat dyes
nylons	top-chrome, acid dyes, SRA, and some direct cotton dyes
vinyons	a few basic dyes and dispersal dyes
aralac	all regular wool dyes and top-chrome
fiberglas	colored only by baked-on resins

into dyes of different colors. Rinse, remove knots, and allow to dry.

The students will have a pattern of concentric circles. Girls may want to do this with silk or other fabrics (using appropriate dyes, see Table 15–2) to design their own scarves. Attractive effects can be made by a careful selection of color combinations.

15.2d Preparing a mordanted dye

A mordant is used with certain dyes so that the dyes adhere to the fabric. Students can prepare a 0.01 M aluminum sulfate solution, boil a piece of white cotton cloth ($6'' \times 6''$) in the solution for 3 minutes, and transfer the cotton to a bath consisting of 2 cc of concentrated NH_4OH and 20 cc of water. You may want to establish the equation to show that aluminum hydroxide has been precipitated in the cotton fibers.

Next remove the cotton and press out the fluid; dye it in a suspension of 0.25 gram alizarin to 50 cc of water. Also introduce a piece of cotton which has not received a preliminary treatment in the mordant. After 15 minutes, students can wash both pieces in water. Is there an advantage in using a mordant before the dye?

15.3 Nutrients in foods

In everyday life probably no individual submits the foods he eats to nutrient tests, nor does he undertake chemical investigations relating to the elements and compounds that compose the foods he eats. However, youngsters are often interested in repeating the nutrient tests on common foods such as the remains of their own lunch. They discover that starch, sugar, fats, and proteins are chemicals that can be identified in the foods we consume.

15.3a Testing for fats

Students probably know that foods containing fats or oils leave a translucent spot on unglazed paper. For another test they can soak the mashed or chopped food sample in carbon tetrachloride or ether in a well-ventilated room or under a hood for about 15 minutes. (*Caution: Ether is highly explosive; avoid using flames or sparks.*) Remove the sample (decant or filter if necessary) and let the solvent evaporate from the dish (under a hood). Students will find globules of fat remaining in the dish. If students weigh the original sample and then weigh the fat residue (recommended procedure is to weigh the empty dish and then the dish plus fat, and subtract), they can calculate the approximate percentage of fat in the sample.

15.3b Test for proteins

Pure proteins such as casein, powdered skim milk, or egg white in various concentrations may be used in establishing the specific test. Then students can test samples of their lunch for proteins.

Biuret test. Proteins give a characteristic test reaction with Biuret reagent, which is a combination of two solutions—3 per cent copper sulfate and concentrated potassium hydroxide. The two solutions should be kept in separate containers until used. Only a few drops of each solution are required for the test. When students are going to perform the test on food samples, each solution can be placed in small medicine dropper bottles for convenience. A stock solution for use in quantity may be prepared by adding 25 cc of a 3% copper sulfate solution to a liter of 10% potassium hydroxide.

The light blue reagent turns blue-violet in the presence of proteins. The test is quantitative as well as qualitative: the darker the color, the greater the amount of protein present for any given quantity of reagent. The test is sensitive to as little as one part of protein in a million parts of water.

Xanthoproteic test. In this older test for protein, a sample of food such as boiled white of egg when heated to boiling in concentrated nitric acid turns yellow if proteins are present. To confirm this test, wash the sample in water and add an alkali such as ammonium hydroxide. The sample should turn from yellow to orange if protein is present.

Millon test. Millon's reagent is made by gently heating 1 part (by weight) of mercury in 2 parts (by weight) of concentrated nitric acid (sp. gr. about 1.42) until the mercury "dissolves"; then dilute with two volumes of water. To a dilute solution of 1 per cent egg albumin (prepared from powdered egg albumin) add 3 or 4 drops of the reagent. Bring gradually to the boiling point.

A protein like albumin yields a white precipitate which gradually turns red upon continued gentle heating. Secondary intermediate proteins, such as proteoses, yield a red solution.

15.3c Testing for starch

When an iodine solution such as Lugol's solution is added to a starch, the substance turns blue-black in color. (This reaction is also used in reverse as a test for iodine; see 11.4b.) Prepare Lugol's solution by dissolving 5 grams of potassium iodide in 1000 cc of warm water; add 2 grams of iodine crystals, which will dissolve. (Ordinary tincture of iodine diluted with water may also be used.) Demonstrate the test on starch paste; then students can add a few drops to a sample of food from their lunch. Small amounts of starch produce a very faint blue or greenish tint. Tests are more successful (the reaction is faster) on boiled foods than on raw foods.

Converting starch into simple sugar.[6] Have students add a pinch of corn starch to about 5–10 ml of water and heat to boiling to produce a starch solution. Then concentrated HCl is added, and the solution is heated in a Bunsen flame for two minutes. This brings about hydrolysis of the starch. Then the test tube is placed over the sink, and solid sodium carbonate is added until there is no more gas emission. This removes excess acid. A slight excess of sodium carbonate may be in the bottom of the test tube with no damage. Boil with Fehling's or Benedict's solution and note the orange (yellowish red) precipitate of cuprous oxide. This is a positive test for glucose sugar. For directions on the preparation of Fehling's solution see reactions which distinguish aldeydes from ketones, 14.4d.

[6] For a demonstration on the conversion of starch into sugar by saliva see pp. 58 and 59 of the companion volume, *A Sourcebook for the Biological Sciences* by E. Morholt, P. Brandwein, and A. Joseph (Harcourt, Brace, 1958).

Benedict's solution. This test solution, as is the case with many test solutions, can be made a number of ways. The following preparation is from the 40th edition of the *Handbook of Chemistry and Physics*. With the aid of heat, dissolve 173 g of sodium citrate and 100 g of anhydrous Na_2CO_3 (200 g of crystalline Na_2CO_3) in 800 ml of water. Filter, if necessary, and dilute to 850 ml. Dissolve 17.3 of $CuSO_4 \cdot 5H_2O$ in 100 ml of water. Pour the latter solution, with constant stirring, into the carbonate-citrate solution, and make up to 1 liter. The amounts can vary as long as the proportionate relationships are kept the same. The solution can be purchased ready made. In the presence of simple sugars, when heated, a precipitate forms whose color varies in relation to the amount of simple sugar present.

Testing for simple sugar. First establish the test for simple sugars (not table sugar) using Benedict's (see above) or Fehling's solution (see 14.4d). (Students should heat samples of each pure nutrient in Benedict's or Fehling's solution.) Also show the reaction with Karo syrup or samples of students' lunches. Add the solution to a sample of food and heat to boiling. Students should observe the series of color changes, and the end color. Various color changes characterize the amount of simple sugar present: green indicates about ½ per cent of simple sugar in the sample, yellow shows the presence of 1 per cent or more, and an orange-red indicates more than 2 per cent.

Students should also test ordinary table sugar, sucrose, to learn that a complex sugar does not give this color reaction with Benedict's or Fehling's solution.

Clinitex tablets and Clinistix are sold in drugstores to test for sugar in urine (mainly for diabetics). They are easier to use than Benedict's and Fehling's solutions. The sample is simply dissolved and the tablet or stick added. No heat is required.

15.3d Testing for sucrose

In this test a solution containing 5 mg or more of sucrose gives an identifying reaction. You may want to have students use this at some time in a study of foods, or in identification of the soluble end-products of digestion which pass through a membrane.

Heat 1 cc of the sucrose solution (or one suspected of containing sucrose) with an equal amount of a saturated solution of ammonium nickel sulfate and a few drops of HCl or H_2SO_4. As the solution boils, a yellow color will appear, and then a deep red color results that will remain when the liquid cools.

Inverting complex sugar into simple sugar. Students may want to change complex table sugar into simple sugar and then test with Benedict's solution to show that they have produced the change. Slowly boil the sugar in water containing a weak acid, such as dilute HCl, for a few minutes. Then neutralize with sodium carbonate, adding until there is no further gas emission. Test with Benedict's solution (see above) for simple sugar.

15.3e Testing for minerals

By using the tests described below, students can demonstrate the presence of mineral ash in a substance or food that has been burned. Furthermore, they can identify some of the elements in the ash. Strongly heat the sample to be tested with a Bunsen burner until only a white ash remains with no evidence of unburned carbon (black). Add the ash produced to 10 ml of water, heat to boiling, permit to cool, and then filter. Use the filtrate for tests.

Chlorides in food. Students may show that chlorides are present in the ash of burned foods by testing for the chloride ion (see 11.2d).

Iron in liver. The presence of iron in liver can be shown by testing the ash with potassium ferrocyanide. A deep blue color (precipitate) will be produced in the presence of ferric ion. If this does not show a positive test, try potassium ferricyanide which gives a dark blue color with *ferrous* ions. Both tests should be made. Students may want to test blood for minerals just as they did a food sample and then test for the presence of iron in the ash.

Sodium in foods. Almost any food held in a flame will show the characteristic yellow sodium flame because sodium compounds are found in almost all plants and animals. A simple spectroscope may be used to identify the sodium lines. (See 20.5a.)

15.3f   Testing for water

Students can learn that all foods, even some that appear quite dry, contain water. They can heat the food sample in a dry test tube. Water evaporating from the food will condense on the sides of the tube. For an approximate quantitative determination, students can weigh a food sample, then heat it in a Pyrex test tube connected to a condenser, collect the water, and weigh it after the sample is reduced to ash.

15.3g   Testing for vitamins

Test for vitamin C. The reagent for the vitamin C test is a solution of sodium 2, 6-dichlorobenzene indophenol, a blue dye; the blue color is bleached by vitamin C. Semiquantitative assays can be made by determining the number of drops of the reagent that can be cleared of color by a standard quantity of different citrus and vegetable juices. Standardize the reagent as follows. Take ½ cc of 10 per cent as-

corbic acid solution (one commercial preparation is called Cecon) and dilute with 50 cc of water to make a 1 per cent solution. Then see how many drops of "indophenol" can be bleached by all of this solution. Then any 50-cc sample that clears this number of drops contains 1 per cent vitamin C. If it clears twice as much indophenol, it contains 2 per cent, and so on.

Test for vitamin A. Add carbon tetrachloride to an opened capsule of vitamin A concentrate in a large porcelain dish or a white soup bowl. Using tweezers, add one crystal of antimony trichloride. (*Caution: Antimony trichloride is caustic.*) The white crystals will turn bluish purple.

15.4   Cosmetics

You will want students to know that many familiar chemicals are used in the preparation of the perfumes, powders, toothpastes, and creams that are part of our life. In some chemistry classes, students can prepare perfumes, creams, powders, deodorants, and many other toiletries in the laboratory. Other special preparations may be reserved for club or project activities. We have described only a small sampling from the broad field of cosmetology. Students who wish to read further should consult standard references such as *New Practical Formulary*, M. Freeman (Chemical Publishing Co., 1955); *Formulary of Perfumes and Cosmetics*, R. M. Gattefosse (Chemical Publishing Co., 1959); and *Chemical Formulary*, H. Bennett (Chemical Publishing Co., 1957).

This section describes some recipes for perfumes and flavors, toothpastes, deodorants, face powder, nail polish and remover, creams, and lipsticks, as well as suggested techniques for the analysis of cosmetic products.

TABLE 15-3
Flavors and odors of essential oils

isoamyl acetate	banana
methyl anthranilate (methyl aminobenzoate, o)	grapes
benzaldehyde	almond
geraniol (2,6-octadiene-8-ol 2,6)	roses
diphenyl ether	geranium
cinnamic aldehyde (phenyl acrolein)	cinnamon
vanillin (4-OH-3-MeO-benzaldehyde)	vanilla
methyl salicylate	wintergreen
ethyl butyrate	apricot, peach
methyl butyrate	pineapple
octyl acetate	orange
methyl acetate	peppermint

15.4a Perfumes

In the manufacture of perfumes, fragrant substances (essential oils; see Table 15-3) are blended in alcohol. Students can prepare terpineol, a perfume base which has the odor of lilacs.[7] Measure off 25 cc of water into a beaker and add 2 drops of concentrated phosphoric acid. Next introduce into the solution a marble-sized piece of terpin hydrate. Cover the beaker to prevent excess evaporation and let the mixture boil gently for 10 minutes. Finally filter and notice the odor of terpineol in the filtrate. (Some unchanged terpin hydrate may also be present.)

Students can also prepare two esters, one that has the odor of acacia blossoms and a second that smells like orange blossoms. Pour 20 cc of methyl alcohol into a large test tube. Now dissolve 2 grams of beta-naphthol in the tube. Carefully add, drop by drop, concentrated sulfuric acid until no further change seems to occur. Note the odor of acacia blossoms. The mixture may have to be warmed slightly if heat is not generated in the mixture. Be

careful in handling these substances; their odor may be pleasant, but since they are mixed with H_2SO_4 avoid contact with the skin. Repeat the experiment using ethyl alcohol instead of methyl alcohol. The ether produced has the odor of orange blossoms.[8]

Modern perfumes are often bouquets of many flower fragrances. As a project some student or small group of students may want to prepare some of the ambitious formulas which are used commercially.[9] As an introduction to the complexity of the preparation, the following are given as examples from the Gattefosse formulary.

Simplified modern perfume.[9] Prepare this mixture (modify quantities proportionately for individual needs).

vetiver oil	50 g
bergamot oil	50 "
jasmine oil absolute	10 "
rose oil absolute	10 "
neroli oil	10 "
sweet orange oil	60 "
nerol	280 "
cinnamic alcohol	100 "
panaxol base	200 "
benzyl acetate	40 "
methyl ionone	75 "
methyl nonyl acetaldehyde (10 per cent)	50 "
C_9-aldehyde (10 per cent)	20 "
musk xylene	50 "

Boys in class may prefer to prepare the following fragrance.

Russian leather.[9] Combine the following ingredients (vary the quantities proportionately, if desired).

[7] V. R. Damerell, *Laboratory Experiments in College Chemistry*, Macmillan, N.Y., 1952.

[8] From *Using Chemicals,* a resource unit for a course in physical science, Bureau of Secondary Curriculum Development, N.Y. State Education Department, Albany, 1956.

[9] R. M. Gattefosse, *Formulary of Perfumes and Cosmetics,* Chemical Publishing Co., N.Y., 1959.

pyrogenous essence of cedar	50 g
wood complex	125 "
clary sage oil	50 "
bergamot oil	50 "
cinnamic alcohol	100 "
geranyl acetate	70 "
benzyl acetate	50 "
isoeugenol	50 "
eugenol	50 "
terpineol	25 "
geraniol	75 "
citronellol	40 "
ethyl vanillin	45 "
artificial amber	60 "
resinodour labdanum	130 "
musk ambrette	40 "
concentrated castoreum	10 "
concentrated civet	15 "

Eau de cologne stick. Pour the following ingredients into a flask with reflux condenser.

soap flakes	10 grams
28 per cent ammonia	3 grams
alcohol (SDA 40)	77 cc
perfume oil (added later)	10 grams

Reflux for half an hour, add the perfume oil, and pour into small molds. (Vary the quantities to meet individual requirements.)

This may also be made into deodorant sticks if 0.1 to 1.0 per cent phenol or p-amino benzoic esters are added.[10]

Perfume wax. This solidified perfume stick or mold for a container is convenient in travel.

Jasmine flowers wax is one of many that may be found in Gattefosse.[11] Combine 10 grams of beeswax, 5 grams of artificial jasmine, and 5 grams of concrete jasmine perfume. Melt this mixture in a container

in a water bath; pour into small flat containers or into molds.

15.4b   Toothpastes and powders

The base for tooth powder and paste is finely divided chalk which is not hard enough to scratch tooth enamel. Students may make a powder or paste in this way.[12] Combine 125 grams of precipitated chalk (available at drugstores at low cost), 95 grams of magnesium carbonate (a polishing material), 30 grams of powdered sugar, and 30 grams of powdered white soap. Mix this thoroughly so that the powders are well distributed. If a flavor is desired, add about 5 drops of oil of wintergreen, cinnamon, or peppermint to a small quantity of the powder. Force this through the fine mesh of a tea strainer and mix with the rest of the batch of powder. If students prefer a paste, add equal parts of glycerin and water to the powder until a paste of a familiar consistency results.

An inexpensive but effective powder can be prepared by mixing 1 part by weight of powdered table salt and 2 parts of baking soda. The salt serves as an astringent and the bicarbonate reacts with food particles in the mouth.

Another powder can be made by mixing thoroughly 4 grams of powdered chalk, 1 gram of powdered sugar, and 1 gram of sodium bicarbonate. Students can flavor this with a few drops of oil of peppermint or wintergreen.

Another toothpaste can be made from 16 oz precipitated chalk, 4 oz shredded pure castile soap, 4 oz pure orris, 4 oz sugar, and sufficient sodium salicylate; sift the materials together; gradually

[10] H. Bennett, *The Chemical Formulary*, Vol. X, Chemical Publishing Co., N.Y., 1957.
[11] R. M. Gattefosse, *Formulary of Perfumes and Cosmetics*, Chemical Publishing Co., 1959.

[12] *Using Chemicals*, a resource unit for a course in physical science, Bureau Secondary Curriculum Development, New York State Education Dept., Albany, 1956.

dissolve the mixture in pure glycerin to the desired consistency.

15.4c Miscellaneous products

Deodorants and antiperspirants. An effective antiperspirant which checks perspiration but does not destroy the odor can be made by preparing a 15 per cent solution of aluminum chloride.

Another antiperspirant which is less harsh and dries faster than aluminum chloride contains borax.[13] Prepare a solution containing 15 parts of aluminum chloride, 5 parts of aluminum sulfate, 0.5 parts of borax in 100 cc of distilled water.

Mouthwash.[14] A pleasant-tasting mouthwash can be prepared by combining the following ingredients.

alcohol (ethyl)	98.7 parts
dentifrice essence	1 part
10 per cent tincture benzoin	0.1 part
oleo-resin of vanilla	0.2 parts
liquid red coloring	

Dentifrice essence can be prepared by combining 6 grams of essence of mint, 1 gram clove oil, 2 grams anise oil, and 1 gram of essence of vanilla.

Brushless shaving cream. Mix 300 g ammonium stearate with 30 g white (clear) mineral oil. Perfume as desired. This can also be used as cold cream.

Shaving soap (solid). Reduce these quantities as desired. Heat in a double boiler for 30 minutes 160 g castile soap powder, 80 g rose water, 20 g cocoa butter, and 10 g sodium bicarbonate. Then add 40 g glycerin and pour into molds.

Styptic powder. Reduce each of these ingredients to a fine powder and mix thoroughly: 4 U.S.P. anhydrous alumi-

num sulfate and 1 g U.S.P. zinc oxide. Modify the quantities to meet the needs of the class. Students can also make a styptic pencil by allowing aluminum sulfate to crystallize in a tubular mold.

Liniment. Students may prepare an athlete's rubdown by mixing 2 parts of methyl salicylate with 10 parts of ethyl alcohol and 5 parts of witch hazel.

Brilliantine.[15] Semiliquid brilliantine can be prepared by melting at 40° C 10 grams hydrophilic petroleum jelly and 10 grams of petroleum oil. Then add 30 grams of water and mix well to homogenize the preparation.

Shampoo. Combine the following ingredients to prepare a mild shampoo.

liquid soap	100 cc
triethanolamine lauryl sulphonate	10 cc
water	90 cc
perfume and color	trace

Lipstick and rouge

Theatrical, nonindelible lipstick.[16] Prepare the quantities as needed for use in the classroom.

petrolatum	16 oz	(480 g)
paraffin	9 oz	(270 g)
mineral oil	4 oz	(120 g)
carnauba wax	1½ oz	(45 g)
lanolin	2 oz	(60 g)
lake color	4 oz	(120 g)

Heat in a double boiler over an electric hotplate. Pour into cylindrical molds of lipstick size, and allow to harden.

Indelible lipstick.[16] Modify these quantities for the size of the class. Weigh out these ingredients.

castor oil	24 oz	(720 g)
glyceryl mono-stearate	8 oz	(240 g)

[13] M. Freeman, *New Practical Formulary,* Chemical Publishing Co., N.Y., 1955.
[14] R. M. Gattefosse, *Formulary of Perfumes and Cosmetics,* Chemical Publishing Co., N.Y., 1959.

[15] R. M. Gattefosse, *Formulary of Perfumes and Cosmetics,* Chemical Publishing Co., 1959.
[16] Adapted from Bennett's *The Chemical Formulary,* Vol. II, Chemical Publishing Co., 1957.

stearic acid	2 oz	(60 g)
cetyl alcohol	2 oz	(60 g)
tetrabrom fluo-rescein	2½ oz	(75 g)
erythrosine	1 oz	(30 g)
oil-soluble red	4 grains	
perfume	⅜ oz	(11.3 g)

(Tatrazin or ponceau may be used in place of oil-soluble red.) Directions are the same as those for preparing theatrical lipstick.

Rouge. Mix 600 g pure fine talc, 50 g gum arabic, and about 30 g carmine powder (vary the amount of carmine to obtain the desired shade). A few drops of an essential oil may be added as perfume.

Face powder and talcum powder. A simple face powder can be made in small batches by mixing 50 g pure talc powder, 50 g finely powdered magnesium carbonate, 50 g zinc white, 30 drops of orris oil, and 20 drops of rose oil. To color the powder use varying amounts of powdered carmine, starting with ½ g, to get the desired flesh tint.

Students may prefer to use this simple recipe for making face powder. Mix 20 g powdered talc with 8 g magnesium carbonate. Add color and a few drops of rose oil or other essential oil. Without color this is a good talcum powder.

Another recipe consists of 40 parts of fine cornstarch, 1 part of talc, and 1 part of orris root; color and scent to suit.

To prepare a simple talcum powder combine the following materials.[17]

talcum	94.0 g
magnesium stearate	2.5 g
calcium carbonate	2.5 g
titanium oxide	1 g
lavender compound	trace

Vary the quantities to suit individual needs.

[17] R. M. Gattefosse, *Formulary of Perfumes and Cosmetics,* Chemical Publishing Co., 1959.

Bath salts. Epsom salt crystals dyed and scented with oil of Paris rose make bath crystals. Trisodium phosphate crystals, which soften the water, can also be used.

Bubbling bath salts can be made by mixing 20 parts of Epsom salts, 6 parts of table salt, 1 part of boric acid, and 1 part of sodium bicarbonate. The acid will release the carbon dioxide from the bicarbonate, forming bubbles.

For large amounts of bubbles use 16 oz boric acid, 16 oz of borax, 2 oz table salt, and 16 oz of sodium bicarbonate.

Cold cream. These creams are emulsions containing a continuous oily phase.

white beeswax	10 g
paraffin	5 g
mineral oil	20 cc
borax	1 g

Melt together the first 3 ingredients in a beaker set in a water bath. In another beaker dissolve the borax in 25 cc of distilled water. Then add the borax solution to the mixture of melted oil and waxes in the first beaker. Let the mixture cool after it has been stirred; add a few drops of rose oil or other aromatic oil and pour into jars.

Hand lotion. Most skin-soothing lotions contain similar ingredients, although the quantities may vary. Here are two lotion recipes which have been used by teachers.

lotion 1

powdered tragacanth	0.2 g
boric acid	3 g
distilled water	4 cc
glycerin	5 cc
witch hazel	5 cc

Stir together the first 3 materials and let stand overnight; later add the glycerin and witch hazel. After this is well mixed by stirring, strain through a cheesecloth and add a drop of rose oil or other aromatic oil.

                  lotion 2

bay rum	30 g
glycerin	10 g
carbolic acid	10 drops
(preservative)	

Mix in the order given. In each case vary the quantities to meet the needs of the class.

Nail polish remover. These removers contain acetone and often ethyl acetate. An oil such as castor oil or olive oil is sometimes added to prevent excessive drying. Prepare the following solution, modifying the quantities as needed for small groups or individual work.

ethyl acetate	6 cc
castor oil	1 cc
acetone	20 cc

Shake the solution; use cotton soaked in the remover to test its ability to remove nail polish.

The following remover is acetone-free so that it has advantages over the usual polish remover.[18]

butyl acetate	1 part
ethyl acetate	2 parts
propyl alcohol	2 parts

Sunburn remedy. A soothing lotion for sunburn can be prepared by adding 1 per cent solution of hydrous chlorobutanol U.S.P. to a 12 per cent solution of glycerin. (*Caution: Some people are allergic to chlorobutanol or other derivatives of butanol.*) Tannic acid (even strong tea) mixed with clear, greasy surgical jelly makes a good burn or sunburn lotion.

15.4d Analyzing cosmetics

We have described several methods for preparing some cosmetics and lotions in the classroom or laboratory.

[18] R.M. Gattefosse, *Formulary of Perfumes and Cosmetics,* Chemical Publishing Co., 1959.

You may also want to stress the chemist's role in testing the ingredients of cosmetics and other commercial preparations. Students can bring to class samples of their tooth powder or paste. A study of kinds of adulterants and other additives may be meaningful in your classes.

Students can test for the presence of the detrimental chlorate ion in tooth powder or paste by dissolving a bit of the paste or powder in water. Add drop by drop 5 ml of $AgNO_3$ solution; if a precipitate forms, add the $AgNO_3$ solution until no further precipitation forms. Filter, add 5 ml of 6 M KNO_2 to the filtrate, and add 3 more drops of $AgNO_3$ solution. A white precipitate is a positive test for a chlorate.

They may also want to test the abrasiveness of tooth powders by rubbing samples against clear plastic and comparing scratches. Use pure precipitated chalk as a standard.

Discover the elements present by means of a flame test (see 10.3b). Add 15 cc of dilute HCl to a sample of the paste or powder. If a gas is produced, bubble it through limewater or bromthymol blue solution. The formation of a white precipitate in the limewater or a change in the color of bromthymol blue to yellow indicates that the gas produced is CO_2 and therefore the paste or powder contains $CaCO_3$.

15.5 Maintenance of materials

Students, as well as their parents, use many chemicals at home that are mainly related to the maintenance of materials. Some applications of these chemicals have been treated elsewhere (fire extinguishers, 9.5c; softening of water, 4.7b; bleaches, 11.2b).

In this section we describe some preparations of soaps, stain removers, water- and fireproofing materials, disinfectants, mortars, cements, rust inhibitors, building materials, paints and lacquers, and so forth. Many cross references to other chapters are indicated to show the chemistry of the reactions.

15.5a Building materials

Cement. Cement is made from lime-containing materials such as limestone, chalk, oyster shells or from slag and clay-containing substances such as clay or shale. The finely ground mixture of these substances is heated and changed into "clinkers" which are reground and mixed with gypsum. Cement is a mixture largely composed of calcium silicates and calcium aluminates. If pure cement is used, sand must be added before adding water.

The components of an "average" Portland cement are [19]

Ca_3SiO_5	tricalcium silicate	40.7%
Ca_2SiO_4	dicalcium silicate	32.1%
$Ca_3Al_2O_6$	tricalcium aluminate	10.7%
$Ca_4Al_2Fe_2O_{10}$		8.9%
$CaSO_4$		2.9%

Concrete is the same material (cement plus sand) plus crushed stone or gravel. Without the gravel the cement may be used to cement stone. The correct sand, gravel, and cement proportion varies with the purpose.

Mix the cement with water until it is the right consistency, somewhat stiff; it should not run easily but pour with a heavy slowness.

Waterproofing concrete. To waterproof concrete completely coat it with sodium silicate (water glass). A concrete floor that is to be painted must be first coated with sodium silicate in order to prevent chemicals in the concrete from reacting with the paint.

Plaster. Patching plaster (as commonly sold in small boxes for home use) depends

[19] Harry H. Sisler, Calvin A. Vanderwerf, Arthur W. Davidson, *General Chemistry: A Systematic Approach*, Macmillan Co., N.Y., 1949, p. 694.

upon the presence of calcium oxide to retard the hardening process. Ordinary plaster of Paris (as sold in bags) hardens rapidly after mixing with water and must be worked and smoothed rapidly. To slow down the hardening of plaster of Paris add about 1 to 5 per cent calcium oxide (quicklime). Citric acid will delay the setting of plaster of Paris several hours (1 oz of acid per 100 lb of plaster of Paris). Glue, dextrin, and gum arabic are other additives which delay setting.

The finest molding plaster is dental stone or dental impression plaster which can be purchased from a dental supply house.

Mortar. Mortar and cement are often confused. Mortar is sand mixed with calcium hydroxide formed by the reaction of quicklime (calcium oxide) with water. In hardening, the carbon dioxide in the air reacts with the quicklime to form calcium carbonate. Mortar is used to join stone or brick. Today, however, straight cement and sand are often used in place of mortar.

15.5b Adhesives

Plastic cement. Plastic cements such as Duco are used as adhesives with paper, wood, and chinaware. A simple plastic cement can be made in the laboratory by adding 10 cc of amyl acetate to 1 gram of celluloid (cellulose nitrate). Toothbrush handles (generally made of cellulose acetate) allowed to dissolve in acetone by simply standing in a closed jar produce a good lacquer. Thin with acetone as necessary.

Plastic varnish. A demonstration simulating a plastic varnish consists of merely diluting one of the plastic cements with a suitable solvent to a consistency suitable for brushing or spraying. Thus, a cellulose acetate base cement may be thinned with acetone. A cellulose nitrate base cement may be thinned with ethyl or butyl acetate. Many commercial lacquers contain cellulose nitrate dispersed or dissolved in a wide variety of solvent combinations. Consult such texts as Henley's *Twentieth Century Formulas,* Norman W. Henley Publishing Co., N.Y., 1955, and other formularies for exact composition of various lacquers.

15.5c   Paints and lacquers

Oil paints dry as the result of the oxidation of the linseed oil. Varnishes of several different kinds made from plant oils, such as tung oil, also work this way. Alkyd and synthetic resin varnishes and enamels dry by polymerization in some cases, and oxidation in others. (*Caution: Oil paints and lacquers are highly inflammable and must be stored in fireproof metal lockers. It it best to mix only as much as you need for immediate use.*)

Outside paint. Mix thoroughly the following materials; add tinting colors in oils as desired from tubes or small cans.

heavy paste white lead[20]	16 oz
raw linseed oil	1½ oz
pure turpentine	1½ oz
drier	½ oz

(*Caution: Lead paint is poisonous and should not be used on objects that will be bitten or tasted by children.*)

Stucco or brick paint. Mix the following materials until there are no lumps.

soft white lead paste	16 oz
boiled linseed oil	7 oz
turpentine	⅓ oz

Enamels. Enamel paints are made by simply substituting varnish for linseed oil in any paint recipe (see above).

Rust-proofing paint. Mix thoroughly the following ingredients.

[20] Zinc or titanium white are better but more expensive.

red lead	1 lb
raw linseed oil	3½ oz
drier	⅙ oz

Aluminum paint. The best all-around outside metal paint is the so-called aluminum paint which consists of tiny flakes of an aluminum-bronze alloy. Simply mix the flakes in varnish as desired, and it is ready to use.

15.5d   Fireproofing and water-proofing

Fireproofing fabrics.[21] Here are two solutions useful for fireproofing fabrics in the laboratory. Either solution should be brushed in until the fabric is soaked. (*Note:* Solution 2 is removed by laundering.)

solution 1	
ammonium phosphate	6 oz
ammonium chlorate	4 oz
ammonium sulfate	2 oz
water	5 pints

solution 2	
aluminum sulfate (alum)	27 oz
borax	3 oz
boric acid	1 oz
water	200 oz

Note that modern stage curtains and many drapery fabrics are glass and hence need no treatment.

Fire-extinguishing liquid.[22] To 95 parts of carbon tetrachloride add 5 parts of solvent naphtha to reduce the production of toxic fumes in fires.

Fireproofing canvas.[22] Soak the canvas to be fireproofed in a solution containing 1 pound of ammonium phosphate, 2 pounds of ammonium chloride, and ½ gallon of water. (Vary the quantities, keeping the

[21] M. Freeman, *New Practical Formulary,* Chemical Publishing Co., N.Y., 1955.
[22] H. Bennett, *The Chemical Formulary,* Vol. X, Chemical Publishing Co., N.Y., 1957.

same proportions to meet specific needs.) After soaking, let the fabric dry in the air.

Waterproofing fabrics. A simple water-proofing solution consists of 1 lb of zinc sulfate in 1½ gallon of water. The cloth is soaked in the solution and allowed to dry; excess crystals can then be brushed off. Another waterproofing solution is as follows.

lead acetate	½ lb
tannic acid	1 oz
sodium sulfate	½ oz
alum	5 oz
water	2 qt

Dip cloth to be waterproofed in the solution. After the cloth has dried, test the cloth.

15.6 Household chemistry

15.6a Stain removal

Ink eradicator. Laundry bleach (sodium hypochlorite) is a commonly used ink eradicator.

Stain removers. A committee of students can use information from Table 15-4 and demonstrate how several kinds of stains can be removed from cloth.

Oil stains on leather, wallpaper, concrete. Students can demonstrate the removal of oil stains. Mix Fuller's earth with carbon tetrachloride to make a paste, and place over the stain. (*Caution: Carbon tetrachloride fumes are toxic.*) Allow to stand 24 hours or more until the Fuller's earth is dry. Brush off the Fuller's earth. Repeat if part of the spot persists.

Rust and ink remover.[23] Prepare both of the following solutions and soak the stained fabric alternately in each solution, rinsing the fabric in water between immersions.

[23] H. Bennett, *The Chemical Formulary*, Vol. X, Chemical Publishing Co., N.Y., 1957.

TABLE 15-4
Stain removers

blood	ammonia (dilute)
candle wax	lard and benzene[1]
chewing gum	benzene[1] or carbon tetrachloride[2]
cod liver oil	amyl acetate
enamel	amyl acetate plus acetone[3]
fruit	pour boiling water through stain; then pour on 3% hydrogen peroxide
grass stains	alcohol
ink	add 3% hydrogen peroxide and hold in front of steam from a kettle; apply dilute oxalic acid solution and rinse thoroughly
iodine stains	ammonia water or hypo
lacquer	acetone or amyl acetate[3]
mildew	Javelle water[4]
paints and varnish	carbon tetrachloride[2] or benzene[1]
perspiration	hydrogen peroxide (3%) and soap
scorches (cotton only)	potassium permanganate 5% solution followed by 3% hydrogen peroxide

[1] *Caution:* Inflammable. [2] *Caution:* Fumes are toxic. [3] Do not use on rayon. [4] Do not use on silk or wool.

Solution 1. One part of ammonium sulfide solution to 19 parts of water.

Solution 2. One part of oxalic acid (poison) to 19 parts of water.

Dry-cleaning fluid.[23] Mix together the following ingredients to make a dry-cleaning fluid that can be used on fine fabrics with good results.

glycol oleate	2 oz
carbon tetrachloride	60 oz
naphtha	20 oz
benzene	18 oz

Reduce or increase the quantities, keeping the same proportions to accommodate class needs.

15.6b Rust control

Prevention of instrument rusting. The rusting of bright steel surfaces can be prevented by applying a thin coat of crude lanolin. Or prepare a benzene-oil solution by dissolving one part of paraffin oil in 200 parts of benzene.[24] After the instruments have been washed in hot water and dried in a current of warm air (if possible), dip them in the solution, manipulating the instruments so that their surfaces are completely coated. (Open and close scissors or similar tools so that their surfaces are coated.) Then place the instruments on a glass plate to dry in a warm room.

Removing rust from instruments. Let the instruments remain overnight in a saturated solution of zinc or tin chloride. In this procedure the rust is removed by reduction. Rinse in clear water; wash in hot soda and soap solution and dry.

15.6c Soap

Making soap. The main steps in the making of soap can be attempted as a laboratory activity. This is one procedure,[25] among many, that you may want to have students use. (See also 14.4g.)

Melt 30 grams of tallow (about 3 teaspoonfuls) in a hot water bath; slowly pour 25 cc of 30 per cent NaOH solution into the tallow and mix well by stirring. Next boil this mixture (without the water bath) for 10 minutes and carefully remove from the flame. Prepare 100 cc of 7 per cent sodium chloride solution and add to the mixture. Let this settle; cut the soap into bars the next day.

This is another suggestion for preparing soap in the laboratory. Quantities may be varied to meet the needs of the class. In an evaporating dish gently melt a level tablespoon of lard or beef tallow; add 10 cc of 30 per cent NaOH solution to the melted fat. Then continue to boil gently for a half hour. It may be necessary to add

boiling water to replace the volume. If the material is too greasy, add more sodium hydroxide.

Finally separate the soap from the glycerol by putting the mixture in a large beaker with as little as possible of the boiling water. Stir in 2 cc of crystalline sodium chloride (ordinary salt) and let it cool. When it is cold, lift out the soap, wash in cold water, and set aside to dry for a week or so.

Cleaning action of soap. Students will also want to show that the cleaning action of soap is an emulsifying process. Have students explain these demonstrations. Prepare a mixture of 15 cc of kerosene and 15 cc of water in a large test tube and shake. What happens? Then add 1 cc of soap solution and shake again. What is the action of the soap? You may want to show by means of models that the "oily" end of the soap molecule (the R group) dissolves in oils and fats, while the "salty" end (the bound sodium) dissolves in water. This ties the oil and the water together; this explains how soap "cuts" grease. (See also 14.4g.)

Cleaning action of detergents. Compare the cleansing action of soaps and various commercial detergents.

Almost all "detergents" contain a wetting agent which enables the soap to reach the fiber or material under treatment. You may want, at this point, to compare the action of soaps or detergents in "hard" and "soft" water.

Also test for the presence of free alkali by treating samples of pure soap and detergent with an indicator. Add 10 cc of water containing 2 drops of phenolphthalein solution to about 2 cc of each of the soap and detergent samples to be tested. What happens in each case?

15.6d Bleaches

Many bleaches are used in the home. Dyed fabrics may be soaked in the

[24] M. Freeman, *New Practical Formulary*, Chemical Publishing Co., 1955.
[25] S. Wilson and M. Mullins, *Applied Chemistry*, rev. ed., H. Holt, 1947.

bleaches so that students can examine the results.

Javelle water. Javelle water is a bleach made by mixing 8 oz of sodium carbonate in 16 oz of boiling water to which you add 4 oz of chloride of lime. Finally dilute by adding 32 oz of cold water. Be very careful to prevent splattering while mixing chemicals in the boiling water. Do not use sediment at bottom of bottle.

CAPSULE LESSONS

Ways to get started in class

15-1. Have students prepare slides of different fibers for examination under a microscope, hand lens, or a microprojector. Which fibers are of plant origin? Of animal origin? How are they manufactured? How have several synthetics been made—rayon as well as nylon, Dacron, and others?

15-2. Arrange one or several laboratory periods in which students can test sample swatches of materials that they have brought from home. Students can apply the burning tests and some of the chemical tests described in this chapter. Some students may want to report on proper cleaning methods for clothes made of these fabrics. What are the advantages of each kind of fiber in clothing? In home furnishings?

15-3. Simulate the making of synthetic textile fibers by producing rayon through the cuprammonium process (or by producing nylon).

15-4. Prepare several problems for the class to investigate: unknown fibers that students must identify by running through several tests; samples of different rayons that must be identified.

Students can use a hall case to prepare effective demonstrations of ways to identify textile fibers.

15-5. You may want to begin by demonstrating the use of a commercially prepared sugar testing tablet obtained from a drugstore. The tablets are part of a kit containing a reference color chart; the kit is used by doctors or by diabetics themselves in testing for the quantity of glucose in urine. Prepare varying solutions of glucose: ¼, ½, ¾, 1, 1½, and 2 per cent solutions. What color reactions are produced?

Show a chart of nutrient values of foods. Establish the reasons for knowing the composition of foods that we eat. How are food samples tested for the presence of nutrients? Plan laboratory work using the demonstrations described in this chapter.

15-6. Students can bring in cans of fruit juices for laboratory work. Use "indophenol" first on pure ascorbic acid, then on frozen, on canned, on boiled fruit juices. Also discover the effect on vitamin C of sodium bicarbonate, which is often added to keep vegetables green in color while cooking.

15-7. Have students determine the composition of carbohydrates—show that they contain carbon, hydrogen, and oxygen. Similarly, what elements make up proteins? Groups of students may work on different nutrients and pool their data as a summary.

15-8. You may want to have a group of students divide up the area of synthetic fibers, each member of the group preparing a class report on chemical constituents, properties, and uses of a particular type of fiber.

15-9. Prepare a talcum powder, a toothpaste or powder, a hand lotion, or an antiperspirant. Establish the use of several common chemicals in cosmetics and toiletries. Groups of students in the laboratory may plan to prepare specific recipes (some are offered in this chapter).

15-10. Students can report on the value of such organizations as testing bureaus in department stores, consumers' reports, and similar private testing agencies.

15-11. A group of students may want to explore the recipes for all kinds of cosmetics, drugs, and pharmaceuticals in some of the formularies listed at the end of the chapter.

15-12. Students can demonstrate the action of blueprint paper (2.2b) or they may want to prepare trays of developer, acid short stop, and hypo, and develop prints from their own negatives.

15-13. A small committee of students can show the use of plaster of Paris in producing good impressions. What is the main chemical ingredient? How does plaster differ from mortar? When is cement used? What is the use of concrete?

15-14. In a summary of many aspects of applications of consumer chemistry, several films or strips are available. (Please refer to listing at the end of this chapter.)

Consumer chemistry is a broad field with many applications for those students who wish to do projects or a long-range research activity. Where can a student get help for a project in textile chemistry, or in dyeing, or an experiment using tests for nutrients, vitamins, or a study of the effect of food preservatives, or a project to test the effectiveness of soaps and detergents, or even to make a new perfume? Among the parents of students and among your colleagues there may be an expert in some specialized area. It may also be possible to invite a contractor to talk about building materials, or an operator of a cleaning plant to describe textiles and spot removal. A member of the local Board of Health might speak on insecticides and chemicals used in water purification and sewage disposal. A druggist might report on new drugs.

You may find it practical to visit a pharmaceutical plant, a cosmetics or food processing plant, a candy plant, or a textile establishment. A trip might be planned to visit building construction in action—the preparation of cement and the laying of bricks—prefabricated parts—insulation materials—chemical reactions involved in some of the weathering actions.

Nearby colleges that give courses in some of these specialties may loan a film or a piece of equipment on request. Many industrial corporations have free films, booklets, and teacher's kits available. (Please refer to the listings at the end of this chapter.)

BOOKS AND PAMPHLETS

These are only a few of the books which are pertinent to the work discussed in this chapter. These and many other references classified by subject and with complete bibliographical data are given in the bibliography at the end of the book.

Alexander, W., and A. Street, *Metals in the Service of Man,* Pelican, 1954, $0.85.

Bennett, H., ed., *The Chemical Formulary,* Chemical Publishing Co., 1957.

Brauns, F., *The Chemistry of Lignin,* Academic, 1952.

Chamot, E., and C. Mason, *Handbook of Chemical Microscopy,* Vol. I, 3rd ed., Wiley, 1958.

Charlot, G., *Qualitative Inorganic Analysis,* Wiley, 1958.

Clark, G., and G. Hawley, eds., *Encyclopedia of Chemistry,* Reinhold, 1957.

Cook, A. H., ed., *The Chemistry and Biology of Yeasts,* Academic, 1958.

Couzens, E. G., and E. Yarsley, *Plastics in the Service of Man,* Pelican, 1956, $0.85.

Damerell, V. R., *Laboratory Experiments in College Chemistry,* Macmillan, 1952.

Dartnall, H., *The Visual Pigments,* Wiley, 1957.

Duffin, D., *Laminated Plastics,* Reinhold, 1958.

Elkins, H., *The Chemistry of Industrial Toxicology,* 2nd ed., Wiley, 1959.

Faith, W., D. Keyes, and R. Clark, *Industrial Chemicals,* 2nd ed., Wiley, 1957.

Fox, S., and J. Foster, *Introduction to Protein Chemistry,* Wiley, 1957.

Freeman, M., *New Practical Formulary,* Chemical Publishing Co., 1955.

Gattefosse, R. M., *Formulary of Perfumes and Cosmetics,* Chemical Publishing Co., 1959.

Hawk, P., B. Oser, and W. Summerson, *Practical Physiological Chemistry,* 13th ed., Blakiston-McGraw-Hill, N. Y., 1954.

Harwood, J., H. Hausner, J. Morse, and W. Rauch, *The Effect of Radiation on Materials,* Reinhold, 1958.

Hillebrand, W., G. Lundell, and H. Bright, *Applied Inorganic Analysis,* 2nd ed., Wiley, 1953.

Jacobs, M., *The Chemical Analysis of Food and Food Products,* 3rd ed., Van Nostrand, 1958.

Jenkins, G., J. Christian, et al., *Quantitative Pharmaceutical Chemistry,* 5th ed., McGraw-Hill, 1957.

Jones, G., *Glass,* Wiley Methuen, 1956.

King, E., *Qualitative Analysis and Electrolytic Solutions,* Harcourt, Brace, 1959.

Lange, N., *Handbook of Chemistry,* 9th ed., Handbook Publishers, 1956.

Langer, M., *My Hobby is Photography,* Hart, 1956.

Lubs, H., ed., *The Chemistry of Synthetic Dyes and Pigments,* Reinhold, 1955.

Lyon, T. L., *The Nature and Properties of Soils,* Macmillan, 1952.

Matthews, J. M., and H. Mauersberger, eds., *Textile Fibers: Their Physical, Microscopic and Chemical Properties,* 6th ed., Wiley, 1954.

Miner, D., and J. Seastone, eds., *Handbook of Engineering Materials,* Wiley, 1955.

Moeller, T., *Inorganic Syntheses,* McGraw-Hill, 1956.

Moncrieff, R., *Man-Made Fibers,* Wiley, 1957.

Morrison, G., *Solvent Extraction in Analytical Chemistry,* Wiley, 1957.

Mrak, E., and G. Stewart, eds., *Advances in Food Research,* Vol. 6, Academic, 1955.

Meyer, L., *Laboratory Manual for Introductory Chemistry,* Macmillan, 1952.

Nebergall, W., and F. Schmidt, *College Chemistry,* Heath, 1957.

Nordmann, J., *Qualitative Testing and Inorganic Chemistry,* Wiley, 1957.

Riegel, E., *Industrial Chemistry,* 6th ed., Reinhold, 1954.

Riley, C., *Our Mineral Resources,* Wiley, 1959.

Riley, M., *Plastics Tooling,* Reinhold, 1955.

Scientific American, "Sir William Perkins," February, 1957.

Taylor, F. S., *A History of Industrial Chemistry,* Abelard-Schuman, 1957.

Venkataraman, K., *The Chemistry of Synthetic Dyes,* vol. I, II, Academic, 1952.

Vergara, W., *Science in Everyday Things,* Harper, 1958.

Vickerstaff, T., *The Physical Chemistry of Dyeing,* Interscience, 1954.

Vogel, A., *Elementary Practical Organic Chemistry,* Longmans, Green, 1958.

West, E., and W. Todd, *Textbook of Biochemistry,* 2nd ed., Macmillan, 1955.

Whistler, R., and C. Smart, *Polysaccharide Chemistry,* Academic, 1953.

Wilson, S., and M. Mullins, *Applied Chemistry,* Holt, 1949.

Winchell, A., *The Optical Properties of Organic Compounds,* 2nd ed., Academic, 1954.

FILMS AND FILMSTRIPS

This partial list is intended only as a guide toward film and filmstrip selection. Refer to the more complete listing at the end of the book where films are classified by subject and where a key to abbreviations and addresses of distributors are given. The cost of film rental, of course, is subject to change. Films are sound and black and white unless otherwise specified.

Basic Fibers in Cloth (f, s), N. Y. State College Agric., Cornell, $1.50.

Big Kitchen (f, s, c), Modern Talking Pictures, free.

Canned Meat Story (f, s, c), Modern Talking Pictures, free.

Constructive Chemistry (cellulose, rubber), (f, s), Institutional Cinema, $2.00.

Drama of Portland Cement (f, s, c), Modern Talking Pictures, free.

Growth of a Nation (livestock feeding) (f, s), Modern Talking Pictures, free.

Paper and Pulp Making (f, s), Indiana U., $2.00.

Paper Work (f, s, c), Modern Talking Pictures, free.

The Questing Mind (f, s), General Motors, free.

The Rival World (insecticides) (f, s, c), Shell, free.

The Science of Soap (f, s), EBF, $2.50.

Soap: Production and Cleansing Action (f, s), Indiana U., $2.00.

Speaking of Rubber (f, s), Modern Talking Pictures, free.

Story of Perfume (f, s, c), Coty, free.

Story of Research (orlon, acrylic fibers) (f, s, c), DuPont, free.

Synthetic Fibers (f, s), Indiana U., $3.50.

Synthetic Rubber (f, s), U. S. Bureau of Mines, free.

Testing Foods and Nutrients (fs, c), Popular Science through McGraw-Hill, $6.00.

This is Life (meat processing) (f, s, c), Modern Talking Pictures, free.

Vitamin Rivers (f, s, c), Modern Talking Pictures, free.

Yesterday, Today and Tomorrow (food packing) (f, s), Modern Talking Pictures, free.

FREE AND INEXPENSIVE MATERIALS

This is only a partial listing of free and inexpensive materials available to the teacher at this time. A directory of addresses is given at the end of the book. Many of these materials are distributed to teachers without charge. Where there is a small fee, the cost is indicated, although the prices are subject to change. While we recommend the material for use in the classroom, we do not necessarily endorse the products advertised.

ABC's of Hand Tools, General Motors.

An Outline of the History of Chemistry (wall chart), Mallinckrodt.

The Art of Making Fine Glassware, Cambridge Glass Co.

Chemicals from Farm and Forest Products, Manufacturing Chemists Assoc.

Chemistry: The Conquest of Materials, K. Hutton, Pelican, 1957, $0.85.

Color Dynamics, Pittsburgh Plate Glass.

Concrete Pamphlets, Portland Cement.

Fundamentals of Building Insulation, Insulation Board Institute.

How Heat Resistant Chemical Glassware is Made, Corning Glass.

Isotopes Work In Industry, Isotopes Extens., U.S. A.E.C.

Section Three PHYSICS

CHAPTER 16

Pressure

Several demonstrations to measure pressure—both air and liquid pressure—and many of the applications of pressure in daily living are described.

Extensions of the effects of air pressure on daily weather have been described in Chapter 3, Weather.

16.1 Air pressure
16.1a Weight of air

The weight of a given volume of air is easily determined by first weighing an evacuated glass flask of the round-bottomed type and then weighing it with air at normal atmospheric pressure. Students should avoid the use of football or basketball bladders, inner tubes, or other inflatable objects since the buoyancy of the surrounding air tends to cancel the increase of weight after inflation.

If a large enough beam balance is not available, students can make one from a yardstick or meterstick (Fig. 16-1). Drill a hole in the center of a meterstick and place in it a snug-fitting glass tube (½″ to ⅜″ bore). File the length of a nail (8-penny, common) to a wedge to make a triangular knife edge. Insert the wedge, knife edge up, through the tube and hammer it into a cork mounted in a burette clamp on a ring stand. The stick will now swing easily since the knife edge against glass is virtually frictionless.

Use a 1000-cc *round-bottomed* flask. If your vacuum pump is particularly good, there is danger that a flat-bottomed Erlenmeyer flask or Florence flask may implode due to air pressure. Hang the evacuated flask at one end of the stick and balance it with weights at the opposite end; then allow the air to enter and weigh

Fig. 16–1 Beam balance made from a meterstick. The fulcrum of the balance is a nail filed to a sharp triangle, resting against the inside of a glass tube.

glass tubing

nail

it again. Students might be encouraged to calculate the weight of one cc of air from the known volume of the flask and the weight of 1000 cc of air at normal atmospheric pressure.

16.1b   *Pressure of air*

If a vacuum pump is available, students can use it to evacuate a one-gallon rec-tangular can. Lead students to the recognition of air pressure as the force that acts on the outside surface. Now take a similar can and mark off its entire surface into 1″ squares, using a crayon or china marking

Fig. 16–2 Normal air pressure collapses a partially evacuated tin can.

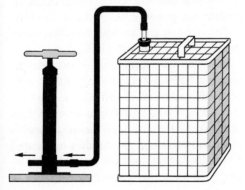

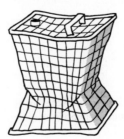

pencil (Fig. 16-2). Repeat the evacuation with a pump. If students count the number of 1″ squares and multiply the total by 14.7 pounds per square inch, they can approximate the force in pounds that acted on the outside surface of the can.

In another method, steam is used to force some air out of a can. First add a few ounces of water to a gallon can that is fitted with a cap or stopper. Remove the cap and boil the water in the open can for three or four minutes. Then remove the source of heat and cap the can immediately. Let the can cool by standing, or sponge it with water to speed the cooling process. Because the steam in the can cools and condenses, reducing the vapor pressure inside the can, the normal external atmospheric pressure is greater than the internal pressure and the can collapses.

Students can evacuate a can without using a vacuum pump (Fig. 16-3). Almost fill a one-gallon rectangular can with water and fit it with a one-hole stopper containing glass tubing of 5/16″ bore. To the glass tube attach about 25′ of rubber tubing which also has a bore of 5/16″. Drop the end of this tubing out of a window. Then have a student hold the can over his head. As the water runs out of the tubing because of gravity, air will not be able to come in to replace it. Here again, the outside atmospheric pressure collapses the can. Students may want to repeat this using a can which has been marked with 1″ squares on its six surfaces, and calculate the total force on it.

A bell jar and a vacuum pump can be used in several ways to demonstrate air pressure. Stretch a sheet of heavy rubber cut from an automobile tire inner tube over the bottom of a bell jar and fasten it with strong rope or tape. Evacuate the bell jar with a vacuum pump. Students should be ready to explain why the rubber sheet is forced into the bell jar and takes the shape of the inner surface of the jar.

Or place a partly inflated balloon in a bell jar. Seal the bell jar's bottom edge with Vaseline to a glass plate. When the bell jar is evacuated with a vacuum pump, the balloon will become inflated; its internal pressure forces the walls of the balloon outward to balance the lower pressure of the air in the bell jar.

Another variation of the same demonstration uses a bottle half filled with colored water and closed with a one-hole stopper carrying a tube into an open flask or beaker (Fig. 16-4). This apparatus is placed inside a bell jar. As air is evacuated from the bell jar (either from the top or the bottom), the pressure around the

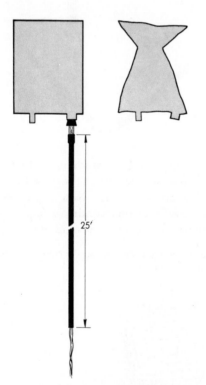

Fig. 16-3 Evacuating a can full of water by attaching a long hose to it and draining it by gravity.

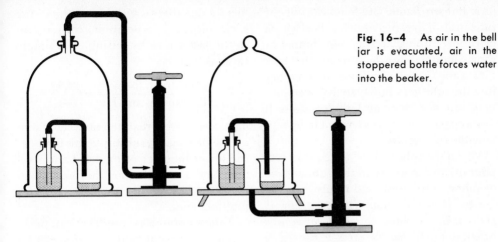

Fig. 16-4 As air in the bell jar is evacuated, air in the stoppered bottle forces water into the beaker.

stoppered bottle drops and the atmospheric pressure above the water (in the stoppered bottle) forces the water out into the empty beaker.

16.1c *Measuring air pressure*

Handling mercury. At the very least, continued exposure to metallic mercury can produce contact dermatitis; often, a person allergic to mercury or its compounds may develop systemic poisoning evidenced by severe swelling, extensive rashes in various parts of the body, and loss of hair.

Torricelli barometer. Fill with mercury a barometer tube or (if one is not available) a 3′ glass tube with a bore of at least 3/16″, one end of which has been sealed

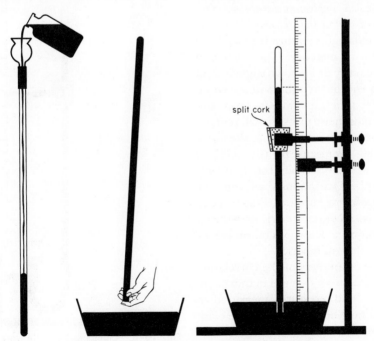

split cork

Fig. 16-5 Steps in making a Torricelli barometer.

in a Bunsen flame. Students can fill the tube easily if they first attach a short length of rubber tubing and a small funnel or short-stemmed thistle tube to the long glass tube (Fig. 16-5). Pour the mercury into the tube very slowly so that a continuous stream without air bubbles results. If any air spaces form, remove them by tapping the tube gently.

When the tube is filled to the very top, pour off any mercury in the rubber tube or funnel into a dish and return it to the bottle. (*Caution: Avoid losing mercury in places where it cannot be picked up; mercury vaporizes slowly and the vapor is harmful to people who are constantly exposed to it.*) Now carefully remove the rubber tube over a sink and, holding the thumb over the open end of the tube of mercury, invert the tube into a shallow dish containing enough mercury so that the finger sealing the tube is also immersed. Now withdraw the finger. Clamp the tube upright. (*Caution: If you do this often, wear rubber gloves or use some implement over the end of the tube; repeated contact with mercury is dangerous.*) Students can measure the height of the column of mercury. They will find that the mercury drops down slightly from the sealed end of the tube and a column nearly 760 mm high at sea level and normal atmospheric pressure will remain. This distance is measured from the top of the curved meniscus to the level of mercury in the reservoir dish. Students should explain variations that would be found at different altitudes. Students can check the correct atmospheric pressure for the day against a classroom barometer or a Weather Bureau report.

A clear-cut analysis of the correlation between pressures measured in mm or cm of mercury and pressures measured in lb/in² can now be presented to the class. Develop the notion that since 760 mm is normal atmospheric pressure as read on a mercury barometer and 14.7 lb/in² is

merely another way of expressing the same thing, we can determine the pressure in the latter unit by setting up a simple ratio as follows:

$$\frac{\text{Pressure in lb/in}^2}{\text{Pressure in mm Hg}} = \frac{14.7}{760}$$

Thus, we merely read the number of mm on the barometer, substitute this figure as the lower member of the left-hand fraction, and then solve for the pressure in lb/in² by the usual method of cross-multiplication.

J-tube barometer. Students can make a more convenient mercury barometer for class demonstrations by filling a barometer tube through a small thistle tube and rubber tubing as already described (Fig. 16-5), but this time continuing to fill until the mercury just enters the very

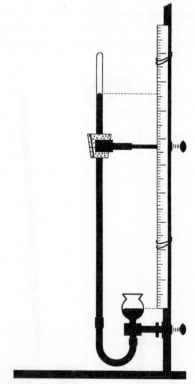

Fig. 16–6 Clamping both the barometer tube and thistle tube (connected by rubber tubing) to a ring stand.

bottom of the thistle tube. While holding the thistle tube in its upright position, raise the barometer tube as in Fig. 16-6, and clamp both the barometer and the thistle tube to a ring stand. The mercury level will drop slightly in the barometer tube until the difference between the mercury levels in the thistle tube and in the tube of the barometer is about 760 mm or less, depending on the local atmospheric pressure and altitude. To make a permanent mercury barometer, attach a meterstick alongside for measuring the height of the column (Fig. 16-6). Cover the mouth of the thistle tube with cloth to keep out dust.

Direct-reading mercury barometer. Another variation of a homemade barometer can be made with a 36″ length of ½″ bore glass tubing that has been sealed at one end in a flame and bent to form a J (Fig. 16-7). The J-tube should be formed around an asbestos-covered broomstick or other piece of round stock having a diameter of approximately 1¼″ to 1¾″. The diameter of the J's curve is not critical. (Tubes already shaped can be purchased.) Fill the tube with mercury; then prepare a small pulley (2″ diameter Bakelite is suitable) with iron counterweights as follows. Attach a thin piece of fishline to one end of a piece of iron rod that is slightly less than ½″ in diameter and 1″ long by drilling a hole in the iron rod. Slide the rod into the ½″ glass cylinder of mercury. Pass the cord over a small pulley to which a cardboard arrow has been cemented. At the other end of the cord attach another piece of iron of slightly less weight than the first, to counterbalance it. The J-tube and pulley are mounted on a piece of plywood. Place a paper scale behind the arrow and attach a meterstick beside the J-tube. The scale can be checked daily by measuring the difference between the mercury levels in the tube and the top of the column. After

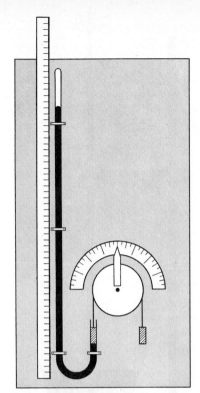

Fig. 16-7 Fitting a J-tube with weights and pulley to operate a dial indicator.

several weeks students can calibrate a fairly accurate dial whose divisions are in terms of the number of mm rise or fall as observed on the stick.

Vacuum in space above mercury in a barometer. To show that the space above the mercury in a mercury barometer is a vacuum, attach an 8″ length of rubber tubing to a 30″ length of narrow-bore (at the most ¼″) glass tubing. The rubber tubing should be of the ordinary thin-wall variety used as gas lines for Bunsen burners. Avoid the use of pressure-type tubing since it will not work properly in this application. Close the free end of the rubber tubing with a pinch clamp. Now fill the tube with mercury as in Fig. 16-5. Set the tube up as a Torricelli barometer as in Fig. 16-8. The rubber tube will be compressed flat by the external atmospheric pressure. (Since part of the space is occu-

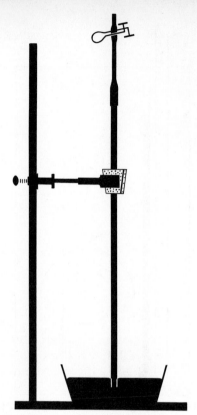

Fig. 16–8 The collapse of the rubber tube indicates that a vacuum exists above the column of mercury in a barometer tube.

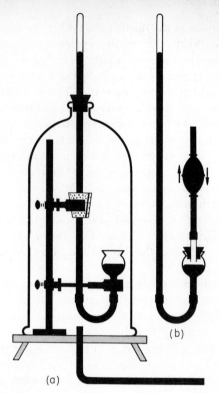

(b)

(a)

Fig. 16–9 Using a barometer to show changes in pressure: (a) mounting barometer in a bell jar on an evacuation stand, (b) using a two-way syringe bulb.

pied by mercury vapor molecules due to the vapor pressure of mercury, we have only a partial vacuum.)

Buoyancy of air. On a vacuum-pump stage under a bell jar stand a small balance. On one pan of the balance place a sealed hollow brass ball and balance it with weights. When the air around the ball is pumped out, students should see that the ball apparently becomes heavier because air supporting it has been removed. When air is re-admitted, the balance returns to equilibrium.

16.1d Changes in atmospheric pressure

What happens to the height of the mercury in a barometer when the atmos-

pheric pressure drops? Place a mercury barometer inside a bell jar sealed to the plate of a vacuum pump (Fig. 16-9A) and pass the tube through a rubber stopper fitted to the bell jar. Point out what happens to the column of mercury when the pump is started—when air is returned to the bell jar.

Fig. 16-9B shows a simpler demonstration of the same effect. Increases and decreases in pressure produced by the two-way syringe cause the column of mercury to rise and fall.

Gases under pressure act like liquids under pressure in that each transmits pressure undiminished in all directions. You may want to have students refer to activities related to Pascal's law (see 16.5b).

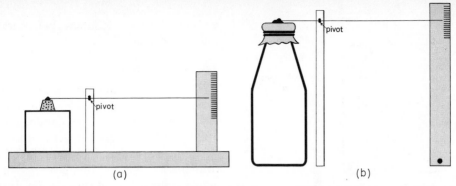

Fig. 16–10 Model aneroid barometers: (a) from sealed tin can, (b) from milk bottle sealed with rubber diaphragm. The indicator stick with its scale should be about 10″ from the pivot.

Aneroid barometer. There are several commercial types of aneroid barometers that students can examine. Some students may also want to try to make simple barometers that illustrate the principle upon which they work.

Commercial models. In one classroom model available, the pressure inside the barometer can be varied by means of a bulb and rubber tube. Changes in atmospheric pressure can also be demonstrated with the ordinary clock or desk aneroid barometers by placing them inside a bell jar from which air is slowly evacuated. To show increased pressure, blow air through a rubber tube into the jar. Do not increase or reduce the pressure beyond the limits of the instrument.

Altimeter. Students will want to demonstrate how an altimeter works. Many give the altitude and the atmospheric pressure on separate scales. If an altimeter is available, students can place it inside of a bell jar and remove the air gradually by means of a vacuum pump. (Do not evacuate beyond the highest altitude reading of the instrument.)

The actual effect of altitude upon barometric readings can be shown by having a committee of students carry an altimeter or aneroid barometer from the basement of your school building to the roof. A definite difference in reading will be observed if the building has at least three floors above the basement.

Homemade aneroid barometer. As a class activity each student can assemble an aneroid barometer from an empty milk can (Fig. 16-10A). They will need to heat the can to cause some of the air to escape by expansion and then seal the two holes in the top by soldering them or stoppering them with sealing wax. Then cement a cork to the center of the top of the can and cement a 10″ broomstraw or balsa wood strip to the cork (Fig. 16-10A). Place a wood block behind the straw and position one finishing nail above and one below the straw so as to prevent either upward or downward movement at this point. Make the effort arm very short and the resistance arm long to magnify the motion. The broomstraw serves as the needle of the barometer. Students can place a wood block covered with paper behind the pointer to serve as the scale. Now the barometer is ready for calibration. A committee of students can record the position of the pointer on the scale and note the daily barometric reading as given by a local radio station or an accurately calibrated mercury barometer. From time to time the homemade aneroid barometer should be checked against an accurate instrument.

Temporary aneroid barometer. A tempo-

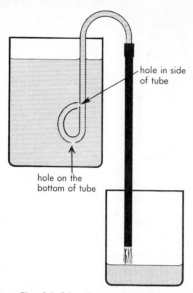

hole in side of tube

hole on the bottom of tube

Fig. 16–11 Automatic siphon.

a vacuum cleaner, a fountain pen containing a rubber sac.

16.2a Siphon

The common siphon is a hose or a bent glass tube filled with water. One end is placed in an elevated jar containing liquid and the other end, in a lower, empty jar. Students can make an automatic siphon from glass or copper tubing. File or blow a hole at the place indicated in Fig. 16-11, and bend the tube into the shape shown. The loop has an approximate diameter of 3″. Attach a rubber tube and suddenly lower the siphon into the jar of water. Water will flow out of the end of the rubber tube.

The hole in the sidewall of the down-tube is much smaller than the bore of the tube. When the siphon is plunged into the water, there is an inrush of the fluid into the larger end hole while the water enters the smaller hole much more slowly. Note that air is being pushed up the vertical tube by the incoming water from the end hole. The water that enters through the side hole, however, breaks into this stream of air, causing air bubbles to interlace with water droplets as they both move upward. This forms a column of "froth" whose average density is very much less than that of a solid column of water, and is easily lifted by the water coming around the bent tube as it establishes its own level. The piston-like action of the froth as it rises in the vertical tube fills it with the mixed fluid. As a result, a few drops of the froth run over the top of the tube and start down the long arm. This brings more of the water into the bent section, forcing more of the froth past the upper bend. The process is cumulative; in a short time, the entire siphon is filled with unmixed water and continues in operation.

Commercial siphons are also available from scientific supply houses (see directory

rary aneroid barometer can be made by simply stretching balloon rubber across the mouth of a very warm milk bottle. Then use a bit of chewing gum to fasten a broomstraw to the center of the rubber. Set up a scale on a piece of cardboard alongside the bottle. Support the scale on a wood base by means of tacks as in Fig. 16-10B. As the air in the bottle cools, the pressure will drop inside the bottle. Then if the atmospheric pressure increases, the rubber sheet will be forced further down. If the atmospheric pressure drops below the pressure inside the bottle, the balloon rubber will rise and the broomstraw indicator will move in the opposite direction. Eventually air molecules from the outside will diffuse through the rubber into the bottle, but this takes several days.

16.2 Air pressure and its effects

Students can demonstrate how several commonplace devices use some application of atmospheric pressure. Air pressure can be demonstrated in the mechanics of a drinking straw, a rubber bulb syringe,

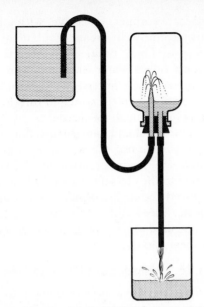

Fig. 16–12 Fountain in bottle created by siphon action.

in appendix) and some pet shops.

Fountain in a bottle. Air pressure can also be used to operate a fountain inside a bottle (Fig. 16-12). Fit a two-hole stopper to a wide-mouth bottle. Then pass a long medicine dropper through one hole of the stopper, with the point inside, and connect the outside end to an 18″ length of ¼″ rubber tubing. Insert into the other hole a short length of glass tubing connected to a 24″ length of ¼″ rubber tubing. Now fill the bottle about ⅓ full of water and put the stopper in place. Place the shorter rubber tube into a jar of water and let the 2′ tube drop into another jar placed at a considerably lower level. With the tubes in place, quickly invert the bottle. As some of the water runs from the longer tube, the pressure above the medicine dropper is reduced and air pressure forces water to spray into the bottle from the higher jar.

16.2b   Pumps

Lift pump. Another useful device oper-

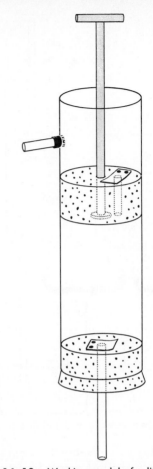

Fig. 16–13 Working model of a lift pump.

ated by atmospheric pressure is the simple lift pump. You may have a small iron farm-type lift pump to demonstrate. Or you can make a large homemade model, which is often more suitable for demonstrations in class than the small commercial glass or plastic models (2″ to 3″ diameter) used for student laboratory work. Make a large demonstration lift pump from a heavy (⅜″ thickness) clear plastic tube (Fig. 16-13). Fit the bottom with a one-hole stopper which has a rubber flap valve, and a long glass tube. A cork to serve as a piston can be fitted with a dowel handle. An additional hole is drilled through the cork and covered with a small

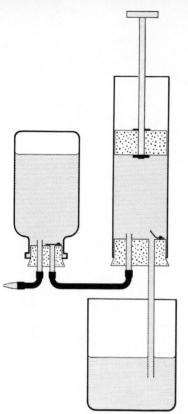

Fig. 16–14 Working model of a force pump.

rubber flap valve as shown. A spout may be made by drilling a hole in the side of the cylinder about two inches below the top and inserting a short piece of glass tubing anchored in place with sealing wax or a rubber gasket. Clamps and ring stands can be arranged to hold the apparatus in position.

Students should be ready to explain what happens when the long tube is dipped into a reservoir of water and the piston is pushed down, then pulled up again.

Force pump. The construction of a force pump is similar to that of a hydraulic press (16.5b) except that a pressure "tank" replaces the piston and cylinder of the jack (Fig. 16-14). A pressure tank may be made from an inverted bottle fitted with a

two-hole stopper. One hole, with a flap valve, connects by means of tubing to the pump section. A nozzle is attached to the second hole. Water entering from the pump section compresses air in the upper section of the bottle, which in turn forces water out through the nozzle.

Centrifugal and gear pumps. Small inexpensive pumps of these types may be purchased. Their operation may be made visible to the class if the metal covers are removed and replaced with ¼″ clear sheet plastic. Sheet rubber from an inner tube can be used as a gasket between the plastic sheet and the pump.

16.2c Magdeburg hemispheres

You can have a student demonstrate air pressure on a dramatic scale. After greasing the edges of a pair of Magdeburg hemispheres, place them together and evacuate the air with a hand or electric vacuum pump. Then close the valve on the hemispheres. Use the apparatus in a tug of war between two students or hang weights from it to show the effect of air pressure. (*Caution: Make sure the valve does not leak.*) Some teachers surreptitiously open the valve and call upon the "littlest one" in class to pull the hemispheres apart.

Vacuum pumps. If good electric or hand vacuum pumps are not available, you may be able to purchase a war surplus aircraft engine vacuum pump which can be driven by a ½-hp motor. The best vacuum obtainable with these is three inches of mercury, which is adequate for the experiments described in this chapter.

16.3 Boyle's law

One apparatus to demonstrate Boyle's law uses a large hypodermic syringe. The narrow opening must be sealed tightly by crimping and bending the needle; then place the piston into its barrel. Fasten the

Fig. 16–15 For each kilogram of sand added to the bucket, note the change in the volume of the confined air. For this demonstration the syringe should be attached to a block of wood. This, in turn, can be clamped to a table edge. To seal, crimp the needle (pinch the sides together and bend). (Bucket not drawn to scale.)

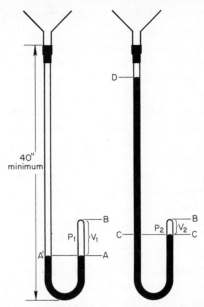

Fig. 16–16 Boyle's law verified by adding the amount of mercury until the volume of confined air is reduced by half.

syringe into a rubber-covered burette clamp. The clamps are set on a ring stand and the stand is clamped to a table edge. Make a leather strap as in Fig. 16-15 that passes over the top of the piston, and from the lower ends of the strap hang a bucket. Note the original reading of the position of the piston against the scale on the syringe. If it has no scale, place a millimeter scale alongside it. Then add sand to the bucket in one-kilogram increments. For each kilogram read the change in volume on the scale. Then plot the force or weight against the reciprocal of the volume.

For another demonstration of Boyle's law, prepare a closed manometer (Fig. 16-16) and add mercury until it stands at the same level in both the closed and open arms. The pressure exerted by the air con-

fined in the closed arm is now one atmosphere. The reasoning to support this conclusion may be stated in a series of steps.

1. Suppose both tubes were open. If any quantity of mercury were now poured into the U-shaped section, the levels in both arms would be the same. This would occur because both the air pressures and liquid pressures in both arms would be exactly equal.

2. Now imagine that we close one of the two tubes without disturbing the equilibrium. Since the liquid levels remain the same, the pressure of the enclosed air must still be one atmosphere just as it was before closure.

3. Reasoning backward, then, if mercury is poured into a closed manometer until the levels in the arms are equal, the gas pressures above both liquid arms must be equal. Since the open arm is subjected to a pressure of one atmosphere, the pres-

sure inside the confined space must also be one atmosphere.

Measure the distance in cm between point A and point B (Fig. 16-6) and call this V_1. Although this is a linear measurement, the uniform cross section of the tube permits us to refer to it as a volume because, for this condition, volume will always be proportional to the column length. We shall call the pressure of the confined air at this point P_1 (it is one atmosphere, as stated before).

Now add sufficient mercury to the open tube to cause the volume of the confined air to shrink to one half its former value; that is, distance BC will be half BA. This new volume is called V_2. Finally, measure the distance from C to D along the open tube. You will find that it comes out very close to 76 cm. Thus, to reduce the volume to one half its former value at one atmosphere, it was necessary to add enough mercury to make the total pressure *two atmospheres*. (One atmosphere of air pressure still acting on the open tube *plus* one atmosphere equivalent of mercury—76 cm.) Thus, doubling the pressure has reduced the original volume to one half, demonstrating the inverse relationship between pressure and volume of gases.

$$\frac{P_1}{P_2} = \frac{V_2}{V_1}$$

At a constant temperature the pressure exerted on a gas is inversely proportional to the volume the gas occupies.

Students should also be able to derive a relationship between pressure and density of gases.

$$\frac{P_1}{P_2} = \frac{D_1}{D_2}$$

Pressure of air is directly proportional to its density. For example, doubling the pressure must double the density (since the volume is decreased by half).

Expansion and compression of air. If students add 5 cc of water to a graduate cylinder, then follow with an additional 15 cc of water, they find that the water is not compressed but occupies a total of 20 cc in the graduate cylinder. However, if air were used in place of water, the results would be different. Students can show the compressibility of air by pumping air into a bicycle tire or a football complete with outer casing. As a rough calculation estimate the capacity of your pump and multiply this by the number of thrusts you use to pump up the tire or football. Conversely, the expansibility of the air can be shown by the bounce of the football, or the effect of expanding air (heated in a test tube) can be shown in popping a cork. You can also show how heated air in the room expands (see 18.2c, 18.3b). Place a partially inflated balloon under a bell jar standing on a vacuum pump. What causes the balloon to expand when the air is removed from the bell jar? Students can show the same effect by tying a rubber sheet across the mouth of a beaker and fastening it securely with cord. Place this on a vacuum-pump stage and cover it with a bell jar. When the pump is started and air is removed from the bell jar, the air within the beaker expands, pushing out and distending the rubber sheet.

The same principle can be illustrated by a demonstration described earlier in this chapter (see Fig. 16-4).

Students can examine the "spring" or compressibility of air in several ways. Fit a steel rod closely into a brass tube closed at one end. Insert the steel rod as a plunger. Push down on the plunger sharply; when the hand pressure is removed, the plunger springs back because the trapped air acts as a coiled spring. Light engine oil can be used to make a seal and act as a lubricant. (If the plun-

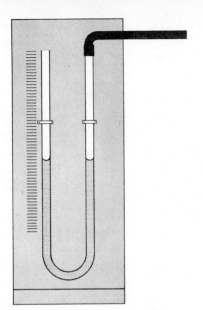

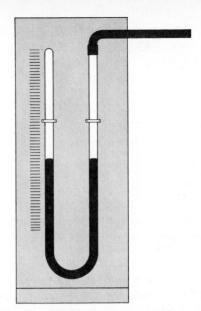

Fig. 16–17 Open manometer used for measuring low pressures. (Liquid is water.)

Fig. 16–18 Closed manometer used for measuring high pressures. (Liquid is mercury.)

ger does not return to the original position, it is probable that some air has leaked out of the tube.)

Next fill the brass tube with water and insert the closely fitting steel rod. When students press down on the plunger, it moves only slightly, if at all. If the plunger is now struck with a hammer, students can see that water is almost incompressible because the whole tube acts like a solid steel cylinder.

16.4 Pressure gauges

Because barometers are designed to measure pressure of one atmosphere or less, other pressure gauges are needed to measure very low and high pressures.

16.4a Open manometer

Small changes in pressure can be measured with an open manometer (Fig. 16-17), which can be made by students. Bend a length of glass tubing as shown in Fig. 16-17. Fill the tube with water colored

with red ink or eosin. Rule off a scale in inches or centimeters and mount the manometer to an upright wooden support. With both ends of the manometer open, the levels in the arms will be the same. As pressure is applied from, say, an illuminating gas jet, the level in the right arm will descend while that in the left arm will rise. The difference in levels may be used to find the pressure from the relationship

$$P = hd$$

where $h =$ level difference. If density is measured in g/cm^3 and the liquid is water, then the pressure is numerically equal to the difference in level. The unit is, of course, g/cm^2.

16.4b Closed manometer

A closed manometer is more practical for use in measuring high pressures. In this case, use mercury in preparing the manometer shown in Fig. 16-18. The mercury stands at the same level in both arms when the pressure is one atmosphere. When the

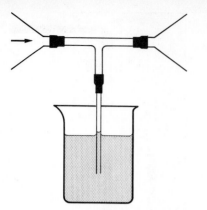

Fig. 16–19 Venturi tube: effect of moving air stream or pressure. Note level of water in tubes.

pressure is increased, the mercury rises in the closed arm, compressing the air confined there according to Boyle's law (see 16.3). Prepare a scale to read in inches or centimeters. The pressure required to establish a level difference in the closed manometer is found by taking into account both the change of levels in the arms and the amount of compression undergone by the trapped air. Since volume changes follow Boyle's law, the calculation of pressure change is not difficult. If mercury is used in the manometer and the levels in the arms are the same to start, then the pressure required to cause a level difference may be found from the equation:

$$P_2 = 13.6 \, (h_1 - h_2) + P_1 \, (h_1/h_2)$$

where P_1 is the atmospheric pressure, h_1 is the level in the closed tube before applying pressure, h_2 is the level with pressure applied, and P_2 is the new pressure. The first right-hand member gives the pressure as indicated by the change of level of mercury (density = 13.6 g/cm³) while the second right-hand member gives the Boyle's law correction. In this equation, pressures must be measured in g/cm².

Students may want to examine a Bourdon spring gauge. This gauge is graduated to read zero when the pressure is one atmosphere, and indicates the increase in pressure over the normal atmospheric pressure.

16.4c Bernoulli effect

You will want students to develop the notion that as the speed of a fluid (gas or liquid) increases, there is a decrease in pressure and, conversely, when there is a decrease in velocity of the fluid, the pressure is increased.

Venturi tube. Venturi tubes of glass or plastic (Fig. 16-19) can be made or purchased for class demonstration. Let the connection to the center of the constriction of the tube dip into a beaker of water; use the exhaust end of a vacuum cleaner or a powerful fan to blow air through the Venturi tube. As the air passes the constriction of the tube (which consists of T-tube and funnel stems), the pressure drops as indicated by the rise of water in the tube.

With a modification of this technique show how a change in pressure can be measured by the visible change in the size of an illuminating gas flame. Attach a rubber tube from a source of illuminating gas to the Venturi tube (Fig. 16-20). After the gas replaces the air in the tube, ignite the jets, which are of the same bore. Students should be able to explain why the gas flame is shorter in the constricted part of the tube.

Ping-pong ball and funnel. As part of a group report, a committee of students can perform the succeeding demonstrations for the entire class.

Connect a compressor to the stem of a funnel, turn on the compressed air, and hold the funnel in an inverted position (Fig. 16-21A). Then place a ping-pong ball in the funnel. Instead of being blown out, the ball remains in the funnel. Students should be able to explain that the air rushing over the sides of the ball re-

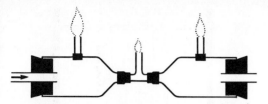

Fig. 16-20 The smaller flame at the constriction shows the lower gas pressure at the constriction of a Venturi tube.

duces the downward pressure, and atmospheric pressure then forces the ball up into the funnel.

Ping-pong ball and compressed-air stream. In this variation of the preceding demonstration, a stream of air will hold the ping-pong ball in mid-air. Connect glass tubing having a bore of ⅜″, drawn to a ⅛″ tip, to a compressor with rubber tubing. Turn on the compressor and place a ping-pong ball in the upward stream of air (Fig. 16-21B). Students should find that the stream holds the ball almost stationary in mid-air. The air stream should be viewed as being conical in general outline with the ball sitting in the center like a ball of ice-cream. As the ball tends to move in any direction, it begins to leave the cone of air. With no air moving past the emerging portion of the periphery, normal atmospheric pressure acts upon this part of the ball while the rest of it is in the lower-pressure region of fast-moving air. This causes an unbalanced force on the ball directed toward the center of the cone; thus, the ball moves back to its initial position. If the stream of air is moved slightly to right or left, the ball will move with the air stream.

Effect of air stream between two suspended objects. If two balloons, ping-pong balls, bottles, or even apples are suspended from a cross bar supported by 2 ring stands and air is blown between them from the exhaust of a vacuum sweeper, they are pushed together by normal air

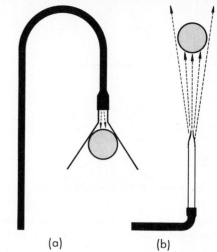

(a)   (b)

Fig. 16-21 Bernoulli effect: ping-pong ball and funnel.

pressure as the result of the reduced pressure between the curved surfaces (Fig. 16-22A).

Cardboard disk and spool. Another simple demonstration of the Bernoulli effect utilizes a thread spool and a cardboard disk fitted with a pin in the center (Fig. 16-22B). If the disk is held against the bottom of the spool with the pin in the spool hole (to center it) and air is blown down through the hole, the cardboard disk does not drop off. Instead it remains in place because the air pressure is reduced between the disk and the spool end, and as a result normal atmospheric pressure forces the disk up against the bottom of the spool.

Applications of Bernoulli's principle. Students will find many commonplace applications of the Bernoulli effect. Students can explain how an atomizer paint sprayer or automobile carburetor works. If a carburetor is available, examine the constriction (like the Venturi tube) in the throat, and also the fuel jets. It may be possible to fill the carburetor bowl with water and blow air through the air intake of the car-

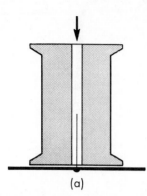 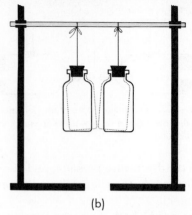

Fig. 16–22 Bernoulli effect: (a) air blown through the spool will not blow card away, (b) a stream of air between the bottles lowers the pressure so that normal pressure pushes them together.

buretor with a vacuum sweeper; the water will be forced out of the bowl by atmospheric pressure into the low-pressure area created in the Venturi, and it will spray out of the fuel nozzle.

Students will refer to the Bernoulli effect on an airfoil to demonstrate how an airplane wing is shaped to develop upward thrust (see Chapter 24).

16.5 Liquid pressure

Hydraulic balance. Both Pascal's principle and the laws of liquid pressures may be nicely demonstrated by a homemade hydraulic balance. Connect a vertical glass tube about 2 meters long to a rubber hot water bottle laid on the floor. Place a wooden board of about the same surface area as the bottle on its flat surface. When the bottle is filled with water and a student stands on the board, the liquid level in the tube rises, but the water does not spray out the top as one might expect. It rises to a height that is very nearly the same as the height of the individual standing on the board. The pressure of the water is equal to the height of the liquid column multiplied by the density of the water. The *total upward* force it exerts on the top surface of the bottle (and hence upon the board and individual) equals the pressure multiplied by the area of the surface of the bottle, according to Pascal's principle. Since the average density of the human body is approximately the same as that of water, the force the individual exerts downward on the board is approximately equal to the product of his height and the area of force application. Since the densities are approximately the same, the height of liquid and individual will also be nearly the same; it should be remembered that the area of force application is also the same for both the upward-pushing liquid in the bottle and the downward-pushing body above.

16.5a *Pressure: depth and direction*

Marriot's bottle. Marriot's bottle, a simple device to show that pressure increases with depth, can be made from a bottle or tall can with three equidistant holes set in a vertical line as shown in Fig. 16-23. (Directions for drilling holes in glass are given in Chapter 25.) If a thin glass tube covered with rubber tubing is placed into each drilled hole, the water flow will be smoother. For best results, plug the holes,

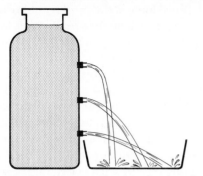

Fig. 16–23 Marriot's bottle: the length of streams shows greater pressure with greater depth.

fill the container with water, and then remove all the plugs at the same time. Students should have a pan ready to catch the water. The pressure of the water at the different depths is indicated by the length and velocity of the stream of escaping water. The taller the container used, the more graphic the effect produced.

Pressure bottle. This is a very simple demonstration of the relationship of water pressure to depth. Stretch a sheet of rubber across the mouth of a wide-mouth bottle and fasten it with cellulose tape or rubber bands. What happens to the rubber sheet when a student gradually lowers the bottle into a deep tank of water? Students

should recognize that increased water pressure pushes the sheet deeper into the bottle. The same bottle can also be tilted to show that the pressure at any specific depth is equal in all directions.

U-tube gauge. Students can also make a U-tube gauge from the bulb of a thistle tube. Cover the bulb with sheet rubber and fasten it with rubber bands. Then connect the stub of the thistle tube with rubber tubing to a U-tube containing colored liquid (Fig. 16-24). Students can lower the thistle tube into a deep container of water. As the depth increases, the rubber diaphragm over the thistle tube is forced inward in proportion to the water pressure. Students can explain that the air in the thistle tube is forced into the U-tube where it displaces some of the colored water.

16.5b Measuring liquid pressure

Pascal's vases. Many teachers begin a study of the measurement of liquid pressure by using Pascal's vases. One commercial device uses a can connected to a container with a diaphragm bottom so that the pressure can be read directly on a pressure gauge when a reservoir is raised

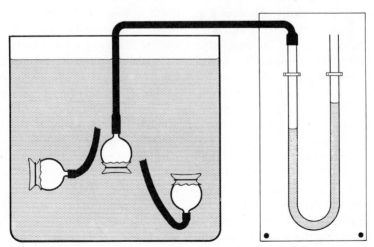

Fig. 16-24 U-tube gauge for measuring liquid pressure.

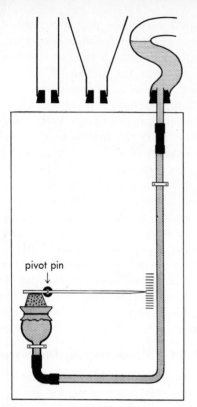

Fig. 16–25 Pascal's vases used to show that pressure depends only upon the height and is independent of the shape of the container.

sel. Since force is the product of pressure and area on which the pressure acts, to get equal forces with equal pressures, we must also have equal areas.

A similar apparatus can be made by bending a wide plastic tube into various odd shapes. A straight tube of the same material and a glass funnel complete the group. Each vessel is connected successively (not simultaneously) to the same manometer; in each case, the vessel is filled to the same level as the previous one. The manometer will indicate pressure for each trial.

Another variation can be made in class by connecting containers to a U-tube manometer. Or have students make a water-pressure depth gauge by covering with thin sheet rubber a thistle tube (Fig. 16-25) attached to a 3′ rubber tube. The inside of the thistle tube and its connected rubber tube are filled with colored water. When the pressure changes, the rubber sheet causes the cork to move. Note the light indicator needle made of balsa wood resting on the cork. It is held in contact with the upper cork surface by the weight of a rubber-band wound around the short end. The indicator is pivoted to form a lever of fractional mechanical advantage. Such a lever multiplies distance rather than force, providing magnification of the rubber diaphragm movement.

Pascal's syringe. The commercial form of Pascal's syringe consists of a glass sphere with many small holes attached to a glass tube and plunger. The sphere is filled with water and as the plunger is pushed, water is forced out of the holes with equal pressure in all directions (Fig. 16-26A). Although this works very well, it is a fragile piece of apparatus. A student can design an unbreakable syringe for a class demonstration by drilling equidistant holes in a hollow rubber ball. Fit with a rubber tube attached to a supply of

or lowered. When Pascal's vases of different shapes are used successively with this gauge, students can readily discover that pressure depends on the height and is independent of the shape of the container. This is a good place to emphasize the difference between pressure and force acting on a whole surface. If the base areas were *not* the same, the pressure at the bottom of each vessel would *still be the same* for equal water levels. Pressure is independent of total area or the shape of vessel. It depends only upon the height of the liquid and the density. The pressure gauge, however, measures the depression of the vessel base diaphragm as a whole; hence, the gauge is measuring the *total force,* not the pressure acting on the bottom of the ves-

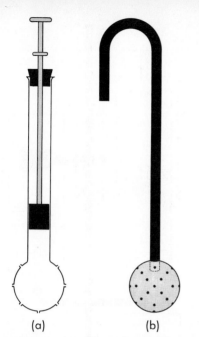

(a)   **(b)**

Fig. 16–26 Pascal's syringes: (a) fragile glass syringe, (b) student-made model using a rubber ball.

flowing water (Fig. 16-26B). The water supply may be the tap or a reservoir made from a large tin can or jar.

Hydraulic press. Glass and plastic operating models of a hydraulic press are sold by scientific supply houses (see directory in appendix). The plastic models are more durable than the glass. Or students can construct a simple working-model hydraulic press. They will need to fit a straight wall lamp chimney or a 2″ diameter clear plastic tube with a two-hole stopper fitted with two glass tubes as shown in Fig. 16-27. For the piston, select cork that is slightly smaller than the internal diameter of the tube. Wrap some waxed soft cotton cord around the cork so that it fits inside the tube snugly but can still slide back and forth. Now drill a hole ¼″ in diameter in the center of the cork and cement a dowel rod of the same diameter into it. A good cement for this is Pliobond which is hot-water soluble, will bond

to glass, and has some flexibility. Finally, make a rubber flap valve over the two-hole stopper by tacking a small square of rubber sheeting over one of the holes on the end of the stopper that will go inside the tube.

Then assemble the lifting section of the jack or press by setting up a second glass or plastic cylinder fitted with a cork-and-dowel piston like the one already described. The bottom of this cylinder should also contain a one-hole stopper equipped with a short glass tube and a flap valve. Now connect the glass tube without the valve of the first cylinder to the glass tube of the second cylinder (the lifting section) with rubber tubing. Then place the down-tube of the first cylinder in water as in Fig. 16-27, and operate the dowel handle. On the upstroke, students should see that water enters the first cylinder. On the downstroke, the valve closes and water is forced into the second cylinder where it lifts the piston.

Heavy-duty hydraulic presses that can exert pressures as high as 50,000 pounds per square inch can be purchased from scientific supply houses (see appendix). You will want students to demonstrate the parts and the operation of an automobile hydraulic jack. Compare the piston, cylinder, and pump section with the parts of the working model. It is also possible to transform the automobile jack into a hydraulic press by operating it inside a strong steel frame made of long steel bolts and heavy plates of steel (Fig. 16-28).

Strength-of-materials machine. By equipping the hydraulic press shown in Fig. 16-28 with a pressure gauge and some auxiliary fittings, it may be converted into a strength-of-materials machine with which several industrial tests can be made on various materials.

If a new hydraulic automobile jack is to

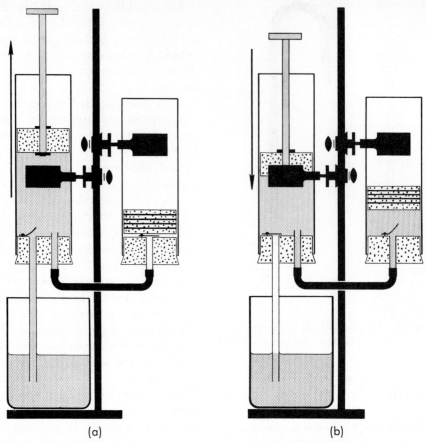

Fig. 16–27 Model of a hydraulic press: (a) on the upstroke, (b) on the downstroke.

be purchased, be sure it is the type intended for use under the car axle or rear end, not a high-bumper type. In addition, examine it to make certain that it has a refill opening which communicates with the inside of the large cylinder.

The pressure gauge. Remove the plug that seals the oil-refill opening by unscrewing it counterclockwise with the proper wrench. Determine the type of thread and the diameter of the threaded hole. If you cannot do this yourself, your hardware store man can give you this information upon inspection. Obtain a pressure gauge (0 to 50,000 lb/in² or thereabouts) having the same size and type of thread as the jack bushing. (A

little hunting around machinery supply houses in your community will either turn up the proper gauge or will lead you to a supply house to which you can write.) Using a small amount of nonsetting plumbers' compound worked into the roots of the male threads, secure the gauge to the jack. If the threads are brass, do not exert too much wrench pressure. In the event that you cannot obtain a gauge with matching threads, any good "heavy" hardware store can supply you with adaptors, reducers, elbows, couplings, etc.

The frame. To obtain the maximum usage from a strength-of-materials machine, the frame (Fig. 16-28A) should be substantially stronger from all points of

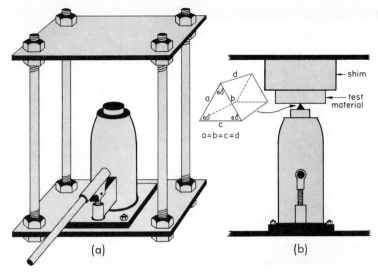

Fig. 16-28 Automobile jack as a hydraulic press: (a) steel frame, (b) with triangle of hard steel to test materials against notching.

view than any of the materials to be tested. In planning ahead, try to obtain ⅜″ steel plates measuring about 6″ × 8″ rather than ¼″ plates if possible. The ½″ steel bolts can be threaded along their entire length to leave plenty of room for anchoring nuts. Alternatively, you can use ½″ steel rods threaded at each end. In relation to the amount of strength you want to build into the frame you place 1 nut below and 1 nut above, 1 nut below and 2 nuts above, or 2 below and 2 above at each of the four corners. The objective is to construct a frame of the shape indicated in Fig. 16-28A. The jack need be held down only at two corners. Drill two holes in opposite corners of the jack-base and two matching holes in the frame base-plate. Machine bolts, either ⅜″ or ½″ type, may be used to hold the jack in position.

Compression test. Compression tests are generally performed on materials such as concrete, asbestos shingles, hollow metal objects such as carrying and storage cases, and so on. The object to be tested is placed on the jack head, shimmed up by steel blocks or plates so that it will reach the upper frame plate, and the jack operated (Fig. 16-29A). The gauge is observed as the process continues. The compression shattering point is easily noted as the pressure suddenly drops when testing brittle materials; the same is true of hollow metallic objects since the pressure will drop sharply as the elastic limit of the material is passed.

Resistance-to-notching test. File a steel wedge having a base area slightly smaller than the jack head and having reasonably sharp edges (Fig. 16-28B). Heat the wedge in a Bunsen flame until it is cherry red, and then plunge it into a can of cold water to harden it. With the wedge on top of the jack head and the sample to be tested resting on its apex, shim out the space above the test material so that the group is held securely by the top frame plate. Always use tempered steel for shimming material.

For comparison testing, it is important to use specimens of similar physical size, say, 2″ long, 1″ wide, and no less than ½″

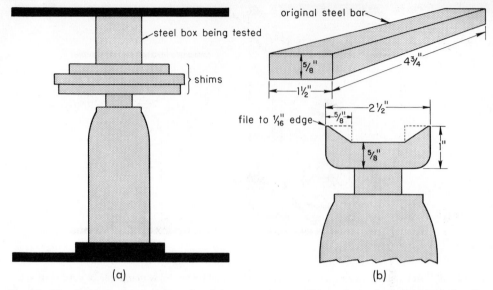

Fig. 16–29 Strength-of-materials testing: (a) compression test, (b) test jig for the resistance-to-bending test, (c) setup for resistance-to-bending test, (d) resistance-to-notching test.

thick. Tests may be run on scrap pieces of aluminum, brass, copper, zinc, and other nonferrous alloys. Avoid the notching test on steel or case-hardened steel. Starting with a soft metal such as aluminum, run the pressure up high enough as read on the gauge to cause a measurable notch to appear in the metal; then, using the same pressure, repeat the test on the other metals. Try it on hardwoods, too. Look for microscopic cracks in metals at the apex of the notch; this is an important industrial method of determining structural notching resistance. The depth of the notch for equal pressures on various materials establishes their relative resistance.

Resistance-to-bending test. Shape a piece of steel to the dimensions and form shown in Fig. 16-29B. After final shaping at red heat, allow it to cool slowly to anneal it. Then grind or file the arms of the "U" to 1/16″ edges. The width of the steel bar initially should be about 1½″ (see insert in Fig. 16-29D).

Using any kind of material including steel, nonferrous metals, wood, glass, etc., operate the jack until the material either shatters or bends enough to reach the bottom of the test jig (Fig. 16-29C). For shatterable materials, the breaking pressure is considered the point at which the gauge reading drops sharply; for bending materials, the comparative strength is indicated by the *maximum* gauge reading during the bending process, carried through until the sheet has reached the bottom of the jig. Always compare approximately equal thicknesses and widths of materials in all of these tests, i.e., equal cross-sectional areas.

Hardness test. The hardness of a metal can be judged on a comparative basis by exerting pressure on the specimen by means of a steel ball bearing resting on the jack head. Using various metals of the same approximate dimensions as well as wood, Masonite, Prestwood, vinyls, linoleum, and thermosetting plastics, rest the material to be tested on the jack head, place the ball bearing on the material,

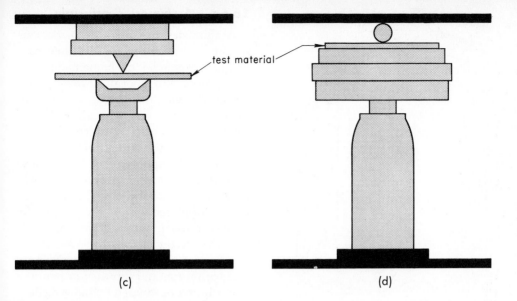

test material

(c)   (d)

and fill in the space below with shimming plates. Find the depth to which the ball bearing sinks into each material with *equal pressures* as read on the gauge. Obviously, the pressure range for the nonmetals will be appreciably below that for the metals (Fig. 16-29D).

16.6 Upward pressure in water

Measuring upward pressure. In one technique students will need a glass chimney or wide glass tube about 1″ to 2″ in diameter. One end should be ground smooth by rubbing with emery powder or carborundum powder. Cylinders with ground ends may also be purchased. Then attach a thread to the center of a 2″ × 2″ glass square by means of Duco or model airplane cement. Place the square against the ground bottom of the cylinder and pull the thread through the cylinder. A student can hold on to the thread and lower the cylinder and square into a jar of water. Now release the tension on the thread; because of the upward force of the water the glass square remains in position

against the bottom of the cylinder.

Students can measure this pressure by slowly pouring a known quantity of water from a graduate cylinder or burette into the glass cylinder (Fig. 16-30). The glass square will not be dislodged until enough water is added to provide a downward pressure equal to the upward pressure; at this point the glass square will fall to the bottom. Students should recognize that the weight of the water poured into the cylinder is almost equal to the total upward force. The weight of the glass plate must be added to the downward force of water. (Since one cubic centimeter of water weighs one gram, the volume of water in cubic centimeters will be numerically equal to the total force of the water. Students can also find the pressure by dividing the total force in grams by the area of the cross section of the cylinder, in cm².)

Have some students show the same principle using another technique. They can float a tall glass upright in a basin of water and place weights, in the form of lead shot or sand, into the glass until the

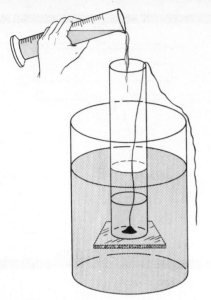

Fig. 16-30 Glass square will not fall away until inside downward pressure equals or exceeds the upward pressure of the water.

rim of the glass is just at the surface of the water. Now remove the glass from the water, dry it, and weigh the glass and its contents. This weight is equal to the total upward force on the glass. (The pressure can be readily calculated only if the glass is cylindrical.)

16.6a *Archimedes' principle*

Archimedes' principle can be demonstrated by means of an overflow can, either commercial or homemade (Fig. 16-31). In group laboratory work or as a demonstration students can fill the can with water and use a small beaker or catch bucket to trap the overflow. Lower an object on a string into the overflow can and record its apparent loss in weight as indicated on a spring balance; water will flow out of the overflow can. The weight of this displaced water is equal to the apparent loss in weight of the object. To find the weight of this displaced water, either weigh the catch bucket both empty and with water and subtract, or pour the water into a graduated cylinder or flask and measure its volume (1 cc of water weighs 1 g).

For a floating object the apparent weight in water is zero; the displaced water from the overflow can will be approximately the same weight as the object. Due to surface tension effects, the weight of the displaced water is seldom as great as it should be. The error introduced may be as large as 8 or 9 per cent, but can be accounted for by observing the curved

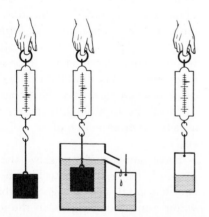
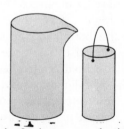

Fig. 16-31 Overflow cans for demonstrating Archimedes' principle. Students can make this device in the laboratory, and follow the steps as shown.

meniscus in the overflow can just as the last drop of water comes out.

Or students can weigh an 8″ square of sheet aluminum. Then bend the sides of the sheet to form a shallow pan. If they now float it in a pneumatic trough equipped with an overflow tube and weigh the displaced water, students should find that the weight of the displaced water will equal the weight of the aluminum sheet. Some students will think that aluminum floats because it is a light metal. If possible, repeat the demonstration using thin sheet iron in the form of tin plate or galvanized iron. Again, students should find that the pan will float, and the displaced water will weigh the same as the sheet of metal.

Archimedes' balance. This is a commercial apparatus consisting of a metal bucket of cylindrical shape and a closely fitted, solid metal piston (brass, nickel-plated) that has *exactly* the same volume as the inside of the bucket.

To show Archimedes' principle rather dramatically, arrange the cylinder and bucket as illustrated in Fig. 16-32. Add enough weights to the left-hand pan to bring the system into perfect balance. Now bring a beaker ¾ full of water up under the piston so that the latter is completely submerged; no part of the bucket should be under water, however. The left side will dip downward as the buoyant force of the water on the piston takes effect. With the beaker supported in position (piston still submerged) by a textbook or wood block, carefully add water to the bucket until it is *just full.* At the instant of filling, the balance of the system will be restored.

Students usually reason in these steps:

1. The volume of the piston is exactly equal to the inside volume of the bucket.

2. Therefore, the weight of the water held in the bucket must be equal to the weight of the water displaced by the piston.

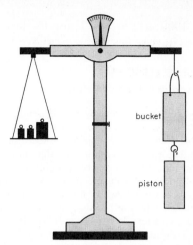

Fig. 16-32 Archimedes' balance.

3. But the weight of water added to the bucket was equal to the loss of weight (buoyant force) of the piston since this weight of water restored balance after the piston had lost weight.

4. Hence, the loss of weight must be equal to the weight of the displaced water by equating (b) and (c).

Hydrometers. The kinds of hydrometers most familiar to students are the automobile battery hydrometer and the antifreeze hydrometer for the automobile radiator. You can demonstrate the action of a battery hydrometer by *slowly adding sulfuric acid to water* while stirring rapidly to make a 20 per cent solution. Place a hydrometer float, which you have removed from a battery hydrometer, into the solution and have students record the reading. Have them also take a reading of plain water.

Then measure the specific gravity of water and of several antifreeze mixtures with an automobile antifreeze hydrometer. As the concentration of alcohol contained in the antifreeze mixtures increases, the specific gravity decreases. Other hydrometer floats with lower ranges for less dense fluids are available from scientific supply houses. Hydrometers for liquids that weigh less than water have scales that read 1000 and lower. Those for heavier liquids have scales that read above 1000.

The battery hydrometer reads from 1100 to 1280.

CAPSULE LESSONS
Ways to get started in class

16-1. Start a lesson by asking students to design an experiment to show that air has weight. Develop a discussion concerning the strengths and weaknesses of the proposed designs that students describe in class.

16-2. Have students explain the principle involved in the following: lift pumps, medicine droppers, drinking straws, atomizers, and vacuum cleaners. What keeps an airplane up?

16-3. Students can help you make a Torricelli barometer and also demonstrate different kinds of barometers (including homemade ones). Have students compare the readings with those given in weather reports. Invite students to design a barometer for high-altitude flight.

16-4. Begin a lesson by having a student report on Boyle's experiments related to the "spring" of the air. As described in the Harvard Case History Series, a committee of students can demonstrate several of the activities suggested in this chapter to measure the "spring" of the air.

16-5. Simulate upper atmospheric conditions by putting an aneroid barometer or an altimeter inside of a bell jar on the stage of a vacuum pump as described in the chapter. Students can translate pressure into the equivalent in altitude. They should be ready to explain how these instruments operate. Do not pump below the limits of the scale.

16-6. At times you will want to summarize some of the ideas related to air or liquid pressure with a film or filmstrip. Have you used *Putting Air Pressure To Work* (McGraw-Hill), *Preface to Physics* (Indiana), or *Harnessing Liquids* (Shell Oil)?

16-7. A short case history can be developed, using a Harvard Case History as a guide. Or consult other references for background material: G. Holton's *Introduction to Concepts and Theories of Physical Science* (Addison-Wesley, 1958), p. 370–75; Bonner and Phillips *Principles of Physical Science* (Addison-Wesley, 1957) p. 249–62; Magie's *Sourcebook of History of Science*, p. 84.

16-8. Introduce Pascal's law by demonstrating a hydraulic automobile jack. Use a laundry or other lightweight spring balance to measure the small force needed to lift an automobile.

(*Caution: Keep students at a safe distance.*) Elicit from students an explanation of how a small force can lift a car.

16-9. A student might begin a lesson on pressure by using a model of a diving bell made of an inverted glass funnel connected to rubber tubing equipped with a pinch clamp. Small toy figures may be put inside of the bell before it is lowered into a jar of water. (The toys can be put on a shelf and held in place with celluose tape so that they are easy to handle.) Why do the figures remain dry in the funnel? Compare this device with those used to remove men from wrecked submarines. Students can compute the water pressure acting on the bottom surface of the "bell" at different depths.

16-10. With some classes you may want to develop laws of flotation. Why does a sheet of galvanized iron float if the edges and corners are folded up with pliers to make a tray? Have students devise ways to show the loss of weight of objects in water, and compare the weight of water displaced. Students should reach a generalization concerning the conditions needed for an object to float in water. Substitute other fluids such as salt water. Develop a definition of specific gravity.

16-11. A student might use Pascal's vases in giving a report to the class. Which contains more water? Check by using a pressure gauge to find that pressure is the same in all the vases, independent of the shape of the container. Elicit from students many of the applications in daily living that use the same principle.

16-12. You may want to show a model Pelton water wheel operated by pressure from a water faucet. Have the water spin a bicycle-lamp generator. Elicit an explanation of the effect of changing water pressure upon the work done by the Pelton wheel. A Pelton wheel is a water wheel having cup-shaped buckets on the rim of the wheel. An inward extension of any one of the buckets falls along the spokes; hence the buckets are radially placed. The Pelton wheel is used in lieu of a turbine when the supply of water is small but the pressure (head) is great. Turbines are used where the flow is large with a moderate head, as at Niagara.

16-13. Plan a laboratory activity in which all students can measure water pressure at various depths. Use the thistle tube tightly covered with rubber sheeting (or similar devices described in this chapter) and attached to a U-tube filled with colored water.

16-14. Have a student conduct a review before an examination by showing a filmstrip, or have a panel of students prepare questions to ask as review.

PEOPLE, PLACES, AND THINGS

You may want to arrange a field trip through local factories to show the various applications of pressure. The trip might include a visit to a garage where the hydraulic lift can be seen; a mechanic might explain the application of the Venturi tube in the automobile exhaust and the use of pressure in the gasoline engine. Other visits may include a gas-liquefying plant, ice house, soft drink bottling plant, and gas plant. Another trip might be arranged to the local weather station. Engineers and technicians in local firms might give a talk before the class on such topics as the use of pressure in the refrigerator, paint sprayer, freezer, and pumps. A local college might loan you apparatus for demonstrations.

Books and pamphlets

These are only a few of the books which are pertinent to the work discussed in this chapter. These and many other references classified by subject and with complete bibliographical data are given in the bibliography at the end of the book.

Bonner, F., and M. Phillips, *Principles of Physical Science,* Addison-Wesley, 1957.

Holton, G., and D. Roller, *Foundations of Modern Physical Science,* Addison-Wesley, 1958.

Menzel, D., ed., *Fundamental Formulas of Physics,* Dover, 1960.

Miller, F., Jr., *College Physics,* Harcourt, Brace, 1959.

Semat, H., *Fundamentals of Physics,* Rinehart, 1958.

Sproull, R., *Modern Physics: A Textbook for Engineers,* Wiley, 1956.

Swenson, H., and E. Woods, *Physical Science for Liberal Arts Students,* Wiley, 1957.

Sutton, R., *Demonstration Experiments in Physics,* McGraw-Hill, 1938.

White, M., K. Manning, R. Weber, *Practical Physics,* 2nd ed., McGraw-Hill, 1955.

Films and filmstrips

This partial list is intended only as a guide toward film and filmstrip selection. Refer to the more complete listing at the end of the book where films are classified by subject and where a key to abbreviations and addresses of distributors are given. The cost of film rental, of course, is subject to change. Films are sound and black and white unless otherwise specified.

Aerodynamics (f, s), Indiana, $3.50.

Aerodynamics (f, s, 2 rls), Almanac, $3.50.

Applications of Pascal's Law (f, s), MN1730 C & D 12 and 12, Civil Aeronautics Admin., Washington, D. C., free.

Archimedes' Principle (f, s), Indiana U., $1.50.

Atmospheric Pressure (f, s), EBF.

Basic Hydraulics (f, s, c), Indiana, $2.00.

Gas Laws and Their Application (f, s), EBF.

Harnessing Liquids (f, s), Shell, free.

Heat and Pressure (f, s), Institutional Cinema, $2.00.

How an Airplane Flies, (f, s, 6 in series), Shell, free.

Large Forces Acting on the Body (f, s), Indiana, $3.00.

Mechanics of Liquids (f, s), Ideal, $2.00.

Preface to Physics (f, s), Indiana, $3.75.

Putting Air Pressure to Work (f, s), McGraw-Hill.

Theory of Flight (f, s), EBF, $2.50.

Water Power (fs, c), Popular Science through McGraw-Hill, $3.25.

Free and inexpensive materials

This is only a partial listing of free and inexpensive materials available to the teacher at this time. A directory of addresses is given at the end of the book. Many of these materials are distributed to teachers without charge. Where there is a small fee, the cost is indicated, although the prices are subject to change. While we recommend the material for use in the classroom, we do not necessarily endorse the products advertised.

Adventures in Jet Power, General Electric, free.

Electricity Around Us, General Electric, free.

Life and Times of Leonardo Da Vinci, International Business Machines, free.

The Science of Flight, O. Sutton, Pelican, 1955, $.85.

CHAPTER 17

Force and motion

We have limited our selection of demonstrations in the vast area of force and motion, work, energy, and power. Demonstrations for developing the concept of force—component vectors and resolution of forces, centripetal force, gravity, and the law of moments—are described, and Newton's laws of motion are developed as the basis for classical physics. Within this context, inertia, gravitational acceleration, periodic motion, and angular motion are considered. Other aspects of force and motion are developed in other chapters in relation to air pressure, water pressure, expansion, Bernoulli's principle, rocketry, and projectile trajectory. (See index.) Several demonstrations are also described to develop interrelationships among the concepts of energy, work, and power, and a brief introduction to machines is provided.

17.1 Force

This section refers to "force" which is independent of the pull of gravity; that is, force parallel to the earth's surface. Units for measuring force of any kind are based upon the effect of a push or pull on a mass, and thereby describe the manner in which a force produces a change of motion of the mass. In class, students will distinguish between the magnitude and direction of a force: forces acting in the same plane at the same time, in the same or opposite directions in a straight line, or at an angle to each other so that, depending on the point of application of the force with respect to the state of equilibrium and the center of gravity, there will be different motions: (a) translational motion, or motion in which all the particles of the body move along similar paths simultaneously (translation may be along a straight line or along a curved path); (b) rotational motion, or motion in which various parts of the body describe different paths at the same time.

The gravitational unit of force in the cgs system (centimeter-gram-second) is the gram; in the mks system (meter-kilogram-second) the gravitational unit of force is not defined and is never used; in the British system, the pound is the gravitational unit of force. The cgs *absolute unit*, however, is the dyne of force; the mks absolute force unit is the newton; and, finally, the British absolute unit of force is the poundal. (For a discussion of mass see 2.1a.)

17.1a Composition and resolution of forces

By composition of forces students can find the resultant of two or more concurrent forces (forces acting on the same point) in the same plane. The resultant is the single force which produces the same result as that effected by all the forces. When the body upon which the forces act

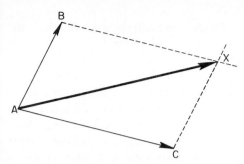

Fig. 17–1 *AX* represents the resultant force from the two forces *AC* and *AB*.

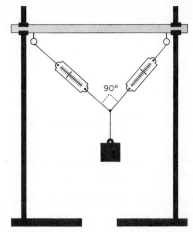

Fig. 17–2 Finding the components of a force by using two spring balances.

does not move, we may find the equilibrant force, that is, the force equal and opposite to the resultant force.

You will want students to represent forces with arrows drawn to scale which indicate both the direction and the point of application of the force and the magnitude of the force. They may diagram examples of addition of forces, subtraction of forces, and two forces acting in two directions from the same point of application (Fig. 17-1). The diagonal *AX* represents the resultant force—i.e., that force which produces the same result as the two forces *AC* and *AB*.

Using spring balances. Have students find the components of a force by using spring balances. Attach two screw eyes about 18″ apart on a board. (The distance is not critical.) Then support the board in a horizontal position with the screw eyes down by resting it in clamps set on two ring stands or on two vertical upright boards. Hang two identical spring balances, one from each screw eye, and attach one end of a string to the bottom hook of one balance. (Instead of a board one can hang the spring balances from nails in the blackboard molding.) Attach a weight equal to about one half the full-scale reading of the balances to the string, as shown in Fig. 17-2, and then fasten the free end of the string to the other balance.

Adjust the string length so that the string forms a right angle at the point where the weight is attached. Each balance will give a different reading if the two parts of the string are not equal. The weight will balance the two angular forces acting along the strings, and the readings on the balances will be the two components of the force. The resultant will have the same magnitude as the weight but will act in the opposite direction—straight up. If students shift the position of the attachment of the weights, thereby changing the lengths of the component arms, they may be able to predict the change in the components. (*Note:* Whenever the weight is shifted, the point of support of at least one of the strings will have to be changed to keep the angle 90°.) At any time the sum of the squares of the readings of the balances will equal the square of the weight— provided, of course, that the strings are arranged to form a right triangle. Naturally the units of measurement will have to be consistent, that is, the units of the spring balances and the weight must be the same. Have students diagram the parallelogram of forces and the equilibrant. If students hang the spring bal-

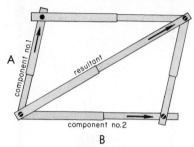

Fig. 17–3 Curtain-rod parallelogram for showing the components of a force.

ances from the blackboard molding, they can diagram the forces and the parallelogram directly on the blackboard.

Using marked ropes. Students might use a sled on snow or ice or a toy express wagon on the floor. Using a spring balance, first lift the front of the sled or wagon to measure the vertical force; then pull horizontally to measure the horizontal force necessary to maintain a constant velocity. Finally pull at the most comfortable angle. The pulling force at any angle will be equal to the square root of the sum of the squares of the force needed to lift the sled slightly and the force needed to move it horizontally at uniform speed. These were the vertical and horizontal forces, respectively, measured previously. This can be done graphically by marking three ropes in inches with quick-drying paint (like the "colored dope" used for model airplane finishing); the marks represent units of force. Arrange the vertical rope at right angles to the horizontal rope. Students can outline the other two sides to complete the rectangle and show that the number of inches of the diagonal rope will provide the resultant or pulling force. This resultant will be approximately the same by either the graphic or the arithmetical method. Experimental error in graphic construction seldom permits obtaining an answer that is as precise as the answer obtained from the algebraic method.

Single and multiple forces. A clear distinction can be made between a single force producing an action and two or more forces producing an action. Attach two spring balances to a brick or cube of stone or some other mass which has sufficient friction to produce a reading. Move the object over a surface, pulling upon it simultaneously with both balances and in a line parallel to the horizontal. Compute the resultant and use this with a single balance to create the same movement of the mass.

Using commercial component devices. Commercial devices in which the component and resultant arms can be varied are available. In some devices, string is used to represent the resultant, which is always the diagonal of the parallelogram formed by the two components.

Curtain-rod parallelogram of forces. Students will need five flat, telescoping curtain rods from which they must cut off the right-angle ends and drill a 5/32" hole 1" from each end of each rod. Use 6/32" machine screws to join the five rods into a quadrilateral with a diagonal (Fig. 17-3) and avoid tightening the nuts all the way. Add a second nut to each one to lock the nut on the screw, thereby leaving the curtain rods free to move. Students can adjust the lengths of the telescoping rods so that they form a parallelogram. The arms marked A and B in Fig. 17-3 are the components. For any type of parallelogram and for any size of arm $\div_M$, that is, any magnitude of component $\div_M$, the resultant is found by measuring the diagonal. Since the curtain rods are adjustable in length, it is possible to set the sides of the parallelogram for a variety of dimensions. When this is done, the diagonal or resultant adjusts in length appropriately.

Components of force on a sailboat. You may want to have students use a small sailboat with a weighted keel, an adjustable rudder, and a single Marconi-rigged sail on a boom that is adjustable in all directions.

If a steady wind on a pond or pool is not available, use an indoor tank and an electric fan. Students should observe that when a wind blows from the rear of the boat, there is no component problem if the rudder is straight. However, when a sailboat tacks, a component problem is set up. With the wind or fan 45° off the left side (from the front) set the boom off to the starboard (to the right when facing the bow) about 30° and note that the boat will move ahead into the wind (but not directly into it).

The action of the wind in producing a motion as seen in the demonstration is best explained by referring to two separate vector diagrams, Figs. 17-4A, 17-4B. The wind vector in 17-4A is AX; this produces two components of force on the sail, AC perpendicular to the sail and AB parallel to the sail. Clearly, AB is of no further concern since it plays no part in either driving the boat or tipping it. The component AC, however, may now be resolved into two new components as in Fig. 17-4B, this time referring to the keel line of the boat. AC produces force AD in the direction desired, that is, along the keel forward, hence is the driving force. AE acts at right angles to the keel, producing a tipping force that causes the boat to list to one side as it moves in the direction of the keel line. The keel reduces the lee movement.

The crane problem. In the upright rod of a tall sturdy ring stand, drill a 1/16″ hole about ¼″ of the way through the rod. The hole should be drilled about halfway from the top of the upright. Cut a piece of ⅜″ dowel stick about 18″ in length; drive a 1½″ wire brad into one end and cut off the head with a bolt cutter or a pair of diagonal pliers; screw a small cup hook

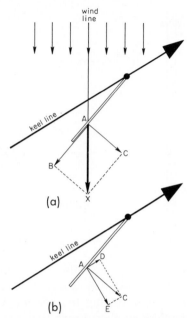

Fig. 17-4 Tacking sailboat: (a) wind vector AX produces two components of force, AC and AB; (b) component AC in Fig. 17-4a can be resolved into 2 other force components, AD and AE. It is AD that drives the boat forward at an angle into the wind.

into the other end. Now assemble the stand and dowel as shown in Fig. 17-5A, making certain that the angle between dowel and upright is exactly 90°. Use a large draftsman's triangle or a blackboard protractor.

The aim of the demonstration is to show that the force exerted by spring balance #1 is the equilibrant for the two component forces. The components are (1) vertical component downward caused by the 1000-g weight hanging from the end of the dowel; (2) horizontal component to the right produced by the *push* of the dowel stick against the point of application. Measure angle a with a large protractor; then transfer the actual forces to the blackboard in the form of a vector diagram. The 1000-g weight is force AB; the reading of spring balance #1 is force AY.

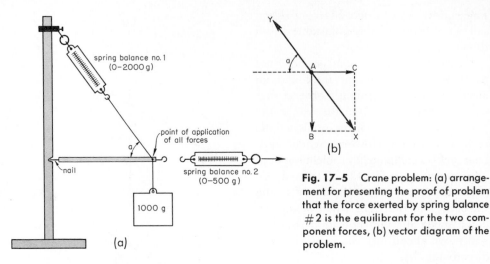

spring balance no.1
(0-2000 g)

point of application
of all forces

nail

spring balance no. 2
(0-500 g)

1000 g

(a)

(b)

Fig. 17–5 Crane problem: (a) arrangement for presenting the proof of problem that the force exerted by spring balance #2 is the equilibrant for the two component forces, (b) vector diagram of the problem.

Now hook spring balance #2 to the dowel hook and very gently pull to the right while observing the pointer. Read the balance at the instant that the nail pulls out of the hole in the upright rod; this is the horizontal component caused by the push of the boom. Transfer this reading to the vector picture, showing it as a pulling force set to the same scale as the others (this is force AC). (See Fig. 17-5B.) Since a resultant is equal and opposite to the equilibrant, extend AY in the opposite direction to form AX, a vector of equal length. This is the resultant, obtained from the definition of the equilibrant. Now clinch the argument by completing the parallelogram geometrically and prove that this second method also yields a resultant equal to AX in magnitude and direction.

17.1b Torque: moment of a force

Pivoted meterstick. There are several commercial devices that use a pivoted meterstick with sliding weights to produce any desired moments of force. Such a device can also be made in the classroom. Drill holes at 1″ (or 10-cm) intervals on a meterstick and mount it on a nail (Fig.

17-6A and B). To show downward forces, weights can be attached by means of battery clips. Show upward forces by passing the hook of a spring balance through one of the holes. In all cases, students can show that the sum of the products of the distance from the pivot and the weight on one side is equal to the sum of the products on the other side when the system is in equilibrium.

As an example, set up the arrangements illustrated in Fig. 17-6A and B. Since the meterstick is pivoted at its center, its weight will not affect the results and may be ignored. Or the experimental approach might take the line in Fig. 17-6C. Hang all the weights as shown but put your finger rather than a spring balance under the 80-cm mark to maintain the stick in equilibrium. Have the students read and record the weights and distances from the fulcrum; then calculate what the spring balance would read at the 80-cm mark. Corroborate their findings by actually taking the measurement. The moments equation for this particular setting is

$$40A + 30B + 20C + 30D = 20E + 40F$$

Replacing the letters with the weights

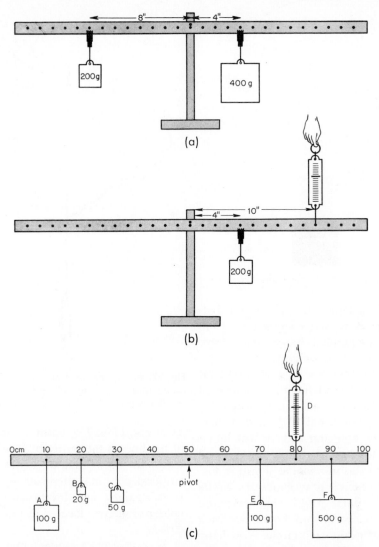

Fig. 17–6 Using a pivoted meterstick to show moments of force: (a) the sum of products of distance and weight on one side equal to that on the other side, (b) upward forces are negative, (c) with several weights on one side balanced by one weight to the other.

given in the diagram, we have

$$(40 \times 100) + (30 \times 20) + (20 \times 50) + 30D =$$
$$(20 \times 100) + (40 \times 500)$$
$$4000 + 600 + 1000 + 30D = 2{,}000 + 20{,}000$$
$$5600 + 30D = 22{,}000$$
$$30D = 16{,}400$$
$$D = 16{,}400/30$$
$$D = 547 \text{ g}$$

Although this answer has been rounded back to three significant figures, it is still more precise than the usual spring balance reading. Students should be able to explain the experimental errors that crop up in this exercise.

Some teachers make the ratios of distance and effort readily observable by

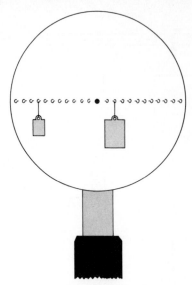

Fig. 17-7 Moment wheel.

employing a long, thick plank and balancing it on a wedge-shaped fulcrum.
Mark off the plank in units; then use students themselves as weights.

Moment wheel. Use a jig saw to cut out
of ¼″ plywood a disk having a diameter of
two feet. In the exact center drill a ¼″
hole. Now pass a nail (¼″ in diameter)
through the hole and nail the disk into a
four-foot long section of 2″ × 4″ wood
and mount this in a vise as shown in Fig.
17-7. On the circle draw concentric circles
about 1″ apart. Along the horizontal
diameter screw in cup hooks one inch
apart, that is, on each circle. Now hang
weights in various combinations on the
hooks to act as forces to bring about
balance; compute the moments.

17.1c Center of gravity and stability

The center of gravity of an irregularly
shaped object is the point of balance.
Students can show this by hanging a
plumb bob or weight suspended from a
string from different points of the object,

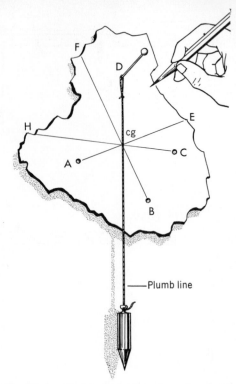

Fig. 17-8 Finding the center of gravity of an irregularly shaped object. (From R. Brinckerhoff, et
al., *The Physical World,* Harcourt, Brace, 1958.)

as in Fig. 17-8. The point of intersection
of the lines is the center of gravity. They
can also show that a model airplane
suspended from a single string so that it
rests straight and level will have the
center of gravity located in line with the
string.

As a project, a student may want to
construct the apparatus described below
to demonstrate the importance of position
of center of gravity in determining stability. Drill a 1″ hole through the 4″ face
very close to one end of a 2″ × 4″ block of
wood. Fill the hole with lead wool or thin
solder pounded in place to form a massive
slug. Have the class note that the block
will stand on end and resist toppling only
when the slug is low; if the block is now
stood erect on its opposite end, with the

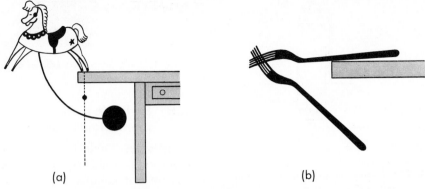

(a)   (b)

Fig. 17-9   Objects can be balanced off geometric center by counterbalancing.

slug up high, it can be toppled over by the breath.

If possible show a commercial model of the Leaning Tower of Pisa, and locate its center of gravity.

Students can compare the stability of bodies by using a round milk or soda bottle to demonstrate the three kinds of equilibrium. With the bottle resting on its side, the center of gravity is always at the same height—the vertical center of the bottle—no matter how much the bottle rolls, and thus the bottle is in neutral equilibrium. On the other hand, with the bottle standing on its open mouth the center of gravity is above the center of the bottle; thus the bottle is in unstable equilibrium and it tips over easily. However, when the bottle rests on its base, the center of gravity is below the center of the bottle, and it is in stable equilibrium. A ball is another example of neutral equilibrium; no matter how it rolls the center of gravity is at all times in the center of the ball.

Students can also show how objects can be balanced off geometric center by "positioning" the center of gravity. In Fig. 17-9A, the toy horse can be held off center because the counterbalancing of the weight shifts the center of gravity. Similarly, two forks can be used to show the same principle (Fig. 17-9B).

17.2   Motion

17.2a   Newton's first law

A body remains at rest (or in motion with uniform velocity) unless it is acted upon by an unbalanced external force. This property of all real bodies is called *inertia.* When, however, we want to make measurements and calculate answers to problems, we find it more convenient to drop the qualititive term "inertia" and use instead quantities we can measure: *inertial mass* for the resistance to motion of a body at rest (measured in mass units such as the gram), and *momentum* for the tendency of a body in motion to continue in motion (measured in mass velocity units, such as gram $\times$ cm/sec).

Bodies at rest. The coin-card-tumbler experiment is a classic demonstration of the law of inertia. For details see inertia in 2.1a.

There are other ways to demonstrate the principle. Students can place a piece of thin paper under a standing fountain pen cap as shown in Fig. 17-10, so that part of the paper extends over the edge of the table. With a moistened finger they can then slap downward against the unsupported end of the paper. The paper will move away and the cap remain standing. Or suspend a heavy weight,

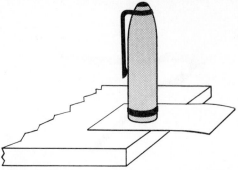

Fig. 17–10 Inertia: the pen top will remain in place if the paper it rests upon is quickly pulled away.

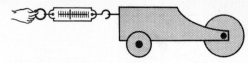

Fig. 17–11 Measuring the inertia of a "frictionless" cart.

such as a bundle of books or a small sandbag, from the center of a thin string. Pull steadily on the bottom of the string; it will break *above* the weight. But if you pull the bottom of the string suddenly, the string will break below the weight because of the weight's inertia.

Measuring inertial mass. Students may try the following activities as demonstrations or as part of a laboratory period.

Towing a "frictionless" cart. Measure the force required to move a commercially made "frictionless" cart forward at a selected constant velocity using a spring balance with a range of 0 to 500 g (Fig. 17-11). Stop the model; then pull on it sharply to start it into motion and note the reading of the spring balance. This reading will be many times greater than the force needed to keep the cart rolling at a constant velocity.

Swinging a suspended weight. Place a weight made from a bundle of books or a cloth bag of sand in the center of a suspended string and quickly pull the lower string sideways with a spring balance until the weight starts swinging; record the reading. Then arrest the motion. By gradually pulling on the lower string, again set the weight in motion. Once the weight is swinging, record the force needed to keep it swinging over the same distance for each swing.

17.2b Bodies in motion: momentum and inertia

"Frictionless" objects. For demonstration purposes certain materials can be used which all but eliminate the element of friction. Following are several suggestions.

Ice. You can take out the dividers from an ice cube tray and freeze a slab of ice that will move freely on plate glass provided the glass is at room temperature. Blocks of wood or bricks can be set on top of the ice to add mass. A clothespin attached to a piece of wood can be used to hold the end of a length of paper tape if a timer is being used (see 17.2d).

Dry ice. A block of dry ice on a Masonite surface or on the top of a stone demonstration table makes an excellent "frictionless" body. It rests on millions of "ball bearings" of the subliming gas. (*Caution: Use tongs or wear gloves when handling dry ice.*)

Dry ice puck. Take a piece of Lucite ½" thick by 4" square. From one side drill a hole in its center about the size of a pin (this can be enlarged later if necessary). From the other side drill a hole 1/16" to ¼" in diameter about ¼" into the block. In this hole mount a 1" tube which stands perpendicular to the surface. Over this secure the open shell of one half of a flush toilet float. A rubber gasket cut from a piece of sheet rubber or inner tube is placed between the float and the Lucite. Screws (several) can be used to hold the half of the float in place. To operate place dry ice under the float half and firmly screw the rim down on its gasket, being careful not to turn the screws so tightly that the threads in the fragile plastic are stripped. With the tip of a round file en-

Fig. 17-12 "Frictionless" cart that can be made in the laboratory. (PSSC of Educational Services, Inc.)

large the pinhole until the escaping CO_2 provides sufficient cushion for the puck to ride on plate glass virtually without friction.

If, instead of Lucite, a block of finely polished steel is used, the puck can be set in motion about a strong magnet simulating the earth's revolution about the sun.

"Frictionless" cart. A cart useful for student experiment can be constructed as in Fig. 17-12. A piece of $2'' \times 4''$ wood is shaped as shown and three skate wheels mounted. The front bumper may include the bent hacksaw blade for experiments having to do with imparting motion from one body to another. The clothespin can hold the tape from a timer (Fig. 17-20). The length of the cart should be such that bricks can be stacked upon it as a means of increasing mass. Comparisons can be made between one cart with two bricks striking a cart with one, two carts meeting each with equal mass and speed. Combined with a timer (Fig. 17-20) many quantitative experiments having to do with inertia, momentum, and mass can be designed.

Exploder. A simple but very effective exploder for imparting motion to two "frictionless" carts can be made from a screen door hinge and two pieces of wood as shown in Fig. 17-13. Note the use of a piece of hard cotton awning cord as a safety restraint. This should not be omitted. This exploder can be attached to the front bumper of the "frictionless" cart described in the preceding paragraph. A screen door V hook and eye serves as a release mechanism.

Inertia devices. Various methods for demonstrating the inertia of bodies in motion are available. One of the simplest makes use of a small ball and shoe box. Remove the cover and knock out one end of the box. Put the ball in the box and move the box along the table with the open end forward. Suddenly stop the motion of the box. Why does the ball continue in motion at its original velocity? Students should recognize that an object in motion remains in motion unless stopped by some external force.

Students can use a slingshot to show momentum. When the sling is pulled back and then released, the sling pocket is in motion with its pellet for some time; then the sling stops its motion, but the pellet continues to move through the air because of its momentum.

On some occasions you may want to have students conduct the following demonstration. Attach the rubber band to two

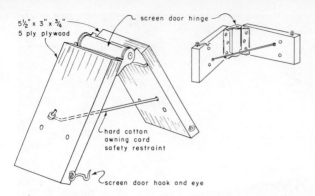

hard cotton
awning cord
safety restraint

screen door hook and eye

Fig. 17–13 An exploder made from two pieces of wood and a screen door spring hinge. (PSSC of Educational Services, Inc.)

ring stands fastened to the table by C-clamps. Place a ping-pong ball on the rubber band in a sling. Pull on the balance and record the reading. Let go, and observe what happens. At first, the rubber band and the ball move forward together; then the ball is propelled forward by momentum from the rubber band when the sling is arrested. Now propel steel balls of different weights, in each case pulling the rubber back the same distance. You may find that firing the balls straight up is easiest.

Duration of force (impulse). Use the door of your room as a demonstration tool. Leave it ajar about ¾ of the way; then slap it sharply enough with your hand so that it just closes and latches. Open it again to the same position and push it gently closed with your little finger. Elicit from the students that in the first case, there was a large force applied for a short time; in the second case, the force was small but was applied for a long time; and both accomplished the same result because both actions gave the door the same momentum (mass × velocity). Relate this to the follow-through in a golf drive, a tennis drive, and a long hit in baseball as compared with a bunt.

17.2c   Newton's third law

Students can relate examples from their experience—what happens when one jumps out of a boat onto a dock, and what happens when a bullet is fired from a gun —to demonstrate that whenever a body acquires momentum, some other body acquires an equal and opposite momentum. Or they may say simply that to every action there is an equal and opposite reaction.

Reaction balloon. Inflate a balloon with air and release it; watch the speed of the balloon as it is propelled by a jet of escaping air. Students will recognize that its movement is in a direction opposite to that of the escaping air.

Reaction car. In this demonstration, tape a carbon dioxide cartridge to a lightweight model railroad flatcar on a length of straight track. Release the cartridge with a special "gun" that may be purchased in hobby shops. Watch the car move at high speed in the opposite direction from the discharge of the gas (Fig. 17-14).

The track should stretch over the top of the normal demonstration table, i.e., at least 8 feet. At its end should be a sponge rubber bumper, crumpled paper, or a pillow to take up the shock.

A spring balance may be attached to the car by a two-foot length of stout twine. The balance should have a maximum reading of 2000 g. In this way, the reaction thrust may be measured and use made of Newton's second law as well as the third

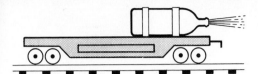

Fig. 17-14 Reaction car with CO_2 cartridges as propellant.

law. Compute the acceleration of the car by determining its mass and substituting in the equation

$$a = \frac{f}{m}$$

where a is the acceleration in cm/sec^2, m is the mass of the car in grams, and f is the reaction force measured as above but converted to *dynes*. (A 1-g mass weighs 980 dynes; hence the reaction thrust measured in grams on the balance may be converted to dynes by multiplying by 980.)

Hero engine. Demonstrate the essential similarity between an engine designed 2000 years ago and modern rockets by building a sturdy working model of a Hero steam reaction engine (Fig. 17-15). Fit a cork to a 500-ml Pyrex flask and attach to the cork a long bolt (¼″ diameter) fastened to a roller skate wheel. Support the wheel in a wide burette clamp on a ring stand. Then carefully insert two right-angle bends of glass tubing (¼″ bore) through holes in the cork. Pour an inch or two of water into the flask and stopper it tightly. Heat the water to boiling over a Bunsen burner. Trace the path of the steam as it escapes from the two glass tubes, causing the whole apparatus to rotate in the opposite direction.

Care should be taken to assure safety in this demonstration. Heat should be applied only so long as required to demonstrate that rotation does occur. Prolonged heating may cause the bottle to blow away from the stopper, especially if there is a constriction in the end of either right-angle tube due to excessive fire polishing.

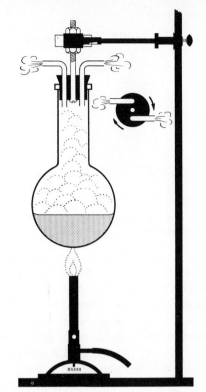

Fig. 17-15 Hero steam reaction engine.

A working model of a Hero engine may also be purchased from scientific supply houses. (See appendix.)

Blowtorch engine. If a plumber's blowtorch is mounted on a board resting on low-friction wheels or in a toy flatcar on tracks and set into operation, it will act as a rocket motor (Fig. 17-16). You may have to give the car a slight starting push. As the burning gases shoot out of the nozzle, the torch assembly will move off in the opposite direction.

Model electric trains. A group of students may want to set up this demonstration of action and reaction. Cut out two disks of thin plywood or fiber board large enough to carry a circular set of tracks. Attach a set of tracks on each board with small bolts. On the bottom of one circle mount six sets of wheel trucks (wheels

Fig. 17–16 Blowtorch acts on the same principle as a rocket motor.

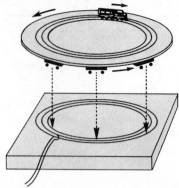

Fig. 17–17 Action-reaction: as the engine moves in one direction, the turntable moves in the other.

down) removed from model trains, in such a way that they will fit on the circular track on the other board (Fig. 17-17). At least one of the trucks should carry a third-rail pickup shoe. This shoe should be connected to the center rail of the upper track. The chassis of the truck (this gets power from the outside rails) should be connected to the two outer rails above. Place the trucks (with the board and upper track attached) on the track of the other circle, and connect this bottom track to a toy electric train transformer. Place a locomotive on the upper track as shown in Fig. 17-17. Then turn on the current. Have your students explain why the locomotive remains relatively fixed in place while the turntable spins under it, if the locomotive is massive and the turntable is light. If they are of nearly the same mass, the locomotive will proceed as fast clockwise as the turntable moves counterclockwise as viewed by a fixed observer. Students can explain this on the basis of the second law.

Cannon and two cars. Action-reaction forces can be effectively demonstrated by the use of two reaction cars. Place two toy train flatcars on a straight track. Load a block of wood on one car and a spring-loaded toy cannon on the other in such a way that when the cannon fires, the ball

hits the block of wood on the other car. When this happens, the cars if identical in mass move apart and stop, each one the same distance from the starting point.

Swing on rollers. To show the reaction of a swing support to its swing, place a small working model of a swing on a wood base that rests on glass rods as rollers (Fig. 17-18A). Then attach a small weight to the swing and set it in motion. As the swing moves in one direction, the support slides back over the rollers in the opposite direction.

Other devices. Students may make models of rotary lawn sprinklers which can be attached to a faucet with rubber tubing. Compare the direction of the water spray with the direction of the lawn sprinkler.

Have a student step on a roller skate with one foot and then take a step forward with the other foot. Why does the skate move backward?

Have one student pull on a spring balance that is attached to another held by a second student. A small committee of students can take readings on both scales. How do the readings compare? Why?

Pour a small amount of water into a large Pyrex test tube and seal the test tube with a cork stopper. Suspend the tube

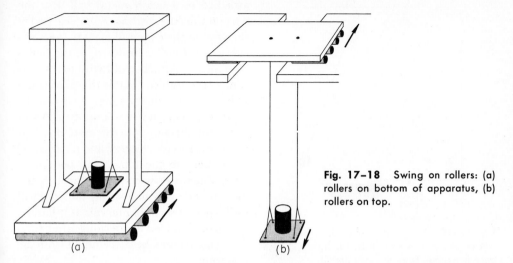

Fig. 17–18 Swing on rollers: (a) rollers on bottom of apparatus, (b) rollers on top.

horizontally by means of two loops of wire over a Bunsen flame (Fig. 17-19). As the tube is heated, watch the stopper pop out; note the recoil of the test tube and the spilling of some of the water.

17.2d Newton's second law

Newton's second law states that the acceleration of a body depends upon two factors: its mass and the force applied to it. If the force is large, the acceleration is

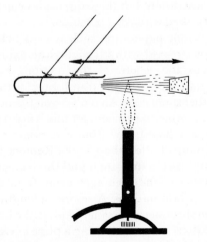

Fig. 17–19 As the cork goes one way the test tube goes the opposite.

large, implying a direct proportion; if the mass is large, then a given force will cause a small acceleration, implying an inverse proportion. Putting these proportions into symbols, we may write

$$a = k\frac{f}{m}$$

where a is acceleration, f is force, m is mass, and k is a constant of proportionality. When the units are properly chosen (e.g., a in cm/sec^2, f in dynes, and m in grams), the constant drops out and the law assumes its familiar form

$$f = ma$$

Students should be able to show that this may be written in a form often known as "impulse equals momentum" equation. If they define acceleration as rate of change of velocity (v/t), the law may be written

$$ft = mv$$

or impulse (which is ft) equals momentum (which is mv).

You may want to start the topic of acceleration with a demonstration using simple calculations. We shall limit our

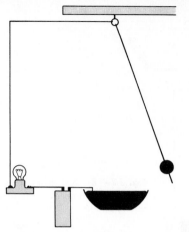

Fig. 17–20 Timing device using a pendulum whose period is two seconds. The light will flash once a second—twice in every period.

discussion to uniformly accelerated motion. Fortunately, the most common acceleration in real situations is a uniform one —gravitational acceleration. The rest of the discussion of Newton's second law is concerned with the force of gravity and its accelerating effects on various objects in different situations.

Demonstrating acceleration with toy trains. A toy electric locomotive can be used to illustrate the second law. Students can connect the locomotive to a 0–500-g spring balance and measure the force required to hold the locomotive stationary at half power. Measure the force as the power is increased. The acceleration that the locomotive would have acquired if it had not been prevented from moving is determined from $a = f/m$ as follows: (1) convert the force measured in g on the spring balance to dynes by multiplying by 980 as previously described; (2) divide this force in dynes by the mass of the locomotive in g, thereby giving the potential acceleration in cm/sec^2.

Timing device. A convenient timing device is a pendulum whose period is 2 seconds (Fig. 17-20). Use thin copper wire

attached to a heavy metal ball. Cut the wire so that the distance from one end of the wire to the center of gravity (geometric center if ball is uniform) of the ball is 38.9 inches. Attach a stiff wire to the bottom of the ball so that as the pendulum swings, the wire passes slightly below the surface of mercury in a soup dish. A second wire, dipping into the mercury, connects in series to a battery and a lamp and from there to the top of the pendulum wire. Since the wire passes through the mercury on every half-swing, the light will indicate one-second intervals as it flashes. Lengths required for periods other than two seconds may be determined from the equation

$$L = \frac{T^2 g}{4\pi^2} \times 12$$

where T is the period in seconds, g is gravitational acceleration (32 ft/sec^2), and π is 3.14. L will come out in inches.

1/120 second timer. A student who is handy with tools can make up an a.c. 1/120 second timer for motion studies involving moving carts, pendulums, or any other objects in motion (Fig. 17-21A). The difference between uniform velocity and accelerated motion is not only set forth by its operation, but these quantities can be measured with good precision.

A long paper tape, such as stock ticker tape (treated with magnetic iron oxide), keeps the record of the motion. First obtain any 120-volt transformer with a rather small core. An old 6.3-volt filament transformer is excellent for this. These can be purchased new from electronics distributors for less than $1.00. Remove the outer casing first, then pull the I-shaped section of the shell core away from the other laminations. Assemble a length of iron sheet stock the same width as the laminations to the core, using a piece of vinyl electrical tape to hold its position at one end. Through the extended end of the

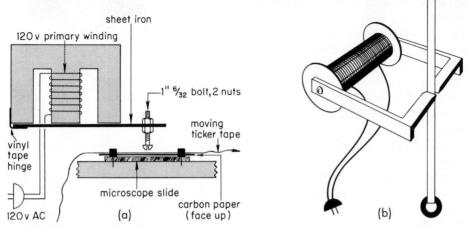

Fig. 17-21 1/120 second timers: (a) made from an electric vibrator, (b) a recording head; magnetic field "marks" the magnetic tape 120 times per second.

armature, secure a 1" 6/32 machine bolt with a pair of nuts, one on each side of the armature. This entire assembly may be supported by a clamp and ring stand; this arrangement makes it possible to lower or raise the vibrator as required.

On a small baseboard under the assembly, place a microscope slide held in place by four thumbtacks. Place some ordinary carbon paper face up on the slide and let the ticker tape pass between the tacks over the carbon paper as it moves. When the vibrator is lowered to the correct point, the machine screw head will bounce up and down, leaving a series of dots on the moving tape where it has been pressed against the carbon paper.

Note that the 120-volt primary winding of the transformer is plugged into the a.c. line. Since the alternating current reaches its peaks once every 1/120 second, the dots on the moving tape will be spaced this distance apart in time. The tape should be cut so that it passes between the tacks; the tacks can thereby act as a guide to keep the tape in place.

Magnetic timer.[1] When a strip of re-

[1] Developed by John Marean, Reno High School, Reno, Nev.

cording tape attached to a moving or falling object is passed between the poles of a 60-cycle electromagnet, it will have pulses impressed on it at intervals of 1/120 second. If the poles have sharp faces, the interface of opposite polarity on the tape is a sharp, dark line after development.

The pulses imposed on magnetic recording tape may be made visible by depositing very finely divided magnetic iron oxide (Fe_3O_4) on the tape. This will concentrate at the points of magnetism, particularly where the magnetic field reverses sharply. A developing "solution" is made up of the iron oxide dust in carbon tetrachloride or Visimag (available from audio equipment companies). Immerse the tape in the solution. When the tape has thoroughly dried, the magnetic areas are easily distinguished. For easier, cleaner measurement, these areas may be lifted from the recording tape by means of transparent adhesive tape. The developing method is capable of resolving some 200 lines per centimeter.

A recording head can be made as shown in Fig. 17-21B. It consists of a coil of #32 wire wound on an insulated threaded iron bolt. Pole pieces of 1/16″ right-angle iron brackets bent and filed to chisel edge are bolted to the ends of the armature. The gap is not extremely critical; it can range from two or three tape thicknesses up to two to three millimeters; and it can be easily adjusted by bending the poles or by beveling one of nuts against which the poles are held and then rotating the coil armature. A coil about 2 cm long by 1.5 cm diameter, which has a d.c. resistance of 80 ohms, produces a very satisfactory field when connected to 120-v a.c.; it does not overheat if operated intermittently for 10 to 20 seconds.

This magnetic apparatus can provide usable data for accelerations in any direction. If 50 cm of the tape are attached to an object of a few hundred grams, some 30 to 40 points may be obtained for a velocity-time graph.

Device for releasing steel balls simultaneously. An excellent means for getting simultaneous and instantaneous release of steel balls or bearings uses an electromagnet. When the current is cut off, the balls start rolling down the incline at the same moment and without delay (Fig. 17-22).

Independence of gravitational acceleration and weight. Only the *acceleration* of a freely falling body is independent of weight; the *force* of gravity is directly proportional to the mass of the body.

You will want students to demonstrate

Fig. 17–23 Free-falling coin and feather: (a) in a vacuum, (b) in air at normal atmospheric pressure. Tubes used in this demonstration are about 100 cm long and 5 cm in diameter.

the force of gravity with its manifestations undistorted by air resistance. They may use a "guinea and feather" tube and a vacuum pump. If a commercial tube is not available, fit a 3′ strong glass or plastic tube 2″ in diameter with a solid stopper at one end and a one-hole stopper at the other. The one-hole stopper carries a glass or metal tube which leads to the vacuum pump by means of a pressure hose (Fig. 17-23). Place a dry coin and feather inside the tube. Evacuate the tube and invert it.

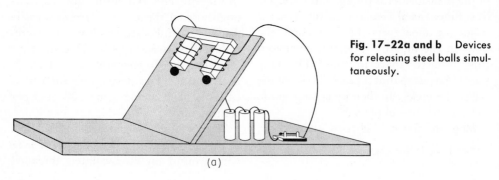

Fig. 17–22a and b Devices for releasing steel balls simultaneously.

Observe that the coin and feather fall with the same acceleration. Next release the vacuum and invert the tube again to show that the resistance of the air present in the tube slows the fall of the feather more than that of the coin.

Shape and rate of fall. First drop an aluminum ball and a sheet of aluminum foil that has been shown to have the same mass as the ball. The foil will fall more slowly due to the partial balance of its weight by air resistance. Then crumple the foil into a tight wad and show that the reduced surface causes the retarding force of the air to diminish, and that the wad and ball both fall with approximately the same acceleration.

Acceleration of falling bodies.

Using pulley and weighted line. Attach a line to a commercial "frictionless" cart or a new ball-bearing roller skate on a table, and pass the line over a pulley attached to the end of the table. Then hang a weight on the end of the line and place weights in the cart (or on the roller skate). Have one group of students time the descent of the weight while another group measures the distance covered by the cart. The data can then be substituted in the following equation

$$\bar{v} = \frac{d}{t}$$

where $\bar{v}$ is average velocity.
The students have the distance and the time, and can find the average velocity over the time interval.

If you increase the mass of the cart by increasing the weight in it, the acceleration and therefore the velocity will decrease; increase the force on the cart by increasing the weight on the line, and the acceleration will increase according to the formula for the second law of motion

$$a = \frac{f}{m}$$

Using sinkers spaced on a line. Attach steel balls or lead sinkers about ½″ in diameter to a fish line at points that are at increasing distances from the floor as follows: the lowest ball should be 3″ from the floor, the next 1′ from the floor, the next 2′3″ from the floor, then 4′, 6′3″, 9′, 12′3″, and finally 16′. Suspend the line vertically and release it by cutting or burning the line at the top. Place a large sheet of metal under the point of suspension. The metal balls will be heard to strike the metal sheet at a constant frequency, about ⅛ second apart. A high-ceilinged room, as found in a gymnasium, is a good place to try this demonstration. (*Caution: Keep students at a safe distance.*)

A second variation of this demonstration consists of hanging another set of weights on a similar line at points that are equidistant from each other. Then the second line should be cut so that the students can hear the increasing frequency of impact at the bottom.

Inclined plane as a special case of free fall. Motion along an inclined plane is most easily demonstrated by the device shown in Fig. 17-24, a 12′ V-trough, at an angle to the horizontal (no more than 10°), with one side covered with aluminum foil and with ½′ square aluminum foil contacts on the other side. The contacts are one foot apart and connected in parallel outside the trough. "Liquid" or "cold" solder can be used to attach wire (B & S #24 or #26) to aluminum. The wires from each side of the trough are connected

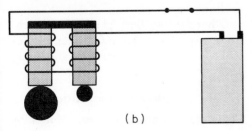

(b)

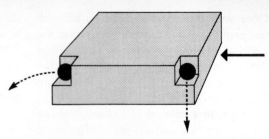

Fig. 17–25 Both balls will hit the ground at the same instant after the block is struck where right arrow indicates.

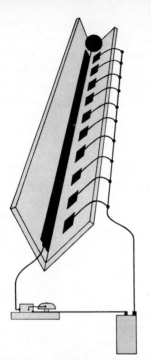

Fig. 17–24 Device used to show that an inclined plane is a special case of free fall.

in series to an electric bell and batteries. A metal ball is rolled down the trough and as it passes each contact, the circuit is completed momentarily and the bell rings. As the ball accelerates, the bell will ring more and more frequently. A metronome set for 4 beats per second can be used to time the acceleration at any point.

Measuring gravitational acceleration. In this demonstration, a solid lead or steel ball no larger than 1″ is dropped from the highest point in the school into a tub of water. (Make certain that no one is in the way, and that it is a windless day.) Students can use a stop watch to determine the time of descent. Then measure the vertical distance accurately and use the formula $d = \frac{1}{2} gt^2$ to find g.

17.2e Projectile motion

Tracing the path of a bullet. The effect of gravitational acceleration upon the path or trajectory of a bullet is easily demonstrated. Place white paper along the blackboard and cover it with carbon paper held with cellulose tape. Shoot a large steel ball from a toy spring cannon with the barrel held firmly against the blackboard at an angle to the horizontal. The ball will make a parabolic trace along the carbon paper which will be transferred to the white paper.

Two balls: one shot, one dropped. One type of commercial apparatus uses a spring and bolt to release two balls simultaneously; one ball is shot horizontally and the other is dropped vertically. Students should find that both balls strike the ground at the same time. A similar device can be made from a block of hardwood about $4″ \times 4″ \times 2″$. In two opposite corners cut out a $1″ \times 1″ \times 1″$ cube using a saw and chisel. Then clamp the block to the corner of a table. Place a ½″ to ¾″ steel ball bearing into each notch. Now tap one end of the block. Watch how the ball at the end that was hit drops off while the ball at the other end is ejected horizontally (Fig. 17-25). Both balls hit the ground simultaneously.

Other devices. Several additional techniques are described in Chapter 24, Engines: Automobiles, Airplanes, and Rockets.

17.2f Rotation and vibration

Simple harmonic motion. You may

want to project uniform circular motion on a straight line in the plane of a circle to have students see that simple harmonic motion is a special case in which acceleration is proportional to displacement in relation to some fixed point. (See also 19.2a.)

Periodic motion as a "shadow" (linear) of uniform circular motion. Use a phonograph turntable set on its side with a small ball attached at the edge (not on the rim). Students will notice that when a spotlight is directed on a screen or blackboard there is a shadow on the ball. The light beam should be nearly parallel. While the ball on the turntable moves with uniform motion in a circle, it throws a shadow on the screen which moves with simple harmonic motion.

Pendulum. You may want to introduce the topic with a duplication of Galileo's pendulum experiment. The bob of a pendulum swinging through an arc is moving down similar inclined planes. The times of fall or the periods are exactly the same.

Students can show this by suspending a ball of iron or steel and one of wood on ropes at least 2 meters long and letting them swing through equal arcs. The period of a pendulum depends upon the length of the supporting string and is independent of the weight of the bob and, to a limited extent, is also independent of the size of the arc.

Examining the time of swing. Suspend a steel ball about ¾″ in diameter from a thin thread about 180 cm long. (Attach the string to the ball with sealing wax.) Set the pendulum in motion through a 10- or 12-cm arc. If two students work as a pair, one can count the swings and the second student can keep track of time with the second hand of a watch. They should count to 100 swings and record the elapsed time.

Then increase the amplitude of the swing to 30 cm and gather data for 100

swings. Other pairs of students might record their findings when the amplitude of swing is increased to almost two meters.

Other pairs of students may use bobs of other masses—wood, lead—to see the effect on the swings of the pendulum.

Comparing the lengths of pendulums and their periods. Thus far, students have found that the periods of pendulums of equal lengths swinging through *short* arcs are independent of the weight and material of the bobs and of the amplitude of the arc. Now students can find that there is a relation between the periods of the pendulums and their lengths.

In the laboratory students can discover for themselves that the periods of two pendulums are directly proportional to the square roots of their lengths. Adjust one pendulum so that it is only ¼ of its original length. Students working in pairs can take the time of 100 swings. Another group of students should take the time of 100 swings of another pendulum which is 1/9 of its original length.

Students can use the equation

$$t = 2\pi \sqrt{\frac{l}{g}}$$

where t = period, l = length, and g is gravitational acceleration.

Hooke's law. In some classes you will want to have students find the relation between force acting on an elastic body and the displacement that is produced.

Show students in a demonstration, or have students rediscover as a laboratory activity, Hooke's law, which states that within limits of perfect elasticity the stretch produced in a body by a distorting force is proportional to the force. Students can suspend a coiled spring from a support, and attach to the end of the spring a weight holder with a pointer. Attach a scale in millimeters (or inches)

to the support. Students should read the
scale when no weights are on the holder
and when one, two, three, four, and five
100-gram weights are added.

Next remove the 100-gram weights
successively, recording the reading on the
scale after each removal, and compare the
amount of extension of the coiled spring
as additional weights are added. Examine
the readings as the weights were removed.
Was the coil perfectly elastic? Was the
limit of perfect elasticity exceeded? Can
students express an equation to show this
simple proportion?

Students should be able to explain how
to calibrate a spring balance to read in
grams if it were unmarked.

Centripetal force. In some classes students will want to estimate the factors
that affect the magnitude of centripetal
force: the mass and speed of the body
(square of the speed) and the radius of a
circle in which it revolves. Students will
learn that in uniform circular motion the
acceleration of a moving body is directed
toward the center.

In a laboratory activity, students can
suspend a 2- or 3-kg ball from the ceiling
of a large room so that it can be set
swinging in a large horizontal circle without endangering students. Arrange the
ball so that it circles about 15 centimeters
above the floor. Students can stand at
different parts of the circle and time the
number of revolutions per second. Have
them time some 50 revolutions and then
compute the revolutions per second. Then
measure the radius of the 4 or 5 points at
which students are stationed and get the
mean radius of the circle. Students can
hold metersticks perpendicular to the floor
and as close as possible to the moving ball
without touching it to get the exact
limits of the circle. Then find the velocity
since the radius and the number of revolutions per second are known. Weigh the

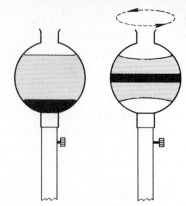

Fig. 17-26 Rotator with bulb containing colored
water and mercury.

ball; convert from weight to mass; and
substitute the known quantities in the
equation

$$f = \frac{mv^2}{r}$$

where m is the mass in grams, v is the
velocity in cm per sec, and r is the radius
in cm. The result, f, will be the centripetal
force expressed in dynes. This force can be
verified empirically by holding the ball
over the points where the radii were taken
and attaching a spring balance to a
second hook on the ball. Hold the balance
parallel to the floor; find the mean of the
spring balance readings and compare
with the results computed earlier.

Students can also use the commercial
centripetal rotator to which is attached
two circular bands of metal. Note the
oblate spheroid when rotated. Then substitute the glass ball into which colored
water and a layer of mercury are added;
when rotated, this turns into two red
bands with a heavier silver band in
the center. Students readily explain that
the heavier particles are thrown off
further from the center (Fig. 17-26). Students can demonstrate a governor on a
steam engine, explain why sharp curves
along a highway are banked, why water

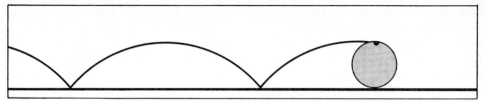

Fig. 17–27 Generating a cycloid.

will stay in a pail whirling in a vertical plane, and how a man-made satellite is put into orbit.

Building a cycloid track. A committee of students can construct this track as a long-range project. The cycloid (Fig. 17-27) is an unusual curve at the end of which a rolling steel ball will always have the same velocity regardless of its starting position on the curve. Students will need to lay out the curve on paper. Cut a wooden disk 6″ in diameter on a jig saw and then drill a hole the size of a pencil lead about ¼″ from one edge and fit the point of a pencil into the hole. Place wrapping paper against the blackboard with the edge resting along the chalk rail. Start rolling the wheel along the rail so that the pencil lead rests against the paper. As the wheel rotates, the pencil will trace the path of a point near the circumference, a cycloid.

Students will then need to bend two brass lengths of 1″ × 1″ angle stock about 1/32″ thick to follow the curve. (They may substitute two strips of thin flexible wood applied side by side to form the right angle.) The wood must be very smooth and should be covered with aluminum foil. Now mount two boards approximately ⅞″ × 6″ × 48″, joining them together to form a right angle as in Fig. 17-28. Drill a ⅛″ hole at the end of each cycloid surface of the angle stock in order to fasten the cycloids with wood screws into the position shown in the figure.

Then students can take apart an old electric bell and separate the two parts of the electromagnet. One pole of the magnet is now attached with cellulose tape to the top of one of the curved strips. The other magnet is held loosely in the track

Fig. 17–28 No matter at what point in the cycloid a ball is released, it will terminate its run at the same speed.

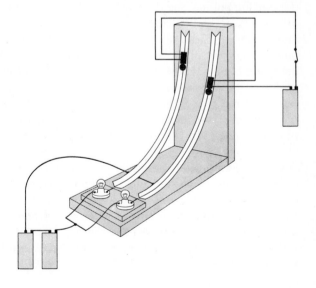

with cellulose tape so that it can be moved up or down along the curved track.

Finally students will place the stopping block at the base of the cycloids. Attach to one side of a wooden block $1'' \times 2'' \times 3''$ two strips of $1''$ wide copper or other non-ferrous metal. Place the block in front of the exits of the cycloid tracks so that the metal strips on the block are about $\frac{1}{4}''$ away from the curved metal tracks. Connect each piece of metal strip to a miniature lamp socket and attach the other side of each lamp socket to two dry cells. Place 3-volt flashlight bulbs in the miniature sockets. Connect the flashlight bulb circuit to the two cycloid tracks. In this manner when the balls strike the metal strips at the end of their tracks, they will complete the connection and the lamps will light. Connect the two magnets in series with dry cells and a switch as shown.

Let $\frac{1}{2}''$ to $1''$ steel ball bearings or iron balls roll down the cycloid tracks. Place the steel balls against the magnets at different points on the curve with the switch "on." Open the switch; watch how the breaking of the circuit stops the current to the electromagnets and causes the simultaneous release of the balls. Although the starting point along the track may be different, both balls hit the bottom at the same time as indicated by the simultaneous lighting of the two lamps. Students can experiment with the apparatus to determine the reasons why steel balls released from two different points reach the bottom at the same time. Where is velocity increased? Where is it reduced along the way?

Gyroscopes. Gyroscopes make striking demonstrations, and students are interested in finding out how they work. Many students know that the gun platforms on tanks and on ships at sea are gyro-stabilized so they can remain on target in spite of a ship's pitch and roll. But they may not know that simple tops are gyroscopes. There are many possibilities for classroom demonstrations.

Sources of gyroscopes. Students can begin by using the simple gyroscope tops sold in toy stores. Commercial gyroscopes are also available from science supply houses (see appendix). Some are set into rotation by winding a cord and then pulling it rapidly; others, by holding the rim of the gyroscope against a rotating rubber wheel on the shaft of an electric motor. Any small electric motor with a one-hole rubber stopper forced over the end of its shaft can spin a gyroscope.

Excellent gyroscopes, gyrocompasses or directional indicators, turn-and-bank indicators, and artificial horizons used in aircraft may also be obtained from surplus supplies available from the regional General Services Administration of the government. Many dealers in government surplus equipment sell these instruments. Often they advertise in such magazines as *Popular Science* and *Popular Mechanics*. Most of these gyroscopes are operated by a motor-driven vacuum pump attached to the fitting in the instrument case. Low-pressure compressed air can also be used to drive the gyro wheel by reversing the connections. These gyroscopes spin at speeds up to 18,000 rpm and make excellent classroom demonstrations when removed from the instrument case.

The "violent" briefcase. Since a heavy small wheel or pulley on the shaft of a motor acts as a gyroscope, try putting in an attaché case a power supply connected to a small motor with a heavy wheel spinning on its shaft (Fig. 17-29). When a student lifts the brief case, the entire case will turn and twist violently. Only a strong grip will hold it still. The motor size should be as large as will fit the attaché case and should have a speed of at least 1700 rpm. The fly wheel should be of

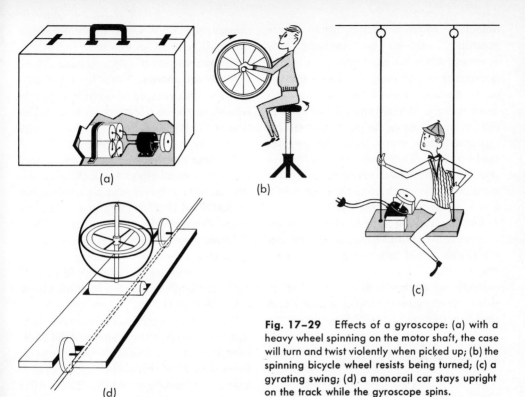

Fig. 17–29 Effects of a gyroscope: (a) with a heavy wheel spinning on the motor shaft, the case will turn and twist violently when picked up; (b) the spinning bicycle wheel resists being turned; (c) a gyrating swing; (d) a monorail car stays upright on the track while the gyroscope spins.

lead with virtually all of its weight concentrated in its rim. If you use a 6-v motor you can use four dry cells of the #6 type for a power supply. Other ways to show the "power" of a gyroscope are suggested in Fig. 17-29B, C, and D.

Precession. Once a gyroscope is rotating in one direction, students can show that it tends to remain erect in spite of disturbing forces. It will precess and wobble slightly. If you reverse the direction of rotation of the gyroscope wheel, the precession will be in the opposite direction.

If you hang a spinning gyroscope at the end of a string and set the entire unit swinging like a pendulum, it will execute peculiar motion patterns as the gyroscope's precession and the swing of the pendulum interact.

17.3 Energy

Energy exists in many interchangeable forms; the relationship between energy and work is a concept which needs special development. Teachers often begin with the simplified definition that energy is the capacity to do work; in turn, work is measured in terms of the distance that a body is moved by a known force against some resisting force. Developing this further, teachers elicit how work is measured by multiplying the distance through which an object moves by the force that has been applied to it in the direction of motion.

Students learn that much of the work done merely overcomes friction; not all the energy applied actually moves an object, for much is wasted. Using simple machines, students can measure how economically work has been done, which is a measure of *efficiency*. Then they may go on to measure *power*, the rate at which work is done. When James Watt tried to sell his first engines, he could not tell his customers how many horses his engines could replace. Therefore, the unit "horse-power" was derived experimentally by measuring the work done by a horse in a given period of time (power).

Finally, making a given task easier involves the use of simple machines, whether the simplest tool or a complex aircraft is examined.

Study of energy will be followed by demonstrations on the topics of power and simple machines.

17.3a   Forms of energy

Students can demonstrate a number of specific forms of energy that are used by man in daily living. There are many demonstrations under several topics in this book. You may want to check the table of contents and the index for those useful to you.

Light energy. Use various kinds of lamps as examples of light energy, or refer to sunlight as an energy source.

Heat energy. Operate an electric heater, or burn small pieces of wood on an asbestos sheet, or burn charcoal in a char-coal stove to show heat energy.

Mechanical energy. Have a student demonstrate muscular motion, or operate a model gas or steam engine as examples of this form of energy.

Chemical energy. Fill a Pyrex beaker one third full of cane sugar and stand it in an enamel basin. Then carefully add concentrated sulfuric acid to the sugar. Notice the black carbon mass that results when the sugar reacts with the acid. In some classes you may want to demonstrate internal-combustion engines (18.8b), explosive mixtures (18.8c), and fuels (14.3).

Electrical energy. Tune in a TV program as an example of electrical energy. Also show an electric spark with an induction or Tesla coil. For chemical energy producing an electric current see 13.2.

Nuclear energy. Show nuclear energy by using a small alpha-track cloud chamber, or make a cosmic-ray cloud chamber as described in 23.1e, or use a spinthariscope. For more details see Chapter 23.

Other times, prepare a radioautograph of some uranium ore by placing a piece of the ore against a sheet of x-ray film (used by dentists); then develop the film a week later. (See 23.1i.)

Thorium, another radioactive substance, is found in the mantles of the Coleman and other makes of gasoline lanterns. Place a piece of this mantle cloth against a sheet of film for a week. (See 23.1i.) After development, look for the pattern of the cloth on the film.

17.3b   Conversion of energy

There are several ways students can show how one form of energy is changed into a second and then into a third or fourth kind of energy. Only a few simple demonstrations are described here; you will think of several modifications for your classroom. You may also want to check the table of contents and the index for other demonstrations.

From chemical to thermal to mechanical, and so on. Set a model steam engine in operation. (See 18.8a.) This burning of fuel represents a change from chemical to heat energy. Students can observe that expansion of steam in the steam engine cylinder involves a change from heat to mechanical energy. Heat was needed to change liquid water to steam which, in turn, can produce mechanical energy.

You can also show how mechanical energy can be changed into electrical energy. Set up a steam engine spinning a bicycle generator which, in turn, is connected to a lamp. Here mechanical energy is changed to electrical energy. In turn, the glowing lamp shows a conversion of electrical energy into light and heat energy.

Starting with chemical energy. Begin this conversion series by using a storage battery to show how chemical energy can be changed into electrical energy. (See 13.2.) Then have the battery operate an electric motor so that mechanical energy is obtained from electrical energy.

Now if students attach a tiny grindstone to the axle of the motor, or fasten some sandpaper on the shaft with cellophane tape, they can demonstrate a change from mechanical to heat energy. Just hold a piece of metal against the spinning stone or sandpaper and notice the results.

Starting with nuclear energy. Refer to the radioautograph of a key, uranium ore, or a thorium gas mantle as described above (for greater detail see 23.1i). This shows the changes that start with nuclear energy. The gamma rays emitted by the radioactive material represent a form of radiant energy into which the nuclear energy has changed; the chemical changes wrought in the film emulsion illustrate the change from radiant energy to chemical energy.

Show the radium dial of a watch or a spinthariscope as an example of a transformation of nuclear energy to chemical energy and then to light energy.

17.4   Work

Have students discover how much work they do when they walk upstairs to class from the school entrance. They will need to measure the height in feet from the entrance to the classroom floor and then multiply their own weight by this distance.

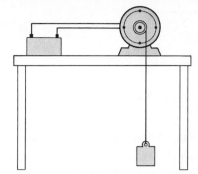

Fig. 17–30 Measuring the work done by an electric motor by finding the weight it will lift and the distance the weight is lifted.

Other students can use a pulley in this problem and pass a sash cord through a suspended single fixed pulley and attach some known weight to the cord. Pull the other end of the cord horizontally and measure the distance the weights have been moved along a measuring tape. Estimate the work done in foot-pounds by multiplying the distance in feet by the weight in pounds.

Or use a scale with a large dial (of the type used in fruit stores) to measure the force needed to move a 5-pound weight along the top of the desk. Multiply this force in pounds by the distance in feet to find the work done in foot-pounds.

Lift a weight upward on a rope in front of a scale printed on white cardboard (or use measuring tape fastened or taped to the blackboard). The student can stand on a chair near the board and loop up foot after foot of cord. Multiply the weight in pounds by the distance in feet through which it was moved to find the work done.

Students can also measure the work done by an electric motor. Attach a string to the shaft or flywheel; find the largest weight that can be lifted (Fig. 17-30). Then multiply the weight in pounds by the distance in feet that the weight has been lifted.

Fig. 17–31 Friction: (a) measuring the force needed to overcome friction, (b) measuring the effect of rollers.

17.4a Efficiency and friction

Friction. Have several students pull a large carton or wooden box loaded with books across the floor. Then use a large spring balance to measure the force required to move the box along with uniform velocity. Now place a ball-bearing roller skate under each corner of the box and again measure the force needed to pull the box of books with uniform velocity (Fig. 17-31). The reading made with the ball-bearing rollers should be almost zero (on a smooth floor). The difference in readings should be close to the actual force required to overcome friction.

Coefficient of friction. Take the weight of the same box; divide this amount into the amount of force needed to pull the box with and without the roller skates. Students will now have the coefficient of sliding friction as well as the coefficient of rolling friction. (Students can use dowel sticks or pieces of broomsticks in place of ball-bearing rollers to find the coefficient of rolling friction.) At other times, ask students to estimate the coefficient for the skates before and after lubrication.

Friction and heat. The fact that heat develops from friction can be readily demonstrated. Fit a smooth piece of brass pipe which has an outer diameter of 1½″ with a threaded cap as shown in Fig. 17-32, and into the opposite end fit a cork. Then place a few drops of water into the pipe and fasten it into the jaws of a ½″ electric drill. Such a drill can usually be borrowed from the school shop or from an automobile mechanic. Then locate two small pieces of old automobile brake lining and place these between the jaws of a large pair of pliers so that they touch the pipe. Set the drill into rotation; after a few minutes students should observe that the resulting friction heats the water so that steam forces the cork out of the pipe.

17.4b Efficiency of machines

To estimate the efficiency of a machine it is necessary to compare the work input with the work output.

Efficiency of movable pulleys. One simple method uses a set of movable pulleys in this way. Hang a 20-pound weight on the lower movable pulley (Fig. 17-33). Measure with a spring scale the force needed to lift the weight; then measure the distance that the force rope was moved. Multiply the force in pounds by distance in feet to get the work input.

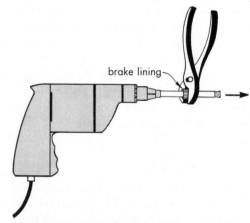

brake lining

Fig. 17–32 Friction produces heat: when the brake lining is pressed against the turning iron pipe, water inside the pipe changes to steam, thereby causing the cork to pop.

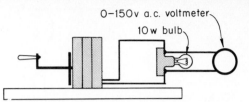

0–150v a.c. voltmeter

10 w bulb

Fig. 17–34 Set up for approximating the efficiency of a hand generator (magneto).

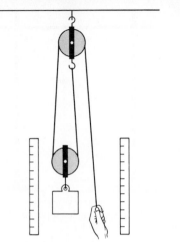

Fig. 17–33 Raising a weight with one movable pulley and one fixed pulley.

Next measure the distance that the weight was moved and multiply this by the weight. With the ordinary pulleys, the input and the output will not be the same; the work done on the force rope (input) will be the greater. The difference is the number of foot-pounds needed to overcome the friction in the pulleys. Find the efficiency in per cent by dividing the output work by the input work and multiplying by a hundred. Weights may also be used to make the load move upward very slowly with uniform velocity.

Efficiency of a toy electric locomotive. Connect an a.c. voltmeter and an ammeter to a toy electric train track and the transformer. (Use d.c. instruments if you use HO scale model trains.) Then operate a locomotive on the track at the highest possible speed that keeps the locomotive on the track. Multiply the voltage by the current (in amperes) to get the power (in watts). Then express this in horsepower by dividing by 746, and multiply this by 33,-000 to express it in foot-pounds. A locomotive may draw about 25 watts (about 1200 foot-pounds per minute). Now measure the work by attaching a spring balance to

the locomotive so that students can find the force it exerts when it draws 25 watts. Multiply this by the distance around the track it travels in one minute. When this product is compared with the input wattage, an efficiency of 25 to 50 per cent may be found, depending upon the condition and the type of locomotive.

Efficiency of a small machine. The following procedure at best leads to a very rough approximation but can be used to show that input is often much greater than output in small electrical generators. Select a hand generator or magneto connected to a light bulb and have students calculate its efficiency as follows. First find the output. Connect a 0–150-volt a.c. voltmeter across the bulb, preferably of 10 watts, as shown in Fig. 17-34. Then turn the generator until the voltmeter reads 120. (At the same time, count the number of revolutions per minute, and estimate the force exerted on the crank; these will be used to calculate the input.) At 120 volts the output should be 10 watts, which gives maximum brilliance of the bulb. (This is 10/746 of one horsepower, since 746 watts equals one horsepower.)

Find the input by multiplying together the force on the crank (which has been estimated with a spring scale), twice the length of the handle (2 × 3.1416), and the number of revolutions per minute. (*Note:* Convert inches to feet.) By dividing this result, in foot-pounds per minute, by 33,-000 foot-pounds per minute (one horsepower), students can get the fraction of a

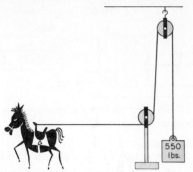

Fig. 17-35 Arrangement for repeating Watt's experiment for finding one horsepower.

horsepower developed by the hand (input). The formula for this computation is

$$P = \frac{F \times 2\pi r \times N}{\text{time}}$$

The result should be many times as great as the 10/746 of one horsepower developed in the bulb (output). This low efficiency is due partly to friction and partly to the very low electrical efficiency of small generators.

If the magneto operated a 2-watt neon lamp, this would be 2/746 of 33,000 foot-pounds per minute or the equivalent of 88 foot-pounds of work per minute. The work done by hand would be at least 10 times as great. With a 10-watt incandescent lamp, the horsepower is 10/746 of 33,000 foot-pounds per minute or 442 plus foot-pounds per minute. Here again losses due to friction in the bearings and to magnetic and electrical inefficiency in the machine exist.

17.5 Power

17.5a Horsepower

Watt's experiment. Students can repeat James Watt's experiment for finding one horsepower if a stable of horses is located nearby. Students will need a strong horse, a heavy rope about 50 feet long, a pulley, and a weight of 550 pounds.

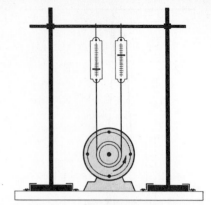

Fig. 17-36 Measuring horsepower of an electric motor with a Prony brake.

Attach the rope to the weight and pass it over a pulley as shown in Fig. 17-35. Now have a horse pull the rope which is attached to its harness. (If you have a Western saddle, the rope can be attached to the horn.) Time the horse for one second, two seconds, up to ten seconds. Measure the height to which the horse raises the weight during these time intervals. Notice that the horse moves the weight at the rate of about one foot in a second. One horsepower equals 550 foot-pounds per second or 33,000 foot-pounds per minute.

Measuring horsepower with a simple Prony brake. Make a simple Prony brake by fastening two ring stands to a strong board as shown in Fig. 17-36. Place clamps near the top of each stand and attach spring balances. Halfway between the bases of the ring stands place a small electric motor or model engine whose horsepower is to be tested and place a pulley on its shaft. Connect a piece of thin rope (about 3/16″ in diameter) between the spring balances so that the rope passes under the pulley. Now adjust the tension on the ropes until both balances have the same reading.

Set the motor or engine into operation at full speed. Pull up on one balance until the engine or motor almost stops. Imme-

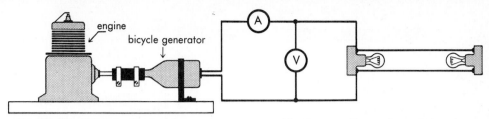

Fig. 17-37 Using an electrical dynamometer to measure horsepower. The small gasoline engine can be replaced by an electric motor.

diately read the force on the two balances. The difference between the two readings is the force exerted by the motor. Measure the diameter of the pulley and multiply by 3.14 to find the circumference. Divide by 12″ to convert to feet. Then find the rated speed in rpm on the name plate or in the instruction book for the motor or engine. Multiply the three figures—the force in pounds, the circumference in feet, and the speed in rpm—and then divide by 33,000 foot-pounds per minute to get the horse-power.

Students can also use a motor of known horsepower in the same way to check the result.

Measuring horsepower with an electrical dynamometer. Horsepower of modern engines is measured with an electrical dynamometer, which is an electrical generator spun by the engine under test. Measure the output in watts and then divide by 746 watts to get the horsepower. Set up an electric dynamometer using a small 110- to 120-volt electric motor with a known horsepower, preferably 1/30 to 1/60 hp, marked on the name plate. Borrow a generator used to operate the headlight of a bicycle. Connect the two shafts by means of heavy snugly fitting thick rubber hose, and fasten the motor and the generator to a board (Fig. 17-37). Connect the generator to several electric light lamps and to an a.c. voltmeter and ammeter as shown in Fig. 17-37. Now connect the motor to the house current. (Operate as many miniature lamps from the generator as

possible without causing them to dim.) Read the voltage and current in amperes from the meter. The product of volts and amperes = watts. Then divide this by 746 watts to get the horsepower. The answer will be approximately the same as the rated horsepower unless there is an error due to the electrical and frictional losses in the generator.

Measuring boy power. A bicycle is a good device for measuring a student's horsepower. Measure the diameter of the circle through which the pedals revolve. (This is usually 14″ or 1⅙′.) Measure the push of each foot by having a seated student press alternately with each foot on a bathroom-type scale. Average the two forces. (The push will be between 50 and 100 pounds.) Then have the same student ride the bicycle at full speed for 10 seconds, counting the number of revolutions of the pedals. Multiply by six to convert this into rpm; then multiply together the force measured earlier, the circumference of the pedals, and the rpm of the pedals. Divide by 33,000 foot-pounds per minute to get the horsepower developed by a student; this usually falls between 1/10 and 1/5 horsepower.

17.6 Machines

17.6a Levers

In all experiments dealing with a meterstick as a lever, it must be remembered that the stick itself may weigh as much as 200 g and that this weight may be consid-

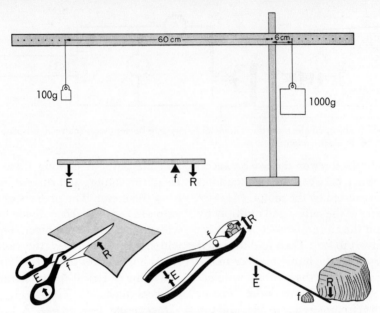

Fig. 17–38 First-class levers.

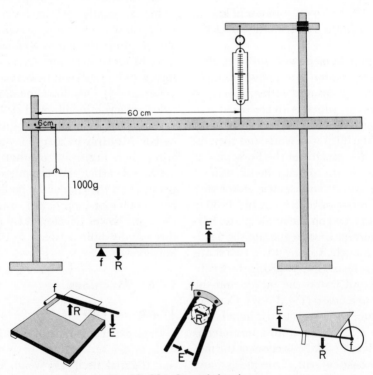

Fig. 17–39 Second-class levers.

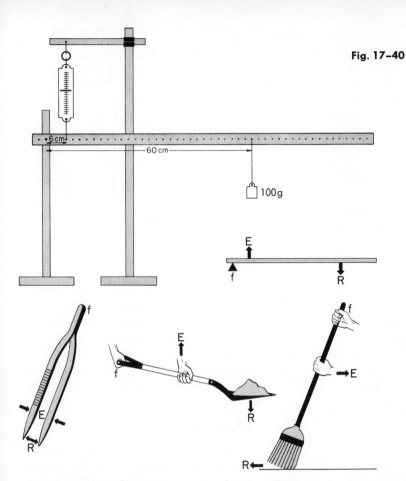

Fig. 17–40   Third-class levers.

ered to be acting from the center of gravity of the stick. The significance of the meterstick's weight may be reduced by using very large masses as the resistance and effort. In such cases, the percentage error will be small enough to be ignored (i.e., R = 500 g, E = 1000 g). Since such large weights may not be available, it is suggested that the weight of the stick be taken into account by adding its moment (wt × distance to fulcrum from the 50-cm mark) to the moment of the force which it aids. Thus, if the fulcrum is to the left of the 50-cm mark, the weight becomes a clockwise force; if the fulcrum is to the right of the 50-cm mark, the weight of the stick is a counterclockwise force.

The principle of the lever can be shown with any rod or bar. In fact, the simple apparatus shown in Fig. 17-38 can be used by students to demonstrate all types of levers. This device can be made by drilling ⅛″ holes at intervals along a meterstick which is then supported on a nail as a fulcrum. Or you may prefer to purchase pivoted meterstick supports sold by scientific supply companies (see appendix). You can then slide the supports to any position along the stick and secure them with a set screw. Students will need at least three—one at the fulcrum and two for hanging the weights.

First-class levers. With the meterstick or yardstick set on a nail or suspended from a support as a fulcrum, attach weights to the right and left sides. Hang the weights by means of wires passed through the holes drilled in the stick or attached to the supports, as shown in Fig. 17-38. Have students discover that the stick will balance when the products of the arm and the attached weight are equal on both sides. For example, a 100-g weight placed 60 cm from the fulcrum will balance a 1000-g weight located 6 cm from the fulcrum on the opposite side. In this instance, the mechanical advantage of the lever is 10, since only 100 g were required to balance 1000 g. The mechanical advantage can also be calculated from distances of the lever arms: the resistance arm of 6 cm is 1/10 the effort arm of 60 cm; hence the MA is 10.

Have students explain why the following are examples of first-class levers: shears, crow bars, pliers, automobile emergency brake handles, and rocker arms on overhead valves of engines.

Second-class levers. Using the same apparatus, place the fulcrum at one end of the stick, and suspend the other end from a spring balance, as shown in Fig. 17-39. The resistance weight can be attached anywhere along the meterstick between the fulcrum and effort. When students change the weight or its position, the reading of the balance will change. Students can show how a paper cutter, a nut cracker, an old type of can opener, or a wheelbarrow are examples of second-class levers.

Third-class levers. Now move the fulcrum to one end of the stick, hang a weight 60 cm from it, and suspend the stick from a spring balance between the fulcrum and the weight at 6 cm from the fulcrum (Fig. 17-40). Now the resistance arm is 60 cm and the effort arm is only 6 cm. Since the effort arm is one tenth as long as the resistance arm, the MA of this lever is 1/10,

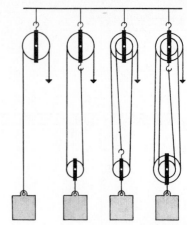

Fig. 17–41 Special pulley arrangements.

and the effort that must be expended is greater than the weight instead of less. In such a lever, force is sacrificed for distance, speed, or convenience of operation. Groups of students will be ready to explain to the class how tweezers, tongs, a broom, or a shovel are examples of third-class levers.

17.6b Pulleys

Large commercial pulleys give the advantage of increased visibility in class demonstrations. However, if they are not available, washline pulleys combined in double or triple clusters can serve as double and triple pulleys. If ceiling eyebolts are not built into the room, you may want to have the custodian build a framework of wood 2 × 2's to support the pulleys when lifting heavy loads. In the laboratory students can use the standard low-friction plastic pulleys. They are, however, limited to about 2 kilograms maximum load.

When using pulleys arranged as in Fig. 17-41, show that the mechanical advantage is equal to the number of supporting ropes. (The rope to which the force is applied is not included as a supporting rope. The only time an effort rope is counted as a supporting rope is when it is pulled up-

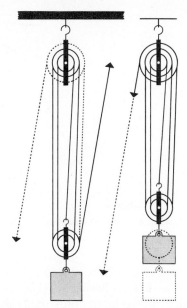

Fig. 17–42 Pulley with a mechanical advantage of 5. An extra pulley is needed (see right) if the convenience of pulling down is wanted.

ward.) A simple way to show how this applies is to ask a student to lift a bench of known weight with one hand. Then he lifts with two hands, each hand supporting half the weight. This is the same as the rope arrangement for two single pulleys arranged as a block and tackle. A second student adds his two hands, and now the weight is distributed among the four hands. This is similar to the four ropes of a double pulley block and tackle. If a third student adds his two hands to lift the bench, there will be 6 supporting hands, each carrying ⅙ of the load. This is comparable to a triple pulley block and tackle. Each rope can be considered as a supporting arm.

Combinations of pulleys. After students have threaded a single fixed, then a single movable pulley, they will want to combine pulleys to increase the MA, that is, to have a smaller effort force raise a large resistance. Have them estimate the number of ropes acting on the movable block sup-

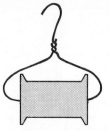

Fig. 17–43 Pulley made from a spool and coat hanger.

porting the weight. (Students will remember to include the weight of the movable blocks in the pulley system in computing the total resistance.)

Figure 17-42 illustrates how a mechanical advantage of 5 can be obtained with the effort acting either upward or downward. The drawing at the right shows that one additional fixed pulley is needed to obtain this MA if we wish the convenience of pulling downward; if, on the other hand, we can tolerate an upward-acting effort, the same MA can be obtained with one less fixed pulley. This is seen in the drawing at the left. Thus, the only function of the fixed pulleys is to reverse the direction of the applied effort. They do not affect the MA of the system.

Students will soon learn that to get an MA of an even number the fixed end of the cord should be attached to the fixed pulley block. When the threading of the pulley is started at the movable pulley block, the MA will be an odd number. (See the two systems in Fig. 17-41.)

As a project some students may make several fixed pulleys from spools attached to wire clothes hangers. Pull down the cross bar of each hanger; cut off each wire about 9″ from the hook and bend the ends to thread through a spool as in Fig. 17-43. Adjust this pulley so that the spools spin easily and bend down the ends extending out of the spool so that it is held in place.

Students can prepare strings with loops

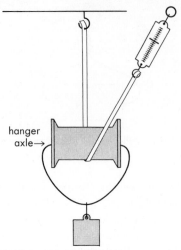

hanger
axle→

Fig. 17–44 Thread spool pulley used with a spring scale to measure effort.

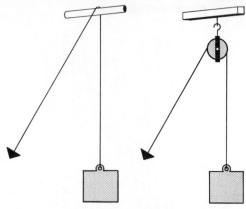

Fig. 17–45 A length of doweling can act as a pulley.

at each end to which weights can be attached. Prepare a single fixed pulley. How much effort is needed to lift a weight of 50 grams, 100 grams? They should also measure the distance that the effort is moved and the distance that the resistance is lifted. Bring in the principle of work. What is the mechanical advantage of a single fixed pulley? What is the advantage in using a fixed pulley?

Also have a student report on the performance of a differential pulley. Students may be ready to explain how the MA of a differential pulley is twice the radius of the larger of the two coaxial pulleys divided by the difference in the radii of these pulleys. Why is the MA greater when there is a small difference in the radii of the two coaxial pulleys?

Excellent pulley substitutes can be made of cotton or linen thread spools with wire-hanger axles as described above. Figure 17-44 shows one of these in use with a spring scale to measure the effort. The resistance is the weight attached to the wire.

Acceptable results can be obtained when pulleys are not available by passing the cord over a smooth, waxed piece of

doweling of ⅜″ diameter and supporting its end so that it is horizontal (Fig. 17-45). When replaced by a commercial laboratory pulley, the results become much better due to the decrease in friction.

17.6c   Wheel and axle

Standard wheel and axles may be used but these are usually small. For a clearer demonstration you can mount a large wheel so that it can rotate about its axle. Fasten a bar of aluminum from one edge of the wheel through its center and partially toward the other edge. To one side of center, the bar is the same length as the wheel radius; to the other side, it is only a few inches long (Fig. 17-46A). In this way there are two "wheels" of different radii mounted on the same axle. When a force is applied to the rim of a wheel with a 12″ radius and a short arm 4″ long measured from the wheel's center to which a weight is attached, the force needed to move the weight is only ⅓ that of the weight since the 4″ resistance arm and the 12″ effort arm give an MA of 3. Students may understand that the center of the wheel acts as the fulcrum of a simple lever. The force arm is the radius; the resistance arm is the short arm.

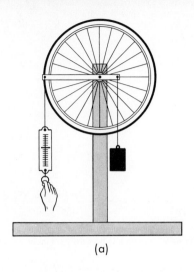

(a)

Fig. 17–46 Demonstration wheel and axle made from a bicycle wheel.

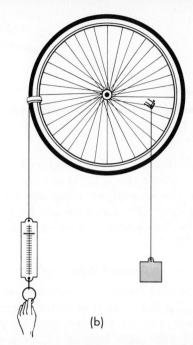

(b)

Mount a spoked bicycle wheel on its regular ball bearings so that the friction is almost zero. Students can clamp a weight to a spoke at any desired distance from the center (Fig. 17-46B). Then measure the distance and the force at the rim required to lift the weight. (A spring balance attached with tape to the rim can be used to measure the force.) The force should be the weight divided by the MA; the MA is found by dividing the wheel radius by the distance of the weight from the center of the wheel.

It may be possible to get an old-fashioned automobile crank and set it up in bearings made by drilling and oiling holes in blocks of wood or by securing loosely with metal strips into a groove across the surface of the board as in Fig. 17-47A. Attach a weight to the axle by means of tape or with fishing cord through a hole drilled in the crank. Measure the radius of the shaft. (It is usually ¾".) Then measure the length of the crank. The MA will be found by dividing the length of the crank by the radius of the shaft. Divide the MA into the

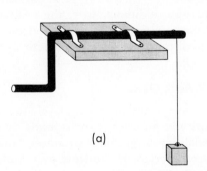

(a)

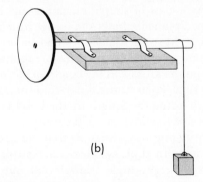

(b)

Fig. 17–47 Crank (or wheel) and axle setups.

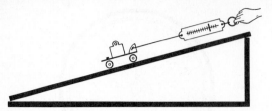

Fig. 17–48 Inclined plane—a sloping board.

weight to find the force required. Then check with a spring balance to see if the force checks with the computed figure. This same demonstration can be made with a disk or wheel and shaft as in Fig. 17-47B.

17.6d Inclined plane

The most elementary inclined plane is a sloping board. In class demonstrations students can use boards 4′ long set on a box 1′ high (or 8′ long on a 2′ support). Commercial inclined planes, though usually shorter, are also useful. Place a weight on a "frictionless" cart or well-oiled roller skate. With a spring balance, as in Fig. 17-48, measure the force required to pull the cart up the incline. Next weigh the cart with its load. Students should find that the force is only ¼ of the weight. Then show that the MA is the ratio of the length of the inclined plane to the height the load is lifted. If the length and height are changed, students should find that the MA will vary in proportion.

As a class of simple machines, the inclined plane includes the wedge and the screw. Make a wedge of wood or use a commercial steel wedge. Measure its maximum thickness and the length of its sloping side. Then students can find the MA by dividing the length by the height (in this case the thickness of the wedge).

Students may also show that the screw is an inclined plane. Have each student wrap a right-angle triangle cut out of paper around a pencil as shown in Fig.

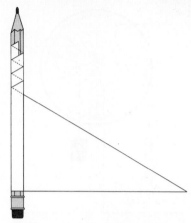

Fig. 17–49 A screw is basically an inclined plane.

17-49 so that the base of the triangle remains even as the paper is rolled. Observe the "threads" that are formed. Students should notice that the spirals or "threads" along the pencil are really the length of an inclined plane. Also show students an automobile screw jack and have them explain the MA of the device.

Students can also find the MA of a screw by counting the number of threads per inch; they can then compute from this the distance between the threads (the pitch). As a check, you may also want to have them measure the pitch directly with calipers. Measure the diameter of the screw. The mechanical advantage is the ratio of $\pi \times$ the diameter of the screw (effort distance) to the pitch (resistance distance). With a screw jack, the handle provides additional MA; the resistance distance is again the pitch, and the effort distance is twice the length of the handle.

17.6e Gears

Have a student use a bicycle to compare the number of turns made by the pedal wheel and the rear wheel. How is speed increased? Students may build a simple device to illustrate the principle by

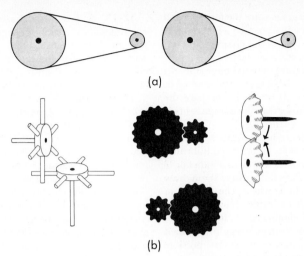

Fig. 17–50 Belt and gear systems: (a) using different size spools; (b) using Tinkertoys, notched circles of wood, and soda-pop caps.

using small and large spools connected by a rubber band. Hammer two long nails into a block of wood; the nails serve as axles for a small spool and a larger one (Fig. 17-50A). Connect the spools with a belt (a rubber band). How many turns are made by the small spool when the large spool makes one turn?

Also show how the direction of the one spool can be changed by twisting the belt (the rubber band).

Demonstration models of gear systems can be made by meshing soda pop caps (Fig. 17-50B). Flatten out the caps so that disks are formed. Mount them with nails so that they mesh on a block of wood. The gears should turn easily; as one cap is turned, students can observe the direction the second and the third gears turn. In essence, they will recognize that these devices multiply speed, distance, or force. Similar devices can be made with Tinkertoys or with dowels that have brads as gear teeth.

CAPSULE LESSONS
Ways to get started in class

17-1. Introduce the concept of acceleration of gravity by using the apparatus that releases two balls of different weights which strike the floor simultaneously. Have the class explain why balls of different weights hit the floor at the same time.

17-2. A student may want to report on the escape velocity (approximately 25,000 miles per hour or 7 miles per second) or the speed that a rocket must attain to escape the pull of gravity, after having exhausted its fuel near the earth's surface. This may serve as an introduction to force of gravity or centrifugal force. You may want to clarify the idea of escape velocity by

pointing out that an object rising at any speed can escape the earth's gravity as long as the thrust that provides the speed does not fail.

17-3. Use a long window pole as a first-class lever to lift a large weight with a small force. Develop the principle of work. Students can bring models of small tools and toys to class and explain different kinds of levers.

17-4. Set up a triple-pulley block and tackle to lift a fairly heavy weight. Ask students to estimate the amount of force needed to lift the weight. Then develop the idea of mechanical advantage of single-, double-, and triple-pulley block and tackles.

17-5. Students can measure the force needed to overcome inertia when starting a bicycle. Use the technique described in this chapter, and test model trains and cars.

17-6. As a laboratory activity, have students study the parallelogram of forces as described in this chapter. If there is time, also prepare the materials for demonstrating the components of the forces acting on a sailboat.

17-7. Have students demonstrate several examples of the different kinds of equilibrium, using commercial models as well as a soda bottle placed in different directions. Have them draw diagrams and explain where the center of gravity lies in each example. How are these notions utilized in designing cars? How could we find the center of gravity in an irregularly shaped object? Students can try to devise possible methods; have them demonstrate the plumb line method with any irregularly shaped flat object you have on hand.

17-8. At some time you may want to begin with a sound film, such as *The Earth in Motion* (EBF). There are several you may want to use in introducing or reviewing the concepts of machines and work.

17-9. Demonstrate Newton's laws by providing laboratory activities, demonstrations, and student lecture-demonstrations.

17-10. Students may develop the laws of the pendulum in a well-planned laboratory period.

17-11. Ask each student to determine how much work he does in coming up from the school entrance to the classroom. Students can develop the formula for work. Have students include the weight of their books in their total weight and multiply this by the vertical height of the room floor from the street level. Develop a discussion of the meaning of work in physics.

17-12. Model railroad train enthusiasts may want to demonstrate the measurement of horsepower of their model engines by following the procedure described in this chapter. These students may want to drive a small generator by means of a model locomotive electric motor to measure the number of watts generated. A comparison of the number of watts (volts × amperes) against 746 watts (one hp) will give an approximation of the horsepower.

17-13. A group of students may display examples of the six kinds of energy (heat, chemical, nuclear, electric, light, and mechanical) and their transformation into other types of energy. Discuss the kinds and transformations of energy used at home or in a factory.

17-14. You may want to begin by raising a problem concerning the effect of friction on the force needed or the work that must be done. Set up a commercial block and tackle or its equivalent in size and have students determine the mechanical advantage from the number of supporting ropes. The students will divide this number into the resistance to get the theoretical force that is needed. Then test the actual force (the effort). It may be as great as a third more than the estimated force. Students should recognize that the difference is due to friction. Now introduce the methods used to overcome friction.

17-15. You may want to develop the law of work for machines (effort × distance equals resistance × distance) by suspending a ruler in a loop of string and balancing it with coins at each end. If twice as many coins are stacked in a heap, where should this be placed to balance the smaller heap at the opposite end? Show how a single fixed pulley is really an equal-armed lever. Have students develop the principle of work in other machines—inclined plane, wheel and axle.

17-16. In some classes you may want to introduce the concept of machines and mechanical advantage by supplying students with several kinds of machines that they can manipulate (lever, inclined plane, pulleys). Present a problem which gives an object of a definite weight that must be moved a given distance. Have students determine which device to use to accomplish their objective with the least effort force.

17-17. As a summary lesson, a committee of students can show a film or filmstrip and have prepared questions to ask in review. There are several films available. Have you seen *Laws of Motion* (EBF), *Machines Do Work* (Institutional Cinema), or the filmstrips on *Mechanics* (McGraw-Hill)?

PEOPLE, PLACES, AND THINGS

It may be possible to borrow simple machines from garages, moving companies, or similar companies engaged in using machines to make work easier in daily living. Students may plan a field trip to a factory, a large garage, or a building construction site, and list as many "machine principles" as possible. Some teachers often work closely with shop teachers in developing club programs or temporary projects, and to help science students use shop equipment. Laboratory equipment may be borrowed from a college department or films may be borrowed from the college film library; a local film library or regional office of an industrial firm may have free films or filmstrips available.

BOOKS AND PAMPHLETS

These are only a few of the books which are pertinent to the work discussed in this chapter. These and many other references classified by subject and with complete bibliographical data are given in the bibliography at the end of the book.

Beiser, A., ed., *The World of Physics,* McGraw-Hill, 1960.

Bonner, F., and M. Phillips, *Principles of Physical Science,* Addison-Wesley, 1957.

Holton, G., and D. Roller, *Foundations of Modern Physical Science,* Addison-Wesley, 1958.

Krauskopf, K., *Fundamentals of Physical Science,* 4th ed., McGraw-Hill, 1959.

Leighton, R., *Principles of Modern Physics,* McGraw-Hill, 1959.

Miller, F., Jr., *College Physics,* Harcourt, Brace, 1959.

Physical Science Study Committee (PSSC), *Physics,* Heath, 1960.

Pokras, L., T*he Properties and Structure of Matter,* McGraw-Hill, 1958.

Richtmyer, F., E. Kennard, and T. Lauritsen, *Introduction to Modern Physics,* 5th ed., McGraw-Hill, 1955.

Ridenour, L., *Modern Physics for the Engineer,* McGraw-Hill, 1954.

Sears, F., *Mechanics, Wave Motion and Heat,* Addison-Wesley, 1958.

Semat, H., *Fundamentals of Physics,* Rinehart, 1958.

White, M., K. Manning, and R. Weber, *Practical Physics,* 2nd ed., McGraw-Hill, 1955.

FILMS AND FILMSTRIPS

This partial list is intended only as a guide toward film and filmstrip selection. Refer to the more complete listing at the end of the book where films are classified by subject and where a key to abbreviations and addresses of distributors are given. The cost of film rental, of course, is subject to change. Films are sound and black and white unless otherwise specified.

Energy and Its Transformations (f, s), EBF, inquire local film library.

Friction (f, s), Ideal, $2.00.

Galileo's Laws of Falling Bodies (f, s), EBF, $1.50.

Horsepower (f, s), Almanac, $2.00.

How a Watch Works (f, s, c), Association, free.

Introduction to Vectors: Coplanar Concurrent Forces (f, s), Indiana, $2.75.

Laws of Conservation of Energy and Matter (f, s, c), Coronet, inquire local film library.

Laws of Motion (f, s, c), EBF, $4.00.

Lever-Age (f, s), Shell, free.

Machines Do Work (f, s), Institutional Cinema, $2.00.

Mechanics (f, s, series 44 lessons in introductory physics), EBF, inquire rental.

Mechanics (3 fs), McGraw-Hill, $3.00 each.

Nature of Heat; Nature of Energy (f, s, c), Indiana, $2.00 each.

Physics at Home (f, s), Institutional Cinema, $2.00.

Principle of Movements (f, s), Indiana, $2.75.

Simple Harmonic Motion (f, s), McGraw-Hill, inquire rental.

Uniform Circular Motion (f, s), McGraw-Hill, inquire local film library.

What is Horsepower? (fs, c), Popular Science through McGraw-Hill, $6.00.

You and Horsepower (fs, c), Harcourt, Brace, $6.00.

FREE AND INEXPENSIVE MATERIALS

This is only a partial listing of free and inexpensive materials available to the teacher at this time. A directory of addresses is given at the end of the book. Many of these materials are distributed to teachers without charge. Where there is a small fee, the cost is indicated, although the prices are subject to change. While we recommend the material for use in the classroom, we do not necessarily endorse the products advertised.

ABC's of Hand Tools, General Motors.

Gyroscopes Through the Ages, Sperry Gyroscope.

History of Measurements (posters), Ford Motor Co.

Manual of Carpentry, U.S. Steel Corp.

Precision (A Measure of Progress), General Motors.

Science at Work (series of resource units), General Motors.

A Thousand Science Projects, Science Service.

CHAPTER 18

Heat and heat engines

In this chapter we shall describe some activities to show the effects produced by heat energy: change in temperature, expansion or contraction, and change of state. In addition, there are some demonstrations and laboratory activities concerning heat transmission, specific heat, and the mechanical equivalent of heat, together with suggestions for demonstrating different kinds of heat engines.

18.1 Heat

Much heat energy is produced as a result of chemical action. You may want to refer at this time to the energy transformations shown in oxidation (7.1c, 7.1d) and fuels (14.3); students will probably need to review the concepts concerning molecules and diffusion that they have already studied. They can quickly distinguish between heat and temperature: heat referring to the amount of molecular energy possessed by a body as a whole, and temperature being a measure of the average kinetic energy of the molecules that make up the body. Students can compare the temperatures of two beakers of boiling water—50-ml and 150-ml beakers. While both show a reading of 212° F, which beaker of water has more heat?

18.1a Measuring temperature

Students can recognize the need for a thermometer to measure the average kinetic energy of a body's molecules because our sense receptors are not sufficiently accurate. Students can demonstrate the unreliability of human sensations in this way. Prepare three containers of water: one at room temperature, a second containing ice water, and a third containing water hot enough to insert a hand comfortably. If a student places a hand in ice water and then into water at room temperature, he "feels" the second container to be warm. On the other hand, if he places a hand into the water at room temperature after first having it in hot water, he "feels" the water to be cool.

The need for an accurate temperature-measuring device may also be demonstrated as follows. Have a student heat some water in a beaker over a Bunsen burner until it is about 125° F as measured by a thermometer. Let him place his fingers into the liquid and try to remember its degree of warmth. He might then pour out the liquid, refill the beaker with tap water, and without the aid of the thermometer attempt to heat it to the same temperature as before with the aid only of his own senses. Check his guess with the same thermometer as before. Students will generally make an error of 10% or more in this operation.

Students may want to calibrate the laboratory thermometers or to prepare a thermometer at this time. (In addition to material in this chapter there is informa-

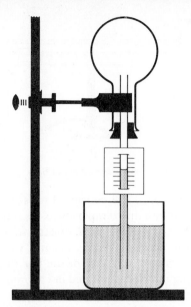

Fig. 18-1 Air thermometer.

tion on thermometers in 3.1a.) You may prefer to postpone this activity until students are ready to study expansion of gases, liquids, and solids (18.2). We shall first describe the simple calibration of a thermometer; the preparation of a mercury thermometer is given in 18.2b.

Air thermometer. Students can demonstrate the principle upon which a thermometer is based: heat causes expansion. (See also 3.1a.) They can easily prepare an air thermometer of the kind that Galileo used (Fig. 18-1) by inserting glass tubing through a one-hole stopper that closes a flask. Invert the flask into a beaker of water to which a dye has been added to increase visibility (or you may want to employ the air thermometer described in 18.2c which uses a U-tube manometer). A white card with India ink "calibrations" helps to make this look like a measuring instrument and also improves visibility. Prepare the air thermometer as shown in Fig. 18-1; then place your hand over the bottle to warm the air inside it. Bubbles of air will be seen to escape from the lower

end of the tube. After you have counted about 15 bubbles, allow the air in the flask to contract by removing your hand; the liquid should rise about halfway up the tube. Set the zero calibration mark opposite the liquid level. Warming the flask will drive the air down in the tube, while cooling it will have the effect of elevating the liquid column.

Calibration. Students can check the accuracy of the fixed points of several Fahrenheit and centigrade thermometers in the laboratory (or establish fixed points in making a thermometer); many teachers find this a successful laboratory activity.

A Fahrenheit thermometer can be calibrated by placing a bulb in a mixture of equal weights of ammonium chloride (sal ammoniac) and ice; mark the lowest point to which the mercury falls as so many tenths of a degree above or below 0° F. Fahrenheit himself believed the lowest temperature man could produce artificially was by means of a freezing saline mixture. If the thermometer is correct, it should read exactly zero in this mixture; the number of tenths up or down from zero indicates the error of the thermometer in this region. In short, Fahrenheit established the size of his "degree" by calling the freezing mixture temperature "zero" and the body temperature "100 degrees," and then dividing this distance off into 100 degrees.

Later put the bulb in steam over boiling water at one atmosphere pressure; mark the high point of the mercury as fractions of a degree above or below 212° F. The freezing point of water, 32° F, can also be checked by inserting the thermometer into a mixture of crushed ice and water.

A centigrade thermometer can be checked or calibrated in steam from boiling water (100° C) and in a mixture of crushed ice and water (0° C). Students can estimate the intervals on each ther-

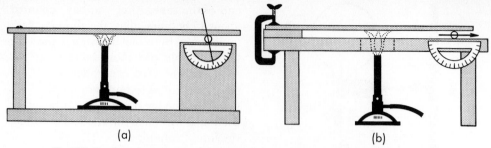

Fig. 18–2 Two devices for measuring the linear thermal expansion of metal bars.

mometer, Fahrenheit and centigrade, and compare them (1 C° equals 1.8 F°). They should be able to explain the derivation of the equation $t_C = 5/9\ (t_F - 32)$. Thermometers containing mercury are more precise than alcohol or other types because mercury has a uniform coefficient of expansion, and hence permits of equally spaced divisions. Students can explain that alcohol thermometers are better for measuring low temperatures since the freezing point of alcohol is substantially lower than that of mercury.

18.2 Thermal expansion

18.2a Solids

You may want students to use a commercial linear expansion apparatus or have them build a homemade model to show the differential expansion of several solids (Fig. 18-2). In preparing the workable model, strips or bars of different metals are secured at one end, while the other ends rest on a piece of glass tubing. Lay the glass tubing on a smooth board and insert a wad of paper with a cardboard pointer attached into one end of the tubing (as shown in Fig. 18-2). Before starting set the pointer so that it points parallel to the lay of the rod. Note that the rods whose thermal expansion is to be compared are now heated equally and for the same duration of time through a hole in the sup-

porting board. Of course all rods should start at the same temperature. As rod expands, the tubing rolls due to friction, thereby carrying needle around with it. The increase in length of the bar due to heating may be calculated in cm or inches by measuring the diameter of the glass tubing, preferably with a vernier caliper. After the number of degrees of rotation has been determined from the protractor scale under the needle, the actual expansion may be determined from the equation

increase in length $=$

$$\frac{2\pi D \times \text{angle moved in degrees}}{360°}$$

where D is the diameter of the tubing.

If it should happen that there is no gas supply available, a propane or butane torch will do as well. These torches are sold in hardware stores for about $6.00.

Students can calculate the linear expansion of several metals by using the equation

$$k = \frac{L_2 - L_1}{L_1(t_2 - t_1)}$$

where k is the coefficient of linear expansion, L_2 is the new length after expansion, L_1 is the initial length of a hollow rod, t_2 is the final temperature, and t_1 is the initial temperature. Commercial models use hollow metal tubing heated by steam from a copper steam generator or a pressure flask. Thus, the initial temperature of the tube is

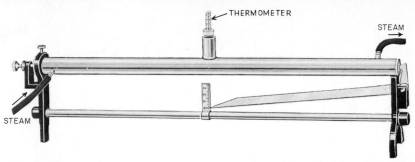

Fig. 18–3 Commercial device for measuring linear expansion of a metal with each one degree rise in temperature. (Welch Scientific Company.)

the same as the room temperature, while the final temperature is very close to 100° C.

A group of students can demonstrate the increase in length of a solid when heated through a 1 C° change in temperature. The apparatus consists of several rods of materials to be tested, with one end fixed in position as shown in Fig. 18-3. Each rod is inserted into a metal steam jacket attached to a steam generator. Readings are made on the scale along which a pointer moves. Before heating the rods, students should establish the ratio of the length of the long arm to the length of the short (often bent) arm of the levers. The lever arms move in relation to the degree of expansion of the heated metal. Students can measure this small amount of expansion in millimeters because the free end of the expanding rod pushes against the short arm of the lever which, in turn, moves the long arm of the lever over a graduated scale so that the small increase in length is magnified.

Once the principle is known, students can continue with the procedure. After they have measured the original length of the rod to be tested, they should replace the rod, fasten the steam jacket into the frame, and fasten with the thumbscrew. Adjust the screw at the fixed end of the rod so that the tip of the long indicator arm stands at zero on the scale. Carefully

insert a thermometer in the stopper closing the opening of the jacket. Heat the steam generator. Compute the coefficient of linear expansion by finding the ratio of the lengths of the long arm of the lever and the smaller one. Since the original length of the rod and the temperature change are known, then

$$\frac{\text{total expansion}}{\text{original length}} = \frac{\text{expansion per unit}}{\text{length}}$$

$$\frac{\text{expansion per unit length}}{\text{temperature change (in °C)}} =$$

coefficient of linear expansion (change in length per unit length per degree)

Comparing linear and surface expansion. Students should explain the bending of a compound bar when heated, and apply this information to the operation of a thermostat. They should also be ready to describe the operation of metallic thermometers.

18.2b Expansion of liquids

Making a liquid thermometer. Students can demonstrate the differential expansion of several kinds of liquids before actually making a liquid thermometer. In one simple procedure, fit several 50-ml Florence flasks with one-hole stoppers and equip them with 3' lengths of glass tub-

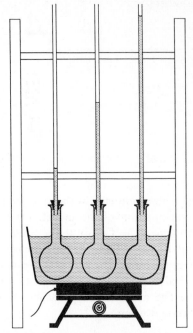

Fig. 18-4 Thermal expansion in liquids.

Fig. 18-5 Driving air from a thermometer tube.

ing (¼″ bore). Students can fill each flask with a different liquid and heat them all at low heat on an electric hot plate or in a water bath with an electric immersion heater, to provide equal heating as shown in Fig. 18-4. In this way, inflammable liquids like alcohol can also be used because flames or sparks are absent. When a water bath with an immersion heater is used, excellent results can be obtained by comparing the expansion rates of water, isopropyl alcohol, methyl alcohol, carbon tetrachloride, mercury, and pure glycerine. Have students observe and record the varying distances that the liquids rise in the tubing; they can use the millimeter rulers or prepare a scale on paper and attach this to the tubing. With all liquids started at room temperature (20° C), the amount of expansion of alcohol from 20° to 30° should be noted; this should then be compared with the expansion of alcohol from 50° to 60° C. This will demonstrate the nonuniform expansion of alcohol. The same procedure should be followed with water, taking the expansions from 20° to 30° C and then from 85° to 95° C. Finally, the *uniform* expansion of mercury should be observed over the same ranges used for the water. (You may want to compare liquid expansion with that of gases, 18.2c.)

After students have recognized the different rates of volumetric expansion of these liquids, you may want them to make a mercury thermometer.

Making a mercury thermometer. This is the most frequently used thermometer in the laboratory because mercury has a co-efficient of volumetric expansion that is nearly constant over the range of temperature measured by the ordinary thermometer. It is also the safest to make in the laboratory because the alcohol-type thermometer may catch fire in the process of preparing one.

Thermometer tubing (¼″ outer diameter) may be obtained from scientific supply houses. Seal one end of an 8″ length of tubing in a Bunsen flame and connect a mouthpiece of rubber tubing to the other end. Heat the sealed end of the tube and blow a bulb (see Chapter 25). Now remove the rubber tube mouthpiece and invert the thermometer tube into a small beaker of mercury (Fig. 18-5). Heat the bulb gently until air bubbles cease to

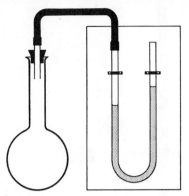

Fig. 18–6 Connecting an air thermometer to a manometer.

escape from the submerged open end of the tube, and let the thermometer cool a bit while standing in the mercury. Watch the mercury rise in the tube. When the tube is filled, seal the other end and allow the thermometer to cool to room temperature. As the mercury contracts, a vacuum is formed.

Now students can calibrate the thermometer. First place the bulb end in a mixture of ice and water and watch until the level of mercury remains fixed; mark this level with a file scratch as 0° C. Then place the bulb in a steam generator and mark the point at which the mercury remains constant as 100° C. Using these two marks as reference points, students can divide the space between the fixed marks into 10 or 100 equal parts to make a usable though only approximately accurate thermometer. Compare this operation with the calibration of a Fahrenheit thermometer as described in 18.1a.

18.2c *Thermal expansion of gases*

Air thermometer. You may first want to demonstrate that air expands by heating an empty flask which has a balloon slipped over the mouth. Why does the balloon become inflated? Or invert a flask so that its mouth is submerged in a container of water (as described earlier). Heat the flask gently by moving the flame back and forth under the glass, and watch the bubbles of air enter the water. As the flask and its confined air cool, students can observe the quantity of water that rises up the neck into the flask. This is a rough estimate of the quantity of air that was forced out of the flask due to expansion of the air within it.

Students can show the almost uniform cubical expansion of gases in several ways. In one simple technique, prepare the air thermometer already described and connect it to a U-tube manometer that is filled with water containing a dye (as shown in Fig. 18-6).

Or you may prefer to use a larger and sturdier version made with a small Pyrex beaker. The volume and pressure of the air can be measured at room temperature. Now when the temperature is raised, both the volume and the pressure will change as students record the change in mercury level.

Through laboratory activities and demonstrations described below students can investigate Charles' law and Gay-Lussac's law, and compare these with Boyle's law. From these students can reach a summary of all the gas laws.

Gay-Lussac's law. In a laboratory activity you may want students to observe first hand that when a gas is heated in a closed container with its volume kept constant, the pressure exerted by the gas against the container increases proportionately as the temperature rises in such a manner that the ratio between pressure and temperature always has the same numerical value. For every one degree change in absolute temperature this coefficient of pressure expansion of a gas is 1/273 of its value at 0° absolute. This pressure coefficient of expansion may be calculated by substituting the laboratory readings in the equation

$$\frac{P_1}{P_2} = \frac{t_1 + 273}{t_2 + 273} = \frac{T_1}{T_2}$$

where P_1 is the initial pressure, P_2 the final pressure, t_1 the initial centigrade temperature, t_2 the final centigrade temperature, T_1 the initial absolute temperature, and T_2 the final absolute temperature.

Assemble the apparatus in Fig. 18-7. However, before sealing the test tube (or commercial container) add a few drops of concentrated sulfuric acid to the container to remove traces of moisture from the air or other gas to be tested. Connect the container of dry air by means of the right-angle bends or rubber tubing to the open U-tube containing mercury. This U-tube is made of two straight lengths of glass tubing connected by a length of rubber tubing. As shown in Fig. 18-7, the right-hand part of the U-tube assembly is movable upward or downward with respect to the left half of the U-tube; the latter is fixed in place so that it cannot move. Bring the mercury in the fixed tube to a definite level by raising or lowering the movable tube. The levels in the two tubes will probably not be the same since the pressure of the air in the test tube will have been changed by this adjustment. Record the reading of the mercury in the fixed tube (the left tube) and call this the *reference* level. As the level is returned to this point after each manipulation, we may be sure that the volume of the dry air is constant when each reading is taken. Read the barometer in mm of mercury and record this reading.

Now note how many mm higher or lower the mercury stands in the movable tube as compared with the reference level; let us assume that it is higher in the movable tube. Thus, the pressure of the air in the test tube is equal to the barometric

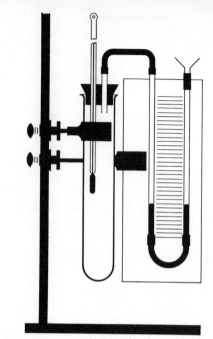

Fig. 18-7 Verifying Gay-Lussac's law: when volume is constant, the pressure of a confined gas increases proportionately with the temperature.

pressure *plus* the difference in the readings. Since the temperature is that of the room, say 20° C, then we now have our first two readings for the pressure and absolute temperature (room temperature centigrade plus 273 = absolute temperature). That is, we now have the values of P_1 and T_1, with the volume at some reference figure which will not be permitted to change.

Now plunge the test tube into a container of ice and water. As the dry air contracts, the level in the reference tube will tend to rise since the pressure in the test tube is being reduced. Wait until the system stabilizes; then adjust the movable tube until the reference level is the same as before. Again take the difference between the reference level and the level in the movable tube, add to this the barometric pressure, and you will have P_2. The new temperature, T_2, is 0° + 273 = 273° absolute, assuming that the temperature

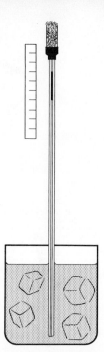

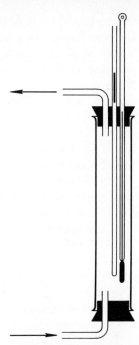

Fig. 18-8 Testing the coefficient of volume expansion as given by Charles' law. If the tube is to be used over several days, insert a plug of calcium chloride to keep it dry. (See also Fig. 18-9.)

Fig. 18-9 Apparatus for verifying Charles' law: a barometer tube with mercury plug and a thermometer held inside a glass cylinder. (See also Fig. 18-11.)

of the ice and water is at zero degrees centigrade.

Repeat this procedure with the test tube submerged in 100° C steam. By following the same steps, you can obtain P_2 and T_3 (100° C + 273 = 373° absolute). When the steam jacket is removed, quickly lower the movable arm to prevent the contracting dry air from causing mercury to spill over into the test tube. The values for the various pressures and temperatures (with volume constant) may now be substituted in the Gay-Lussac equation previously stated to show the constancy of the ratios of pressure to absolute temperature.

Charles' law. While some students are computing the pressure coefficient of expansion, other student committees can plan to test the volume coefficient of expansion, as given by Charles' law.

In this situation, the confined gas is

kept under constant pressure and heated. Students should find that the volume of the gas increases at the same rate (1/273) at which its pressure increases when the volume is kept constant.

In a barometer tube of about 1.5-mm bore, sealed at one end, arrange a column of dry air about 25 cm long and a thread of mercury some 3 cm long as shown in Fig. 18-8. Use a capillary funnel to get the mercury into the narrow-bore tube.

Carefully stand the barometer tube upright in a container of crushed ice. Attach a tube containing calcium chloride and cotton packing to the open end of the barometer tube to prevent moisture from entering if the tube is to be used over several days. Before taking a reading, gently tap the tube to be sure that the mercury index does not shift position. Then measure the distance of the air column from the top of the mercury level to the top of the tube. Since the mercury thread can move freely, the pressure on the air column beneath it remains constant at all times, provided that the barometric pressure does not change over the interval of the experiment. Since this is highly unlikely, we shall assume the pressure to be constant. The volume of air trapped beneath the mercury thread is, of course, the difference between the total length of the tube and the distance of the bottom of the thread to the top of the tube. Since the cross-sectional area of the tube bore is constant, the *length* of the air column in mm may be used in place of *volume* of air. The students should see that the ratio of old length to new length must be the same as the ratio of old volume to new volume since the cross-sectional area cancels out in the division.

Next take a reading when the tubing stands in steam. Insert the tube through the rubber stopper of a steam generator after steam flows from the upper vent in the generator for a few minutes; adjust the height of the tubing in the stopper so that the upper level of the mercury is even with the top of the cork. Then measure the distance of the air column from the top of the cork to the upper end of the tubing.

Students should be ready to use their readings to compute the results and show that when a gas is heated at constant pressure, the volume is directly proportional to the absolute temperature.

$$\frac{V_1}{V_2} = \frac{t_1 + 273}{t_2 + 273} = \frac{T_1}{T_2}$$

You may choose to use an alternate preparation, the one shown in Fig. 18-9. In this case the barometer tubing containing a thin thread of mercury is inserted into the two-hole rubber stopper of the larger glass tube. The other end of the larger tube is equipped with a one-hole

Fig. 18–10 Commercial device for comparing the rates of thermal conduction in metals. (See also Fig. 18–11.) (Central Scientific Company.)

rubber stopper. Ice water is passed through the outer tube first so that the air of the inner tube falls to 0° C; then measure the length of the air column in the narrow tube. Release the ice water; slowly wash through with gradually warmer and warmer water. Next pass steam through the outer tube. What is the increased length of the inner column of air when air is heated to 100° C?

Students should finally summarize all the gas laws: Boyle's, Charles' and Gay-Lussac's laws.

If they are available, gas thermometers containing air, hydrogen, helium, or nitrogen can be demonstrated.

18.3 Heat transfer

18.3a Conduction

Standard demonstration conductometer. One commonly used conductometer con-

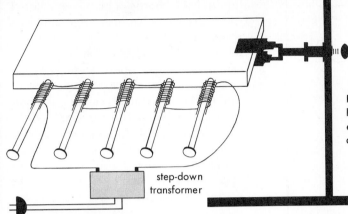

Fig. 18–11 Asbestos board holds the metal rods in this electric conductometer. (See also Fig. 18–10.)

step-down transformer

sists of five rods of different metals (usually iron, copper, aluminum, nickel, and brass) of the same dimensions set into a metal ring as in Fig. 18-10. A match head is attached by means of candle wax to the end of each rod, and the center disk is heated.

The students can observe how the matches ignite in the order of conductivity of the metal rod. Some teachers use, instead of matches, wax washers cut from a candle which melt and fall off the ends. Or you can attach pennies by means of candle wax.

Electric conductometers. Another conductometer that can be made depends upon electric heating which provides a more uniform heat (Fig. 18-11). Make five holes of ¼″ diameter in an asbestos board and fit five rods (¼″ diameter) of equal length but of different metals into the holes. Wrap each rod at one end with asbestos paper and twist ten turns of nichrome wire (#22) around the asbestos, forming a series circuit to each rod. The rods should be at least 5″ long; the wire winding should occupy no more than 1″ snug against the asbestos block. At the other end of the rods attach match heads, coins, or wax washers, as in the standard conductometer. Connect to 12-volt batteries or a 15-volt transformer capable of delivering up to 7 amperes.

Davy safety lamp. You will want to show students that a flame will not pass through a wire gauze because of conduction. See Davy safety lamps in 7.1d.

Conduction in liquids. Also show that liquids do not conduct heat so well as metals. Into a large test tube place pieces of ice and hold them down with a wire grid. Then add water and heat the top part of the tube, holding the bottom of the test tube. Students can explain why the water boils at the top of the tube, producing steam, while the ice at the bottom remains unmelted.

Students will think of many applications of nonconductors or insulators: Why do coffee makers have wooden handles? Why are loosely textured woolens warm?

18.3b Convection

In liquids. There are several ways to demonstrate convection in liquids. A simple method utilizes the convection tube, which can be purchased from a supply house or can be made from glass tubing of ½″ diameter. Carefully heat and bend the ends (see 25.2b), and join the tops to a glass T-tube as in the apparatus for showing the water cycle in 3.2e. Have stu-

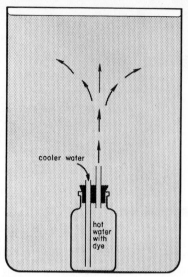

Fig. 18–12 Convection currents in a liquid are evident when the hot water in the submerged bottle is dyed. (See also Fig. 18–13.)

dents watch as a drop of India ink is put on the bottom. Then carefully add water; heat one side as shown. Students should explain why the India ink rises up the heated arm and circulates down the cold side.

Or you may prefer to drop a pellet or two of sodium hydroxide to the bottom of the thoroughly dry convection tube. Then add water very slowly. Place a few drops of an indicator such as phenolphthalein into the top and heat the tube. As the dissolved hydroxide reaches the top by convection, the indicator will turn pink. (If the class is not familiar with the color change in the use of this indicator, it can be demonstrated beforehand in a test tube.) A third variation employs a single crystal of potassium permanganate dropped into a lower corner of the apparatus. As the tube is heated, the material goes into solution. Elicit the role of convection and diffusion in the movement of molecules.

Other devices for showing convection. Another demonstration of convection in liquids uses a bottle of hot water colored with a dye, placed inside a large jar of cold water (Fig. 18-12). Fit a 50-ml wide-mouth bottle with a two-hole stopper that contains one short tube extending upward and a longer tube that extends downward into the bottle, almost reaching the bottom. Fill the bottle with hot water colored with dye and apply the stopper. Lower it into a tall glass jar of cold water. Students should see the colored water rise out of the upper tube as the result of convection. The warmer water which has less density rises up to the top. Recall the expansion of liquids and gases (18.2b, 18.2c). The colored water at the bottom of the bottle is gradually replaced by cold clear water that enters through the long tube. Why will the circulation stop when the water in the bottle and the water in the jar reach the same temperature?

There is another device that uses a flask fitted with glass tubes as in Fig. 18-13, with one tube reaching the bottom. Both tubes rise up 2′ to a rubber stopper fitted into an inverted bottle from which the bottom has been removed (see 25.3a for instructions).

Pour water into the upper bottle so that it runs into the lower one until the latter is full. The lower bottle might initially have a bit of red ink in it so that the liquid will be tinted. Then carefully fill the upper bottle until the liquid covers the ends of both glass tubes. When the flask is heated, the circulation of tinted liquid from the lower tube into the upper one will be clearly visible.

In gases. Students can use pinwheels, lightweight ribbons, or strips of thin aluminum or tissue paper to show convection currents above a radiator or other heater in the classroom. With very thin tissue-paper streamers attached to a long stick or the window pole, you can trace the ventilation and air circulation as well as the

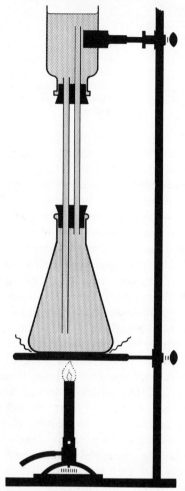

Fig. 18-13 Hot water rises from the lower to the upper bottle. Dye in the lower bottle makes this process visible. (See also Fig. 18-12.)

convection of the air heated by radiators in the room.

One device often used for illustrating convection in gases is the well-known smoke box. A commercial model with a glass front and rear wall or a homemade model can be used. Students can design one specifically to show convection.

Smoke box. This box is made of four slats of wood grooved to receive panes of window glass (8″ × 15″) (Fig. 18-14). Depth of the box is about 5″. If the wood

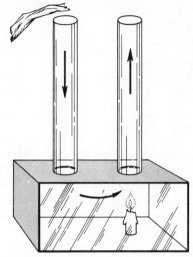

Fig. 18-14 Smoke box for showing convection currents in air.

cannot be grooved, the glass can be fastened with strong plastic tape. You will need two lamp chimneys (glass cylinders or kerosene lamp chimneys can be used). Cut two holes in the top of the box, each slightly smaller than the chimneys to be used, and secure the chimneys in place by means of a cross piece of wood. Or cut the holes in the top of the box exactly to fit the outer diameter of the chimneys. To increase the visibility of white smoke you may want to paint the inside of the box black. It is best not to use too strong a light source.

Place a small lighted candle under one chimney. Show the path of the convection currents by holding ignited touchpaper (use the commercial product or filter paper soaked in 5 per cent potassium nitrate and allowed to dry) in the upper opening of the other lamp chimney. The smoke will descend down the cold chimney, move across the smoke box, and float up the warm chimney. Cigarette smoke can also be used in place of touchpaper.

If you want to show further that it is heat (and not the burning gases from

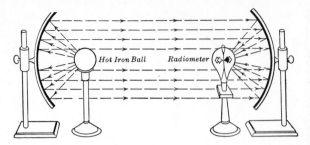

Hot Iron Ball   Radiometer

Fig. 18–15 Focusing radiant energy with parabolic reflectors. (From N. H. Black and E. P. Little, *An Introductory Course in College Physics*, Macmillan, 1948.)

the candle flame) that produces the convection current, substitute the heating element of a small automobile cigar lighter unit for the candle. Connect the lighter unit to a storage battery. (Use a 12-volt battery for a 12-volt unit, and a 6-volt battery for a 6-volt unit.) Repeat the demonstration with the smoke or touchpaper.

18.3c Radiation

If the hand is held alongside (not above) an electric light bulb, heat is felt. Students will explain that this sensation of heat is not due to conduction or convection because there is virtually no gas in the bulb, and the glass itself is a poor conductor. This is an example of radiation of heat, not a transfer through a body nor expansion causing convection currents. If a book is held between the bulb and the hand, there is no feeling of heat; heat rays like light rays travel in straight lines. How does solar heat reach the earth?

Heat transfer through a vacuum. Take a pint bottle of the flat sort, fill with water, and stopper with a one-hole stopper. Insert a thermometer and measure the temperature. Set the bottle inside a bell jar on a vacuum stand and evacuate. Outside the bell jar turn an electric heater toward the enclosed bottle of water. Note the increase in temperature.

Electric light bulbs possess a considerable degree of vacuum. Take a clear glass bulb and mount its bulge in a hole in a Masonite board. Turn on an electric heater from the opposite side. Students

can feel the heat passing through the near vacuum in the bulb.

Radiometer. Have students explain how a radiometer detects radiant energy. They should see that the four vanes are attached to a vertical axis and that it can rotate easily. One side of each vane is coated black and the other side is silvered. All radiometers contain a small amount of residual gas, usually air. As a matter of fact, without a small quantity of gas present in the bulb, there would be no operation. Since black is a better absorber of heat than a silvered surface, the dark side of each vane becomes warmer than the shiny side. The air molecules in contact with the black side therefore take on added kinetic energy in the immediate vicinity of the surface of the vane. Thus, fast-moving molecules collide more frequently with each black surface than with each silvered one. This causes an unbalanced force on each vane, tending to make it move away from the high-speed molecules. Watch the direction of rotation; the black surfaces lag while the bright surfaces lead in the direction of rotation. The operation of a radiometer does not depend upon radiation pressure in any way.

Reflecting and focusing radiation. In some classes you may want to show how radiant energy can be reflected by concave mirrors to a radiometer (Fig. 18-15). Obtain two large parabolic mirrors from old radiant electric heaters and make certain they are as highly polished as pos-

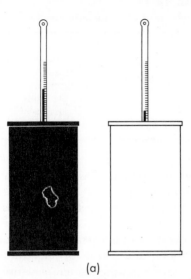

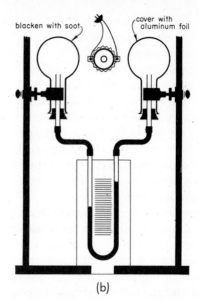

Fig. 18–16 Comparison of heat absorption by black and white surfaces: (a) two cans and thermometers, (b) two flasks equidistant from heat source connected to manometer.

sible. Each mirror should be at least 1′ in diameter, or more if possible. Determine the focal length of each one by facing it toward the sun to obtain parallel incident rays. Note where the light comes to a focus on a small white card held in the path of the reflected rays. The focal length is the distance between the geometric center of the reflecting surface and the spot where focus is obtained, along the principal axis of the mirror.

Heat to red heat an iron ball that measures at least 2″ in diameter. Place this at the principal focus of one of the mirrors. Position the second mirror at a distance from the first that is at least ten times the diameter of either mirror. Place a radiometer at the focus of the second mirror. Show that the radiometer rotates rapidly; then remove the mirrors and demonstrate that the direct radiation is not sufficiently intense to produce rotation.

Absorption of radiant heat. The absorption of infrared radiation depends upon the nature of the absorbing surface. Dull black surfaces absorb a maximum whereas highly polished surfaces absorb little and reflect most of the radiation. Take two large (1 qt or more) fruit juice cans whose tops are intact except for the two holes punched for pouring. Buff one can to a high polish with metal polish or jeweler's rouge; blacken the other can with soot from a luminous candle flame or paint with dull black paint. If soot is used, it can be fixed with spray-on lacquer. In the center of each can make a hole large enough for a one-hole test tube stopper. Through each stopper insert a thermometer. Seal the pouring holes with sealing wax, adhesive tape, or friction tape (Fig. 18-16A). Place a small electric heating unit equidistant from the two cans. Students should notice that the polished can reflects most of the heat and shows little increase in temperature while the temperature rises rapidly in the blackened can.

You can substitute two identical flasks, one sooted or painted black, the other covered with shiny aluminum foil. Fit each flask with a one-hole stopper and a glass tube and fill with alcohol colored with a dye such as methylene blue or red ink. Or use two small flasks such as those previously employed as air thermometers, using water colored with dye (Fig. 18-1). Blacken one air thermometer bulb and cover the other with aluminum foil or aluminum paint. Place an electric heater unit or an electric bulb of high wattage equidistant from both thermometer bulbs. Which thermometer registers the higher temperature? Remove the source of heat. Which flask loses heat faster?

Pressure of expanding air. In an effective demonstration students can read changes in pressure resulting from expanding air. Connect a manometer to a pair of air thermometer bulbs, one blackened and the other silvered, as shown in Fig. 18-21. Equidistant between them place a 660-watt heating coil and socket so that direct radiation from the heater reaches both bulbs with equal intensity. Note that the mercury in the arm of the manometer connected to the black bulb is depressed while the mercury in the other arm rises. This apparatus shows a pressure differential developed as a result of two different rates of heat absorption.

18.4 Law of heat exchange
18.4a Specific heat

Heat is a form of energy and may be described metaphorically as the energy which flows from one object to another due to the difference in their temperatures. More exactly, heat flow is the transfer by molecular impact of the kinetic energy of the molecules in a substance of higher average molecular kinetic energy to a substance whose average is lower.

There are two basic heat units: the calorie and the Btu (British thermal unit). A calorie is defined as the heat required to raise the temperature of one gram of water through one centigrade degree; the Btu is similarly described as the heat needed to

TABLE 18-1
Specific heat of some substances

water	1.000	gold	0.032
ice	0.502	iron	0.113
air	0.24	lead	0.031
aluminum	0.217	mercury	0.033
brass	0.094	platinum	0.032
copper	0.093	silver	0.056
glass (ordinary)	0.200	zinc	0.093

warm one pound of water through one Fahrenheit degree.

The *specific heat* of a substance is the number of calories needed to raise the temperature of one gram of a substance one centigrade degree (or the number of Btu needed to raise the temperature of a pound of a substance one Fahrenheit degree). Thus, the specific heat of water may be given as either 1 cal per g per C° or 1 Btu per lb per F°. In another way, specific heat may also be defined as the number of heat units given up by a unit of mass when its temperature drops one degree.

Comparing specific heat of metals. Arrange a holder to support bars of different metals of equal weights. Immerse these into oil and heat to at least 150° C. Transfer this whole support onto a layer of paraffin so that students can observe the depth to which each bar sinks into the paraffin. The metal having the greatest specific heat gives off the largest amount of heat on cooling and sinks deepest into the paraffin. For example, of four metals, iron sinks deepest, zinc and copper next, and lead least (smallest specific heat). Students can check their observations against a table of specific heat (Table 18-1). Students should also note that water has the highest specific heat of any common substance. Perhaps students can begin to recognize the effect of a body of water on the climate of a region—that it would tend to cool an area in summer and warm it in winter, that is, tend to slow down the rate of temperature change in the air of nearby land areas.

Specific heat of water. Students can also find the high specific heat of water. They will need balls of different metals of the same mass. Heat the balls in boiling water and then place them on a cake of ice; at the same time pour an equal mass of boiling water onto another cake of ice. Students can observe that the size of the depression melted into the ice will vary with the specific heat of the substance. Point out the fact that the specific heat of water is one calorie per gram per C degree (1 Btu per pound per F degree); compare with the equivalent figures for other substances. You might also call attention to the fact that calorie and Btu are defined in terms of the specific heat of water.

Specific heat of a metal. When a hot metal is placed into cold water, the heat given up by the cooling metal is used in warming the water. The units of heat given off by a hot body are equal to the heat units gained by the cold body, provided that no heat is lost to the surroundings.

Students can observe this in the laboratory by using a calorimeter. You will want to provide them with different materials for study: lead, aluminum, and copper shot, iron and steel pellets, and glass beads. Each group of students will need a steam generator, a double-walled calorimeter, a small dipper, a thermometer, a glass stirring rod, and a balance.

In place of a steam generator and commercial dipper, you might have your students bring the shot up to the boiling point of water by filling an ordinary bent tablespoon or a small tea strainer about half full of the metal and immersing the combination in a beaker of boiling water. If you do not have commercial calorimeters, you can make one by lining the inside of a medium-sized battery jar with crumpled newspaper and then "floating"

a 500-ml beaker on this insulation. A cover is not necessary if the students work quickly. (See homemade calorimeter later in this section.)

A procedure for each group might be developed in this way. Find the mass of the material to fill ½ of the dipper. Fit the dipper into the steam generator containing water and adjust a thermometer so that the bulb is in the center of the metal pellets; boil the water until the temperature of the metal becomes constant. One student in each group should find and record the mass of the inner cup of the calorimeter and fill it ⅔ with water which is 5–10° below the room temperature. Also find the mass of the water and record. Fit this cup in the gasket of the jacket of the calorimeter and record the temperature of the hot metal and that of the water before they are mixed.

Carefully, without splattering, pour the hot metal into the water, stir until a constant temperature is reached, and record this temperature. When students find that the final temperature is about 5–10° above the room temperature (recall that the initial temperature was 5–10° below that of the room temperature), the heat loss to the surroundings is approximately cancelled by the heat gained from the environment. Hence, the heat exchange can be assumed to be without loss.

All the groups of students in the laboratory can use their data to find the specific heat of lead, iron, aluminum, or other metals. They know the masses, the specific heat of water and of the calorimeter, and the change in temperature; use the formula for the law of heat exchange—heat lost equals heat gained, or, calories out of the metal equal the calories into the water plus the calories into the calorimeter (usually made of copper or aluminum).

Homemade calorimeter. Students can construct a workable calorimeter from two tin cans (Fig. 18-17) if a commercial insu-

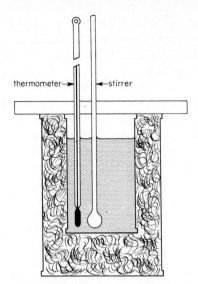

thermometer→ ←stirrer

Fig. 18-17 Calorimeter made from two tin cans.

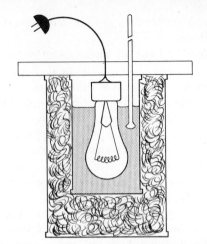

Fig. 18-18 Measuring heat equivalent of electrical energy by means of a tin-can calorimeter.

lated one is not available. They will need a #2½ can as an outer container and a #1 can for the inner one. Insulate the inner can by packing the space between the cans with asbestos, rock wool, or glass wool. Then fit a cover (either wood or a two-hole stopper) to close the inner can. Into one hole insert a thermometer and into the other a stirrer made of a ¼″ dowel stick with a small cross piece of wood. It takes about 10 minutes for water and calorimeter container to reach the same temperature.

Students can show heat from one mass absorbed by another body. Put 50 grams of water at 50° C and 100 grams of water at 10° C into the inner container. Cover it, stir, and read the thermometer. The final temperature of the 150 grams of water should be close to 23.3° C. To find the accuracy of their readings use the law of heat exchange—heat lost equals heat gained.

A thick glass beaker may be used in place of the calorimeter if readings are taken rapidly, but the results will not be very accurate.

$$\text{heat lost} = \text{heat gained}$$
$$(50 \text{ g @ } 50° \text{ C}) = (100 \text{ g @ } 10° \text{ C})$$
$$50 \,(50 - t) = 100 \,(t - 10)$$
$$2500 - 50t = 100t - 1000$$
$$3500 = 150t$$
$$23.3° = t$$

Check: 100 g at 10° has 1000 calories
50 g at 50° has 2500 calories
———————————————
150 g at 23.3° has 3500 calories

Heat equivalent of electrical energy. The heat equivalent of electrical energy is easily measured by submerging the glass bulb of an incandescent lamp in a measured weight of water in the calorimeter. Be very certain that at least ½″ of the neck of the lamp is clear of the water so that there will be no danger of wetting the lamp socket contacts or the connecting wires (Fig. 18-18). Determine the initial temperature and mass of the water. Leave the glowing lamp submerged for about 15 minutes. At the end of a carefully timed period, measure the rise of temperature of the water. A standard 100-watt lamp releases a total of 21,600 calories in 15 minutes since

$$H \,(\text{cal}) = P \,(\text{watts}) \times t \,(\text{seconds}) \times 0.24$$
$$H = 100 \times 900 \times 0.24 = 21,600 \text{ calories}$$

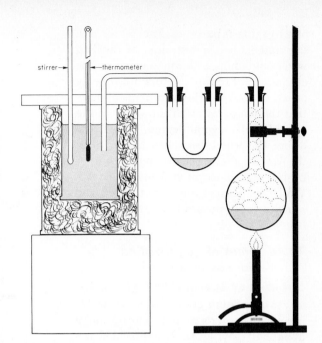

Fig. 18–19 Determining the heat of condensation by the method of mixtures.

This energy appears in the form of *both* heat and light, but predominantly in the form of heat. The heat gained by the water and calorimeter is then determined and compared with the heat generated by the electric power. From 90% to 95% of the electrically generated heat will appear in the form of heated water, indicating that most of the power is wasted as far as illumination is concerned.

18.4b Heat of fusion

How much heat is needed to melt a gram of ice? Students can use the method of mixtures to find the heat of fusion—the number of calories needed to melt a gram of any substance without any temperature change. When the ice melts, heat energy is absorbed by melting ice and thereby prevents a rise in temperature.

Method of mixtures. As a laboratory activity students can check that the heat of fusion of ice is about 80 calories per gram. If they have already found the specific heat of a metal in the laboratory,

have them devise an experiment such as the following. They can weigh a calorimeter, heat about 300 g of water to about 40° C, pour this into the calorimeter, and weigh again. Then add 100 g of crushed ice, stir with a glass rod, and record the temperature throughout. Weigh the calorimeter containing melted ice. Finally, students can use the equation for computing heat of fusion of ice

$$\text{heat gained} = \text{heat lost}$$
$$\text{melting ice} + \text{warming ice water} = \text{warm water}$$
$$\text{in calorimeter} + \text{calorimeter}$$
$$(m_i \times HF) + (m_{iw} \times \text{final temp}) = (m_{ww} \times \text{temp change}) + (m_{cal} \times s_{cal} \times \text{temp change})$$

where m_i = mass of ice, m_{iw} = mass of ice water which is same as mass of ice, HF = heat of fusion of ice (80 cal/g), m_{ww} = mass of warm water in calorimeter, m_{cal} = mass of calorimeter, s_{cal} = specific heat of calorimeter metal.

You may want to have students show the reverse process, that is, in freezing of water heat is given off. Prepare a container of a freezing mixture of cracked ice and salt and embed a test tube of distilled water containing a thermometer into the crushed ice. Prevent the tube from being jarred or shaken. Have students observe that the temperature of the water in the test tube falls several degrees below 0° C before the water begins to freeze. Start the freezing process by stirring slightly or by placing an ice crystal into the tube. Watch the temperature rise to 0° C and remain constant until all the water is frozen.

18.4c Heat of vaporization (or condensation)

Method of mixtures. The heat necessary to change one gram of water at 100° C into steam (water's heat of vaporization) is about 540 calories. In the laboratory it is easier to show the reverse action, that heat is given off when steam condenses in a calorimeter cup of water.

Assemble the apparatus as in Fig. 18-19, using a round-bottomed Florence flask equipped with a one-hole stopper through which steam is delivered to a trap to prevent water (condensed steam) from flowing into the calorimeter cup. Students will need to weigh the calorimeter cup, nearly fill it with water at a temperature of about 10 C° below room temperature, and find the mass of the water. Let the water in the flask boil vigorously for a few minutes and check that steam flows out of the trap. Then insert the tube from the trap into the water in the calorimeter. Use the thermometer to stir gently without striking the walls of the container until the temperature rises 10° above the room temperature. (This partially reduces an error due to heat lost to the room.)

Separate the calorimeter from the apparatus; watch for the temperature to become constant. Record this temperature and find the mass of the water and the cal-

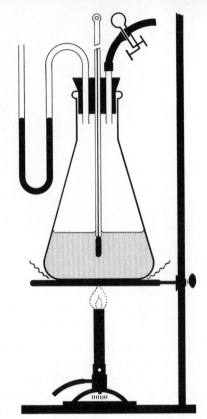

Fig. 18–20 Effect of pressure on the temperature at which water will boil.

orimeter. Determine the mass of steam that condensed in the water. Students can calculate the heat of condensation, which is also the heat of vaporization. A committee of students may want to repeat the procedure, using different temperatures and a different mass of water.

18.4d Effect of pressure on the boiling point of water

In an interesting laboratory activity students can find the pressure and temperature at which water boils, then determine the effect of changing pressure on the boiling point.

Equip a three-hole stopper with a thermometer, an open manometer, and an outlet tube for steam (glass bend with a small section of rubber tubing) as shown in Fig. 18-20. Insert the stopper into a flask that is half full of water, and heat. Students will first observe the bubbles of air and later the larger bubbles of steam that form at the bottom of the flask, rise to the top, and condense on leaving the outlet tube and striking the air. Students should watch the temperature rise to 100° C and then remain steady. Carefully apply a screw clamp and *partly* close the outlet valve. (*Caution: Do not close completely—an explosion can result.*) Why does the manometer show an increase in pressure, and the thermometer a rise in temperature?

Now remove the Bunsen burner so that the water begins to cool a bit. Connect an aspirator to the outlet tube to reduce the pressure in the flask. What is the temperature at which the water begins to boil again?

Some teachers use the method shown in Fig. 18-21 to demonstrate the effect of reduced pressure on the boiling point of water. This method is not quite as informative because there is no provision for reading the pressure or the temperature.

Boil a round-bottomed Florence flask half full of water; remove it from the flame and cork tightly. Support the inverted flask on a ring stand as shown and pour cold water on the flask. As the steam is condensed, lowering the pressure on the water, the water boils again.

Develop the notion of vapor pressure as well as the idea that the boiling point of water (or a liquid) is defined as the temperature at which its vapor pressure is one atmosphere. Why can't eggs be cooked at high elevations such as high mountains? What is the value of using pressure cookers?

In another variation, you can show that if air is exhausted from a flask half filled with water, the liquid boils at a temperature much lower than 100° C. Fill a round-bottomed Florence flask halfway with tap water and insert a two-hole stopper containing a thermometer and a glass outlet tube. Have the bulb of the thermometer in the water. Connect an exhaust pump by rubber tubing to the glass outlet. Support the flask in a cork ring, record the temperature, and start pumping air (and water vapor) out of the flask. Students can see the air bubbles rise first and can then watch the water boil at room temperature.

Pressure of a saturated vapor. At some time, you may want to show students how molecules of a vapor bombard a surface and exert increased pressure. Prepare two Torricelli tubes with mercury. Use a curved medicine dropper to insert a few drops of ether into one tube. (*Caution: Ether is explosive. When there is a possibility that ether will fume, there should be no flames or sparks in the room.*) When the ether rises to the top of the mercury and evaporates to produce saturation, watch the mercury drop. If a meterstick is placed upright in the mercury, students can read the pressure in

Fig. 18–21 Effect of reduced pressure on boiling point of water.

the control. Compare the original height with the fall in centimeters in the experimental tube. This will be a measure of the saturated vapor pressure. Increase the vapor pressure again rapidly by fanning a Bunsen flame across the top of the tube so that the column of mercury is pushed down still further. What happens to the mercury column if ice is placed near the top of the Torricelli tube?

You may want to refer at this time to distillation and also to distillation of fuels (fractional distillation described in Chapter 14). A mixture half water and half alcohol can be used to study the temperature points at which alcohol and water vaporize in distillation.

18.5 Energy used in effecting a change of state

18.5a Cooling by evaporation

Have several students apply alcohol to one hand while wetting the other hand with water. Ether may also be used. (*Caution: Keep room ventilated. Allow no flames or sparks—ether is explosive.*) Wave the hands. Which hand feels cooler? Which fluid evaporates faster? What relation seems to exist between rate of evaporation and removal of heat?

Show that the evaporation of ether can remove heat rapidly enough to freeze water. Place a test tube containing a few cc of water in a small container of ether. Blow air through the ether with a hand pump or an aspirator to cause rapid evaporation. Students can observe that some water is soon frozen. Or you may place a few cc of ether on a watch crystal positioned on a thin square of glass or plywood. If you put a few drops of water under the watch crystal, the water will freeze as the ether evaporates, thereby sealing the dish to the thin square. What would be the effect on the rate of evapo-

ration if air were removed by an exhaust pump from an enclosed area over the ether so that the ether molecules evaporated still faster?

Elicit the factors affecting the rate of evaporation. Students should be ready to explain that when air is bubbled through the ether the evaporating surface of the ether is greatly increased. Molecules are able to evaporate into the air bubbles as well as from the surface of the ether. They can now summarize the factors that affect the rate of evaporation of a liquid: nature of the liquid, temperature of liquid, degree of saturation and density of the gas into which molecules are to escape, amount of surface of liquid exposed, and rapidity of circulation of air over the liquid.

From this, some teachers lead into a study of evaporation (and the degree of saturation of the air in which evaporation takes place) and a study of relative humidity. What is the effect of temperature of the air on the amount of moisture that it can hold? What is the effect of the amount of moisture in the air on the rate of evaporation? Methods for the determination of relative humidity and of dew point have been described in Chapter 4.

18.5b Cooling and change of state

After students have learned that a solid requires heat to change to a liquid (heat of fusion), you may want to have them investigate the release of heat as a liquid changes to a solid. Many teachers have students make a graph of the cooling curve through the change of state of acetamide or naphthalene crystals.

Change of state of acetamide. Support a test tube nearly full of acetamide crystals in a hot water bath. Place a thermometer into the acetamide and heat the beaker until the melted acetamide reaches 95° C. Then raise the test tube out of the beaker and clamp it to a ring stand to cool. Hang the thermometer from the ring stand so that it hangs into the test tube of acetamide, leaving the temperature range from 95° down to 40° visible without moving the thermometer.

At half-minute intervals, students can record the thermometer readings until the temperature of the acetamide falls to 50° C. Then they can plot the readings on a graph, using the time intervals on the horizontal axis and the temperature changes on the vertical axis. At what point do crystals first appear? At what point does solidification take place? What statement can be made about the temperature changes when a crystalline substance changes state?

Rapid evaporation: dry ice. You may want to show how the larger heat of vaporization rather than the heat of fusion is put to use in getting low temperatures. Attach a cloth bag to the stopcock of a cylinder of liquid carbon dioxide. Open the stopcock; as the liquid carbon dioxide rushes out of the bag, the liquid rapidly evaporates and freezes to form the crystalline dry ice. The solid also sublimes rapidly, reaching temperatures down to −78.5° C.

You may wish to freeze mercury to solid form. Place a small quantity of dry ice and a little acetone in a beaker. Use a test tube with a few cc of mercury in it to stir the mixture so that students can see the mercury solidify.

Formation of fog: condensation of water vapor. When the temperature drops, water vapor condenses on dust particles in the air, thereby cooling the atmosphere and forming fog. When moisture condenses on the ground or on any objects, dew is formed.

Prepare two large bottles containing 2 cc of water so that saturation can be produced. (Saturation occurs in a few min-

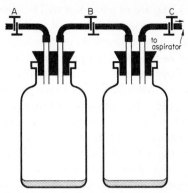

Fig. 18–22 Influence of a drop in pressure upon temperature can be shown by suddenly lowering the pressure in a bottle whose air is saturated with water vapor.

utes in a room at normal temperature.) Close the stopcocks at A and B in Fig. 18-22. Attach an exhaust pump and remove air from the one bottle so that the air pressure is reduced. Close the stopcock C and open the stopcock at B so that the vapor from the second bottle expands rapidly, resulting in a falling of the temperature below the saturation point. Students should see fog form in the bottle. (If a small quantity of smoke is added to the bottle at the start, fog may be more visible to students in a classroom.) You may want to relate this to dew point and to cloud formation (3.2c, 3.2d).

18.6   Mechanical equivalent of heat
18.6a   *Joule's law*

This demonstration of Joule's law (a modification by Hirn) gives a rough estimate.[1] Error may run high because there is some loss of heat through radiation and conduction due to the time it takes to get a thermometer reading. Students will need to roll up heavy brown paper or cardboard and fasten it securely with cellophane tape and string to make a tube 1 meter long and about 6 cm in diameter.

[1] Modified from C. Holley and V. Lohr, *Mastery Units in Physics,* Lippincott, 1952.

One kilogram of lead shot will be used. It may be necessary first to cool the lead shot in ice water to lower its temperature 2 or 3° below the room temperature. Close one end of the paper tube with a tightly fitting cork and pour in the cool shot; close this end of the tube with another cork. For later use, prepare a third cork which has a thermometer run through it. Now begin to invert the tube slowly, back and forth several times (about 10 times), so that the shot falls from one end of the tube to the other. Have students hold the tube in the middle rather than at the ends so that the heat of the hands does not affect the temperature reading to be taken at the end of 10 turns. (Paper and cork are poor conductors of heat.) Hold the tube upright; quickly remove one cork and replace it with the one holding a thermometer. Carefully tilt the tube so that the lead shot surrounds the bulb of the thermometer without striking it so hard as to break it. After students record this initial temperature of the shot as being 2 or 3° below room temperature, they will be ready to start the demonstration.

Now replace the original cork and begin the demonstration by inverting the tube (held in the middle) back and forth for 100 times in succession. If students alternately put each end of the tube on the desk, they will prevent the cork from being forced out of the tube. Elicit which stages show potential energy and kinetic energy. Which kind of energy is converted into heat?

After 100 turns, quickly replace one cork with the cork containing the thermometer and record the final temperature. When students measure the distance in cm from the top of the lead shot to the end of the tube, they will have the mean height through which the shot falls.

In the calculations performed by the students, they will have to take account of the different units used in measuring heat and mechanical work. On the one hand, the heat energy gained by the lead shot is given by

energy gained =
$$m(g) \times .sp.ht(cal/g/°C) \times (t_2 - t_1)$$

This expression gives the energy gained in *calories,* as a dimensional check will show. On the other hand, the mechanical work is

work done = no. of inversions $\times$
mass of shot (g) $\times$ height (cm) $\times g$

Since g is 980 cm/sec^2, the work done comes out in dyne-cm or *ergs.* This answer should then be converted to *joules* by dividing it by 10^7 since 1 joule = 10^7 ergs. At this point, the heat energy in calories may be converted to joules by making use of the mechanical equivalent of heat in the metric system. That is,

1 cal = 4.19 joules

Hence, the answer in calories should be multiplied by 4.19 to obtain the value of the heat energy in joules. Until this is done, no attempt should be made to equate the heat gained by the shot with the work done in inverting the lead-filled tube.

18.7 Heating systems
18.7a *Hot-air convection heating system*

Students can make a simple hot-air heating system by nesting two tin cans so that there is a space of ½″ between them. Drill a hole in the side of the smaller can and fit a piece of copper tubing into the hole as a chimney. Invert the two cans now and drill a hole at the corresponding point in the larger can to permit the metal chimney to leave the "hot-air furnace" (Fig. 18-23). Then drill several

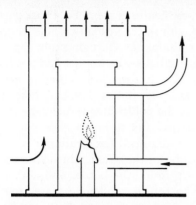

Fig. 18–23 Model of hot-air convection heating.

holes in the part that is now the top of the larger can; also drill a 1″ hole or punch a hole with a juice can opener near the edge of the larger can to serve as the fresh air opening for the air to be heated. Finally, place a burning candle under the smaller can or "fire box." Students should trace the smoke of the candle rising out of the chimney, but the warmed air will rise out of the top openings of the larger can. These represent the registers found in the floor of a hot-air heated house.

A more elaborate apparatus involves fitting each hot-air hole with a tube of sheet metal to represent the pipes that would carry the heated air to individual rooms. Tissue ribbons or smoke may be used to trace the movement of air through the hot-air jacket (the larger can) as it is heated.

18.7b Steam heating systems

One-pipe steam heating system. This heating system can be made from a Pyrex flask fitted with a one-hole stopper and glass tubing that leads to one or more "radiators" (Fig. 18-24). If more than one "radiator" is used, a Y-tube can be used for the branches. Represent each "radiator" with an inverted 100- to 200-ml bottle fitted with a two-hole stopper. One hole receives the steam. Fit a glass tube

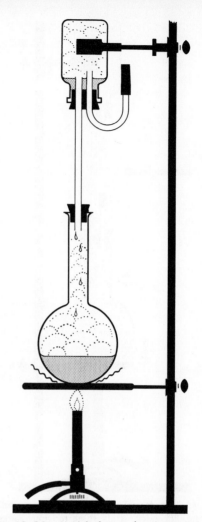

Fig. 18–24 Model of steam heating system.

into the other hole of the stopper and connect a rubber tube that represents the air valve. Demonstrate the path of steam in this way. Trace the rise of the steam by convection and expansion to the radiators. Point out the return flow of the cooler condensed water down the walls of the pipe (tubing) to the boiler. The flask or "boiler" can be heated by gas or by means of an electric hot plate.

Students will be able to observe the failure of steam to enter an air-bound radiator if the air valve is clamped with a pinch

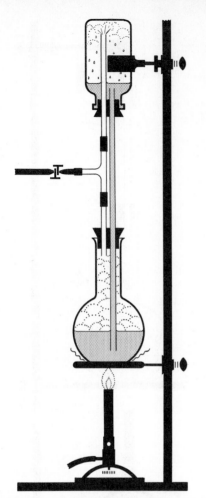

Fig. 18–25 Model of a two-pipe steam heating system. For extra safety some teachers make a small hole in the upper end of the top bottle.

clamp or spring-type clothespin. (*Caution: Do not work the apparatus with all the air valves closed; an explosion may result.*)

Some students like to make a model house using copper-tubing radiators in each room. Remember to open the rubber air valves. Students can also cut an old air valve in half with a hack saw to see how the valve unit allows air to escape but closes as steam pressure builds up in the radiator.

Two-pipe steam heating system. Large buildings, including many schools, have a two-pipe heating system. Fit a flask partly filled with water with a two-hole stopper that contains one short glass tube that extends just below the stopper and one long glass tube that reaches to the bottom of the flask (Fig. 18-25). The long tube represents the cold water return; the short one carries the steam to glass bottle or flask "radiators." Each radiator has one long tube for the steam, which enters and rises up inside the bottle, and a shorter tube to return condensed water to the long cold-water return tube in the flask. The system must be fitted with a rubber safety valve as in Fig. 18-25. This safety valve should consist of a short length of rubber hose on the horizontal leg of the T-tube. If a small quantity of high-temperature grease is smeared on the horizontal leg before placing the rubber tube on it, the tube may then be clamped with no danger. If the steam pressure is allowed to build up beyond a few lb/in² gauge pressure, the grease will permit the rubber tubing to be blown off easily.

Two-pipe heating systems frequently employ a partial vacuum. The pressure in the system is lowered by means of a vacuum pump or a steam aspirator. This permits water to boil and form steam at a lower temperature (see 18.4d), thereby increasing efficiency. You can demonstrate this by connecting a hand-vacuum pump to the T-tube.

18.7c   Hot-water heating system

The hot-water heating system is an excellent application of convection in liquids (Fig. 18-26). A Pyrex flask (the "boiler") filled with colored water is fitted with a two-hole stopper equipped with one tube that descends to the bottom of the flask ("the cold-water return") and is connected to an expansion tank, its opening flush with the tank's bottom. The other tube starts at a point high in the water of the

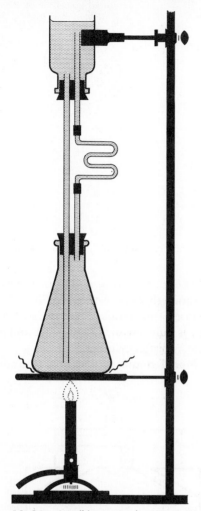

Fig. 18-26 An all-hot-water heating system.

rents is to place a pellet of sodium hydroxide in the "radiator" and use clear water plus a few drops of phenolphthalein in the "boiler." The clear water in the "radiator" turns red when the warmed water from the "boiler" reaches the sodium hydroxide in the "radiator."

18.8 Heat engines

Heat engines convert chemical energy into heat and mechanical energy. The first engine was probably the reaction engine made by Hero in Alexandria more than 2000 years ago. (For demonstrations of reaction engines, see Chapter 24.) It is the kinetic energy of heated gas molecules that moves a piston, drives a turbine blade, or produces the thrust of a jet engine (see Chapters 2 and 24).

You may want to have students report on the background of engine "inventions." They may begin with the cannon—an engine that converts the chemical energy of gunpowder into mechanical energy, as was demonstrated by the French physicist Papin. He showed that a cannon could do useful work by lifting a weight instead of shooting a cannon ball. Then Newcomen developed this concept into an engine that depended upon the release of energy from the condensation of steam; Newcomen engines were used to operate pumps in mines for some 200 years. Finally, James Watt developed the modern double-acting reciprocating steam engine that made steamships and the first locomotive possible. Internal-combustion engines were developed later; the first, operated on illuminating gas, appeared in 1853. By 1870 successful gas engines were in use. Aircraft, with their requirements for high-horsepower engines in lightweight packages, led to the development of modern engines. And more recently, in jet engines and rockets, the principle of the Hero engine has been put back to work.

Pyrex flask and is shaped to represent a radiator. This tube empties well above the bottom of the expansion tank. Instead of the bent tubing, a bottle can be used to represent the radiator; the expansion tank can be made of a bottle with its bottom removed or a large Pyrex funnel.

The entire system must be filled with water before heating. If colored water is placed in the "boiler" and clear water in all the other parts of the system, students can watch the circulation.

Another way to show convection cur-

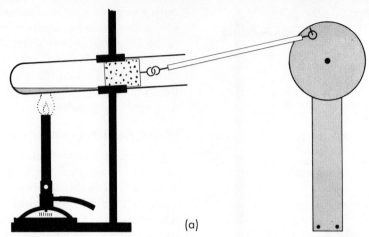

(a)

Fig. 18–27a and b Steam pressure turns the wheel one half revolution. A Pyrex test tube should be used.

18.8a   *External-combustion engines*

The release of mechanical energy from steam can be easily demonstrated. Place 3 cc of water in a heavy Pyrex test tube, and clamp the tube to a ring stand so that it is tilted upward at a 45° angle away from the class. This is most effective if a target is used. (A few trial shots will indicate where the target should be placed.) Cork the test tube and heat it until the water boils; the steam forces the cork out of the tube. The popping cork will fly off and hit the target. Some teachers wrap the test tube in copper screening to avoid possible scattering of the glass if it should break.

Steam engines. The action of a piston can be demonstrated by fitting a well-greased cork into a wide Pyrex test tube. Attach one end of a dowel stick to the cork by means of two screw eyes and connect the other end to a wheel as in Fig. 18-27A. With the test tube slanted slightly, add 1 or 2 cc of water, check the smoothness of movement of the greased cork, then move the cork to a point near the end of the tube containing the water. Apply heat, causing the water to boil briefly. The steam pressure will drive the cork to the

other end of the tube and cause the wheel to rotate through ½ turn. In Fig. 18-27B, a closer approximation to the steam engine is shown with flask as boiler and glass tube as piston cylinder.

Model steam engines. Some students

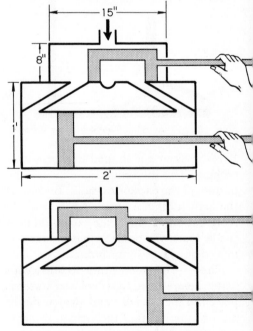

Fig. 18–28 Cutaway diagram and moving wood parts illustrate the action of a steam engine.

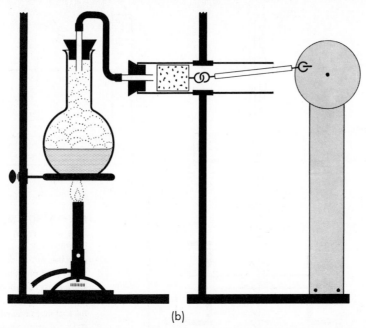

(b)

may have model steam engines that they can demonstrate in class. In most of the model engines the water in the boiler is heated by an electrical heating unit. Some teachers remove the heating unit and heat the boiler with an alcohol burner or a Bunsen burner so that the model more accurately represents the use of a fuel to change water into steam. A can of Sterno (alcohol in solidified paraffin) also makes a good source of heat for model steam engines.

Valve gear. The action of a valve can be demonstrated by building a model of the valve and the piston with attached connecting rod having the dimensions shown in Fig. 18-28. Wood stock, $1'' \times 1''$, is excellent for making the valve and piston. On the blackboard draw a cross-sectional diagram of the rest of the steam engine to fit around the model valve and piston. Colored chalk can be used to make the cylinder stand out. A student can hold the piston and rod in position against the diagram on the blackboard or a large chart. Have another student hold the

valve rod. As one student moves the piston, the other student can move the valve rod to the correct position for the next stroke.

Steam turbines. The principle of the turbine can be shown by aiming a jet of steam from a glass nozzle at a turbine (or pinwheel) (Fig. 18-29). An ordinary toy

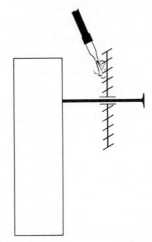

Fig. 18–29 Principle of the turbine can be shown by directing a jet of steam at a toy pinwheel.

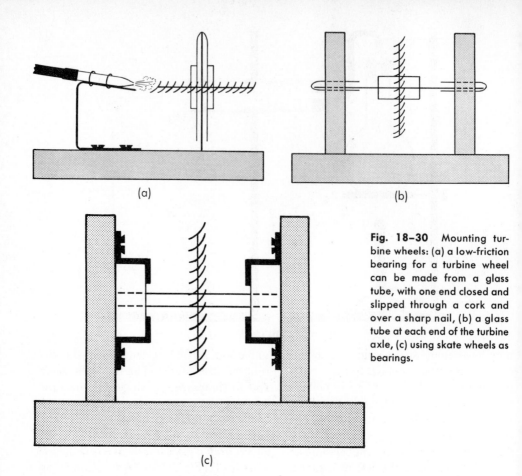

Fig. 18-30 Mounting turbine wheels: (a) a low-friction bearing for a turbine wheel can be made from a glass tube, with one end closed and slipped through a cork and over a sharp nail, (b) a glass tube at each end of the turbine axle, (c) using skate wheels as bearings.

plastic pinwheel can be used or one can be cut from stiff aluminum foil. You can make your own turbine. Remove the top of a tin can with a mechanical can opener, and use it as a form for cutting a turbine wheel. At every ¼″ along the circumference draw a line to the center of the circle. Into each line make a ⅜″ cut with metal cutting shears. In the center drill or punch ½″ hole. Make a low-friction bearing as follows. Seal one end of a 2″ length of glass tubing (¼″ bore) and insert it into a ¼″ hole bored in the center of a cork of ½″ diameter (Fig. 18-30A). Or use two glass tubes to mount the turbine vertically (Fig. 18-30B).

Bend the sections of the tin can top be-tween each pair of ⅜″ cuts with pliers. Set each blade at an angle of approximately 45° and have each curve slightly. Slide the cork into the hole in the disk. A piece of board about 4″ × 4″ × ¾″ with a 3″ finishing nail driven through the center acts as the base. File the nail head to a sharp point. Then complete the assembly of the turbine by slipping the glass tube-cork-and-turbine-wheel unit over the nail. Show students how to operate the turbine. Attach a medicine dropper tube to a strip of metal that is fastened by nails or screws to the base, and pass steam through it to the turbine wheel blades. Adjust the angle of the nozzle tube to attain the maximum speed of rotation.

Fig. 18–31 Internal-combustion chamber in which gas and air mixtures are ignited by electric spark. The cylinder is wrapped with two layers of cellophane tape for safety: (a) collecting gas by water displacement, (b) arrangement for ignition.

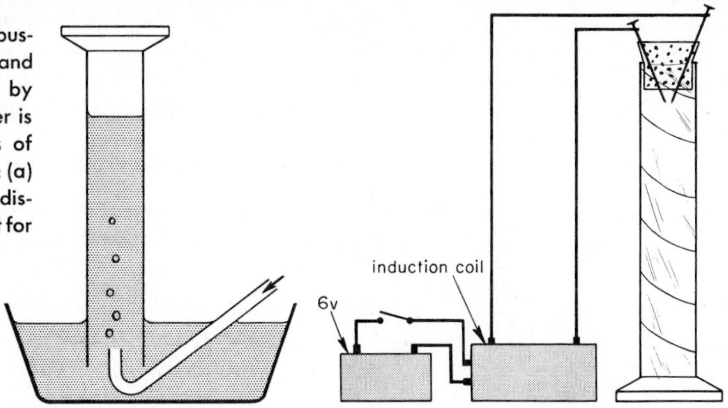

induction coil

6v

(a)   (b)

The same turbine wheel can be mounted vertically instead of horizontally (Fig. 18-30B). Skate wheels can be used as bearings. Solder a ¼″ metal rod or bolt a long ¼″ bolt through the center of the wheel. Fasten the wheels to a board by means of two metal straps (Fig. 18-30C).

Commercial steam turbine models are also available from scientific supply houses. If the front cover of a commercial model is removed to expose the turbine, students can observe the action of the steam against the rotating blades of the turbine.

18.8b *Internal-combustion engines*

Combustion chamber. A safe internal-combustion demonstration can be made by carefully wrapping a tall glass cylinder (250 ml or smaller; anything larger is dangerous) with two layers of cellophane tape (Fig. 18-31). A large cork carrying two nails with points set at 45° (Fig. 18-31B) acts as both the piston and the spark plug. Have illuminating gas or natural gas enter the cylinder by water displacement as shown in Fig. 18-31A. Then let the cylinder stand open to allow air to combine with the gaseous fuel (17 seconds for illuminating gas, 24 seconds for natural or bottled gas). Careful timing as indicated will result in a proportion of 10 parts air to

one part of illuminating gas or 20 parts of air for complete combustion of the methane (CH_4), which forms 90% of natural gas. Hook the end of #28 copper wire to each nail head, making sure that the wires do not touch, and attach the two free ends of the wire to the secondary terminals of an induction coil. The induction coil primary connects to a switch and batteries as in Fig. 18–31B. (*Caution: Keep the switch in the open or "Off" position while assembling the apparatus.*) Now place the cork into the top of the cylinder and turn on the current. Students will see the fuel burn in the cylinder and hear a loud explosion that drives the cork (piston) up toward the ceiling.

Internal-combustion cannon. Commercial models of this cannon are available from scientific supply houses, or students can build one to be used as permanent equipment of the department. Use a block of wood 2″ × 2″ × 6″ to serve as the cannon barrel; drill a 1″ diameter hole 5″ down the center as shown in Fig. 18-32. Two nails driven across from opposite sides into the center of the hole, with their points ⅛″ apart, will serve as a spark plug. Connect the secondary of an induction coil to the nails and place a drop of gasoline or ether in the "cannon" and allow it

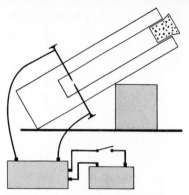

Fig. 18–32 Internal-combustion cannon.

to vaporize for a few minutes. Then close the hole of the "cannon" with a cork and turn on the current, being certain the cannon is pointed away from students. The fuel and air mixture burns rapidly, and the cork will fly across the room. (*Caution: Ether and gasoline are both inflammable and explosive. They should not be used in the presence of flame or sparks in the classroom or laboratory.*)

Internal-combustion can. A clean (½ pint) paint or varnish can (for safety's sake no larger) of the friction-lid type makes a spectacular model of an internal-combustion engine. Punch a hole in the side of the can, near the bottom, just large enough to take the bushing of a standard automobile spark plug. Your garage or service station can find a nut of the right size to fit the plug. Secure the spark plug tightly in this hole, with the discharge points inside the can. Connect the can and plug terminal to the secondary binding posts of an induction coil; the primary is connected to four dry cells in series or a 6-volt storage battery through a spring type of switch, such as a telegraph key. Using a medicine dropper, drop three drops of white or high-octane gasoline in the can, replace the lid tightly, then warm the can in your hands for at least 3 minutes to vaporize the gasoline and force it to mix with the

air in the can. Close the switch, keeping your face well away from the top of the can. The spark causes ignition of the mixture, forcing the cover off with a loud pop.

18.8c *Air-fuel mixtures*

Explosive mixture can. A can with a friction lid can serve as an excellent model for demonstrating the nature of an explosive mixture (Fig. 18-33). First drill a ¼″ hole in the center of the lid and a ⅜″ hole at the side of the can near the bottom. Fill the can with illuminating, natural, or bottled gas through a rubber tube fitted into the bottom hole. When gas begins to come out of the top hole, disconnect the gas source and leave the bottom hole open. Now ignite the gas at the top hole with a match. At first, there should be a large yellow flame at the top hole, but after a few minutes the flame should gradually become smaller and less visible. As gas is consumed, air enters through the bottom hole; when the air and remaining gas in the can have the proper air-gas ratio for an explosive mixture, a violent explosion forces the cover upward into the air. It is best to try this demonstration before the class meets. Be sure to have the class stand at a safe distance (about 6 feet).

Combustion mixture tubes. One successful method uses four 250-ml cylinders

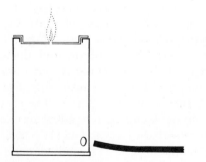

Fig. 18–33 Can for preparing explosive mixtures of gas and air.

filled with fuel gas (use water displacement), with the following ratios of gas to air: a) all gas; b) ½ gas and ½ air; c) ¾ gas and ¼ air; d) ⅞ gas and ⅛ air. When the proper mixture is in each cylinder, cover the mouth of each cylinder (still under water) with a glass square, remove them from the water, and stand them upright. Now ignite the mixtures one by one by lifting the glass cover and quickly inserting a long burning wax taper. Students should observe that a) will burn with a yellow flame and dense black smoke; b) will have more flame and less smoke; c) will burn with some blue flame; d) will flash suddenly, showing the presence of a more explosive mixture.

Model gasoline engines. Cutaway model engines are available from scientific supply houses, or students can operate model airplane engines on an open window sill or in the school yard. Small gas engines such as those found in lawn mowers, water pumps, and washing machines make good working models for class demonstrations. You may want to refer at this time to the study of automobiles and airplane engines in Chapter 24.

Operating cutaway engines. If the school shop will collaborate, an excellent project for a class group or club is the construction of a cutaway of a small automobile or airplane engine to expose cylinders, pistons, valves, crankshaft, and camshaft.

Students can obtain engines from a junk yard; it may be possible to obtain old aircraft engines from the Air Force through the General Services Administration. Dismantle the engine and cut away a little less than one half of the block and cylinder heads. Reassemble heads; the starter operated by four automobile batteries (24 v) can be used to turn the crankshaft slowly so that the class can see the different parts in action.

Please refer to the operation of automobile engines and ignition systems as developed in Chapter 24.

Diesel engines. Students can show first that a bicycle tire or basketball pump gets hot as the air contained in it is compressed. Then show the effect of the compression of a gas on the production of heat. This may be shown by using a fire syringe with dry paper that has been soaked in potassium nitrate as tinder. Instead of potassium nitrate, you may prefer to place a few drops of carbon disulfide on a piece of cotton and drop this to the bottom of the tube for a minute or so; then remove the cotton. Insert the piston, and this compression will quickly generate enough heat to ignite the vapor so that a flash will be seen. (It may take a few trials to determine the amount of carbon disulfide to use.) Relate this work to Joule's law.

If one of the students has a model airplane diesel engine, he can be invited to operate it in class, or you can purchase one for class demonstrations. If possible, arrange to have students inspect a diesel engine in a bus, truck, tractor, or pumping or power station.

CAPSULE LESSONS
Ways to get started in class

18-1. In some classes begin by asking students to judge the temperature of several containers of water. Or a student can place one hand in very warm water and the other in cold water. Then have him transfer each hand to a container of water at room temperature. What are his impressions of the temperature of the containers of water? Develop the need for thermometers. Students may calibrate a thermometer or check the fixed points of several thermometers as described in the chapter. Compare heat and temperature. Then you will want to move along into specific heat of substances.

18-2. In a laboratory activity students can determine the specific heat of a metal. It may be possible for students to plan an experiment using the methods of mixtures.

18-3. After students know that expansion by heat causes a change in state, they can determine the heat of fusion of snow and/or the heat of condensation of steam. They can demonstrate applications that show heat is given off when water freezes.

18-4. What is the effect of pressure on the boiling point of water? Use any one of the several demonstrations described in this chapter to establish a definition of boiling.

18-5. Begin by demonstrating the freezing of mercury. Lead into a discussion of the factors involved in change of state. Students can review the kinetic theory of molecular motion.

18-6. How can heat be transferred from place to place? Without giving explanations, you will want to demonstrate conduction, radiation, and convection. Then have students describe what has happened. In which case are

molecules moving faster? In which case is kinetic energy passed along the line? How can energy be transferred by radiation?

18-7. Demonstrate Joule's law and calculate the mechanical equivalent of heat. Elicit the role of friction and establish the loss of heat in calculating the efficiency of a machine.

18-8. How are our homes heated? Students may construct models of home heating systems and explain how they operate.

18-9. Perhaps students will report on the different kinds of heat engines. Demonstrate in class the operation of an internal-combustion engine. Show the heat produced as a result of compression. Use cutaway models in class, if possible.

18-10. Students may relate the role of black and shiny bodies and their ability to absorb and radiate heat. What effect has this on absorption and radiation of radiant energy from the sun? Explain the climate near an ocean. What conditions cause land and ocean breezes?

18-11. As a summary of some area of this topic, you may want to show a film or filmstrip.

PEOPLE, PLACES, AND THINGS

Over a period of years many teachers glean a remarkably fine assortment of teaching aids either made by students in class (calibrating thermometers, building models and cutaways of engines) or toy engines that have been contributed. Students working in garages often bring to class spark plugs, storage batteries, and carburetors.

BOOKS AND PAMPHLETS

These are only a few of the books which are pertinent to the work discussed in this chapter. These and many other references classified by subject and with complete bibliographical data are given in the bibliography at the end of the book.

Finck, J., *Thermodynamics,* Bookman, 1955.
French, A., *Principles of Modern Physics,* Wiley, 1958.
Hausmann, E., and E. Slack, *Physics,* Van Nostrand, 1958.
Holton, G., and D. Roller, *Foundations of Modern Physical Science,* Addison-Wesley, 1958.
Krauskopf, K., and A. Beiser, *Fundamentals of Physical Science,* 4th ed., McGraw-Hill, 1960.
Leighton, R., *Principles of Modern Physics,* McGraw-Hill, 1959.

Miller, A., *Roberts Heat and Thermodynamics,* 5th ed., Interscience, 1960.
Miller, F., Jr., *College Physics,* Harcourt, Brace, 1959.
Rogers, E., *Physics for the Inquiring Mind,* Princeton U. Press, 1960.
Semat, H., *Fundamentals of Physics,* Rinehart, 1958.
Sproull, R., *Modern Physics: A Textbook for Engineers,* Wiley, 1956.

FILMS AND FILMSTRIPS

This partial list is intended only as a guide toward film and filmstrip selection. Refer to the more complete listing at the end of the book where films are classified by subject and where a key to abbreviations and addresses of distributors are given. The cost of film rental, of course, is subject to change. Films are sound and black and white unless otherwise specified.

Carnot Cycle (f, s), McGraw-Hill, inquire local film library.
Energy and Its Transformations (f, s), EBF.
Energy at Work Series (5 fs), Popular Science through McGraw-Hill, $3.00 each.
Energy Is Our Business (f, s, c), N.Y. State Dept. Commerce, free.

Heat (series 15 lessons in introductory physics) (f, s), EBF.

Heat (4 fs), Popular Science through McGraw-Hill, $3.00 each.

Heat (f, s), Science Slides, $3.50.

The Heat Engine (f, s), Shell, free.

Heat: Its Nature and Transfer (f, s), EBF.

How Heat Travels (fs), Popular Science through McGraw-Hill, $3.50.

How We Measure Heat (fs), Film Strip of the Month.

Introduction to the Heat Engine (f, s), Shell, free.

Modern Physics Serves: Heat (set of 5 fs), Popular Science through McGraw-Hill, $3.25 each.

Nature of Heat (f, s, c), Coronet, inquire local film library.

Service Unseen (air conditioning) (f, s, c), Modern Talking Picture Service, free.

Steam for Power (f, s, c), N.Y. State Dept. of Commerce, free.

The Steam Turbine (f, s), Young America, inquire local film library.

Thermodynamics (f, s), EBF.

Thermometers (radiation pyrometers, electronic potentiometers) (fs and lectures), Minneapolis-Honeywell, free.

FREE AND INEXPENSIVE MATERIALS

This is only a partial listing of free and inexpensive materials available to the teacher at this time. A directory of addresses is given at the end of the book. Many of these materials are distributed to teachers without charge. Where there is a small fee, the cost is indicated, although the prices are subject to change. While we recommend the material for use in the classroom, we do not necessarily endorse the products advertised.

Automobile (charts; also resource materials kit), General Motors; inquire cost.

Chemical Problems of the Automobile, General Motors, free.

Diesel, The Modern Power, General Motors, free.

Four-stroke Cycle and Flame Travel (chart), General Motors, free.

Gasoline by Synthesis; Natural Gas, Standard Oil of N.J., free.

Man-Made Magic (steam turbine), General Electric, free.

Miracle of Ice from Heat, Servel Inc., free.

Short Stories of Science and Invention (by Kettering), General Motors, free.

Story of Combustion, Chrysler, free.

Story of the Turbine, General Electric, free.

CHAPTER 19

Sound and music

Sound is such an immediate part of our everyday life—from simple person-to-person communication to hearing a complex symphony—it is taken for granted. And study of sound has led us into the field of ultrasonics, with applications in the fields of medicine, food processing, chemistry, and navigation.

The simple tuning fork, a complex musical instrument, and the intricate ultrasonic generator are dependent on similar basic principles which can be demonstrated in the classroom. All these devices and the phenomena relating to their use utilize the transmission of energy by longitudinal waves. These waves are compressional in nature, and, unlike electromagnetic waves such as light and radio, require a material medium through which they can travel.

19.1 Properties of sound

19.1a *Propagation of sound*

Sound in a vacuum. Show that the transmission of sound requires a medium by suspending an electric bell in a bell jar. Evacuate the jar with a vacuum pump, and show that the sound level diminishes, although the hammer of the bell is still vibrating as violently as before.

Students can use a modification of this demonstration in group work, using a heavy glass jar instead of the bell jar.

Assemble the apparatus shown in Fig. 19-1, suspending the bell with rubber bands from a three-hole stopper in the glass jar. Into one hole insert a glass tube connected to a vacuum pump by means of rubber tubing. Insert brass bolts into the other two holes to serve as binding posts and connect to the bell with very thin copper wires. Attach the leads from the binding posts on the outside to a switch and two dry cells as shown in Fig. 19-1. During the evacuation of air from the container no part of the bell should touch the walls of the container.

Sound through air. Have students hold a sheet of tissue paper or onion skin paper stretched taut on an embroidery hoop and hold it parallel to one side of a vibrating tuning fork. If they place a fingertip or the ear to the paper, they will feel the vibrations.

Sound through a liquid. Some students may have heard rocks banged together under water. Insert the stem of a tuning fork into a hole bored into a large cork. Set the tuning fork in vibration and hold it so that the tuning fork rests on the surface of water in a container standing on a resonating box. Students will hear the vibrations of the tuning fork transmitted from the cork through the water and into the air of the room.

Sound through a solid. One way to show that solids transmit sound is to have students hold one ear against the desk and

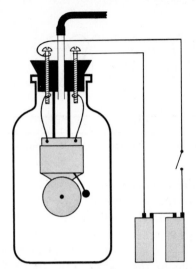

Fig. 19–1 Suspending a bell in jar which can be evacuated.

cover the other ear with a hand while a student or the teacher holds a vibrating tuning fork against the surface of the desk. In another method, use a long stick or beam instead of the table.

19.1b Speed of sound

A fairly precise measure of the speed of sound can be obtained over a long distance. If the sound of the noon whistle of a local factory can be heard at your school, and if the factory is quite distant, have one student locate himself just outside the mill in a telephone stall, establish contact with another student by telephone in the school, and signal the commencement of the blast. The student at the receiving end can start the stopwatch at the verbal signal and stop it when he hears the blast. You or your students will be able to think up variations of this experiment. Corrections will need to be made in the calculations for errors due to temperature variations. At 0° C sound travels 1090 feet per second, at 20° C, 1130 feet per second. The increase in speed is 2 feet per second per C degree.

19.2 Models of sound waves
19.2a Mechanical models

Compression and rarefaction. There are many commercial models available from supply houses, and several devices can be constructed by students.

Model of longitudinal waves. In this demonstration students can see that the force imparted to particles by a pull or a push travels a long distance while the individual particles travel only small distances. Suspend 5 to 8 small drilled steel balls in a row so they just touch each other (Fig. 19-2). Pull the first ball back and let go, so that it strikes the second ball. Watch how the balls in between do not seem to move while the end ball is pushed out about as far as the first ball was pulled. This is also available as a commercial model.

Analogy of coil spring. A window-shade-roller spring with folded pieces of paper placed on the coils at equidistant points (Fig. 19-3) can serve as a model to show rarefactions and compressions. Stretch the spring horizontally between two supports and set it into vibration horizontally, causing pulses to move back and forth along the length of the spring. Students will see the pieces of paper go through a slight back and forth motion that is analogous to compression and rarefaction.

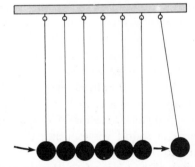

Fig. 19–2 A force moves from ball to ball without moving any ball but the last one in the series.

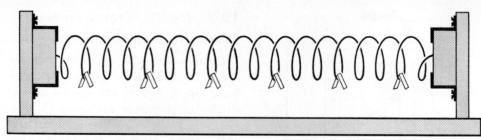

Fig. 19–3 Compression and rarefaction using a window-shade roller spring. (Not drawn to scale.)

Simple harmonic motion. Attach a rubber ball to the surface of a phono turntable. The ball should be near the edge. From behind illuminate with a spot. When the turntable turns, the shadow of the ball describes simple harmonic motion. The shadow cast from the side of a turning crank can also be used.

19.2b Making sound waves "visible"

Sound waves can be traced or made "visible" in several ways. Students can construct some of these devices, or commercial apparatus may be purchased.

Tracing of a vibrating tuning fork. One simple apparatus uses a vibrating tuning fork that has a thin pointer attached to one prong. Students can make these by attaching a broomstraw with a Duco-type cement to an ordinary tuning fork. Now prepare the tracing material. Smoke a 12″ length of glass plate with a candle flame. Clamp the tuning fork so that the pointer or broomstraw just touches the smoked surface as shown in Fig. 19-4. Set the tuning fork vibrating and move the smoked glass under the straw at constant speed. Students should observe a tracing which appears as a clear line in the soot of the tuning fork's motions. Compare the patterns of sound waves using different pitch and different intensity. The higher the pitch of the tuning fork, the closer the spacing of the waves on the graph (assum-

ing the glass is always drawn along the fork at the same speed).

In another method for visualizing sound waves, cover the lens of a slide projector with aluminum foil that has a pinhole in the center (Fig. 19-5). You may cement a piece of aluminum foil to *each* tine of a tuning fork for balance. Direct a light beam from the pinhole at one foil reflector on the tuning fork. Pick up the reflected beam with a plane mirror and direct the beam at a wall or screen. When the fork vibrates, the dot of light will oscillate. If the mirror is turned slowly, a wave pattern is visible on the wall or screen. Suggested distances: lantern to fork, about 1 foot; fork to mirror, about 3 feet; mirror to wall, not critical.

Manometric flame apparatus. There are several kinds of commercial devices available from scientific supply houses (see appendix). They depend upon the rarefaction and compression of sound waves

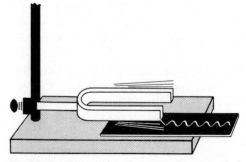

Fig. 19–4 Tracing the vibrations of a tuning fork onto smoked glass.

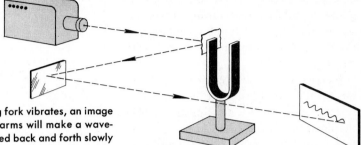

Fig. 19-5 As the tuning fork vibrates, an image reflected from one of its arms will make a wave-like motion. Mirror is moved back and forth slowly about a vertical axis.

acting against a disk that forms one wall of a fuel gas reservoir. A rotating mirror (see below), usually spun by hand, projects onto the wall the variations in the height of the flame produced. When tuning forks of different pitch are used, students can compare the patterns produced by different frequencies.

To make your own manometric flame

apparatus, take a #2 juice can. Remove the top and in its side place a 2" to 3" glass nozzle made from ¼" glass tubing drawn out to 1 mm. When the apparatus is assembled, the opening is filed back to the dimension that works best. (See below under sensitive flame.) The nozzle can be sealed in place with putty, sealing wax, or mucilage. In the bottom of the can near

Fig. 19-6 Using flame to visualize sound waves: (a) manometric flame device, (b) rotating cube of mirrors for reflecting flame, (c) flame alone. (Scale has been exaggerated for emphasis.)

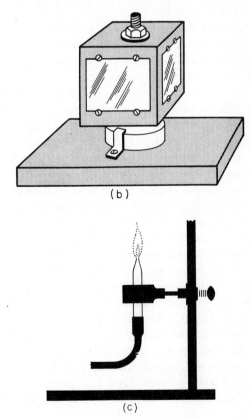

(b)

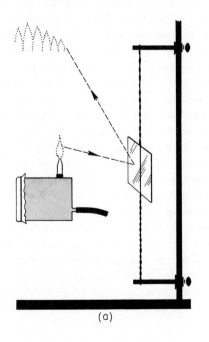

(a)

(c)

the edge opposite the side with the glass nozzle, seal in place a glass or brass tube of a size to take rubber tubing. Over the open top of the can, stretch a rubber sheet diaphragm and secure in place with string (Fig. 19-6A).

Run gas through the device until all air has been flushed out, and light the glass nozzle. Sound waves striking the rubber diaphragm will cause the flame to flicker by varying the pressure of fuel gas within the can. The flame is reflected by a rotating mirror (see below) which casts a flickering image of the flame onto the wall or a screen.

Rotating mirror. To make a crude rotating reflecting mirror, take a ring stand and with two rubber bands mount a two-sided chromium plated camping mirror (3″ by 5″) as in Fig. 19-6A. One way to attach the rubber bands is to punch or drill two holes, one at each end of the mirror. The bands can be looped through these before being stretched to an anchoring point. Twisting the rubber bands makes the mirror rotate.

A better rotating mirror (Fig. 19-6B) can be made in the following manner. Take a block of wood 3½″ to 4″ square. Through its center run a bolt of sufficient extension and of a size that will fit snugly into the center of a roller skate wheel. On each side secure pocket mirrors of the sort available in a variety store. Mount the cube in the skate wheel with nuts and washers, making sure there is sufficient clearance for the cube to turn. The skate wheel in turn is mounted on a wood base. The whole can be rotated by hand or, by adding a pulley, by a small electric motor which is controlled by a rheostat. Another way to make a rotating mirror is described in this section under graphing sound waves with a neon lamp oscilloscope.

Sensitive flame. Heat a 6″ piece of ⅜″ bore glass tubing over a wing top on a

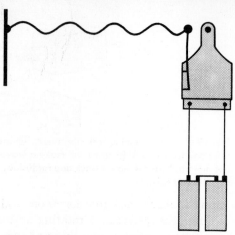

Fig. 19-7 The hammer of an electric bell can produce waves in a line.

Bunsen burner. Draw out the glass carefully until it comes apart in two pieces. Using a fine triangular file, very gradually enlarge the opening in one of the drawn-out ends until it is just barely visible. Try it out as a nozzle on the end of a rubber hose connected to the source of fuel gas. The flame should be long, narrow, and silent. If unsuccessful, file back just a little bit more and try it again. Repeat this procedure until you obtain a flame that responds violently to hand clapping. If the flame is just right, the increase in pressure over the nozzle as a result of a passing sound wave will make the flame shrink visibly (Fig. 19-6C).

Some students can try to make a more permanent record by letting the shadows of the flame fall on the blackboard in a darkened room. Here the heights can be marked on the blackboard and comparisons can be studied.

Showing standing waves. Commercial vibrators that operate on battery current or on the 120-volt house current are available. If one of these vibrators is attached to the free end of a string (and the other end fastened to a wall), the string will form standing waves when the

Fig. 19-8 A slinky, a long, loose metallic coil with great stretch, is used to transmit waves and pulses. (William Vandivert, courtesy of *Scientific American*.)

tension is right. Nylon fishing line is excellent for this demonstration.

As a substitute you can use an ordinary electric bell which will produce standing waves in the same ways as the commercial vibrators (Fig. 19-7). Remove the gong and attach the string directly to the hammer; operate the bell with 6 volts of battery current or 8 to 12 volts from a transformer. Many teachers find that this demonstration is most striking in a darkened room when a chalk-white string is used against a black background and a spotlight or the beam of a projector's light is focused on the standing wave in the string.

Waves and pulses with a slinky. As illustrated in the photograph in Fig. 19-8, students can transmit pulses and observe the reflection of pulses out of phase. They can also observe the effect of superimposing waves. This can be done by starting a second faster pulse that will overtake a slower first pulse, or by starting a pulse from the opposite direction. You can also cancel a pulse by sending two pulses, out of phase, one to the left and the other to the right of the slinky.

Graphing sound waves with a neon lamp oscillograph. This neon lamp oscillograph is an electronic variation of the manometric flame apparatus described earlier in this section. If a 2-watt split-plate neon bulb is connected to the primary of the output transformer of a radio or to the loudspeaker of a public address system using an output transformer in reverse, it will vary in intensity as the loudspeaker signals change. If the neon lamp throws its beam on a two-sided metal mirror that is rotated by a small electric motor, the mirror will throw a graph of the sound waves on a white paper screen. Use a motor of the low-voltage type (so that its speed can be adjusted by means of a small rheostat) and secure it so that its shaft is vertical to a baseboard. Saw a vertical slot in the shaft, insert the metal mirror into the slot, and solder it in place. When sound ema-

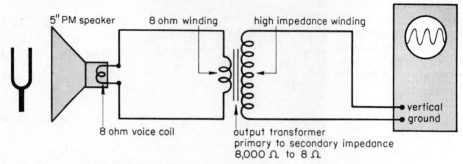

Fig. 19-9 Graphing sound waves on a cathode-ray oscilloscope.

nates from the loudspeaker, disconnect the speaker and use the neon lamps alone. Adjust the speed of the motor with the rheostat until the graph is visible on the white paper.

Using a cathode-ray oscilloscope. An oscilloscope is very useful for showing the meaning of wave length, amplitude, and frequency. If your school owns a cathode-ray oscilloscope with a built-in amplifier (all oscilloscopes built after 1945 have amplification sufficient for the purpose), connect a 5″ permanent magnet dynamic loudspeaker and an output transformer as shown in Fig. 19-9. Hold a tuning fork near the speaker cone and adjust the oscilloscope sweep frequency and synchronization to obtain a stationary pattern. The number of cycles are easily counted, and comparisons can be made

with forks of different frequencies—preferably those separated by one octave (such as a 256 vps and a 512 vps). The speaker and output transformer may be purchased from any of the larger mail-order electronics distributors, such as Lafayette Radio, 165-01 Liberty Avenue, Jamaica 33, N.Y. Note that the output transformer is connected so that the low-impedance coil goes to the speaker-voice coil while the high-impedance winding is joined to the vertical deflection terminal and the ground post of the oscilloscope.

Ultrasonics. A cathode-ray oscilloscope equipped with a low-power public address amplifier and a crystal microphone will produce visible sine waves on the screen when a Galton whistle is blown near the microphone. This whistle, available from pet shops, produces sounds that are too

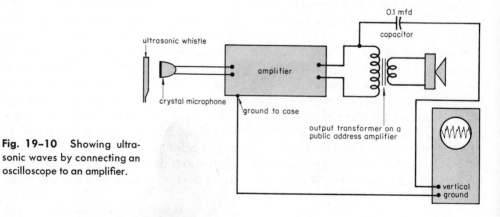

Fig. 19-10 Showing ultrasonic waves by connecting an oscilloscope to an amplifier.

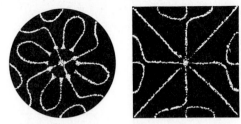

Fig. 19–11 Patterns such as these are produced when the edge of thin sheet metal is stroked with a violin bow. They are called Chladni figures after their discoverer.

high in frequency for the human ear to hear. By carefully adjusting the horizontal sweep frequency and synchronization controls of the oscilloscope, you can produce a display of sinusoidal waves although the only sound heard will be a soft hissing of the breath through the Galton whistle. The frequency of the whistle can be determined by reading the sweep frequency from the oscilloscope dial and counting the number of complete cycles visible. The ultrasonic wave frequency is obtained by multiplying the number of cycles visible by the sweep frequency in cycles per second. The oscilloscope connections are shown in Fig. 19-10. Note that the audio signal is fed to the oscilloscope through a 0.1 mfd capacitor directly from one leg of the output transformer primary winding. If no signal is obtained from this leg, try connecting the capacitor to the other terminal of the primary. All such connections should be made with the power plug of the amplifier removed from the a.c. receptacle.

With an audio-generator (which may be borrowed from a radio repair shop) students can listen to the threshold of audible sound and observe the pattern on the screen. (Note that all cathode-ray oscilloscopes require an adjustment of the frequency control when the input frequency changes.)

Focusing sound waves on a powdered

surface. This demonstration makes sound waves "visible" and shows that sound waves (like light) can be focused. If parabolic reflectors are available, sound waves produced by a police whistle at the focus of the reflector operated by compressed air can be focused on a sheet of metal that has been covered with lycopodium powder or very fine talc. Ripples will disclose the presence of the sound waves. A very loud noise is needed. The reflector may have to be tried at various angles.

If thin sheet metal is stroked along the edge with a violin bow, sound will be produced. If sulfur, cork dust, or other fine powder is on the sheet, various patterns will be formed (Fig. 19-11).

Students can demonstrate the reflection of sound waves in this way. Use two parabolic mirrors described above; place a watch at the focus of one of the mirrors. Across the room a student holding an ear trumpet at the focus of the other mirror should hear the sound.

19.2c Generating waves

The ripple tank. The techniques of building ripple tanks and vibrators as well as many demonstrations using the ripple tank are described at length in 20.2.

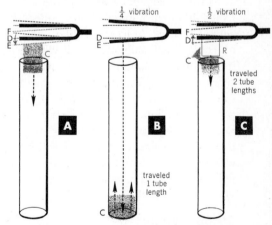

Fig. 19–12 Resonance in a tube of air. (From R. Brinckerhoff, et al , *Exploring Physics*, Harcourt, Brace, 1959.)

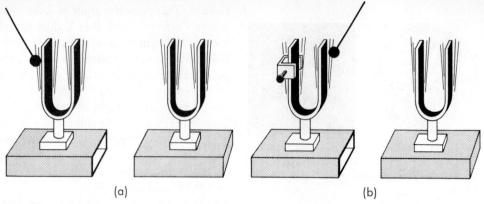

Fig. 19-13 Producing beats: (a) both forks vibrate in complete resonance, and no beats are produced; (b) with one fork a little out of phase, beats will be heard.

19.3 Characteristics of sound waves

19.3a Resonance

Students can stand a glass tube in water, as in Fig. 19-12, and vibrate a tuning fork just above it. With some practice they will find that resonance will be produced when the length of the tube above the water level is one quarter the wave length of the sound. Thus the wave length of any tuning fork used will be four times the height of the column of air in the tube.

Many objects have a fairly well-established frequency of vibration called the *natural resonant frequency.* When such an object is struck sharply, it will vibrate at its natural resonant frequency. If it receives sound waves of the same frequency, it will begin to vibrate. If, while pressing the loud pedal, you sing at the exposed strings of a piano in the pitch of particular strings, these strings will begin to vibrate in sympathetic resonance and will be heard in a quiet room after the voice has stopped.

19.3b Beats

For this demonstration students will

need two resonator boxes fitted with tuning forks of the same frequency to serve as the basic apparatus for demonstrating beats. If commercial resonator boxes are not available, you can make them by knocking out one end of a wooden cigar box and gluing a small block with a hole in its center to the top of the box to hold the tuning fork. Box size must be adjusted for particular frequency. One fork should be equipped with a rider. (Use a small screw-type pinch clamp.) First set the tuning forks into vibration without the rider (Fig. 19-13A). Repeat with the rider on one fork; beats (interference) will be produced (Fig. 19-13B). (You can also demonstrate interference with the ripple tank as described in 20.2.)

Beats with a sonometer. Set up two identical strings on the sonometer some distance apart so that they may each be put into vibration separately by means of a violin bow (Fig. 19-14). Adjust the strings so that each produces the same pitch. Stop the vibration, attach a small bolt and two washers to one string as shown, and set both strings into vibration again. As interference takes place, beats will be heard. For details on how to build a sonometer see 19.5a.

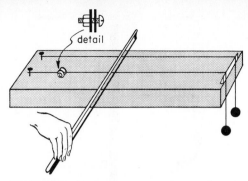

Fig. 19–14 Beats on a sonometer can be produced first by tuning two strings to the same pitch and then attaching a small weight to one of the strings and bowing both strings simultaneously.

Other times you may want to use the loudspeaker-microphone arrangement and cathode-ray oscilloscope (Fig. 19-9) as described earlier in this chapter. Set two tuning forks, one with a rider, into vibration to produce beats. Watch the pattern of the beats on the screen of the oscilloscope.

19.3c Doppler effect

Have students show the increase or decrease in pitch as the source of sound moves toward or away from the listener. One student can swing in a circle overhead a small air whistle at the end of a 4′ string. As the whistle approaches a second student, the pitch will increase; as the whistle moves away, the pitch decreases. Simple toy devices that show the Doppler effect in this way are also sold commercially. Students may remember the increasing pitch of an approaching whistle of a locomotive or an auto horn and the decreasing pitch as the sound moves away.

The ripple tank described in 20.2 is a graphic way to demonstrate the Doppler effect. Hold the rippler in the hand and attach a plastic bead to the vibrating arm. First start with the rippler in a stationary position but vibrating in the hand so that circular waves can be seen. Then gently move the rippler forward. Watch how the waves ahead of the rippler are closer together, indicating a shortening of wave length, while the wave pattern behind shows waves farther apart, indicating an increase in the wave length. Relate this to the differences in pitch of sounding objects moving toward or away from an observer.

19.3d Finding the wave length of a tuning fork

To find the wave length of a tuning fork whose frequency is not known, lower a 1″ glass tube into water and change the length of the tube by raising it and lowering it while the tuning fork is vibrating over the open top of the tube (Fig. 19-15). When resonance occurs, measure the length of the tube above the water level. This will be one quarter the wave length of the tuning fork. Multiply by 4 to

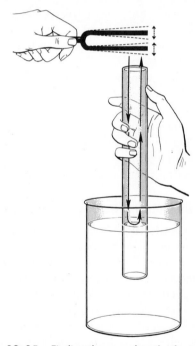

Fig. 19–15 Finding the wave length of a tuning fork by finding the length of a closed air column which resonates with it. (R. Brinckerhoff, et al, *Exploring Physics*, Harcourt, Brace, 1959.)

get the wave length of a tuning fork. Actually this is an approximation; for accurate results students must consider the internal diameters of tubes.

$$\text{wave length} = 4(L \text{ plus } 0.4d)$$

where L = length of tube above water and d = diameter of tube.

If an open tube is used in place of the tube shown in Fig. 19-15, two close-fitting telescoping tubes will be needed. Here the length of the resonant tube is ½ the wave length. Thus, multiplying by 2 gives the wave length of the tuning fork.

19.3e Making sounds visible in a vibrating column of air

Sift some lycopodium powder or fine cork powder into a horizontally placed glass tube whose length is at least 3′ and whose diameter is about 1½″. Use a fishtail burner top and a tube to blow air across the end of the tube (Fig. 19-16A). Watch the particles vibrate and fall into nodes and loops.

When a piston is pulled inside a Kundt's tube (½″ diameter) containing lycopodium powder, loops and nodes are visible on the standing wave patterns set up in the powder (Fig.19-16B). Stroking is accompanied by pulling a rosin-coated cloth along the projecting portion of the piston rod.

19.3f Magnetic audio-generator

A simple audio-generator (Fig. 19-17) can be made from an iron-toothed gear wheel rotated by an electric motor, using a rheostat or variable resistance to control the speed. Assemble the apparatus so that the teeth move past the pole of an alnico magnet connected with a 50-turn coil of #24 wire. Have the coil feed into a loudspeaker output transformer that is operated in reverse (i.e., the secondary is used as the primary, and the primary as the

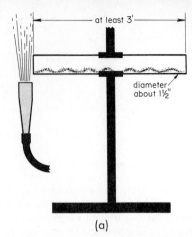

(a)

Fig. 19-16 a and b Standing waves: (a) in a 3′ by 1½″ glass tube containing lycopodium powder, (b) in a commercial Kundt's tube containing cork dust. (Welch Scientific Company)

secondary), and connect this to the input of a cathode-ray oscilloscope (see 19.2b, using cathode-ray oscilloscope).

Students can see the pattern of the sound produced as the shifting magnetic field generates current which can be seen on the screen. Vary the speed of the motor; as the speed increases, the frequency of the waves produced will increase, and this can be seen on the scope. A loudspeaker can be used either with or instead of the oscilloscope if the transformer feeds its output into the microphone input of the amplifier.

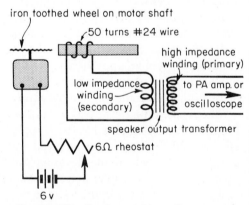

Fig. 19-17 Simple variable audio-generator.

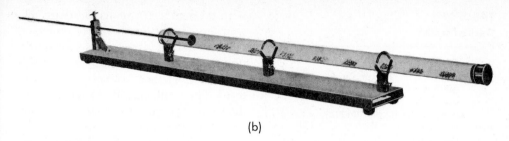

(b)

19.4 Absorption of sound
19.4a Acoustics

After a study of parabolic mirrors used for reflecting sound, you will want to refer to parabolic shapes that are used as the reflection board for orchestras. Students can explain that the dead spots in an auditorium are the places where reflected and incident waves cancel each other out. (Also refer to nodal lines on the interference patterns in a ripple tank as covered in Chapter 20.)

Have students talk from different places in a large gymnasium or auditorium. Can the rest of the class hear the reverberations? A loudspeaker from a public address system may also be used for this purpose. Students can plan the next demonstration on the soundproofing qualities of different materials. They may also obtain samples of different sound-absorbing boards and tiles from the school custodian or a building supply company.

19.4b Sound-absorbing materials

As a project students may want to demonstrate the sound-absorbing qualities of different materials by making a miniature soundproof room inside a strong wood box (Fig. 19-18). The box is lined with a layer, at least 2″ thick, of rock wool or other fibrous sound-absorbing materials. A slot in the center holds 8″ × 8″ sheets of materials to be tested and divides the box into two compartments. Hang in one compartment a 1½-volt electric bell connected to a

switch and one dry cell, or the 3-volt connection of a toy transformer. In the other section connect a carbon telephone microphone to four dry cells and a 0–100-range milliammeter. Students can connect the bell and observe the readings on the meter with different materials in the slots. The better the sound-absorbing quality of the material, the lower the reading on the meter. Test several samples: Celotex, plasterboard, rock wool, wood, and others. Compare these insulators with substances such as metal and glass. If an earphone is substituted for the milliammeter, the difference in sound-absorbing qualities can be heard.

19.4c Decibels

The decibel is a unit used to measure

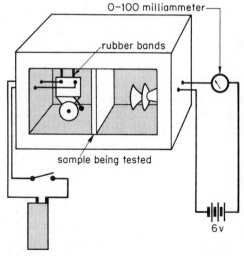

Fig. 19-18 Box for testing the sound-absorbing quality of materials.

TABLE 19-1
Decibel scale*

threshold	0
noise in average home	32
quiet office	37
quiet radio in home	40
noise in city residential area	45
restaurant	50
noisy office	57
stenographic	70
noisy factory	85
boiler factory	97

*Adapted from Bell Laboratories Decibel Scale.

sound intensity and is based upon the fact that our ears respond logarithmically, rather than linearly, to sounds of different intensity. For example, if the *power* of a given sound is assigned a value of 1 unit and is increased to 10 units of power, the ear will hear it as an approximate *doubling* of sound level. Now if the power goes up to 100 units, the audible level will only be three times that of the original. Since the logarithm of one (to the base 10) is 0, the log of 10 is 1, and the log of 100 is 2, the ear is responding logarithmically. In recognition of this physiological behavior, the bel was defined as

$$\text{bels} = \log_{10} \frac{P_1}{P_2}$$

where P_1 is the reference sound power and P_2 is the power being compared with the reference. Since this is a very large unit, the decibel (db) has become standard. Since there are 10 db in each bel

$$\text{decibels} = 10 \log_{10} \frac{P_1}{P_2}$$

19.5 Music

Generators of sound such as tuning forks that produce a pure tone consisting of a single pitch accomplish results that are very different from the effects produced with musical instruments. Students may want to report on the early studies of Helmholtz that give the basis for understanding resonance, and the work of Miller and others in their studies of wave patterns. They will learn that overtones produced by the vibrating parts determine the quality (or timbre) of the sound of the musical instruments. The nature of the musical scales and the mathematical relationships of its notes can be demonstrated in class or in the laboratory.

19.5a Overtones

To demonstrate overtones, start with a pure tone (middle C) produced by a tuning fork with a pitch of 256 vibrations per second (vps). If possible, show the wave form with an oscilloscope by feeding in the sound waves with a microphone (see 19.2b). Then demonstrate a sonometer with a string tuned to 256 vps. Students will recognize that though the pitch is the same, the over-all sound quality is different. If possible, also show the difference between the waves made by the tuning fork and by the sonometer by using an oscilloscope.

Sonometer. A sonometer can show the various possible modes of vibration of a string in the study of quality of sound, overtones, and harmonics. The basic demonstration technique consists of hanging tiny paper riders, uniformly spaced, along the length of the string. The bridge is then placed one more unit of spacing away from the last rider, and the string is bowed at a point that is 1 space away from the bridge (Fig. 19-19). In A of this figure, the bridge is shown under the center of the string and the rider halfway between the remote end and the bridge. The string is then bowed halfway between the bridge and the other end. For this arrangement, the rider will immediately fly off, showing that the center of the string is vibrating while the ends

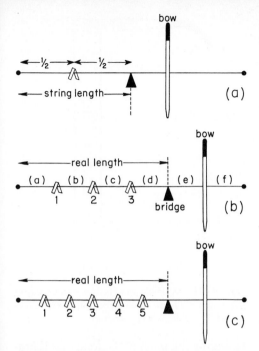

Fig. 19–19 Where to place the paper riders, the bridge, and the point of bowing when demonstrating string vibration on a sonometer.

eral other nails further on along the board, you will be able to vary the tension on the string by moving the spring from one to the other. A bridge can be made of a wood wedge.

Using either the sonometer or the homemade string apparatus, show that the pitch of a string is a function of the tension of the wire, its mass per unit length, and its length. (For further details see 19.5b, string instruments.)

Harmonics of a vibrating string. Stretch a steel sonometer wire on a wooden frame so that the ends of the wire are electrically isolated from each other. (If your regular sonometer is wood or plastic, it may be used just as it is.) Assemble a strong U-magnet (preferably one of the new alnico types with high flux density), a small audio-amplifier, a loudspeaker output transformer used in reverse, and an oscilloscope. The low-impedance secondary of the output transformer is used as the primary and is connected across the ends of the sonometer wire; the primary (high-impedance winding) is connected to the vertical terminals of the scope. The amplifier's loudspeaker should be left connected. The U-magnet may be held in a ring stand and clamp assembly so that the wire can vibrate between its poles. When the magnet is above the center of the string and the string is plucked near its end, the fundamental mode of vibration will be seen on the oscilloscope screen and heard on the speaker as a result of the voltage in-

are held fixed. This is to be expected, of course. Now change the arrangement to that shown in B. The full string is divided into 6 parts, a through f. Riders are hung between parts as shown, with the bridge separating part d and e, and bowing taking place between e and f. Now only riders 1 and 3 will be thrown off while rider 2 will remain in place. This shows that the real string is vibrating in two parts, rider 2 being at a node or point of zero vibration. In C, the string is in 8 parts; when bowed, only riders 1, 3, and 5 fly off, leaving 2 and 4 undisturbed.

If you do not have a commercial sonometer, you can make one by hammering two 8-penny nails into a board about 4½' long. Twist one end of a standard guitar steel G string around one of the nails, and tie off the other end to a strong spring held to the other nail (Fig. 19-20). By placing sev-

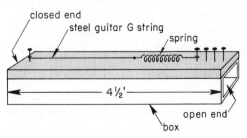

Fig. 19–20 Basic plan for a sonometer.

duced in the wire as it cuts the field of the U-magnet. To hear and view the second harmonic, place two U-magnets in position, one over the $L/4$ (length of vibrating part of string divided by 4) and the other over the $3L/4$ position, with their poles reversed in position. For the third harmonic, three U-magnets are used, placed respectively at $L/6$, $3L/6$, and $5L/6$, with successive magnets reversed in polarity. Higher-order harmonics can also be detected by placing magnets properly for them.

Perhaps students from the school band or orchestra can demonstrate the tone quality of different instruments. Compare middle C on a violin, on the piano, and on a tuning fork (256 vps). Notice how the difference in the overtones produces the different qualities of tone that enable us to recognize the different kinds of instruments being played.

Now set forks of 256, 512, and 1024 vps into vibration, first individually and then simultaneously, so that students can hear the effect of overtones.

19.5b   *Musical instruments*

After a study of overtones and of resonance, students can make many kinds of musical instruments to hear different tonal qualities.

Basic wind instrument. To make a simple wind instrument students will need a glass tube, a long bolt or threaded rod, and some felt. Cut several circles of felt to make a felt washer about ½″ thick so that it just fits inside the glass tube; bore a ¼″ hole through it to make a washer. Fasten the bolt or threaded rod to the washer and place it in the glass tube. Test the model by blowing air across the top of the tube with a Bunsen burner wing top attached to a rubber tube (Fig. 19-21). As the rod and washer are moved up and down, the wave length of the tube is changed, thereby

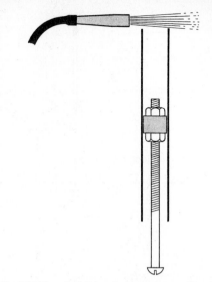

Fig. 19-21   A simple wind instrument. Changing the length of the air column changes the tone produced. The slider is a felt washer.

changing the pitch of the tone that is produced. Toy shops often sell similar instruments containing a rod that slides in and out to change the pitch.

Students can demonstrate the principle of the trombone with two glass or metal tubes, one of which fits closely inside the other. Blow air across one end while varying the total length by sliding the tube up and down.

Control of pitch. You will need to call upon the musicians in class or the members of the school orchestra for this demonstration. Have a student play a bugle to show the limited number of notes that can be produced. Then have someone play a trumpet. Show the operation of the valves that change the length of the tubes to increase the number of notes that the instrument produces.

Or connect a bugle mouthpiece or the mouthpiece and reed of a saxophone to pipes of different lengths to show the effect of the length of the resonating tube on the pitch. If you have an oscilloscope, sound the various instruments singly and in vari-

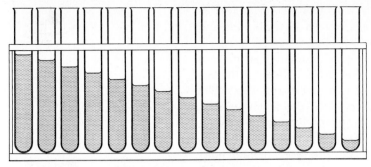

Fig. 19–22 Test tube organ.

ous combinations before a microphone that goes to an amplifier and thence to the oscilloscope. Compare the same notes on different instruments, a discord and a harmony, and so forth (see 19.2b).

Organ pipes. You may be able to get one or more organ pipes from a factory. (Imperfect pipes can be purchased for a nominal fee.) As substitutes for organ pipes, use open and closed pipes of different lengths, and blow across the mouth of each.

Test tube musical organ. Set up 15 test tubes in a long test tube rack, and add different amounts of water (Fig. 19-22). Tones are produced when air is blown across the tops of the tubes by means of rubber tubing and a wing top. Adjust the wave length of each test tube by varying the water levels until two octaves of a major scale result. Now mark the water levels with tape on the outside of the tubes and replace the water with modeling clay to make a permanent test tube musical organ.

Bottle musical organ. An instrument similar in principle to the test tube organ can be prepared by a student in a few minutes. It consists of bottles of several sizes for producing different notes when compressed air is blown across the mouth of each bottle.

String instruments. A weighted string sonometer can be used to show the principles of string instruments. The weights show the effect of tension upon pitch.

Pitch of a violin. Have a student tighten and loosen strings of a violin or a guitar to demonstrate how pitch is affected by string tension. Have students listen to strings of different materials of the same length. Apply tension by attaching weights or spring balances to these strings. Show the differences in pitch and quality of the different strings by plucking or bowing them and, at the same time, changing the length or tension of the strings. Increasing the length (or decreasing the tension) will lower the pitch, and decreasing the length (or increasing the tension) will raise the pitch. Have a student play a violin or a guitar and explain how he raises the pitch of a string by shortening it with his fingers.

Homemade ukulele. Students can make a ukulele from a cigar box with ukulele strings (Fig. 19-23). They should be able to demonstrate the principles of string instruments.

Percussion instruments. As a home assignment students can make drums of different pitch by stretching leather, heavy

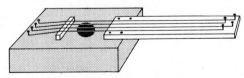

Fig. 19–23 Homemade ukulele.

plastic, rubber, or other membranes across tops of tin cans, wooden boxes, barrels, and other hollow containers.

Model marimba. Students can make a working marimba (Fig. 19-24) with glass cylinders, pieces of wood, and water. The glass cylinders, with the water level in each adjusted properly, serve as resonators under pieces of hard, dry wood which are cut until they produce a definite note. Strike the pieces of wood with a small mallet. The resonators (glass cylinders) should be directly under the centers of the pieces of wood and up very close, about ½″.

Other percussion instruments. Student members of the orchestra can demonstrate other percussion sounds: chimes, gongs, cymbals, triangles, and so forth.

In fact, the test tube and bottle musical organs described above as wind instruments can be used as percussion instruments by tapping the test tubes or bottles lightly with a wooden mallet instead of blowing air across the tops.

Independent instruments. Very often a lively discussion can follow the question: How would you classify the piano? Students should be able to recognize that the sound is produced by vibrating strings (characteristic of string instruments) and that the emitter of sound waves is hit with a hammer (characteristic of percussion instruments). Many authorities hesitate to classify the piano as belonging to any one of the three types of instruments. How shall we classify the organ, harp, electronic organ, and harpsichord?

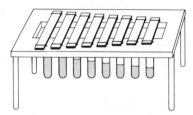

Fig. 19–24   Model marimba.

Fig. 19–25   Working model of vocal cords.

Human voice

Vocal ranges. Select students who sing fairly well to explore the voice range in class. Use a piano to show the range on the keyboard for the bass, baritone, tenor, alto, and soprano. Examine the piano keyboard to notice the range of frequencies. If possible use an oscilloscope for each range (see 19.2b). Also compare the ranges of the violin, cello, "Bull fiddle" with the ranges of human voices and the piano scale. Do the same with wind and reed instruments. If possible, have students play the clarinet, alto saxophone and bass saxophone, a French horn, trumpet or cornet, and then a sousaphone for the bass.

Mechanical vocal chords. A student can construct a working model of vocal chords from a cardboard tube 1″ in diameter fitted with a one-hole stopper that contains a glass or metal tube (Fig. 19-25). Connect the tube to an air pump or compressor. Across the opposite end of the cardboard tube stretch two sheets of thin rubber (cut from a toy balloon) and secure to the tube with rubber bands or tape.

When air is blown through the tube, vibrations are produced resulting in sound. If you tighten the rubber sheets, the pitch of the sound will be higher and if you loosen them, the pitch will be lower. Prepare several sets, each adjusted to a different pitch by proper stretching of the sheet rubber. The higher-pitched sets could represent vocal chords of women, while the lower-pitched chords could represent those of men. Three of these can be made to "sing" a chord when operated simultaneously.

19.5c Simple harmonics

Siren disk. A siren disk attached to the shaft of a motor whose speed can be controlled by a rheostat is useful in teaching the mathematical basis of harmony. Students will notice that the disk contains concentric rings of holes, each ring having a different number of holes. Connect an air supply to a rubber tube, and direct the air stream at one row of holes while the motor rotates the disk. Then adjust the speed until a tone is produced of the same pitch as one played on a violin or some other tuning source. Next give rubber tubes to other students. Have them blow air through other rings of holes simultaneously. If the ratios of the number of holes in each ring are whole numbers, such as 3:2, 5:4, and so on, major chords are produced. Most siren disks are also provided with one ring of unevenly spaced holes to show the comparison between noise (irregular vibrations) and musical tones (regular vibrations).

Making and using a siren disk. Have some of your students make a siren disk according to the following specifications. Cut a perfect circle with a radius of about 7″ from a piece of stiff, straight cardboard. Using the center of the disk as the center of concentric circles, draw 4 circles with radii of exactly 1½″, 3″, 4½″, and 6″, respectively. Using a good protractor, measure off successive 60° angles around the center so that you can divide the disk into 6 equal "pie" segments.

Working first with the innermost (1½″ radius) circle, place a sharp pencil dot at each intersection of the circle with the segment lines (Fig. 19-26). This gives 6 equally spaced points. With a protractor and dividers or a compass, mark off 3 equally spaced dots between each segment dot. This will give you 24 equally spaced holes.

Repeat the procedure on the next circle outward, except that you must mark 4 equally spaced dots between each segment dot to yield 30 dots altogether. On the next circle, you will want 5 equally spaced dots between each segment dot for a total of 36 dots. Finally, mark 7 equally spaced dots between each segment dot to obtain 48 holes. If the cardboard is to be the final model of the disk, each hole is now punched or drilled to a diameter of approximately ⅛″, mounted on a rotator, and used as previously described with a jet of air. If you want your siren disk of metal, use the cardboard as a template, punching through each point with a metal center-punch with the cardboard super-

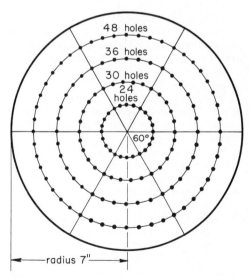

Fig. 19–26 Producing the musical sequence of *do, mi, sol, do* on a siren disk.

imposed over a disk of sheet aluminum (16 gauge is best) or even heavy galvanized iron. Then drill ⅛″ holes at each punch mark.

As the disk is rotated at a constant speed, direct a jet of air against each row, first the innermost, the second, the third, and finally the outermost row. Students should recognize the musical sequence *do, mi, sol, do.* Increase or decrease the speed of rotation to demonstrate that the relationship from tone to tone remains the same though the pitch changes.

Develop the notion that the ratios of 24:30:36:48 or 4:5:6:8 produce the musical sequence *do, mi, sol, do.* Notice the harmonious combination of 2 notes an octave apart (24:48 or 1:2). Compare another musical interval—24:36 or 2:3. Also listen to the vibration ratio of 36:48 or 3:4, and 24:30 or 4:5. Develop the combination of vibrating ratios of 4:5:6 all sounded together to form the major diatonic scale made of 3 major chords.

Savart's wheels. The same results can be obtained with Savart's wheels which are toothed disks that are rotated by a motor. Hold cards against the rotating teeth of the Savart's wheels to produce notes. The ratios of the number of teeth on the wheel will also show the relationship of the tones of a chord.

CAPSULE LESSONS
Ways to get started in class

19-1. Begin with a clock alarming in air under a bell jar and then evacuate the jar. Try to restore the air before the alarm runs down so that students can hear the sound again. Develop the notion that sound waves create vibrations in the air and set up waves traveling in all directions in the medium. What kinds of substances transmit sound waves? How fast does sound travel in air, water, and steel?

19-2. Students can demonstrate the transmission of sound waves through solids and liquids using the demonstrations described in this chapter. What factors affect the speed of sound? Describe experiments to determine accurately the speed of sound.

19-3. At one time make the effect of sound waves visible with an oscilloscope. Directions are given in 19.2b. Develop the notions of pitch, quality, and loudness.

19-4. You may want to have a laboratory activity in which students can study the effect of sound on manometric devices. Develop the basic principles of sound waves.

19-5. At some time, show a film in review of the characteristics of sound waves and their transmission. Have you shown the film *Waves* (Educational Services, Inc.) or *Sound Waves and Their Sources* (EBF)? Others are listed at the end of this chapter.

19-6. If possible, begin a lesson by having a student demonstrate a high-fidelity amplifier, and compare the playing of an identical recording on a high-fidelity player and a standard player. Students will enjoy picking out the types of musical overtones that are missing and noticing the difference in sound distortions.

19-7. Have a student show the difference between ultrasonic and audible sound by using a commercial oscilloscope or a student-made model. Use a crystal microphone and an amplifier. For ultrasonic sound use a Galton whistle. Compare the wave pattern of the ultrasonic and audible whistle on the screen.

19-8. Demonstrate standing waves by having a heavy white card vibrate by means of the hammer of a large electric bell from which the gong has been removed. First whiten the rope with chalk to make it visible. Shine a spotlight on the rope or use the beam of light from a projector to illuminate the cord in a darkened room. A student will need to hold the free end of the rope and adjust the tension by hand until standing waves are produced. Or use a clothesline or rubber tubing attached to a wall at one end and operated manually at the other end. Compare transverse and longitudinal waves. Use a large turn spring-coil slinky attached to a support, and give the lower end of the spring a quick pull. Students can watch how the disturbance moves along the coil to the top. What kind of wave motion is this?

19-9. For one lesson period you may want to

show the nature of sound waves by using the analogy of waves in a ripple tank. (For details and demonstrations see Chapter 20, Light and Color.)

19-10. Students can demonstrate a working model of the vocal chords. Air can be blown through the "larynx" made of a cardboard tube with rubber membranes. Compressed air can be used, or blow through the bottom of the tube. Also make models with shorter cords of stretched rubber to represent vocal chords of a female, and longer cords to represent vocal chords of a male. Adjust the tension to change the pitch of the artificial vocal chords.

19-11. Students in the school orchestra or musicians in class will want to play string, wind, reed, percussion instruments, and explain how each instrument produces different notes. Develop an understanding of pitch, loudness, quality of sounds.

19-12. If possible, use a commercial or homemade oscilloscope to show a tuning fork producing a pure tone simultaneously with the same note played by a musical instrument. Feed the sound into a microphone and amplifier before it enters the cathode-ray oscilloscope. A local radio or TV repairman may loan an oscilloscope to the school or perhaps come to demonstrate its use.

19-13. As projects, students may want to build simple musical instruments and show how they work. These may become part of the permanent audio-visual equipment of the department.

19-14. In some classes, you may want to use a microphone and amplifier feeding into a cathode-ray oscilloscope to show the pattern of the sound waves produced by each of the notes of a piano.

19-15. Use a disk with drilled holes arranged in concentric rows of 24, 30, 36, and 48. Develop the ratios of harmonious notes. Have a student pianist or a music teacher demonstrate chords and harmony on the piano. Elicit the arithmetical relationship of the frequency of each note by referring to the piano keyboard.

PEOPLE, PLACES, AND THINGS

If possible, have students visit the rehearsal of the school orchestra to listen to the different instruments. It may be possible to invite a music teacher to speak on the mathematics of music. In a visit to a radio broadcasting station students can see the sound waves on the station's oscilloscope. There may be in your classes an expert on high fidelity who can give a short talk about his interest.

Toy musical instruments can be purchased in neighborhood novelty stores to show reed, wind, and string instruments. It may be possible to purchase musical instrument charts that are large enough for the whole class to study together.

Books and pamphlets

These are only a few of the books which are pertinent to the work discussed in this chapter. These and many other references classified by subject and with complete bibliographical data are given in the bibliography at the end of the book.

Buddenbrock, W. von, *The Senses,* U. Michigan Press, 1958.

Cable, E., R. Getchell, and W. Kadesch, *The Physical Sciences,* 3rd ed., Prentice-Hall, 1957.

Horton, J. W., *Fundamentals of Sonar,* U.S. Naval Institute, Annapolis, 1957.

Leighton, R., *Principles of Modern Physics,* McGraw-Hill, 1959.

Mendenhall, C., A. S. Eve, D. Keys, and R. M. Sutton, *College Physics,* 4th ed., Heath, 1956.

Pierce, J., and E. David, Jr., *Man's World of Sound,* Doubleday, 1958.

Sears, F. W., *Mechanics, Wave Motion and Heat,* Addison-Wesley, 1958.

Van Berge, J. K., J. R. Pierce, and E. E. David, *Waves and the Ear,* Doubleday, 1960.

Films and filmstrips

This partial list is intended only as a guide toward film and filmstrip selection. Refer to the more complete listing at the end of the book where films are classified by subject and where a key to abbreviations and addresses of distributors are given. The cost of film rental, of course, is subject to change. Films are sound and black and white unless otherwise specified.

Basic Physics Series on Sound (f, s, 4 in series), Indiana U., $2.00 each.

Doppler Effect (f, s), McGraw-Hill, inquire rental local film library.

Faster than Sound (f, s), Institutional Cinema, $2.00.

Fundamentals of Acoustics (f, s), Ideal, $2.00.

How Sound Travels (fs), Popular Science through McGraw-Hill, $6.00.

Nature of Sound (f, s), Ideal, $2.00.

Principles of Ultrasonics (f, s), McGraw-Hill, inquire rental local film library.

Progressive Waves: Transverse and Longitudinal (f, s), McGraw-Hill, inquire rental local film library.

Quiet, Please! (f, s, c), Indiana U., $3.00.

Science in the Orchestra (f, s, 3 in series), Indiana U., $2.50 each.

Science of Musical Instruments (fs, 3 in series), Popular Science through McGraw-Hill, $6.00 each.

Simple Waves (f, s), PSSC, Educational Services, Inc., Modern Talking Pictures, inquire rental.

Sound (f, s, series 11 lessons) EBF, inquire rental.

Sound Recording and Reproduction (f, s), EBF, $2.50.

Vibration Motions and Waves (f, s, 2 rls), Institutional Cinema, $3.00 each.

World of Sound (f, s), Teaching Film Custodians, free.

FREE AND INEXPENSIVE MATERIALS

This is only a partial listing of free and inexpensive materials available to the teacher at this time. A directory of addresses is given at the end of the book. Many of these materials are distributed to teachers without charge. Where there is a small fee, the cost is indicated, although the prices are subject to change. While we recommend the material for use in the classroom, we do not necessarily endorse the products advertised.

Benade, A., *Horns, Strings, and Harmony*, Doubleday, 1960, $.95.

Griffin, D., *Echoes of Bats and Men*, Doubleday, 1959, $.95.

Scientific American, "More About Bat Radar," August, 1958.

Van Bergeijk, W., J. Pierce, and E. David, *Waves and the Ear*, Doubleday, 1960, $.95.

CHAPTER 20

Light and color

Up to the seventeenth century, light was thought to consist of a stream of corpuscles. Then Huygens developed the wave theory to explain much of the behavior of light—reflection, refraction, and double refraction. Until the advent of the nineteenth century most workers in the field accepted the corpuscular theory. Then in the early 1800's Young, Fresnel, and Foucault demonstrated the phenomena of interference and diffraction which the original corpuscular theory could not explain, and it was postulated that light was really waves of short wave length. In 1873, when Maxwell calculated that the velocity of certain electromagnetic waves was almost exactly the velocity of light, the wave theory of light became widely accepted.

But this theory did not account for emission effects. It remained for the quantum theory developed by Planck, Einstein, and others during the twentieth century to account for these. "The present understanding in the face of apparently contradictory experiments emphasizes the fact that light appears to be dualistic in nature. The phenomena of light propagation may best be explained by the electromagnetic wave theory, while the interaction of light with matter, in the processes of emission and absorption, is a corpuscular phenomenon."[1] This is not easy to ex-

[1] F. W. Sears, and M. W. Zemansky, *University Physics*, 2nd ed., Addison-Wesley, 1955, p. 718.

plain to high school students. Perhaps the best approach is to use whichever model best explains the phenomenon we are dealing with—and not be concerned about "what light really is."

There are many classroom demonstrations to show phenomena associated with light. In the last part of the chapter, some demonstrations for the study of color are suggested.

20.1 Properties of light

20.1a Light travels in straight lines

The rectilinear propagation of light (one of the first properties recognized) can be demonstrated by students in several ways. Light passes through aligned apertures. Students can prepare this setup to show the path of light. With a fine pin puncture a small hole in the center of each of three cards. These holes should be about 1/100 of an inch in diameter. Then stand each card in a wooden block (or support with a bit of modeling clay) and line up the cards (Fig. 20-1). Darken the room and place an automobile headlight bulb connected to a 6-volt battery behind one of the end cards. Notice how light passes through all three cards (when all the holes are exactly aligned).

Casting of shadows. In another demonstration, you may want to place a one-foot square of cardboard two feet from the bulb

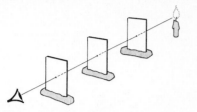

Fig. 20-1 Light from the candle travels only in a straight line.

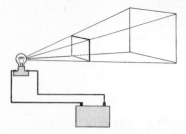

Fig. 20-2 Threads tracing the light to the corners of the card and to the corners of the shadow.

of an automobile headlight that is connected to a battery. Darken the room so that a large square shadow will be thrown on the wall. Then run threads from the center of the bulb to the corners of the cardboard and then to the square shadow (Fig. 20-2). Each of the threads will be in a straight line. Turn off the bulb, substitute a two-foot square of cardboard, and use threads to locate the corners where the shadow should form. Turn on the lamp bulb so that students can see that the shadow falls within the predicted area. This can be repeated with objects of different shape.

You may want to refer at this time to eclipses and the formation of shadows (Chapter 5).

Pinhole camera. Knock out one end of a covered shoebox and construct a small rectangular wood frame that just fits inside the box. Cover one face of the frame with tracing paper and place this inside the box so that it is free to slide. Drill a 1″ hole in the center of the closed end of the box, cover it with aluminum foil, and make a pinhole in the center of the foil with a very fine needle (Fig. 20-3). Aim the pinhole at a well-lighted scene, and look into the open end of the box. Move the tracing paper screen back and forth inside the box to change size of image. If students view a well-lighted object in the room, they can trace straight lines from the image through the pinhole to the object.

20.1b Reflection and refraction

There are many demonstrations of reflection and refraction in the literature. In this section we present some of the more successful ones, each with a lens diagram. But first we shall describe three gadgets which can simplify almost any demonstration that uses mirrors, lenses, or prisms.

20.1c General devices for work with light

Optical bench. The optical bench is a convenient device for demonstrating lenses. Several types are sold by scientific supply houses (see appendix). In its basic form, it consists of a meterstick mounted on legs with special holders that clip to the meterstick to support lenses, lights, or a screen. More expensive types use rigid steel rods for the framework.

An optical bench is most easily made by using a standard meterstick, two blocks measuring 1¾″ × 2¾″ × 4″ cut from a piece of common 2″ × 3″ stock used as

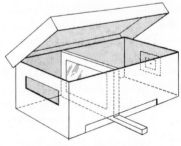

Fig. 20-3 Pinhole camera.

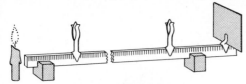

Fig. 20-4 Optical bench.

supports for the stick, and standard lens holders. The blocks should be grooved about ¾″ deep to receive the edge of the meterstick. The screen may be a piece of white cardboard similarly supported, and the source of light may be an ordinary candle or a clear, 32 CP carbon filament lamp such as is found in most schools (Fig. 20-4). Vary the positions of the lenses, and each time focus the glowing carbon filament or

TABLE 20-1

Relation of distance of object to distance of image (for lens with 1′ focal length)

distance of object	distance of image	width of image as compared with object
very far away (the sun)	1.00 ft	exceedingly small
100 ft	1.01 ft	1/100 size
10 ft	1.11 ft	1/9 size
5 ft	1.25 ft	1/4 size
3 ft	1.5 ft	1/2 size
2 ft	2 ft	same size
1.5 ft	3 ft	2 times larger
1.25 ft	5 ft	4 times larger
1.11 ft	10 ft	9 times larger
1.01 ft	100 ft	100 times larger
1.00 ft	very far away	enormously large
less than 1 ft	no real image	

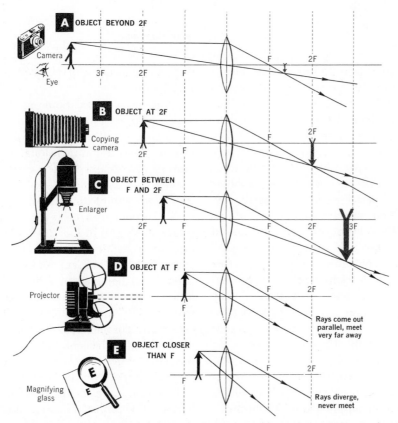

Fig. 20-5 Diagrams of some optical devices. (From H. Ruchlis and H. Lemon, *Exploring Physics*, Harcourt, Brace, 1952.)

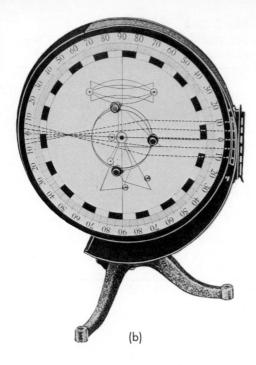

(b)

(a)

Fig. 20–6 Commercial optical disk. (Welch Scientific Company.)

candle flame upon the screen. Use the apparatus to show each of the applications of the lens illustrated in Fig. 20-5. Adjust the relative lens distances from the light according to the chart in Table 20-1. For lenses other than 1′ focal length the proportionate relationships are the same.

Optical disk. An optical disk is another convenient device for teaching optics. Adjustable light slits are located at one side of the disk. A kit of thin cross sections of lenses, prisms, and mirrors can be purchased from a scientific supply house (see appendix) to accompany the disk. Special screws hold the parts in position so they fit into outlines on the disk. Let a parallel beam of light from a lantern slide projector (with the objective lens removed) pass through light slits made in disk's side (Fig. 20-6A). A special projector for use with lens studies is available from scientific supply houses. The protractor scale that is printed around the disk can be used to measure the angles of the

incident, reflected, and refracted rays. (See Fig. 20-6B.)

Large smoke box. Some students can make a large smoke box for demonstrations in optics. The advantage of a smoke box is that three-dimensional beams of light can be obtained. Use a cardboard or wooden container about 2′ × 2′ × 3′. Remove one side of the box and replace it with a sheet of glass, clear plastic, or cellophane as shown in Fig. 20-7, so that the interior of the box is visible. Through another side of the box, cut out two armholes about 5″ in diameter. In a third side, cut a series of parallel slits about 2″ long, ⅛″ wide, and ½″ apart. Students may find it easier to make the slits if they cut a square 4″ × 4″ out of the center of the side of the box, cut slits in a sheet of heavy paper, and paste the paper over the square.

Place a parallel-beam light source or a lantern slide projector (minus its objective lens) facing the slits. Fill the box with smoke from a cigarette or touchpaper.

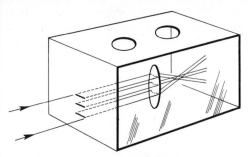

Fig. 20-7 Smoke box for making beams of light visible.

(Instructions for preparing touchpaper are given below.) Have students insert in succession different lenses through the armholes and hold each lens so that visible rays pass through it. Students can observe the effect produced by lenses of different focal lengths, concave lenses, prisms, and mirrors. (Mirror demonstrations using this smoke box are described later in this section.)

Making touchpaper. Soak mimeograph paper in a 5 to 10 per cent KNO_3 solution. When the paper is dry, roll it into a thin tube and light one end of the tube.

Sources of parallel-beam light. A parallel beam of light is needed for many optical demonstrations. These light sources are available from scientific supply houses, or you can prepare several substitutes for class work.

A focusing flashlight or a lantern slide projector with the objective lens removed can be used. If many sources are needed for group work in the laboratory, you can get a good approximation of a parallel beam by placing in front of an ordinary incandescent lamp a sheet of opaque material with a narrow slit in it.

Demonstrating a reflected beam. In the laboratory, groups of students can show a reflected beam of light in several ways.

In smoke. One striking demonstration of reflection of light uses a small mirror placed at the bottom of a smoke-filled glass tank, an aquarium for instance, with a protractor mounted inside. (Use a cigarette or burning touchpaper as a source of smoke.) Cover the tank with a sheet of cardboard in which a $1'' \times \frac{1}{8}''$ slit has been cut (Fig. 20-8) and shine a light through the slit so that it strikes the mirror at the approximate angle shown in Fig. 20-8. The incident beam and the reflected beam will be visible in the smoke, and the angles they make can be measured with a large protractor.

In water with eosin or fluorescein. Use the same apparatus as described above, but this time fill the tank with water colored with a little eosin or fluorescein in place of smoke. Again direct the ray of light through the slit. The slit must be in contact with the water. The glow of the beams of light is due to the fluorescence of the dye. Students should see the beams clearly in this medium. Can students trace the angles of incidence and reflection and find them to be equal?

With mirrors. In demonstrating reflection by mirrors, use a carpenter's folding ruler placed in front of a mirror, as in Fig. 20-9. When the angles are properly adjusted, students should see two rulers.

Also set up a large mirror facing the class on a demonstration table in the center front of the classroom. Ask students in one outer row of seats to name which students they can see in the mirror. Do these

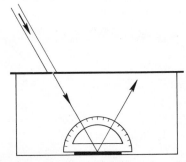

Fig. 20-8 Reflection of light made visible in a smoke-filled aquarium.

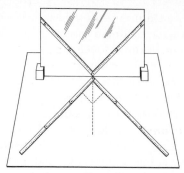

Fig. 20-9 Reflection in a mirror.

students, in turn, see the first group? (If you have movable furniture, arrange the seats in rows for this demonstration.) Stretch a string from each student in one outer row to the center of the mirror and back to the corresponding student (the one in the same left-to-right row) seen in the mirror. Students can measure the angles of incidence and reflection formed by the strings, and they will find these to be equal. As they work back from the front seats, the angles will be smaller and smaller, but for each position the angle of incidence will be equal to the angle of reflection.

One-way mirrors. If possible, obtain some one-way glass or use a lens from a pair of one-way sun goggles. Students can observe that the silver layer is so thin it reflects about one half the light and allows the other half to pass through. Devise demonstrations to show their use.

Parabolic mirrors. When parabolic mirrors are available, they can be used with a parallel-beam light source. A large shaving mirror of the magnifying type is a parabolic mirror. A sheet of shiny tinplate or a chromium-plated photographic ferrotyping plate can be curved to form one dimension of a parabolic mirror.

To show the path of the beams use the smoke box described earlier in this section. The same apparatus can show the effects of mirrors of various curvatures, both concave and convex types. Make a convex mirror by bending, in reverse, a chromium-plated sheet of metal. One type of convex mirror is used decoratively in a circular gold Colonial frame.

A concave mirror can be made using small mirror sections as in Fig. 20-10. By changing the relative position, concave mirrors of different curvatures can be produced. When the mirrors are reversed and the light source is applied from the opposite side, a convex mirror results.

Have your students experiment with a shaving mirror to produce both real and virtual images. If the source of light, for instance, a 25-watt incandescent lamp, is placed inside the principal focus of the mirror—that is, quite close to the mirror surface—students can stand back at almost any distance and see a virtual, enlarged, upright image of the lamp. In Fig. 20-11, the formation of a virtual image is diagrammed. Now have them move the lamp quite far from the lens so that it is well beyond the principal focus. For this condition a real, inverted, smaller image

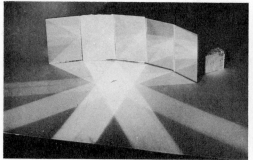

Fig. 20-10 A concave mirror made from sections of plane mirror. (PSSC of Educational Services, Inc.)

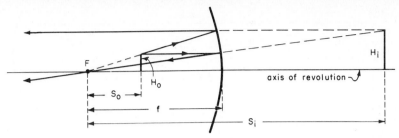

Fig. 20-11 Diagram of the formation of a vertical image in a concave mirror. (From PSSC of Educational Services, Inc.)

will be projected in the space between the mirror and the source (Fig. 20-12). Look for this image by moving the eye back and forth as well as sideways between the mirror and the lamp. The location of the real image can be predicted if the focal length (f) of the mirror is known or can be measured by applying the equation

$$S_i = \frac{f^2}{S_o}$$

where S_i is the distance of the real image from the focus when the object is located at a distance S_o from the focus, and the focal length of the mirror is f. The remaining mirror equations given below should be derived by the students using similar triangles and the rules of plane geometry (Fig. 20-13).

$$\frac{H_i}{H_o} = \frac{f}{S_o}$$

and

$$\frac{H_i}{H_o} = \frac{S_i}{f}$$

Once these are derived, your students should be able to combine them to obtain the equation given above

$$S_i = \frac{f^2}{S_o}$$

Your students should discover for themselves that a convex mirror cannot produce a real image under any circumstances. Have them show why this must be so from the geometry of the mirror and the law of reflection.

Periscope. Students often prepare a re-flecting periscope from a long mailing tube or from shoe boxes taped end to end. The length of the tube can be any size needed to enable viewing over a wall. Cut apertures in the cardboard, using Fig. 20-14 as a guide, and mount plane mirrors at 45° so that the mirror at the upper end faces the scene to be viewed and the lower mirror faces the eye as shown.

Reflecting-image range finders. A simple range finder can be made from three sticks as shown in the photograph (Fig. 20-15). At right angles nail a 2' stick to the end of a 4' stick. Over the right-angle joint place a small pocket mirror at exactly 45° with the front facing into the angle made by the sticks. At the end of the short stick nail or bolt a third stick (3' long) in such a way that it can pivot. On the side facing

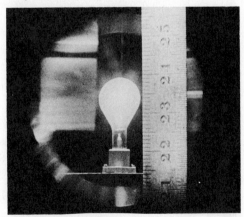

Fig. 20-12 A parabolic mirror forms this real image of a light bulb that is located about 17 meters in front of this image, while the parabolic mirror is about two meters behind. (PSSC of Educational Services, Inc.)

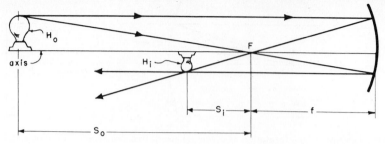

Fig. 20–13 The real image may be located by tracing two rays. (From PSSC of Educational Services, Inc.)

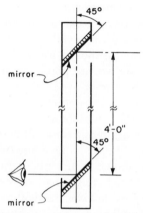

Fig. 20–14 Plan for a student-made periscope. (From PSSC of Educational Services, Inc.)

the 45° mirror mount with glue a second small mirror. Have students sight from the end of the stick over the top of the fixed 45° mirror until they see the image in the mirror in line with the object they see in the distance. The instrument can be calibrated by testing it over long distances. Mark these distances on the long stick. For parallax measurement of distance with a cross-staff see 2.1c.

Another type of range finder can be built within a wood box that is about 3″ × 8″ in cross section. Scrape off half the silver and black paint from a small mirror, and position it in the box as shown in Fig.

Fig. 20–15 A range finder made from three sticks and two pocket mirrors. (William Vandivert, courtesy of *Scientific American*.)

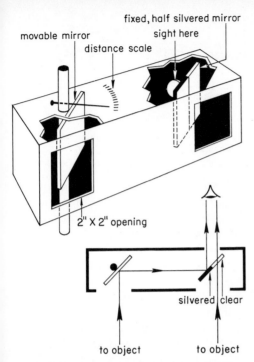

Fig. 20–16 A simple range finder whose parts are contained in a box.

20-16. Notice the three openings in the box—one behind the half-silvered mirror for sighting, two in front for light admission. The opening used for sighting should be about the size of a dime. Glue a second mirror to a dowel which can be turned and use a nail or pointer as an indicator. Sight from the back opening through the split mirror. When the two parts of the split image coincide, the range is being measured. The instrument is calibrated against measured distance, and a scale is marked at the top of the box as shown. Some cameras use a range finder of this type.

20.1d   Refraction

Demonstrating a refracted beam of light
Refraction at air-water surface. Students can show that the greater the angle of incidence, the greater the bending or refrac-

tion of light. Again use a rectangular fish tank, but this time fill the tank ¾ with water dyed with eosin. Make a thick cardboard cover with a slit 1″ × ⅛″ to fit the tank snugly. Fill the space above the water with smoke and direct a strong beam of light through the slit. Students should find the beam of light visible in the smoke, and also in the water because eosin is fluorescent. Notice how the light refracts sharply at the surface of the water.

Students should be ready to explain the following observations. Why does a pencil held in water appear bent? Would you spear a fish by aiming high or low? Why does a piece of wire seen obliquely through glass appear broken? Perhaps a student can make a penny visible in the following way. Place a penny at the bottom of a small container so that the edge of the vessel just hides the coin from view. Now pour in water and see the coin make an appearance.

Measuring the angle of refraction. Special water cells equipped with a protractor on the rear wall are available for this purpose from supply houses (see listing in appendix). Or a glass cell can be made from two pieces of window glass 4″ × 5″. Bend a piece of soft rubber into a U-shape and place it between the two sheets of glass.

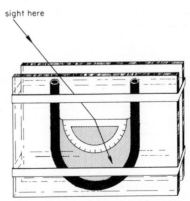

Fig. 20–17 Cell for measuring angle of refraction of light beam in liquids.

Hold the glass against the rubber tube with heavy rubber bands or tape (Fig. 20-17), and fill the cell with water. Place a protractor against the rear glass plate as shown and shine a narrow beam of light from above into the water whose level matches that of the protractor. Students should observe the refracted beam in the water. (A few drops of eosin added to the water will make the refracted beam more visible.) Use the protractor to measure the angle of refraction. With another protractor above the water measure the angle of incidence at the same time. The beam of light can be made more visible with chalk dust. Also fill the cell with other liquids and compare the angles of refraction. Check the results with a table giving indices of refraction of different materials (Table 20-2).

Snell's law. Students can verify Snell's law by tracing the path of a ray of light through a flat square of glass. They should proceed as follows.

1. Lay the square of glass in the exact center of a clean white sheet of paper. Using a sharp hard pencil, draw a clean outline around the glass square.

2. Place two pins (A and B) in the paper (cardboard backing will hold the pins without marring the table) so that the line between them makes an angle of about 30° with the normal (Fig. 20-18 and Fig. 20-19, part 1).

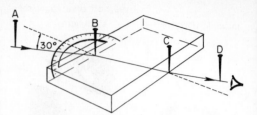

Fig. 20–18 Arrangement of materials for deriving Snell's law.

3. Crouching down low enough, place the eye at table level on the other side of the glass square (Fig. 20-18) and place two more pins (C and D) so that they appear to be in a straight line with A and B as seen through the glass (Fig. 20-19, part 2).

4. Remove the glass square and draw in the incident ray through the holes left by A and B, and the emergent ray through the holes left by C and D (Fig. 20-19, part 3). Then connect the end of the incident ray with the beginning of the emer-

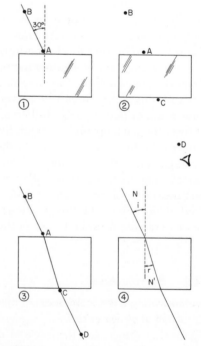

Fig. 20–19 Step-by-step process in deriving Snell's law.

TABLE 20-2

Indices of refraction for some common liquids[1]

bromine	1.66
glycerine	1.47
water	1.33
carbon disulfide	1.63
methylene iodide	1.74
carbon tetrachloride	1.46
ethyl alcohol	1.36

[1] All values are for light of wave length = 5839 angstrom units.

gent ray inside the glass boundary lines.

5. Construct normal NN′ geometrically or with a large protractor. Then measure the incident angle (i) and the refraction angle (r) as in Fig. 21-19, part 4. Substitute in the equation for Snell's Law

$$\text{index of refraction} = \frac{\sin i}{\sin r}$$

thus determining the index of the glass. Now change the incident angle by taking new positions for pins A and B, and repeat. After trials with at least four different angles of incidence, it will be clear that the ratio of sines is a constant. This is Snell's law.

Prepare a rectangular cell made of Lucite that contains clean water (Fig. 20-20), and have students repeat the same procedure with water or other liquids. (See working with plastics, 14.5d.)

20.1e Prisms

Students can study how light beams are bent in a prism. Hold the base of the prism flat and place it in the path of a narrow light beam. Then shift the base side up and test the effect of using different angles for the incident beam. Notice how the beam will bend toward the base in both cases. Why? Now place two triangular prisms base to base and use two light beams entering from two slits as shown in Fig. 20-21A. Have students explain why one beam will be bent upward and the other downward. They can repeat this activity, using light from a series of parallel slits.

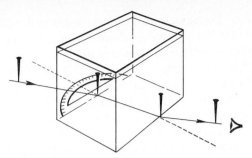

Fig. 20–20 A clear plastic box can be used to apply Snell's law to liquids.

Inexpensive, student-made prisms. Students can make simple prisms for class work. A triangular prism cell can be made from three glass microscope slides. Seal the edges and one end with cellophane tape. Fill the cell with water, seal the other end, and then use it as a prism.

Triangular glass prisms found in crystal chandeliers are useful. Military surplus prisms originally made for binoculars may be available. (Studies of prisms and dispersion are described under color in this chapter.)

20.1f Lenses

Convex lens. Some teachers introduce the laws of image formation with convex lenses by substituting lenses for prisms and repeating the demonstrations described in the preceding section. Use a large lens with a curvature somewhat similar to that of two prisms placed base to base. A side-by-side comparison shows that converging beams are similar. The smoke box described earlier in this chapter is useful here.

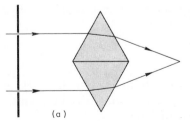

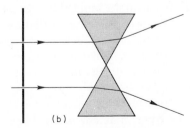

Fig. 20–21 Using prisms to introduce convex lenses (a) and concave lenses (b).

Concave lens. You may want to begin by demonstrating light beams passing through two prisms that are placed apex to apex as shown in Fig. 20-21B. Then students can use a concave lens and compare its similarity to the two prisms in the apex-to-apex position by repeating the demonstration using the lens in place of the prisms. Students can trace the diverging rays, and also use the concave lens as a hand lens to find the small, virtual image produced. Have students compare this image with that produced by a convex lens. Also use concave lenses on a simple optical bench as a laboratory activity. A small candle mounted on a movable block can be used as a light source.

Refraction in lenses. Introduce refraction in lenses by using a large, double convex lens in a darkened room. First use the lens to focus the light from a flame of a candle onto the wall so that students can see its image enlarged and inverted. Then repeat the procedure using convex lenses of shorter focal length; students should be ready to explain why the image remains inverted and will be large when the focal length is shorter. Have students diagram the different image formation in their notebooks. Compare these results with the images obtained when concave lenses are used.

Finding the focal length of a lens. A student can demonstrate a simple method for finding the focal length of a convex lens. Have him hold the lens at least 25′ from a well-lighted window, and focus the image of the window on a piece of white paper fastened on the wall behind the lens. It will be necessary to move the lens back and forth until the smallest and sharpest image is obtained. The distance from the center of the lens to the image is an approximation of the focal length.

In a second method, use a lighted candle or a carbon filament lamp. Place a

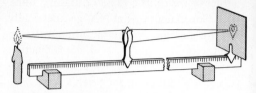

Fig. 20-22   Finding the focal length of a lens.

meterstick to the right of the light as shown in Fig. 20-22, and set the lens in a holder on the meterstick so that the center of the lens is aligned with the center of the light source. To the right of the lens, place a small white sheet of cardboard on a stand to serve as a screen. Focus the image on the screen by moving the lens and the screen until an image of the same dimensions as the flame or filament falls on the screen. The distance from the lens to the screen divided by two is the focal length.

Lens aberrations. Have students use uncorrected, inexpensive, spherical lenses to focus a light source on a screen in a darkened room. They do not get a sharp image at F_2 when the light is at F_2 or at two focal lengths away. Have students compare the lens equation

$$\frac{1}{f} = \frac{1}{S_o} + \frac{1}{S_i}$$

with the lens maker's formula

$$\frac{1}{f} = (n-1)\left(\frac{1}{R_1} + \frac{1}{R_2}\right)$$

where n is the index of refraction and R is the radius of curvature of each side of the lens. After a laboratory demonstration, students can summarize the drawings shown in Fig. 20-23 and use the following equation to find image and object relationships.

$$\frac{H_i}{H_o} = \frac{S_i}{S_o}$$

where H_i is image height, H_o is object height, S_i is image distance, and S_o is object distance.

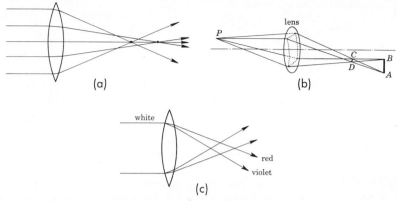

(a)

(b)

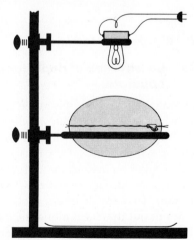

white

red

violet

(c)

Fig. 20–23 Lens aberrations: (a) spherical aberration for lenses whose surfaces are spherical arises because there is a longer focal length for rays through the lens center than for those nearer the edge; (b) off-axis astigmatism arises when the object is not on the lens axis; in the above the vertical line *BA* is in focus at a greater distance than the horizontal line *CD*, yet each is part of the same image; (c) chromatic aberration arises from the fact that the index of refraction for light in glass varies according to wave length. (From F. Miller, Jr., *College Physics*, Harcourt, Brace, 1959.)

Model of the lens of the eye. A transparent plastic bag (polyethylene) can be used as the base for a large working model of the lens of the eye. First cut out two equal circles of the plastic sheet and cement them together around the edges with plastic cement (available in hobby shops), leaving a small side aperture. Then fill this sphere with water and close the aperture with a wide clip or clamp. Use this "lens" to focus a beam from a carbon filament lamp by setting it on a ring attached to a ring stand (Fig. 20-24). First obtain a sharply defined image of the filament of the lamp on a paper screen by moving the ring upward or downward as necessary. Then lift the screen to a slightly elevated position by placing a book under it. The image should become blurred. By pulling outward or pushing inward on the sides of the lens, its curvature may be changed to bring the image back into focus. This is somewhat similar to the way the lens of the eye accommodates to objects at different distances.

Nearsightedness and farsightedness. Students will remember that "nearsighted-ness" is due to an elongation of the eyeball (Fig. 20-25A) and "farsightedness" arises from the opposite condition (Fig. 20-25B).

A local optometrist, oculist, or optician is often glad to supply a teacher with lenses. For the following two demonstrations, lenses for correcting near- and farsightedness should be used. They should have no astigmatic correction since that would introduce distortion.

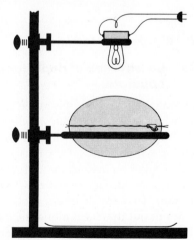

Fig. 20–24 A water-filled plastic bag can act as a rough model of the lens of an eye.

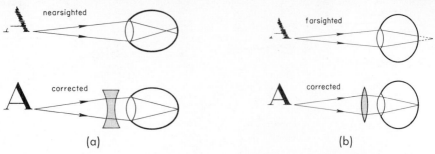

Fig. 20–25 Lenses to correct (a) nearsightedness, (b) farsightedness.

For farsightedness, focus an image through a projector lens onto a screen (analogous to the retina) and move the projector a little toward the screen. The image focus is now behind the screen. Now take a convex spectacle lens and refocus. This might all be readied beforehand so as to know how much to move the projector for the particular lens.

For nearsightedness, move the projector a bit away from the screen so that the image comes to a focus in front of the screen. Now introduce a concave spectacle lens and bring the image into sharp focus.

An optical bench can be set up using a candle, lenses, and screen arranged as to simulate near- and farsightedness.

20.2 Ripple tank techniques

20.2a Construction of ripple tank apparatus

The tank. The tank itself is made of ordinary window glass to which wood strips about 1″ by 1″ are secured with aquarium cement or a good grade of tile mastic cement. A window set in its frame and calked to make it waterproof can serve as an excellent tank. In many demonstrations you will want to put up fences along the sides of the tank in order to prevent unwanted reflections. These fences can be made of wire mesh covered with bandage gauze.

For most demonstrations the water depth is 10 mm. Provision should be made for supporting the tank horizontally on its own legs, although a pair of straight chairs will do nicely in an emergency.

Underneath the ripple tank, place a 150-watt clear, straight filament lamp mounted in a #2½ fruit can; no special optical system is necessary. To approximate more closely a point source of light a hole about 2″ in diameter can be cut in the side or bottom of the can and the light mounted in relation to it with the filament in a vertical position. The ceiling can be used as a projection screen if it is not too high; otherwise an old bedsheet stretched on a light wood frame can be mounted above the tank to serve as the screen (Fig. 20-26B). The whole setup can be reversed as shown in Fig. 20-26A if that proves handier.

Wave generation. Waves and ripples may be generated in several ways. You can dip your finger into the tank with slow rhythmic strokes, and observe the circular waves thus produced. One or more dropping funnels mounted over the tank provide an excellent source of controlled pulses. The drops of water should not fall more than ¼″ to avoid splashing. A medicine dropper can be used in the same fashion. A piece of doweling or metal rod laid in the tank and rolled back and forth produces straight waves. A Pop-It bead or similarly shaped material mounted on the end of a hacksaw blade can serve as the

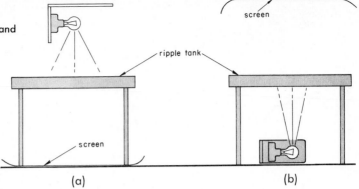

Fig. 20-26 Light source and the ripple tank.

screen

ripple tank

screen

(a)   (b)

source of higher frequency wave patterns. One end of the hacksaw blade can be anchored to a block of wood in such a fashion as to allow varying the length of the part of the blade that is set in vibration.

Motor-driven vibrators. A miniature toy electric motor such as the inexpensive Distler "Minimotor" (available by mail order from Lafayette Electronics, 165–08 Liberty Ave., Jamaica 33, New York, catalog number F-258) is mounted on a meterstick as shown in Fig. 20-27. The motor shaft is 3/32″ in diameter; drill a hole 1/16″ in diameter in a small wood dowel and force the dowel on to the shaft. Sink a wood screw into the dowel at right angles; directly under the meterstick insert a 1¼″

round-head wood screw. Connect the motor to a dry cell in series with a 10-ohm rheostat or potentiometer.

With the aid of a C-clamp, secure the stick to a second meterstick with a 1¼″ wood block between them. To one end of the lower meterstick attach an 8″ length of wood that has been planed to a sharp edge to produce straight waves. Circular waves are easily produced by a Pop-It bead attached to the end of a doweling with a small nail. Two beads or two meterstick vibrators can be used when two sources of waves are desired; this requires two motors and vibrator assemblies. Alternative ways of constructing vibrators are shown in Fig. 20-28. In Fig. 20-28A the

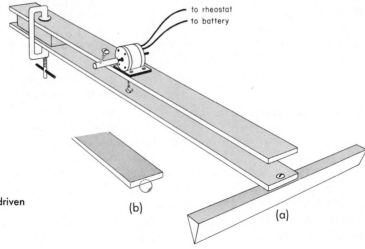

to rheostat
to battery

Fig. 20-27 A motor-driven ripple tank vibrator.

(b)

(a)

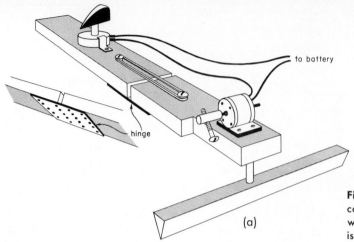

to battery

hinge

Fig. 20–28 Two ways to construct ripple tank vibrators which use a wave whose shaft is made to be out of balance.

(a)

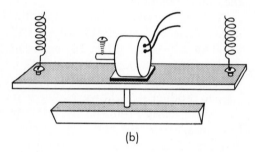

(b)

hinge is a piece of tin from a tin can; a rubber band supplies the vibrating tension. In Fig. 20-28B one or more springs are attached to each end of the vibrator. The springs should be so mounted and of sufficient strength to provide rotational stability.

The details of the construction of motor-driven vibrators can be as varied as the persons building them. Students often find it a challenge to design their own.

20.2b *The study of waves*

By analogy the waves in a ripple tank permit visualization of phenomena that must otherwise be relegated to blackboard descriptions. The wave theory does not tell the whole story about light but it is a major part of our present understanding of optical phenomena. You may want to make reference to the corpuscular or quantum nature of light. Many of these demonstrations are applicable to both sound and light.

Propagation of waves. Motor speed in ripple tank wave production is fairly critical. Experiment with various rheostat settings until you can obtain sharp, well-separated shadows of the crests and troughs of the water wave on the screen; you may also find that you can effect substantial improvements in the display by changing the relative distances of the light source and screen from the ripple tank.

As a first demonstration, use the Pop-It bead vibrator to produce circular waves. The bead is a point source from which the waves spread out in circles in the ripple tank. Point out that this is a two-dimensional display and elicit from your students the fact that a point source of light in real space produces concentric spherical, rather than circular, waves.

An additional concept that you might introduce at this time is that as the distance from the point source increases, the wave fronts begin to approach linearity, and that at great distances the fronts can be represented by parallel lines. Here again, the motion of parallel planes in real three-dimensional space should be emphasized since the use of the term "plane parallel waves" is common in the literature. The use of a very distant object for determining the focal length of a convex lens is an important application that the student will encounter in the laboratory; if he understands why the waves that reach us from distant bodies are essentially plane parallel waves, this concept will not have to be retaught when lenses are studied.

The use of a linear wave generator, such as the straight stick, can now be justified experimentally. The dimensions of the tank are not sufficiently large to permit circular waves to become plane parallel waves; hence we produce them artificially with suitable equipment so that they may be studied. Thus we simulate long path distances.

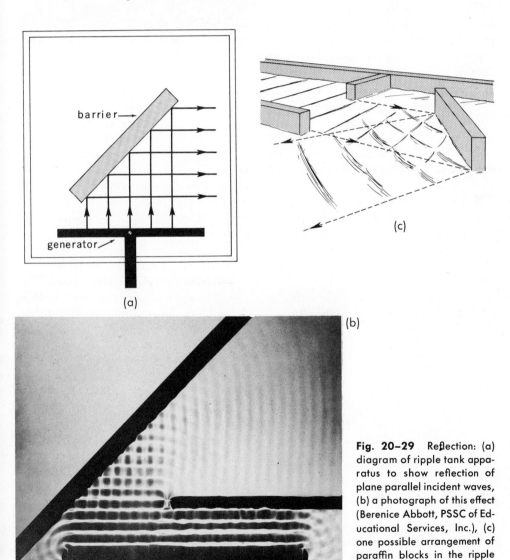

Fig. 20-29 Reflection: (a) diagram of ripple tank apparatus to show reflection of plane parallel incident waves, (b) a photograph of this effect (Berenice Abbott, PSSC of Educational Services, Inc.), (c) one possible arrangement of paraffin blocks in the ripple tank.

Reflection: plane parallel incident waves. Reflection from a plane mirror may be simulated in the ripple tank by placing a wax block (or a short board) at an angle of 45° to the plane waves generated by the rippler (Fig. 20-29A). It will be observed that the wave train is reflected at 45° from the normal so that the incident and reflected waves appear to form a square grid pattern (Fig. 20-29B). For water waves and light waves, the angle of incidence equals the angle of reflection, each angle being measured between the ray in question and the normal to the reflecting surface. In Fig. 20-29C is shown one possible arrangement of blocks.

If two barriers (paraffin blocks) are placed perpendicular to each other to form a 45° angle to the waves as in Fig. 20-30, the waves will be focused along a line that bisects the angle made by the barriers.

Circular waves in an ellipse. Using a 3' length of 1¼" wide sheet metal or linoleum, form an ellipse by joining the ends of the metal together with tape or paper clips. You may want to use a length of rubber tubing as in Fig. 20-31.

Use a wax block at each side of the ripple tank to apply pressure to the ellipse in

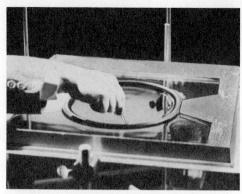

Fig. 20-31 Generating circular waves at one of the foci of an ellipse. (Alexander Joseph.)

order to keep it an ellipsoidal shape. With your finger or medicine dropper generate a single circular wave at one of the foci of the ellipse. Observe the image of the moving wave. The wave reflected from the opposite end of the ellipse converges at the focus. The circular wave returns to the focus at which it was generated. If you put sufficient energy into the original single circular wave, it will travel back and forth along the major diameter of the ellipse, with the foci showing up distinctly.

Reflection: circular incident waves. The image in a plane mirror appears to lie as far behind the reflecting surface as the original object is in front of it; the image is virtual, of course, because there are no real light rays coming from behind the mirror. The ripple tank shows this when used as follows: produce a single wave by dipping a pencil point sharply into the water. A flat barrier will then reflect the wave so that both the incident and reflected wave fronts are circular. Careful observation of the distances will show that both the original source of the disturbance and the "virtual" image are equidistant from the front surface of the barrier (Fig. 20-32).

Reflection from concave and convex surfaces. A coffee tin may be cut to form a

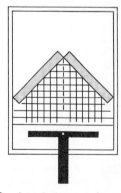

Fig. 20-30 A variation on plane reflection of straight waves in which the waves are focused down a line bisecting the angle made by the barriers.

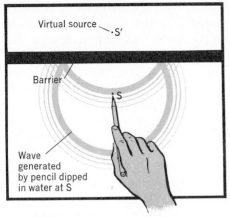

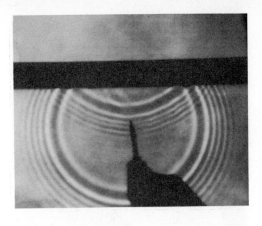

Virtual source — ·S'

Barrier

Wave generated by pencil dipped in water at S

S

Fig. 20–32 When circular incident waves are reflected from a plane surface, the reflection appears to have started from behind the reflector. (From R. Brinckerhoff, et al., *Exploring Physics*, Harcourt, Brace, 1959.)

semicylindrical concave reflecting surface that can be used to illustrate reflection from curved mirrors. Barriers set at angles at either side will serve to anchor the reflector (Fig. 20-33A). When placed in the path of the straight waves, the reflection will focus at a point one half the radius of the curve. The cylindrical tin may then be reversed to demonstrate the spreading out of waves reflected from a convex surface (Fig. 20-33B). These curved barriers can also be readily made from rubber tubing. For advanced students, it would be worthwhile at this point to investigate the geometry of curved mirrors and derive the equation

$$f = \frac{R}{2}$$

where f is the focal length of the mirror and R is the radius of curvature.

Reflection of circular waves by a parabola. Take a strip of sheet metal or linoleum $1\frac{1}{4}''$ wide and about $14''$ long. Curve it to form the approximate shape of a parabola. Place this on edge in the water and hold it in the shape of a parabola by means of wax blocks placed against the ends. Find the focus of the parabola by experi-

menting with your finger or drops of water as wave generators. When you have found the focus, the waves reflected by the parabola will be straight waves (Fig. 20-34).

Reflection of straight waves by a parabola. Generate single straight waves by rolling a length of doweling back and forth. Have these waves move into an open parabola as in the demonstration immediately above. Observe the straight wave produced by reflection (Fig. 20-35).

Measuring wave length. For this experiment you will need a meterstick and the handstrobe (see 20.9). Place the stick on a paper screen so that the images of the waves travel down the length of the meterstick. Next strobe the waves with the rheo-

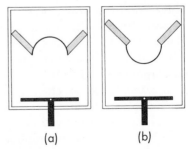

(a)   (b)

Fig. 20–33 Positioning tin reflecting surfaces in the ripple tank.

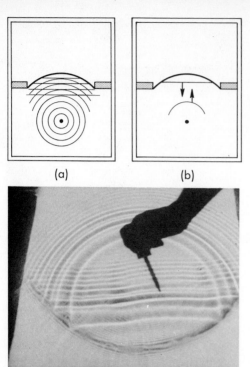

(a)   (b)

Fig. 20–34 Reflection of circular waves by a parabola. The wave generator in the photograph is a medicine dropper filled with water. (Photo by Alexander Joseph.)

stat adjusted for the longest wave length. When the waves on the screen below appear to be "stopped" by the rotating strobe, read the wave length of a single wave which is the distance on the meterstick covered by one bright band and one dark band (Fig. 20-36). Then increase the speed of the wave generator and measure the wave length of waves that have a shorter wave length. After a bit of practice you will be able to read the wave length directly by scanning the moving waves.

Standing waves. The phenomenon of standing waves is fundamental to an understanding of interference effects and related experimental observations on the behavior of light. As a first approach to this subject, place a straight barrier in the center of the tank and use the plane-wave vibrator. With the motor speed properly adjusted, the reflected waves will interfere with the waves traveling in the opposite direction to produce a series of motionless standing waves. The bright lines are the maxima where the water is moving up and down rapidly; the dark lines are the minima (or nodes) where the water remains undisturbed. Measure the distance between nodes and between adjacent maxima, and by comparing these distances with the wave length of the ripple before reflection, show that they are ½ wave length apart. Prove why this should occur by discussing the actual physical structure of node in the water wave as a point where the incident wave tries to move the water up (or down) while the reflected wave exerts an equal force in the opposite direction. In contrast, a maximum (or antinode) is a result of two displacement forces working in the same direction, resulting in an increased disturbance of the medium. After students thoroughly understand the phenomenon of standing waves, some teachers lead into other interference effects caused by superposition of wave trains going in the same direction.

Huygens' principle and diffraction. As originally proposed by Christian Huygens (1629–1695), a fundamental wave principle states that every point on an advancing wave front acts as a source from which new waves continually spread. This principle has far-reaching applications in all wave phenomena, and is the starting point for studies of diffraction and interference. An extremely provocative demonstration of Huygens' principle can be given with the ripple tank. Using the straight-wave vibrator, set up a series of sharply defined waves, with no barriers in the tank. Parallel to the oncoming straight waves, place two blocks of paraffin or weighted boards to form a "slit" that is several times wider than any ripple wave

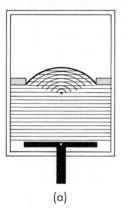
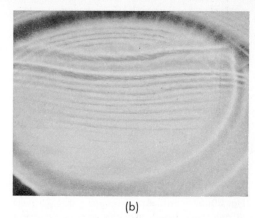

(a)   (b)

Fig. 20-35 Reflection of straight waves by a parabola produces circular waves. (Photo by Alexander Joseph.)

length. Each of the wax blocks should be shaved to an angle of 45° at the slit. (See Fig. 20-39.) It will be observed that the straight waves come through the opening without being seriously affected. Now make the slit narrower and narrower. When the width of the opening approximates one wave length, the straight waves will emerge from the opening as nearly perfect circular arcs (Fig. 20-37). Since every point in a straight wave front lies along a straight line, the formation of an arc from one of these points is a vivid proof of Huygens' principle. In a discussion of this demonstration students should recognize that the width of the opening is not the only determining factor in the production of circular waves from a plane wave front. One must compare the width of the slit to the length of the wave. In short, the larger the wave length is in relation to the opening size, the clearer the results.

One of the important implications of Huygens' principle is that a series of very closely spaced point sources, each producing circular waves, should ultimately give rise to a wave having a straight wave front. This can be shown on the blackboard geometrically with a series of circles

having their centers on the same straight line. As the radii grow larger, the most advanced points (in the direction of propagation) on each circle come closer to each other so that the tangent to these points soon becomes the combined wave front of all the original wavelets.

The ripple tank offers a dramatic demonstration of this effect. Hammer a number of nails in a stick along a straight line so that their points come through about ¼" apart. Shingle nails are excellent for this purpose because they are short and

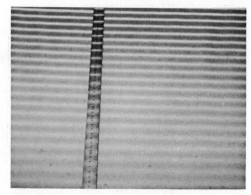

Fig. 20-36 Measuring wave length by laying a meterstick across the ripple tank. A strobe light is used to "stop" the waves. With practice one can read the wave length by visually scanning the tank. (Alexander Joseph.)

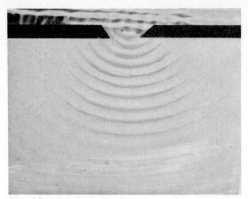

Fig. 20-37 Straight waves going through a slit of one wave length in width emerge as almost perfectly circular arcs. (Alexander Joseph.)

Diffraction may be alternatively defined as the spreading out of waves as they pass through a small opening, or as the bending of rectilinearly propagated waves as they pass the edge of an obstruction. Actually, the second effect is a consequence of the first; that is, the formation of new circular wave fronts at the remote side of a small opening being fed straight waves gives rise to new point sources having propagation directions different from the initial direction. Circular waves radiating from a slit of the order of one wave length, therefore, represent a diffraction effect. Several students may point out that light can bend around corners, just as sound does. However, the amount of bending is extremely small and normally goes unnoticed. Explain this difference in amount by comparing the wave lengths of ordinary sound waves with those of visible light.

Interference. One easy way to show interference effects in the ripple tank is to use a barrier of wax blocks stood end to end to form two rather closely spaced

relatively thick. Or you may use a row of florist's pins. Arrange the stick on the motor drive so that the nail points will dip in and out of the water as the vibrator operates. (The body of the stick should remain clear of the surface at all times.) Thus, each nail point serves as a point source for expanding circular waves which quickly begin to overlap and produce a tangential plane wave front (Fig. 20-38).

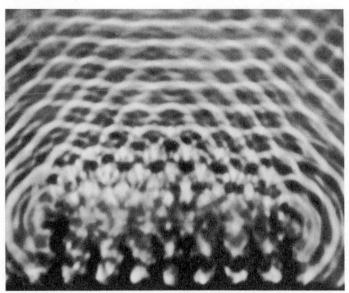

Fig. 20-38 A series of point sources in a line produce circular waves which merge to form a straight wave. (Dr. James Strictland.)

Fig. 20-39 Arrangement of barriers in a ripple tank to produce interference patterns.

Fig. 20-41 Using two point sources of circular waves to produce interference patterns in a ripple tank. (Alexander Joseph.)

openings. Shave each of the edges of the blocks to an angle of 45°. Adjust opening size, distance between openings, and ripple frequency until the best interference pattern is obtained (Fig. 20-39). For some students, a discussion of the meaning of nodal line and its origin should be stimulated. You may want to derive the expression

$$L = \frac{xd}{s}$$

where L is the wave length, x is the distance between nodes at a point s cm from the double source, and d is the distance between openings.

An alternative method for producing in-

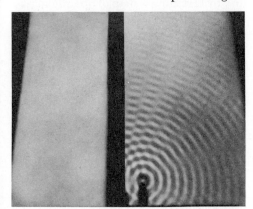

Fig. 20-40 Producing interference patterns using a point source of circular waves close up to a straight reflecting barrier.

terference patterns is to set up a reflecting barrier. Place the bead quite close to the barrier and vary the ripple frequency until the nodal lines are distinct and sharply defined (Fig. 20-40). Explain the nodal lines in terms of standing waves that are in phase at certain points and out of phase at others.

A third and very excellent method involves the use of two beads close to each other on the same vibrator rod (Fig. 20-41). In this case, proper adjustment of meter speed will yield well-defined nodal lines and reinforcements.

You will want to discuss other facts of interference and diffraction as you utilize the ripple tank. For example, the diffraction grating is merely an extension from two closely spaced slits to many such slits. Many teachers use optical diffraction gratings in individual experiments, now that replica gratings have become so inexpensive. It is possible in laboratory work to derive and use the equation

$$nL = d \sin r$$

where n is the order of the spectral line, L is the wave length, d is the slit separation, and r is the diffraction angle from the zero order to the first order.

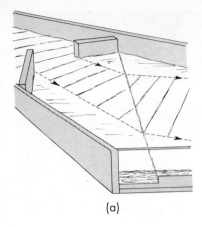

(a)

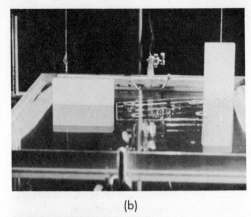

(b)

Fig. 20–42 Refraction: (a) one arrangement of barriers with the glass set at 45° to the incoming straight waves, (b) a photograph of a refraction setup in a ripple tank (Alexander Joseph), (c) refraction of water waves. (Berenice Abbott, PSSC of Educational Services, Inc.)

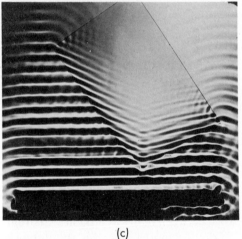

(c)

Refraction. A flat glass plate measuring approximately 5″ × 7″ is supported by "built-up" pillars of washers until its upper surface is no more than 1 millimeter below the water surface. The depth of water in the tank is about 1.5 cm. Ordinary sheet glass used for windows is perfectly suitable.

Arrange the plate of glass so that one of its longer edges presents itself to the oncoming straight wave at an angle of 45° or so (Fig. 20-42A). As the obliquely incident wave fronts pass into the shallow water above the plate, there will be a decrease of velocity and refraction will occur (Fig. 20-42B).

The bending will take place toward the normal according to Snell's law (Fig.

20-42C). You can visualize the normal line by fastening a strip of opaque masking tape along the bottom of the tank at right angles to the edge of the glass plate. The tape will throw a clear shadow on the screen, clearly delineating the normal. Masking tape is also useful to show the line of propagation of the straight waves (i.e., normal to the incident wave fronts) and the line of refraction (i.e., normal to the refracted wave fronts). The incident and refracted angles are easily measured, and the index of refraction of the shallow water may be computed from Snell's law,

$$\text{index of refraction} = \frac{\sin i}{\sin r}$$

where $i =$ the angle of incidence and $r =$ the angle of refraction. Your students may enjoy varying the index of refraction by changing the depth of the water above the glass plate. Using the same method, they can also experimentally verify the equation $v = \sqrt{gh}$. In this type of experiment, students will need to take many readings of the dependent and independent variables (v and h, respectively). Then they will need to tabulate their results and to find the mean, the deviation from the mean, and the probable error.

Focusing by a lens. A semicircular lens can be cut from a glass plate to show how plane waves are focused by refraction. If you can cut glass to shapes, form a "lens" (plano-convex) about 15″ long and about 6″ across its thickest dimension. Use ordinary window glass. Lucite sheeting 3/16″ thick can also be used, as can sheet aluminum providing it is thick enough not to sag. The lens is mounted so that its top is exactly 1 millimeter under the water surface as before. Each end can be anchored with barriers of wax or paraffin set at an angle away from the straight waves (Fig. 20-43).

The diverging action of a concave lens may be demonstrated with equal facility by making up a similar plate with suitable

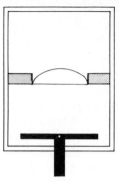

Fig. 20-43 A "lens" cut from glass or Lucite will focus waves in the ripple tank.

edge curvature. In both demonstrations, the "focal length" of the lens should be measured; then the index of refraction should be changed by varying the depth of the water and focal length measured again to show the relationship between f and index of refraction.

Total internal reflection. Cut from glass or plastic a shape with angles of those shown in Fig. 20-44A. Set it on washers so that the water depth is 1 mm or slightly less on its surface. The base of the figure faces the rippler and waxed blocks covered with bandage gauze are placed against the base angles. Get the rippler into operation to generate waves of long wave length. A beam of straight waves will move over the

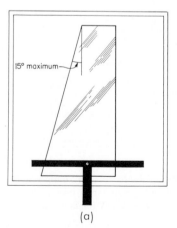

(a)

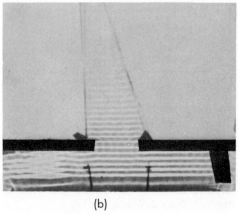

(b)

Fig. 20-44 Total internal reflection demonstrated in the ripple tank. (Photo by Alexander Joseph.)

triangle and will remain inside, being reflected internally by the deeper water (Fig. 20-44B). Now place a glass plate parallel to one side of the figure and separated from it by a distance of less than one wave length of the waves you are generating. The waves will travel across the deep water gap and continue over the new glass plates without being internally reflected. Next move the glass plate more than one wave length away from the side of the triangle, and the total internal reflection will occur inside the figure again. Students can trace the reflection of any single wave.

20.3   Combinations of lenses and mirrors

20.3a   *Telescopes*

Reflecting. Set up a shaving mirror (concave) and a very small plane mirror —possibly 1″ × 1″—as shown in Fig. 20-45B. The plane mirror may be held on the end of a short, stiff piece of wire or mounted on a doweling so that its support does not block too much light. The eyepiece lens should be a short focus type of

about 5 cm or less. The plane mirror should be placed close to the principal focus of the concave mirror and tilted at an angle of 45° as shown. The eyepiece lens may be hand-held and moved back and forth until it produces a virtual, enlarged image of the real image formed by the concave mirror. In other words, the lens is a magnifying glass used to view the real image projected in space by the concave mirror. The object viewed might be a 25-watt lamp at the other end of the room. Since shaving mirrors are not precision surfaces, there will be some distortion, but the principles of the telescope will be quite evident.

Astronomical. An optical bench is handy for this demonstration. You will need two lenses: the objective lens may have a focal length of 10 to 20 cm; the eyepiece lens should be a short-focus type of 5 cm or less. Set up the lenses so that the eyepiece is a short distance (possibly 2 or 3 cm) beyond the principal focus of the objective lens (Fig. 20-46A). Look at a distant object. The real image formed by the objective lens will be inverted; hence, when examined by a second convex lens

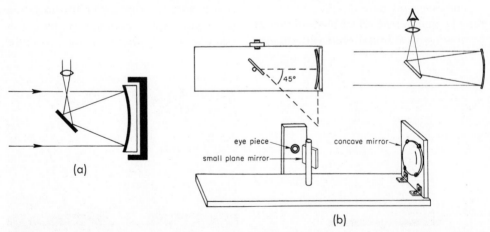

(a)

45°

eye piece

small plane mirror

concave mirror

(b)

Fig. 20–45   Reflecting telescope: (a) the essential relationship of the mirrors and eyepiece (from F. Miller, Jr., *College Physics*, Harcourt, Brace, 1959), (b) a model that can be made from a shaving mirror, a pocket mirror, and a small lens. (From A. Joseph, et al., *Sourcebook for Elementary Science*, Harcourt, Brace & World, 1961.)

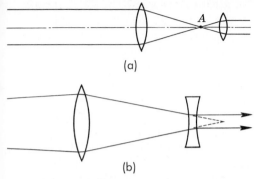

(a)

(b)

Fig. 20–46 Refracting telescope: (a) the relationship of the objective and eyepiece lenses in an astronomical telescope where the image is inverted, (b) a terrestrial telescope keeps the image erect by placing a concave eyepiece inside the objective focus. (From F. Miller, Jr., *College Physics*, Harcourt, Brace, 1959.)

(the eyepiece) used as a magnifier, the eye will see an enlarged virtual image of the real image. Since reinversion does not occur, the final image will still be inverted. This does not matter for astronomical applications.

Terrestrial. The original Galilean telescope was of this design, using a convex lens as the objective and a concave lens as the eyepiece (Fig. 20-46B). Use the same objective as in the astronomical telescope; the eyepiece, however, should be a double concave lens with large curvature, i.e., strongly concave. Using the optical bench once again, place the eyepiece lens a short distance *inside* the principle focus of the objective so that the rays cannot fully converge. Thus, a virtual but *erect* image will form at B, or somewhat beyond it depending upon the spacing of the lenses. Magnification occurs because the image is much closer to the eye than the actual object and thus subtends a much larger angle in the eye. Magnification is increased by using objectives of the longest possible focal length.

For further details on building telescopes see 5.3e.

20.3b Other optical instruments

Compound microscope. A single convex lens used as a magnifying glass is termed a *simple microscope*. Greater magnification can be obtained by combining two convex lenses as in Fig. 20-47, to make up a compound microscope. The small object to be viewed is placed between F and 2F of a very short focus convex lens. This produces a real, enlarged image outside of 2F on the other side of the lens. This image is then viewed by a magnifying lens, again very short in focal length, to produce a very much enlarged virtual image. The optical bench is again useful in this demonstration. Make certain that the object is very small (the head of a pin is suitable) and very well illuminated. Note that two lenses having focal lengths of 2 cm are used in the illustration, that the object is placed at 2.2 cm (just beyond the principal focus), and that the eyepiece is adjusted until it can magnify the real image formed at A. For details on making a compound microscope see 20.3c.

Prism spectroscope. The actual construction of a model of a spectroscope should be a student project because housings must be fabricated. For example, the prism should rest on a horizontal table in

objective L_1
$f = +2$ cm

eyepiece L_2
$f = +2$ cm

A

$s_1 = -2.2$ cm $s_2 = 2\,2$ cm

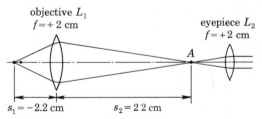

Fig. 20–47 A compound microscope: the object to be viewed is placed just beyond the focus of the objective, L_1, so that a real image is formed at A. This image is very large since the ratio of image distance over object distance is large. Further magnification is secured when the real image at A acts as the object for the eyepiece, L_2. (From F. Miller, Jr., *College Physics*, Harcourt, Brace, 1959.)

the form of a plywood disk about 6″ in diameter, elevated on a wood stand so that it is at a comfortable height. The telescope section should be formed of cardboard or Bakelite tubing in two pieces that fit snugly into one another. Exact dimensions cannot be provided because lens diameters vary considerably. The telescope might be held in a clamp on a ring stand while the collimator lens may be in a standard lens holder. The adjustments are as follows: place the collimator lens so that it is exactly one focal length away from the slit; the prism should be as close as possible to the collimator; the same is true of the objective of the telescope. Effectively, the collimator renders the light from the slit parallel. The prism then disperses the light into its components, but these emerge parallel from the other side. The telescope then forms a real image of the slit at A, and the eyepiece magnifies it for close inspection. For added details on spectroscopes see 5.3f and, especially, 20.5a.

Projector. The commercial film or slide projector uses a pair of plano-convex lenses to concentrate the light from the projection lamp through the transparency (Fig. 20-48). The concave mirror assists in this action by reflecting light that would otherwise be lost in the rear of the lamphouse. The illuminated slide now acts as the object and is located between F and 2F of the objective lens in the front barrel.

For great enlargement, the slide is nearly at the principal focus. The objective merely forms a real, inverted, enlarged image of the slide well beyond 2F on the other side. The making of such a projector is, again, a student project requiring the purchase of condenser lenses and an objective from optical supply houses. The concave mirror must be of metal due to the great heat developed by the lamp. There are lamps which have built-in mirrors. The lamp housing can be made up of galvanized sheet iron or aluminum bent to shape and held together with sheet metal screws. Be sure to provide adequate ventilation if the lamp is more than 50 watts. If 200 watts or more, forced cooling may have to be used. A hand hair dryer (without heating element) is ideal for this.

Detailed instructions for making optical instruments are given in the following sections: simple and compound microscopes, see below in 20.3c; telescopes, 5.3e; spectroscopes, 5.3f and 20.5a; simple enlarger, 20.7c; periscope and range finders, 20.1c.

20.3c Building microscopes

As a club activity, students can make their own simple microscopes with which they can explore crystals, textiles, and living microorganisms.

Simple microscope. In this simple microscope, a glass bead is cemented into plywood. Students will need a square of ⅛″

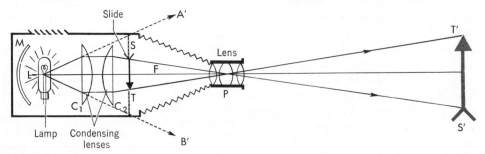

Fig. 20–48 Plan of a typical projector. (From H. Ruchlis & H. Lemon, *Exploring Physics*, Harcourt, Brace, 1952.)

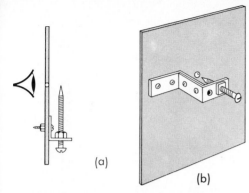

(a)

(b)

Fig. 20–49 Simple van Leeuwenhoek microscopes: (a) the material being looked at is raised on the point of screw past the glass bead lens, (b) the material turns toward the glass bead.

plywood, $3'' \times 4''$. In the center of the plywood, drill a small opening about 3/16″ in diameter and cement a small round glass bead into it (Fig. 20-49A). Use the small beads available from supply houses to increase surfaces for reaction in flasks. Or glass beads can also be made by melting a glass rod in a Bunsen flame. Smaller beads are most effective.

This bead will be the tiny, spherical lens similar to that used by A. van Leeuwenhoek in his microscopes. Mount a small sheet brass angle an inch or so below the lens in line with the lens. Solder a brass nut having 8/32 thread onto the extending angle arm. File the tip of a long brass 8/32 thread screw to a fine point and insert this in the brass nut. Dip the point into some crystals or into a culture of protozoa. Place the lens near the eye and focus by turning the screw and moving your eye.

In a variation shown in Fig. 20-49B a screw is used that moves the object horizontally varying distances from the lens. This is achieved by using two brass angles joined so that one arm is attached to the plywood, while an arm extended in the other direction carries the 8/32 thread brass nut. The center of the nut must be

aligned with the lens so that the 8/32 thread screw goes through the opening and moves toward the lens for focusing.

In using either type of simple microscope, bright light must illuminate the material to be examined.

Tongue depressor microscope. A simpler version of the Leeuwenhoek microscope using microscope slides and screw thread focusing can be made. Join the ends of two tongue depressors with masking tape or adhesive tape to form a hinge and fold them together (Fig. 20-50). Let us call the left side A and the right side B. About $1\frac{1}{2}''$ from the top of A drill a tiny opening to receive a small glass bead as a lens. Use beads having a diameter of $\frac{1}{8}''$ or $1/16''$ for the best magnification. Aligned with this opening, an aperture is drilled in B to admit light; $2''$ below this opening drill a second aperture slightly more than $\frac{1}{8}''$ in diameter. Over this hole attach a 6/32 thread brass or iron nut using model airplane cement. Allow a day for the cement to set firmly and then insert a brass 6/32 thread screw which will be used for focusing. Finally fasten a rubber band around the center of both tongue depressors.

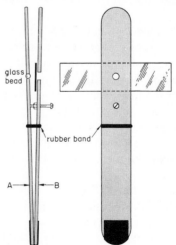

glass bead

rubber band

A — B

Fig. 20–50 A simple version of van Leeuwenhoek microscope.

Attach a prepared microscope slide to side *B* with a rubber band. Place the lens against the eye and focus by turning the machine screw.

Compound microscope. Inexpensive, unmounted lenses to be used for the microscope objectives and eyepieces can be obtained from supply houses. With these, students can construct a compound microscope. Check Fig. 20-51 for details while reading the directions.

Base. (See Fig. 20-51A.) Cut a base from a hardwood such as maple or oak—dimensions, $1'' \times 6'' \times 4''$.

Pillar. (See Fig. 20-51B.) Cut a piece of birch or pine $2'' \times 2'' \times 4''$. With a saw and chisel make a slot in the wood $1''$ wide and $2''$ deep. Drill a $\frac{1}{4}''$ hole $\frac{1}{2}''$ down and $1''$ in from the edge through both walls of the slot.

Arm. (See Fig. 20-51C.) Use $1''$ plywood (7-ply if possible) cut to a curve of a radius that will handle the length of focusing tube required by your particular lenses (see length of focusing tube below). Drill a $\frac{1}{4}''$ hole $1''$ from lower end and $\frac{1}{2}''$ in from edge. Attach to pillar by inserting into slot and using a bolt and wing nut.

Tube holder. (See Fig. 20-51D.) For the focusing tube holder use brass tubing with a $1''$ internal diameter and about $4''$ long. Cut a slot along its length and squeeze together to impart some springiness. Mount on the arm so that it is perpendicular to the stage (see below). Use two $\frac{3}{4}''$ flathead brass screws to secure the tube to the arm, countersinking the heads flush inside the tube.

Focusing tube. (See Fig. 20-51E.) The length of the focusing tube may be calculated in advance as follows.

1. First calculate the position of the real image formed by the objective lens, using the equation

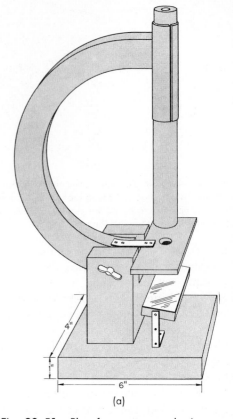

Fig. 20-51 Plan for a compound microscope that can be made by a student.

$$\frac{1}{S_i} = \frac{-1}{(f + .1f)} + \frac{1}{f}$$

where S_i is the distance of the real image from the optical center of the objective and f is the focal length of the objective. In this calculation we are assuming (quite properly) that the object will be placed about 10% further on beyond the principal focus of the objective.

2. Add the focal length of the eyepiece to the result obtained above. This will give you the necessary spacing between the optical centers of the two lenses.

For example, suppose that you are using a pair of lenses, each with a focal length of 2 cm. This yields

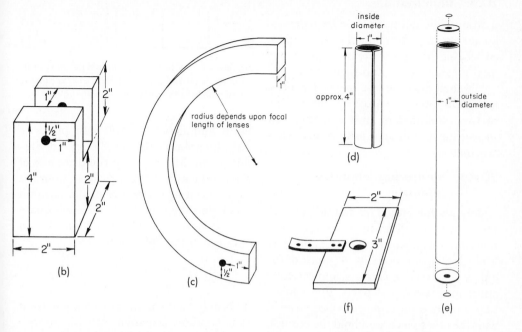

inside diameter

approx. 4"

(d)

radius depends upon focal length of lenses

(b)

(c)

(f)

outside diameter

(e)

$$S_i = -\frac{1}{2.2} + \frac{1}{2.0}$$

thus $\qquad S_i = 22 \text{ cm}$

Adding the focal length of the eyepiece $(22 + 2 \text{ cm}) = 24 \text{ cm}$ total separation. See Fig. 20-47.

The focusing tube should be cut somewhat longer than the figure obtained by calculation, say, 10% longer. Then, the lenses should be temporarily secured in the tube with Scotch tape, and the tube should be tested visually. Final corrections in tube length may then be made with confidence.

To make the tube itself, take a cardboard or metal tube with an outside diameter of 1". Cut a circle of plywood or thick cardboard so that it just fits snugly into the inside diameter of this tube. In the center of this circle, in turn, drill or cut another circle the diameter of the eyepiece lens. Cement the lens in place, slip its circular mounting into the end of the tube, and glue in place. Cut another circle of plywood or thick cardboard for the other end of the focusing tube and mount the objective lens. Insert the mounted lens into the end of the focusing tube temporarily. When the microscope is assembled, test the lens relationship for the best length of tube before permanently setting the objective lens in place.

Stage. (See Fig. 20-51F.) Use tempered Masonite, 3" by 2". Under the objective lens drill a ½" hole in the stage. Attach the stage to the arm with a piece of brass at least 1/16" thick and ¾" wide using ¾" brass screws. Rubber bands can be used to hold a slide on the stage.

Mirror. (See Fig. 20-51A.) Mount the mirror (approx. 2" × 2") onto a piece of wood of about the same size but which has a hole drilled through it from end to end. Mount on angle irons directly under the ½" hole in the stage in such a fashion that the axis in which the mirror pivots bisects the ½" hole and therefore bisects a projection of the objective lens.

20.4 Illumination

Many different units have been defined for measuring "how much light" is present. Table 20-3 gives the most commonly used measurements and their units.

We shall describe two means for measuring luminous intensity by using either of two photometers, and a method for measuring illuminance using a photoelectric meter.

20.4a Measuring luminous intensity

Joly photometer. This simple photometer can be made to measure the luminous intensity of an electric light bulb. Use a block of paraffin about ½″ thick of the type sold for sealing jam jars, and carefully cut it into two equal parts. Place black paper on one piece of paraffin, cover it with the other piece, and hold the paraffin blocks together with rubber bands (Fig. 20-52). Or you may prefer to purchase a commercial model of the same equipment. You will need to purchase some standard candles from a scientific supply house. (Most common white candles emit about two candle power.) Place a meterstick or yardstick on the table; mount the candle at one end, the paraffin blocks near the middle, but free to slide, and the small electric light bulb to be tested, in a base-mounted socket, at the other end. Center the candle flame with the vertically mounted paraffin blocks. Then light the

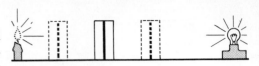

Fig. 20-52 With the Joly photometer the paraffin block is moved back and forth until a point is found where both halves are equally lighted.

lamp and move it until both pieces of paraffin seem to be equally lighted. Students can now measure the distances of the candle and the electric light from the black sheet at the center of the paraffin block and then apply the inverse-square law to find the luminous intensity (in candles) of the light bulb.

$$\frac{I_{(\text{candle})}}{(d_{\text{candle}})^2} = \frac{I_{(\text{bulb})}}{(d_{\text{bulb}})^2}$$

This may be the point at which you want to have students demonstrate the inverse-square law with strings and a projector as described earlier in this chapter.

Bunsen photometer. The Bunsen photometer uses a grease spot in place of the paraffin blocks used in the Joly photometer (Fig. 20-53). A commercial model can be used or the apparatus can be constructed from a cardboard square about 5″ × 5″ with an opening at the center about 2½″ square. Mount a piece of mimeograph paper over the opening and at the center of the paper prepare a grease spot about ½″ in diameter using a drop of oil or fat. Now mount the cardboard square in a slider made for a meterstick or on a wood block. Place a lamp of known luminous intensity at one end. Carbon filament lamps are available that emit 16 or 32 candles. At the opposite end mount the bulb to be tested. Students can adjust the position of the grease spot and the lamp to be tested until the grease spot disappears. Then measure the distance between the grease spot and the filament of each of the lamps. Use the inverse-square equation as

TABLE 20-3
Units of measurement for light intensity

Luminous flux (rate at which visible radiation is emitted)	lumen
Illuminance (rate at which unit area of surface receives visible radiation)	foot-candle (= lumen/sq ft) lumen/sq meter
Luminous intensity	candle (= lumen power)

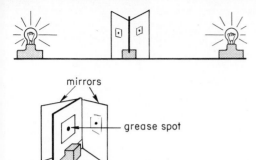

Fig. 20–53 In the Bunsen photometer the center assembly is moved to a point where the grease spot appears to be passing an equal amount of light in each direction. If you mount a mirror, the spot can be viewed from both sides simultaneously.

before to find in candles the luminous intensity of the unknown lamp.

20.4b Measuring illuminance

Photoelectric photometer. One kind of photoelectric photometer depends on light falling on a metallic surface which gives off electrons. Another uses the photovoltaic effect. Connect a Weston photronic cell or selenium light meter element to a galvanometer and hold a match in front of the cell. Students can observe the current produced. Now repeat with a small flashlight to show that an increase in light also causes an increase in current. This illustrates the principle of the photoelectric meter.

Students can make a liquid photoelectric cell by heating a section (about 1" ×

6") of sheet copper in a Bunsen flame until the copper is covered with black copper oxide. Then place it in nitric acid; remove it after about five minutes when there is a red layer visible. The red layer is cuprous oxide which is sensitive to light. Now immerse the sheet in a jar containing lead nitrate solution. On the other side of the jar insert a clean sheet of lead of the same dimensions and connect the metal strips to a galvanometer. Have a student shine a strong light on the cuprous oxide and observe that the galvanometer will show an increase in current reading. What happens to the current reading when the light is moved away?

When students observe that the difference in the amount of light can be detected electrically, they are ready to use a photoelectric foot-candle meter.

Deriving the inverse-square law experimentally. Some teachers have found this procedure effective. A foot-candle meter can be used to derive the inverse-square law. Mount a 25-watt bulb at the end of a yardstick. Have students prepare a two-column table on the blackboard; label one column "d" (distance in feet), the other, "f" (illuminance in foot-candles). The room should be *absolutely* dark. Hold the photometer 1' from the bulb and note the reading. Students can write both numbers in the table. Can they predict the reading at 2'? Then test it at 2'. The reading should be ¼ of the reading found at 1'. Write the values in the table and

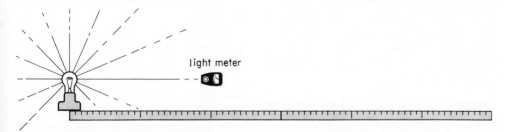

Fig. 20–54 Using a light meter to derive the inverse-square law experimentally.

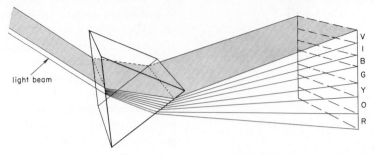

V
I
B
G
Y
O
R

light beam

Fig. 20–55 A prism is held or secured base down in a shaft of light to produce the spectrum.

have students predict the reading at 3'. Again, they can test the results (about 1/9 of the first reading). What distance would give a reading 1/16 of the first reading? (See Fig. 20-54.) Check the prediction and enter the values on the table.

From a study of the data elicit that the 2' reading was ¼ of the 1' reading. Develop the idea that squaring the distance, 4, and dividing this into the reading for 1' will give the meter value for the new distance. At a distance of 3', dividing the square, 9, into the first reading gives the meter reading for 3'. Now repeat this operation for four feet. Students will recognize that in all cases the observed illuminance was equal to the original illuminance divided by the square of the new distance. They can now develop the equation

$$\frac{I_1}{d_2{}^2} = \frac{I_2}{d_1{}^2}$$

20.5 Color

You may want to have students repeat, in a limited way, early experiments to show the dispersion of light into its color components. Students will want to describe Newton's early experiments with light and color.

20.5a Analysis of white light: the spectrum

Color dispersion by a prism. Students

can cover the bottom half of a sunny window with cardboard having a slit about 1″ × ⅛″ so that a parallel beam of light is available. Where sunlight passes directly through the slit, support a prism, base down, in a clamp on a ring stand in the path of the beam. Preparation of an inexpensive prism from microscope slides is covered earlier in this chapter in 20.1e. A spectrum will appear on the floor or on the lower part of the wall facing the slit; if the prism is held base up, the spectrum will be found on the ceiling. Or hold a white card near the prism as a screen (Fig. 20-55).

When sunlight is not available, substitute a photoflood lamp or a projector held behind a slit in cardboard.

"Rainbow." A large-scale demonstration of a rainbow can be carried out on the school lawn if you turn on a lawn sprinkler that produces a fan-shaped spray. Students can adjust the position in relation to the sunlight until a rainbow is visible. However, they should recognize that a rainbow and a spectrum are not exactly the same.

Grating spectroscope. A piece of inexpensive plastic spectrum grating which is actually an interference grating makes a simple spectroscope. These gratings can be obtained at a small cost from a scientific supply house. They are mounted over a ½″ opening at the end of a cardboard tube or shoe box as in Fig. 20-56. A fine

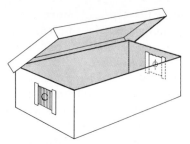

Fig. 20–56 A grating spectroscope.

slit is made in aluminum foil and mounted over a ½″ hole at the other end of the container. The slit should be parallel to the grating pattern. The spectrum can be observed off to one side.

Prism spectroscope. A fine slit prism can be used to show the visible spectrum. The prism should be mounted in a can or box with a collimating tube and slit as in Fig. 20-57. A very fine slit should be used, measuring no more than 0.01 cm in width. This can be made by cementing two slivers of injector type razor blades on the end of the tube. While holding the slit up to the light, adjust the blade positions so that the merest hairline of light can be seen. Then firmly cement in position. The angle between the tubes *must* be determined experimentally before the telescope is finally secured in the box. A water-filled prism may be used as shown in Fig. 20-57, or an ordinary glass prism taken from a crystal chandelier or an old pair of binoculars can be installed in the box. Students can locate the bright lines for specific elements when gas spectrum tubes or a neon or argon bulb are used. Or you may place a small quantity of a metallic salt on wire gauze on a tripod over a Bunsen burner. Invert a tin can with a 1/16″ slit over the top of the wire gauze, covering the salt so that a source of monochromatic light is produced which can be examined with the spectroscope and its wave length compared with a reference scale (see appendix).

Sodium absorption lines. Insert in a lantern slide holder a piece of cardboard with a vertical slit about ⅛″ wide. With the prism standing on end on a ring stand (ring covered with piece of plywood serves as prism table), rotate it to the position of *minimum* deviation of the spectrum observed on the screen. Outline the edge of the prism on the table with a pencil so that it may be returned to this setting later. Now turn the prism about until a *reflection* from any face is seen on the screen, showing an image of the slit. Adjust the focusing of the projector until the slit-image is sharp and clear. Return the prism to the position previously marked. The spectrum on the screen is a continuous type obtained from the incandescent tungsten of the lamp filament. Using the Bunsen burner source of monochromatic light from rock salt (NaCl) crystals, hold the source between the prism and the screen. After a few moments, the dark absorption lines of sodium will be clearly seen in the continuous spectrum.

20.5b Measuring the wave length of any part of the visible spectrum

Surprisingly precise results in the measurement of wave lengths can be obtained with the aid of one of the replica diffraction gratings that are now easily available at low cost from Edmund Scientific Co.,

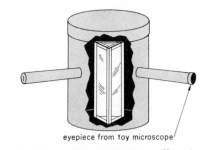

eyepiece from toy microscope

Fig. 20–57 A prism spectroscope. The prism can be made from microscope slides taped together and filled with water.

Barrington, N.J. Set up two meter-sticks at right angles to each other on the laboratory table; for a permanent setup, it is a good idea to fasten the sticks at the proper angle with the help of a flat angle iron (2″ × 2″ × ½″). Mount an Edison screw-type electric socket (flush mounting type) immediately above the right-angle joint and equip it with a 25-watt clear tubular showcase lamp having a long straight filament. Wire a line cord and plug for 120-volt a.c. operation to the socket.

Mount the replica grating at one end of either meterstick, using a single thumbtack pressed into the end of the stick. As you look through the grating, you should be able to see the luminous filament at the other extremity of the meterstick.

A second student placed behind the other meterstick is then told by the observer where to place his pencil point on the second stick. The observer will be able to see three orders of continuous spectra to one side of the luminous source, and he directs his assistant to place his pencil on that point in the first order over which the desired color appears. Suppose the observer wishes to find the wave length of the center of the green band; by watching his assistant move his pencil slowly along the stick, he can tell him when to stop as the pencil reaches the center of the color band (Fig. 20-58).

The distance from the grating to the source is, of course, 100 cm (distance B); the distance from the source to the point where the color being measured appears is called A. Note that a right triangle is formed by connecting the position of the color with the grating position, making an angle between the reference meterstick and this connecting line.

It is next necessary to determine the grating spacing, d. The manufacturer of the grating always specifies the number of lines per inch on his product; first determine the number of lines per cm by dividing this figure by 2.54 since there are 2.54 cm in one inch. Second, determine the spacing between adjacent lines by taking the reciprocal of the number of lines per cm just obtained. This will come out as a very small number, and is referred to as d. Since the basic grating equation is

$$\text{wave length} = d \sin \theta$$

and since the sine of θ is found from the quotient of A over the hypotenuse of the right triangle, the wave length may be found directly from

$$\text{wave length} = d \times \frac{A}{\sqrt{A^2 + B^2}}$$

A good variation on the procedure above is to substitute a monochromatic sodium source (Bunsen burner and rock salt) for the 25-watt lamp. In this case, only the D lines of sodium will be visible (unresolved) so that this method of wave length determination may be checked against the accepted value for the D-line wave length (5.89×10^{-5} cm).

Thin film diffraction. Thin film diffraction and colors can be observed in oil films on the surface of water, or in thin glass

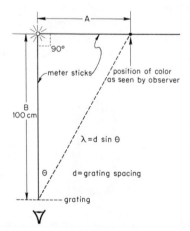

Fig. 20–58 Measuring the wave length of various colors with a diffraction grating.

that is blown into a bubble over a Bunsen flame. When two microscope slides are placed against each other, separated only by a hair at one end, light is reflected from the two slightly different thicknesses near the wave length of light and hence produces interference patterns. You will also want to refer to demonstrations of interference, using the ripple tank as discussed earlier in this chapter.

20.5c Additive mixing of spectrum colors

With a prism. Students can use the same apparatus as was used in the analysis of white light with a prism. Place a second prism whose apex is in the opposite direction at a point where the spectrum was visible on a card (Fig. 20-59). Students should observe that the second prism will recombine the colors that were separated by the first prism, and throw a beam of white light if a screen is placed behind it.

With a transparent color wheel. The primary colors can be shown by making a color wheel composed of six triangular cutout sections, each just under 60° wide. Cut two circles 1′ in diameter out of heavy cardboard. With a razor blade cut out 6 equally spaced triangular shapes with apex angles a little under 60° (Fig. 20-60A). In the center make a hole of a size to fit the shaft of a small electric motor. In the order red, green, blue, red, green, blue, cement pieces of cellophane or gelatin over each of the triangular openings. Use one circle to anchor the whole together. If students place a light source behind one section and spin the wheel on the shaft of a

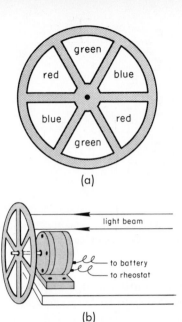

(a)

(b)

Fig. 20–60 Additive color wheel. At about 180 rpm the colors will blend into white.

small electric motor connected with a rheostat, the colors will combine to form white when the wheel is rotated at about 180 rpm (Fig. 20-60B). (Colors must be spectrally pure. Gelatin filters such as those used on stage lights can be obtained in almost any shade of any color from large stage lighting firms in New York.)

With a color box. A second group of students might demonstrate the additive mixing of white light with a color box. Divide a wood box (about 1′ square) into three compartments to hold electric light bulbs as in Fig. 20-61. In each subdivision there is a 50–60-watt bulb in a socket. Connect each to a 200-ohm rheostat. Cover each compartment with two layers of colored cellophane; use red in the first compartment, blue in the second, and green in the third. Then cut out the end of the box parallel to the cellophane layers and cover it completely with heavy tracing paper or, preferably, ground glass. Adjust the lights by turning the appropriate

Fig. 20–59 What one prism breaks up another can put back together.

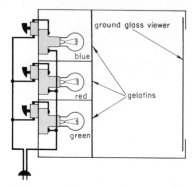

Fig. 20-61 Additive color box. Correctly adjusted, the three colors combine to make white light.

rheostat until the three colors, viewed through the screen, combine to form white light.

Red, green, and blue are the three primary colors for transmitted light (and color television), and are often known as "additive primaries." Careful adjustment of the rheostats can produce all the other colors. Some colors require only two colored lights. Commercial color boxes, which use the same principle, are sold by scientific apparatus companies.

With projected colors. Focus three lantern slide projectors, each with a two-layer colored cellophane slide (one red, one green, one blue), on the same area of a screen. Have students explain the appearance of an area of white light (Fig. 20-62).

To achieve the opposite effect—blackness—use one slide projector with a slide made of three layers of cellophane (red, blue, and green). Magenta, yellow, and cyan (blue-green) are a second set of primaries.

20.5d Subtractive colors

You may want to have students use several demonstrations to show that an object appears a certain color because it reflects (or passes) that color and absorbs (or subtracts) all others.

Colored objects. Illuminate a red object with red light (use a red bulb, a red cellophane or gelatin filter in front of a reflector or spotlight, or a red cellophane slide in a slide projector). The red object will still appear red. Now change to a blue light by using blue filters in the same light source; students see that the object appears black because no color is reflected. Now change to a purple light; the object will appear red because it reflects the red part of purple and absorbs the blue part. On the other hand, a blue object illuminated with red light will look black. In blue or purple light, it will appear blue. Have students suggest other objects and illuminations of different colors and explain the results.

Opaque (painted) color wheel. Many students know that magenta (sometimes called red), cyan (or blue-green), and yellow are "primary colors" for work with paints. How can they relate this fact with the class discussion of the three primaries of light: green, red, and blue? They will learn that yellow paint looks yellow because it absorbs everything but yellow.

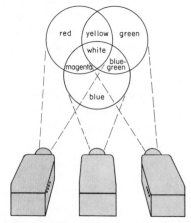

Fig. 20-62 Mixing colors from three projectors to make white.

This is readily seen to be equivalent to absorbing the "minus" of yellow, that is, blue. In the same way, the "minus" of cyan is red (orange-red) and for magenta it is green. Thus, combining the three pigment primaries (magenta, cyan, and yellow) by subtraction should be equivalent to combining the three light primaries (green, red, and blue) by addition.

Subtractive and additive colors compared. Whirling an opaque colored wheel which has been appropriately colored (see below) will result in a near white. This is not different in principle from combining the primaries from three projectors and projecting the light on a screen to produce white light. Both are additive. When the opaque colored disk whirls, reflected light —in every respect the same as the light reflected from a screen—goes to the eye and there mixes to produce the sensation of whiteness.

There is a difference between subtractive and additive colors. Red, green, and blue projected separately upon a screen produce white. The same will occur for the so-called subtractive colors—magenta, yellow, and cyan. The difference between these two sets of primaries is simply that red, green, and blue are each only one color while magenta (red and blue), yellow (red and green), and cyan (blue and green) are each mixtures of two colors. Hold yellow in front of a magenta gelatin; only red passes through, green and blue being subtracted. Hold a red filter in front of a green filter; the result is yellow by addition.

If your school has a stage and lighting crew, you can obtain some gelatin filters that closely approximate spectral colors. It is interesting to try the combinations listed below and have your students explain the resulting colors. Preferably, have them predict what the combined color will be when the white light of a lantern-slide projector is passed through the combination. Try such combinations as red and green, red and dark blue, blue and magenta, blue and cyan, red and deep yellow, etc.

Making a color wheel. Groups of students may prepare these color wheels. Cut out a cardboard disk, divide it into 3 segments, and color each segment with a "primary" color, particularly the "spectral hues," using water color, crayon, or tempera. Then place the disk on the shaft of a small electric motor. (If one color shows up while the wheel is spinning, paint or paste over part of it with one of the other colors.)

When the colors are in balance, a creamy white color should be produced. Often the result will be a dirty, rather dark gray or gray-brown. This does not indicate that the theory is wrong, but rather shows how impure most pigments are.

Absorption of light by pigments. You may want to show the absorption effects in paints. Use "pure" colored paints of any kind and daub a bit of four colors on a white dish. Mix two of the colors together, add a third and then a fourth, and examine the new color each time. Students will notice that at each step the color loses some of its intensity due to the fact that more light is being absorbed and less reflected.

20.6 Monochromatic light

20.6a Yellow light

Examine variously colored objects in monochromatic light. If you drop sodium chloride into the flame of a Bunsen burner or place a NaCl tablet on a wire screen on top of a Bunsen burner, pure color or monochromatic yellow light will be produced like that of the sodium-vapor lamps used on some highways to increase visibility in foggy weather. Look at a person's face and note the cadaver-like aspect of it. This happens because all the pinks and reds of the features appear gray or black since the monochromatic yellow light contains no red for reflection. Then examine hanks of various colored cloths and note how difficult it is to tell the true color under this light. This must be performed in a totally dark room. Keep a box of artist's chalk crayons out of sight until the room is dark except for the sodium light. Then challenge the students to tell the colors of the various pieces.

20.6b "Invisible" light

Infrared light. You may want to repeat some of the classic observations to show radiation just below the visible spectrum. Hold a large prism in front of a strong light so that a spectrum is projected on a card. Hold a thermometer a minute or so in the blue part of the spectrum; compare with a temperature reading taken in the red. Now, keeping the thermometer in the blue light, compare this reading with a reading just beyond the red edge of the visible spectrum. The increase in temperature readings beyond red shows that radiation has been refracted by the prism beyond the visible range.

Ultraviolet light. A bank of two, three, or four 2-watt argon lamps that fit standard base mounting sockets makes a simple ultraviolet light source. In a darkened room, illuminate minerals, ores, oils, and even teeth with the ultraviolet light; new colors will become visible. Clothing and plastics with dyes that glow brightly in sunlight will glow even more brightly in ultraviolet light. Special fluorescent paints that show colors only in ultraviolet light can be purchased from scientific supply houses and used to paint objects or pictures; in normal light hardly any color is

visible, but in ultraviolet light the painted picture is vivid. For details on making ultraviolet boxes see 4.3b.

Commercial ultraviolet light sources can also be purchased. When using commercial sources, avoid having students look directly at the ultraviolet light because it can damage the retina of the eye. An artificial sun lamp or any arc lamp with an ultraviolet filter makes a good source.

Some of the materials that fluoresce in ultraviolet light are petroleum products, metallic sulfides, eosin and fluorescein, and dyes of different kinds and fabrics dyed with them.

Focusing infrared light. An infrared bulb or electric heater unit can be used as a source of infrared light. If you focus this light, you can ignite a piece of paper with it, or even cook a "hot dog" for a striking demonstration. Use a parabolic mirror to focus the infrared light. Or make a lens by filling a Florence flask with a violet solution of iodine crystals in carbon tetrachloride.

Students can report on the use of infrared in night photography, and describe the many kinds of camera filters.

Polarized light. You can use a calcite crystal or the more commonly used polaroid to show polarized light. Lenses can be removed from polaroid sunglasses, or polaroid material can be purchased in disk or sheet form.

As a first experiment in the laboratory students can hold one sheet of polaroid near a light source and place a second sheet in front of the first. When the polaroid crystals are lined up on both sheets, light will pass. If the sheet is rotated 90°, much of the light will be blocked off. They can also observe specimens under the microscope, with and without polaroid disks set above and below the specimen.

Shine a spotlight on a shiny surface and

have students use polaroid sunglasses to observe the effect. The glare coming from the smooth surface is horizontally polarized. The vertical component of the polaroid lenses will eliminate the glare.

Take one picture of the subject from a given position. Now move the camera about 4″, being careful to keep its angular orientation approximately the same, and take a second picture of the same subject. When these pictures are projected by two side-by-side projectors having crossed polaroid sheets in front of the lenses, a three-dimensional reproduction will be seen on the screen if the viewer wears crossed polaroid goggles having the same axes as those on the projector.

To demonstrate one use of polarized light in research, make small I-beam sections from plastic mechanical drawing triangles. Place the specimen inside the slide carrier compartment of a projector with polaroid sheet on each side and bend the specimen. The stress lines in the plastic caused by bending or compression will be projected on the screen in colors. Adjust the relationship of the polaroids with respect to each other for the best image.

20.7 Photographic equipment

The equipment used in photography is generally expensive, yet there are many simple student-made devices that can be prepared.

20.7a Print box

One of the most useful devices the photography "bug" can have is a print box. A simple one can be made at a low cost (Fig. 20-63A). Students can build a wooden, light-tight box about 10″ deep, 12″ long, and 8″ wide. Place two base mount sockets on the inside bottom and an ordinary wall type toggle switch on the outside, as shown. Drill a ¼″ opening near the bot-

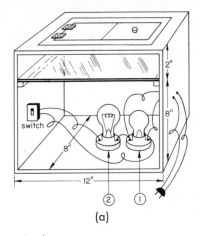

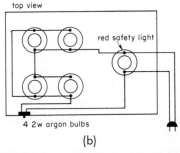

Fig. 20–63 Print box: (a) for use with 100-watt bulb, (b) arranged for use with "cold light."

tom to receive the electric light cord for the lamp. Connect the outside end of the cord to an ordinary two-prong plug; connect the inside wires to socket 1 and then run a wire from this socket to the switch. Now connect the other side of the switch to one side of socket 2, and connect the unused side of socket 2 to the side of socket 1 that does not run to the switch.

Next nail two strips of wood to the inside walls, 8″ above the bottom. Cut two glass sheets to rest on these strips; and between the two glass sheets place two layers of tracing paper to act as diffusers.

Into socket 1, screw a small red safelight bulb (purchased from a photographic shop), and into socket 2, screw a 40-watt electric light bulb. The white light will be controlled by the switch. The red lamp will stay on regardless of the switch position. For those interested in using "cold light," four sockets, each carrying a 2-watt argon bulb, can be connected in parallel in lieu of socket 2, as shown in Fig. 20-63B.

Cut a tightly fitting cover from ⅞" wood for the box. Centering it, trace the outline of an old wooden printing frame on the wood cover and cut out this area with a coping saw. Inset the printing frame and fasten it in place with thin brads. Then use a small hinge to attach the folding cover of the printing frame to the edge of the set-in frame. Remove the locking clips that come with the printing frame, and fasten a knob to one side of the cover with a flathead screw (with the head on the inside of the cover) and secure the knob by means of a nut. The last step is to fasten the top of the box in place with wood screws.

The larger the printing frame, the greater the range of sizes of negatives that can be printed. Masks for different-size negatives can be cut from black paper or aluminum foil. Experimentation will indicate the appropriate exposure times for making contact prints. See capsule lesson 20-7 for a laboratory activity.

20.7b Portable darkrooms

Loading box. Some students who want to do photographic work may not have a closet or small room that can be completely darkened. Students can build a portable darkroom from a carton or wooden box with a light-tight cover (Fig. 20-64). This cover carries an extra layer that fits the inside of the box snugly. Two armholes are cut in the side about 5" in diameter and fitted with two sleeves made of lightproof material such as auto inner tubes, oil cloth, etc. If using cloth, elastic bands sewn into the sleeves can improve the lightproofing. For extra safety paint the inside surfaces of the box black. To use the box, place the materials to be handled inside the box and set the lid into place.

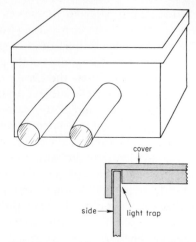

Fig. 20-64 Portable darkroom made from a wooden box.

Then slide your arms into the sleeves and load film into developing tanks or film-holders or carry on any other operation that must be done in total darkness. A little practice is all that is needed to do these things by "feel."

Loading bag. For some 75 years, traveling photographers have used loading bags for loading film or putting film into tanks for development. A bag can be made from lightproof cloth with two sleeves and a zipper.

Daylight printing and enlarging. Construct a 2' × 3' wooden base of ½" or thicker plywood. Drill holes in the base for the electric cords of the print box or enlarger and a safelight bulb. (A small bulb wrapped with several layers of red cellophane makes a usable safelight.) Next build an external framework of 2" × 2" wood members. The height of the frame will be determined by the height of the equipment to be used in the darkroom. Cover one side of the frame with plywood containing two 5" holes with lightproof sleeves. The other surfaces (the top and 3 sides) should be covered with two layers of red cellophane. Place the necessary trays of developer, water, and fixer inside the box. In daylight, students can examine the enlarging and developing process by looking through the red cellophane. Some teachers close the sides and use two layers of glass with red cellophane between the layers for the top and sides. Wood molding strips hold the glass to the framework.

20.7c Simple enlarger

An enlarger can be made from an old bellows camera that has been mounted and adapted as follows. Use Fig. 20-65 as a guide. First construct a lamp house. Start with a smooth 1″ thick board that is 1′ × 4′. Toward one end place a porcelain base socket and connect this to a wire and switch and plug, and insert a 100-watt frosted bulb into the socket. Then obtain a rectangular can from which one end is

cut or, preferably, a can with a cover that can be removed. Cut a hole in the can so it can be put over the lamp; cut another small hole for the wire. Fit the open end with a sheet of ground or opal glass. (If ground or opal glass is not available, a substitute may be made by inserting two sheets of tracing paper between two plates of glass and taping this "sandwich" together.)

Next place two sheets of a good grade of window glass against the open side of the lamp house. Remove the back of the bellows-type focusing lens camera and place the opening against the two sheets of glass as shown. Secure the camera by means of small clamps if you wish to be able to remove it for use as a camera; otherwise it can be fastened to the board with wood

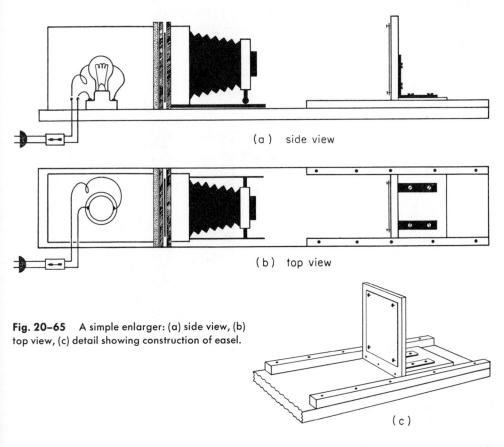

(a) side view

(b) top view

Fig. 20–65 A simple enlarger: (a) side view, (b) top view, (c) detail showing construction of easel.

(c)

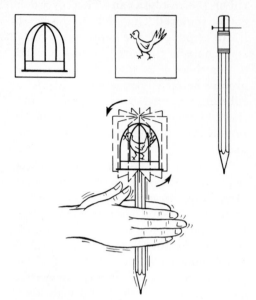

screws. As an easel for the enlarger paper, use a flat $9'' \times 12''$ sheet of plywood (1" thick) fastened to a base by means of two angle irons and wood screws. The base slides between two wood rails as shown in Fig. 20-65. Students will need to work in darkness.

For very fast exposure of paper, a small #1 photoflood lamp may be used in place of the 100-watt lamp. The negative to be enlarged is placed between the sheets of clear glass.

20.8 Motion pictures

Persistence of vision. Take movies of the class at different camera speeds and then project the film. Use the bird-in-the-cage apparatus made from a dowel and card (Fig. 20-66) to demonstrate persistence of vision. Or use flip books made by students.

Fig. 20–66 When the pencil is twirled, the bird appears to be in the cage. (From A. Joseph et al., *Sourcebook for Elementary Science*, Harcourt, Brace & World, 1961.)

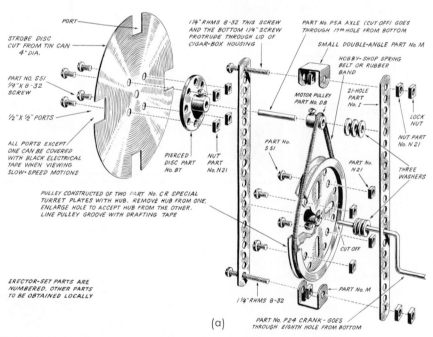

Fig. 20–67 a and b Stroboscope that can be made from parts in an erector set. (From PSSC of Educational Services, Inc.)

Sound track and photocell. Have students examine the sound track and pull it past a photocell hooked on an amplifier and speaker. Use a strong light behind the film and exclude all other light. Or use a projector and pull the film through by hand to show that incorrect speed changes the light passing into the photocell and thereby alters the sound. This can be demonstrated during a regular projection by changing the projector from sound to silent speed or by introducing resistance in the circuit from the outlet to the projector, causing the projector to slow down and thereby altering the rate the film travels past the photocell.

20.9   Stroboscope

From an erector set. A stroboscope can be made from an erector set (Fig. 20-67). Use a rubber band for the belt, and as an upper pulley on the shaft roll on masking tape tightly to form a shaft of ¼″ diameter.

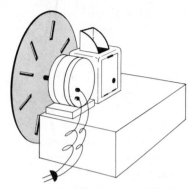

Fig. 20-68 Mounting a motor-driven stroboscopic disk in front of a camera lens.

For the large bottom pulley use two small paint can covers or a 2″ pulley. When students use covers, these must be soldered to the erector set shaft.

On the upper shaft place a 3″ heavy cardboard disk with four equally spaced ½″ openings. Calibrate the disk first by finding how many turns the upper disk makes for one turn of the crank handle. Then multiply this by the four holes. This will stop high-speed motion. For example, a fan blade covered with white tape will appear to stop on a rotating electric fan. It is necessary to time the number of turns per minute. The speed is the number of turns multiplied by the ratio previously established between the disk and the crank multiplied by four.

Taking stroboscopic pictures. The photographic process makes it possible to "freeze" various positions of the object as seen through the disk stroboscope. (See Fig. 20-68.)

Any camera with a bulb or time shutter release may be used. This makes it possible to expose the film during a controlled time interval. The polaroid camera is a good choice as it produces prints almost immediately. For a box camera, a plus 1 lens attachment should be used to enable sharp pictures to be taken at a distance of

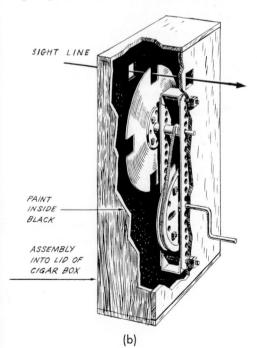

SIGHT LINE

PAINT
INSIDE
BLACK

ASSEMBLY
INTO LID OF
CIGAR BOX

(b)

about 3½'. Most fixed-focus box cameras are focused for a normal object distance of about 15'.

The stroboscope should be driven by a synchronous motor in order to simplify time measurements. A 450-rpm 6-watt synchronous clock motor[2] is suitable, provided it is used with a disk with 4 radial slits. These are sold by electrical supply houses. Motors from phonograph turntables and electric clocks are synchronous. The disk may be of black paper, 6–8" in diameter. If the slit subtends a central angle of about 10°, individual exposures of about 1/250 second at the rate of 30 per second will be obtained. By taping 2 or 3 of the slits, exposure rates of 15 or 7.5 per second can be obtained.

Note that if the width of the slot is changed, the effective exposure time is changed while the number of exposures per second is unaffected.

The simplest lighting procedure is to use a small flashlight of the penlight style as the moving source in a semidarkened room. For example, the penlight may be attached to a string and used as a pendulum. Good images will be obtained using medium- or high-speed film even with an aperture equivalent to that in a box camera (f/16). Other ways of using the penlight flashlight on moving objects may arise in class discussion.

If the moving object which is to be photographed is not, in itself, luminous then it should be made highly reflective. Using white paint is one method. Another technique is to use a polished steel ball bearing as the moving object. In these cases it is essential that the background be as dark as possible. An open door into an unlighted room makes a very satisfactory black background.

In general, films normally available will be suitable, provided they are rated at an ASA exposure index of 80 or higher. Polaroid films type 42 or 44 are suitable. Polaroid projection slide film is particularly suitable as results may be examined by projection, thereby making considerable enlargements possible.

If a roll film camera is used, it may be possible to insert a single sheet of cut film over the focal plane of the camera (in a dark room or changing bag). In this way a single exposure may be processed without the need of going through an entire roll. If the camera has a film counter peephole, this should be covered with opaque tape when using sheet film.

In most cases films should be developed about 25% longer than usual to increase contrast. A hard film developer should be usually used, such as D76, DK60A, or other recommended developers. For quicker results, tray developers ordinarily used for paper may be used for development times on the order of 2–4 minutes.

A distance scale in the picture may be obtained by placing a ruler in the plane of the moving body and then taking 2 exposures of about 1/25th second of the penlight lamp at 2 points on the ruler a known distance apart (for f/16). The separation of these 2 image points when measured on the finished picture will provide a calibration scale. These exposures are preferably made on the same negative as the one with the record of motion (a double exposure).

---

[2] Any synchronous motor from about 300 rpm (6 watts) to 1800 rpm (9 watts) will do; however, the lower frequency is more useful.

CAPSULE LESSONS

Ways to get started in class

20-1. Before beginning the topic of reflection of light, show such mirrors as concave shaving mirrors, convex wall mirrors, a rear-view auto mirror, reflectors' inside projectors, and the mirrors of a simple periscope. Develop an understanding of the application of each kind of mirror.

20-2. You may be able to borrow from an optometrist samples of different kinds of lenses. Use a parallel beam light source and have students observe what each lens does in the light beam.

20-3. A student committee could prepare a demonstration of lenses of varying focal length. (Use a microscope objective for extremely short focal length, and a telescope objective for a lens of long focal length.) Develop the lens equations.

20-4. In some classes, introduce the topic of lenses with demonstrations of typical optical instruments that may be available in school, such as microscopes, telescopes, binoculars, projectors, opera glasses, among many.

20-5. Some teachers use a good film or filmstrip to summarize the main points of light, mirrors, or lenses. You may want to use *Lenses* (United World), *Light* (EBF), *The Nature of Color* (Ideal), or a film from the PSSC series.

20-6. Arrange for student camera enthusiasts to demonstrate as many types of photographic exposures as available. They can show the principle of the exposure meter by connecting a photronic or selenium light cell to a galvanometer (as described in this chapter). Then shine lights of varying intensities at the light cell.

20-7. Have each student develop a print from his own negative as a laboratory activity. Ordinary dark shades are sufficient for darkening the room, or use a portable darkroom as described in this chapter. Prepare trays of standard paper developer, a stop bath (3 per cent acetic acid or white vinegar), and hypo as a final fixer. Then wash all the prints in running water for 15 minutes. In a summary discussion evaluate the results.

20-8. Have students set up a display of student-made print boxes, enlargers, light sources, copy devices, and other photographic equipment that is relatively easy to make and use at home. This is a useful and satisfying hobby activity that many students explore further.

20-9. It may be possible to demonstrate several kinds of telescopes. Show how one long focus and one short focus lens can be set up in a tube to make a simple telescope (described in Chapter 5).

An amateur astronomer might demonstrate a reflecting telescope. If possible have him show the hand grinding of a lens. Consult Ingall's reference *Amateur Telescope Maker* for valuable guidance (see bibliography in appendix).

20-10. Begin the topic of color by having each student make a simple color wheel. Then test each one on the spinning shaft of a small electric motor. If one color predominates, remove the excess of that color.

Students can also show the mixing of paint colors. Compare the primary colors (blue, yellow, red) of paints with the primary colors for TV (green, blue, red).

20-11. Have students make photographic color slides of the spectrum of a strong beam of light and the spectrum of the sun. Use an exposure meter to get the correct exposure, and project the slides after they have been processed.

20-12. Develop some ideas about invisible light. Demonstrate the heating of a frankfurter by a focused beam of infrared light from a heater or an infrared bulb.

Also use an ultraviolet light source or several two-watt argon lamps to show ultraviolet fluorescence. Some typical materials that may be used are described in this chapter and in Chapter 4.

20-13. Introduce the notion of the reflection of light by using the smoke box as described in this chapter. Develop the principles concerning incident and reflected beams and the velocity of the light beam passing from air to water or to glass and back to air.

20-14. Plan a laboratory lesson using mirrors and pins to establish incident and reflected rays, images, and objects.

20-15. Calculate the wave length of light from the visible spectrum, using inexpensive plastic diffraction gratings (described in this chapter).

20-16. A student might report to the class on the use of a spectroscope, and, if possible, demonstrate the principle upon which it operates.

20-17. In some classes or in club work, students can build a photometer and demonstrate its use.

PEOPLE, PLACES, AND THINGS

The uses of light, techniques for handling it, and sources of information about it exist in almost every community. Clerks in camera shops are often experts on the techniques of photography, and may be willing to give a class talk. The local lens grinding or photographic developing house can make an excellent source of information for a report to the class. You may want to investigate the use of light in photo offset printing and lithography. Rare is the area that does not have at least one amateur astronomer who will discuss the making and handling of telescopes. The "amateur scientist" section in *Scientific American* is another avenue of information. Popular magazines such as *Popular Science, Popular Mechanics,* and *Mechanics Illustrated* often describe devices and techniques of use in the study of light and color.

BOOKS AND PAMPHLETS

These are only a few of the books which are pertinent to the work discussed in this chapter. These and many other references classified by subject and with complete bibliographical data are given in the bibliography at the end of the book.

Bennett, A., D. Gray, et al., eds., *American Institute of Physics Handbook,* McGraw-Hill, 1957.

Boucher, P., *Fundamentals of Photography,* Van Nostrand, 1955.

Buddenbrock, W. von, *The Senses,* U. Michigan Press, 1958.

Ference, M., Jr., H. Lemon, and R. Stephensen, *Analytical Experimental Physics,* 2nd ed., U. Chicago Press, 1956.

Forsythe, W. E., *Smithsonian Physical Tables,* 9th ed., Smithsonian Institution, 1954.

Hausmann, E., and E. Slack, *Physics,* 4th ed., Van Nostrand, 1957.

Holton, G., and D. Roller, *Foundations of Modern Physical Science,* Addison-Wesley, 1958.

Ingalls, A., *Amateur Telescope Making,* Scientific American, 1955.

Jaffe, B., *Michelson and the Speed of Light,* Doubleday, 1960.

Mendenhall, C., et al., *College Physics,* 4th ed., Heath, 1956.

Miller, F., Jr., *College Physics,* Harcourt, Brace, 1959.

Murray, H., *Color in Theory and Practice,* Wiley, 1952.

Richtmeyer, F., E. Kennard, and T. Lauritsen,

Introduction to Modern Physics, 5th ed., McGraw-Hill, 1955.

Sears, F. W., *Mechanics, Wave Motion and Heat,* Addison-Wesley, 1958.

Stong, C. L., *Amateur Scientist,* Simon and Schuster, 1960.

White, H., *Modern College Physics,* 3rd ed., Van Nostrand, 1955.

FILMS AND FILMSTRIPS

This partial list is intended only as a guide toward film and filmstrip selection. Refer to the more complete listing at the end of the book where films are classified by subject and where a key to abbreviations and addresses of distributors are given. The cost of film rental, of course, is subject to change. Films are sound and black and white unless otherwise specified.

Behind Your Snap Shot (f, s, c), Eastman Kodak, inquire rental.

The Case for Color (f, s, c), DuPont, free.

Color and Light (f, s, c), Indiana U., $3.00.

Compound Microscope (f, s, c), Bausch and Lomb, free.

Curves of Color (f, s, c), General Electric, free.

Doppler Effect (f, s), McGraw-Hill, inquire rental.

Eye and the Camera (fs), Popular Science through McGraw-Hill, $3.00.

Formation of Crystals in Polarized Light (f, s, c), Indiana U., $2.00.

Fundamentals of Photography (f, s), Indiana U., $2.50.

Introduction to Optics (f, s, c), (PSSC, Educational Services, Inc.), Modern Talking Pictures, $5.75.

Light (f, s, series 18 lessons), EBF, inquire rental.

Light Control through Polarization (f, s, c), Polaroid Corp., free.

Light: Lenses; Light: Refraction (f, s), Indiana U., $2.00 each.

The Light in Your Life (f, s, c), General Electric, free.

Magic of Fluorescence (f, s, c), General Electric, free.

Measurement of Speed of Light (f, s), McGraw-Hill, inquire rental.

Measurement with Light Waves (f, s, 1½ rls), Ideal, $3.00.

Modern Physics Series: Light and Sound (4 fs), McGraw-Hill, $3.25 each.

Nature of Color (f, s, c), Ideal, $4.00.

Nature of Light (f, s), Ideal, $2.00.

Perfect Parallel (f, s, c), Libby-Owens-Ford Glass Co., free.

Photographic Darkroom Procedures Series (6 fs), Mc-Graw-Hill, $6.00 each.

Refraction (f, s), U. W. Educ., inquire rental.

Speed of Light (f, s) (PSSC, Educational Services, Inc.), Modern Talking Pictures, $5.75.

The Spectroscope (f, s, c), McGraw-Hill, inquire rental.

Spherical Mirrors; Lenses (f, s), United World, $2.00 each.

FREE AND INEXPENSIVE MATERIALS

This is only a partial listing of free and inexpensive materials available to the teacher at this time. A directory of addresses is given at the end of the book. Many of these materials are distributed to teachers without charge. Where there is a small fee, the cost is indicated, although the prices are subject to change. While we recommend the material for use in the classroom, we do not necessarily endorse the products advertised.

Ansco: *Developing and Printing Made Easy,* $.25; *Description of Illustrated Lectures,* free loan; *For Black-White Photography,* $.25.

Eastman Kodak: *Developing, Printing and Enlarging,* $.35; *How to Take Better Kodachrome Pictures,* $.35; *How to Make Good Pictures,* $1.00; *How to Make Good Movies,* $2.00; *Kodak Reference Handbook* (2 vols.) $4.00 each; *Photographic Production of Slides and Filmstrips,* $.50.

Enlarging Photographs, Federal Manufacturing and Engineering Corp.

Milestones in Optical History, Bausch and Lomb.

Optical Kit, Cenco, $14.95.

Optics and Wheels, General Motors.

The Story of Light, General Electric.

CHAPTER 21

Currents and fields

Students can work with devices from pith ball electroscopes to Van de Graaff generators, motors, and transformers. There are many opportunities for laboratory work and for demonstrations in the study of currents and fields—experiences that students will need for the more detailed studies of electromagnets, induced currents, radio, television, and the application of electrical principles in communication and industry.

21.1 Electrostatics

21.1a Presence of electrostatic charges: electroscope

Student-made electroscopes. If a standard electroscope is not at hand, students can make one from several kinds of materials. For example, they can hang a strip of folded thin aluminum foil or gold leaf from a bent wire in a bottle as shown in Fig. 21-1. Over the top of the wire slip the ball from the end of a hollow curtain rod. In place of gold leaf use the foil found on a small mica condenser taken from a radio set. Electroscope leaves can also be made by spraying two pieces of fine lens tissue, each about $\frac{1}{4}'' \times 1''$, with an extremely light almost transparent coat of aluminum paint. As shown in Fig. 21-1B, pass pins through two pieces of the tissue, and hold the pins by means of wire to the bottle. Two pith balls

sprayed with aluminum paint and suspended on silk threads can also act as an electroscope.

A more accurate electroscope can be made by starting with a small sliding curtain rod of the type that has ball ends. Use the half that is hollow. Cut off all but 8'' from the ball end; fit a 1-quart milk bottle or other large bottle with a stopper or cork. Make an opening in the center of the cork to hold the curtain rod snugly. Pass the rod through the cork and leave 2'' of the ball end projecting above the cork and flatten out 2'' of the bottom end of the rod. As in Fig. 21-1C, attach a piece of electroscope foil by means of cellulose tape and lower it into the bottle. A paper scale placed inside the bottle in advance can be used to measure deflection.

Projection electroscope. The leaves of an electroscope can be made visible to the entire class if you remove the bellows from a $3\frac{1}{4}'' \times 4''$ slide projector and place the electroscope in front of the slide compartment so that the leaves are centered in the slide area. Now focus the leaves on the screen or on a wall (Fig. 21-2). Students will notice that the leaves appear inverted and enlarged. When you perform demonstrations using an electroscope, the results will appear magnified many times on the screen.

Sensitive and stable electroscope and electrometer. A sensitive electroscope can be converted into an electrometer. An ordinary coffee can as shown in Fig. 21-3 is used; bore a ¾″ opening in the side of the can. Lay the can on its side and attach a wood base. Drill an opening 5/32″ in diameter through the center of a piece of polyethylene rod ¾″ in diameter. Force the polyethylene into the ¾″ hole in the can. Bend a ½″ wide strip of aluminum sheet (about #24) into the shape shown. Drill a 5/32″ hole at the center of the bend at the top of the strip of sheet metal and pass a 1″ long, 8/32-thread machine screw through the hole in the strip and also through the polyethylene. Attach an 8/32 wing nut to hold the parts in place. In a position which is in line with the center of the can drill two very small openings through the strip just large enough to insert a needle through the openings.

Remove the needle and pass it through the center of a 4″ length of drinking straw covered with a metal foil coating. Move the needle in the opening so that it becomes slightly larger than the needle. With a scissors clip off small bits from the end of the drinking straw until it balances vertically. Now place the straw between the strips in the can and pass the needle through the strips and the straw, completing the electroscope. It will be found to be unusually sensitive.

You can convert this electroscope into an electrometer by placing a circular scale in the circular base of the can under the lower end of the straw; this can be calibrated by charging the electroscope with

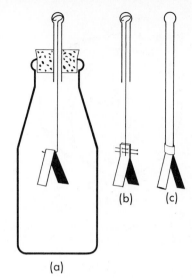

Fig. 21-1   Electroscope that can be made by students.

known high-voltage d.c. Only one terminal of the power source need be touched to the electroscope knob; the other terminal should be left disconnected from the electroscope and should be positioned at some distance away. A Wimshurst static machine is a good high-voltage source for calibration. Its output voltage may be taken as approximately 20,000 volts per cm of spark discharge. Thus, if its discharge spheres are 1 cm apart, the deflection of the electroscope at the instant of spark discharge represents a potential of about 20,000 volts. Another way to convert the electroscope into an electrometer involves charging capacitors; touch one

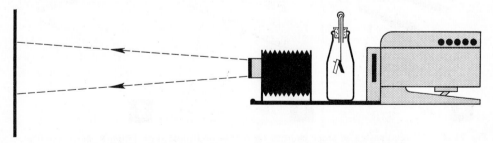

Fig. 21-2   Projecting the leaves of an electroscope upon a screen.

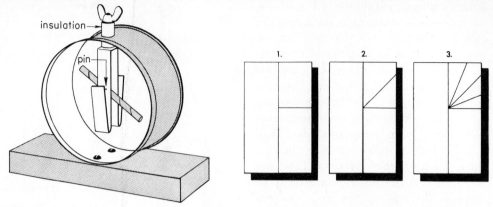

Fig. 21-3 Electroscope mounted in a coffee can can be also used as an electrometer. (Redrawn from PSSC of Educational Services, Inc.)

terminal of the high-voltage capacitor to the wing nut that serves as an electrode. (*Warning: Use extreme care in handling high voltage; use very small capacity high-voltage mica capacitors having a capacitance in microfarads below .0005.*)

Effect of charge on an electroscope. Have a student first rub a glass rod with silk and then bring it near (but do not touch) the electroscope. Students will observe that the leaves separate. Now repeat using a hard rubber rod rubbed with wool and note the same effect. Students may contribute the notion that both leaves were acted on by something from each

of the rods which caused them to repel each other. Was it the same thing in both cases?

Simple electrostatic attraction and repulsion. Several students will be ready to contribute suggestions for a procedure to answer this question. Rub the glass rod with silk again and suspend it by a silk thread (Fig. 21-4). Bring a second glass rod (also rubbed with silk) near one end of it; the rod swings *away*. Do the same thing with a hard rubber rod rubbed with wool or fur, and the glass rod swings toward it. Then whatever we have here comes in two varieties; each repels its du-

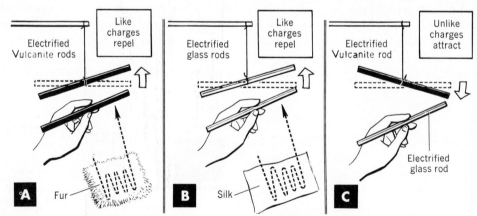

Fig. 21-4 The relationship of static charges on rubber and glass rods. (From R. Brinckerhoff et al., *Exploring Physics*, Harcourt, Brace, 1959.)

plicate and attracts its opposite.

You will want to have students explain these demonstrations. Attach threads to two balloons and hang them from a cord stretched across the room. Then rub both balloons with fur or wool. The balloons separate because they have similar (negative) charges which repel each other.

Or rub a hard rubber comb or vulcanite rod with fur or wool and bring it near one of the charged balloons; it will be repelled by the similar charge on the comb or rod. But if a glass rod rubbed with silk is placed near one of the balloons, the glass rod will attract the balloon, indicating that the charge on the glass rod is opposite (positive).

Dancing dolls.[1] W. G. Whitman suggests an interesting variation of the electrostatic effect. Cut out small paper dolls of very thin tissue paper, place them in a pie pan, and cover the pan with pliofilm or other kinds of plastic films. When students rub the surface of the pliofilm with wool or fur, the dolls should dance.

Electrostatic plastics. When students are not able to produce a good electrostatic charge by rubbing a glass rod with silk, Clark[2] suggests the use of a rod of Lucite rubbed with polyethylene film. The rod acquires a positive charge; the negative charge is acquired by the polyethylene film.

As a variation rub the glass rod with sheet rubber (baby diaper type). This will set up an excellent plus charge on the glass.

21.1b Quantitative measurement of electrostatic repulsion

In this method for measuring electrostatic repulsion an ordinary platform balance is used as a measuring device (Fig.

[1] W. G. Whitman, *Science Education,* 28:3, Apr.–May, 1944.

[2] F. Clark, *American Journal of Physics,* January, 1955.

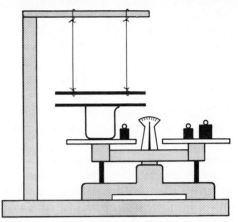

Fig. 21–5 Measuring the amount of electrostatic repulsion between two charged vulcanite rods.

21-5). On one side of the balance place a beaker or glass tumbler to act as an insulator, and balance its weight on the other platform with weights. Charge two identical vulcanite rods simultaneously by rubbing them with fur. Place one charged rod across the top of the glass standing on the balance and suspend the other rod from silk threads directly above it; or support it on two glass rods held by two ring stands. If the rods come in contact, the pan carrying the rod will be depressed by the repulsive force. Then add fractional gram weights until the pan is in balance again. When ordinary vulcanite rods are used, the weight required to balance the repulsion will be about one gram depending on the dimensions of the rod.

The attractive force between charged glass and a vulcanite rod can be measured by adding fractional weights to the side that carries the vulcanite rod.

Induced electrostatic charges. You will want students to demonstrate a different series of attraction-repulsion phenomena. So far we have been dealing with the interaction between two charged bodies, with like or unlike charges. What happens when a charged body is brought near an electrically neutral body?

Inflate two balloons with air. (Since most balloons are made of synthetic rubber, stretch the balloons in width and length several times before inflating.) Then rub one balloon against a piece of fur or wool, touch it against the wall or ceiling, and release it gently. Why does it remain there? Students may think through an explanation although it is not as simple as the previous one. In this case the negatively charged balloon placed near the neutral wall repels the electrons that are on the surface layer of the wall, pushing them away from the surface into the wall. This leaves the surface of the wall with a slightly positive charge (induced charge) which in turn attracts the negatively charged balloon. The force of attraction is great enough to counteract the downward gravitational pull on the balloon, so that the balloon remains in place.

Can a student demonstrate the negative charge on the balloon by bringing it near an electroscope? He will not be able to demonstrate the positive charge on the wall, however, because it exists only in the presence of the balloon.

You may want students to show the same effect by placing a dry sheet of paper against the blackboard and stroking it repeatedly with fur or wool. After sufficient stroking, the paper will remain against the blackboard. If you lift one end of the paper from the blackboard, it will fall back because of the attraction. These demonstrations are more effective in dry weather than on days of high humidity or rain. (When steam heat is on, the relative humidity usually drops 25% to 50% indoors.)

Groups of students may work together to show more graphically that these phenomena must be due to induced charges. Have students suspend several dry puffed wheat or puffed rice kernels from silk threads. First bring hard rubber combs that have been charged by rubbing with wool or fur next to the grains; the grains will be attracted. Then they can bring glass rods charged by rubbing with silk near the grains; they will again be attracted. It is apparent from this that the induced charge near the original charged object always results in attraction because it is always opposite in sign from the original charge.

Contact and induction charging of electroscope. Use a simple leaf electroscope to show the two ways in which an electroscope can indicate a charge on an object, and how they differ. Rub a hard rubber rod with wool or fur and bring it *near* the electrode of the electroscope; the leaves will stand apart. Remove the rod; students can see the leaves fall back immediately. Now *touch* the same rod (recharged if necessary) to the electroscope; the leaves will again stand apart. Remove the rod; this time the leaves will remain apart for some time.

If this demonstration is done after the ones described above, the students should be able to explain what has happened. The first time, the negative rod induced a positive charge on the electrode and a negative charge on the leaves; the electroscope as a whole was still electrically neutral. When the rod was removed, the charges immediately were reoriented and no net charge was left on the electroscope. The second time, the negative rod transferred electrons to the electroscope; the whole instrument was negatively charged; removing the rod had no effect on removing charge. The electroscope can be discharged quickly if a student touches the electrode. Why?

Using the electroscope to determine sign of charge. So far we have used the electroscope to show the presence of charge. Can the students devise a way to use it to distinguish between positive and negative charges? They should be able to see that a *charged* electroscope can do this.

Charge an electroscope by contact, as described above, or by *induction* as follows. Bring a negatively charged rod near the electrode; touch the opposite side of the electrode with your finger. Some of the repelled electrons will go through you rather than down to the leaves; when the finger is removed, there will be a net positive charge on the electroscope. (Or have a student give it a negative charge by using a positive rod to induce the charge in the same way.)

Do students know the sign of the charge on the electroscope? To use it as an indicator, touch a body with unknown charge to the knob. If it is of the same charge as the electroscope, the leaves will spread further apart; if it is oppositely charged, they will move together. You will want to have students demonstrate this effect with known charges first; in this case, several charged electroscopes will be needed in advance.

Site of electrostatic charge. Charge a metal bucket by connecting it to a Wimshurst electrostatic generator (or Van de Graaff generator). Now place an electroscope *inside* the bucket or connect the electroscope terminal to the inside of the bucket by means of a thin wire. The electroscope will not show a charge. However, if you place the electroscope near the *out-*

Fig. 21-6 Faraday's bag shows a charge only on the outside, even when pulled inside out. (Welch Scientific Company.)

side of the bucket or if you connect the electroscope to the outside, it will show a charge. What would happen if we could turn the bucket inside out. We can't, but we can repeat the demonstration with a conical silk bag called Faraday's bag (Fig. 21-6). First charge the rim with an electrostatic generator, and show the presence of a charge on the outside of the bag by using an electroscope. Then use the silk string (be careful not to touch the bag or it will become discharged) to pull the cone inside out, and test the new outside surface; it will again show a charge. In both cases, only the outer surface shows a charge.

Standard pear-shaped electrostatic charging form. Charge this device (Fig. 21-7A) with an electrostatic generator and show that the charge is concentrated near the pointed end rather than at the round

Fig. 21-7 Place of charge: (a) the charge on a pear-shaped form gathers at the pointed end, (b) when the surface of a charged ball is covered with cups, the charge moves to the outer surface of the cups. (Welch Scientific Company.)

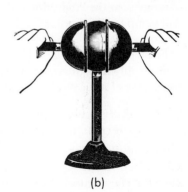

(a)   (b)

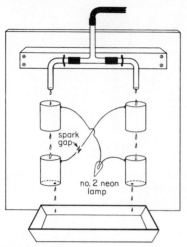

Fig. 21-8 Kelvin waterdrop apparatus for generating static electricity.

end. If you can slip two metal cups that have insulating handles over a charged metal ball, the charges can be transferred from the surface of the charged ball to the cups (Fig. 21-7B).

The deflection of an electroscope brought near the first pear-shaped object will be greatest near the pointed end. Students will recognize why lightning rods have pointed ends. Students can demonstrate the value of a lightning rod by making a model of a house from a small cardboard box. Use wire to make a lightning rod extending over the roof of the house and into a ground. Then ground one end of an electrostatic generator and bring one terminal near the "lightning rod." A spark will jump to the "rod" and flow into the ground.

Electrostatic whirls and bells available from supply houses are used to show the conversion of static electricity into motion.

21.1c   Kelvin waterdrop electrostatic generator

The simplest of the continuously operating electrostatic generators is the well-known Kelvin waterdrop apparatus (Fig.

21-8). This can be mounted on a piece of hard Masonite or Transite (asbestos rigid board). On top of the board arrange glass tubes connected to tubing that is attached to a source of water.

Students will need four #2 cans arranged as shown in Fig. 21-8. The bottoms have been removed from the two upper cans, while the two lower cans have holes for draining off the water. Notice that the upper left can is connected to the lower right can, and the upper right can is connected to the lower left can.

Pick up the charge from either of the upper cans and connect to an electroscope or Leyden jar which is grounded at the lower end.

Water drips into the center of the upper can without touching it. (Avoid drafts in the room which may deflect the drops.) The drops are charged as they drop down the glass tubing. Leaving the glass tubing, they charge the top can by induction and then charge the lower can by contact. This is the reason for the crossed connections. A very great potential difference can be built up in this device; in fact, a charge is built up with each drop. This can be observed by watching the movement of the foil of a connected electroscope. The rate of drop production should be adjusted to about 2 per second.

21.1d   *Van de Graaff generator*

A simple, nonelectronic Van de Graaff generator can be made as a student project at very low cost and with relative ease. It can be used in place of a Wimshurst machine. An inverted circular aluminum baking pan is used for the base. Cut a hole in the center as shown in Fig. 21-9. Through this opening slip a tall plastic juice container (of the type made for refrigerator use) from which the bottom has been cut away. Open an 8" or 10" sheet metal geography globe at the equatorial seam. Cut a hole in the lower half of the globe by drilling a circle of small holes and finishing the cut with a small cold chisel and file. Slip this over the top of the container. (If a geography globe is not available, use two circular baking pans placed face to face to form an approximate sphere.)

Next place into the lower half of the globe a circular plywood disk about 6″ in diameter and with a 3″ hole in its center. Mount two brass angles about 2″ × 2″ opposite each other and bolted to the plywood. Then place a brass rod as a shaft through the upper holes of the angles. Remove the shaft and slip 2 one-hole rubber stoppers, top ends together, over the shaft to serve as an upper pulley.

Then fasten a 2″ × 2″ square of copper window screening to the plywood so it almost touches the rubber belt by means of small wood screws; use a short length of copper wire to connect this screening to the metal of the ball.

Bolt two miniature 1½- to 3-volt motors of the type sold in hobby shops to the inverted bottom of the pan so that they face each other. The connections lead to 2 or 3 (3- to 4½-v) dry cells and are made in such a way that the motors turn in the same direction when facing each other, that is, so that the belt is driven in the same direction by both motors. The motor shafts facing each other both fit into a 1″ rod of plastic. First drill a small hole on each side and then force the shafts of the motors into opposite ends of the plastic rod. You may be able to get a piece of plastic from a plastic handle of an old appliance. Wood from a broomstick can be used if it is first thoroughly treated with clear lacquer. Slip a rubber belt about 1/16″ thick and 1½″ wide over the upper and lower pulleys. Then place screening at the bottom as the lower electrode. Both screen electrodes should be about ⅛″away

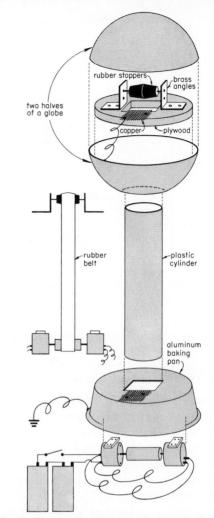

Fig. 21-9   Breakaway view of a Van de Graaff generator that can be built by students.

from the belt. Run wires to the batteries. To hold the plastic cylinder in place, you can bolt wooden supports around it where it rests on the aluminum pan. To test the operation hold a stiff wire attached to a wood handle against the base and at a distance of 1″ from the globe or upper electrode. A strong spark will jump. Up to 200,000 volts (20,000 volts per cm in air) can be generated by this Van de Graaff machine. It is sometimes necessary to

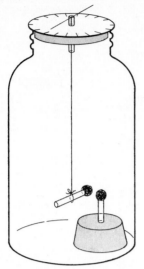

Fig. 21–10 Torsion balance for demonstrating Coulomb's law.

connect the base to a water pipe as a ground.

21.1e   Coulomb's law

To demonstrate Coulomb's law students can construct a device which is a simplified torsion balance. The demonstration is effective only when relative humidity is low. From the top of a wide-mouth gallon jar (mayonnaise jar) support a long unspun nylon fiber (Fig. 21-10). At the top the fiber passes through a narrow gauge glass bushing on which rests a toothpick as an indicator. Under the toothpick place a 360° plastic protractor. To the bottom end of the fiber attach a small glass rod carrying a tiny aluminum ball made from foil. Standing at the bottom of the jar is a glass rod set in a wide cork as a base with a similar aluminum ball at the upper end. The two balls are at the same level. Open the cover and charge both balls by touching them with a charged vulcanite rod. Then note the deflection. Turn the toothpick indicator needle 15° to balance out the repulsion. Repeat for another 15° and

note that the twist required is greater; then repeat for an additional distance. Students solve some problems by applying the inverse-square law for attraction and repulsion.

The same apparatus can be used with magnets to get the inverse-square law relationship for magnetic attraction and repulsion. The hanging glass rod is replaced by a commercial cylindrical magnet about ¼" in diameter and 2" to 3" in length. A similar magnet is vertically secured to the wood block below by means of paraffin or sealing wax. Exactly the same procedure is used for determining the law relating to magnetic attraction and repulsion as was employed for determining electrostatic forces.

21.2   Storing electric charges

21.2a   Leyden jar

If a Leyden jar is not at hand, you may want to have one made by students as a project. They can pour aluminum paint into a milk bottle and quickly pour it out again so that the inner surface is coated with aluminum. Wipe off the paint from the inner walls about an inch from the

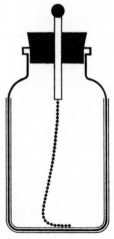

Fig. 21–11   Leyden jar.

mouth of the bottle. Then paint the outer surface of the bottle with aluminum paint within an inch of the top. Or you may prefer to coat the outer and inner walls of a wide-mouth jar with shellac and then line and coat the jar with a layer of aluminum foil. Stand a clean bare copper wire inside the bottle or jar as an internal connection; stand the bottle on a piece of bare copper wire to make the external connection. You may want to make a top for the jar and a charging post as in Fig. 21-11. An old electric switch pull chain makes an excellent inner contact.

First charge the Leyden jar by connecting the internal wire to an electrostatic generator. Then disconnect the generator and discharge the jar by means of a "shorting loop" (with a nonconducting handle) by first touching the outer surface and then bringing the other end of the loop near the internal connection. A spark will jump.

21.2b Electrophorus

If a Wimshurst machine is not available, a simple device—the electrophorus —can be used to charge the Leyden jars or other devices. Make an electrophorus by filling a pie tin with a thick layer of molten sealing wax or melted breakable-type phonograph records. If you melt the breakable-type phonograph records, you can use the pie tin. Keep the gas flame very low and melt gradually; otherwise, a strong smell develops. Attach a flat disk of aluminum to a broomstick handle about 4″ long by drilling the center of the disk to take a 2″ wood screw through the circular end of the handle. Charge the wax surface by rubbing briskly with a dry piece of cat's fur. Bring the disk down flat against the wax surface, touch the top of the metal disk with the finger, remove the finger, and finally lift the disk from the wax. Now bring the edge of the metal disk near the end of the finger or knuckle; a sizable spark will be produced. (*Note:* Such electrostatic effects do not work well on damp days.)

21.2c Capacitors

Students soon recognize that the Leyden jar is a forerunner of the capacitor (formerly called a condenser).

Principle of the capacitor. From this activity, students may come to recognize that a capacitor is a combination of conducting plates separated by an insulator. You will need an electroscope than can hold a sizable charge to demonstrate the principle of the capacitor. Connect a metal plate resting on insulating material to the electrode of the electroscope. Charge the plate with an electrostatic generator and observe that the electroscope leaves move further and further apart. Now use a second insulated metal plate and ground it. Bring this plate near the first one and students should notice that the leaves fall back a bit. Add more charge to the first plate; show that it is now capable of holding much more charge than before, and it takes much more of a charge to make the leaves spread as much. (Perhaps you will want to carry this further by inserting a glass plate between the two metal ones; it will increase the capacitance of the plate attached to the electroscope.)

To extend the idea of the properties of capacitors, repeat the demonstration with larger metal plates, varying the distances between them, and using different insulators. Students can observe that the capacitance increases with the area of the plates and the insulating ability of the substance between them, but decreases as the distance between plates is made greater.

In variable capacitors, as the plates intermesh, the areas involved increase, thereby increasing the capacitance. Stu-

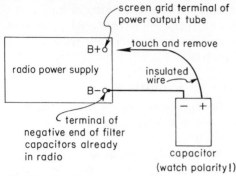

screen grid terminal of
power output tube

touch and remove

B+

radio power supply

insulated
wire

B−

terminal of
negative end of filter
capacitors already
in radio

− +

capacitor
(watch polarity!)

Fig. 21–12 Charging a high-voltage capacitor.

dents can buy variable capacitors from a shop that has junk radios. (See Chapter 22 for the use of capacitance in radio tuning.)

Demonstrating high-voltage capacitors. A television power supply filter capacitor, called a "doorknob type," can be charged with an electrostatic generator to make an excellent class demonstration. These capacitors are rated at 20 to 30 kilovolts and have a capacitance of 500 micro-microfarads (mmfd); they are available from any large electronic distributor such as Lafayette Radio in Jamaica, N.Y., or Allied Radio in Chicago. Since they are unpolarized, no precautions need be taken in this respect. Connect the capacitor terminals across the discharge rods of a Wimshurst machine (or to the base and ball of a Van de Graaff generator) to charge it. Remove it with caution, handling one wire at a time, using rubber gloves or nonconducting tongs. The shock from one of these small capacitors is unpleasant but certainly not particularly dangerous for an individual with a normal heart.

Ordinary radio or television filter capacitors rated at 400 to 600 volts with capacitances from 4 mfd to 20 mfd or more may be given a high-energy charge by connecting them temporarily across a source of high voltage, such as the power supply of a radio receiver. First, these capacitors are electrolytic and are polarized; hence, it is important to note which terminal is marked "+." With the power supply turned off, clip the negative end of the capacitor to the "B−" point of the power supply (very often the chassis itself is at B− potential), leaving the other lead disconnected. Turn on the radio and allow it to warm up for about 15 seconds; then touch the other capacitor lead to a B+ point on the power supply. Handle this wire by means of its own insulation, preferably while wearing rubber gloves. Remove the lead just touched to B+ from the supply, turn off the radio, and remove the B− capacitor lead. When the two leads are touched together, the class will observe a very hot, energetic spark (Fig. 21-12).

Measuring potential. This device approximately measures high voltage by the spark method. It consists of a glass tube containing two corks. One cork carries a small metal rod with a metal ball at the end. The other cork has a hole in it with an 8/32 brass nut cemented to the cork to which in turn is soldered a copper wire lead. A brass 8/32 threaded rod or long 8/32 thread screw passes through the nut. On the inside end of the brass rod or screw a small metal ball is soldered as in Fig. 21-13. At the other end of the threaded rod attach a long plastic handle. Along one

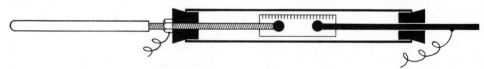

Fig. 21–13 The length of the spark indicates the approximate voltage.

side of the glass or clear plastic tube paste a millimeter scale. Measure the voltage of a spark by adjusting the distance between the metal balls until the spark just stops jumping. Measure the distance between balls on the millimeter scale. Each cm jump is 20,000 volts; thus, each mm jump is 2000 volts. This device can then be used to measure the voltage output of electrostatic generators or the potential of a charged capacitor. Do not touch bare metal parts during the test.

21.3   Current electricity

21.3a   Conductors

Teachers use many devices to lead students into a study of currents from electrostatic charges. You may want to attach a wire (carefully) across the plates of a capacitor and have students discuss what happens in it. Or ground an electroscope and have students explain what happens to the charge in it. Some teachers begin with an analogy. They fill a long glass tube with enough marbles or beads to fill the tube. As one marble is pushed into one end, a marble will come out the other end (not the same marble). This can illustrate what happens when a charged body is connected to a wire. Some teachers prefer to develop the idea of potential from charged bodies before introducing current or use the analogy of gravity and potential energy.

Fall of potential. Using binding posts or Fahnestock clips, secure three pieces of nichrome wire, all one meter in length, to a blackboard on legs. If possible, select nichrome sizes to be B & S gauge #30 or 32 (very thin) for one of the lengths, #24 for the second length, and #16 or 18 for the third length. Connect these in series as shown in Fig. 21-14. Connect a 6-volt storage battery with its positive terminal going

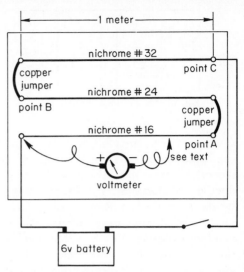

Fig. 21-14   Arrangement for measuring fall of potential along a wire conductor.

to one end of the lowermost wire; to the same point, connect the positive terminal of a 0-6-volt voltmeter. Now shift the negative voltmeter lead from point A, to point B, to point C, taking readings for the three positions. Determine the resistance of each piece of nichrome wire from the wire tables in the *Handbook of Physics and Chemistry,* and compare the voltage drop across each one with the resistance. You will find that the fall of potential across any two points is always proportional to the resistance between those two points. An alternative procedure is to measure the drop across each piece individually by shifting both voltmeter leads so that the instrument is in parallel successively with the #16, then the #24, and then the #32 wire, recording the drops in each case. The voltmeter leads will have to be reversed as each change is made to keep it reading in the right direction.

21.3b   Conductors and nonconductors

Charge one electroscope by connecting

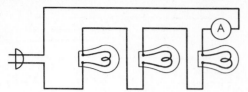

Fig. 21–15 Three bulbs in series.

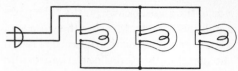

Fig. 21–16 The left bulb is in series with the two parallel-connected bulbs to the right.

a wire between the charging rod of the one electroscope and the electrode of a second electroscope. Also test the conductivity of glass, hard rubber, and other insulating materials. Repeat using wires and nonconductors in series with a 110-volt lamp and socket to show that current does not move through a nonconductor and, further, that all metals are not equal in their conductivity. Also use a carbon rod to show that it is a conductor although a nonmetal.

21.3c Simple circuits

Series and parallel circuits. Hook up a board of three porcelain base mounting sockets. First hook lamps in parallel using wires with alligator or battery clips. (All three bulbs are hooked up as the two right hand lamps in Fig. 21-16.) Test the total current with an a.c. ammeter. Use lamps of the same age and wattage. Then test the current in each lamp. The total current is the sum of the current in each lamp. Then change to three bulbs of different wattage and note that again the total current is the sum of the individual currents. (*Caution: Do not change connections while power is on.*)

Now students can change the sockets into a series connection with one ammeter in series (Fig. 21-15). When three identical lamps are in series, each lights dimly but equally, and the current through each is equal. If one bulb of lower wattage is inserted into the circuit, the current drops and the other two bulbs are dimmer. The current in the circuit is everywhere the same. Show how this is an application of resistances in parallel and in series.

If as in Fig. 21-16 you have part of a circuit in parallel, and this in series with another circuit, first treat the parallel group as a unit and add it to the series group as a single unit in a series circuit.

21.3d Resistance in series and in parallel

In a laboratory lesson, have students measure the resistance of a group of three different resistances by any of the methods described earlier in this chapter. Or use standard marked resistances that do not have more than 5% error. This type of resistance as well as some that have 1% accuracy are available from radio supply houses. Have students connect three in series and test the resistance so they can learn that the total resistance is the sum of the individual resistances. Place an ammeter in series in any part of the circuit to show that the current flow is the same in all the resistances. Students can develop the equation

$$R_t = R_1 + R_2 + R_3$$

$$R_t = \text{total resistance}$$

When students connect the same resistances in parallel, they will find that the total resistance is smaller than the smallest individual resistance. Show that the reciprocal of the total new value, R_x, is found by the following equation which is the sum of the reciprocals of the individual resistances. Thus the students substitute each R in the denominator

$$\frac{1}{R_x} = \frac{1}{R_1} + \frac{1}{R_2} + \frac{1}{R_3}$$

21.3e Ohm's law

Connect an ammeter in series with a battery, a known resistance, and a voltmeter across the resistance. The relationship of resistance to voltage will equal the reading of the ammeter, or

$$I = \frac{E}{R}$$

Repeat with different voltages by changing the number of battery cells and by changing the resistance. Set up situations where voltage and resistance are known, where resistance and current are known but voltage is unknown, and where resistance is known but current and voltage are unknown.

Effect of temperature on a resistance. Students can show the effect of temperature on a resistance by measuring the resistance along a length of nichrome wire. (This is described earlier in this chapter.) Heat the nichrome wire with a Bunsen burner and take a new reading. Also measure the resistance of a tungsten lamp when it is cold, and compare with the lamp current and voltage when the lamp is hot. A carbon pencil lead or a carbon lamp filament behaves in the opposite way. If the resistance when cold is measured and then the pencil lead is heated, the resistance drops. In the case of the carbon lamp filament the resistance will be less when operating than when the lamp is cold. Remind the class that metals have an increased resistance upon heating. Carbon is just the opposite. The same is true of the general class of materials called semiconductors.

21.3f Fuses

Make up a fuse board as shown in Fig. 21-17. A cleat socket to take regular 120-volt lamps is placed on the board in such a way as to make the circuit straightforward. Wire the board as shown using

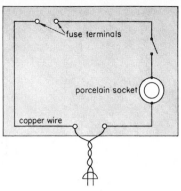

Fig. 21–17 Board for demonstrating a fuse in a circuit.

#18 wire, including two binding posts or clips between which a 2″ length of *fuse wire* can be connected. If your room is protected by a 10- or 15-ampere fuse, never use fuse wire having a capacity greater than 2 amperes.

To show normal, safe operation screw a 100-watt lamp into the socket and close the switch. The 2-ampere fuse wire will sustain this load since the current is somewhat less than 1 ampere. To demonstrate overload, replace the lamp with a 660-watt heating coil, and close the switch. It may take a minute or two, but the fuse wire will finally melt and open the circuit. A short circuit may be shown next. Move the students at least 10 feet from the board; then short-circuit the cleat socket terminal with an insulated clip lead or stiff, bent wire. The 2-ampere fuse wire will burn out instantaneously without harm to the room or hall fuse.

Have students show cartridge and plug fuses. If possible, obtain a "Minibreaker" (circuit breaker that screws into standard plug fuse socket) and standard circuit breaker for demonstration. These may be used to show overloads *but not short circuits*. On short circuit, the chances are good that the school fuse will "go" first, making a replacement necessary.

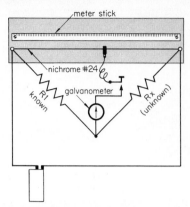

Fig. 21–18 Slide-wire bridge for measuring resistances.

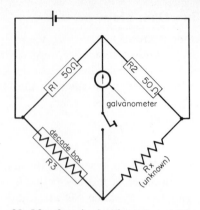

Fig. 21–19 Standard Wheatstone bridge for measuring resistances.

21.3g *Measuring resistance*

Slide-wire bridge. One of the oldest and most accurate devices for measuring resistance is the Wheatstone bridge described below. (Other ways to measure resistance are described earlier in this chapter.) The type commonly used in secondary schools is the low-cost, slide-wire bridge. A slide-wire bridge is available from supply companies, or you may want to make one from a length of #22 or 24 nichrome wire, a meterstick, an inexpensive radio resistor, a dry cell, and a galvanometer (Fig. 21-18). Connect the ends of the nichrome wire to the resistance and battery as shown and use a battery clip and insulated wire to make the sliding contact on the nichrome wire. Connect a galvanometer and a telegraph key or some other type of spring-return push-button that is normally *open* in series as shown in the diagram. Connect the unknown resistance to points X and Y. Attach the clip near the center of the slide wire and tap the key with a swift motion to establish a *very brief* contact while you watch the galvanometer. Move the clip to one side or the other while you repeat the fast tap procedure until you find a point where the galvanometer shows zero deflection. For this condition, the bridge is said to be balanced and the equation given below may be applied. Note that the resistance R_1 fixed in the circuit must be changed for different ranges of resistance. (50 to 100 ohms is useful for low ranges.)

$$\frac{\text{Millimeters to left of balance point}}{\text{Millimeters to right of balance point}} = \frac{\text{Resistance of } R_1}{\text{Unknown resistance } (R_x)}$$

Standard Wheatstone bridge. If decade resistance boxes are available, a standard type bridge can be set up as in Fig. 21-19. Inexpensive radio resistors can be used to make these decade boxes for each student by constructing the system shown in Fig. 21-20.[3] The resistors are ½-watt types, preferably of 1% accuracy. Three decades are shown in the figure. By proper manipulation of the battery clip leads, it is possible to set up any resistance from 0 to 999 ohms in steps of one ohm. Note that this is done by means of a total of only 12 resistors. For example, to give the decade board a total resistance of 864 ohms, the following connections would be made: clip 1 to A, clip 2 to D, clip 3 to G, clip 4 to H, clip 5 to M, and clip 6 to O. For 407 ohms, the

[3] Patent applied for by Harvey Pollack.

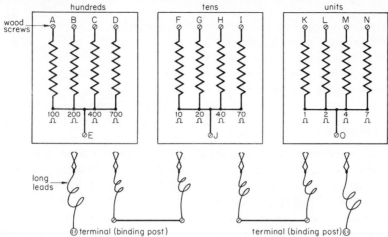

Fig. 21–20 A substitute for a decade box which uses inexpensive radio resistors. All connections should be firmly soldered.

connections would be clip 1 to C, 2 to E, 3 directly to 4, 5 to O, and 6 to N.

In planning Wheatstone bridge experiments, several important details should be borne in mind. The decade box will replace R_3 in Fig. 21-19; the unknown resistor will be used in the position labeled R_x; resistors R_1 and R_2 can be made equal to each other, thus simplifying the applicable equation as shown below; if the battery voltage is fixed, say, at 3 volts, the student must be prepared to change both R_1 and R_2 to other known values in order to obtain a sizable deflection of the meter when the bridge is unbalanced. For most purposes, when the decade board has a maximum of 999 ohms as in this case, R_1 and R_2 might be 50 ohms apiece. The equation is

$$\frac{R_x}{R_3} = \frac{R_2}{R_1}$$

which becomes

$$R_x = R_3 \times \frac{R_2}{R_1}$$

but if $R_1 = R_2$, then the fraction becomes unity and we have

$$R_x = R_3$$

21.4 Magnetic fields

The property of attraction possessed by ores of magnetite was known to ancient Greeks. In the twelfth century these ores were called "leading stones" or lodestones when they were found to take a north-south position.

You may want to show that magnetite, when freely suspended, takes a north-south position. There are many applications of the properties of magnets but by far the most important reason for studying magnetism is to have students understand the relationship between magnetism and electricity, for this is the basis of generators and most other electrical power equipment. This relationship is a two-way road: 1) electromagnetism—a conductor carrying current sets up a magnetic field around the conductor; 2) electromagnetic induction—a moving or changing magnetic field sets up (or induces) current in a conductor in the field.

In this section suggestions for demonstrations and laboratory activities on magnetism are considered first, followed by a development of some of the basic principles involved in electromagnetism and its applications (including most meters and electric motors). Finally, demonstrations of electromagnetic induction and its applications (induction coils, generators, transformers, among many others) are introduced.

21.4a   *Properties of magnets*

Magnetic materials. Students can show that a strong magnet will attract some materials and not others. They can show that it will attract nickel (a Canadian nickel is nearly pure), cobalt, iron, and steel. (These are the same materials which can themselves be magnetized.)

"Natural" magnet. Have students demonstrate that an arrow-shaped piece of lodestone (magnetite) will exhibit the same magnetic properties as the magnet used above. Then suspend it on a string where it will act as a magnetic compass. Have students label the end that points roughly to the north; check this against the needle of a magnetic compass.

Attraction and repulsion of poles. Suspend with a thread and copper wire stirrup a bar magnet that has its poles marked. Then have a student place another magnet with marked poles near the poles of the suspended magnet to show the attraction of the opposite poles and the repulsion of similar poles. Students will recognize that this force probably can be measured. They can develop the relationship, F (in dynes) $= \dfrac{m_1 m_2}{d^2 (\text{cm})}$, where m_1 and m_2 are pole strengths. If m_1 and m_2 are unit poles separated by 1 cm, then the force will be 1 dyne.

Test tube magnet. Fill a test tube halfway with iron filings and apply a cork. A student can stroke the test tube in one direction only with the north-seeking pole of a magnet, and then bring the test tube near a compass. Test its polarity again,

after shaking the test tube. Some teachers use this demonstration as an analogy to represent the "breaking down" of a magnet into small portions, each of which acts as a magnet.

Needle magnet model. Students will need a standard magnet model box, or they can set up 24 sewing needles all magnetized and suspended in 4 rows of 6 needles each. Needles are easily magnetized by stroking with a strong permanent magnet. To make the point of the needle an N-pole, stroke from the center of the needle outward toward the point, using the S-pole of the permanent magnet. Insert the needles into drinking straws and attach these to loosely held threads which in turn are run through fine holes in an overhead piece of plywood and are matted on top so that the threads can turn with a minimum of resistance. Arrange the needles a little over a needle length apart. The poles should point at random at the beginning of the demonstration. Then one student can pass one pole of a bar magnet beneath or above the needles. The class can see how the needles are rearranged in some specific orientation: all north poles will point in one direction, and south poles in the opposite direction. A commercial model is also available which uses tiny magnets pivoted on needles.

Measuring magnetic force (the inverse-square law). A simple torsion balance for measuring magnetic force can be made by suspending a magnet from a piece of surgical gut, nylon fiber, or thin copper wire (Fig. 21-21). Note that the string is anchored, top and bottom, by means of stiff rubber bands. A toothpick or sliver of wood slipped in the gut can serve as an indicator. A plastic protractor under the indicator is used as a scale. Set the zero of the scale under the needle. In using the torsion balance, students can bring one pole of a bar magnet near the like pole of the suspended bar magnet, and read the deflection in degrees.

21.4b The earth's magnetic field

Principle of magnetic compass. You may want students to explain the principle of a magnetic compass. Suspend an ordinary bar magnet with unmarked poles in a copper wire stirrup (see Fig. 21-21) held by a thread. After it comes to rest, mark the end that points north as the north-seeking pole. Then repeat the same procedure on a commercial pivot if available. Or suspend magnetized steel knitting needles on a stirrup; or use smaller magnetized sewing needles inserted into pieces of straw floating on water. You can mount a U-magnet on the point of a pencil stuck in a Bunsen burner (Fig. 21-22A). You will also want to show a mariner's or an aircraft navigational compass when these are available.

Making a navigational compass. As a project, an individual or group of students may want to make this type of compass. They will need a large flat cork. Drill a

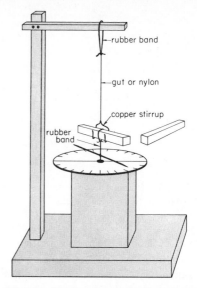

Fig. 21–21 Torsion apparatus for measuring magnetic force. All except the suspended magnet should be made of nonmagnetic materials such as wood.

¼″ hole in the center. Then seal the end of a glass tube (5/16″ outside diameter) in a Bunsen flame. This glass tube is then inserted into the cork. Now mount a 4″ sewing needle in a board (Fig. 21-22B) so that the point is up and the eye is im-

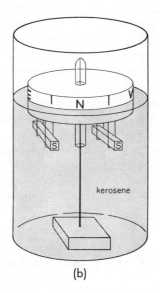

(a)　　　　　(b)

Fig. 21–22 Model compasses: (a) U-magnet on point of a pencil, (b) type of compass used on ships.

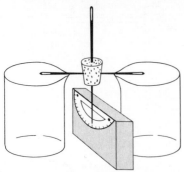

Fig. 21-23 Dipping needle for showing the angle of the earth's magnetic field.

bedded in a wood base. By means of copper wire, suspend from the cork a pair of thin bar magnets with like poles pointing the same way. If students slip the assembly over the needle, the glass tube will act as a bearing; mark a scale around the edge of the cork. Set the compass in a jar of kerosene; the magnets will pivot so that they point north-south. (The liquid damps the compass movement for easy reading.) This type of mounting produces a damped compass typical of the construction of aeronautical and ships' compasses.

Dipping needle. If possible, demonstrate a commercial dipping needle, or have students make one using two embroidery needles, a cork, a steel knitting needle, and two tall beakers (Fig. 21-23). First insert the knitting needle through the center of the cork and then insert the two smaller needles at right angles into the sides of the cork. Rest the needles on the spouts of the two tall beakers. Adjust the knitting needle in the cork until it is balanced and then magnetize it by stroking the needle in one direction with a bar magnet. It will then dip and line up with the dip angle of the earth's magnetic field for your locality.

21.4c Demonstrating magnetic field patterns

Temporary patterns. In a short labora-

tory activity, students can show the fields of force around bar and horseshoe magnets. They can place a sheet of paper over a magnet and sift iron filings on the paper. Tap the paper gently and watch the iron filings become temporary magnets by induction and set themselves in the direction of the lines of force. Students can trace the lines of force emerging from the north pole and passing to the south pole, a convention introduced by Faraday. What happens if glass is substituted for the paper?

Students can trace the curved path of the magnetic lines of force around a magnet in this demonstration. Place a bar or horseshoe magnet under a shallow glass container of water. Insert a strongly magnetized sewing needle into a small cork and let it float upright in the water so that the north pole of the needle is submerged. Students should be able to follow the path of the needle and cork as it moves like an independent pole (a north pole), when it is placed at the north pole of the bar magnet at the beginning of the demonstration. Why does the needle move from the north to the south pole of the magnet?

Also have students place small compasses along the path from one pole to the other of a bar or horseshoe magnet.

Permanent magnetic patterns. At times, students may want to make permanent copies of magnetic fields. They will want to examine the field of a bar magnet, horseshoe magnet, and also two similar poles, and two opposite poles of bar magnets placed about half an inch apart. These permanent patterns are worthy of exhibit in display cases or on bulletin boards.

Pattern in wax. Students can prepare a pattern of a magnetic field, using iron filings on waxed paper. Gently heat the pattern so that the filings become imbedded in the softened wax. Some teachers prefer a method that lessens the risk of the paper flaring up in a flame. They use file folders coated with wax. Heat paraffin in a shallow tray on an electric stove or hot plate. Slide the sheets of file folder through the paraffin, holding the sheets in the tips of the corners with forceps. After the paraffin has hardened, set the magnets on the coated sheets and sprinkle iron filings on them; tap gently. When the field is formed, quickly pass the flame of a Bunsen burner over the waxed surface to soften the wax (but not scorch the paper). Or you may prefer to have students use a heating lamp with a reflector just above the surface. In either case, upon removal of the magnet when the wax has hardened, a permanent magnetic field pattern remains.

Some teachers often use ordinary cardboard and spray the filings with a clear lacquer. Cans of lacquer of the aerosol type are available from hardware stores.

Photographing lines of force. One method uses fast blueprint paper. Prepare the field with a magnet, using iron filings sprinkled on blueprint paper in direct sunlight, or under an arc lamp, or #2 photoflood lamp. After exposure to light for 10 to 15 minutes, remove the magnet and filings, develop the paper in water, and set it aside to dry.

In another method, photographic contact printing paper is used; in fact, out-of-date paper can be used. Students will need to prepare developing solution for the printing paper, a stop bath (3 per cent acetic acid or pure white vinegar), and a fixing bath (hypo). In dim light, students can write their names in pencil on the back of the photographic paper so they can identify their work later on. Then set small magnets on the paper and prepare a field with filings. Complete darkness is not essential. Expose to a 100-watt lamp for 10 seconds, remove the magnets and filings,

TABLE 21-1
Magnetic inclination (dip), in degrees, by locality*

Alabama	64	Kentucky	69	Ohio	72
Alaska	70	Maine	75	Oklahoma	65
Arizona	59	Maryland	70	Oregon	68
Arkansas	64	Massachusetts	73	Pennsylvania	71
California	60	Michigan	74	Puerto Rico	49
Colorado	67	Mississippi	63	South Carolina	66
Connecticut	72	Missouri	69	South Dakota	73
Delaware	71	Montana	71	Tennessee	67
Florida	57	Nebraska	70	Texas	66
Georgia	64	New Hampshire	73	Utah	66
Hawaii	39	New Jersey	71	Vermont	74
Idaho	69	New Mexico	64	Virginia	69
Indiana	69	New York	74	Washington	71
Iowa	72	North Carolina	67	West Virginia	70
Kansas	68	North Dakota	75	Wisconsin	75
				Wyoming	70

* These figures are approximate only and are based upon the U. S. Coast and Geodetic Survey of 1911 and 1912.

and place the paper in the developer. As soon as a clear image of the magnetic field appears, transfer to stop bath, then into hypo for 30 minutes; finally wash in running water for one hour. The next day students can claim their photographs of the magnetic fields and discuss their technique.

21.4d Making "permanent" magnets

Magnetizing with the earth's field. First show that a soft, wrought iron bar is not magnetized. Hold it at the angle of the magnetic declination for your location, with the upper end pointing north (see Table 21-1). Holding the bar at this angle, sharply strike the upper end of it with a hammer several times, and check the poles with iron filings until it is magnetized.

You can also magnetize the bar by the earth's field if you leave it in the angle of declination for several months. The tapping only serves to hasten the realignment of the atoms in the iron bar. Students may try to learn if radiators or other iron pipes have become magnets, that is, if they have north and south poles.

Magnetizing with a coil. Students can make a magnetizing coil by winding a 300-turn coil of #14, 16, or 18 cotton-covered or enameled wire over a hollow cardboard-tube core 1″ in diameter. Secure the turns with shellac, clear lacquer, or cellophane tape. Or use a field coil from an automobile radio dynamic loudspeaker. Either coil will operate on 6 volts d.c. from a storage battery or a d.c. power supply. Place the steel object to be magnetized inside the coil, and turn on the current for a few seconds. (Tapping the steel object while it is inside the coil helps to align its molecules.)

Barkhausen effect. Slip a bar of hard steel into one end of the field coil of an old dynamic speaker. Connect the coil to radio earphones or a telephone receiver. If a radio earphone is used, the field coil should have an impedance of 500 to 1000 ohms; if a telephone receiver is used the impedance should be 75 to 100 ohms. Then connect a magnetizing coil to direct current and slip it slowly over the other end of the steel bar. A series of clicks will be heard in the phone; it is thought that this effect is a confirmation of the "domain theory." In any case, what happens is that atoms or groups of atoms are aligned by the coil; as they move into position, a tiny electrical impulse is produced, which the receiver picks up and transforms into sound.

Next remove the magnetizing coil and heat the same end of the bar with a Bunsen burner. Clicks again will be heard as the iron atoms move into their original random position (heat causes demagnetization).

If the earphone is placed against the microphone of a public address system, the sound can be amplified and heard by the entire class. With a P.A. system de-signed for microphones of various impedances, the pickup coil can be connected directly to the amplifier after selecting the correct microphone impedance setting.

21.5 Electromagnetism

The significance of Oersted's discovery in 1819 is apparent today in the dependence of industry on conversion of electrical energy into mechanical energy. You will want to have students repeat Oersted's discovery—the existence of a magnetic field around a conductor carrying current. Please note that throughout this book the electron current convention is used; that is, electrons are considered to flow from the − terminal to the + terminal in the wires outside the source. This dictates the use of Left-Hand Rules in all cases.

21.5a Magnetic field around a conductor

Several demonstrations are described below in which students can show that when a conductor carrying an electron flow is held in a north-south direction above a compass needle, the needle will be deflected in a definite way. When the electron flow is north, the pole of the needle will be deflected to the east, and when the electron flow is reversed so that it flows south, the north pole of the needle will be deflected to the west. Have students use the Left-Hand Rule for determining the direction of the lines of magnetic force around a straight conductor carrying a flow of electrons.

Making a galvanometer. As a project for a home assignment, students can make a galvanometer from a dry cell, a paper cup, thread, a coil of insulated wire, and a magnetized needle.[4] Around the top of a paper cup wind some 50 or more turns

[4] This and other fine demonstrations are described in *Edison and Faraday Experiments You Can Do* (1958), available from Science Service, Washington, D.C.

of insulated wire so that both ends of wire are free to be connected later to a dry cell. Magnetize a needle, small enough to swing and rotate freely within the paper cup. Place the magnetized needle in a stirrup or support of plastic tape and suspend from a thread hung across the paper cup. You will need to punch small holes in the cup to fasten the thread.

Let the freely moving needle point north; connect the wires to the dry cell and watch the needle swing. Switch the connections to the dry cell and again watch the needle swing.

Oersted's experiment. Connect one end of heavy copper wire to one cell of a storage battery and place a large compass needle a few inches from the wire. Wearing asbestos gloves or holding the wire with a pair of tongs, adjust the wire so that it is parallel to and above the needle. Momentarily touch the other end of the wire to the other terminal of the battery. With current in the wire, the needle will swing to a new position of 90° to the wire, lining up with the wire's magnetic field.

Using iron filings or midget compasses. This is another way that students can show the magnetic field around a wire. Insert a ¼″ brass or aluminum rod into two corks, with a cardboard disk or square around the center of the wire, and support the device in a ring stand (Fig. 21-24). Connect the ends of the rod to a storage battery for about 3 seconds. At the same time, another student can sprinkle iron filings on the cardboard. As the cardboard is tapped, circular patterns of filings form around the wire or rod. At other times, you may want students to use several midget compasses (½″ diameter) set in circles on the cardboard around the current-carrying rod. Can students explain why all the needles line up to form a circle? (The compasses can also be cemented to the cardboard.)

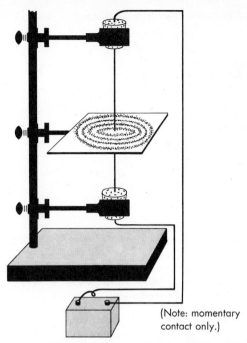

(Note: momentary contact only.)

Fig. 21-24 Duplicating Oersted's experiment.

Using oils and seeds. Although people are well aware of the appearance of a magnetic field, very few have had the opportunity to see the patterns produced by electric fields. These were first done by Michael Faraday and illustrated in his book, *Experiments in Electricity*. The following procedures are based on his work. (The liquid medium he used was turpentine. Here CCl_4 covered with mineral oil is used. The particles which will align themselves with the electric field are "bent" grass seeds, one of the smallest grass seeds available from seed houses. The high-voltage source is a 7000- to 8000-v neon sign trasformer. To each of the two secondary terminals or leads attach a 20-megohm (20 million ohm) ½- or ¼-watt radio resistor. (They cost about 10 cents each.) This is to cut the current flow to a safe level. Place the transformer into a closed wooden box; bring out the primary cord and plug through a hole and exit each of the high-voltage leads through

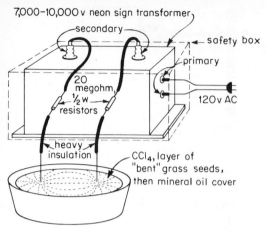

7,000–10,000 v neon sign transformer

secondary

safety box

primary

20 megohm ½ w resistors

120 v AC

heavy insulation

CCl_4, layer of "bent" grass seeds, then mineral oil cover

Fig. 21–25 Electric field patterns outlined by "bent" grass seeds suspended in a medium of carbon tetrachloride covered with mineral oil. The seeds act as dipoles and arrange themselves at the interface of the two liquids.

a shallow glass dish about 4″ to 6″ in diameter. First pour in a ¼″ layer of carbon tetrachloride. Next sprinkle in several hundred "bent" grass seeds. Then add a ¼″ layer of mineral oil of the type sold in drugstores. The two liquids will form an interface or boundary in which the seeds, being able to move somewhat freely, will align themselves with the electric field, each acting as a dipole. For the first experiment simply connect one high-voltage wire to a stiff wire standing vertical in the liquid layers supported by a glass or wood insulator. The seeds will form a radial pattern. (*Caution: Make all connections while the plug is disconnected from the 110-volt circuit.*) Next add a second parallel wire to the first as in Fig. 21-26A. This time a dipole pattern will form as illustrated in the photograph. With the current off, try two parallel metal bars connected to the high voltage. The seeds will show the parallel lines of force between the plates and the fringing lines near the ends as in the photograph in Fig. 21-26B. A high-voltage induction coil may be used for these experiments but it will not work as well. The 20-megohm resistors are not required if

separate holes several inches apart (Fig. 21-25). Screw down the box cover so that no one will accidently get his hands in contact with the high-voltage terminals or leads before the current has passed through the 20-megohm resistors. Next prepare the field pattern container. This is

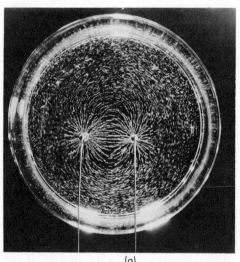

(a)

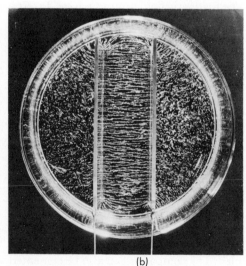

(b)

Fig. 21–26 Electric fields: (a) dipole pattern, (b) parallel lines of force. (PSSC of Educational Services, Inc.)

you use an induction coil operated by a 6-volt battery.

To show the field between two similarly charged rods use two vertical rods ½" apart with both connected to a single high-voltage terminal. The other high-voltage terminal is not used. If you wish, the glass dish may be placed on the stage of an overhead projector and the electric field projected on the ceiling or forward to a screen by means of a mirror.

Some people prefer to show the electric field in a dry medium. The same high-voltage supply is used with black paper as a background, with the rods entering the paper at right angles to the surface of the paper. For particles use fine, very dry Epsom salt crystals or dried pig hair clippings which are very short. Dried pig hair cut into very short lengths for this purpose is sold by some scientific supply houses. If the dry particles are sprayed with clear lacquer after the high voltage is turned off, a permanent pattern will remain. You may want to try this photographically by using photographic or blueprint paper as the background. After the field forms, shut off the high voltage and hold a strong light over the pattern. Develop the photographic paper in the usual way; develop the blueprint paper in water. Other types of fields can be demonstrated with the dry or wet type of field pattern: a rod and a bar; a single charged rod inside a grounded metal ring 3" in diameter and 1" high.

To prevent confusion remind the students that the magnetic field is at right angles to the electric field when current is flowing.

21.5b Properties of electromagnets

You will want to plan laboratory periods so that students can show the basic principles of electromagnets. What factors affect the strength of an electromagnet?

Connect a length of #16 or 18 insulated copper wire to a low-voltage d.c. source. If students now dip the center of the wire into a heap of iron filings or brads, they can examine the amount that is attracted. What happens when the current is disconnected? Now they can wind 10 turns of the same wire around a ½" cardboard or plastic tube. Connect the current again and place the coil in brads or iron filings. Why are more attracted now? Now wind another layer of the same wire, making 20 turns, and show the increased attraction.

Then students can place an iron core inside the coil and observe the greatly increased attraction. After testing the effect of increasing turns and the insertion of an iron core, they can increase the current and show the increase in magnetic attraction.

Finally, bring an electromagnet near a suspended magnet to show that the electromagnet follows the laws of attraction and repulsion like any permanent magnet.

21.5c Magnetic field resulting from electric field

Assemble an old 78-rpm phonograph record on the shaft of an electric fan. Hold wool or fur gently against the rotating disk. A compass needle will be attracted toward the rotating disk.

Now, for example, suppose that the record is rotating counterclockwise as viewed from the front. This means that a large excess of electrons is rotating counterclockwise since the disk becomes negatively charged. This movement of electrons constitutes an *electron current* in a circle within the plane of the record. Using the Left-Hand Rule for Coils, the fingers form a circle in the same direction as the electron current (i.e., counterclockwise) so that the thumb is seen to point *into* the plane of the record. This is the direction of

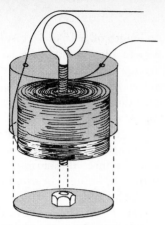

Fig. 21–27 Lifting electromagnet.

the magnetic field; hence a compass held near the rotating record will deflect so that its N-pole points inward. If the direction of rotation can be reversed, the compass will swing around in the opposite direction.

The *electric* field consists of lines coming from electrons within the plane of the record; the magnetic field produced by the same moving electrons is at right angles to this plane. Thus, the electric and magnetic fields are at right angles to each other.

21.5d Applications of electromagnetism

Can students name devices used at home or in industry that utilize an electromagnet? They can demonstrate many applications in class or in the laboratory: telegraphs, radio speakers, telephones, magnetic yoke of TV set (see Electronics, Chapter 22). Only lifting magnets, bells, generators, transformers, and motors will be discussed at this point.

Lifting magnets. A working model of a lifting magnet can be constructed and operated on 6-volt direct current (Fig. 21-27). Students will need a steel pipe cap (3″ in diameter) with ½″ steel eye-bolt in the center. Onto the bolt wind 200 turns of #14 to 18 cotton-covered wire. Drill holes in the cap for the ½″ bolt and the

coil leads. The coil lead holes should be insulated with plastic tape. When the coil is tightened into place inside the cap, the bolt head must be flush with the cap's edges. A fiber washer can be used on the bolt to hold the coiled wire. The iron core and field coils from old radio dynamic speakers also make good lifting magnets but require 110–120 volts d.c. This can be provided by a 3-amp selenium rectifier rated at 120 v r.m.s. (Method for getting direct current is described under diode as rectifier in 22.2a.)

Electric bell. Develop the principle of the electric bell by starting with an electromagnet. Arrange it so that it attracts a hacksaw blade or other strip of flexible iron. Turn the current to the electromagnet on and off to show that you get a single motion for each time that the current is on. This represents the single stroke gong of the type used for fire drills in school; it rings once for each depression of the signal button. Then assemble one (or more if a stiffer spring action is wanted) hacksaw blade on a wood block so that it rests a short distance above the poles of an electromagnet (Fig. 21-28). The electromagnet is held in place by two wooden blocks. About 60 turns of #14 to 18 cotton-covered wire on each arm should be sufficient. Connect one side of the electromagnet to the battery and the other side of the electromagnet to the blade of the hacksaw.

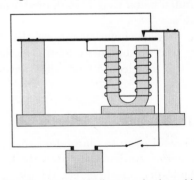

Fig. 21–28 A model bell using a hacksaw blade.

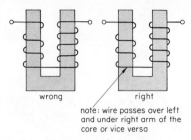

wrong right

note: wire passes over left
and under right arm of the
core or vice versa

Fig. 21–29 The right and wrong ways to pass from one arm to the other when wrapping a U-core.

Then set up a vertical strip of brass or copper behind the magnet with the end bent over to make contact with the top of the hacksaw blade. File the contact end of this strip to a point. Connect the bottom of this contact strip to the other side of the battery. When the current is on, the hacksaw blade will move down breaking the circuit, thus eliminating the magnetic field. Then the hacksaw blade springs back and touches the contact point and the action starts again. Thus a continuous buzzer is made. An electric bell can be made if a bolt is put through the hole at the free end of the hacksaw blade and placed to strike a gong every time it is drawn to the electromagnet.

Making electromagnets. In general, lifting and bell-type electromagnets might be made up according to the following specifications, although precision in these respects is not too critical.

1. Use as much soft iron in the core as space permits.

2. Plan on the use of a 6-volt storage battery or 4 dry cells in series to provide 6 volts.

3. Use #24 or #26 cotton-covered wire (very common sizes). #24 will give you about 50 turns per inch of winding; #26 gives about 60 turns per inch. Enameled wire may be used just as well, if available.

4. Wind no less than 100 turns around

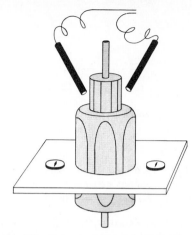

Fig. 21–30 Using compasses to detect the magnetic field around the armature of an electric motor. The carbon electrodes are connected to a d.c. source. When they are touched to opposing sides of the armature, the compass needles align themselves with the magnetic field.

each leg of the U. See Fig. 21-29 for the correct passage from one arm of the U-core to the other.

21.5e Electric motors

Principle of the electric motor: the commutator. You may want to begin with a demonstration to show the law of magnets —like poles repel, unlike poles attract. Suspend a bar magnet in a copper wire stirrup as in Fig. 21-21. Holding another magnet in hand, move it so as to keep the suspended magnet revolving to show that the motion is maintained by the reversal of the poles. Next hang a 50-turn circular coil between the poles of a horseshoe magnet. Connect the coil leads to a 6-volt battery. Students can observe that the coil will turn and stop; continuous rotation requires reversal of poles. In addition, the current must reach the coil by some means other than the suspended wires since they will twist on each other. Students can show this reversal of poles with the armature from an automobile generator (may be available from a garage).

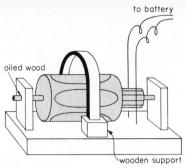

to battery

oiled wood

wooden support

Fig. 21–31 A 6-volt armature mounted on well-oiled wood bearings and placed in a magnetic field will turn when current is applied.

Fig. 21–32 St. Louis motor, a commercial device used to demonstrate action of an armature in a magnetic field. (Welch Scientific Company.)

Place the armature through an opening in a piece of Celotex or beaver board and connect two carbon rods to wires which lead to a storage battery; touch the carbon rods to the commutator. Sprinkle iron filings on the board so that the fields of the magnets form. If students place compasses at the points where the field indicates the presence of poles, the ends of the compass needles will point to the poles (Fig. 21-30). If students turn the armature a half turn, keeping the carbons stationary, they can note that the poles reverse, as indicated by the compass needles. They may need to repeat this several times to develop the principle of reversal of poles by commutator rotation.

Demonstration motor. Students should be ready to identify the parts of several demonstration models of d.c. motors. Mount a 6-volt armature on two bearings made by drilling holes in 1″ blocks of wood nailed to a board (Fig. 21-31). Lubricate the holes by soaking them with oil and place a large horseshoe magnet in the position indicated in the illustration so that the armature windings are between the poles. Next touch two wires connected to a 6-volt d.c. source to the opposite sides of the commutator. Students should be able to explain why the armature spins.

Or you may want to develop the principles of the motor with a commercial St.

Louis motor (see appendix for supply houses), as shown in Fig. 21-32. Here students can remove the bar magnets, push them apart, or hold them close together to study the operation of the armature.

To demonstrate a series motor replace the horseshoe magnet (Fig. 21-31) with an electromagnet made by winding a U-shaped iron bar with 100 turns of #24 cotton-covered wire. Connect it in series with one of the wires from the battery as shown in Fig. 21-33. Then students can connect the electromagnet coil across the two commutator brush wires as in Fig. 21-34 to show a parallel or shunt motor.

A compound wound motor consists of a field that contains two distinct coils: one of these is a series winding and has a relatively low resistance (few turns); the other

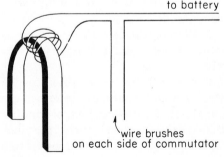

to battery

wire brushes on each side of commutator

Fig. 21–33 Essential wiring to show a series motor. (See also Fig. 21–31.)

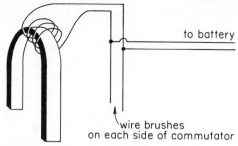

wire brushes
on each side of commutator

Fig. 21–34 A parallel or shunt motor can be demonstrated if wired in this manner. (See also Fig. 21–31.)

to battery

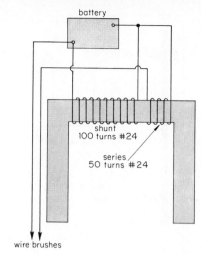

battery

shunt
100 turns #24

series
50 turns #24

wire brushes

Fig. 21–35 The circuit of a compound-wound motor.

is a parallel or shunt winding with considerably more turns to increase its resistance. These may be wound alongside one another or in the form of separate layers. If you use a shunt coil of 100 turns of #24 wire, a suitable series coil would contain possibly 50 turns of the same size wire for use with a 6-volt battery. (See Fig. 21-35.)

Alternating-current motors. Show a synchronous motor removed from an old electric clock. If you can get a three-phase a.c. motor, you can again point out the rotor and the stationary field coil connected in delta or Y as in the case of the three-phase electric generator. Small three-phase a.c. motors are available from stores that sell surplus aircraft parts. Phonograph motors are also good examples of simple a.c. induction motors. Students will notice that there are no brushes or commutator segments in this type of motor. The armature has no windings. Alternating current (60 cps) is supplied to the field magnet; as the field grows and decays as a result of the sinusoidal current, induced eddy currents in the squirrel cage bars of the rotor oppose the growth and decay according to Lenz's law. Since the armature can move, this opposition is evidenced by the armature *following* the changing field.

Electric motor efficiency. The efficiency of an electric motor can be measured by the methods used for measuring the horse-power of a motor as developed in Chapter 18. Since 746 watts is the equivalent for one horsepower, a motor's efficiency can be readily calculated if its rating is known. The horsepower of the motor expressed in watts (746 per hp) divided by the motor's rated wattage consumption will give the motor's efficiency. The smaller the motor, the less the efficiency.

21.5f Electric meters

D'Arsonval movement. You may want to begin with a laboratory activity in which students use working models to develop the principle of the d'Arsonval movement (Fig. 21-36). Wind a coil (1¼″ diameter) with about 50 turns of #28 or 30 cotton-covered magnet wire, and secure the turns by means of cellophane tape. Leave about 10″ of wire extending from one end of the coil and remove the insulation. Attach the other end of the coil to a short section of pull chain from a key chain or electric light socket, and then attach the upper end of the chain to a cork or stopper supported by a clamp. A toothpick inserted between the turns of wire will serve as an indicator needle, and a

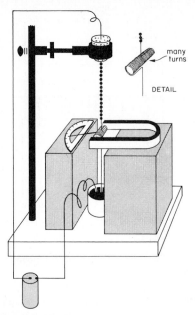

many
turns

DETAIL

Fig. 21–36 The d'Arsonval movement can be used to indicate the relative strengths of various voltages.

protractor can be used as a scale. Then support a horseshoe magnet with the poles around the coil. Put the bare extended wire in a container of mercury or salt water to make a contact; another bare wire leads into the mercury or salt solution to make the external connection. For a source of current, connect a dry cell to the end of the pull chain and to the external contact wire in the mercury or salt water. The coil will turn between the magnet poles. If students increase the voltage by adding another dry cell, they will see the coil turn through a greater angle.

You may want to follow this with another demonstration showing a suspension-type d'Arsonval galvanometer. The parts can be compared with a large disassembled voltmeter or ammeter. Students can compare the core, magnet, and moving coil.

Measuring voltage. Standard galvanometers are available with proper resistances included. When schools lack these combinations, any galvanometer or milliammeter can be used as a voltmeter if equipped with a series resistance. You can use miniature radio resistors as resistances for different voltage ranges; these can be removed from old radio sets or purchased from a radio parts supply house. A 500,000-ohm variable resistor (volume control) can be connected in series with the meter. Adjust the shaft for maximum resistance and connect to a battery of cells with the voltage range desired. Then gradually turn the volume control until the maximum scale deflection occurs on the meter. Maximum deflection should now be interpreted as representing the voltage of the source. For example, if the battery used is 6 volts, a full-scale deflection of the meter with the series resistor left as it is should be interpreted as a 6-volt reading. By reducing the voltage in known steps (e.g., from 6 to 4.5 to 3.0 to 1.5), a new paper scale pasted on the glass of the meter can be calibrated in terms of voltage.

Care in using electrical meters. It is important to warn students that ammeters are always connected in series with a circuit; they will burn out if connected in parallel. Many teachers place a small automobile fuse of the maximum capacity of the meter in series with the meter to prevent it from burning out in case of a misapplication or an overload. Milliammeters are more delicate and require special fuses called "Littlefuses" which are sold by large radio supply stores.

Some school meters contain removable shunts when used as an ammeter. Make certain that the proper shunt is used for the current in the circuit. Check before making connections. In the case of voltmeters with various range series resistances, make certain that the correct one is used for the voltage range for which it is

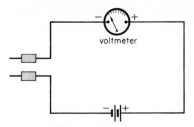

Fig. 21–37 Using a voltmeter to compare voltage drops with known resistances.

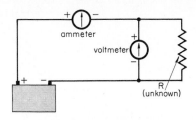

Fig. 21–38 Voltmeter and ammeter used in combination to measure resistance.

to be used. Voltmeters can also be protected by the proper size of "Littlefuse."

Meters should not be placed in hot or damp places and must not be dropped or shocked mechanically. A wire placed across the terminals when not in use in a circuit prevents excess vibration of the coil. Repairing meters is a delicate job. Replacement parts are available for large demonstration meters. However, great skill is required in remounting a coil.

Large numbers of high-grade surplus military meters are available from surplus parts stores. Some are missing shunts or require the addition of resistances or shunts.

Meter for measuring resistance. The most common instrument used to measure resistance is the ohmmeter which can be read directly and requires no computation. (For other ways to measure resistance see 21.3g.) A very low-range milliammeter or voltmeter can be converted into an ohmmeter. Commercial models use a 0–1 ma. meter movement for readings up to 5 million ohms. However, such high ranges are not needed for the classroom unless they are used to check radio and TV sets.

A voltmeter may be used as an ohmmeter with limited measurement range. If a battery having a potential equal to the maximum voltage reading on the scale of the voltmeter is connected in series with a pair of test prods and the meter (Fig. 21-

37), the instrument may be calibrated to read in terms of the resistance connected between the prods. With the test prods short-circuited to each other (zero resistance between them), the meter will merely read full scale since it is connected directly across the battery. As resistances are added in the circuit by connecting across the separated prods, a voltage drop will occur in the resistance, causing the meter reading to decrease. For example, if a 1000-ohm resistor causes the meter reading to decrease 1 division from the maximum, this point may be calibrated as 1000 ohms directly on the scale or on a curve drawn on a sheet of graph paper.

You will want to calibrate the meter. Introduce known resistances (such as decade resistance boxes or radio resistors as discussed in 21.3g) in the circuit and mark the readings in ohms on the scale. The high-resistance readings will fall to the left of the scale while the low-resistance readings will fall to the right. Two radio tip jacks can be used as prods for testing.

In another method you can convert a milliameter or galvanometer into an ohmmeter by connecting a volume control resistor of 500,000 ohms in series in the same way as in making a voltmeter. The scale will not be linear when used to measure resistance. When the control is adjusted for maximum scale reading, introduce known resistances into the circuit and

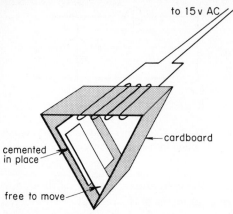

to 15 v AC

cardboard

cemented
in place

free to move

Fig. 21-39 Simple a.c. meter. There are two pieces of thin sheet iron in the cardboard frame. One is cemented down; the other is free to move.

mark the scale in ohms. When this is done, the calibration is complete.

Voltmeter-ammeter. The use of a voltmeter and an ammeter or milliammeter is another method for measuring resistance. Connect the unknown resistance in series with the ammeter and battery and in parallel with the voltmeter as shown in Fig. 21-38. Students can take the readings from the voltmeter and ammeter and substitute in the equation for Ohm's law

$$\text{resistance (ohms)} = \frac{\text{voltage (volts)}}{\text{current (amperes)}}$$

A.c. meters. Alternating-current meters are widely used because of the prevalence of a.c. in the United States. As a project, a student can show the principle of the a.c. meter with little equipment. Begin by cutting a triangular form out of cardboard (Fig. 21-39) and wind 100 turns of #22 cotton-covered wire on it. Then cement inside one surface a strip of sheet iron or a piece of tin plate cut from a tin can. Place a very thin piece of sheet iron inside of the form so that it just rests against the cemented one. Connect the coil to the 15-volt secondary terminals of a toy electric train transformer. The loose piece of metal

will move away from the other piece by repulsion; how much it moves is a measure of the voltage in the coil. Regardless of the way the electrons are flowing or how quickly the current direction is reversed, the two metal sheets will have the same poles so that they continue to repel each other. If a needle and scale are attached to the moving sheet of metal (the vane), the voltage can be varied so that different readings are obtained. (Inexpensive small a.c. meters can also be purchased from radio parts supply houses.)

At some point you may want to demonstrate an a.c. meter and open the case to show the curved moving vane. Also show that a d.c. meter of appropriate range can be used to measure a.c. by connecting it in series with a midget radio selenium rectifier. A capacitor of at least 1 mfd should be connected across the meter. With this connection, the meter will read the *peak* value of a.c. (about 1.4 times the effective value of the a.c. line voltage). Students should observe that a.c. ammeters use coils with a few turns of heavy wire, while a.c. voltmeters use hundreds of turns of fine wire. Why?

21.6 Electromagnetic induction

A basic discovery in electricity and magnetism—electromagnetic induction—was made independently by Faraday and Henry in the first half of the nineteenth century. Here lay the basis for the generator and hence for the distribution of the electric power available today.

In this section some of the basic demonstrations have been described. You will want students to recognize that the motor and generator can be considered as "opposite" machines, in that the motor turns electrical into mechanical energy, while the generator turns mechanical into electrical energy. Students then recognize that these should depend upon "opposite" phenomena: in the motor a current sets up a field which attracts other magnets to produce motion; in the generator, the relative motion of magnetic field and coil produces current in the coil.

21.6a Using a galvanometer to show small currents

Before beginning the demonstration of Faraday's work, students can learn how a galvanometer is used to measure small currents of electricity. Connect a galvanometer in series with a 100,000-ohm resistance of the type used in a radio receiver; touch the connections to a dry cell or flashlight cell so that students can read the small amount of current. You may want to use a low-range milliammeter if a galvanometer is not available, or use a voltmeter, and short-circuit the voltmeter resistance by connecting a piece of bare wire across it. Then shift the needle to the right of zero with the adjustment screw found on the face of the meter.

21.6b Faraday's experiment

To repeat Faraday's first experiment, use a strong electromagnet. Close the magnetic gap with pieces of steel as shown in Fig. 21-40. In the gap between the pieces of steel, spin a copper disk on the shaft of a motor. Connect two wires to a galvanometer; touch one wire to the rim and the other wire to the center of the spinning disk. Can students explain why a minute electric current will register on the galvanometer?

21.6c Induction in a coil

Demonstrating the principle of induction. Students can connect a single loop of thick copper wire (#14 enameled or cotton-covered wire) to the terminals of a galvanometer. Then move the pole of a strong magnet within the wire loop or at a

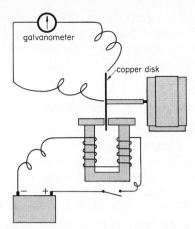

Fig. 21–40 Early Faraday generator: inducing a current by spinning a copper disk between the poles of a magnet.

close distance to the loop. Standard alnico magnets are preferred, but students can also use strong permanent magnets of the type removed from discarded loudspeakers. If in doubt about the location of the poles, students can use a piece of steel to find the area of maximum attraction. When the magnet is moved, students should observe the slight deflection of the galvanometer needle, indicating that a small current was produced.

Next they can wind the wire into a two-turn loop and repeat the demonstration. Also try 5, 10, 15, and more turns of wire. Elicit the notion that the deflection of the galvanometer will increase as the number of turns is increased.

Students will also want to move the coils over the magnet. Take the same coils of wire and connect them in turn to the galvanometer with flexible wire. Then move the coils over the magnet. They will see that the same deflection results from the same number of turns of wire, as long as motion is involved—lines of force are cut. Increase the speed of motion to show the increase in output current. Stop all motion and have the magnet remain stationary inside the coil; there is no current. No mechanical energy was supplied to move the coil or magnetic field, and no electrical energy can result. Students will recognize that here lies the basis of the generator.

21.6d Henry's experiment

Joseph Henry's original electromagnetic induction experiment can be shown by students. They can wind two coils on an iron ring and connect one coil to a galvanometer and the other coil to a dry cell. Then students can connect and disconnect it again to show the deflection of the needle whenever the magnetic field builds up or collapses as the result of turning the current on or off.

Commercial induction coils. Induction coils such as a Ford Model T or TT Fordson tractor ignition coil can be purchased from supply or mail order houses. Dismantle one end and remove one side of the case; melt away some of the pitch to expose the small primary and large secondary coil. Students will recognize that the making and breaking of the vibrator contacts at the end of an induction coil builds up the field and then causes it to collapse. In transformers, the a.c. with its changing current direction accomplishes the same thing.

Current induced by the earth's magnetic field. Students will want to show how to cut the earth's magnetic field. Connect a 20-foot length of standard insulated wire to a galvanometer while two students hold the ends, and swing the wire rapidly as if it were a jump rope. As the wire cuts the earth's magnetic field, current will register on the galvanometer.

They can also show this by using a wire loop about 3′ × 8′. Connect the two ends to a galvanometer. Have two students hold the loop and turn it rapidly for a half turn. Watch the galvanometer register a small amount of current.

Or they may want to make a 3′ loop of 50 turns of wire and set it so that it can spin. Attach flexible wire and connect it to the galvanometer. Then rapidly spin the loop for a few turns while students watch the reading on the galvanometer.

21.6e Self-induction

Connect a large coil wound around a large iron core, or a loudspeaker field coil in its container in series with a battery. Break the circuit and notice the spark. Connect a small neon bulb across the point where you intend to break the circuit; it will light up when the circuit is broken. What happens is that the collapse of the magnetic field upon breaking the circuits induces a current in the coil as the magnetic field passes through the coil.

21.6f Generators

Building generators. After students have learned the principles of electromagnetic induction, you will want to assemble a simple generator by spinning a magnet inside a fixed coil. Then use a bicycle generator of the same type. If you have a commercial handcranked magneto, use it to operate a neon bulb. Old telephone handcranked magnetos can also be used for this purpose. In the first case the coil was stationary and the magnetic field turned; in the second instance the magnetic field was stationary but the coil turned.

To show the operation of an a.c. generator, obtain any multipolar generator such as the one used in an automobile, or use any electric motor whose brushes can be removed. It is necessary to expose the commutator so that a portion of it can be covered with tape (Fig. 21-41). Using vinyl electrical tape, wrap all but a small part of the commutator, leaving a small section exposed. Fit two rings made of copper foil around the taped portion, leaving a space between them, and fashion a pair

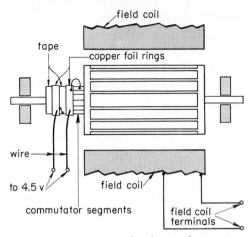

Fig. 21–41 Apparatus for showing how an a.c. generator works.

field coil

tape
copper foil rings

wire

to 4.5 v

field coil

commutator segments

field coil
terminals

of light wire brushes that will remain in contact with the rings as the armature is turned by hand. Solder either ring to any commutator segment; then solder the other ring to another segment displaced from the first by 180°. For the outside ring you may have to make a small hole in the tape.

Locate the terminals of the field coils. Since the field coils are connected in series, you should find the terminal that represents the beginning of the series and the one that connects to the end of the series. A galvanometer with a 10-ma shunt (approximately) should then be connected across the field coil terminals. (A galvanometer without a shunt may be endangered by excessive induced current when the armature is rotated.)

When the armature is rotated slowly, the galvanometer will be seen to deflect one way, then the other, in a sinusoidal type of variation. This is, of course, alternating current generated by an armature energized with direct current; furthermore, the direct current can flow in only one direction in the armature coils to which the slip rings are connected. Hence, first an S-pole approaches a given field

coil; then an N-pole passes it, causing the output current direction to reverse.

If the tape is now removed and the d.c. from the battery applied to the regular brushes and commutator, the output current will be d.c. rather than a.c. The commutator serves the function of reversing the current in each armature pole as it approaches a given field coil, causing the same pole to approach in every case. Thus, the induced current is unidirectional.

Motors and generators. To show the motor and generator relationship set up the electric swing in Fig. 21-42. Notice that there are four dowels about 18″ high set into a 2′ by 6″ board about ⅞″ to 1″ thick. Then wind two coils of 100 turns of #28 magnet wire and suspend them from the tops of the dowels like two little swings. Connect the coil ends as shown in the figure and then fasten two permanent horseshoe magnets on the dowels so that the coils each pass one pole. Start one coil swinging. Immediately the other coil swings. Then the other coil swings and vice versa until torsion in the wire and air friction stop it. This can be used to challenge the class. Some teachers like to use this device to introduce the generator-

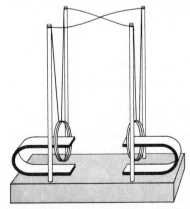

Fig. 21–42 An electric swing. One coil acts as a generator and the other acts as a motor.

motor relationship. What happens is that current is induced in the first swinging coil as it cuts through the magnetic field of the wire. This current flows to the other coil which then has a magnetic field that is either attracted or repelled by the stationary magnet field. This results in motion. On its return swing it has current induced in it, and the opposite coil is energized. This keeps up automatically for some time. If you you insert a galvanometer in the circuit, the reversal of current flow will be self-evident.

21.6g Lenz's law

Whenever a current is induced in a wire, the direction of current always opposes the direction of motion. Using a handcranked magneto connected to a 10-watt, 110-volt bulb, students will notice that the faster they try to spin the armature, the more difficult it becomes. This can also be demonstrated by using a very large coil through which you lift a strong permanent magnet suspended on a spring balance with the coil connected to a galvanometer. The faster you attempt to pull the magnet through the meter, the greater the force required. Do not attempt to measure the pull until the original deflection produced by inertia has stopped. The magnetic field produced by the induced current acts to oppose the motion.

21.6h Transformers

Step-up transformer. A neon sign transformer connected to a piece of neon tubing can be used as a demonstration of a step-up transformer. Students should be able to identify the large secondary and the smaller primary coils if the transformer can be dismantled. (*Caution: Be careful of the high voltage.*)

You can also dismantle a radio power transformer and show the same type of small low-voltage primary filament windings and the large high-voltage secondary windings.

Building a transformer. On occasion, some students may want to make a transformer. In building one with power ratings up to 250 watts, there is an advantage in using a core with $1\frac{1}{4}'' \times 1\frac{1}{4}''$ cross section, for these transformer cores are easily obtained from burned-out or abandoned old-type radio sets. They will need 6 turns per volt or 720 turns on the primary for this cross section. (Use #24 enameled wire.) For the secondary coil, wind directly over the primary and use heavy wire depending on the voltage. For 12 volts, wind 72 turns of wire; for 6 volts, wind 36 turns, and so on. This model can be used to demonstrate the turns-to-volts ratio, the same in primary and secondary.

CAPSULE LESSONS
Ways to get started in class

21-1. You may want to have students show common examples of electrostatic phenomena, and develop discussion around several of the demonstrations described in this chapter. Students can state the nature of the charges, and the ways to determine whether objects hold the same or different charges.

Several students may want to make electroscopes as individual project activities (some are described in the chapter).

21-2. Begin the topic by charging Leyden jars, commercial and student-made jars, with a Wimshurst machine or other electrostatic generator and develop the notion of a condenser or capacitor. Discuss the uses of capacitors.

21-3. Have students show high-voltage electrons with commercial or student-made Tesla coils. Commercial Van de Graaff generators are available for school use that can also be demonstrated for this purpose. Lead into a dis-

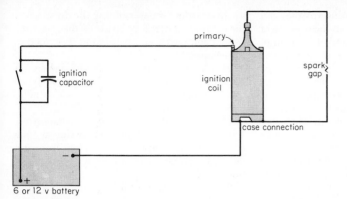

primary

ignition
capacitor

ignition
coil

spark
gap

case connection

6 or 12 v battery

Fig. 21–43 An auto ignition coil producing high-voltage sparks.

cussion of storage of electrons and differences in potential.

21-4. An automobile ignition coil can be used to produce a high-voltage spark. Connect the primary to a 6- or 12-volt battery or d.c. source. Place a knife switch in one leg of the circuit. Then place an automobile ignition capacitor across the knife switch, and connect the wires to the center high-voltage terminal and to the case (Fig. 21-43). Make a ⅛″ gap between these two wires. Turn the switch on and off to produce the spark. Attach a spark plug to the same two wires to show the spark.

21-5. Students can use small toy electric train transformers to demonstrate variable voltage. Use a coil of bell wire in series with a 200-watt lamp and a second coil connected to a flashlight bulb with the coils placed side by side around a piece of iron. The flashlight bulb will light, demonstrating the principle of the transformer.

21-6. At some point you will want to show a film on electrostatics or circuits. Have you reviewed *Electrostatics* (EBF) or *Basic Electricity* (Minneapolis-Honeywell)?

Several filmstrips have the advantage of a slower pace for discussion and review. You may want to examine *Electromagnets* (Young America) or *Modern Physics Series: Electricity* (McGraw-Hill).

21-7. Have students learn to read ammeters and voltmeters operating in a d.c. circuit connected to a small electric motor and lamps. What effect does the type of wiring, series or parallel, have on the circuit current and on voltage?

21-8. Ask a student to demonstrate a multimeter made from a kit or one that is designed by the student. Have the student show how he uses the meter to measure voltage, current, and resistance. Such meters may be borrowed from the school shop or from a radio or TV repairman.

21-9. As a project, students may show a.c. meters measuring voltage and current connected to a model railroad or connected to a breadboard layout of the wiring of a house.

21-10. Invite a radio amateur or radio repairman to demonstrate the use of meters in checking a radio or TV set.

21-11. In a laboratory activity, students can use many types of magnets and study magnetic fields. (Excellent alnico magnets can be removed from burned-out, permanent magnet loudspeakers.) They can demonstrate the magnetic lines of force with iron filings or with small compasses.

21-12. Or begin by getting a model geography globe that contains a strong permanent magnet, or electromagnet connected to a battery and switch. Orient the magnet inside the globe so that the south pole acts as the north magnetic pole. Place this pole just north of Hudson Bay above the Arctic Circle. Place small compasses on the surface of the globe to show the magnetic field. These compasses can be held in place with a few drops of Duco-type glue or model airplane cement.

If possible, display an aircraft compass, a mariner's compass, a marching compass, and various pocket-size magnetic compasses. A student can report on angle of declination as part of the topic for the day's work.

21-13. You may want to have some classes prepare special exhibits for display cases of magnetic fields made on blueprint paper, pictures made on ordinary photographic contact printing paper, or patterns of magnetic fields using iron filings imbedded in wax.

21-14. Have students make an electromagnet as a laboratory activity. In this way they can discover the relationship between the strength of the electromagnet and the number of turns of wire, the amount of current, and the effect of an iron core inserted into a coil.

21-15. Have students list the small home appliances that use the principle of the electromagnet—telephone, electric bell, electric mixer, and small vacuum cleaner, among others. They may also indicate uses in industry—automobile starter motor, lifting magnet, telegraph, even electric train models. Some appliances may be brought to class, and students can explain how they operate. A committee of students can set up a working model of a telegraph sender and receiver.

21-16. Many students will want to make electromagnets as projects to show they have learned the principles involved in their use. These can become a permanent part of the department's equipment.

21-17. A committee of students can summarize the main ideas developed in class about magnetism and electromagnetism by preparing questions and by using a film or filmstrip. Some films and filmstrips are listed at the end of this chapter; others are listed in the appendix.

21-18. At some time a student can begin a lesson by repeating Oersted's discovery. Develop the basic rules for determining the direction of the current and the polarity of the magnets. (Small compasses can be used as described in this chapter.)

21-19. Develop the principle of a generator by moving a magnet in a coil of wire (attached to a galvanometer). Elicit the factors that influence the amount of flow of current.

21-20. A student may want to demonstrate Faraday's or Joseph Henry's experiments (described in this chapter). Then elicit from students the factors basic to electromagnetic induction.

21-21. In a laboratory period, committees of students may move among several setups and answer questions on their work: preparation of a bell and buzzer circuit, telephone, and telegraph circuits, and so forth.

21-22. You will want to look into the many available kits in magnetism and electricity. Some contain very clear diagrams, directions, and materials. One company offers setups for some 300 experiments with equipment for demonstrations on general science and physics. This is written by V. Spitzenbergen and supplied by O. K. Distributors, P. O. Box 74, Outremont, Montreal, P. Q., Canada. The price for the series is $295.

PEOPLE, PLACES, AND THINGS

Any large automotive garage provides many applications of the laws of currents and fields. Perhaps you will want a committee to report on the principles that lie behind the testing and repairing of electric circuits and devices in the automobile. It may be possible to arrange a field trip to a local hydroelectric or steam electric generating station. A report can be made by a student or group of students on the devices and techniques used to distribute electricity. A student might do a report on the testing devices used in a radio-TV repair shop. There may be an electrical engineer on the staff of a nearby industrial concern or university who would be willing to speak on the problems of generating and distributing electricity or on the future of electricity as an energy source.

BOOKS AND PAMPHLETS

These are only a few of the books which are pertinent to the work discussed in this chapter.

These and many other references classified by subject and with complete bibliographical data are given in the bibliography at the end of the book.

Angelo, E., Jr., *Electronic Circuits,* McGraw-Hill, 1958.

Avery, M., *Household Physics,* 3rd ed., Macmillan, 1955.

Bennett, A., and D. Gray, et al., eds., *American Institute Physics Handbook,* McGraw-Hill, 1957.

Bitter, F., *Magnets: The Education of a Physicist,* Doubleday, 1959.

Blanchard, C., C. Burnett, R. Stoner, and R. Weber, *Introduction to Modern Physics,* Prentice-Hall, 1958.

Ference, M., Jr., H. Lemon, and R. Stephensen, *Analytical Experimental Physics,* 2nd ed., U. Chicago Press, 1956.

Forsythe, W., *Smithsonian Physical Tables,* 9th ed., Smithsonian Institution, 1954.

Fowler, R., and D. Meyer, *Physics for Engineers*

and Scientists, Allyn and Bacon, 1958.

French, A. P., *Principles of Modern Physics,* Wiley, 1958.

Gilbert, W., *On the Magnet,* ed. by D. Price, Basic Books, 1958.

Holton, G., and D. Roller, *Foundations of Modern Physical Science,* Addison-Wesley, 1958.

Scientific American, "Strong Magnetic Fields," Feb., 1958.

Scott, W. T., *The Physics of Electricity and Magnetism,* Wiley, 1959.

Semat, H., and R. Katz, *Physics,* Rinehart, 1958.

FILMS AND FILMSTRIPS

This partial list is intended only as a guide toward film and filmstrip selection. Refer to the more complete listing at the end of the book where films are classified by subject and where a key to abbreviations and addresses of distributors are given. The cost of film rental, of course, is subject to change. Films are sound and black and white unless otherwise specified.

ABC's of Hand Tools (f, s), General Motors, free.

Basic Electricity (f, s, c), Minneapolis-Honeywell, free.

Basic Electricity as Applied to Electronic Control Systems (f, s, c), Indiana, $4.50.

Care and Use of the Jig Saw; Of the Drill Press (2 fs, c), Popular Science through McGraw-Hill, $6.50 each.

Coils and Electric Currents (f, s), Institutional Cinema, $2.00.

Electric Motors Series (4 fs), Ill. U. Voc. Agric., $2.10 each.

Electricity and Magnetism (f, s, in the series 24 lessons in introductory physics), EBF, inquire rental.

Electrodynamics; Electrostatics (f, s), EBF, inquire rental.

Electromagnets (fs, c), Young America, $6.00.

Elements of Electrical Circuits (f, s), Ideal, $2.00.

Freedom and Power (Franklin to Edison) (f, s, c), General Electric, free.

Introduction to the Automotive Electrical System (fs, c), Delco-Remy Divis., free.

Magnetism (fs), General Electric, free.

Measurement of Electricity (f, s), U. Indiana, $2.00.

Modern Physics Series: Electricity (6 fs), McGraw-Hill, $3.75 each.

Ohm's Law (f, s), Coronet, inquire rental local film library.

Principles of Electricity; Power by Which We Live (f, s, c), General Electric, free.

Principle of the Generator (f, s), U. Indiana, $2.00.

Series and Parallel Circuits (f, s), Ideal, $2.00.

Sources of Electricity (f, s), Institutional Cinema, $2.00.

FREE AND INEXPENSIVE MATERIALS

This is only a partial listing of free and inexpensive materials available to the teacher at this time. A directory of addresses is given at the end of the book. Many of these materials are distributed to teachers without charge. Where there is a small fee, the cost is indicated, although the prices are subject to change. While we recommend the material for use in the classroom, we do not necessarily endorse the products advertised.

ABC of Home Wiring, Cunningham and Walsh.

ABC's of Hand Tools, General Motors.

Alexander Graham Bell, and telephone pamphlets, Bell Telephone System.

Alternating Current, Simply Explained, Wagner Electric Corp.

Amazing Story of Measurement, Lufkin Rule Co.

Edison and Electricity; Electricity Around Us; Steinmetz: Latter Day Vulcan; and others, General Electric.

Electrical Fundamentals; Electrical Energy, Chrysler Corp.

Electricity and Wheels, and others, General Motors.

Everyday Electricity Charts (set of 8 wall charts in 2 colors; vacuum cleaner, automatic washer, etc.), Westinghouse, $1.00 set.

History of Measurement (posters), Ford Motor Co.

How Man Put Electricity to Work, Consolidated Edison.

Magnetism and Electricity, Service Reference Book, Chrysler Corp., inquire cost.

Man-Made Magic, General Electric.

Manual of Carpentry, U.S. Steel.

Motors: Make the World Go Round (directions for making tin can motor), General Electric.

Precision: A Measure of Progress (reading micrometer), General Motors.

Story of Western Union, Western Union Telegraph.

CHAPTER 22

Electronics

The demonstrations in this chapter introduce basic principles of the telegraph, telephone, microphone, radio, transistor, television. The radio has been developed in detail from the spark transmitter and crystal receiver through radio tubes, transistors, and into television. These demonstrations serve the dual purpose of presenting the fundamental principles used in radio and television and of providing a review of magnetism and electricity.

22.1 Communication by wire

22.1a Telegraph

You may want to begin the study of the telegraph by holding an electromagnet in a clamp just under a clamped hacksaw blade (Fig. 22-1). Students can turn the magnet current on and off to attract and release the blade.

If some students want to make an iron-hinge armature telegraph (Fig. 22-2), they will need a wood yoke of 1″ stock which they can get from the end of an apple box. Place a wood screw or nail at point A, and fasten a 2″ iron hinge at B so it just rests on the head of screw or nail placed below at A. At C place a #12 iron wood screw and wind 5 layers of #22 cotton-covered wire around it. Make a sending key from a spring-type clothespin; connect it in series with the hinge sounder and battery.

Students can operate the telegraph by pressing the clothespin.

A less complex telegraph model can be made using metal cut from a "tin" can. Wind 100 turns of #22 wire around each nail of the sounder (Fig. 22-3). When carrying the wire from one completed coil to the beginning of the next, be sure to cross around the other side of the second nail so that the direction of the second winding will be reversed. In this way opposite magnetic poles form at the two nail heads.

Students can compare the parts of the homemade telegraph key and sounder with a commercial key and sounder; point out the magnet coils and armature and

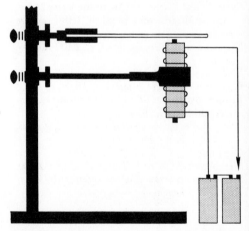

Fig. 22–1 The essentials of a telegraph receiver: a strip of iron that is attracted by an electromagnet.

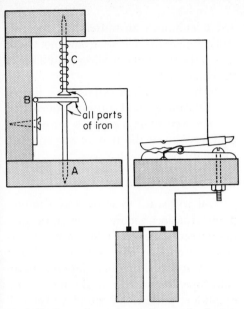

Fig. 22-2 Telegraph sender made from a clothespin, receiver made from an iron nail and iron hinge.

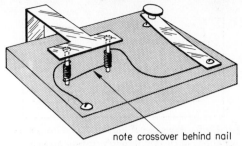

note crossover behind nail

Fig. 22-3 Strips of metal from a tin can make up this telegraph receiving and sending unit.

show how the armature is attracted and produces the click. They can also set up a complete 2-way telegraph circuit with relays using equipment as shown in Fig. 22-4.

22.1b Telephone

Principle of the telephone transmitter. You may want students to manipulate the apparatus in Fig. 22-5[1] which shows the effect of compressing carbon particles on the flow of current.

Cut two metal disks to fit into a beaker. Solder a length of bell wire to each of the disks. Place one disk at the bottom of the beaker and cover it with an inch layer of carbon granules. Satisfactory carbon granules can be made by rubbing the carbon electrode removed from a large dry cell with a coarse wood rasp. Hold the elec-

trode in a vise and rasp the granules onto a piece of paper below the filing point. Cover this layer with the other metal disk. Connect in series a small light bulb and two dry cells with the two metal disks. Notice the change in brightness of the light bulb when you press down on the top disk compressing the carbon granules. You may want to substitute an ammeter in the circuit in place of the bulb to measure changes in quantity of current.

From this demonstration, students can refer to the telephone. What causes the diaphragm in the transmitter to vibrate? How does this affect current?

Model telephone. Students can make a large working model of the telephone microphone and receiver from readily obtainable parts (Fig. 22-6). They should learn the effect of compressing carbon particles and the use of the electromagnet so that they can describe how sound waves are changed to electrical impulses and then changed back to sound waves.

[1] From *Using Electricity*, a resource unit for a course in physical science, Bureau of Secondary Curriculum Development, New York State Education Department, Albany, 1953.

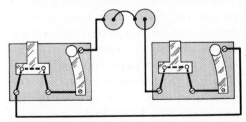

Fig. 22-4 One way to wire two sending and receiving telegraph units.

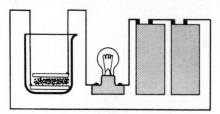

Fig 22–5 Principle of the telephone transmitter: variations in current through carbon particles.

Construct a microphone by drilling an opening (1″ in diameter) through the length of a 3″ × 3″ × 5″ piece of wood and then cut away a quarter section of the wood as shown. Remove the carbon rod from a dead dry cell and use a hack saw to cut the rod into half-inch wafers. Close one end of the wood block with a piece of sheet metal and put the carbon wafers into the hole. Finally attach the wood block to a board and mount a flexible sheet of metal in front of the open end with a block of wood. Place a spring between the metal sheet and the wafers and make connections to the pieces of metal at the ends of the block.

To build the receiver, students will need to wind on an iron core (1″ diameter), 300 turns of #18 cotton-covered wire and mount the magnet horizontally on a board; place a thin sheet of iron in front of one end of the core. Students can now connect the microphone and receiver in series with a 6-volt battery or several dry cells and an ammeter as shown.

Press the metal diaphragm of the microphone and watch the diaphragm of the receiver move with an accompanying increase in the reading on the ammeter. The carbon disks are compressed just as the carbon grains are in the regular telephone microphone, thereby increasing the current. If students move the microphone diaphragm rapidly, the iron diaphragm of the receiver will also vibrate rapidly.

You may want to disassemble a standard telephone transmitter and receiver and compare the fine electromagnet windings of the telephone receiver with those of the giant model.

Perhaps a student can devise a simple circuit using a small container of carbon particles (graphite) and show the effect of compression on the flow of current in a flashlight bulb.

22.1c Microphone

You will want to show that a microphone transforms sound waves into a varying current. Students can connect a carbon microphone in series with a 6-volt battery and the input of a cathode-ray oscilloscope. If a student speaks into the microphone, patterns of sound waves will appear on the screen. Or connect a 1.5-volt dry cell and microphone in series with a 0–10-ma milliammeter and speak into the microphone; the milliammeter will show "average" variations in current.

Students can also demonstrate the action of a crystal microphone such as the one used in the public address system. An old phonograph crystal cartridge removed

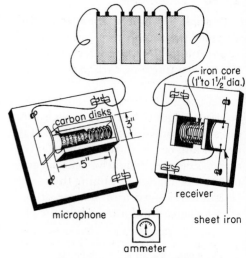

Fig. 22–6 Model telephone

from a pickup arm can be used to show the principle. Connect the terminals to a low-range voltmeter; place a needle in the holder and tap the needle lightly with a ruler. The voltmeter should show a reading of a fraction of a volt to 1 volt. Sound waves impinging upon the crystal of a microphone are converted into electric current in the same way.

Or students can operate a one-way telephone circuit by following the diagram in Fig. 22-7.

22.2 Electrical communication

22.2a *Electromagnetic waves*

Transmitting electromagnetic waves. You may want to start this topic with a device that will generate electromagnetic waves and show a visible effect (Fig. 22-8). Connect the primary of an induction coil to a battery and switch. Then connect the end of the secondary of the induction coil (farthest from the vibrator) to a wire strung from the front to the rear of the room, as an antenna. Now attach the other secondary terminal to a ground connection such as a water pipe or radiator. Make a spark gap of two stiff copper wires between the two terminals of the secondary of the induction coil. Then turn on the switch.

Now you will need a neon wand. (You can get a neon sign maker to make a

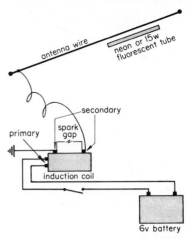

Fig. 22-8   Electromagnet waves generated from the antenna wire will cause the neon tube to glow. (See also Fig. 22-9.)

straight neon tube for a very small sum, or use a neon spectrum tube obtained from a scientific supply house. Or a 15-watt fluorescent lamp tube can be used equally well.) Hold the wand parallel to the antenna wire. Students can see the tube glow. As you move it away, the glow will get dimmer; it should be effective over two feet.

Receiving electromagnetic waves. Students can build a device to pick up radio waves generated by the apparatus in Fig. 22-8. Set up another antenna parallel to the first one and connect this to an ordinary standard-size porcelain socket (Fig. 22-9). Any size wire, bare or insulated, can be used for the antenna and its connections. The other socket connection connects to a water pipe or radiator as a ground. Screw a 2-watt neon bulb into the socket while the induction coil is in operation. The bulb will glow. The passage of the electromagnetic waves through the first antenna induces sufficient current in the second antenna to light the bulb.

Changing electromagnetic waves into sound waves. You can remove the socket

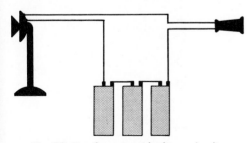

Fig. 22-7   One-way telephone circuit.

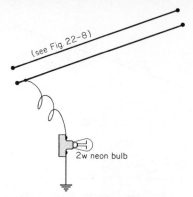

(see Fig. 22-8)

2w neon bulb

Fig. 22-9 Electromagnetic waves induce a current which, in turn, lights the neon bulb.

used in the demonstration above and replace it with a pair of earphones or an ordinary telephone receiver and a crystal detector connected in series (Fig. 22-10). It is best to use a crystal detector of the germanium fixed type such as the 1N16 or 1N34. (These are inexpensive and can be purchased from a radio supply house.) Students should hear with the earphones the signal set up by the oscillating spark. Or the signal can be picked up by any radio receiver in the room.

Demonstrating resonance with a loop oscillator and receiver. First make two loop antennae on wood frames, using the dimensions given in Fig. 22-11, and wind 7 turns of #18 or 20 gauge bell wire on each loop. Use one of the loops as an oscillator by connecting one side of it to a spark gap made from two binding posts and two 2″ finishing nails. Connect the other side of the loop to one terminal of the secondary of an induction coil. Then take a large variable capacitor of 365 mmfd of the sort found in radio receivers, and place it in a battery jar filled with mineral oil or clean engine oil. Connect one side of the capacitor to the free terminal of the secondary coil and the other side to the free side of the spark gap to complete the circuit (Fig. 22-12). A 20,-

000-v capacitor or appropriate Leyden jar can also be used. Connect the primary of the coil to a 6-volt battery and switch. (*Note:* If the capacitor arcs, you can make a substitute from alternate sheets of aluminum foil and thin glass with about 10 plates, 6″ × 8″.)

Build the receiver by connecting the second loop to a similar radio tuning capacitor and a 1- or 1½-volt lamp of the type made for single-cell flashlights. An NE-2 neon lamp may also be used. Bring the second loop near the first; tune the capacitor. When the circuit is in resonance, the lamp should light brilliantly.

You may want to show that a change in the inductance of the coil requires a change in the capacitance of the capacitor to keep the resonance. Remove one of the connecting wires from the receiving loop and connect it to the second turn of wire (thereby shortening the coil) by means of a battery clip. Retune the capacitor to get the lamp to light. Check the position of the plates to show that a greater area of the plates is meshed, giving increased capacitance.

Diode as a rectifier. To show the rectification action of a crystal diode use a small

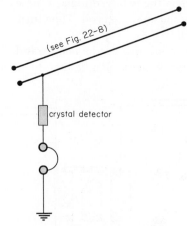

(see Fig. 22-8)

crystal detector

Fig. 22-10 Crystal detector.

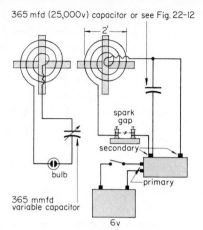

365 mfd (25,000v) capacitor or see Fig. 22-12

2'

spark gap

secondary

bulb

primary

365 mmfd variable capacitor

6v

Fig. 22–11 Loop oscillator and receiver used to demonstrate resonance.

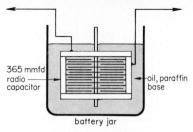

365 mmfd radio capacitor

oil, paraffin base

battery jar

Fig. 22–12 Capacitor in oil.

selenium rectifier (65-ma, 120-volt rms rating) obtainable from radio supply companies. Connect the diode in series with the 110-volt circuit and a 2-watt (or smaller) neon lamp. Across the 110 input place a second neon bulb (Fig. 22-13A). As in the case of the vacuum-tube diode the neon tube across the 110-volt circuit will have both plates glowing, indicating the presence of a.c., whereas the one in series with the crystal diode will have only one plate glowing, indicating the direct current resulting from the rectification of the a.c. by the diode.

A vacuum-tube rectifier circuit may be set up in a similar manner, using a 117L7/M7GT tube (available at any electronic store where tubes are sold). Obtain an *octal* type of radio socket and wire the socket into the circuit shown in Fig. 22-13B. Note that the diagram showing the pin numbering of the socket is a *bottom view;* the schematic diagram of the tube has been numbered in correct correspondence. Be sure to use 120-volt neon lamps (nite-light type) since these have dropping resistors (R in the figure) built into their bases. You will need two standard Edison sockets for the neon lamps.

The octal socket may be supported above a wood base by means of two ½″ brass spacers.

This apparatus demonstrates the process of rectification. An alternating voltage impressed across the two plates of a neon lamp causes alternate ionization of the gas near each of the plates, the result being that each appears to glow constantly as a

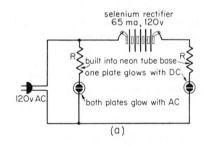

selenium rectifier 65 ma, 120v

R

built into neon tube base

one plate glows with DC

R

120v AC

both plates glow with AC

(a)

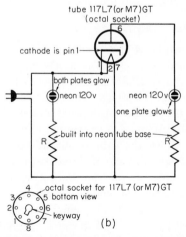

tube 117L7 (or M7)GT (octal socket)

6

cathode is pin 1

2 7

both plates glow

neon 120v

neon 120v

one plate glows

built into neon tube base

R

R

4

octal socket for 117L7 (or M7)GT

3 5 bottom view

2 6

keyway

1 7

8

(b)

Fig. 22–13 Diode as a rectifier: (a) using a small selenium rectifier, (b) using a vacuum tube.

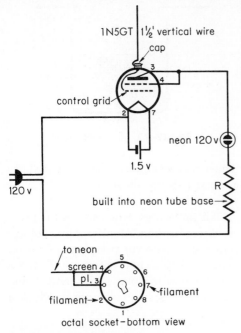

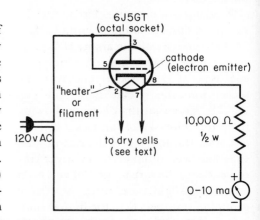

Fig. 22-14 The action of the grid in a triode can be shown with this circuit.

socket, effectively converting it into a triode. Connect a vertical wire to the grid cap at the top of the tube and the 120-volt a.c. line cord as shown in the diagram. When power is applied to both filament and plate, the neon tube will glow. As a rubber rod previously rubbed with fur is brought near the vertical wire, the neon lamp will be extinguished for a minute or two. This occurs because the negative rod drives electrons by repulsion into the control grid of the tube; when the grid becomes negative, it acts as a barrier to the electron stream in the tube so that the electrons can no longer flow from the filament to the plate and thence through the neon tube. In a minute or two, the electrons on the grid will leak off through paths along the glass tube and the neon tube will re-light. This occurs faster on moist days than on dry days since a moist glass path has a lower resistance than a dry one.

This demonstration offers evidence that a negative grid can control the flow of plate current in a triode and that the more negative the grid is, the smaller is the plate current.

Triode filament temperature and plate current. The plate current in a vacuum

result of persistence of vision. Actually, the electrodes are flashing on and off at the a.c. line frequency (60 cps). When d.c. is applied, however, only the positive electrode glows so that the difference in the effect of a.c. and d.c. is easily discernible.

22.2b The triode

Principle of the triode. The action of the grid in a triode is nicely shown by setting up a 1N5GT sharp-cutoff pentode tube in the circuit given in Fig. 22-14. This tube fits into an 8-pin octal socket which may be obtained at the same radio supply store where the tube is purchased. Note that a bottom view of the socket is shown to indicate the pin-numbering sequence. The 1N5GT filament (pins #2 and #7) requires only 1.5 volts which may be obtained from a single dry cell; the screen grid in this tube is connected to the plate by joining pins #3 and #4 right at the

Fig. 22-15 Showing the effect of temperature on plate current.

tube consists of thermionic electrons emitted from the filament and attracted to the plate by electrostatic forces. To show that the number of electrons emitted by the filament (hence the magnitude of the plate current) is governed by the temperature of the filament of the tube, you may set up the circuit shown in Fig. 22-15. Such a demonstration illustrates the importance of applying the proper filament (or heater) voltage to a vacuum tube.

Set up the circuit as shown in the diagram. The 6J5GT tube plugs into an octal socket and its electrodes terminate at the pins indicated. Without connecting the filament to a voltage source, plug in the line cord to a 120-volt a.c. source. You will note that the plate current as read by the 0–10-ma milliammeter is zero because thermionic emission cannot occur from a cold cathode. Now apply 6 volts to the heater from 4 dry cells in series (or a 6-volt storage battery or 6.3-v step-down transformer) and allow the tube to heat for at least 15 seconds. The plate current reading should be recorded. Now try 4.5 volts from three dry cells and note that the plate current is reduced. Repeat with 3 volts from two dry cells. In each case, the electronic emission from the cathode diminishes as a result of the reduced temperature of the filament which serves to heat the cathode.

Plate voltage and plate current. The same 6J5 can be set up in the circuit of Fig. 22-16 to illustrate that the plate current of a vacuum tube varies in the same sense as the plate voltage, although the relationship is not a strictly linear one.

The 6J5 heater is connected to a 6-volt source and the tube allowed to warm up (see previous demonstration). The plate controlling potentiometer is a 10,000-ohm, 2-watt wirewound type used in radio and television. With the wiper of this "pot" moved all the way to point A, full plate

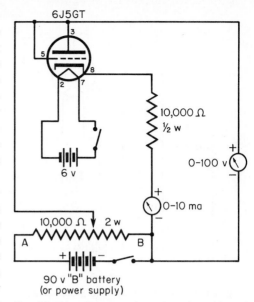

Fig. 22-16 Circuit to show the relationship of plate voltage and plate current.

voltage is applied from the B battery to the tube. (If a variable d.c. laboratory supply is available, it should be substituted for the B battery). The voltage may be read off on the d.c. voltmeter connected from the plate of the tube to B −. A record should be made of both the plate voltage and plate current at this setting. Now run the wiper toward point B in small steps, reading each new value of applied voltage and plate current. Tabulate these values and construct a graph to show how plate current (dependent variable, hence plotted on the y-axis) varies with plate voltage (independent variable, x-axis). Your graph should show reasonable linearity over quite a range, indicating that plate current varies in the same sense as plate voltage and is nearly in the same proportion.

Grid voltage and plate current. In this demonstration, the plate voltage on the 6J5 is held fixed at 90 volts by B_3 (Fig. 22-17), no resistor is used in series with the plate milliammeter, and the heater volt-

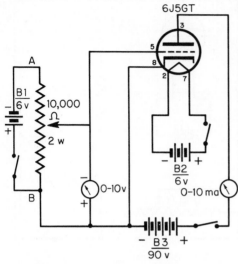

Fig. 22–17 Grid voltage and plate current.

age is fixed at 6 volts by B_2. The difference of potential between grid and cathode, however, is made variable from zero to −6 volts on the grid by means of the 10,-000-ohm, 2-watt potentiometer connected across B_1, the grid "bias" battery. The actual voltage difference between the grid and cathode is measured by a 0–10-volt voltmeter connected as shown.

After warming up the heater as before, move the wiper of the potentiometer to point A. This makes the grid more negative than the cathode by 6 volts; the plate current should be very close to zero with this setting. Call the students' attention to the fact that this is the same situation as we encountered by bringing a charged rubber rod near the vertical wire in a previous demonstration. Now move the wiper toward B in a series of small steps, reading the grid-cathode voltage and plate current for each setting. Construct a graph of plate current (dependent variable) vs. grid voltage (independent variable). The graph will clearly show that a very small change of grid voltage produces a substantial change of plate current. You should call

attention to the fact that the plate voltage variations plotted in the demonstration using the circuit of Fig. 22-16 did not exercise nearly as much control over the plate current as did the grid voltage changes just plotted. This behavior is essential to an understanding of amplification. That is, small changes of grid voltage produce much larger plate current variations than do the equivalent changes of plate voltage. Thus, if a small varying a.c. signal is applied in such a way as to change the voltage of the grid with respect to the cathode periodically, the plate current will surge up and down in accordance with the frequency of this signal. Due to the large plate current variations, the output signal will be of much greater amplitude than the input signal, thus illustrating voltage amplification.

Triode amplification. For this demonstration, you will need a crystal phonograph cartridge in its tone arm. If you have a record player without an amplifier, the cartridge will very likely be the crystal type if the record player is more than 7 or 8 years old. Many of your students have old record players at home from which the tone arm can be removed for experimental purposes. If an old 78 rpm record is placed on a turntable with the cartridge connected directly to a pair of 5000-ohm headphones, the music will be clearly heard although the volume will be quite low (Fig. 22-18A). Students should listen to the music at this level without amplification.

Next set up the circuit of Fig. 22-18B. In this arrangement, the cartridge is in series with the little 1.5-volt bias battery going to the grid. As the needle follows the record groove changes, the cartridge generates a small EMF which adds to and subtracts from the bias battery voltage. This causes the grid voltage to wobble around its static value in synchronism with the record variations. Thus the plate current of the 6J5 fluctuates *over a wide range.* This will be heard as a greatly amplified sound in the headphones. The amplification normally obtained from a 6J5 operated at the voltages given in Fig. 22-18 is about tenfold. The class will be able to hear the music from the headphones from almost any point in the room with amplification.

The 500,000-ohm resistor connected across the cartridge has the function of completing the circuit from the negative end of the 1.5-volt bias battery to the grid of the tube. Crystal cartridges have very high impedance and should be shunted by a resistance to assure proper operating bias.

22.2c   Radio reception

Radio detection. A radio wave of the usual amplitude-modulated type consists of a very high-frequency electric and magnetic field moving through space. The high-frequency wave is called the carrier. Superimposed upon the carrier is a modulation wave form having a frequency that is usually in the audible range (audio frequency). The amplitude-modulated wave appears graphically as in Fig. 22-19A. Note that its body and substance is the high-frequency component or carrier, while the amplitude of the carrier fluctuates at the rate dictated by the modulating frequency. A tuning fork held in front of a microphone at the radio studio would produce a complex wave of this nature. Of utmost interest is the fact that there are two audio frequency components 180 electrical degrees out-of-phase with each other; that is, at any instant, when one audio component reaches a given positive value, the other component attains an equal negative value. When such a wave is re-

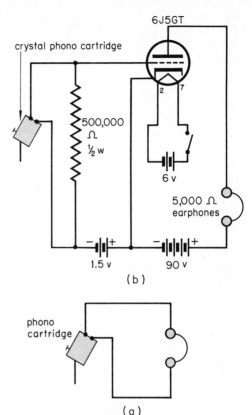

Fig. 22–18   Triode amplification in (b) is compared to absence of amplification in (a).

ceived at a receiving antenna, the modulation components cancel each other out if nothing is done to prevent it.

The function of the radio detector is to eliminate one of the audio components while leaving the other untouched; this prevents cancellation and makes it possible to extract the audio component for further amplification and reproduction in a loudspeaker. This is easily accomplished by simple rectification by means of either a crystal diode or a vacuum-tube diode. Since the voltage induced in a receiving antenna by a passing wave is a.c., rectification wipes out half of the carrier, leaving the other half and just one of the audio components.

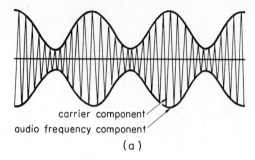

carrier component
audio frequency component

(a)

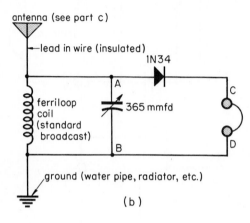

antenna (see part c)

lead in wire (insulated)

1N34

A

ferriloop coil (standard broadcast)

365 mmfd

C

B

D

ground (water pipe, radiator, etc.)

(b)

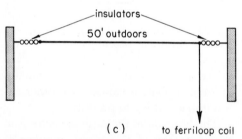

insulators

50' outdoors

(c)   to ferriloop coil

Fig. 22–19 Radio detection: (a) graphic model of amplitude-modulated radio waves, (b) circuit of simple crystal receiver, (c) antenna for crystal set.

A simple crystal receiver is nothing more than a resonant circuit which selects the particular frequency to be detected, a diode, and a pair of headphones. No batteries are required because the radio station itself supplies the power to operate the headphones through the medium of the wave it broadcasts. Your students can obtain the parts needed for a simple crys-

tal set from any of the electronics parts houses. They will require standard broadcast "loopstick" antenna coil, a 365 mmfd variable capacitor, and a 1N34 crystal diode, in addition to the headphones (Fig. 22-19B). The antenna is important, especially if you are located at a considerable distance from the broadcast station. String about 50 ft of any kind of wire between two insulators, keeping the wire well away from metallic objects, including the building structure (Fig. 22-19C). The lead-in wire comes off the end of the antenna and may be any length. Wire the circuit carefully, soldering all joints and keeping the leads between parts as short as possible. Once the receiver is constructed, tune the variable capacitor until a station is heard. Then disconnect the headphones from points C and D and reconnect them across A and B. Note that nothing is heard when the phones are in the latter position. This demonstrates the need for detection as provided by the crystal diode.

To show that a vacuum tube will perform the same function, use a 6J5 with its grid connected to its plate as shown in Fig. 22-20 in place of the crystal diode. In this case, a heater battery (or transformer) is required to establish thermionic emission; otherwise the components are the same as for the crystal set.

Radio receiver detection and amplification. As a final project in radio reception, some of your students may be interested in building a two-stage receiver consisting of a crystal detector and a triode amplifier. To make this economical to operate, you will want to suggest the use of a battery-type tube such as a 1A5GT rather than the power-consuming 6J5 used in previous experiments. The circuit given in Fig. 22-21 is somewhat refined to give it optimum performance. Here is a list of parts you

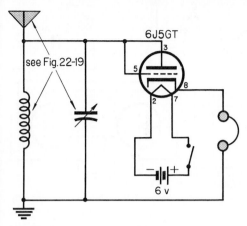

Fig. 22–20 Radio wave detection, using a vacuum tube as a diode.

will need to buy; unless you live in a large city, the best approach to this kind of purchasing is to order everything from a single distributor by mail.

1 Broadcast ferriloop antenna coil
1 365 mmfd variable tuning capacitor
1 1N34A diode
1 200 mmfd mica capacitor, low voltage
1 500,000-ohm, ½-watt carbon potentiometer

1 0.01 mfd paper capacitor
1 octal socket
1 1A5GT tube
1 single-pole, single-throw toggle switch
1 500,000-ohm ½-watt resistor
+ miscellaneous materials such as wood or Bakelite for a panel and base, 90-volt B battery, 1.5-volt A battery, 5000-ohm headphones, antenna and ground wire, hookup wire, etc.

The main precautions to be observed in wiring this receiver are these: make all leads short and direct; solder all joints cleanly; use tinned copper wire of B & S gauge #22 or #24 with good insulation for hookup purposes; be certain that bare wires do not touch each other and so cause possible damage to the tube or batteries.

You might ask your students why no switch is needed in the B battery leads. They should point out that B current can flow only when thermionic emission occurs and that if the filament switch is open, there can be no plate current. Thus when the filament switch is open, the B

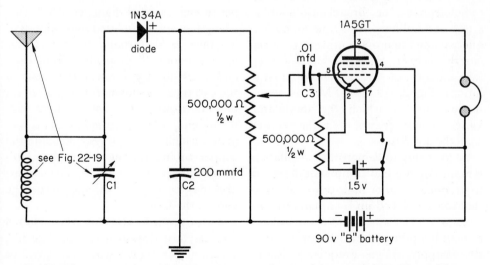

Fig. 22–21 A two-stage radio receiver consisting of a crystal detector and a triode amplifier.

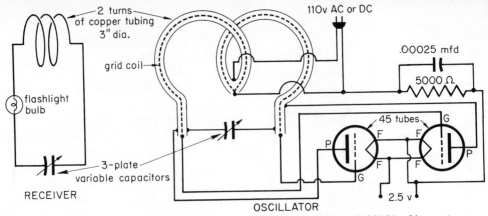

Fig. 22–22   High-frequency oscillator and receiver. The 5000-ohm bias and .00025-mfd capacitor may be omitted and the connections completed with wire.

battery circuit is automatically opened as well.

22.2d   Oscillation

Demonstrating electrical oscillation. Every radio and television transmitter starts with an *oscillator*. This device produces alternating voltage at radio-frequencies and forms the basis for the generation of the carrier wave. A transmitter, therefore, consists of an oscillator followed by a series of amplifiers which build up the power until it attains the desired value. If the transmitter is used for radiotelephone or broadcast, another group of amplifiers—this time audio-frequency amplifiers—are utilized to *modulate* the carrier. Such modulation may take the form of AM (amplitude modulation) (Fig. 22-19A) or FM (frequency modulation) in which the modulator varies the frequency of the carrier rather than the amplitude.

A good way to demonstrate oscillation is to use commercial equipment designed to produce a rather high-powered wave that can be picked up by a separate antenna a few feet away, and made to light a small lamp in mid-air. (Central Scientific Supply, High Frequency Radio Transmitter.) In the absence of such equipment, you can construct an oscillator that is quite effective for demonstration.

You will need a pair of 45 tubes or any small transmitting triodes such as the type 210 or its equivalent. If you use 45's, the filament voltage required is 2.5 volts at 3 amperes which can be obtained from a step-down transformer of suitable rating. Other triodes may require different filament power; this should be checked before planning on the filament source. Your distributor will provide this information.

Around a rolling pin or bottle (3" diameter) form a 2-turn coil using soft copper tubing, external diameter of ¼". Pass a length of vinyl-insulated solid wire, B & S gauge #20, through the two turns, leaving about 6" protruding from each end. Carefully file a hole in the center of the two turns as shown in Fig. 22-22 and pull out a short section of the inner wire for making a later connection. A three-plate variable capacitor resonates with the copper tubing coil at a very high frequency (approximately 50 megacycles) and may be soldered directly across the ends of the large coil.

Two 4-prong sockets should be mounted on a baseboard measuring about 8" × 12", positioned in such a way that it will be easy to solder each end of the copper tubing to its respective grid as shown in the diagram. Note that the plate of the left-hand tube connects to the left end of the large coil but that its grid connects to the *right* terminal of the inner coil; a similar cross-over exists in the connections to the other triode. Be certain that there are no inadvertent short-circuits, especially at the point where the inner coil emerges from the hole in the copper tubing. In operation, this oscillator will produce an easily detectable radio wave.

The detector or "receiver" consists of a three-turn copper tubing coil, 3″ in diameter, a 3-plate variable capacitor, and a flashlight lamp in its socket. When the two units are complete, plug the oscillator into the a.c. line with its tuning capacitor fully meshed. Bring the receiver near the oscillator and carefully tune its capacitor. If resonance is established, the lamp should light brilliantly with the two units separated by several inches. If it does not, try a partly meshed condition for the transmitting capacitor and repeat the process. Try reversing the a.c. plug, since this sometimes provides better operation over longer distances.

Transmission of speech and music. Inexpensive phono-oscillators, available at many of the radio supply centers, can be used to transmit a voice modulated signal up to 50 feet. Any ordinary radio may be used to receive these signals. Although these oscillators are designed to be used with a crystal phono cartridge, a crystal microphone may be substituted in its place for voice broadcasting.

Determine whether your class has a licensed radio amateur. He will be happy to set up a receiver in the classroom and transmit from his home station. If funds are available, you might invest in a pair of Citizens Band tranceivers (transmitter-receiver combinations) for which no license is required.

22.2e *Transistors*

Transistors are solid-state devices that can duplicate most of the functions performed by vacuum tubes. Although the simplest form of transistor contains three elements (like the triode), its fundamental theory of operation differs altogether from that of its vacuum-tube counterpart. Despite this fact, useful comparisons between the two can be drawn to help the student understand how a transistor can amplify or oscillate.

The circuits given in this section are all based on the standard common-emitter connection. When the transistor is used in this type of circuit, the source of electrons may be considered to be the *emitter;* hence, this element is comparable to the *cathode* in a triode (Fig. 22-23A). The receiver of electrons is the *collector*. Since this element also represents the output electrode in the common-emitter circuit, it may be likened to the *plate* of a triode, insofar as function is concerned. Finally, the transistor *base* serves as a control element for the electron flow between the emitter and collector; hence, it may be compared to the *grid* of a triode.

Fig. 22-23B illustrates the basic common-emitter circuit. A signal source such as a microphone or phono pickup applies a small varying voltage between the base and emitter of the transistor, causing a very small alternating current to flow in the base-emitter circuit (I_b). Normally a small direct current flows in the collector-emitter circuit due to the action of the battery, even when the base-emitter circuit is open or unconnected. Note that the emitter is *common* to both the base and collector circuits, just as the cathode is common to the grid and plate circuits in a triode. Due to the fact that the base is a very thin section of semiconductor between the collector and emitter, the small alternating base-emitter current from the

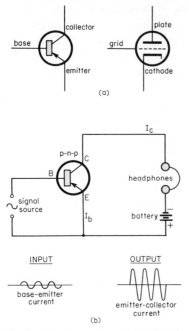

Fig. 22-23 Transistor circuit: (a) emitter element analogous to cathode in a triode, (b) basic common-emitter circuit.

signal source produces a substantially larger variation in the emitter-collector current (I_c). In effect, this is current amplification. The headphones in the collector circuit pass a larger alternating current than was initially available from the signal source, thereby effecting a *gain* of 10 or more.

The tremendous popularity of transistorized circuits as used by experimenters and students is easily explained. Transistors need no filament or heater power. They can therefore operate at high efficiencies. The transistors shown in the following circuits consume approximately 0.04 watt each, yet are capable of amplification that approaches medium-gain triodes. The compactness and ruggedness of the transistor make it highly desirable in portable amplifiers, radio receivers, and radio transmitters. Transistors generate so little heat that they can be housed

in miniature cases which need no provision for ventilation. When operated within ratings, they are virtually indestructible and have a useful life of indefinite length.

When students work with transistors, they should be made aware of the two varieties and of the battery polarity precautions that must be observed with each variety. Incorrect connections will invariably damage the transistor beyond repair. For all of the circuits given in this section, a single battery is used. *It is very important that the students first determine whether the transistors they will work with are p-n-p or n-p-n types.* This information should be obtained from the manufacturer's or distributor's literature.

Note: If the transistor is p-n-p, the collector battery must be polarized so that the collector is *negative* with respect to the emitter.

Note: If the transistor is n-p-n, the collector battery must be polarized so that the collector is *positive* with respect to the emitter.

The schematic symbol for the transistor has been standardized, as shown in Fig. 22-23, for the p-n-p type. An n-p-n transistor is shown in the same general way, except that the emitter arrow head is pointed *away* from the base rather than toward it.

The following circuits are tested designs that typify experimental construction practice. Although the component values are quite standard, it may be found that some experimentation is necessary, especially where substitutions in transistor types are made, in order to obtain optimum performance. For additional circuits of all types, refer to the listing of booklets available from such manufacturers as Sylvania, Raytheon, and General Electric. Many of these will be sent to you free on request; others sell for $.35

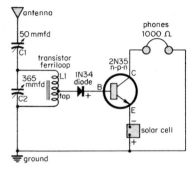

Fig. 22-24 Solar battery-operated transistor receiver.

to $1.50 and may be ordered from electronics distributors.

Solar battery-powered receiver. This simple, battery-operated transistor receiver will produce clear reception with ample selectivity and volume. Although a good antenna and ground are necessary for best results, a Lafayette MS-166 taped transistor loopstick antenna or similar antenna loopstick does provide an excellent impedance match to the transistor, with more gain than the average loopstick, Signals are coupled through C1 to the tuned circuit made up of L1 and C2 (Fig. 22-24). Variable capacitor C2 is used for station selection.

Transistor amplifier. Students especially interested in radio may want to make a transistor amplifier for use in demonstrations. This two-stage transistor audio amplifier (Fig. 22-25) will do the work of a much larger vacuum tube amplifier. The amplifier requires only 6 volts from

a midget battery. The total drain is 0.08 watt. Two Raytheon transistors are needed, types CK721 and CK722. (If other transistors are used, they should be of the p-n-p type.) A simple but sensitive microphone of the crystal variety feeds into a UTC type SO-6 "Sub-Ouncer" transformer (T1). The other transformer, T2, is a UTC type SO-3 "Sub-Ouncer" audio transformer. The switch is essential to prevent rundown of the battery. Other parts are listed in Fig. 22-25.

Regenerative receiver. A regenerative receiver is highly sensitive and efficient. A "tickler" winding, L2, can be made easily by winding 10 to 15 turns of plastic-covered hookup wire around the middle of L1. Add R1 and C4 to above circuit. A 0.01 mfd coupling capacitor, C3, is substituted for 1N34 diode (Fig. 22-26). This circuit amplifies and detects the RF. Operation is similar to other regenerative receivers. Signals picked up by antenna-ground system are coupled through C1 to the tuned circuit consisting of C2 and L1. Varying the setting of C2 selects the desired signal, which is then transferred (through C3) to the base-emitter circuit of the transistor.

Short-range voice transmitter. In this short-range transmitter, the headphone serves as an inexpensive microphone. This circuit requires a feedback winding, L2, in addition to regular parts as shown (Fig. 22-27). For operation, connect the transmitter to a good ground and run an

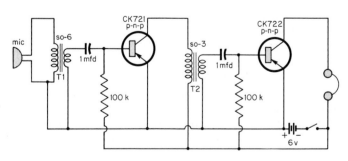

Fig. 22-25 Two-stage transistor audio amplifier.

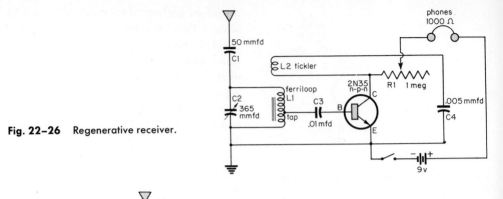

Fig. 22–26 Regenerative receiver.

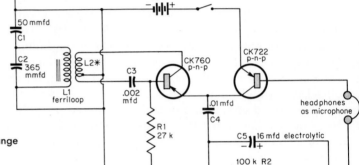

Fig. 22–27 Short-range transmitter.

*20 turns of #30 wire, tapped 5 turns from "base" end, wound over ferriloop

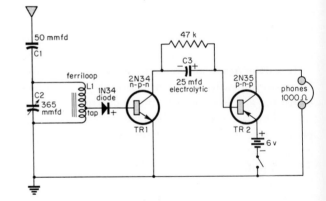

Fig. 22–28 "Complementary" nonregenerative receiver.

antenna lead to within a few feet of a standard receiver. Tune receiver to a dead spot on the dial. Then tune C2 and listen for live background hiss or acoustic feedback. Reverse connections to L2 if no signal is heard.

"Complementary" transistor receiver. This receiver is not regenerative and does not require the tickler winding, L2. Direct coupling between the collector of the n-p-n transistor, TR1, and the base of the p-n-p unit, TR2, is possible because of the opposite d.c. characteristics of these two types. Broadcast signals picked up by a good antenna-ground system are coupled through C1 to the tuned circuit.

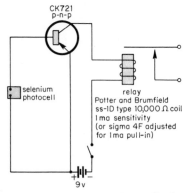

Fig. 22–29 Selenium photocell relay.

Variable capacitor C2 selects the desired signal which is transferred to base of TR1 through low-impedance tap on L1 (Fig. 22-28).

Transistor photocell relay. The selenium photocell used in the sun-powered receiver becomes a signal source in this circuit (Fig. 22-29). The "sun battery" generates current when it is exposed to light, and after it is amplified, the current triggers a relay.

22.2f Television

When small-screen television sets are discarded, it may be possible to get one for classroom and laboratory study. In addition, TV kits are fairly inexpensive, and you may want to demonstrate the parts or help students build a set as a project.

Several radio houses sell inexpensive oscilloscope kits which contain a small cathode-ray tube that operates on the same principle as the TV picture tube.

FM sound signal. You will want to have students demonstrate that the sound portion of the video set is an FM receiver by borrowing an FM set that tunes completely across the frequencies below and above the FM band. The sound of TV stations will be picked up. The FM range is included in the middle of the channels of the vhf TV stations between Channel 6 and Channel 7. To show the dual nature of TV reception, operate a video set with the sound off and the picture on and pick up the corresponding sound on an FM radio.

Antennas. If you have no antenna available for demonstration work, you can make one by using two sticks as shown in Fig. 22-30. The length of arms depends on which channels you plan to receive. By way of example, the following list gives the length of arm that should be used for the different channels.

Channel	Arm length (in inches)
2–6	33
7–13	26
14–30 (vhf)	22
31–47	18
48–64	15
65–83	13

Tack copper wire to each arm and connect the centers to a length of standard 300-ohm TV lead wire, which contains two wires in a flat plastic ribbon.

Face the plane of the wires (or of the antenna) broadside toward the station you are trying to receive. Tune in the same

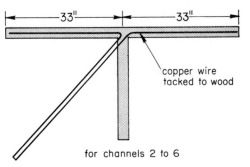

for channels 2 to 6

Fig. 22–30 A TV antenna can be made by tacking copper wire to sticks whose lengths vary according to groups of channels to be picked up. (Adapted from Dr. Theodore Benjamin.)

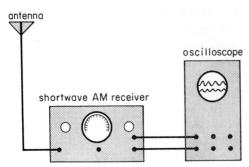

antenna

oscilloscope

shortwave AM receiver

Fig. 22–31 Picking up AM video signal and displaying it on an oscilloscope.

video channel as one heard on the FM set. For the demonstration use separate antennas for the TV set and the FM. (Many FM sets need only a short length of wire as antenna.) Place a grounded metal sheet in front of the antenna to show shielding.

AM video signal. When students understand the operation of the FM sound portion of the TV set, you may want to borrow an AM short-wave receiver that tunes down to two meters. Tune in the signal of a standard TV station. Students will hear a variable buzzing signal, which is the AM signal of the video picture that is going over the air. Now if an oscilloscope is connected to the speaker of the set, as in Fig. 22-31, they will see a graph of the video signal.

Crystal TV pickup. You may want to make an antenna for the channel of a TV station near the school if you are within 25 miles of the station and there are no obstructions along the line of sight. A tuning capacitor can be made from two sheets of metal that are about $2'' \times 3''$. Bend each sheet at right angles across the $2''$ width of a point $1''$ from one end; drill a hole in the smaller side of each piece (Fig. 22-32). Place a flat-head bolt in each hole, attach a nut on it, and connect one antenna lead to each plate.

Connect crystal-type high-impedance

earphones and a fixed crystal diode (of the high-frequency type) to the capacitor in the arrangement shown in Fig. 22-32. Set all the parts on a sheet of glass placed on a wood-top desk or table. Students can tune by changing the distance between the metal plates: the higher the channel, the greater the distance needed between the plates. The sound that is heard is the AM video signal.

Rectilinear propagation of the video signal. In general, electromagnetic waves of TV signals obey the rules for the transmission of light (see Chapter 20). This can readily be shown if a small TV receiver is available. First operate the receiver on the side of the school facing a TV station. Then, if the school building has a steel frame, move the antenna and set so that the building is between the TV station and the set; reception will be very poor. If the school's construction does not block the video waves, then move the set and antenna to a location behind a hill. In some localities, signals cannot be received directly because of surrounding mountains, hills, or even tall buildings. Here any signal comes in by reflection. You may be able to locate the object from which the signal is reflected by using a local map.

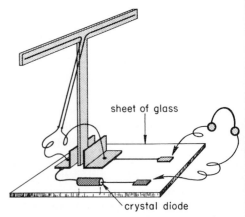

sheet of glass

crystal diode

Fig. 22–32 Crystal TV-video signal pickup.

If the set shows a picture with "ghosts" or partly duplicated pictures, each "ghost" or additional picture is a reflected signal that arrives a fraction of a second later. Try to locate the cause of the "ghost" by measuring the distance from the station to the reflection point and then to the set. Since the wave travels at approximately 186,000 miles per second, students can divide this distance by 186,000 to find out how long the reflected signal takes to get from the transmitter to them. Next get the direct distance from the station to the set and divide again by the speed of light. The "ghost" signal will be arriving a tiny fraction of a second later than the main signal.

Picture tube. To show that electrons in motion, even in the free space within a TV picture tube, constitute an electric current like that in a wire, obtain a good picture on an operating television receiver and bring a strong magnet near the screen. Since moving electrons generate a magnetic field, the field of the outside magnet and those produced by the electrons interact, causing the electron streams to change direction. This distorts the picture in a very obvious fashion. Point out that most modern television receivers use exactly this principle for producing the scanning lines; the magnetic field needed for this is generated in the yokes around the neck of the picture tube. Hide a *strong* magnet in your jacket pocket and stand near the screen. The distortion that occurs when you move around can be quite amusing.

Scanning. Turn on the set. As soon as there is a pattern of lines or a picture on the face of the picture tube, have students come close enough to observe the 485 active horizontal lines which make up the image. These are the traces of a scanning beam that moves horizontally across

the screen, goes off, and returns a little below the first line. The beam traces 525 lines in 1/30 of a second (standard in the United States) with about 485 of them visible on the screen.

Screen phosphors. You can show that electrons cause the white material on the face of the picture to glow by using a section of a broken TV picture tube screen. Tape the sharp edges with two layers of adhesive tape, and connect a spark from a high-voltage induction coil to it to make it glow.

Or use an old fluorescent tube. Connect the end terminals to the secondary of an induction coil, a Ford model TT tractor coil, or a small Tesla coil. Have students connect the primary to a 6-volt battery or to a toy train transformer. Point out that the white coating on the fluorescent tube and on the inside of the TV picture tube face is of similar composition. The coating will glow when hit by the high-voltage electrons from the induction coil. Move a strong magnet next to the tube; portions will darken as the electron beam bends, just as in a TV tube.

High-voltage supply. Students can identify the medium-voltage B supply by showing the low-voltage rectifier which changes the 110-volt a.c. house current to d.c. A serviceman can tell you which tube this is if you give him the make of the set. (*Caution: Make certain that the set is disconnected from the 110-volt circuit and allowed to stand overnight before touching inside parts.*)

Identify the flyback oscillator, a special circuit that boosts the d.c. input voltage from approximately 300 volts to 15,000 volts of a.c. or more.

Also point out the high-voltage rectifier tube used to change high-voltage a.c. to high-voltage d.c. for the picture tube. This tube may be enclosed in a separate metal box in the set. It may be operated anywhere from 5000 to 20,000 volts depending on the set and picture tube size.

Color television. You may want to have students recall at this time the primary colors. If you can get the face of an old color TV picture tube, students will be able to see, by means of a low-power microscope, dots of material that glow red, blue, and green on the inside of the face. (Watch out for the sharp edges of the broken glass.) There will be groups of three dots arranged in triangles.

It may be possible, too, to get an old tricolor picture tube to show students the three-electron gun type of picture tube used in color sets. Inside this tube they can see a thin sheet-metal mask containing about 250,000 fine holes. Each hole acts almost like the pinhole of a pinhole camera for a triangle of three dots. Instead of a light beam, an electron beam passes through.

A separate circuit controls each color gun so that its beam passes through the correct pinhole to strike the correct color phosphor on the screen. In a sense you have three separate receiving tubes in one envelope, one for each TV primary color —blue, red, and green.

CAPSULE LESSONS
Ways to get started in class

22-1. Begin with a modification of Marconi's transmitter (described in this chapter) to show the transmission of electromagnetic waves. Show that the receiving antenna picks up a signal. Connect a microammeter or sensitive galvanometer in series with the antenna, and an 1N16 or 1N34 crystal detector and a ground. The meter will indicate that current is received. Develop the idea that the rectifier changes the high-frequency current to d.c.

22-2. Use a commercial or homemade radio oscillator to demonstrate the generation of radio waves and the reception of the energy by neon bulbs.

22-3. Using a commercial bread-board type of radio receiver, have students develop the functions of the main components.

22-4. Students may want to build a simple crystal receiving set. Use 10 turns of cotton-covered (#30) wire wound around a 1″ cardboard tube. Then shellac the wire to the tube. Sandpaper the wire to remove the insulation. Use a sheet metal arm pivoted by a screw to make contact. Connect it in series with a crystal, earphones, a long antenna, and a ground. If a radio station is very near, a short length of wire can serve as the antenna.

22-5. If possible, have a radio amateur or radioman use an oscilloscope to show the wave pattern in the radio frequency section of the set and in the loudspeaker circuit. Also develop the idea of AM and FM.

22-6. Try to arrange a visit to a local radio broadcasting station, radio amateur station, airport radio station, or the local police radio station. Plan beforehand the aims of the field trip.

22-7. As a summary you may want to show the films *Electronics* (EBF) or *Transistor* (Bell Telephone) or the filmstrip *How Color Television Works* (McGraw-Hill). A group of students, prepared as "experts," can show the filmstrip and ask effective key questions to develop the main points.

22-8. It may be possible to visit a local television station. Perhaps the engineer will introduce students to the video and audio amplifiers, the wave patterns of the signals on the station oscilloscope, the transmitter, and the antenna. He may also demonstrate the methods used to check the frequencies within the channel assigned to the station.

22-9. Perhaps a committee of capable students will dissect an old TV receiver and rearrange the component parts on a large board with the names and function of each major part listed on the board. A paper circuit may be drawn between the parts by referring to the circuit obtained from the manufacturer, a TV repairman, or by referring to a text such as Kiver's *Television Simplified.*

22-10. As part of a lesson, students can display picture tubes of different sizes; also use a cathode-ray oscilloscope to show the vertical and horizontal control of the electron beam.

22-11. Begin a lesson by using a Crookes tube or a simple cathode-ray tube containing a single flat phosphor-coated metal plate operated by an induction coil to produce an electron beam. Then use magnets to move the beam. At the same time, show students how the magnet control yoke operates (taken from an old TV receiver).

22-12. You may want to introduce the principles of color television by showing the primary colors for TV. Project simultaneously through blue, green, and red cellophane slides (as described in Chapter 20). Or use three flashlights covered with different TV primary colors and shine the three beams at a white screen in a darkened room.

22-13. Perhaps a few students can build a solar energy transistor set from one of the several kits available. They can teach the lesson with demonstrations.

PEOPLE, PLACES, AND THINGS

You may find it worthwhile to have a qualified technician from a local radio or television station explain to the class the operation of broadcast equipment. You might arrange a field trip to the station or have a group of students visit and make a report. Local television and radio repairmen can be a source for worn out and weak parts. These can be dismantled and examined. Few neighborhoods lack an amateur radio operator who talks by voice and code to other amateurs over the country and, often, overseas. These amateurs are often delighted to speak to a class.

BOOKS AND PAMPHLETS

These are only a few of the books which are pertinent to the work discussed in this chapter. These and many other references classified by subject and with complete bibliographical data are given in the bibliography at the end of the book.

Garner, Louis, *Transistor Circuits,* Coyne Publishers.

General Electric Co., *Transistor Manual.*

Henney, K., and A. R. Glenn, *Principles of Radio,* Wiley, 1952.

Kiver, M. S., *FM Simplified,* Van Nostrand, 1953.

Marcus, A., and W. Marcus, *Elements of Radio,* Prentice-Hall, 1953.

Pollack, Harvey, *Transistor Circuits and Theory,* American Electronics.

Radio Relay League, *Radio Amateurs Handbook,* Hartford, Conn., 1957.

FILMS AND FILMSTRIPS

This partial list is intended only as a guide toward film and filmstrip selection. Refer to the more complete listing at the end of the book where films are classified by subject and where a key to abbreviations and addresses of distributors are given. The cost of film rental, of course, is subject to change. Films are sound and black and white unless otherwise specified.

An Adventure in Electronics (f, s, c), General Electric.

Automation (f, s, in The Search series), Young America, inquire rental local film library.

Automation in Television (fs, c), Admiral, free.

Basic Electronics (f, s, c), Minneapolis-Honeywell, free.

Bottle of Magic (electron tube) (f, s, 2 rls), Western Electric, free.

Cathode Ray Oscilloscope (f, s), Indiana U., $2.50.

The Diode (f, s), Indiana U., $2.75.

Electromagnetic Radiations (f, s) (PSSC, Educational Services, Inc.), Modern Talking Pictures, 1961, $5.75.

Electronics (f, s, 8 lessons), EBF, inquire rental, regional office.

Electronics in Automation (f, s, c), DeVry, free.

Exploring with X-rays (f, s), General Electric, free.

Highways for the Telephone (f, s), Bell Telephone, free.

How Color Television Works (fs, c), Popular Science through McGraw-Hill, $6.00.

Mr. Bell (f, s), Association, free.

Naturally It's FM (f, s, c), General Electric, free.

Piercing the Unknown (computers) (f, s, c), Modern Talking Pictures, free.

Radio Receiving: Principles (f, s), Ideal, $2.20.

Radio; Television (fs), Young America, $3.50 each.

Receiving Radio Messages; Sending Radio Messages (f, s), Indiana U., $2.00 each.

Sound and the Story (Hi-Fi) (f, s, c), Inst. Visual Tr., free.

Television (6 f, s) (6 fs), McGraw-Hill, inquire rental of films and purchase of filmstrips.

This is Automation (f, s, c), General Electric, free.

Transistor (f, s), Bell Telephone Co., free.

Triode (f, s, 2 rls), Almanac, $3.00.

This is only a partial listing of free and inexpensive materials available to the teacher at this time. A directory of addresses is given at the end of the book. Many of these materials are distributed to teachers without charge. Where there is a small fee, the cost is indicated, although the prices are subject to change. While we recommend the material for use in the classroom, we do not necessarily endorse the products advertised.

A Dictionary of Electronic Terms, Allied Radio Corp., $.25.

Electronic Shortcuts (germanium diode), Sylvania Electric, $.25.

Great Names in Science (Ampère and others; 6 transcribed 15-minute radio programs), 33⅓ rpm, $6.00.

Radio and Television (booklets and charts), Sylvania Electric, inquire cost.

Science at Work Series, General Motors.

A Story of Electronics, General Electric.

A Thousand Science Projects, Science Service, $.25.

Other free and inexpensive aids in teaching are listed at the end of Chapter 21.

CHAPTER 23

Nuclear and solar energy

You may want to have students reconsider all forms of energy—heat, light, mechanical, electrical—in the kinetic or the potential state, and contrast these forms of energy with that energy bound in the nucleus of atoms, and with the new direct applications of solar energy as batteries.

Many teachers demonstrate the effect of radioactive ores or isotopes on an electroscope or a Geiger counter. Students can compare the intensity of radiation and the effectiveness of different shieldings in absorbing radiations. On a small scale, it is possible to reproduce the classic experiments of Rutherford, build a small model of a mass spectrograph, a Wilson cloud chamber, a spinthariscope, and a Geiger counter.

Solar energy batteries are available and small radio kits using these batteries can be purchased.

Some teachers like to begin with models of atoms, thereby defining the particles found in atoms; other teachers prefer to start with a discussion of kinds of radiations and ways to detect them and measure their intensity. The following cross references may be of aid: atomic models, 6.4, and Brownian motion, 1.2.

23.1 Particles and radiation

23.1a Path of electrons

Students can see the path of a beam of electrons using a Crookes tube, or a cath-ode-ray tube of the type shown in Fig. 23-1. Connect the electrodes to the secondary terminals of an induction coil or to a Ford Model T or TT ignition coil. Then attach the two primary terminals in series with a switch and a 6-volt source of direct current as shown. With the current on, students can observe the beam in the tube. (*Caution: Do not touch any parts while the current is on.*) If the beam is not sharp, reverse the battery connections or the two induction coil secondary connections of the cathode-ray tube.

Students should recognize that they see the path of the electrons, not the electrons themselves. Can students see the beam deflect slightly from a straight path? The deflection of the beam is due to bending by the earth's magnetic field. J. J. Thomson used this method to measure the charge-to-mass ratio of the electron. If a cathode-ray oscilloscope or a TV picture screen is

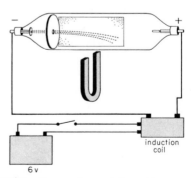

Fig. 23–1   Electron beam deflected by a magnet.

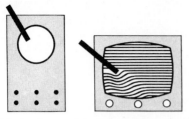

Fig. 23–2 Image distortion results when a magnet is brought close to an oscilloscope or TV screen.

used, the electron lines on the screen can also be deflected (Fig. 23-2).

23.1b A modification of the Thomson e/m experiment

Students should be encouraged to read J. J. Thomson's original account of the ingenious experiment in which he established the ratio of the charge of an electron to its mass. Then the experiment described below may be set up as either a demonstration or a laboratory exercise. It is possible to obtain the value of e/m (charge-to-mass ratio for electron) to the correct order by means of this inexpensive, easily available material. The trick involves the use of a tuning eye 6E5 tube that costs about $1. The electromagnet is wound on a tube of cardboard, plastic, or aluminum 6.2 cm in diameter. Two layers of #16 enameled wire form the solenoid of 174 turns. The coil form or tube is 4″ long and the winding covers 3¾″. With a current in the coil of 6 amperes d.c., a field of 200 gauss (approx.) is formed, or, in mks, 2×10^{-2} webers/meter². The tube fits inside the coil so that the center of the field is in the center of the tube (Fig. 23-3A). The circuit connections, as in Fig. 23-3B, require 6.3 v, d.c. or a.c., on the heater (pins 1 and 6). The cathode pin 5 is connected to the negative of a high voltage d.c. supply or B batteries with a range of 125 to 250 maximum volts. The positive high voltage is connected to the target

which is pin 4. No other tube connections are used.

The moving electrons in the tube will produce a visible trace on the target which appears as an arc whose diameter can be measured in cm. The arc diameter is a function of the target voltage (Fig. 23-3C); all of the factors are related by the following equations.

$$e/m = v/Br \qquad (1)$$

where e is the charge on an electron in coulombs, m the mass of an electron in kg, v the velocity of the electrons in the tube in m/sec, r the radius of the visible arc in meters, and B the field intensity in webers/meter². Since B and r are known, it is necessary to find the velocity of the electrons to complete the right member of equation (1).

The velocity of an electron in an electric field is given by equation (2).

$$Ve = mv^2/2 \qquad (2)$$

where V is the voltage between electrodes. Solving this equation for v and combining with equation (1) yields

$$e/m = 2V/B^2r^2 \qquad (3)$$

Since V, B, and r are all known, the ratio e/m is determined.

The accepted value of e/m for the electron in the mks system, to three significant figures, is

$$e/m = 1.76 \times 10^{11} \text{ coul/kgm}$$

There are several excellent commercial demonstrations of e/m for the electron sold by scientific supply houses (see listing in appendix).

23.1c Detecting radioactive substances

With an electroscope. Charge the electroscope with a rod rubbed with cat's fur. Students can study the rate of discharge of

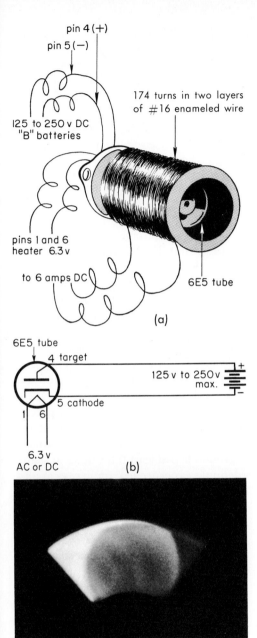

pin 4 (+)
pin 5 (−)

174 turns in two layers
of #16 enameled wire

125 to 250 v DC
"B" batteries

pins 1 and 6
heater 6.3 v

to 6 amps DC

6E5 tube

(a)

6E5 tube
4 target
125 v to 250 v max.
5 cathode
1 6
6.3 v
AC or DC
(b)

(c)

Fig. 23-3 A modification of the Thomson e/m experiment: (a) the 6E5 "Magic Eye" tube inside a solenoid made of 174 turns of #16 enameled wire (after a photograph by Alexander Joseph), (b) the circuit connections, (c) a circular path of electrons is produced whose diameter is a function of the accelerating voltage and the magnetic field. (Alexander Joseph.)

an electroscope when a radioactive substance, such as a piece of carnotite, uranium nitrate, or other ores, is placed near it for a 10-minute interval. Also compare the rate of discharge of the charged electroscope when it is allowed to stand in the air for 10 minutes.

Discharge of electroscope by x-rays. You can demonstrate the relationship between gamma rays and x-rays by using a large electroscope, or place a smaller one in front of the slide carrier of a lantern slide projector (21.1a). Charge the electroscope with a hard rubber rod that has been charged, aim the beam of an operating Crookes tube or cathode-ray tube at the terminal of the electroscope. The x-rays produced by the bombardment of electrons on the metal electrode of the cathode ray or Crookes tube ionize the air and the electroscope is discharged.

Discharge of electroscope by gamma rays. If you bring a sample of uranium or radium ore such as carnotite near the charged electroscope electrode, the air is ionized and discharges the electroscope. If a soft type x-ray or cathode-ray tube is available, it may also be used to discharge the electroscope (Fig. 23-4). This demon-

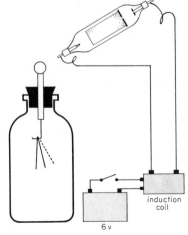

induction coil

6 v

Fig. 23-4 Discharging an electroscope with a "soft" x-ray or cathode-ray tube.

stration is a simplified version of the classic discovery that gamma rays and x-rays were similar. In operating this demonstration, use a small induction coil that runs on 6 volts. Do not use voltage higher than 20,000 volts.

With a Geiger counter. Turn on a Geiger counter and listen to the frequency of clicks from background radiation. Then bring samples of uranium salts, radioactive minerals or ores near the counter tube and compare the frequency of clicking. Also have students bring the illuminated dial of wristwatches near the counter. (Also try certain orange pottery which may contain uranium salts.)

Students can devise ways to show the effect of air, cardboard, glass, sheets of different kinds of metal (including lead) on the absorption of beta particles. For example, what is the frequency of clicking when a uranium salt is held varying distances from the counter? When a sheet of glass, aluminum, or lead is placed between the counter and the source of radiation?

Penetration by beta rays and x-rays. Aim a cathode-ray tube or Crookes tube at one side of a small operating TV picture or oscilloscope (Fig. 23-5). Streaks and lines will appear on the screen. Then place a sheet of heavy aluminum foil between the tube and the screen; there will be some reduction of the streaks. Use a heavy sheet of aluminum; a smaller number of streaks remain. The thicker sheet of aluminum blocks all the electrons (beta particles), and the lines now visible are caused by the x-rays produced. If you place ¼" sheet lead in between, it will absorb all the x-rays, and all the streaks will disappear from the screen.

Tracks in nuclear emulsions.[1] Glass plates measuring 1" × 3" and coated with

[1] This is adapted from a procedure developed by A. Beiser of New York University.

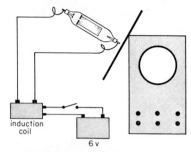

Fig. 23–5 The effect of shielding between the tube and oscilloscope is shown in the disturbance on the screen.

a "nuclear" emulsion may be obtained from Eastman Kodak at about $5.00 per dozen. When properly exposed and developed, such emulsions display tracks of nuclear particles that have passed through the material and have left exposed silver grains behind. Start with plates having an emulsion thickness of 25 microns since these are easier to process.

Tracks of cosmic-ray particles are obtainable by shipping two or three plates, carefully packaged, by air parcel-post to a friend at the other end of the country. It is best to have the plates make the round trip at least three times to assure adequate exposure to cosmic rays at altitudes of 15,000 feet or so in the mail plane.

Exposure to radioactive substances is accomplished by lightly scratching one of the numerals of a luminescent watch with the point of a fine sewing needle. In a darkroom touch the needle point *very lightly* to the emulsion in several places. After repeating this several times, wrap the plate in lightproof paper and set aside for a week or 10 days.

Develop and fix the plates in the standard manner, using D–19 full strength at 70° F for five minutes as the developer and a fresh acid-hypo bath as a fixer. Wash and dry the plates. Should the finished plate have a deposit of metallic silver on the emulsion, it may be removed by *lightly* rubbing it with a piece of cotton moistened in alcohol.

Examine the finished plate under low power on a standard microscope first; then switch to high power to examine the tracks more closely. Short, thick tracks are generally due to alpha particles. Long, thin tracks are often caused by protons. With luck, you may find one or more "stars" which consist of tracks leaving a common point and indicate disintegrations due either to natural radioactive decay or the impact of high-energy cosmic particles with atoms of the emulsion.

23.1d   *Scattering*

Rutherford scattering. There are two phases to a demonstration and laboratory experience with Rutherford scattering, a method for determining an atomic nuclear radius, usually gold. The first step is to cut a ¾″ cylinder from a ½″ diameter glass tube (Fig. 23-6A). In the center of one wall drill a very small hole. (See drilling in glass, 25.2b.) Next coat the inside of the cylinder with a layer of clear lacquer over which you sprinkle activated zinc sulfide as a scintillating screen. Into the little hole insert an alpha source polonium needle. For best results the polonium needle (alpha particles) should be collimated by a metal tube. A section of a disposable hypodermic needle can be adapted for this purpose. Or, place radium dial material inside the hollow hypodermic tube in place of the polonium tipped needle. Set a small piece of gold foil inside the tube so that it effectively becomes a bisecting barrier as shown in Fig. 23-6B. Under the low power objective of a microscope, study the scintillating section of the glass tubing on the side of the tubing remote from the radiating material. The brightest, most frequent scintillations will be seen to occur along a straight line from the radioactive needle, showing that most of the

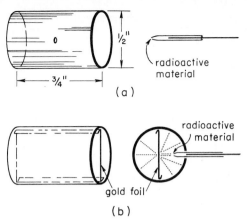

Fig. 23-6   Rutherford scattering: (a) section of glass tube with small hole into which a fine, hollow needle holding radioactive source of alpha particles is inserted, (b) bisecting partition of gold foil and needle in position. The inside of the glass tube is coated with zinc sulfide.

alpha particles penetrate the foil without deflection; there are some scintillations, however, visible at various angles indicating that occasionally an alpha particle collides with a heavy nucleus and is deflected from its straight path. It was from an experiment of this sort that Rutherford concluded that the atom was mostly empty space, containing a very small central nucleus.

Rutherford scattering analog.[2] The forces around the nucleus and the nature of scattering can be represented analogously with a shaped model and rolling balls. You may find this analog to be an excellent group or club project. The individual student who likes to work with his hands may also be interested.

Start with a 2′ × 2′ section of smooth Masonite. Be sure it is flat and unwarped. Cement this to ¾″ (or thicker) plywood (Fig. 23-7A) of the same dimensions to gain a flat surface of high rigidity.

Build an "atom hill" model that repre-

[2] Suggested in H. E. White, *Modern College Physics*, 3rd ed., D. Van Nostrand Co., 1956.

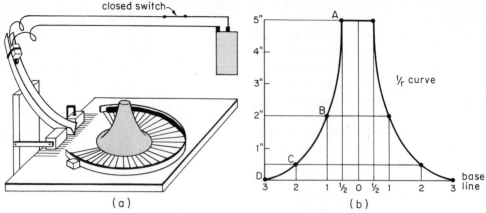

Fig. 23-7 Scattering analog: (a) balls released down trough toward the mound represent alpha particles approaching an atomic nucleus, (b) dimensions for the center cone.

sents the forces surrounding the nucleus of an atom. This hill has a curvature that follows the equation

$$\text{height at any given point} = \frac{R}{r} - 1$$

where r is the radius of an imaginary circle in the base of the hill which would be intersected by a perpendicular dropped from the given point, and R is the radius of base of the hill. For example, suppose you were going to make a hill having a 3″ base radius (diameter of base = 6″), and a flat-top radius at the highest point of exactly ½″ (Fig. 23-7B). Thus $R = 3″$, so that the height of the flat-top above the base would be 3 divided by ½″ minus 1 or 5″. Thus, the hill's maximum height would be 5″. Going down the hill, consider next the height of a point on the projected circle having a radius of 1″. From the equation

$$H = \frac{3}{1} - 1 = 2″ \text{ above the base}$$

point B is 2″ above the base and is located on a circle having a radius of 1″. Continuing to circle C which has a radius of 2″, the height at this point is

$$H = \frac{3}{2} - 1 = \frac{1}{2}″ \text{ above the base}$$

And, finally, the base circle (circle D) has zero height since

$$H = \frac{3}{3} - 1 = 0″ \text{ above base}$$

Intermediate points can be determined and a curve of the desired dimensions drawn on graph paper to serve as a template for establishing the curvature of the hill. Divide the board into 5° or 10° sections, using white ink or paint to mark the segments. You may turn the model in wood on a lathe or you may cast a model in plaster. First take a box about 10″ square and fill it with modeling clay or plaster. Use the template cut from your plot to shape the mold. When the plaster has set (immediately if you are using modeling clay), coat the mold surface with a thin layer of Vaseline. Now pour in plaster and allow it to set overnight. Carefully remove it from the mold the next day. Notice the thick bottom section. This circular section will set into a circle cut out of the center of the 2′ square of Masonite and therefore rest on the plywood under the base. Glue the hill into position. Sand the edge of the hill at the point of contact with the board so the joining edges are smooth and tight. Then thoroughly sand the entire model and shellac carefully.

The next step is to form a sheet metal circular barrier about the hill as in Fig. 23-7A. Thin metal binding used for linoleum will serve well. Secure the circle of metal in position by means of little blocks. An alternative method is to take a strip of ½″ × ½″ wood and make saw cuts every half inch to a depth of slightly more than ¼″. This will permit you to form a circle of the wood with the cuts on the inside of the circle. Fasten with glue and brads. On the inside of the circle place a ⅜″ layer of soft, nonsetting clay. Sticky fly paper might also serve. This will catch the spheres or balls used to represent alpha particles.

Note in Fig. 23-7A that the circle is open at one end. This is the position for the chute to be used to provide energy to the balls to be fired at the "atom model." The chute should be approximately cycloidal; that is, it should terminate on the Masonite board so that the ball leaves it in a horizontal plane. This is to avoid giving the ball a "hop" that might make it bounce. You can cut a groove in the chute or place a half section of tubing on the support. The chute support is fastened to two blocks of wood that slide along the open edge. Parallel lines are drawn on the base ¼″ or ½″ apart for moving the chute horizontally. Use ball bearings ¼″ to ⅜″ in diameter. Mount a magnet taken from a doorbell as a release mechanism. Scotch tape or rubber bands can hold the magnet. Connect the magnet to a dry cell and a switch to operate, simply place a ball bearing against the magnet, and release by opening the switch. The chute is held with a C-clamp for each parallel aiming position. If glass marbles are used, they may be released by hand. This is obviously less accurate.

The chute is moved from center to the right in ¼″ or ½″ steps. Count the number of the hits inside each 10° area and then plot a curve.

$$\frac{\text{number found in angle}}{\text{total fired}} = \frac{n}{N} =$$

fraction of particles found in angle

Particles that approach an atom along a direct line with the nucleus are scattered over the widest angles. This means that they undergo the most deviation from their original path. Particles that pass through the atom at angles that miss the nucleus by wide margins are scarcely deviated. Have students compare deflection from the cone at the outer edges, which is analogous to the coulomb field, to the action near the center, which is analogous to the region of nuclear forces.

If a little trap door or opening is made in the hill in the center near the top, neutron capture can be demonstrated. Students can then see that only a tiny fraction of passing neutrons can be captured. Only those that are dead center and have the correct amount of energy will be "captured" by a nucleus.

23.1e Cloud chambers

Commercial alpha-track chamber. Small, compact alpha-track cloud chambers are sold by scientific supply houses. They require a.c. for the light source and d.c. for the charge on the chamber. The d.c. may be supplied by 2 portable radio "B" batteries (45-volts) connected in series. A simpler and more permanent method of providing d.c. uses an inexpensive radio selenium rectifier. Run one wire from the a.c. source to the negative terminal of the chamber and connect the second a.c. wire to the negative of the selenium rectifier. The positive side of the selenium rectifier is connected to the plus connections of the chamber. If the rectifier is not marked, try it in the circuit; if the chamber does not work, reverse the connections.

Diffusion cloud chamber.[3] The objective of this demonstration is to prepare a container in which condensation trails may be formed by the passage of cosmic rays or other charged particles, giving visible evidence of their passage.

The simple and foolproof cloud chamber of the diffusion type described here is based upon the model developed by Clifford Little at the Physical Science Study Committee at the Massachusetts Institute of Technology in the summer of 1957.

The first items needed are a small, wide-mouthed vacuum bottle and its stopper. An ordinary cottage cheese container of thin plastic (see list of materials with Fig. 23-8 for approximate size) forms the chamber. Small pieces of plastic ¼″ high are set at the bottom as spacers (Fig. 23-8).

A 5″ length of copper tube, ½″ to ¾″ in diameter, should be heated and used to melt a hole through the center of the bottom of the plastic container. The fit should be slightly loose. (If slight cracks occur in the plastic, they will not affect the operation.) A hole of the same size is then drilled or melted through the center of the vacuum-bottle stopper. This fit should also be loose to permit the escape of carbon dioxide from the vacuum bottle. To ensure such venting, use a small nail to punch a hole through the thermos stopper halfway between the center hole and the edge of the stopper.

Next, a 2¾″ disk of sheet copper is soldered against one end of the copper tube as in Fig. 23-8. Paint the top surface of the copper disk with flat black paint for visual contrast.

These parts are assembled as shown in Fig. 23-8. At the top of the plastic container, against the inside walls, place a ½″

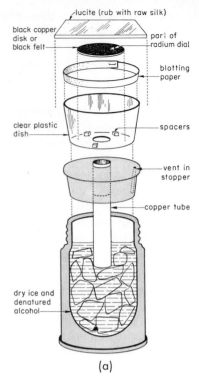

Fig. 23–8a Diffusion cloud chamber: parts of the chamber.

band of thin blotting paper, its ends stapled together to form a ring. It should fit snugly on a slight bias. The container cover is simply a 4″ square of Plexiglas or Lucite, 1/16″ to ⅛″ thick.

Be certain to use gloves or tongs or other protection for the hands for the next operation. Load the vacuum bottle with small pieces of dry ice, and fill with denatured ethyl alcohol. The dry ice will boil at first and then stop. Ventilate the room to carry away alcohol fumes. After a short time, the dry ice will soften in the alcohol. Lower the free end of the copper tube assembly into the vacuum bottle, and secure the stopper tightly. Wet the ring of blotting paper with denatured ethyl alcohol. Place the Lucite cover on the plastic container, and rub the cover with a silk cloth to give it an electrostatic charge.

[3] From the pamphlet *Planet Earth,* a book of experiments by A. Joseph, published in 1958 by the National Academy of Sciences.

Fig. 23–8b Diffusion cloud chamber setup for use with a small projector. (Alexander Joseph.)

(b)

Next, shine the beam of a small projector or small pocket flashlight with a condensing lens through the chamber, and look down into the chamber. Cosmic-ray tracks will soon be seen traversing the chamber.

This apparatus can also be used to show alpha particle tracks. Cut out a small section of a numeral from a radium watch dial. (*Caution: Don't touch radium paint with your hands! Use tweezers!*) Place it in the plastic dish on the black copper disk, and replace the cover. Shine a flashlight or slide projector beam across the plastic chamber. You will see alpha tracks issuing horizontally in all directions from the bit of watch dial.

In damp weather, the plastic top must be charged every 15 minutes or so by rubbing with a silk kerchief. The dry ice and alcohol mixture, however, will last for many hours of operation.

The principle of the diffusion cloud chamber is simple. Since copper is a very good conductor of heat, the copper disk at the bottom of the chamber is kept cold by the dry ice and alcohol. The Lucite cover at the top remains at room temperature, since Lucite is a good insulator and a poor conductor of heat. Thus, the temperature difference between the Lucite cover and the copper disk is about 150 F° or more. Under these conditions, the alcohol vapor from the blotting paper ring is rather dense. The introduction into this vapor of a cosmic ray or other charged particle produces condensation nuclei. A thin "line cloud" or cloud track results, just barely visible. With a strong light (300- to 500-watt slide projector) and a fast-lens, motion-picture camera loaded with high-speed, black-and-white film, it is possible to get pictures of alpha tracks from an alpha source or of the cosmic-ray tracks that enter through the walls of the vacuum bottle and pass across the chamber.

23.1f Observing scintillations

With a microscope. After their eyes have become accommodated to darkness in a dark room or in a photographic darkroom, students can place a radium watch dial on a microscope stage and focus on one dial number with the low-power lens. (Full accommodation may take as long as 30 minutes.) They should see tiny individual flashes. Some success can also be achieved using a magnifying glass. Each scintillation is the result of the action of gamma and beta rays from the radium disintegration. The radium dial paint is mainly zinc sulfide with a trace of radium chloride. The radium in the radium chloride breaks down to release the beta and gamma rays. These rays pass through the fluorescent zinc sulfide, causing it to glow.

You may want to demonstrate a commercial scintillation counter if it is avail-

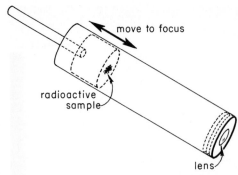

Fig. 23-9 Model spinthariscope.

able. It may be possible to borrow one from a local Civil Defense Agency.

With a spinthariscope. Students can study radiations with a spinthariscope which may be purchased or made in the laboratory. To make, snugly fit the eyepiece of a microscope into a cardboard tube. Inside the tube, place a cork onto which some scrapings from a radium watch dial have been cemented. (*Caution: Do not inhale, or allow scrapings to enter into a wound or into the mouth.*)

Attach a stick to the cork by means of glue as shown in Fig. 23-9. After the eyes have become accommodated to darkness, look through the lens and focus by moving the cork up and down until the scintillations are in focus. In the commercial spinthariscope the emissions from the radium source strike a fluorescent screen composed of zinc sulfide.

Using photographic film. Photographic emulsions are much used in modern nuclear investigations. On the other hand, such emulsions are not strongly affected directly by radioactive emanations, including gamma radiation. The sensitivity of film as a detecting device, however, may be substantially improved by using the scintillation technique.

In a dark room, place a radioactive button or plaque directly in contact with the emulsion of a fast film such as Royal Pan or Super Panchro Press Type B. Wrap the combination thoroughly in black opaque paper held in place with several rubber bands. The lights may now be turned on. Leave the test sample undisturbed for exactly one hour; then develop and fix the film. Note the extent of the darkening.

Now, again working in the dark room, cover the sensitive surface of a fresh piece of film with a thin layer of fluorescent zinc sulfide powder. Place the button or plaque in contact with the surface and carefully wrap as before. After an exposure of one hour, develop and fix this film in exactly the same way as the first and then compare the extent or depth of darkening. The second sample will be found to have darkened considerably more than the first due to the scintillations of visible light produced by the ZnS powder under nuclear bombardment.

23.1g Mass spectrograph analogy

It would be unusual to have a working mass spectrograph to show the separation of elements into their isotopes. However, the principle can be shown by means of an analogy using ordinary things found around the classroom or laboratory. In a mass spectrograph inside a vacuum chamber the element becomes a positive ion when one or more outer electrons are stripped off. These ionized particles then pass through a strong magnetic field which bends their path.

Isotopes of a given element differ; their chemical properties are identical. The extent to which their ions moving through the magnetic field are deflected from a straight path will depend upon the centripetal force caused by the interaction of fields. The amount of deflection then depends upon the mass of the ions.

This follows from the relationship

$f = mv^2/r$, where m represents the mass of the moving body, v its velocity, f the centripetal force, and r the radius of curvature of the path. Since f and v are held constant, the radius of the path is therefore directly proportional to the mass of the ion. Thus, ions of U-234 and U-235 are deflected more than ions of U-238 so that the impact on the silver collecting plate occurs in different positions for these isotopes of uranium.

An analogy can be set up to demonstrate this effect. Use a very strong single pole of an electromagnet and three steel ball bearings of different sizes. As in Fig. 23-10, allow the ball bearings to be released from the top of a cardboard chute one at a time. Each ball must just graze the pole of the magnet without being trapped. This distance can be determined experimentally. For an electromagnet use the magnet of a repulsion coil or wind 600 turns of #14 enameled magnet wire around a 1″ iron core. A 12″ length of an auto's rear axle makes a good core. Operate the magnet on a 6-volt storage battery or a 6-volt d.c. battery substitute. Place newspaper on the table where the ball bearings will hit after they are deflected by the magnetic field. Sprinkle flour or talcum powder over the paper to see the point of first contact of the ball. The ball bearings of greater mass will hit farthest out while the lightest will hit closer. *Note:* Current should be connected to the magnet only at the time that a ball bearing is to be released down the chute in order to prevent undue battery drain.

Another method is to have the balls hit carbon paper in contact with white paper to make a permanent record.

23.1h   *Measuring radiation*

Geiger counter principles. A Geiger tube consists of a metal or glass chamber

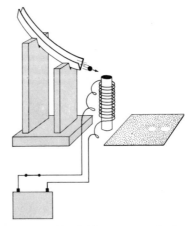

Fig. 23-10   Balls of different mass simulate isotopes.

container in which a central wire carries a high positive charge with a negatively charged cylinder of metal around it. A gas, commonly argon, fills the tube to a pressure of only about .04 atmospheres. Neutron detectors use a boron compound gas. The high voltage ranging from 300 to several thousand volts (depending upon the design and purpose of the counter tube) is supplied by small dry batteries or a power supply. The charge is so adjusted that no electron current flows from the negative to positive in the gas-filled space. However, any entering particle that ionizes the gas causes the gas to become conducting, and electrons flow from the negative to the positive for that instant. Normally, when a gas is triggered into ionization by a high-speed particle, the gas tends to remain ionized even when the trigger has passed on. If this were permitted to occur, only one count would be recorded and the system would go dead until the high voltage was removed to de-ionize the gas, then reapplied. Self-quenching action is accomplished by introducing a small amount of chlorine or bromine with the ionizable gas. The momentary flow of electrons is recorded directly or through an amplifier. Counts

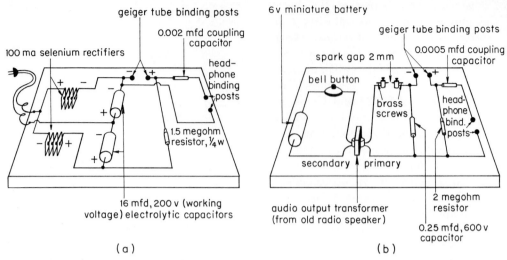

Fig. 23-11 Geiger counter circuits that can be put together by students at low cost: (a) for 110 volts a.c., (b) for battery operation.

are read per minute or, on some meters, in roentgen units. For instance, the present maximum permitted exposure daily dose is 30 milliroentgens (30 thousandths of a roentgen per day).

Often, after students construct a simple earphone type of Geiger counter, they add a sensitive milliammeter or microammeter to determine count-rate more precisely. Such meters require calibration in terms of counts/minute.

This is most easily accomplished by using a calibrated radioactive source obtainable from scientific supply houses or local laboratories. Such a source consists of a plaque or button of radioactive material clearly marked with its emission rate in counts/minute. Before beginning to calibrate the meter, remove the radioactive source to a distance and establish the background count in your locality due to cosmic rays and local radioactive rocks and soils. Call the background meter reading in scale divisions BR. Now bring the calibrated source to the recommended distance from your probe and note the scale reading. Subtract BR from the scale

divisions read with the source and mark the new point with the number equal to the source rating in counts per minute. Since the scale will be quite linear, the value of each scale division in terms of counts/minute is thus established.

110-volt a.c. Geiger counter.[4] The simple, homemade cosmic-ray Geiger counter diagrammed in Fig. 23-11A brings the possibility of laboratory work with cosmic rays and radioactive materials within the scope of the science classroom. The counter circuit is much simpler than the usual radio circuit. It can be constructed for under $20.00, including the cost of Geiger tube and headphones. It is made with standard radio parts and can be built on a bread board in a class period. The unit operates from a regular 110-volt, a.c. power outlet (which reaches, in each cycle, a momentary peak voltage of 150–175 volts). Voltage is doubled in this circuit to provide just over 300 volts to a low-voltage Geiger tube. *Since most tubes are made to operate at higher voltages, be certain*

[4] From *Planet Earth,* a book of experiments by A. Joseph, published in 1958 by the National Academy of Sciences.

that the Geiger tube you get from your supplier operates at 300 volts. (One supplier of these tubes is Electronic Products, Inc., 111 E. Third Street, Mount Vernon, New York.)

The parts to be used in this project are listed with Fig. 23-11A. Using these materials, construct the counter according to the diagram.

Cosmic-ray counts can be detected by simply wrapping your Geiger tube with lead foil to a thickness of 1/16''. This will shield the counter against normal radiation while permitting radiation due to cosmic rays to penetrate the tube. Connect one lead from the headphones to the negative terminal on the tube and the other lead to the positive terminal. Connect the parts as in Fig. 23-11A. When you have completed the circuit, plug into a 110-volt, a.c. power source, and you will have a working cosmic-ray Geiger counter.

(Warning: Do not touch connections while the counter is plugged into 110-volt a.c. power source.)

Battery Geiger counter.[5] This simply constructed Geiger counter can be used to teach the principles of operation of the device and to provide a portable counter of great sensitivity. It may be used to detect cosmic rays if lead foil is wrapped around it, or to detect beta and gamma rays when uncovered. Cover with aluminum foil to detect gamma rays alone. The materials to be used in this project are listed with Fig. 23-11B.

Each time the bell push button closes and opens the circuit of the primary of the output transformer (note the secondary is used as the primary and the primary as the secondary winding), a high voltage is induced in the secondary (see Fig. 23-11B). This voltage is sufficiently high to jump the spark gap (2 mm) and charge the .25-

mfd 600-v capacitor. Repeated opening and closing of the switch builds up the voltage on the capacitor. This voltage then appears across the terminals of the Geiger tube. Each time the gas in the Geiger tube is ionized by radiation, current flows from the capacitor through a 2-megohm resistor. When current flows, the voltage drop across the resistor lowers the voltage across the Geiger tube so that the discharge is quenched, and the tube is then ready for the next ionizing radiation. The voltage drop appearing across the resistor at each pulse operates the high-impedance headphones (or crystal earphones) through a small capacitor.

The momentary-contact switch should be pressed and released sharply about 15 to 20 times. This should charge the capacitor sufficiently to have the Geiger tube operate for several minutes. Pressing and releasing at ½-minute intervals will maintain the voltage. If the counter fails to operate at first, reverse the battery connections. (The polarity of the Geiger tube may be reversed depending on the direction of the windings of the transformer.) The counter will give a background of from 20 to 25 counts per minute and will respond to relatively low levels of beta and gamma radiation and cosmic rays.

Absorption of gamma radiation.[6] The metal slide-tube on a standard Geiger probe absorbs beta and alpha radiations but has negligible effect upon gamma radiation. Lead, however, is used as a gamma absorber in many laboratories to protect personnel. To demonstrate this and to show the dependence of absorption on the thickness of lead used, obtain a gamma source (such as I^{131}, or a gamma-source button) and at least 6 sheets of lead

[5] From *Planet Earth,* a book of experiments by A. Joseph, published in 1958 by the National Academy of Sciences.

[6] Adapted from *Laboratory Experiments with Radio Isotopes, for High School Demonstration,* Samuel Schenberg, editor, sponsored by the Atomic Energy Commission, available from the Superintendent of Documents, Washington, D.C.

measuring about 1/32″ in thickness. Support the Geiger probe in a ring stand clamp and place the gamma source far enough away to obtain a background count. Adjust the meter sensitivity so that the background count is small. Now bring the gamma source close to the probe so that a high meter reading is obtained. Note the reading and then insert one lead plate after the other between the source and probe. Each plate will reduce the count significantly; if these are recorded, it will be found that the reduction in count varies almost linearly with the thickness of interposed lead.

Inverse-square law.[7] Since gamma radiations are electromagnetic in nature, students should be able to extrapolate the inverse-square law for visible light to include these. The validity of the inverse-square law as applied to gamma radiation may be dramatically shown by setting up the following apparatus.

Set up a ring stand, clamp, and ring so that a Geiger-Müller probe is held in the clamp above the ring on which a gamma-source button is placed. The probe should be horizontal with its shield closed. Set the ring so that the gamma-source button is exactly 4 cm below the probe and determine the average counts per minute from the Geiger counter rate meter. Increase the separation between probe and button to 5 cm and record the new average count per minute. Repeat this procedure, in steps of 1-cm separation, until the distance reaches 17 cm.

Now plot a curve in which the separation is given on the x-axis and the counts per minute on the y-axis. Using the same axes, plot a similar curve for the theoretical decline of activity on the basis of the

inverse-square law. The curve obtained from the measured values will be found to approximate the theoretical curve very closely.

X-ray absorption. A large, three-element tube such as a 203 or 811A can serve as a fairly safe source of x-rays. The dealer who sells the tube will identify the electrode connecting pins and will also provide a tube socket to fit. The socket should be steatite or isolantite to prevent arcing.

Connect the grid and plate terminals together with a jumper right at the socket. Supply the filament with the correct voltage as specified by the tube manufacturer from either a transformer or a storage bat-

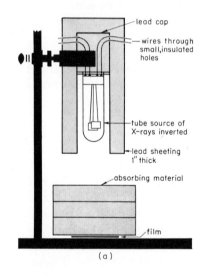

(a)

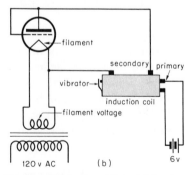

(b)

Fig. 23–12 X-ray absorption: (a) lead encased x-ray source, (b) circuit.

[7] Adapted from *Laboratory Experiments with Radio Isotopes, for High School Demonstration,* Samuel Schenberg, editor, sponsored by the Atomic Energy Commission, available from the Superintendent of Documents, Washington, D.C.

tery. Before making external connections to the tube, form a 1″ thick lead casing around the glass by wrapping sheet lead around it until the required thickness is obtained; cap the top of the case by the same lead thickness. Alternatively, the casing can be cast in plaster of Paris. In any case, it should be leak-tight with respect to radiation. This can be checked by holding it up to a strong light to detect spaces or openings. When complete, the case should be closed on all sides save one; the plate-grid assembly should be facing an open end as in the drawing (Fig. 23-12A).

Wire the tube as shown in Fig. 23-12B. Support the case with a clamp and stand well above the table. Place a piece of photographic film wrapped in aluminum foil under the opening in the case. All connections to the induction coil should be made with high-tension ignition cable.

Using a ten-minute exposure on different pieces of film, try absorbing the x-rays with bricks, slabs of concrete, lead, books, etc. Make your developer and developing time the same for all the films so that the time factor is constant. Have your students arrive at a reasonable conclusion concerning the effectiveness of various x-ray shielding materials.

Plotting the half-life of isotopes. Some school systems have arrangements for getting isotopes like I-131 and P-32 in safe doses and quantities through the AEC. The AEC assigns some local hospital doing isotope work to act as a dispensing agent. Specific precautions must be observed. Place some of the radioactive material into a shallow glass container and bring the probe or counter tube over it at a fixed distance. Take readings daily at exactly the same place and maintain the same distance between isotope and probe. Students can plot the results for two weeks and determine which has a half-life of

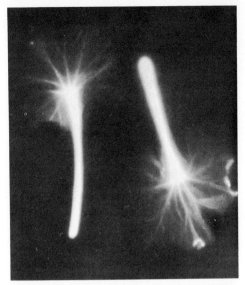

Fig. 23–13 Radioautograph of leaf of Coleus plant from radioactive phosphorus-32 taken up by the plant. (Janita Russo.)

about 8 days and which has a half-life of about 14 days.

23.1i   Radioautographs

If a 10-microcurie dose of radioactive phosphorus P-32 is available from local sources through the AEC, you may want to place a tomato plant seedling in water to which the radio-phosphorus has been added. After some two to five days, remove one leaf and place it against a piece of dental x-ray film or against a piece of Tri-X or Royal Pan film that has been covered with thin lightproof black paper. When this is developed a week or so later, you may get a picture similar to the one in Fig. 23-13.

Or students can use fresh cuttings of plants that have been standing in a water solution of uranium nitrate (uranyl nitrate). How long does it take for the solution to reach the leaves?

Radioautographs of animal bones can be prepared by feeding small doses of P-32 in water. A small animal like a mouse can be treated this way for a week. If the mouse is sacrificed, the bones can be radioautographed.

Explicit details for preparing radioautographs are available in textbooks such as Kamen's.[8] A series of teaching activities and an excellent listing of films and the literature can be found in *Nuclear Science Teaching Aids and Activities* by John Woodburn, Dept. of Health, Education and Welfare, Office of Education, Washington 25, D.C., 1959. Another carefully detailed source is *Teaching with Radioisotopes,* edited by H. Miner, R. Shackleton, and F. Watson, U.S. Atomic Energy Commission, Washington, D.C., 1959.

Pictures by radiations. If a metal key is placed on Super-X film and is then covered with uranium ore for a week, when the film is developed a week or so later a white image of the key is revealed surrounded by a black area that has been exposed to the radiations.

Next repeat the procedure, using radioactive thorium from a Coleman gasoline lantern mantle (obtainable in large hardware stores or from a large mail order house). If an old gaslight mantle is available, it will serve well. Again place the key on Super-X film and cover with a piece of the cut-up mantle so that it almost completely covers the key and film. Develop after a week and make prints. In addition to the shape of the key, students will also be able to make out the weave of the fibers of the mantle which is impregnated with thorium oxide at the factory. A piece of uranium ore or the mantle alone will also give an excellent radioautograph.

[8] Martin D. Kamen, *Isotopic Tracers in Biology: An Introduction to Tracer Methodology,* 3rd rev. ed., Academic, 1957.

23.2 Solar energy

Many scientists believe that solar energy will be the ultimate source of energy after fossil fuels are exhausted. Some scientists think that the hydrogen fusion reaction can be harnessed to do man's work. In that event the heavy hydrogen in sea water could provide an almost endless reservoir of "fuel."

When live green plants convert sunlight into chemical energy in photosynthesis, the conversion efficiency is less than one per cent. Recently solar batteries have been made which have efficiencies as high as 12 per cent. These are used to supply power. Small country telephone exchanges use these solar batteries during daylight hours to charge small storage batteries which, in turn, provide power during darkness.

You can demonstrate the conversion of the energy "photons" in sunlight to the energy of electrons in motion by connecting a *photogenerative* cell to a galvanometer or low-range milliammeter. Be sure to use the type of cell that produces its own voltage (selenium barrier or silicon) rather than a photoconductive type of cell such as cadmium sulfide or cadmium selenide.

Miniature motors can be operated with a group of eight cells, 1″ in diameter. Enough power can be developed to move a small model automobile or turn a very small fan.

Small transistor radios can be operated on a group of nine solar batteries arranged in series. It will be necessary to check that the total voltage of the cells in series equals the voltage of the transistor battery (usually 9 volts). Kits for solar battery-operated transistor radios are also available from supply houses.

CAPSULE LESSONS

Ways to get started in class

23-1. Begin by measuring the radioactivity of uranium salts, radioactive isotopes, and a radium watch dial by bringing each near the probe of a Geiger counter. Two weeks in advance of this lesson, have a student place a radium watch dial against photographic film in a light-proof paper wrapper. Develop the film to see the exposure caused by the gamma rays given off by the disintegration of radium. Guide the discussion into the kinds of particles given off by radioactive materials, or into the rich areas of measuring the kinds of radiations. (Refer to the demonstrations in this chapter.)

23-2. Show other kinds of radiation—cathode-tube radiations and the effect of a magnet on the beam. Develop some of the basic understandings related to measurement of mass of particles—the work of Thomson and of Rutherford.

23-3. What are the kinds of radiations that are emitted from radioactive materials? Develop a discussion using one of the many pamphlets (see listing of free and inexpensive materials) that describes means for protection against radiation.

23-4. In a darkened room, have students use a spinthariscope to examine the scintillations of radioactive paints. Develop the notion of radioactive decay and half-life.

23-5. If possible, use a student-made Geiger counter (described in this chapter) to compare the room background count, a radium watch dial, carnotite ore sample, uranium nitrate or uranium acetate, and a gasoline lamp mantle which contains thorium oxide. Develop the notion of energy transformation.

23-6. Have students use models of atoms showing neutrons, protons, and shells of electrons. Develop the changes that occur in atomic number and atomic weight in transmutation processes.

23-7. Some teachers often repeat some classic experiment—possibly one of Thomson or Rutherford—and have students reconstruct the reasoning that resulted from their original observations and data. Abstracts from their papers can be mimeographed for the class.

23-8. A group of students can build a wooden model of an atomic pile using black wood as graphite, aluminum painted dowel sticks as uranium fuel rods, and grey dowel sticks placed between the other rods to represent control rods. They can use the model in reporting to the class on the operation of the pile. Develop the notions of critical mass, slowing down of neutrons, and neutron absorption as a means for controlling a chain reaction.

23-9. Demonstrate the idea of a chain reaction by using matches or a series of mousetraps. Have students explain the steps in this analogy.

23-10. In one lesson students can use a filmstrip such as *Atoms As You Will Use Them* (Harcourt, Brace) or *Atomic Physics* (5 fs in series, United World), or the film *What Makes Atoms Stick?* (Indiana U.). Develop the peacetime uses of nuclear energy in industry, medicine, and biological research.

23-11. A committee of students can arrange an effective display for a hall case or for the library using illustrations from magazines and free materials.

23-12. Develop a discussion comparing the uranium or plutonium bomb with the hydrogen bomb. What is the difference between fission and fusion? Which kinds of atoms undergo each kind of process? What is meant by radioactive fallout? What is a clean bomb?

23-13. You may want to develop a reading for class. A section from Glasstone's *Sourcebook on Atomic Energy,* or the story of the building of the first atomic pile, or a report of a major discovery (work of Bohr, Fermi, or others), or a reprint of Edward Teller's *The Work of Many People* makes exciting reading for some classes. You may want to add questions, based on the reading, to test students' ability to interpret what they have read. There is much need for an appreciation of the creative work in this area.

PEOPLE, PLACES, AND THINGS

This area of physics is developing rapidly. A local geologist or mining engineer may describe to the class the process of locating and mining uranium ore. The Atomic Energy Commission has films and booklets of demonstrations with radioactive materials and also has set up a procedure whereby schools may procure some of these materials. Check with a nearby college or university physics department on what you may borrow (special apparatus, isotopes, sample ores, and so forth).

BOOKS AND PAMPHLETS

These are only a few of the books which are pertinent to the work discussed in this chapter. These and many other references classified by subject and with complete bibliographical data are given in the bibliography at the end of the book.

Ambartsumyan, V. A., ed., *Theoretical Astrophysics,* Pergamon, 1958.

Birks, J., *Scintillation Counters,* Pergamon, 1960.

Cable, E., R. Getchell, and W. Kadesch, *The Physical Sciences,* 3rd ed., Prentice Hall, 1957.

Condon, E., and H. Odishaw, eds., *Handbook of Physics,* McGraw-Hill, 1958.

Cork, J., *Radioactivity and Nuclear Physics,* 3rd ed., Van Nostrand, 1957.

Curtiss, L., *Introduction to Neutron Physics,* Van Nostrand, 1959.

Eisenbud, L., and E. Wigner, *Nuclear Structure,* Princeton U. Press, 1958.

Elton, L. R., *Introductory Nuclear Theory,* Interscience, 1959.

Faro, U., and L. Faro, *Basic Physics of Atoms and Molecules,* Wiley, 1959.

Glasstone, S., *Sourcebook on Atomic Energy,* Van Nostrand, 1955.

Harwood, J., H. Hausner, J. Morse, and W. Rauch, eds., *The Effects of Radiation on Materials,* Reinhold, 1958.

Hoag, J. B., ed., *Nuclear Reactor Experiments,* Van Nostrand, 1958.

Hooper, J., and M. Scharff, *The Cosmic Radiation,* Wiley, 1958.

Hughes, D., *The Neutron Story,* Doubleday, 1959.

Jelley, J., *Cerenkov Radiation and Its Applications,* Pergamon, 1958.

Rusk, R., *Introduction to Atomic and Nuclear Physics,* Appleton-Century-Crofts, 1958.

Scientific American, "Progress in Solar Power," July, 1956; "Atomic Clocks," Feb., 1957; "Discovery of Fission," Feb., 1958; "Anti-Matter," April, 1958; "Overthrow of Parity," April, 1957; "Ionizing Radiation," Sept., 1959.

Semat, H., *Introduction to Atomic and Nuclear Physics,* Rinehart, 1954.

Thiel, R., *And There Was Light: The Discovery of the Universe,* transl. R. and C. Winston, Knopf, 1957.

Wilson, R., and R. Littauer, *Accelerators,* Doubleday, 1960.

Woodburn, J., "Low-level Radioisotope Techniques," *Science Teacher,* Nov., 1960.

Young, M. E., *Radiological Physics,* Academic Press, 1957.

FILMS AND FILMSTRIPS

This partial list is intended only as a guide toward film and filmstrip selection. Refer to the more complete listing at the end of the book where films are classified by subject and where a key to abbreviations and addresses of distributors are given. The cost of film rental, of course, is subject to change. Films are sound and black and white unless otherwise specified.

Atom and Industry (f, s), N.Y. State Dept. Commerce, free.

Atomic Alchemist (f, s); *Atomic Energy* (f, s); *Agriculture, Industry and Power* (f, s); *Atom Smashers* (f, s), U.S.A.E.C., free.

Atomic Detective (fs, c), Popular Science, 1960, $6.00.

Atomic Physics (f, s, series 9 lessons), EBF, inquire rental.

Atomic Physics (fs, 5 in series), United World, $3.00 each.

Atomic Radiation (f, s), Ideal, $2.00.

Atom Goes to Sea (f, s), General Electric, free.

Bell Solar Battery (f, s, c), Bell Telephone Co., free.

Beyond Uranium (f, s), Indiana U., $5.25.

Cosmic Ray Studies (f, s), Indiana U., $3.00.

Discovery of Radium (f in series *You Are There*), Young America, inquire rental local film library.

Energy From the Sun (f, s), EBF, inquire rental.

Madame Curie (MGM, 2 rls, f, s), Teaching Film Custodians, free.

Medical Aspects of Nuclear Radiations (f, s), Dept. Army, free.

Neutron Story (fs, c), Popular Science, 1960, $6.00.

Nuclear Physics (f, s, 7 lessons in series), EBF, inquire rental.

Our Mr. Sun: The Case of the Cosmic Rays (2 f, s, c), Bell Telephone, free.

Radium (f, s), Institutional Cinema, $2.00.

Taking the X Out of X-rays (f, s), General Electric, free.

What Makes Atoms Stick? (f, s), Indiana U., $4.75.

Why Are Atoms Unpredictable? (f, s), Indiana U., $4.75.

FREE AND INEXPENSIVE MATERIALS

This is only a partial listing of free and inexpensive materials available to the teacher at this time. A directory of addresses is given at the end of the book. Many of these materials are distributed to teachers without charge. Where there is a small fee, the cost is indicated, although the prices are subject to change. While we recommend the material for use in the classroom, we do not necessarily endorse the products advertised.

Atom In Your Hand, Union Carbide.

101 Atomic Terms, Esso.

Atomic Energy How?, What?, Why?, Consolidated Edison, N.Y.

Atomic Energy and the Physical Sciences, U.S.A.E.C., $.50.

The Atomic Revolution, General Dynamics, inquire cost of class sets.

Atoms to Kilowatts, Commonwealth Edison Co.

Atomic Revolution, General Dynamics Corp., inquire cost for quantity orders.

Birth and Death of the Sun, G. Gamow, Mentor, 1952, $.50.

Chart of the Nuclides (26″ x 50″) and booklet, General Electric.

A collection of papers from the *Journal of Chemical Education* related to radioactivity, Nuclear-Chicago Corp., branch offices.

Electromagnetic Spectrum (wall chart, color), Westinghouse, $2.00.

The First Pile, ed. by C. Allardice and E. Trapnell, Technical Information Division, Oak Ridge, Tenn., U.S. Atomic Energy Commission, 1959.

"How a Nuclear Power Plant Operates," *Oil Power,* vol. 60:2, Socony Mobil.

Indian Point Atomic Power Plant, Consolidated Edison, New York.

Inside the Atom, General Electric.

Laboratory Experiments with Radioisotopes, S. Schenberg, ed., U.S. Govt. Printing Office, 1958, $.35.

Major Activities in Atomic Energy Programs, Semi-Annual Report of Atomic Energy Commission.

Nuclear Physics Charts (set of 6 wall charts in 2 colors), Westinghouse, $1.00 set.

Pathological Effects of Atomic Radiation, National Acad. Sciences, $1.00.

Radio Isotopes in Science and Industry, special report of U.S. Atomic Energy Commission, 1960.

Story of the Bell Solar Battery, Bell Telephone.

Teaching with Radioisotopes, ed. by H. Miner, R. Shackleton, and F. Watson, U.S. Atomic Energy Commission, 1959. Obtainable from U.S. Govt. Printing Office, $.40.

The Universe and Dr. Einstein, L. Barnett, Mentor, 1952, $.35.

The Work of Many People (reprint), E. Teller, W. M. Welch Scientific Co.

You Can Understand the Atom, Atomic Energy Commission.

CHAPTER 24

Engines: automobiles,

airplanes, and rockets

Many students are very deeply interested in the mechanics of the automobile, airplane, and rocket engine. Many applications of physical theory are used in these engines: in fact a large part of the course in physics (and chemistry) might be taught around these methods of transportation.

Some engine parts are available for little or no cost; students working as garage mechanics often can bring parts to class for study on a loan basis. Some of these parts can be operated as working models in class.

We shall suggest in this chapter demonstrations for the study of these three engine types; demonstrations on the basic principles of internal-combustion engines are described in Chapter 18. The chemistry of the storage battery is given in Chapter 13, Electrochemistry.

24.1   Automobile

24.1a   A complete automobile engine

Overhead-valve engines are preferable to internal-valve engines for class demonstrations because the operating parts are more easily visible.

If fire regulations permit and certain precautions are observed, an engine can be run in the laboratory or classroom. The engine should be firmly mounted, and the exhaust should be carried out through a flexible pipe to the outside of the building. (*Caution: Work in a well-ventilated room and have a fire extinguisher on hand.*) Some teachers prefer to keep a mounted engine out-of-doors under a cover that can be locked when the engine is not in use.

Students can see the effect of changing the air-fuel ratio of the mixture by adjusting the mixture control on the carburetor when the engine is running. You can also attach an airplane manifold pressure gauge to the intake manifold of the engine; a J-tube barometer can be used as a manifold pressure gauge if it is connected to the intake manifold (Fig. 24-1). Most engines have such a connection, often used to operate the windshield wipers.

The thistle tube of the barometer is fitted with a one-hole stopper and a delivery tube. Rubber tubing connects the delivery tube to the intake manifold. If the manifold has no connection, a hole can be drilled and threaded to receive a 1/8″ pipe nipple. Then, if the engine is tuned correctly, the manifold pressure gauge will read more than 15″ of mercury. If the mixture is made too thin or too rich, the manifold pressure will drop. If you oper-

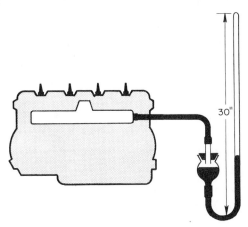

Fig. 24–1 A J-tube barometer connected to the intake manifold of an engine.

ate the engine with one spark-plug wire disconnected, as if one cylinder were not firing, the manifold pressure will also drop.

The pressure developed by compression in the engine cylinder can also be measured with a compression gauge (0 to 150 pounds per square inch range) borrowed from an automobile garage. Fit a one-hole rubber stopper over the connection of the gauge (Fig. 24-2). Remove one spark plug and measure the pressure developed during the compression stroke. With the ignition off, turn the engine over with the starter; at the same time hold the rubber stopper on the stem of the gauge against the spark plug hole and note the maximum reading. An engine that is in good working order will read 120 psi or more. If the compression is less than 90 psi, check whether the valves need grinding or the piston rings are worn.

Use a flashlight to have students observe the position of the piston through the spark-plug hole. Another way to illuminate the interior of the cylinder is to lower through the spark-plug hole a small bulb connected to a battery. If a small enough socket is not available, two thin wires may be soldered to the base of the bulb. The piston is at its highest position (top dead center) at the moment of the maximum compression reading on the gauge.

If the engine has overhead valves, the effect of the proper setting upon manifold pressure can be detected. Simply change the valve adjustment on top with a wrench and note the change in maximum pressure. A thin feeler gauge may be used to show the small space between the rocker arms and valve stems.

24.1b *Transmission*

Standard transmission. Remove the top cover of a standard transmission and shift the gears by applying a steel bar or large screwdriver to the linkage. If the transmission is removed from the car, it can be turned with a crank. An arrow attached to the output shaft will indicate the different speed ratios with each of the gears (Fig. 24-3). In low gear, the output shaft will turn very slowly; in high gear, it will turn at about the same speed as the crank; in second gear, it will turn at about half the speed of the crank; in reverse, the output turns in the opposite direction and at about the same speed as in low gear.

Automatic transmission. The principle of fluid drive, utilized in most automatic transmissions, can be readily demonstrated. Place two identical well-oiled electric fans face to face. Turn on one of

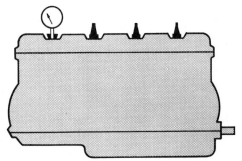

Fig. 24–2 Mounting a compression gauge in a spark plug hole.

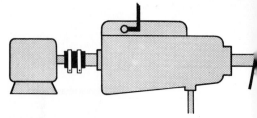

Fig. 24-4 Operating a simple automatic transmission with an electric motor.

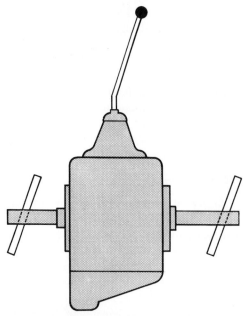

Fig. 24-3 Running steel bars through the input and output shafts of a standard transmission so that their relationship can be made visible at various gear ratios.

them; the other fan will also spin. In the fluid drive system, one set of blades sets a fluid (in this demonstration air is the fluid) into motion, and the fluid spins another set of blades. An old fluid-drive unit may be obtained from an automobile junkyard and opened in class.

Only the simplest automatic transmissions, those that operate electrically, can be demonstrated as independent units. These can be rotated by an automobile starter motor operated on a battery (Fig. 24-4). Battery current must also be supplied to the circuits of the transmission.

If a car with an automatic transmission is jacked up so that its rear wheels are off the ground and chocks or bricks are placed under the front wheels, the car can be operated (out-of-doors); as the engine is accelerated gradually, the transmission will shift automatically.

24.1c Differential

Obtain the rear end of an old automobile of the type that has a removable inspection plate. Cut short the drive shaft and drill a hole through it at a right angle; pass a steel bar through the hole to act as a handle (Fig. 24-5). Students can inspect the pinion, idler, and master gear in the rear end. Then have one student turn the handle attached to the drive shaft, while another student slows down one of the wheels by holding a blackboard eraser against it. Students can see the action of the differential. Completely stop one wheel and watch the other spin around the stationary gear. This shows how the inner and outer wheels can turn at different speeds, as they must in making a turn.

24.1d Cooling system

Use a parked automobile with the hood raised to point out the parts of the cooling system: radiator, water pump, thermostat housing, water jackets, and hoses. If you

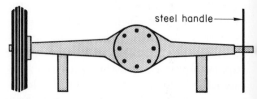
steel handle

Fig. 24-5 Using the rear end of an old automobile to show the effect of the differential by removing one wheel and passing a steel bar through the axle to act as a handle.

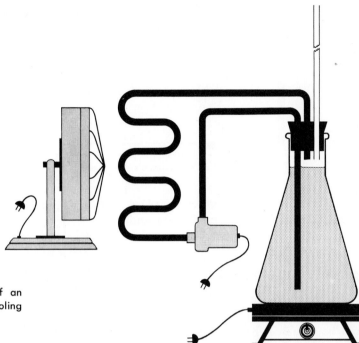

Fig. 24–6 Model of an automobile water-cooling system.

remove the radiator from an engine, run cold water into the water pump and drain the warm water out of the top hose connection into a sewer; measure the difference in temperature of the incoming and outgoing water with an ordinary laboratory thermometer.

In a car with the front grill removed and the engine running, you can show that the hottest water is in the top of the radiator by holding thermometers against the fins at the top and bottom of the radiator. Show the rapid increase in temperature that results if the fan belt slips or is removed. (*Caution: Do not make any changes with the engine running.*)

A model of the cooling system can be made by using copper tubing to make a radiator (Fig. 24-6). Pump water through the tubing from a flask of water equipped with a three-hole stopper and heated by an electric hot plate. Connect two of the stopper holes to the copper coil (one at each end) and the third to a small water pump. Arrange an electric fan to cool the copper coil. Students can compare the temperature of the water leaving and entering the copper coil radiator.

24.1e Electrical system

One way to demonstrate an automobile electrical system is to mount the parts on a large plywood board and use wires with insulation in different colors for each of the different circuits. The automobile generator can be operated directly by a ½ hp electrical motor that operates from a wall outlet (Fig. 24-7). Some teachers prefer to mount the units without any permanent wiring; they connect the wires as the different parts are demonstrated. In this case, the generator, voltage regulator, battery, and starter motor can be permanently connected. The starter motor should be wired with the same heavy-duty cables as those used in an automobile. Use a long

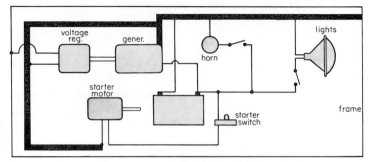

Fig. 24-7   The parts of an automobile's electrical system can be mounted on plywood.

strip of metal to serve as a ground in place of the frame of the car. Lamps, horns, and other parts can be obtained from an auto-bile that has been junked.

24.1f   *Ignition system*

The ignition system can be mounted on a $2' \times 2'$ plywood board and its current can be obtained from a storage battery. Mount horizontally an automobile distributor so that its shaft can be coupled to the shaft of a small electric motor (Fig. 24-8). Set up 6 or 8 spark plugs (depending on the type of distributor used) in a sheet-metal frame. You will also need an ignition coil and a 10- or 20-ohm rheostat. Show students how to use ignition wire to connect the distributor to the spark plugs. The metal frame holding the spark plugs returns to the ignition coil ground circuit. The distributor and coil are also connected to the battery circuit. Now slowly rotate the distributor by hand so that students can observe the individual firing of each spark plug. If you connect a small neon glow lamp across each spark plug, the firing is easier to see. You can demonstrate most of the types of ignition trouble. If water is sprayed inside the distributor cap, the plugs will not fire. Place a defective ignition coil into the circuit, a defective capacitor, or worn points in the distributor, and note the results.

24.2   Airplane

24.2a   *Lift*

At this point you will probably want students to repeat one or more of the demonstrations of the Bernoulli effect described in 16.4c. Students will also want to try a simple demonstration of airfoils.

Simple airfoils. Fold a sheet of paper at one end and hold it under the chin; blow across the top and watch the paper rise (Fig. 24-9). Another simple airfoil can be made from a manila folder which has one

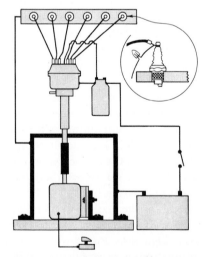

Fig. 24-8   Automotive ignition system. The distributor shaft is coupled to a small electric motor. The upper right shows a spark plug with a neon glow lamp to signal firing.

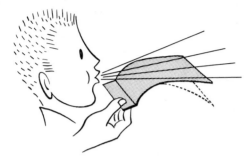

Fig. 24–9 Bernoulli effect.

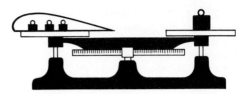

Fig. 24-10 Measuring lift when a stream of air passes over an air foil.

half curved as shown in Fig. 24-10. Place this on a balance platform with weights and blow across the sheet. Students can see that the platform rises, indicating the "lift" action of the paper airfoil. Students can diagram the "lines" around the airfoil that indicate the path of air.

Airflow over a wing. In this demonstration an attempt is made to visualize the airflow over a wing. You can prepare a condensed cloud from dry ice in hot water in this way. Fit a 1-liter Erlenmeyer flask with a one-hole stopper that contains a right-angle delivery tube. Place hot water and dry ice into the bottle and stopper it (Fig. 24-11). (*Caution: Avoid handling dry ice; use gloves or tongs.*) Direct the steam of condensed cloud emerging from the tube at an airfoil. Students should be able to track the path and shape of the airflow over the

wing or other aerodynamic shape.

Streamlining. Students can use the dry-ice and hot-water generator to direct a cloud at streamlined shapes and at irregularly shaped surfaces to show the breaking away of airflow from nonstreamlined bodies. Airflow can be shown on a large scale by placing the demonstration in the space in front of the carrier of a large lantern slide projector, bellows removed, as in Fig. 24-11. Focus the lens; have students describe their observations.

Shock waves. Shock waves can be shown by analogy using the dry-ice and hot-water cloud generator. Prepare knife-edge wing sections as in Fig. 24-11, and direct the cloud stream at a knife edge in front of the slide carrier of a projector. As the edge is tipped up, a distinct separation of layers of air is projected on the screen.

24.2b Classroom wind tunnel

A model wind tunnel is a basic instrument for demonstrating principles of aero-

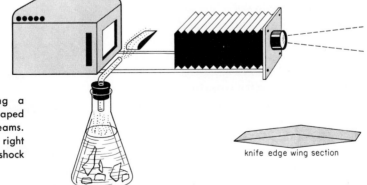

Fig. **24-11** Directing a cloud over variously shaped objects to study air streams. The shape in the lower right is used to demonstrate shock waves.

knife edge wing section

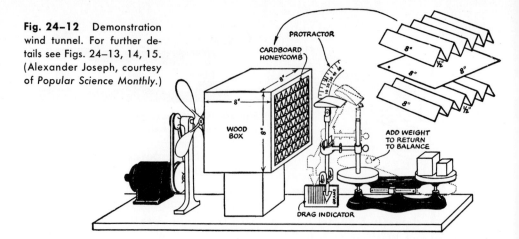

Fig. 24–12 Demonstration wind tunnel. For further details see Figs. 24–13, 14, 15. (Alexander Joseph, courtesy of *Popular Science Monthly*.)

dynamics. An electric fan, a square carton, some manila folders, and a platform balance provide the basic materials for making a classroom demonstration wind tunnel. Shape the manila folders into accordian pleats as shown in Fig. 24-12. Fill a cardboard carton (cross-section diameter $9'' \times 9''$) with layers of the pleated folders and glue them in place. (The drag indicator in Fig. 24-12 is described below.) The pleated folders break up the whirling air from the fan into less widespread disturbances, thereby minimizing the turbulence effects. Without the folders this equipment will not work properly.

A balance is needed to measure forces on the model wings that are to be tested in the demonstration. Cover each pan of the balance with a layer of wood about 2″ thick; drill a hole in the center of the wood cover for the left-hand pan and insert a wood dowel. The wings to be tested are attached to the dowel by means of a thumb screw (Fig. 24-13).

Measuring lift in the wind tunnel. Place the balance in front of the tunnel and set the fan in motion so that students can see the wing lift. Quantitative measurements can be made by counterbalancing the wing and dowel with weights that are placed on the right-hand pan. Turn on the fan and add weights to the left-hand pan until the lift produced on the wing is balanced. Change the angle of attack of the wing so that students can see and record the change in lift force. Test different shapes of wings. Find the lift per square inch; calculate the area of the model wing and divide this into the measured lift.

Measuring drag in the wind tunnel. A drag balance can be added to the wind tunnel. This is constructed by using a burette clamp as a pivot center. The pivot is a V-notch filed into the opposite sides of the burette clamp as in Fig. 24-14. A dowel carrying a single edge razor blade hangs in the V-notch with the cutting edge of the blade centered in the V-notch.

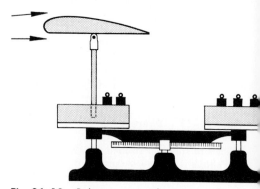

Fig. 24–13 Balance prepared to measure forces on model wings.

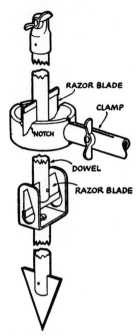

Fig. 24–14 Special balance to indicate drag. (From *The Science of Pre-flight Aeronautics for High Schools*, Macmillan, 1942.)

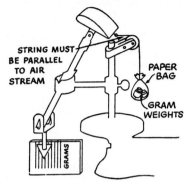

Fig. 24–15 Calibrating the drag indicator. (From *The Science of Pre-flight Aeronautics for High Schools*, Macmillan, 1942.)

Wings are attached to the top of the dowel and a pointer made of cardboard or aluminum and pivoted on a razor edge is attached to the bottom of the dowel. Support the burette clamp on a ring stand. Then calibrate the drag balance in grams as follows. Attach a string and a pulley to the top of the dowel and add small known gram weights to measure the force needed to displace the dowel any given distance (Fig. 24-15). Mark the position of the pointer on a cardboard scale as shown. Test the drag by mounting a wing section or model on the dowel and turning on the fan. As the angle of attack of the wing increases, the drag increases. If the fan speed can be doubled, the drag force will be squared. Drag and lift can be tested not only for wing sections but for whole airplane models.

Measuring air speed in the wind tunnel.
Make a simple air speed indicator from a hinged sheet of thin aluminum (see 3.5b). It can be calibrated before being used in the wind tunnel by holding it out of a car window as you drive in still air; students can record the angular displacement of the sheet as the car is driven at 5, 10, 15, and more miles per hour. This can then be used in a model wind tunnel to measure the air speed produced by the fan.

Or you can make a more accurate Pitot-Static tube air speed indicator. Bend a length of ¼″ glass tubing to the shape shown in Fig. 24-16, and half fill the U-tube portion with water and red ink.

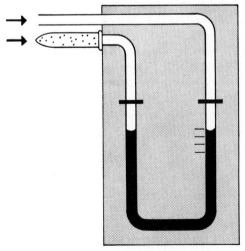

Fig. 24–16 Pitot-Static air speed indicator.

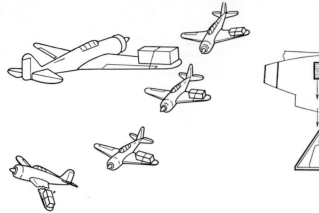

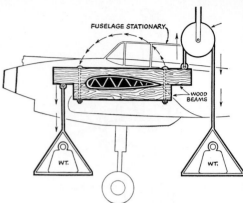

Fig. 24-17 Showing the effects of increasing the stress on a wing. (From *The Science of Pre-flight Aeronautics for High Schools,* Macmillan, 1942.)

Fig. 24-18 Applying torsional forces to a wing. (From *The Science of Pre-flight Aeronautics for High Schools,* Macmillan, 1942.)

Leave the upper tube open and cover the lower tube with a pencil cap that has tiny holes drilled into its sides. Calibrate the instrument on a windless day by riding in an automobile with the device headed into the direction of motion.

24.2c Stress on flying planes

Gravitational. The effect of increasing G's upon a wing can be demonstrated easily and dramatically. An expendable airplane model with built-up wings serves as the test model. Attach a weight to one wing with cellophane tape and move the airplane through the air, by hand, in level flight position. All is well, nothing happens. Now put the model into a dive and then into a sudden recovery. Students can see the loaded wing snap off (Fig. 24-17). In level flight the load was one G, a force that the wing could withstand; during the pull-out, however, the dynamic load was several G's, a force greater than the structural strength of the model wing.

Torsional forces. Gusts and sudden changes in flight attitude produce twisting or torsional forces on a wing. Students can measure quantitatively the ability of a

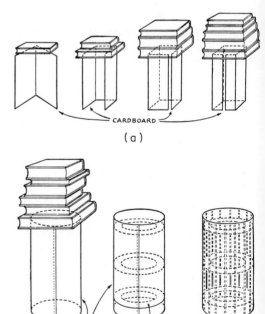

Fig. 24-19 Distributing stress: (a) the more corners in the cardboard, the more weight it can carry; (b) model of "stressed" skin construction. (From *The Science of Pre-flight Aeronautics for High Schools,* Macmillan, 1942.)

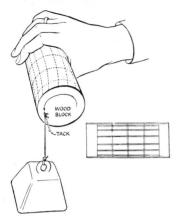

Fig. 24-20 Torsional forces applied to a model of "stressed" skin construction. (From *The Science of Pre-flight Aeronautics for High Schools*, Macmillan, 1942.)

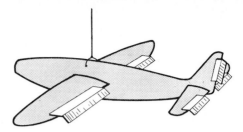

Fig. 24-21 Model airplane with control surfaces made of pieces of index card.

model airplane to withstand these forces. Cut a jig from wood to fit around the wing (Fig. 24-18). Hang weights on the jig; notice that one set of weights is attached to a string that passes over a pulley. Use different weights so that the torsional force applied to the model is varied; then determine its breaking point.

"Stressed" construction. The principle of distributing stress can be shown as in Fig. 24-19A. The great strength built into lightweight "stressed" skin airplanes can be demonstrated by assembling the center of a fuselage section in the form of a cylinder. Prepare thin cardboard or balsa rings about 3″ in diameter, cut notches in the rings (Fig. 24-19B), and cement thin wooden medical swabs into position. Cover the cylinder with strong paper and cement the sticks (called stringers) and rings to the paper. When the assembly is dry, try it on end with books as weights. Test its ability to stand torsion by hanging weights on it from a wooden disk set in one end of the cylinder. To balance the stress a similar disk should be set into the other end (Fig. 24-20). The model should withstand great forces because the skin

distributes these forces over the entire model. Students can compare this with a model prepared without this "skin."

24.2d Controlling airplanes

Demonstrating control of surface reactions. It may be possible to have students demonstrate a model airplane, which is controlled from the ground by lines. They can show the action of the elevator control by hand operation.

Fit a solid model airplane with a control surface made of pieces of index card as shown in Fig. 24-21. Tabs on the horizontal tail serve as elevators, on the vertical tail as the rudder, and on the rear of the wings as ailerons. If these controls are bent as indicated and the model is suspended from a string, the action of each control surface can be shown by blowing air across the model.

24.3 Rockets

You will want to have students review Newton's third law (17.2c) to understand the principle of rockets.

24.3a Measuring thrust

A carbon dioxide cartridge can be used to measure thrust. Drill a hole in the center of a block of wood about 3″ × 3″ × 2″ in such a way that it will snugly hold a carbon dioxide cartridge. Attach four wires, one to each corner of the block, and

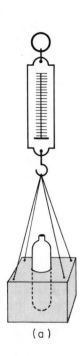

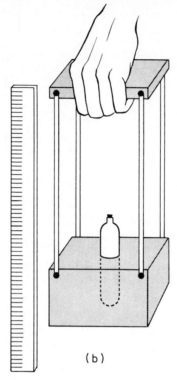

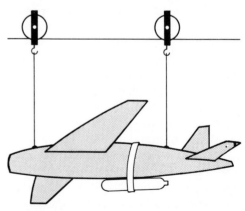

(a) (b)

Fig. 24-22 Measuring the thrust generated by a CO_2 cartridge: (a) using a spring scale, (b) using rubber bands (elastics) and a ruler.

connect them to a spring balance (Fig. 24-22A). Place the cartridge in the hole, with the neck pointing upward. Release the carbon dioxide cartridge with the "gun" so that students can read the amount of thrust indicated on the spring balance during the escape of the jet of carbon dioxide. Now subtract the weight of the wood block and cartridge from the total reading to get the corrected thrust. In Fig. 24-22B, the two wooden squares are connected by heavy rubber bands or elastics. Stretch induced by the CO_2 is measured with a ruler.

24.3b Jet-propelled models

Carbon dioxide jet plane. A demonstration model jet plane can be propelled across the classroom at high speed. Suspend a solid model airplane or glider from two pulleys on a wire as in Fig. 24-23 and tape a carbon dioxide cartridge to the fuselage. At the other end hang a pillow or some other shock-absorbing material in case the model builds up considerable speed by the end of its run. When the cartridge gas is released, watch the model shoot across the room. In which direction does the plane move? When students fol-

Fig. 24-23 A CO_2-propelled jet plane.

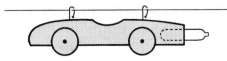

Fig. 24–24 A jet model that uses CO_2.

low the trail of condensed moisture produced by escaping gas, they can develop an understanding of the thrust produced by the expanding gas, according to Newton's law of action and reaction.

Carbon dioxide jet racing car. A group of students can make a lightweight streamlined model automobile from a block of balsa wood and attach lightweight wooden wheels that spin freely on axles made from small nails. In the rear center of the body of the car drill a hole to hold a carbon dioxide cartridge (Fig. 24-24A). Place two bent pins into the top of the car and run a long thin but strong thread or string the length of the hallway or the gymnasium. At the end lay a pillow on the floor as a shock absorber. Pass this string under the pins to serve as a guide. When the cartridge is released, the model can attain speeds as high as 60 miles per hour. Several models can be raced simultaneously, using parallel sets of strings as guides.

Carbon dioxide jet rocket ship. A balsa wood block can be shaped into the form of a rocket with a hole drilled in it to carry a carbon dioxide cartridge. Two screw eyes on the rocket (Fig. 24-24B) hold it on a long wire stretched the length of a gymnasium or long hall. At the end suspend a pillow as shock absorber. When students release the cartridge, the model rocket will skim along under the wire at speeds approaching 60 miles per hour. The escaping jet of gas will produce condensed moisture in the air.

Powder-propellant rocket. An inexpensive solid-fuel rocket motor (such as Jetexengine) can be purchased at a hobby shop. A chemical pellet is used as the propellant. (*Caution: The fuel is inflammable and should be operated out-of-doors.*) Attach this rocket motor to a model airplane that is suspended from a long horizontal wire, or you may prefer to attach it to a flying model. Fasten the engine just below the center of gravity of the airplane model. Then ignite the rocket by lighting a fuse.

Liquid-propellant jet. A commercial model jet engine called the Dyna-jet uses air and special gasoline fuel as the propellant. (*Caution: This must be operated out-of-doors and great care must be taken with the highly combustible fuel.*) A battery is needed for ignition and a source of compressed air is needed to start the jet engine. The engine may be difficult to start so that some preliminary testing and patience will be needed. A safe "rocket ship" which uses water under pressure as a propellant is available in many toy stores.

CAPSULE LESSONS
Ways to get started in class

24-1. Students will enjoy bringing planes to class to demonstrate kinds of aircraft and some principles of flight. They can also report on the history of aviation.

24-2. A club or committee of students might stage an "air show" on the school grounds where they can fly model planes driven by tiny gas engines in a circle tethered and controlled by U-lines. Have them show the effect of air speed changes, and the operation of the elevator.

24-3. It may be possible to plan a visit to a local airfield. If a student is taking flying lessons, he can explain how to control an airplane. You may want to invite a civilian or military pilot to explain the control, takeoff, and landing of an airplane. Perhaps an orientation flight can be organized for students. (Permission from your Board of Education and consent notes from parents are standard procedure for special work or field trips away from class.)

24-4. You may want to introduce the principle of action and reaction by having a student demonstrate a small Jetex toy motor attached to a model airplane. The model hangs from pulleys that ride on a wire stretched between two walls. Or have a pupil demonstrate a model racing car driven by a carbon dioxide cartridge as described in this chapter. A good model will attain speeds close to 60 miles an hour. Develop the principle of action and reaction and its application.

24-5. Begin by demonstrating a Hero engine made of glass or a homemade version such as described in Chapter 18 to show the principle of action and reaction. You may want to move ahead into a study of power or into principles underlying rocket flight.

24-6. Show a recent film that deals with combustion or the operation of a car. There are also filmstrips and films describing principles of rocketry. Have you used *ABC of Jet Propulsion* (General Motors), *Background of Rocketry* (Indiana U.), *Jet Propulsion* (General Electric), or *Introduction to Rocketry* (Indiana U.)?

24-7. Have students report on some basic problems that were conquered in getting a satellite into orbit. Students will be able to interrelate problems of chemistry and physics to give meaning to this area.

24-8. If possible begin by demonstrating a cutaway engine model. Students in the school shop may be able to cut away sections of the cylinder head, block, and crankcase of an engine to expose the moving parts. Apply storage battery current to the generator to turn the engine

slowly. Battery power can also be applied to the starter motor.

24-9. Students can demonstrate model gas, steam, and Diesel engines. Elicit comparisons among the kinds of engines as well as their special applications.

24-10. It may be possible to set up cutaway demonstrations of manual and automatic transmissions. Or have students mount a transmission without its case inside a plastic container.

24-11. Have a student prepare a report on the relative efficiency of different fuels used in internal-combustion engines.

24-12. If there is a steam power electric generating plant in your locality, you may want to arrange a visit to observe the steam turbines. If a model steam turbine is available, students can explain and operate it in class.

24-13. Have students set up a replica of the electrical system of an automobile. They can use second-hand parts operated by a storage battery.

24-14. Perhaps the class can visit an automobile repair shop or go to the school shop to observe the disassembly or assembly of an engine during a complete overhaul. Have students observe the timing adjustment and carburetor adjustment during the tune-up.

24-15. If possible take the class to visit an aircraft engine repair shop at a local airport. They may then be able to compare aircraft and automobile engines. Have them also compare the weight and the developed horsepower (brake horsepower) of each engine.

PEOPLE, PLACES, AND THINGS

Teachers have a responsibility to advise rocket enthusiasts and their parents about the dangers of assembling and launching rocket missiles. Solid propellants are probably the most dangerous, even for an expert. Every step is dangerous for an amateur; the average adult, whether teacher or parent, is generally not qualified to supervise these activities.

Many organized rocket groups over the country help young people design rockets. They stress the principles of physics, chemistry, meteorology, mathematics, space medicine, and ballistics.

The parents of persistent enthusiasts should be apprised of the legal liabilities and restrictions many states have imposed on the parents of minors.

Books and pamphlets

These are only a few of the books which are pertinent to the work discussed in this chapter. These and many other references classified by subject and with complete bibliographical data are given in the bibliography at the end of the book.

Blanchard, C., C. Burnett, R. Stoner, and R. Weber, *Introduction to Modern Physics*, Prentice-Hall, 1958.

Branley, F., *Experiments in the Principles of Space Travel*, Crowell, 1955.

Holton, G., and D. Roller, *Foundations of Modern Physical Science*, Addison-Wesley, 1958.

Richterweger, F., E. Kennard, and T. Lauritsen, *Introduction to Modern Physics,* 5th ed., Mc-Graw-Hill, 1955.

Ridenour, L., *Modern Physics for the Engineer,* Mc-Graw-Hill, 1954.

Schneider, L., and M. Ames, *Wings on Your Future,* Harcourt, Brace, 1955.

Scientific American, "Re-entry from Space," June, 1961; many other articles.

Yates, R., *Model Jets and Rockets for Boys,* Harper, 1952.

FILMS AND FILMSTRIPS

This partial list is intended only as a guide toward film and filmstrip selection. Refer to the more complete listing at the end of the book where films are classified by subject and where a key to abbreviations and addresses of distributors are given. The cost of film rental, of course, is subject to change. Films are sound and black and white unless otherwise specified.

ABC of Automobile Engine; ABC of Jet Propulsion (2 f, s, c), General Motors, free.

Aerodynamics: Forces Acting on an Airfoil (f, s), Indiana U., $3.50.

Airplane Series (10 f,s), M.I.T., free.

Animals in Rocket Flight (f, s), Dept. Air Force, free.

Automotive Mechanics (15 fs in 2 sets), McGraw-Hill, $6.00 each.

Earth Satellite (2 f in ser), Indiana U., $3.00 each.

Flight Into the Future (f, s), Bell Aircraft, free.

Fluid Dynamics (f, s, 4 rls), PSSC, Educational Services, Inc., $23.00.

Guided Missiles (f, s), Dept. Army, free.

Harnessed Lightning (turbojet engine) (f, s, c), General Motors, free.

History of the Helicopter (f, s), Shell, free.

How an Airplane Flies (ser 6 f, s), Shell, free.

Introductory to Rocketry (f, s), Indiana U., $3.00.

Jet Propulsion (f, s, c), Shell, free.

Jet Story (f, s), General Electric, free.

Large Forces Acting on the Body (f, s), Indiana U., $3.00.

Nike (f, s), Bell Telephone, free.

Power Within (internal-combustion engine) (f, s), U.S. Bur. of Mines, free.

Principle of the Generator (f, s), Institutional Cinema, $2.00.

Supersonic Flight (f, s, c), Shell, free.

Theory of Flight (f, s), EBF, $2.50.

Turbojets, Pulse Jets and Ramjets (f, s), Indiana U., $3.00.

FREE AND INEXPENSIVE MATERIALS

This is only a partial listing of free and inexpensive materials available to the teacher at this time. A directory of addresses is given at the end of the book. Many of these materials are distributed to teachers without charge. Where there is a small fee, the cost is indicated, although the prices are subject to change. While we recommend the material for use in the classroom, we do not necessarily endorse the products advertised.

Airplane Charts, United Air Lines.

Automobile Story (resource kit); *Chemical Problems of the Automobile; Diesel: the Modern Power; Short Stories of Science and Invention; Driver Training Kit; How the Wheels Revolve;* many other booklets and charts, General Motors.

"Earth Satellite" in *Oil Power,* vol. 57:4, Socony Mobil.

Frontiers of Space, California Inst. of Technology, $.65.

Life and Times of Leonardo Da Vinci, I.B.M.

Motors Make the World Go Round; Story of the Turbine; Man-Made Magic; Adventures on Jet Power, and others, General Electric.

Pan American World Airways Teacher, Pan American.

Rockets into Space, A. Joseph, Science Research Assoc., $.60.

Satellites, Rockets, and Outer Space, Willy Ley, Signet, $.50.

Science Book of Space Travel, H. Goodwin, Cardinal, $.35.

Smashing the Sound Barrier, R. Brinckerhoff, Science Research Assoc., $.60.

Space Handbook, staff report of congressional committee on astronautics and space exploration, U.S. Govt. Printing Office, inquire cost.

Space Primer, Convair Division, General Dynamics, San Diego, Cal., inquire cost for class sets.

Story of Combustion, Chrysler.

Story of the I.G.Y. and Earth Satellites, Esso.

Section Four TECHNIQUES AND TOOLS FOR THE TEACHER

CHAPTER 25

Skills and tools in the laboratory

Practical laboratory procedures for experimentation and handling apparatus are almost limitless. Many of these suggestions have been included within this book, whenever they seemed relevant or helpful. Of particular interest will be the making up of standard reagents (8.3c) and indicators (8.4f). For other references see the table of contents and the index.

In this section we shall describe such general techniques as working with glass and metal; improvising equipment.

25.1   Laboratory techniques
25.1a   *Transferring materials*

Measuring. There is a key point that students can learn in measurements of weight and volume: errors are minimized if a subtractive method is used. For instance, if students need a beaker containing 5 grams of salt, they could weigh out 5 grams of salt on the balance and transfer it to the beaker. But this leads to two distinct possibilities for error: some material can be lost in transfer, and the balance might be out of adjustment so that it may weigh heavy (or light) each time it is used. Both these sources of error can be eliminated by using a subtractive method. That is, weigh the beaker, then add a 5-gram weight to the balance pan. Add salt to the beaker until the balance is again even. With this procedure, any error in the balance will show up in both weighings, and cancel out.

The same procedure is useful for measurements of volume. For example, in using a burette, students can start with the liquid at some point below the zero mark, and record the level. Then draw out as much as required, and record the new level; subtracting gives the true volume of liquid removed, since any consistent errors in readings will cancel each other.

Liquids. When a liquid is poured from one container into another, a stirring rod should be inserted in such a manner that the liquid flows down the rod. Students will find that with practice this technique can be perfected to the point where hardly a drop is ever spilled.

When pouring from a labeled container (such as a reagent bottle), pour from the side opposite the label so that the liquid does not run down the label.

When the liquid to be transferred has been measured to contain a specific quantity of solute (and the dilution does not matter from then on), students can rinse the last bit of solution out of the original container with a wash bottle (see 25.2b.). Using two small quantities of rinse water is almost 10 times as effective as using one rinse equal in volume to the sum of the two.

Solids. Students should avoid pouring a small quantity of a solid from a stock bottle directly into another container. Instead, they should pour the amount they think they will need into a piece of clean paper; then make a V-trough on one side of the paper and pour the solid down this makeshift spout. (This is especially important in adding the material to a weighed beaker or flask on a balance.) Of course, the excess materials should not be returned to the reagent or stock bottle.

Another uniform laboratory procedure refers to prevention of contamination of stock chemicals or reagent bottles. Students should be instructed not to pour back excess chemicals into stock bottles.

Use of pipettes. Students can check on each other and spot the amateurs in laboratory technique. A fine point: how many place the thumb instead of the index finger over the top of a pipette?

Also, in using the more common liquids, insert the tip of the pipette into the fluid and suck gently (do not inhale at the same time), with the tongue ready to cover the tube, until the liquid is a few centimeters above the calibration mark; then quickly remove the tube from the mouth and cover with the index finger. Bring the liquid level down to the mark by twirling the tube slightly, keeping control with the index finger. Finally, touch the pipette tip to the liquid surface (not to the wall of the container) to remove any excess. (*Caution: Poisonous or volatile liquids should not be sucked with the mouth; use the bulb of a medicine dropper or a gentle vacuum aspirator.*)

25.1b   Preventing "suck-back"

Students will need to be cautioned in advance about "suck-back" when using a flask in which a gas or vapor is generated and then passed through a delivery tube to a collecting bottle. Should the reaction slow down for some reason, the pressure will drop, and it is likely that whatever product has collected will be sucked back into the reaction flask. At the least this will probably ruin the experiment; in many cases it is dangerous because the product is cooler than the reaction flask and can cause the glass to crack or even explode.

Students can prevent this in several ways.

1. Keep the reaction going as evenly as possible; if necessary, intermittently apply heat to the reaction flask.

2. Wherever possible, avoid having the delivery tube immersed in a liquid product; keep the end of the tube just above the surface of the liquid.

3. When terminating this kind of reaction, first remove the collected product, and then either extinguish the flame under the reaction or let it subside of its own accord. (*Caution: Never remove a flame from a reacting mixture while the delivery tube is immersed in a liquid.*)

25.1c *Preventing "bumping" and splashing*

Whenever a boiling reaction is to continue for a length of time, especially when reflux apparatus is used, there is the possibility that the materials in the reaction flask will "bump" or splash. This can be prevented by placing a few clean glass beads or porous clay chips in the reaction flask.

25.1d *Washing glassware*

Most glassware can be washed with warm, soapy water, but when experiments call for chemically clean glassware, extra precautions must be taken. After glassware has been washed by ordinary means, place it in a hot dichromate cleaning solution. This is prepared by pouring one liter of concentrated sulfuric acid into 35 cc of a saturated aqueous solution of sodium dichromate. (*Caution: Never pour the aqueous solution into the acid; avoid spilling on clothes or skin.*)

After the glassware has been standing in this solution for several hours or overnight, it should be rinsed continuously in warm tap water until all the chemical solution has been removed.

Glassware is clean when water completely wets the glass, forming a continuous film; on glassware which is not clean, water collects in drops on the surface.

Greasy and tarry materials on glassware may be removed by soaking the glassware in an alcohol-sodium hydroxide solution. This is prepared by dissolving 120 g of sodium hydroxide in 120 cc of water and diluting to one liter with 95 per cent ethyl alcohol. After soaking, rinse the glassware in tap or distilled water.

Tarry substances that do not respond readily to cleaning by commercial detergents may be removed by using automobile engine oil detergent obtainable from automobile supply stores. Scientific supply houses (see appendix) sell excellent glassware detergents.

25.2 Working with metal and glass

Some practice working with glass and metal will reap worthy benefits for students; in fact, some students can develop sufficient skill to make simple repairs of standard school equipment, and they can also be encouraged to try to make simple equipment for a home laboratory.

25.2a *Working with metal*

Cutting sheet metal. Lay out dimensions on sheet metal with a scribing tool, such as a sharpened nail, awl, or ice pick. Tinner's snips can be used to cut sheet metal (up to #18 gauge); saws made for cutting wood will also cut sheet metal. Duckbill shears are handy for cutting circles and curves. Use a coping saw for thicker sheets; still thicker metal sheets should be cut with a hack saw. In each case the metal should be clamped to the table, and the teeth of the blades should point toward the handle; file the burrs off the cut edge.

Drilling sheet metal. Sheet metal can be drilled with the same drill points used for heavier metal. For most metals carbon drill points can be used, but for steel high-speed bits are better. Place a piece of wood under the metal to be drilled, clamp the metal with a C-clamp to the work table, and mark the point to be drilled with a center punch. Tap the center punch with a hammer to make a small impression in the metal; this gives the drill point a place to start without skidding. Then use either hand or power drills.

Fastening sheet metal. Sheet metal can be fastened together by using Parker or sheet metal screws. Drill a hole with the same dimensions as the thickness of the screw between threads, place the screws into the holes, and tighten them with a screw driver; no nuts are needed. Machine screws with nuts can be used if desired. The most practical screws and nuts to use in the school laboratory are 6/32 and 8/32 thread roundheaded brass screws and nuts ½″ and 1″ long.

Heavier pieces of metal (and plastic) can be fastened together by tapping or threading the metal to receive machine screws for attaching parts or wires. A tap wrench and 8/32 and 6/32 taps are needed. It is advisable to ask the hardware dealer for the correct diameter high-speed drill point for preparing the hole before tapping or cutting a thread of a particular size. One drill is used for cutting a thread, and a second is used for the clearance hole through which a screw will pass without being threaded into place. Hold the work in a vise or a clamp to prevent the material from slipping and breaking the tool. Slowly start to tap; take a half turn and back off a half turn. Then turn again to the point at which you stopped and start another half turn and back off. (*Caution: Avoid forcing the tap; it may snap.*)

Soldering. With practice many students become skilled at soldering. At some time, you may want students to learn this technique. Students can use a common soldering iron heated in a gas flame but an electric soldering iron is preferable. (A 75-watt soldering iron is sufficient for soldering electric wires; sheet metal or heavier pieces need a 150-watt or larger iron.)

The procedure is the same in using the

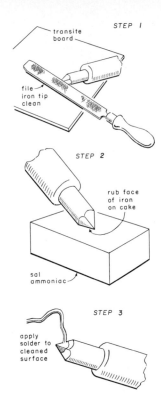

STEP 1

transite board

file iron tip clean

STEP 2

rub face of iron on cake

sal ammoniac

STEP 3

apply solder to cleaned surface

Fig. 25–1 Preparing the soldering iron. (PSSC of Educational Services, Inc.)

irons except that a gas-heated iron needs to be reheated from time to time (Fig. 25-1). When the iron is hot, file the point down to bare copper. The iron is dipped into powdered sal ammoniac (ammonium chloride) or rubbed on cake sal ammoniac and then touched with solder to "tin" the iron to prevent the formation of an oxide coat on the tip; this would decrease the transmission of heat. First clean the parts to be soldered with sandpaper or steel wool; then apply soldering flux. Use noncorrosive soldering paste for nonferrous metals. Ferrous metals and coated metals such as galvanized iron and tin plate need a flux made of 15 per cent zinc chloride solution.

Add solder to each surface that has been fluxed by holding the point of the hot soldering iron against the metal until

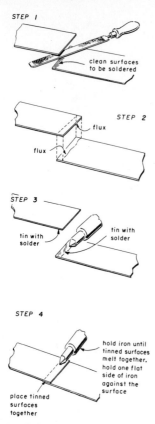

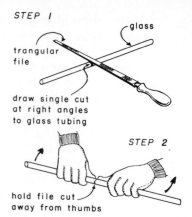

Fig. 25–3 Cutting glass tubing. (PSSC of Educational Services, Inc.)

Fig. 25–2 Soldering two flat pieces together with an overlap. (PSSC of Educational Services, Inc.)

the solder melts into the metal (Fig. 25-2). Now place together the two surfaces to be soldered and apply more solder. Hold the iron against the metal until the metal is heated sufficiently so that the molecules of molten solder combine with the hot surface molecules of the metal being soldered. The solder will take hold when the metal is heated to the melting point of the solder.

Special note for soldering copper or aluminum. Before soldering copper wires, be certain that the wires are clean and completely free of insulation. Some copper wire is insulated with an almost transparent coating of enamel which can be removed with steel wool. Splice together

the copper wire and solder with rosin-core solder. Students can use acid-core solder on nonferrous metals to prevent corrosion.

Soldering aluminum is a difficult procedure for the beginner because it requires special fluxes and special solders. These difficulties can be avoided by making joints using screws and nuts or sheet metal screws. Clean the aluminum with sandpaper to remove the aluminum oxide coating before fastening an electric wire against it under a screw head or a nut.

25.2b   *Working with glass*

Cutting glass tubing and rods. For ordinary-sized glass tubing or rod, draw with one stroke a sharp triangular file at right angles across the glass tubing as shown in Fig. 25-3. Hold the scratch away from the body, and place the thumbs on the opposite side so they touch each other behind the cut. Press with the thumbs, pulling back with the other fingers, and the glass will snap evenly around the tubing.

In cutting tubing of wider bore, make a cut completely around the glass, cover the tubing with cloth, and then snap. Very large tubing should be cut with a glass-tubing cutter (Fig. 25-4A). When the tubing to be cut is more than an inch

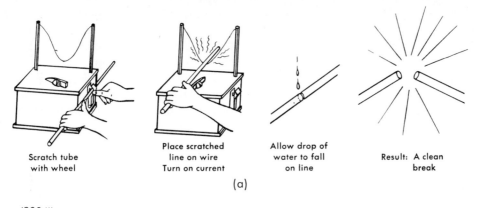

| Scratch tube with wheel | Place scratched line on wire
Turn on current | Allow drop of water to fall on line | Result: A clean break |

(a)

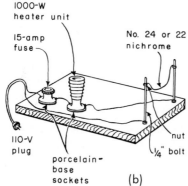

1000-W heater unit

15-amp fuse

No. 24 or 22 nichrome

110-V plug

porcelain-base sockets

nut

¼" bolt

(b)

Fig. 25-4 Electrically heated wire to cut glass: (a) the object to be cut is first encircled with a scratch from the cutter wheel mounted on one side; the scratch is then heated by the hot wire and then cooled quickly by the breath or with water (Welch Scientific Company); (b) equivalent that can be made by a student. (PSSC of Educational Services, Inc.)

in diameter, use the technique for cutting bottles as described later in this section. The hot wire part of the electric tube cutter can be made as indicated in Fig. 25-4B.

In all cases, firepolish the cut ends by holding the cut end of the tubing in a Bunsen flame or in the center of an electric heating unit. When the edge begins to melt, remove the tubing and place on a sheet of asbestos to cool.

Stirring rods. These are easily made from short lengths of glass rod that have been cut in the same way as tubing is cut; firepolish the ends. A flange can be made at the ends by pressing each end while still hot on asbestos sheeting.

Inserting tubing into a stopper. You will want students to avoid accidents by learning the correct way to insert glass tubing into a stopper. Wet the glass tubing, or apply a bit of Vaseline or glycerin. Then grasp the tubing firmly *near the end to be inserted* into the stopper, and "screw" it in. Many teachers have students use cloth or paper toweling to hold the tubing as it is inserted. Never push from the center or the opposite end of the tube; this technique will probably break the tube and can force the jagged end into the palm.

Working glass tubing. At some time you may want to have students work with glass, possibly blow glass, or design simple equipment. Students should heed these instructions in working with glass.

1. Hot glass looks exactly like cold glass, and glass is slow to cool; think before grasping a worked piece of glass.

2. Bent-glass work should be in one plane, unless specifically designed to be otherwise. This can be achieved by making all bends after the first one with the

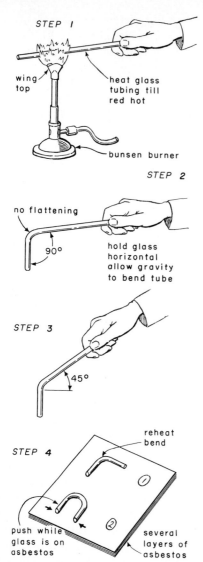

STEP 1

wing top

heat glass tubing till red hot

bunsen burner

STEP 2

no flattening

90°

hold glass horizontal allow gravity to bend tube

STEP 3

45°

STEP 4

reheat bend

push while glass is on asbestos

several layers of asbestos

Fig. 25–5 Bending glass tubing. (PSSC of Educational Services, Inc.)

tubing placed on a piece of asbestos sheet.

3. Students should discard any bend or join that has a flaw, a thin portion, or a significant constriction.

4. It is good practice to wear safety glasses when blowing glass.

5. For "spot work" such as blowing a small bubble or finishing a join, use a Bunsen burner regulated for the typical cone; use the hottest part of the flame. Use a wing top to heat a larger area of glass. Constricted bends usually result from failure to use a wing top.

6. Except for "spot work," glass tubing that is being heated should always be rotated in the flame by rolling it between the thumb and first two fingers of both hands.

7. Never inhale through the tube when blowing glass; the air inside is very hot.

8. All glass that has been heated for working should be annealed (see below).

9. Students should plan ahead when their work involves preparing more than one bend. Which one should be made first for ease in handling? If possible, plan to make cuts before bends or joins; it is sometimes awkward to cut a complicated piece of work.

10. Never put a piece of wet glass into the flame, even if the water is far away from the part that is being heated. If the piece doesn't shatter then and there, it probably will later, when the air inside the tube cools and the water condenses on a piece of glass that is still hot.

Students will probably want to learn several of these five basic techniques for working glass tubing (bend, seal, hole, join, and annealing). They will then be able to prepare simple pieces of apparatus.

Simple bend. Students can bend tubing by rotating a length of tubing over a wing top attachment placed on the burner. Rotate the tube slowly between the thumb and first two fingers of each hand. When the glass becomes soft and begins to sag, students can let it bend by gravity to form a right angle. Some teachers prefer to have students use as a guide the corner of a sheet of asbestos to shape a right angle bend. They can lay the glass on the sheet. For angles less than 90°, remove tube from the heat and hold as shown (Fig. 25-5); then anneal the glass (see below).

Simple seal. It is often necessary to seal off the end of a piece of glass tubing, especially when making a blown piece. Hold the end of the tube in the flame until it closes completely, rotating the tube if necessary. There should be no line visible where the glass has fused.

Simple hole. At times a hole of a specific diameter may be required in a section of glass tubing. Regulate the burner to give a good cone (do not use a wing top). Seal one end of a piece of glass tubing and hold it so that the hottest part of the flame strikes the spot where the hole is to be made. (If you do not want the tube with the hole sealed off, be sure to leave enough distance between the hole and the sealed end for convenient cutting later on.) When the glass is soft, remove it from the flame and immediately blow, gently, into the tube. If it is heated enough, a very fragile bubble will form. (The bubble may pop out suddenly or even burst; this does no harm.) If it is not heated enough, a thick bulge will appear. Students may repeat the operation and try to salvage the piece, although this may not be successful. Once the thin-walled bubble is obtained, gently set the piece aside to cool. When it is cool, break the bubble and file off its sharp edges into the discard crock. If the region with the hole is waved over a flame briefly, the edges will become smooth.

This technique requires some practice. You may have to vary the size of the flame and possibly the length of time for heating the glass to make the aperture of the desired size. If the opening is too large, it can often be made smaller by holding it in the flame a bit longer at this point.

Simple join. Students can learn to join two pieces of glass tubing together to make a Y- or T-tube. They can practice first with two pieces of straight tubing, each about 5″ long. First seal an end of *one* piece and let it cool. Then hold one piece in each hand so that the free ends are in a wide flame at the same time. Rotate both pieces in the flame until the edges become very soft. Then, with the ends still held in the flame, bring them together and hold them firmly in place. Continue twirling the piece, but slowly now, for the join is very weak at this point. Continue heating until the line that marks the join completely disappears. From time to time (whenever the join seems to be about to constrict) remove it from the flame and blow gently into the open end to restore the shape. Do not blow too hard or too much; if a bubble forms, the piece is ruined. Discard any joins which show an angular line where the two pieces came together; this is a strain line, and in use the tube is apt to crack at this point. When the join is completed, set it aside to cool; later it can be annealed (see below).

"Glass solder." Corning Glass Company makes a "glass solder" that permits any piece of glass tubing to be joined to any other. A paste of this material is made in airplane dope. This is placed on the clean surfaces to be joined. These are then clamped together and placed into a home-made oven. The oven is made from a cylinder of asbestos paper inside which are the wires of a 660-watt heating element. The outside of the asbestos cylinder is wrapped with aluminum foil. The glass being joined is heated at 600° C for 30 minutes.

U-tubes. To make a U-tube, students should start with a cooled right-angle bend. Then reheat the tubing at the spot where the second bend is to be, rotating it in the flame. When it is red hot, place it flat on an asbestos sheet and complete the bend by hand. Or students may begin with a straight length of tubing and rotate it over a wing top until it begins to sag; as the tubing is removed from the flame,

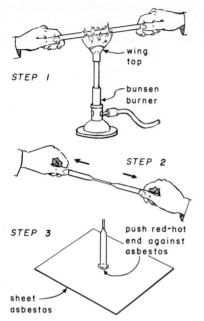

STEP 1

wing top

bunsen burner

STEP 2

STEP 3

push red-hot end against asbestos

sheet asbestos

Fig. 25–6 Making medicine droppers and pipettes. (PSSC of Educational Services, Inc.)

raise the arms upward so that a U-tube forms as a result of gravity.

Larger tubing should be filled with dry sand first, then heated and bent; the sand will prevent collapse of the tube. Avoid overheating, however, or the sand will melt into the glass.

Flares. The end of tubing can be flared by evenly heating it and inserting a copper triangle or carbon block to make the flare.

Pipettes and capillary pipettes. Students can make pipettes in this way. Heat the center of a piece of tubing; remove from the flame and pull until the center thins out slightly (Fig. 25–6). Let it cool and cut it in the center so that two medicine droppers can be made. Select the tubing length desired; firepolish the wide end. (The narrow end should also be firepolished; but be careful not to let it close.) To make medicine droppers to which a rubber nozzle is to be fitted, the wide end

should be heated to red heat and pressed down on asbestos sheeting to form a flange over which the rubber can be placed.

In making capillary pipettes, the same procedure is followed except that the tubing is heated a little more, and the two ends are pulled apart very rapidly— as far as desired. The faster the pull and the further apart the ends are pulled, the finer the capillary. At the same time, you may want students to save lengths of appropriate bore for capillary tubing ready to seal in a laboratory study of melting points of certain substances.

Spiral tubes. A spiral glass tube for a Liebig condenser can be made from a long section of tubing. Heat the glass in a wide flame at a point close to one end, and, as it softens, wrap it around a dowel stick (or broom handle) that has been covered with asbestos paper (Fig. 25–7). Then heat more of the tubing, and turn the dowel so that the hot tubing is wrapped around it. Continue until the desired number of spiral turns is obtained; then anneal the entire unit.

Annealing worked glass tubing. The process of heating glass and making it take new shapes sets up strains in the glass which are usually invisible. However, it is along these lines of strain that the glass is

Fig. 25–7 Making a helix (coil) of glass tubing by bending soft, hot tubing around an asbestos-covered dowel stick.

likely to break if it is suddenly heated or cooled or lightly tapped in the wrong spot. This can be avoided if worked glass tubing is annealed. Set the burner to a yellow flame by reducing the air supply. Heat the worked area of the tubing gently, rotating it in the flame, until it is blackened with soot; do not heat to melting. The glass flows slightly, thereby eliminating strain. Now place it on asbestos until cool; later remove the soot and the piece is ready for use.

Working with Pyrex glass. Similar techniques are used with Pyrex tubing, but a much hotter flame is needed. While a Meker burner may give a hot enough flame, this is a time-consuming procedure. A more practical method employs one of several kinds of blast lamps using compressed air. These are not inherently dangerous in experienced hands. One technique is described here.

A gas-compressed air blast lamp is used to make seals and connections, Y- and T-tubes, as well as to blow Pyrex glass. Special precautions are needed in using a source of pure oxygen gas (please refer to precautions indicated in Chapter 26).

Wash bottles. A wash bottle is a useful piece of laboratory equipment that students can make. It gives them an opportunity to learn basic techniques of cutting glass tubing, making bends and pipettes, and inserting tubing into stoppers.

Many teachers provide a pattern similar to Fig. 25-8 for students to follow. These questions might serve as a guide: How long should tube *A* be to fit the flask? Will the bent tubes go through the stopper, or should they be inserted first and then be bent? Can the bottle be made more versatile by making tube *A* in two parts, with the pipette end a short piece connected to the rest with rubber tubing?

Thermometer bulbs. Students can make a thermometer and calibrate it as de-

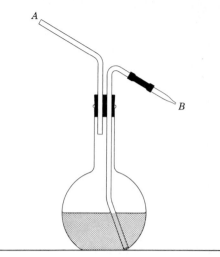

Fig. 25–8 Wash bottle. (E. Morholt et al., *A Sourcebook for the Biological Sciences*, Harcourt, Brace, 1958.)

scribed in 18.1a. (See also 3.1a). They will need 12″ of thermometer tubing which must first be sealed at one end in a flame. While it is still hot, blow gently into the tube, reheating it if necessary, until an even bulb appears. The tube can be filled with alcohol dyed with red ink or eosin; then scale marks can be scratched on the glass. (*Caution: Students should not try to seal the other end after the liquid is in the tube. If a closed thermometer is desired, it can be sealed with sealing wax or a stopper.*)

T- and Y-tubes. These tubes are useful for making three-way connections in certain assemblies. Reread the directions above for a simple join. Begin with a right-angle or acute-angle bend that has long arms and one end sealed. Make a hole on the outside of the spot (see above for making holes) that is exactly the diameter of the tubing. Seal the other end of the tube. Then heat one end of a short piece of the same tubing and the hole in the angle piece at the same time until both are soft; join them together in the flame and hold them there. They will join, but the join line will be visible. The method de-

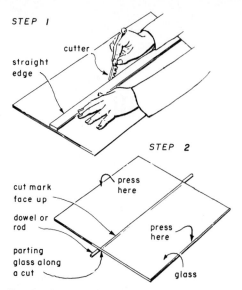

STEP I

cutter

straight edge

STEP 2

cut mark face up

press here

dowel or rod

press here

parting glass along a cut

glass

Fig. 25–9 Cutting glass sheeting. (PSSC of Educational Services, Inc.)

scribed above for the simple join, alternately spot-heating the line and blowing to restore the shape, is now used. A professional-looking T- or Y-tube shows no sign of the join; actually it is usable as long as the line is completely gone, even if the glass near the join looks a bit wavy. Anneal after the piece has cooled.

Wheel-type cutter of sheet glass. A sharp glass cutter is required in the laboratory. (Store the cutting wheel with a thin film of oil so that its cutting edge will not rust.) Cut a paper pattern of the piece to be cut. Place this pattern on the glass, and apply a steel edge or steel rule on the edge to be cut (Fig. 25-9). Work on a flat surface. Apply considerable pressure as you move the cutting wheel along the ruler. You can tell that the wheel is cutting the glass by the sound it makes. Then turn the glass over and place a thin dowel stick or thin metal rod directly under the mark made in the glass by the cutter. Press against the glass on opposite sides of the cut so that the glass will break evenly along the cutting wheel marks.

If a narrow strip of glass is to be cut off an edge of a piece of glass, use pliers to snap off the glass after the cut is made.

Circles can be cut out of sheet glass with a circular glass cutter. Set the radius of the circle to be cut and swing the arm. An ordinary glass cutter can also cut circles if a circular object of the desired dimensions is used as a guide. Or you may even use a string or wire to swing a circle (Fig. 25-10); hold the wire in the center of the circle while moving the cutter around to scribe the circle (apply pressure). To remove the circle that has been formed, side cuts will need to be made.

When a large circular hole in sheet glass is needed, follow the same procedure, but make the additional cuts in the center instead of outside. Carefully tap out the center portions on the cut lines.

Electrically heated wire to cut sheet glass. This procedure can be used for heavy sheet glass, even glass almost an inch thick. First mark a line with the glass cutting tool. Working on a sheet of asbestos to prevent electric shock or fire, place a hot-coil of wire from an electric

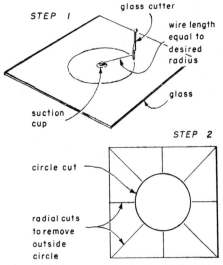

STEP I

glass cutter

wire length equal to desired radius

glass

suction cup

STEP 2

circle cut

radial cuts to remove outside circle

Fig. 25–10 Making a glass circle. (PSSC of Educational Services, Inc.)

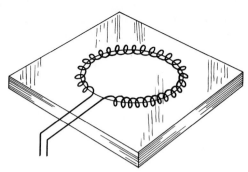

Fig. 25-11 Cutting a circle out of thick glass by heating the scratch with a coil of heater wire.

heater replacement over the cut line. Circles (as for a telescope mirror blank) can be cut by laying the heater wire in a circle along the mark made by the glass cutter (Fig. 25-11).

Using a drill press to cut sheet glass. Large circles or large apertures in heavy glass can also be cut if a drill press is available. A hollow sheet metal tube or tin can is used as the cutter (Fig. 25-12). Place a sheet of wood under the glass and firmly clamp the glass to the drill press table (be sure to use soft wood between the jaws of the clamp and the glass). If a tin can is used for wide diameters, cut away the bottom lip with shears and make notches in the edge. Pass a bolt ¼" in diameter or larger through the center of the other end of the can to hold it in the drill chuck.

Now apply a mixture of coarse carborundum (or emery powder) and water to the glass. With the tube or tin can spinning in the drill press, slowly lower the chuck until the cutting edge of the tube or can touches the glass. Apply very gentle pressure and keep on adding the grinding powder and water mixture. Continue the process until the circle or hole is cut out. It may take an hour or more, but a smooth job will result.

Drilling in glass. For many types of glass apparatus, it is convenient to have a side

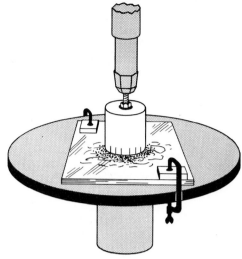

Fig. 25-12 Cutting a circle in glass sheeting by means of a drill press and a tin can with carborundum.

hole for inserting a glass tube or a wire. You may want to drill a hole in the glass. This is not difficult but should not be tried with very thin glass. Sheet glass, cylinders, jars, and bottles can be drilled in this way. Snap off about an inch of the end of a triangular file with a hammer. Insert the tang, or point, into a cork for safety; the other end of this is the tool (Fig. 25-13). Mark the point where you wish to drill the hole. Notice the way it is held in the hand; only one point of the triangular tip is used for cutting, and pressure is applied with the thumb. Once the initial mark is made to locate the point to be drilled, dip the cutting tip of the file in turpentine to cool the glass and make a grinding paste of the glass powder. Then move the file point with a circular motion. If the cutting action stops before you have finished, change to another triangular point. If all three points become dull, snap off another short piece of the file to make a new set of points. Continue, dipping the file in turpentine occasionally, until the point comes through the glass. Dip the end of a thin rattail (round) file in turpentine and

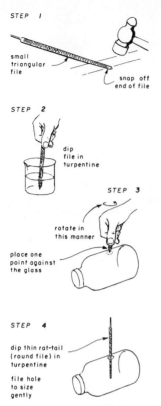

STEP 1

small
triangular
file

snap off
end of file

STEP 2

dip
file in
turpentine

STEP 3

rotate in
this manner

place one
point against
the glass

STEP 4

dip thin rat-tail
(round file) in
turpentine

file hole
to size
gently

Fig. 25-13 Using a triangular file and turpentine to drill a hole in glass. (PSSC of Educational Services, Inc.)

use it slowly to enlarge the hole to the desired size.

Switch to a large rattail file for larger holes. If glass tubing is to be inserted into the hole, first firepolish the tubing and slip rubber tubing over the insert tube. Then slip the tube and rubber covering into the drilled hole. If wire is to be inserted into the hole, it must be sealed in place with hot sealing wax, glyptal (insulating varnish), or epoxy resin. If the container is to be used under vacuum, vacuum cement (purchased from a scientific supply house) must be used as a seal.

25.3 Making simple laboratory equipment

Students working together as a squad

with a teacher can make most of the common laboratory equipment we have described. Many students are encouraged to set up a home laboratory or workshop with equipment they have learned to make as a member of a laboratory squad or a club. Along with the opportunity to perfect skills and techniques, students gain a respect for the equipment they make and work with—it isn't just something to take off a shelf when needed.

25.3a Basic laboratory equipment

Bunsen burner. The ubiquitous laboratory burner is a fairly simple piece of equipment to make. Students will need a 3" square of wood about 1" thick. Drill a ⅜" hole in the center and fit a 6" length of metal tubing (⅜" diameter) in the aperture in the wooden square. Then drill two holes (each ¼" wide) at a point 1½" above the bottom end of the metal tube. Also drill a hole slightly more than ¼" into the edge of the wood block, reaching the center hole (Fig. 25-14). Fit the stem of a medicine dropper (with a curved tip) into this hole; adjust it so the tip turns upward in the center hole. Or use a piece of copper tubing that has been partly pinched and bent over instead of the medicine dropper.

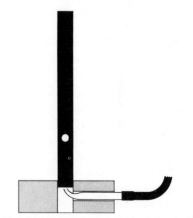

Fig. 25-14 Bunsen burner that can be made by students.

Now students can connect the tube to a rubber hose leading through a hand valve to a source of gas, using either a main supply or a tank of bottled gas.

Electric test tube heater. A cone-shaped electric heater replacement unit can furnish an excellent source of heat. Mount a porcelain-base electric socket on a rigid sheet of asbestos such as Transite or on an asbestos house shingle, and connect an electric iron or a heater cord with a plug to it. Place the heater unit into the socket as shown in Fig. 25-15. Wrap asbestos paper (about ½″ thick) around the heating unit to prevent accidental burns. The heater can then be used for heating test tubes; plug in the cord and hold the test tube (in a holder) in the hollow center of the cone.

Arc furnace. The form for an arc furnace can be made using a chalk box as a mold, with a 2″ diameter cardboard tube in the center and two 5/16″ dowels set in at about 45°. First place a layer of fire clay 1½″ thick at the bottom; then place in the cardboard tube. Pass dowels covered with Vaseline through the opposite walls of the box and into the tube at the approximate angle indicated in Fig. 25-16. Now fill with fire clay or with asbestos furnace cement. It will take many days to set. Place in a very warm, dry place. When the clay or cement is dry, remove the dowels and the cardboard form. Finally tear off the chalk box mold. Firebrick can be used in place of the molded form by drilling out the appropriate holes.

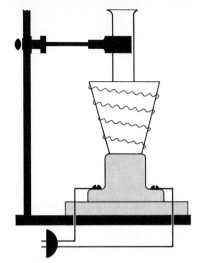

Fig. 25-15 A test tube heater made from a cone-shaped electric heater replacement.

Next insert the 5/16″ diameter arc carbons and connect a battery clip to each one. Insulate by covering with plastic tape. Connect the carbon rods as in Fig. 25-16 in a series circuit with a 1000-watt cone-shaped heater replacement unit or any other 1000-watt heater source such as an iron. Connect all parts with heater cord of the type used for electric irons. Connect to a heavy duty plug. Insert plug into 110-volt. Now touch and then separate the carbons slightly to start the arc. (*Caution: Look at the arc through cobalt glass. Never look at it with unprotected eyes.*) Use tongs to lower a porcelain crucible containing materials that require high temperatures for melting such as brass, aluminum, and so forth.

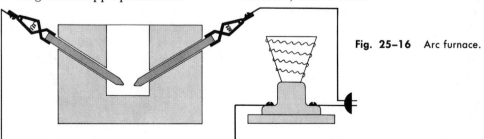

Fig. 25-16 Arc furnace.

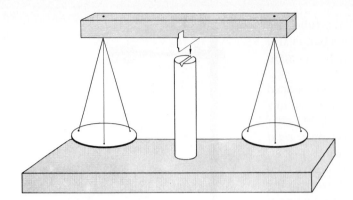

Fig. 25-17 A balance that pivots on the edge of a razor blade.

Laboratory balances and weights. An accurate microbalance can be made of inexpensive materials (see 2.1c).

A fairly accurate all-purpose balance can be made by using the edge of a razor blade as the knife-edge pivot (Fig. 25-17). Students will need to make a wood base about 16″ by 6″. Drill a hole in the wood base the proper size to insert a short length of broomstick, and cover the top of the stick with a circle cut from a thick sheet of copper. File a V-shaped groove in the copper parallel to the short sides of the wood base.

To make the beam, use a piece of wood ¾″ × ¾″ × 12″. In the center make a knife slit about ¼″ deep. Insert a double-edge razor blade into the slit and cement it in place. Drill a hole through each end of the balance at equal distances from the razor blade; cut out two plastic circles (each 3″ wide) for the pans. Drill three small holes, equally spaced (120° apart), around the edges of the plastic disks and attach each pan to the beam by means of three strings. The pans must hang level. Rest the beam on the stand with the razor-blade edge in the V-slot on top of the broomstick post. Balance the beam by adding plastic tape around the end that is too high.

Weights can be made from pieces of sheet lead. Cut up pieces of sheet lead to weigh the quantities you want—1, 10, 20, 50, 100 grams—by testing them on a school balance or a druggist's balance. Coins can also be used as weights if they are first weighed on an accurate balance. Of course, lead wears down quite quickly (coins less quickly), and on occasion students will have to check the accuracy of the weights.

Student-made flasks. When large, clear-glass electric light bulbs made of heat-resistant glass burn out, they can be converted into Florence flasks. Place the bulb in a heavy cloth bag or wrap it in a towel; then twist the brass screw base with a pair of pliers to loosen it but avoid forcing it. It may be helpful to heat the base over a burner first to loosen the cement which holds it. When the base is removed, you will find a long thin sealing tube extending out of the glass neck. Place the flask *under water,* and snip off the end of the pointed seal with a pair of tinner's snips. Then remove the bulb from the water, wrap the bulb in cloth, and knock out with a thin file the center part that supported the filament. Allow the bulb to dry completely and firepolish the cut edge. Finally, heat the bottom of the bulb until it is red hot and immediately press it against asbestos to flatten the bottom. After cooling, the flask is ready for use.

A 100-watt bulb has a capacity of about 100 cc; a 500-watt bulb of a half liter (however, bulb envelope sizes vary). Once a "flask" is made, its capacity can be measured fairly accurately by either of two different methods. Students can measure 100 cc of water in a graduate cylinder, pour the water into the clean flask, and scratch the bulb at the water level with a file. Or they can put the flask on one pan of a balance, add weights to the other pan until the pointer is at the zero mark, and then add a 100-gram weight. Pour water into the flask until the reading is again zero. The flask then contains 100 grams of water; it may be assumed that this is approximately 100 cc, or, for more accurate calibration, calculate the volume from the density of water at room temperature. The water level can be marked with a file or glass marking tool.

Other glassware. Funnels, battery jars, beakers, and other pieces can be cut from strong glass bottles and jars (Fig. 25-18). Once a scratch is made, the glassware is put in contact with hot wire as in such a device as shown in Fig. 25-4.

Measuring devices for liquids. Many students are ingenious in devising equipment for their own home laboratories. For example, plastic measuring cups can be used in place of graduate cylinders. (The plastic ones are useful for all chemicals other than concentrated acids.) Or an 8-ounce baby bottle can be used since it is graduated into ounces and half-ounces. A tall olive jar can be turned into a graduate cylinder by making a scale on the side: add water, one cc at a time, and mark the scale with a file or China marking pencil.

Ring stands. A serviceable ring stand can be made from a length of ¼″ or heavier threaded rod, with two nuts to fit and a wood base. Drill a hole in the wood base and countersink the hole at the bottom of the base; bolt the threaded end of the rod to the top and bottom of the base. Acid-proof the base with black asphaltum varnish or melted paraffin.

Clamps and holders. Small C-clamps and strong spring-back steel clamps used

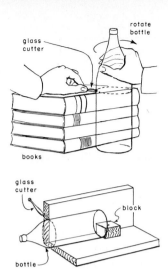

Fig. 25–18 Cutting glass bottles. (PSSC of Educational Services, Inc.)

for holding paper together can serve to hold apparatus to the ring stand. Wooden spring-type clothespins make good holders for heating narrow test tubes.

Wire leads. A group of students on a squad can prepare some wire leads using battery or alligator clips and insulated wire so that these can be used readily when making a temporary circuit.

BOOKS AND PAMPHLETS

Scientific Instruments You Can Make and *Science Exhibits,* both by Helen M. Davis, Science Service Inc., Washington, D.C., 1954, 1955.

Laboratory Glass Blowing (Pyrex glass), Laboratory and Pharmaceutical Sales Dept., Corning Glass Works, Corning, N.Y.

Many science kits are available and vary in price; pamphlets describing specific kits are available from the manufacturers. You may want to look into some of the following.

Library of Science, Science Materials Center, 59 Fourth Avenue, N.Y. 3, *Calculo Analog Computer Kit, Ultra-violet Science Kit, Light and Color Kit, Pre-electricity Physics Kit.*

American Basic Science Club, P.O. Box 524, San Antonio 6, Texas, *Science Kits.*

Polaroid Corp., Cambridge 39, Mass., write for information on the polaroid transparency system that produces black and white positive transparencies in 2 minutes after the shutter is snapped. *Dippit* is used to harden the emulsion.

CHAPTER 26

Science facilities for a science program

Over the country teachers discussing common problems related to science facilities seek solutions for these immediate situations: making the most of inadequate facilities, increasing the possibilities of laboratory experience without a tremendous outlay of money, planning for new classrooms and laboratories, providing project areas within the regular laboratory space, stimulating some students to set up laboratories at home, effectively using the abilities and talents of students in squads. This chapter examines some of the modifications in practice in science classrooms and laboratories.

There is also the constant need to observe specific safety precautions in using and storing chemicals and equipment.

26.1 Space for storage

The varied equipment and chemical supplies used in physics, chemistry, and general science raise the need for storage space and for methods of cataloguing materials and equipment so that materials can be assembled quickly by teachers and student aides.

If equipment and materials are stored in several different places, many teachers develop a filing system of the following sort. On a 3″ × 5″ index card they indicate the cabinet, shelf, or drawer in which each item is stored; these cards are filed in alphabetical order. Some schools use a code number and letter for each storage area, giving each cabinet a letter designation and each drawer or shelf a number. Thus an item on the second shelf in cabinet A would show the code designation A-2. If a large storage room with many shelves is available, each shelf can be coded by letter and subdivided into numbered sections. Each cabinet or shelf should be labeled with its code number.

26.1a Closed storage

Some schools may have separate rooms for storage or built-in closets, while other schools may have to improvise with a series of locked metal cabinets having shelves and drawers of varying dimensions.

In general, it is unwise to store physics apparatus in the same room with chemical reagents because fumes will eventually corrode the equipment. Chemical reagents should be stored in closed metal cabinets, on acid-proof shelves in fireproof, locked storage rooms away from heat. They should be stored at or near floor level, never above the heads of students. Further suggestions for safety in handling chemicals are described in detail in 26.4.

Acids should be stored in a separate section. These, as well as all chemicals, should be stored in alphabetical order much in the manner of a well-ordered prescription pharmacy. The labels can be covered with several coats of label varnish; acids and bases may be stocked in bottles that have molded or chemically etched labels. Use plastic or ground-glass stoppers for strong acids and bases.

Cabinets with drawers of different sizes are desirable for assorted items like corks, rubber stoppers, rubber tubing, short pieces of glass tubing, rods, clamps, clips, and the like, that are always in immediate use.

26.1b   Open storage

Materials to be used in current laboratory sessions need to be stored on a community shelf or in a cabinet. Many teachers find it helpful to prepare (with the help of students on a laboratory squad) "kits" of materials needed for each specific laboratory period. It is then possible to provide opportunities for students to work alone or to move ahead with optional activities, and other equipment can be provided for groups of students working together in an activity. There is a need for students to work in groups, especially when there is a shortage of materials. However, where possible, teachers usually limit a group to three members; otherwise some students in the group tend to lose track of the procedures.

26.2   Work facilities

26.2a   Space for work

Demonstration table. A science classroom needs a demonstration table. These tables usually contain drawers that can be used for storing the "wherewithal" of the science teacher: Bunsen, Fisher, and Meker burners, matches or friction lighters, testing splints and tapers, test tubes, clamps and ring stands, tubing, stoppers and corks. Many models exist. You will find them shown and described in supply house catalogs.

Laboratory tables for students. Traditionally most student laboratory tables are made with a stone top and sink facilities. However when these are lacking, large tables can be used whose tops are covered with acid-proof paint or with black asphaltum varnish.

For home laboratories, students can cover a work area with Transite or other hard sheet asbestos material that is heatproof, fireproof, and a good electrical insulator. Or asbestos shingles, which are less expensive, can be fastened to the table top. Students will need to drill a hole in the asbestos shingles to prevent cracking and then fasten them down with wood screws.

Investigators' corner. Where possible, a corner of the laboratory should be set aside for those students who are doing individual research. This corner should probably be equipped with electrical testing equipment, measuring devices with sources of a.c. and d.c. (26-2c), and, if possible, an oscilloscope. Gas and water outlets and a sink are also useful. When chemical experiments are planned, a permanent or portable hood should be used. A Geiger counter or scintillation counter and special sinks for disposal of radioactive materials should be part of the equipment if work is to be done with radioisotopes (see 23.1h).

Where radio projects are underway, connections to the proper type of antenna, transmission or reception should be available. These antennae should be located outside of the school building, and connections should be carried to the investigators by the correct lead-ins as required by the Underwriter's code. Transmitting lines to the antenna should be carried by means of high-voltage insulators.

It is important that all electrical connections be of a safety type to prevent danger of shock. This is especially important in high-voltage circuits. Before a student plugs a high-voltage system into operation, the teacher should carefully check for possible shock hazards or short circuits. It is also wise to have a special fuse for the circuit to the investigators' corner so that a short circuit will not put the remainder of the room out of operation.

Reading center. Students will find it convenient to have a select reference library in the classroom or combination class-laboratory. Many teachers have compiled these kinds of references in convenient shelves or window ledges: current magazines, college texts, a file of project ideas and open-end experiments, a file of extensions for each laboratory lesson so that students who work faster in the laboratory may move ahead, and scientific tables and reference handbooks.

Demonstration and display space. Space for demonstrations, bulletin boards, a hall case, provide visual aids that focus attention and stimulate learning. Committees of students take responsibility for these display areas when given freedom to be creative. For example,

1. Window sills may be used for mounting weather instruments or for demonstrations requiring light (try mounting a prism on the sill and throwing a rainbow on the opposite wall).

2. Bulletin boards may display current events in science, career information, special TV or museum programs, and charts.

3. Glass-front display cabinets are useful for various exhibits, such as students' projects, or for mineral or crystal collections.

4. Shelf or table-top areas are necessary for demonstrations that must rest undisturbed for days (for instance, diffusion of $CuSO_4$ in water).

In physics laboratories, you may also want to install and make use of ceiling fixtures for suspending pendulums or pulleys or for attaching a target for projectile studies.

Putting window ledges to work. Both indoor and outdoor window ledges can be put to use. Weather instruments (Chapter 3) may be attached on the outside of the window. A rain gauge (3.2e) can be set on a pole outside the building for students to read. Place a thermometer and a wet- and dry-bulb thermometer (3.1a, 3.2b, 25.2b) outside of the window where these can pique the curiosity of students. An anemometer (3.5b) can be set up on the outside to measure wind speed.

On the inside window sills, students can prepare challenging displays of equipment, models, or projects that relate to the current work in class.

Using wall space. Bulletin boards can be prepared by groups of students. These can be changed continuously to coincide with each topic studied in class. Excellent materials can be gathered from such magazines as *Scientific American, Science Newsletter, Science World, Life, Time,* and *Popular Science.* Low-cost and free pamphlets and charts are available for many topics studied in physical sciences (see directory of distributors, appendix). When such materials are arranged by topics and filed in manila envelopes or file folders, they become part of the teacher's vertical file of current materials.

Instead of tacking charts or fastening them with cellophane tape, you may want students to use sheets of lightweight beaverboard or Upson board that can be suspended from the picture molding by means of picture wire and picture hooks. Other display materials can be tacked to cork display boards.

Rejuvenating blackboards. Dull gray blackboards can be revived by washing the slates first with water and mild soap and rinsing with clean water. Then, wearing gloves, wash the blackboards with a solution of black India ink dissolved in distilled water. The boards should dry thoroughly. This simple treatment can be repeated several times during the year.

Using glass-front display cabinets. Glass-front cabinets intended for storage can be converted to display space. Some teachers use the rear half of each shelf for storage and the front portions for display purposes. New equipment, projects, and simple "setups" of demonstrations that present a challenge to the class all belong in the display area, even if only for the day.

Some teachers also use open shelves or book shelves for display purposes. This provides an area for students to exhibit science hobby projects as well as those ideas that grow out of class discussion or laboratory work. An exhibit case stressing students' hobbies can be frequently changed during a month and often stimulates other students who may not have a hobby.

Using illumination. There are times when extra lighting can focus the attention of students in class. Some teachers use a spotlight made from a reflector lamp bulb that is screwed directly into a standard socket and aimed at the demonstration, chart, or display.

At times, it may be effective to display exhibits on a window sill in boxes that are open to the light. Arrange the display so that the side facing the class is open while the opposite side is covered with tracing paper or tracing cloth to admit light from the windows.

26.2b   Water supply

Running water. While some classrooms may lack running water and gas outlets, teachers still do laboratory work. They use a five-gallon carboy or tins equipped with siphons and pinch clamps. Another tin or earthenware crock can serve as a

sink. Electric immersion heaters can be used to provide hot water as can a hot plate with a Pyrex boiler. If the source of running water is a short distance away, a connection can be made. Insert a one-hole rubber stopper into the mouth of the faucet and attach a glass tube that is connected to a long rubber tube to transport circulating water to condensers or other equipment.

Where hard water interferes with chemical reactions, an ion-exchange filter can be purchased and attached directly to the faucet.

Distilled water. It is important to have a supply of distilled water in the laboratory. Small quantities can be purchased from a chemical supply house or from a druggist. Some teachers prepare distilled water with a Liebig condenser or they make a "pie-tin still." (For distillation of water, see 4.72.) Certain ion-exchange resins such as are sold by scientific supply houses will give water almost as pure as distilled water.

A commercial still (gas or electricity) available under government license is used by schools that require large quantities of distilled water (see appendix). Teachers often prepare enough of a supply to last several months because the operating still needs supervision (to observe safety factors).

26.2c   Electricity

There are many ways of getting the kinds of current that are needed in the laboratory. Any plans concerning electrical wiring should best be checked with the school custodian.

A.c. and d.c. sources. Step-down transformers can be plugged into standard 120-volt outlets to provide any required voltage. The same transformers can supply d.c. when selenium rectifiers or the new silicon rectifiers (obtainable from

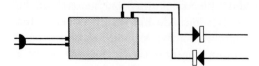

Fig. 26-1 Producing direct current by placing selenium rectifiers into the output circuit of a step-down transformer.

radio supply houses) are put into the output circuit as shown in Fig. 26-1. A battery charger can also supply d.c. To provide a steady flow of d.c., place a 1000 mfd, 24-volt electrolytic capacitor across the d.c.

For students' laboratories at home, a source of low-voltage a.c. can be obtained from transformers in toy electric train outfits. These transformers usually supply 3 to 15 volts in 3-volt steps.

Individual batteries for each experimenter are expensive and often wasteful. The best source of direct current for students is a low-voltage central battery system equipped with a battery charger and outlets at students' desks. However, this is expensive, and it is not usually necessary because 6 volts is used for most laboratory work. This low voltage can be distributed by temporary overhead wires connected to storage batteries; each student's work space has two lead wires suspended from the overhead circuit.

Batteries. When batteries are to be purchased, storage batteries of the alkaline type are preferable. (Less expensive storage batteries may be used if you charge them once a week and have somone keep them charged over the summer.) The Edison (nickel-iron) alkaline battery may be considered expensive but it will last a lifetime. The cadmium-nickel alkaline battery is less expensive and will last many years with proper care. Lead storage batteries can be bought in an auto supply store but they have a much shorter life (1 to 3 years).

Charging batteries. A standard battery charger can be used to keep storage batteries charged. When a charger is not available, use an automobile generator or a 32-volt farm-type generator battery system, driven by a ⅓ or ½ hp electric motor.

For a home laboratory, students can make one of the several batteries described in 13.1a and 13.2. Or selenium or chemical rectifiers can be used with the a.c. wall outlet and a step-down transformer as shown in Fig. 26-1. For high-voltage d.c., students can tap the B (high-voltage) supply of a radio set. (*Caution: Great care must be taken as these voltages are dangerous.*)

You may prefer to use the voltage-doubling circuit of the power supply used in the 110-volt a.c. Geiger counter described in 23.1h.

26.2d Darkroom and photographic equipment

Constructing a darkroom. Many students are interested in photography and they may be helped to gain skill through practice if a darkroom is available. If

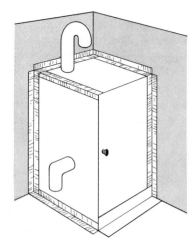

Fig. 26-2 A darkroom can be made in the corner of a room.

there is an available closet in school, a darkroom can be prepared and furnished with a small ventilating fan. Rubber strips cut from an automobile tire tube can be used over the inside edges of the door to block the light that may enter between the door and the jamb.

When a closet is not available, a substitute darkroom can be made in a corner of a room by setting two 4″ × 8″ sheets of wallboard or plywood into a corner using a half sheet (4″ × 4″) as a roof. Seal the edges with thick paper tape and seal the boards to the two walls as shown in Fig. 26-2. Lightproof photographers' cloth (from a photographic supply house) can be used to substitute for the door.

When neither a corner nor a closet can be spared for a darkroom, students can make the simple portable darkrooms that have been described in 20.7b.

Inside the darkroom, arrange the working surface for maximum efficiency. For example, construct strong shelves painted with asphaltum varnish behind the work surface for the storage of chemicals and equipment. Erect a safelight of the proper type for contact or enlarging paper about three feet above the working surface. Lightproof drawers can be built under the working surface so that contact paper is just below the printing box and enlarging paper is just under the enlarger. (See 20.7 for instructions concerning the making of an enlarger and a printing box.)

When running water for washing prints is not available, use a five-gallon jug equipped with a siphon and a crock or plastic bucket as a drain.

26.2e   *Heating equipment*

There are substitute devices that teachers use when gas or heating equipment is not available in the classroom. These are suggestions that students may also use for their home laboratories. Electric hot plates and small electric stoves can be purchased, or cylinders of liquid fuel (propane) with attached burners (see supply houses) are especially adaptable for class use. If there is gas elsewhere in the building, you can carry 2½ minutes of gas supply in a basketball bladder. Alcohol lamps can be used for low-temperature heating; or small alcohol stoves can be purchased.

You may want to refer to methods for constructing other heating equipment: electric test tube heaters (25.3a) and electric immersion heaters (available in many drug and hardware stores). Students can make their own Bunsen burners when gas is available (25.3a).

26.2f   *Refrigeration*

A standard household refrigerator or the complete working mechanism of a refrigerator is useful laboratory equipment for making ice cubes for use in experiments and for storing chemicals which must be kept at low temperatures. If a used refrigerator is made available, be certain that it is a type which uses freon as the refrigerant.

On a small scale, ice and salt or ice and rock salt may be used around a container to produce temperatures below the freezing point.

Extremely low temperatures may be produced by a mixture of alcohol and dry ice or acetone and dry ice. (See 4.6d.)

26.3   **Student squads**

Science teachers who must prepare their own demonstrations for laboratory periods have a heavy teaching load compared to other teachers in the school. When students are organized as a squad, they can reduce the time and energy that go into preparation. Students also gain in manipulative skills and can be given many opportunities for initiating their own small "research" projects under the teacher's sponsorship. In some schools, teachers have special buttons made for squad members, and the fact that students have participated in this kind of activity is noted on their permanent record cards. It is advisable to have consent notes from the parents of squad members on file and to obtain the approval of the school administration.

26.3a   Suggested squad activities

No two schools are the same. In the small school a teacher with ten students must gather together his demonstration material hurriedly; in the large school there may well be "red tape" and long trips to centrally located storage rooms. However, whatever the size of school or type of science program, squads of students can do much that will free the teacher of time-consuming detail.

There follows a suggested listing of squad activities. This is not exhaustive. Separate activities can be combined, or many activities can be even further specialized. A comprehensive description of the methods many teachers employ in using student resources is given in the companion volume, *A Sourcebook for the Biological Sciences* by E. Morholt, P. Brandwein, and A. Joseph (Harcourt, Brace, 1958).

Procurement. Preparation in advance of materials and apparatus needed for a particular demonstration or laboratory period. The activities of such a squad can be keyed to the routine of the particular school. One group may be responsible for preparing setups or equipment ordered, another for returning material to storage. It is suggested that any transport of chemicals and apparatus take place when the halls are relatively empty. Several teachers may pool squad activities.

Clean up. Putting the demonstration table in order at the end of class, seeing to it that all materials are returned to storage, and getting the laboratory ready for use by the next group. This squad may be part of another group concerned with laboratory maintenance, keeping apparatus assembled, watching over long-term demonstrations, and watching for devices that need repair.

Safety. One group can be responsible for designing fire and other emergency drills and can acquaint the rest of the class with what should be done if clothing catches on fire, acid (or caustic) is spilled on skin, if a substance gets in the eye, how dangerous apparatus (and chemicals) are handled, and so forth.

Building apparatus. Many of the devices described in this book can be built by students and, once built, become part of the science department's teaching resources. The same applies to the making of charts and models.

Books. One squad can look into and procure books and periodicals of interest to students of science. In connection with this you may want to write to AAAS, 1515 Massachusetts Ave., N.W., Washington, 5, D.C., for their comprehensive list of paperbacks, *An Inexpensive Science Library* (cost, $0.10).

Research. A group of this sort might devote itself to keeping abreast of current developments in some aspect of science and communicate these happenings by means of a bulletin board or by publication of a mimeographed magazine.

Special jobs. Squads can be formed to run the mimeograph machine, the movie and slide projectors, and other basic laboratory equipment.

Tutoring. Here students can be of great help to each other. A special group might be set up whose purpose may be to help the students in difficulty or to review the student who has been absent.

26.4 Safety in the laboratory and classroom

Basically, safety precautions for the classroom and laboratory involve good planning and common sense in the use of chemicals and equipment. Certain safety steps should be standard operating procedure for all the members of a science department. Students who work on squads should also be trained in their responsibility in establishing good safety practices.

26.4a Disposal of laboratory waste

Silicon steel drain pipes or other non-corrosive plumbing are best for disposal of chemical wastes. Avoid pouring chemicals into a sink that is not equipped with these pipes. Acids and caustics will corrode ordinary pipes and drains. If you lack the proper type of pipe, collect the chemical wastes in earthenware crocks or enamel-lined pails that can be carried to a protected drain or sewer. Flush the sink and pipes with running water after acids or alkalis have been disposed of; strong acids should be poured slowly with cold running water. Avoid pouring one chemical after another; they may react together.

Powdered wastes may be inflammable or explosive and should not be mixed with ordinary waste that is to be burned.

Broken glassware should be collected in earthenware crocks labeled for this purpose.

26.4b Handling gases

The generation of different gases has been described (see index for specific gases). Certain safety precautions for handling gases are in order. Pure oxygen must never be used with tubing, valves, or stopcocks containing grease, as this may result in an explosion when the oxygen oxidizes the grease. It is safer to use rubber tubing with a pinch clamp as a valve for oxygen.

Special oxygen valves can be purchased. In addition, tubing delivering oxygen (and hydrogen) should contain a safety tube to prevent flashback. This type of safety tube is discussed in 7.2a.

The flow of hydrogen should be carefully controlled so that the gas does not escape into the room where flames or sparks might be present. Chlorine should be stored in a room where its fumes cannot attack metals. In addition, never allow chlorine to escape into the air. When chlorine is used in a demonstration, have available a container of hypo dissolved in water into which the delivery tube can be inserted when it is no longer in use. Any chlorine remaining will react with the hypo, producing a sulfur precipitate.

Other gases such as carbon dioxide, nitrogen, and helium which are not combustible should be controlled to prevent excessive concentration of the atmosphere in a small or in an unventilated room (i.e., a concentration of more than 8% carbon dioxide may produce unconsciousness).

26.4c General safety rules

A pamphlet of concise, comprehensive general instructions concerning the responsibilities of the head of a science department, science teachers, and students in maintaining safety is distributed by the New York City Board of Education. We reprint here some of the safety provisions relevant for teachers of science from the pamphlet *For Greater Safety in Science Teaching.*[1] Occasional parenthetical cross references to this sourcebook have been added for convenience.

REGULATIONS FOR SCIENCE CHAIRMEN

File with the principal each term a signed statement that they (the science teachers) have read the rules and that the provisions of this report have been compiled with. A receipt from

[1] New York City Board of Education, 110 Livingston Street, Brooklyn 1, N.Y. Revision in press.

each teacher should be kept on file.

Notify the principal in writing each term, and immediately in the case of emergencies, of any hazards such as

a. Defective gas fixtures, electrical outlets, and connections.

b. Seats so defective that they may cause injury.

c. Inadequate storage cabinets.

d. Lack of fire blankets, extinguishers, fire pails, and sand.

See that a first aid cabinet is ordered and placed in each science laboratory and preparation room and elsewhere as needed, and that ample reserve stocks of tannic acid salve for possible burns, antidotes for poisons, and first-aid material are provided. At least two copies of the Red Cross booklet on First Aid should be kept with each first-aid cabinet.

Inspect first-aid cabinets and fire extinguishers at least once a term.

Make certain that combustible and dangerous materials such as poisons are kept securely locked in a metal cabinet. Acids should be stored in an albarene closet, never in ordinary closets or wooden cabinets. Do not store chemicals which react with each other in close proximity such as glycerin and nitric acid, potassium chlorate and organic compounds, and cyanides and acids, etc. No pupils should have access to such lockers and storerooms or closets in stockrooms.

See that the cabinet for the storing of sodium, potassium, calcium, and calcium carbide has printed on it boldly in white the warning, "In case of fire, do not use water."

See that pupils do not handle materials in cabinets reserved for dangerous substances.

Inspect chemical cabinets and keep on hand the dates of such inspection.

Keep tools and sharp-edged instruments under supervision, and exercise the greatest care when they are used by pupils.

In making electrical connections for the use of stereopticons, film projectors, and the like, use heavy rubber-covered wall plugs (to avoid cracking if dropped) and high-quality cable (double cords within heavy insulation) which will not kink or easily break. This will prevent short circuits and the danger of both electric shock and fire.

Be responsible for acquainting all squad members with the safety rules and regulations at the beginning of their service.

Secure parents' consent in each case for the work of squad members.

See to it that a metal or earthenware waste jar is provided in every classroom where science experiments are performed. Such waste jar and *not* the wastepaper basket should be used for broken glassware, chemical residues, etc.

Discard unlabeled, contaminated, and undesirable reagents.

See that any demonstrations, experiments, or projects dealing with atomic energy or radioactivity are performed in accordance with safety practices in that field.

I. PUPILS

1. Pupils are to be under the direct supervision of a teacher at all times and in all places, as required by the By-Laws of the Board of Education.

2. Pupils are not to carry laboratory equipment or apparatus through the halls during the intervals when classes are passing.

3. Pupils are not to transport dangerous chemicals at any time.

4. Pupils are not to handle materials on the demonstration table except under the direction of the teacher.

5. Pupils are not to taste chemicals or other materials.

6. Before permitting pupils to work with sharp tools, the teacher must be assured that pupils are fully competent to use the tools.

7. At the beginning of each term, pupils should be instructed in general safety precautions.

8. Pupils should be specifically instructed regarding the dangers and the precautions required, at the beginning of each laboratory period where there is a special hazard.

9. Pupils should be cautioned about hazardous activities involving the use of chemicals outside the school—e.g., mixing chemicals to "see what happens," setting fire to gasoline cans, breaking open fluorescent tubes.

II. TEACHERS

1. Teachers must

a. Report to the principal any injury or accident immediately.

b. Arrange for the completion and filing of the proper forms to be signed by

a. the injured party

b. witnesses

c. teacher concerned, or laboratory assistant

2. Teachers must be fully acquainted with first aid treatments.

3. Teachers should notify the chairman of the department of the existence or development

of any hazard that comes to their attention.

4. Teachers are to perform classroom experiments only if they themselves have previously tried them out or have been properly instructed by the chairman or an experienced teacher.

5. When using volatile liquids which are inflammable, such as alcohol, in a demonstration experiment, care must be taken that any flame in the room is at an absolutely safe distance from the volatile liquid.

6. Demonstrations involving explosive mixtures must be so arranged as to shield both pupils and teachers from the results of the explosion. Even when there is no likelihood of an explosion, pupils should be asked to evacuate seats directly in front of the demonstration table whenever there is any possibility of injury to them by the spattering of a chemical, an overturned burner, inhalation of fumes, etc.

7. Large storage bottles of dangerous chemicals such as acids and alkalis, if on shelves, are to be no more than two feet above the floor. If possible, they should be kept on the floor.

8. Never add water to concentrated sulphuric acid. If it is necessary to prepare diluted acid, the concentrated acid should always be added in small quantities to the water, stirring continuously.

9. Handle all corrosive substances with the greatest care. Special precautions should be taken with concentrated sulphuric acid, nitric acid, glacial acetic acid, and concentrated solutions of caustic alkalies and other corrosive chemicals as phenol, etc.

10. White phosphorus must be kept under water in a double container, one part of which is metal. This form of phosphorus must be cut under water. If cut in the open air, the friction may be sufficient to ignite the material with very serious results. Use red phosphorus in place of white phosphorus whenever possible.

11. Residues of phosphorus should be completely burned in the hood before depositing in the waste jar.

12. Combustible materials of all types are to be kept in a metal cabinet or albarene closet provided with proper means for closing and locking.

13. Metallic sodium, potassium, and calcium, and calcium carbide should be stored above water solutions or vessels containing water. Metallic sodium and potassium, after the original container has been opened, must thereafter be kept under kerosene. These substances are corrosive and must not come in contact with the skin.

14. Do not demonstrate devices or equipment brought in by pupils before pretesting.

15. When a motion picture machine or other projection apparatus is sent into nonscience classrooms, a carbon tetrachloride extinguisher should accompany the apparatus.

26.4d *Safety suggestions in chemistry*[2]

1. *Laboratory preparation of oxygen* (see 2.2c, 7.1b)

a. Care must be taken to avoid exposing potassium chlorate, manganese dioxide, sodium peroxide, or any other oxidizing agents to contamination. Dangerous explosions may result from the presence of organic material in an oxidizing agent.

b. In the experiment where oxygen is prepared by heating manganese dioxide and potassium chlorate, make certain that the bottles of manganese dioxide and charcoal powder are not placed on the same shelf or near each other in the laboratory . By keeping them in different parts of the room, the possibility of a pupil's mistaking one for the other, and thereby possibly causing a serious explosion, will be removed.

c. Warn pupils against allowing the carbon from wood splints to fall into the hot potassium chlorate-manganese dioxide mixture. If this should occur, heating must be stopped immediately.

d. If the sodium peroxide method is used for preparing oxygen, the following precautions should be observed to insure safety.

1. Avoid contact of skin with moist sodium peroxide.

2. Make certain that no active sodium peroxide is left in contact with paper or other easily ignitible substance. If paper is used for pouring the chemical into the generator, soak it thoroughly with water before discarding.

3. It is suggested that an Erlenmeyer or Florence flask be used as a generator instead of a bottle, thus avoiding the possibility of cracking the generator due to heat of the reaction.

4. It is suggested that the sodium peroxide be handed out to the pupils in the dry flasks, all ready for use.

5. The water must be carefully controlled by a dropping funnel.

[2] From *For Greater Safety in Science Teaching,* Board of Education, New York City. Revision in press.

6. Teachers should remember and emphasize to pupils that the flask, *after the reaction,* contains a caustic alkali.

e. Oxygen may be safely prepared from a 3–5% solution of hydrogen peroxide which is dropped on either powdered manganese dioxide or pelleted activated charcoal. No heat is necessary.

2. *Experiments on hydrogen* (see 2.2c, 7.2a, 7.2b, 7.2c)

a. All Kipp or other large generators should be equipped with safety devices. If safety devices are not available through science supply houses, they may be constructed by soldering a piece of fine wire mesh over one end of a short piece of brass tubing narrow enough to fit into ordinary black rubber tubing. (See 7.2a for a description of a monel safety tube.)

b. Never ignite hydrogen coming from a generator until you are quite certain that there is no residual air in the generator. One may test for this by taking samples of the evolving gas in a small test tube and bringing these to a Bunsen flame until a nonexplosive sample (no "pop") is obtained. Then, to ignite the generator, fill the test tube with the gas, ignite the gas in the tube, and finally ignite the generator by means of the burning gas in the test tube.

c. As a further precautionary measure, it is suggested that a towel be wrapped around the hydrogen generator before the evolving gas is ignited.

d. In putting potassium on water, use very small amounts of the metal to avoid dangerous spattering. It is suggested that a medium-sized crystallizing dish be used for this experiment, and that an appropriately sized watch glass or glass plate be used to cover it immediately after the potassium is put on the water. The reaction of sodium on water is safer, and should be used when either would do.

3. *Dehydration of sucrose by concentrated sulphuric acid* (see 9.3c).

In this demonstration the spongy lump of remaining carbon often contains some occluded concentrated acid. Pupils should not be permitted to handle the carbon or its container.

4. *Phosphorus*

In using a solution of phosphorus in carbon disulphide to demonstrate spontaneous combustion, great care must be exercised. The solution should be covered with a layer of water and kept in a small, glass-stoppered bottle which is stored in a metal container, the bottom of the container being covered with sand. To use the solution, a medicine dropper is squeezed and inserted below the water into the solution. After use, the medicine dropper is contaminated with phosphorus and constitutes a fire hazard. It is suggested that it be stored in the same metal can as the solution, being attached to the solution bottle by means of a wire holder. Articles having phosphorus on the surface may be made harmless by washing with a solution of copper sulfate. (For other material on spontaneous combustion, see 7.1c.)

5. *Laboratory preparation of rhombic sulphur* (see 9.1a)

a. If carbon disulphide is used as a solvent, open the windows and perform this part of the experiment first, before any of the Bunsen burners are lighted. All watch glasses containing sulphur in carbon disulphide should be placed under the fume hood. The carbon disulphide should be handed out by the laboratory assistant.

b. Carbon tetrachloride, as a solvent for sulphur, is a poor substitute but is much safer than carbon disulphide.

6. *Laboratory preparation of sulphur dioxide* (see 9.2c)

a. Unless exceptionally good ventilation equipment is available, it is inadvisable to perform this experiment in the laboratory, except by demonstration.

b. In any event, pupils should be cautioned against inhaling the gas.

7. *Laboratory preparation of halogens* (see Chapter 11)

a. Warn pupils against inhaling any of these gases. A bottle of ammonium hydroxide should be kept on hand and its vapors inhaled to counteract breathing of halogen fumes.

b. In testing for the halogens, do *not* use carbon disulphide. Carbon tetrachloride works just as well and is noninflammable.

c. It is suggested that chlorine be prepared only by the instructor as a demonstration.

d. Bromine vapor is poisonous and corrosive to the mucous membranes and the skin; it should be collected under water. Liquid bromine should be delivered in sealed capsules, and open stock should be stored in glass-stoppered bottles, sealed with paraffin or collodion.

e. Iodine vapor is poisonous. It should be prepared in small quantities only. (See 11.4.)

f. Hydrofluoric acid is dangerous both in liquid and gaseous form. Soluble fluorides are poisonous.

g. HCl may be safely prepared by students by

adding 2:1 sulphuric acid to solid NaCl in a 300-ml round-bottomed flask through a thistle tube. Moderate heat is required. (See also 11.2c.)

8. *Laboratory preparation of nitrogen and nitrogen compounds* (see Chapter 12)

a. In preparing nitric acid (12.3b), it is suggested that the retort be clamped into position by using a cork collar about ⅔ the way up the tubular portion of the retort, and the clamp tightened securely about the cork. In this manner, the retort can be easily and safely manipulated.

b. Concentrated nitric acid is highly corrosive. Pupils should be cautioned against spilling it on their skin or clothing.

c. Nitrous oxide should not be prepared by students. (See 12.3a.)

d. The preparation of nitrogen by heating a mixture of sodium nitrate and ammonium chloride is likely to produce an explosion if the substances are overheated. Therefore, this method should *never be used as a laboratory experiment*. If performed as a demonstration, make certain that the solution does not boil. If it does, add water. (For other methods of preparing nitrogen, see 12.1a.)

e. The preparation of nitrogen iodide should *never be attempted by students* under any circumstances.

9. *Ammonia fountain* (see 8.2b)

Make certain that the flask used is sturdily constructed. Otherwise, it may be crushed due to the partial vacuum developed in it. If available, use a round-bottom flask. It is stronger than the flat-bottom variety.

10. *Thermite* (see 10.2c)

In performing the thermite demonstration, be very careful in approaching a mixture that has apparently failed to ignite. The mixture may flare up suddenly.

11. *Phosphine*

Pupils must never be allowed to prepare phosphine. A teacher may demonstrate its preparation but the greatest care must be exercised throughout. The generator will explode if air gets in.

12. *Preparation of esters* (see 14.4f)

It is suggested that the materials in the test tubes be heated over a water bath instead of over a direct flame. Strong heat might cause spattering of the sulphuric acid-containing mixture.

13. *Fire extinguishers: demonstration only*

Glass models of fire extinguishers should be tested by the teacher in advance to assure proper

concentration of materials. If acid is too strong, the stopper may be blown out of the bottle and contents spattered upon students. Demonstrate the carbon tetrachloride fire extinguishers in well-ventilated rooms. Warn pupils of possible dangers. (See also carbon dioxide fire extinguisher in 9.5c.)

14. *Soap Making* (see 14.4g.)

Heat fat slowly with constant stirring to prevent spattering.

15. *Plastics* (see 14.5. and 15.1.)

Heat or add chemicals in hood or well-ventilated rooms.

26.4e Safety suggestions for physics teachers[3]

1. Electric current used in the laboratory should be sent through a protective limiting load resistance in order that no more than the desired amount of current will flow under any circumstances.

2. In pupil experiments involving use of the electric current, voltage should be limited to a maximum of 30 volts. This does not apply to electrical laboratories or shops where students have special training and background and suitable precautions are taken.

3. Where circuit breakers are not provided, electric lines to pupils' tables should be protected by enclosed fuses only.

4. In removing an electrical plug from its socket, pull the plug, not the electric cord.

5. In inserting an electrical plug, hold plug so that any flashbacks due to a short circuit will not burn the palm of the hand. This applies as well to holding a soldering iron.

6. In wiring an electrical circuit, make the "live" connection the last act in assembling and the first act in disassembling.

7. When using an electric current, avoid bringing both hands in contact with "live" sections of the circuit. If possible, use but one hand at a time in all manipulations involving an electrical circuit.

8. Electrical extensions used in the classroom for projection machines, etc. should be inspected regularly for defects in insulation and connections.

9. If the current is constantly used near any metal object, the object should be permanently protected with an insulating cover to avoid possible contact. General care should be observed

[3] From *For Greater Safety in Science Teaching*, Board of Education, New York City. Revision in press.

to see that live wires do not contact grounded metallic objects.

10. Exposed live electric switches on the front panels of laboratory and preparation room switchboards should be shielded by a wire cover or other protective device whenever pupils have access to such panels.

11. Connections shall not be made to electrical light sockets for the purpose of operating electrical appliances or for electric light extensions or portable lamps.

12. Multiple plugs shall not be used in electrical wall outlets. Semipermanent electrical connections shall not be made to wall outlets. Electrical apparatus consuming more than 1100 watts shall not be connected to wall outlets. Motor-driven apparatus shall not be connected to wall outlets unless such apparatus is essentially portable. Under no circumstances shall a motor requiring a starting current of more than 1100 watts be connected to a wall outlet.

13. During the charging of a student storage cell, pupils should be kept way from the fine spray which develops. It is harmful if inhaled or allowed to get on skin of pupils.

14. Care should be observed in teacher and pupil handling of a storage battery. In spite of its low voltage, it is a source of danger because of the acid it contains and because of the very high current which may be drawn from it on a short circuit.

15. All types of induction coils should be clearly marked for the low-voltage and high-voltage connections in order to avoid the possibility of shocks.

16. Instructors and pupils should, at all times, be shielded from x-rays and from ultraviolet apparatus.

17. In the handling of radio equipment by teachers and pupils, the following precautions should be observed.

   a. Make certain that the current is off before putting hands into the radio.
   b. Be sure that there is a "bleeder" (high resistance) across the output of the power supply. Otherwise, a severe shock from the charged condenser may result.
   c. In handling the so-called transformerless type of radio, where the tubes are series connected and the set works directly from the line, caution must be observed to prevent any grounded metallic object from coming in contact with the metallic chassis.

   d. In using a standard transformer radio, pupils must be cautioned on the handling of "B" voltages. The high-voltage secondary is in the order of 600 v d.c. Severe burns and shock can result from contact.

18. In evacuating a bulb during the density of air experiments, wrap it in a towel to avoid flying glass if the bulb should be crushed. Also use round-bottom flasks for the process. They are stronger than the flat-bottom variety.

19. In using a pressure cooker to demonstrate variation of boiling points with pressure, be sure to examine the safety valve before use to make sure it is in working order. Also do not allow the pressure to go above 20 pounds.

20. Caution should be observed in the use of the whirling table, Savart's wheel, siren disk, centrifugal hoops, etc. Make certain that the safety nut is securely fastened at all times; the apparatus should revolve at moderate speeds only.

21. Care should be taken to prevent pupil injuries due to sharp edges on mirrors, prisms, and glass plates. They should be inspected before they are handed to pupils, and sharp edges should be removed by grinding them with emery cloth or carborundum stone or by painting the edges with quick-drying enamel. Pupils should be instructed to report at once any sharp-edged apparatus handed to them.

22. a. The practice of removing thermometers, glass tubing, etc. from rubber stoppers as soon as possible after use will prevent the possibility of the glass freezing to the rubber.
   b. To remove thermometer or rod or glass tubing which has been "frozen" into a rubber stopper, the following method has proved safe and efficacious. Use a wet cork-borer, just large enough to slip over the tube, and slowly work the cork-borer through the stopper, thus boring the frozen tube out of the stopper.
   c. As an alternate method to "b" above, it is suggested that the rubber stopper surrounding a frozen thermometer be split open with a razor. The stopper can then be repaired with rubber glue, or can be used as a split stopper.

23. Exercise care in demonstrating, adjusting, or using image tubes of television receivers or cathode-ray oscilloscopes when these tubes are removed from their protective housing. They

can implode with great force. Flying frames can be very dangerous.

26.5 Getting information on facilities and supplies

Many communities are concerned with science facilities, either plans for building a new wing or a school or remodeling ordinary classrooms into science rooms. Where can you get help? Visit other schools and colleges, write to schools which have specialized facilities, consult professional education journals to find manufacturers of equipment and send for their catalogs. Many articles are listed in *Educational Index*, as, for example, such research findings as "The Coordinated Classroom" by D. Harmons, distributed by American Seating Company (Grand Rapids 2, Michigan, 1949).

You will want to use a reference that many teachers have already found most useful, the *Purchase Guide for Programs in Science, Mathematics, and Modern Foreign Languages* which was prepared by the Council of Chief State School Officers, with the assistance of Educational Facilities Laboratories, Inc., and others, (Boston, Ginn and Company, 1959). This reference will assist in the wise and economical purchase of apparatus, equipment, and materials in your school. In this Guide are listed for each science level—elementary science, general science, bi-ology, chemistry, and physics—materials considered *Basic* (i.e., required for use in every classroom and laboratory) for minimal programs in science; *Standard* (i.e., items which give enlarged scope for developing science programs); and *Advanced* (items needed for advanced or specialized work in class or for individual projects).

Also see the following as sources of information on equipment and supplies.

Fisher Unitized Furniture, Bull. FS–227, Fisher Scientific Co., 1458 N. Lamon Ave., Chicago 5, branch offices

Welch All-Purpose Furniture, W. M. Welch Scientific Co., 1515 Sedgwick Street, Chicago 10

Spitz Shadow and Ultraviolet Orreries, Spitz Laboratories, Inc., Yorklyn, Delaware

Catalog of Steel Specimen Cabinets, Chas. Lane Corp., 46 West Broadway, N.Y. 7

Total Experience Science Furniture, E. H. Sheldon Equipment Co., Muskegon, Michigan

Wood Educational Laboratory Furniture, Kewaunee Mfg. Co., Adrian, Michigan

For Greater Safety in Science Teaching, Board of Education, New York City, 110 Livingston St., Brooklyn 1, N.Y.

The major supply houses often have order books which list apparatus and supplies needed in the teaching of all the branches of science; these are available for the asking and provide a wealth of ideas for busy science teachers.

Section Five APPENDIX:

TEACHERS' REFERENCES

Reference tables

In this section we have included several tables that the teacher and student in chemistry and physics will refer to. Below is a listing of the tables that appear within the text; the bold number denotes the chapter wherein the table is included.

TABLE A-1
Altitude, barometer reading, and boiling point

altitude (approx. ft)	barometer reading (cm of mercury)	boiling point (° C)	altitude (approx. ft)	barometer reading (cm of mercury)	boiling point (° C)
15,430	43.1	84.9	3060	67.9	96.9
10,320	52.0	89.8	2400	69.6	97.6
6190	60.5	93.8	2060	70.4	97.9
5510	62.0	94.4	1520	71.8	98.5
5060	63.1	94.9	970	73.3	99.0
4500	64.4	95.4	530	74.5	99.5
3950	65.7	96.0	0	76.0	100.0
3500	66.8	96.4	−550	77.5	100.5

TABLE A-2
Density of liquids

(approximate grams per cubic centimeter at 20° C)

Acetone	0.79	Ether	0.74	Naphtha (petroleum)	0.67
Alcohol (ethyl)	0.79	Gasoline[1]	0.68	Olive oil	0.92
Alcohol (methyl)	0.81	Glycerin	1.26	Sulfuric acid	1.82
Benzene	0.90	Kerosene[1]	0.82	Turpentine[1]	0.87
Carbon disulfide	1.29	Linseed oil (boiled)	0.94	Water, 0° C	0.99
Carbon tetrachloride	1.56	Mercury	13.6	Water, 4° C	1.00
Chloroform	1.50	Milk[1]	1.03	Water, sea	1.03

[1] Not a single homogenous substance. Since the constituents can vary, the density also varies.

TABLE A-3
Specific gravity of common materials

(grams per cc at 20° C)

Agate	2.5-2.6	Granite[1]	2.7	Polystyrene	1.06
Aluminum	2.7	Graphite	2.2	Quartz	2.6
Brass[1]	8.5	Human body (normal)	1.07	Rock salt	2.1-2.2
Butter	0.86	Human body (when		Rubber (gum)	0.92
Cellular cellulose		lungs are filled)	1.00	Silver	10.5
acetate	0.75	Ice	0.92	Steel	7.8
Celluloid	1.4	Iron (cast)[1]	7.9	Sulfur (roll)	2.0
Cement[1]	2.8	Lead	11.3	Tin	7.3
Coal (anthracite)[1]	1.5	Limestone	2.7	Tungsten	18.8
Coal (bituminous)[1]	1.3	Magnesium	1.74	Wood	
Copper	8.9	Marble[1]	2.7	rock elm	0.76
Cork	0.22-0.26	Nickel	8.8	balsa	0.16
Diamond	3.1-3.5	Opal	2.1-2.3	red oak	0.67
German silver	8.4	Osmium	22.5	southern pine	0.56
Glass (common)	2.5	Paraffin	0.9	white pine	0.4
Gold	19.3	Platinum	21.4	Zinc	7.1

[1] Not a single homogeneous substance. Since the constituents can vary, specific gravity also varies.

TABLE A-4
Specific heat of some materials

(calories/gram/° C, from 20–100° C)

Air (constant pressure)	0.24
Alcohol	0.66
Aluminum	0.22
Cellulose (dry)	0.37
Charcoal (at 10° C)	0.16
Clay (dry)	0.22
Copper	0.09
Glycerin	0.57
Granite	0.19
Gold	0.03
Glass (normal thermometer)	0.20
Ice (at $-10°$ C)	0.53
Iron (cast)	0.119
Iron (wrought)	0.115
Lead	0.031
Marble	0.21
Mercury	0.033
Paraffin	0.7
Platinum	0.03
Petroleum	0.51
Silver	0.06
Water	1.00
Water vapor (constant pressure)	0.46
Water vapor (constant volume)	0.36

TABLE A-5
Range of resistances[1]

	ohm-meters (at 0° C)
Aluminum	2.63×10^{-8}
Amber	5×10^{14}
Boron	1×10^{6}
Constantin	49×10^{-8}
Copper	1.54×10^{-8}
Germanium	2×10
Glass	$10^{11} - 10^{13}$
Gold	2.27×10^{-8}
Iron	11.0×10^{-8}
Mercury	94×10^{-8}
Mica (colorless)	2×10^{15}
Nichrome	3.5×10^{-5}
Platinum	11.0×10^{-8}
Quartz (fused)	5×10^{17}
Silicon	3×10^{4}
Silver	1.52×10^{-8}
Sulfur	1×10^{15}
Tungsten	5.0×10^{-8}
Wood (maple)	3×10^{8}

[1] These are approximations since exact values vary, depending upon purity, handling, heat treatment, etc.

TABLE A-6
Coefficient of linear expansion

(approximate expansion per unit length per ° C $\times$ 10⁻⁶)

Aluminum	24	Rubber (hard)	80
Brass	19	Silver	17
Bronze	27	Steel	13
Celluloid[1]	109	Steel (stainless)	18
Cement	10–14	Tin	27
Formica[2]	30	Vulcanite	63
Copper	17	Wood (parallel	
German silver	18	to grain)	
Glass (plate)	.9	beech	.2
Gold	13	elm	.6
Granite	8	oak	.5
Gutta percha	198	pine	.5
Ice	51	walnut	.7
Iron (wrought)	11	Wood (across grain)	
Lead	29	beech	61
Magnesium[3]	27	elm	44
Platinum	.9	oak	54
Pyrex	3.6	pine	34
Quartz (fused)	.4	walnut	48

[1] At 20–70° C   [2] At 20–60° C   [3] At 20–100° C

TABLE A-7
Coefficient of volume expansion

(increase per unit volume per ° C $\times$ 10⁻³)

Alcohol (ethyl)	1.1
Benzene	1.2
Carbon tetrachloride	1.2
Ether	1.7
Gases (at 0° C and constant pressure)	3.7
Glass	.025
Glycerin	.5
Mercury	.18
Petroleum	.96
Turpentine	.97
Water (at 20° C)	.21

TABLE A-8
Electrochemical equivalents

element and valence	symbol and charge on ion (valence)	grams per coulomb or ampere-second
Aluminum	Al^{+++}	9.32 $\times$ 10^{-5}
Copper (2)	Cu^{++}	32.9 $\times$ 10^{-5}
Copper (1)	Cu^{+}	65.9 $\times$ 10^{-5}
Gold (3)	Au^{+++}	68.1 $\times$ 10^{-5}
Gold (1)	Au^{+}	204.4 $\times$ 10^{-5}
Hydrogen	H^{+}	1.04 $\times$ 10^{-5}
Iron (3)	Fe^{+++}	19.3 $\times$ 10^{-5}
Iron (2)	Fe^{++}	28.9 $\times$ 10^{-5}
Lead (4)	Pb^{++++}	53.7 $\times$ 10^{-5}
Lead (2)	Pb^{++}	107.4 $\times$ 10^{-5}
Nickel	Ni^{++}	30.4 $\times$ 10^{-5}
Oxygen	O$^{=}$	8.29 $\times$ 10^{-5}
Silver	Ag^{+}	111.8 $\times$ 10^{-5}
Zinc	Zn^{++}	33.9 $\times$ 10^{-5}

TABLE A-9
Wave lengths of various radiations

radiation	angstrom units[1]
cosmic rays	0.0005
gamma rays	0.005–1.40
x-rays	0.1–100
ultraviolet	2920–4000
visible spectrum	4000–7000
violet	4000–4240
blue	4240–4912
green	4912–5750
yellow	5750–5850
orange	5850–6470
red	6470–7000
maximum visibility	5560
infrared	over 7000

[1] To convert to inches, multiply by 3.937 $\times$ 10^{-9}; to convert to centimeters, multiply by 1 $\times$ 10^{-8}.

TABLE A-10
Periodic table of the elements*

1 H 1.0080																1 H 1.0080	2 He 4.003
3 Li 6.940	4 Be 9.013											5 B 10.82	6 C 12.011	7 N 14.008	8 O 16.000	9 F 19.00	10 Ne 20.183
11 Na 22.991	12 Mg 24.32											13 Al 26.98	14 Si 28.09	15 P 30.975	16 S 32.066	17 Cl 35.457	18 A 39.944
19 K 39.100	20 Ca 40.08	21 Sc 44.96	22 Ti 47.90	23 V 50.95	24 Cr 52.01	25 Mn 54.94	26 Fe 55.85	27 Co 58.94	28 Ni 58.71	29 Cu 63.54	30 Zn 65.38	31 Ga 69.72	32 Ge 72.60	33 As 74.91	34 Se 78.96	35 Br 79.916	36 Kr 83.80
37 Rb 85.48	38 Sr 87.63	39 Y 88.92	40 Zr 91.22	41 Nb 92.91	42 Mo 95.95	43 Tc (98)	44 Ru 101.1	45 Rh 102.91	46 Pd 106.4	47 Ag 107.880	48 Cd 112.41	49 In 114.82	50 Sn 118.70	51 Sb 121.76	52 Te 127.61	53 I 126.91	54 Xe 131.30
55 Cs 132.91	56 Ba 137.36	57 La 138.92	72 Hf 178.50	73 Ta 180.95	74 W 183.86	75 Re 186.22	76 Os 190.2	77 Ir 192.2	78 Pt 195.09	79 Au 197.0	80 Hg 200.61	81 Tl 204.39	82 Pb 207.21	83 Bi 209.00	84 Po (210)	85 At (211)	86 Em (222)
87 Fr (223)	88 Ra (226)	89 Ac (227)															

LANTHANUM SERIES

58 Ce 140.13	59 Pr 140.92	60 Nd 144.27	61 Pm (145)	62 Sm 150.35	63 Eu 152.0	64 Gd 157.26	65 Tb 158.93	66 Dy 162.51	67 Ho 164.94	68 Er 167.27	69 Tm 168.94	70 Yb 173.04	71 Lu 174.99

ACTINIUM SERIES

90 Th (232)	91 Pa (231)	92 U (238)	93 Np (237)	94 Pu (242)	95 Am (243)	96 Cm (245)	97 Bk (249)	98 Cf (251)	99 E (254)	100 Fm (255)	101 Mv (256)	102 No ( )

* Symbols for the elements are those used in the "Trilinear Chart of Nuclides" by W. H. Sullivan (Atomic Energy Commission, 1957). Atomic weights of stable elements are those adopted in 1957 by the International Commission on Atomic Weights. For those elements having no stable isotope, the mass number of the "most stable" well-investigated isotope is given in parentheses. For a definition of "most stable," see inside front cover of the Trilinear Chart of Nuclides.

This chart is adapted from one copyrighted in 1957 by Fisher Scientific Company. (From F. Miller, Jr., *College Physics*, Harcourt, Brace, 1959.)

Supplementary aids to the teacher:

readings and special techniques

There are many aids available for the teacher who seeks to help students gain additional skill in laboratory procedures, or in stimulating their reading of current journals.

Many teachers have used the accompanying suggestions in class, in club work, as ideas for assembly programs, and as a stimulus for those deeply interested students who want to begin a long-range science exploration—a small piece of research to be done over one to two years.

While readings from scientific journals or an historical treatment of a science concept have long been available, there now are many organized groups in science, and from industry, who are turning to the science classroom to provide ideas and varying techniques both for students and for teachers. And teachers have appreciated these aids and use them within the framework of class work for students of different abilities. We begin with examples of readings for students.

Readings

Some teachers provide copies of a reading for each student. These may be read in class and then discussed, or they may be used as extensions of the day's work and can be summarized at home. Other teachers make up a series of questions based on the passage and use these as tests of understanding.

Scientific American has been steady reading for many high school students and is therefore so well known that examples need not be quoted. Teachers can order from the publishers reprints of papers in physical sciences that have appeared in this journal over the years.

The number of paperbacks in science in-creases monthly. There are excellent books in the PSSC series from Harper and other publishers.

Many papers in the *American Scientist* would provide splendid reading material for class work: interpretation and discussion of designs for experiments. Only a very brief perusal of the following paragraphs from a reading from this journal will certainly stimulate the students' thinking.[1]

The carbon dioxide theory has given plausible explanations for the beginning of a glacial period and of the climatic oscillations that occur during a glacial period. What increases the total carbon dioxide amount sufficiently to bring a glacial period to an end? One possibility is that the rock weathering is slowly reduced because of the increasing flatness of the land. In addition extensive glaciation probably reduces the rate of weathering for the fraction of the land surface that is covered by the glaciers. Thus, as the loss of carbon dioxide from the atmosphere for weathering decreases as a glacial epoch nears its end, the amount of atmospheric carbon dioxide slowly increases until finally the surface temperature is too high to allow further growth of the glaciers. An extensive period of mountain building has occurred at intervals of roughly 250,000,000 years during the earth's history and a glacial period has followed in each case during the time interval when sufficient carbon dioxide was removed from the atmosphere.

What is the reason for the recent temperature rise that is found throughout the world? Will this trend toward warmer climates continue for some time? The carbon dioxide

[1] Quoted from p. 311, "Carbon Dioxide and the Climate" by Gilbert N. Plass, *American Scientist,* Vol. 44:3, July, 1956.

theory may provide the answer. We have discussed the burning of fossil fuels which is adding more than 6×10^9 tons per year of carbon dioxide to the atmosphere. If all of this extra carbon dioxide remains in the atmosphere, the average temperature is increasing at the rate of $1.1°$ C. per century from this cause. Since 1900 a careful study of world temperature records shows that the average temperature has been increasing at roughly this rate. Of course, the agreement between numbers could be merely a coincidence.

Wouldn't students want to read the rest of this paper on climatic change, and then pursue current work in the field?

A variety of special techniques

In this section are offered sources of some specialized techniques. These are not usually part of a high school course of study, but they offer stimulus for project work or, even, longer-range research work for individual students or groups in a club activity.

Urea synthesis.[2] Part of a synthesis is presented:

You can repeat Wöhler's synthesis of urea in the home lab without too much difficulty. Because of its instability, ammonium cyanate is prepared by mixing solutions of potassium cyanate and ammonium sulfate. Upon evaporation, the ammonium cyanate is converted into urea: $NH_4CNO \rightarrow NH_2CONH_2$, which is obtained as a white powder mixed with potassium sulfate. The urea is extracted with alcohol, in which potassium sulfate is insoluble.

Dissolve 3 grams of potassium cyanate in 15 cc. of water, and add an equal quantity of ammonium sulfate. After all solids are thoroughly dissolved, transfer to an evaporating dish and heat to dryness, stirring frequently. Continue heating until the solid residue is completely dry. Powder the residue with a pestle, then add 5 or 10 cc. of absolute alcohol (either ethyl or methyl). Heat the alcohol to boiling on a steam bath for about 5 minutes; then filter off the undissolved potassium sulfate. Add to this another 5 or 10 cc. of alcohol and repeat the extraction. Combine the two filtrates and cool thoroughly by immersing the container in an ice-salt mixture. Crystals of urea will separate; filter them off, allow to dry (do not heat).

The complete procedure and methods for identifying urea are described. Organic reactions, preparation of synthetic dyes, perfumes, plastics, are also well treated.

Teaching with radioisotopes. A manual of experiments[3] prepared by science teachers at the request of the U.S. Atomic Energy Commission gives specific details for experiments that are intended to be "open-ended" in order to encourage variations by students and teachers. Here is a brief quotation from p. 39, experiment 7 on "The Use of Radioisotopes in Analytical Chemistry":

Basic question: How can a radioisotope be use to indicate the amount of an element present in an unknown quantity in a solution? (A typical "tracer experiment.")

Procedural suggestions: To a solution with an unknown quantity of iron (made up by instructor beforehand, possibly 0.15 g $FeCl_3$ added to 15 cc of H_2O) add Fe^{59} of known activity. Pipet onto a labeled planchet an identical quantity of Fe^{59} for a control. Add enough NaOH solution to the iron solution to yield a weighable precipitate of $Fe(OH)_3$. Force-filter the mixture through a small Buchner funnel which will accommodate filter paper of planchet diameter. Remove the filter paper with tweezers and cement it to the planchet with a drop of sugar solution. Then evaporate the moisture from the planchet. Compare the count of the dry precipitate with the count of the control sample to determine the fraction of "label" recovered. Then weigh the precipitate and calculate the total iron in the original solution according to the analysis given below. To determine whether precipitation completely removed the element, continue adding NaOH until no increased formation of precipitate is noted. Force-filter and remove about 3 to 5 ml of filtrate to a planchet for evaporation and counting and comparison with the control to see if any of the label was not initially recovered.

Analysis: In the analysis we assume that the Fe^{59} added no significant amount of iron to that already present. The analysis is based on the following relations, in which "prec." means precipitated:

[2] Quoted from p. 62, *Organic Chemistry for the Home Lab,* Burton Hawk (Science Service, Washington, D.C., 1956), $2.00.

[3] *Teaching with Radioisotopes,* edited by H. Miner, R. Shackleton, F. Watson (U.S. Atomic Energy Commission, Washington, D.C., 1959), $0.40.

$$\frac{\text{wt. Fe prec.}}{\text{total wt. Fe}} = \frac{\text{wt. *Fe prec.}}{\text{total wt. *Fe}} + \frac{\text{CPM prec.}}{\text{CPM added}}$$

from which the total weight of the iron is found as

$$\text{wt. Fe} = \text{wt. Fe prec.} \times \frac{\text{CPM added}}{\text{CPM prec.}}$$

Since the iron precipitated is in the form of $Fe(OH)_3$, which is the material actually weighed, the weight of iron in the precipitate is found from

$$\text{wt. Fe prec.} = (\text{wt. prec.}) \left(\frac{Fe}{Fe(OH)_3} \right).$$

where the last term is expressed in atomic weights. In this case it would be 55.85/106.85, or 0.523. Thus the final equation becomes

$$\text{wt. Fe.} = (\text{wt. prec.}) \times \left(\frac{Fe}{Fe(OH)_3} \right) \times \left(\frac{\text{CPM added}}{\text{CPM prec.}} \right)$$

The equipment and the sources of difficulties are listed. There are some sixteen experiments described.

A collection of papers from the Journal of Chemical Education.[4] Willard Libby's paper on *Isotopes in Chemistry Teaching* gives technical information and laboratory experiments. This paper is representative of the many offered in this collection. Dr. Libby presents five experiments to illustrate the use of the methodology just described in the paper, using labeled reagents 6 N H_2SO_4 (10^6 disintegrations per minute S^{35}/ml), 6 N HCl* (10^5 d.p.m. Cl^{36}/ml), and solid Na_2C*O_3 (10^3 d.p.m. C^{14}/mg). The experiments using these radioisotopes are: Analysis of a solution for $SO_4^=$ both radiochemically and gravimetrically; Demonstration of crystal growth and consequent decrease in surface area of freshly precipitated AgCl; Following radiochemically the precipitation of basic carbonates; Assimilation of C^{14} by growing plants; The degree of uniformity of carbon assimilation in three-hour growth of plants.

Equilibrium. Oxidation and reduction. This is number 8 of the *Tested Demonstrations in General Chemistry*[5] available to teachers. Many suggestions are given for demonstrations that involve oxidation and reduction; only three will be quoted here.

Rate of reaction. 1. Match. Burn, raising question of why it needs energy of activation to start it, although once started it con-

tinues burning. 2. Iodine clock reaction. Stop-watch, two 400 ml beakers. Solution A: 2 g KIO_3 + 1000 ml water. Solution B: Dissolve 2 g soluble starch in 500 ml boiling water. Mix equal quantities of solutions A and B, pouring back and forth several times to mix thoroughly. Time the seconds it takes before the solution mixture flashes blue-black. 3. Effect of concentration. Solution A and B (from 2 above), six 400 ml beakers. In beakers place (1) 160 ml A, (2) 160 ml B, (3) 80 ml A + 160 ml water, (4) 80 ml B, (5) 40 ml A + 240 ml water, (6) 40 ml B. Have three students assist you. At time zero mix 1 + 2, 3 + 4, and 5 + 6; note times to flash blue-black for concentrations, 1, 1/2, and 1/4, respectively.

Finding molecular weights. The Manufacturing Chemists' Association has also prepared some open-ended experiments in chemistry, including a teacher information sheet and a student guide.[6] Only a brief quotation is given here to indicate this valuable aid for teachers of chemistry.

This is a "discovery" experiment. The student should reach a generalization from data which he has collected, and use this generalization to find the molecular weight of an "unknown."

The method of finding molecular weights by the effect on boiling and freezing points of solutions is discussed in some texts, but it is seldom included in laboratory manuals. Yet it is not beyond the range of high school students. The method is used for soluble *nonelectrolytes,* but this point need not be emphasized at first. Some students should be asked to experiment further with electrolytes. If no one does, the students should be informed about the effect of the presence of ions on the lowering of the freezing point.

[4] Quoted from p. 92, Related to Training and Experiments in Radioactivity Presented by Nuclear-Chicago Corp., 333 East Howard Ave., Des Plaines, Ill., 1959, free. Also branch offices.

[5] *Tested Demonstrations in General Chemistry,* compiled by H. N. Alyea, and reprinted from the 1955–56 volumes of *Journal of Chemical Education.* Available from the *Journal* (Easton, Pa.) for $1.50.

[6] This experiment was prepared by Paul Westmeyer, University High School, Urbana, Ill., as one of the many experiments offered in the *Scientific Experiments in Chemistry,* Manufacturing Chemists' Association, 1958.

The method in the student guide involves finding the freezing points of solutions, and gives directions concerning possible errors students may make in the laboratory; it offers conclusions and methods for utilizing the data in equations, raises further questions, and offers applications. This is the format for the many fine experiments offered in this chemistry series.

The mass of the electron.[7] Many teachers are now familiar with the experimental physics work developed by teachers in the Physical Science Study Committee (PSSC) at MIT. The laboratory manuals and text materials offer stimulating variations for presenting the major concepts in physics. We give here a brief quotation to show the calibre of the work offered in this area.

An electron, initially at rest, accelerates in an electric field and acquires kinetic energy equal to the product of its charge and the potential difference through which it moves, $\frac{mv^2}{2} = qV$. If the electron with velocity v then moves through a uniform magnetic field perpendicular to its direction of motion, the field exerts a centripetal force perpendicular to the electron's motion and the direction of the field. This force depends on the magnetic field strength B, the charge of the electron, and its speed; $F = Bqv$. The electron will follow a circular path of radius R given by $F = \frac{mv^2}{R}$.

Equating the two expressions for the magnetic force, $F = Bqv$ and $F = \frac{mv^2}{R}$, gives

$$v = \frac{BqR}{m}$$

or

$$v^2 = \frac{B^2q^2R^2}{m^2}$$

Substituting this expression for v^2 in the equation $\frac{mv^2}{2} = qV$ gives

$$m = \frac{R^2qB^2}{2V}$$

Instead of using a tube like that described in the text for accelerating and deflecting electrons, we will use a common, commercial vacuum tube used in tuning a radio. Figure 1 shows the construction of this tube. The electrons emitted by the cathode are accelerated by the potential difference between the cathode and the anode. They move rapidly outward in a fanlike beam, reaching nearly their maximum velocity by the time they emerge from beneath the black metal cap covering the center of the tube. Their speed is approximately constant over the remainder of their path to the anode.

The anode is coated with a fluorescent material which emits light when electrons strike it. Since it is conical in shape, we can see the path the electrons follow as they move outward from the cathode; when we look straight down from above, the conical anode slices the electron beam diagonally, showing the position of the electrons at different distances from the cathode. Two deflecting electrodes are connected to the cathode and, with no magnetic field present, they repel electrons moving toward them from the cathodes and from a wedge-shaped shadow behind them (Figure 2). . . .

Connect the coil and tube as shown in Figure 4. Set the anode potential to between 90 and 250 volts and then vary the current flowing through the coil until the curvature of the edge of the shadow is estimated to be the same as some small round object whose radius can be easily measured such as a dime, the center cap of the tube, or a small circle scratch on a piece of transparent plastic.

Make measurements for several different anode potentials and calculate the electron mass. (Note: 1 volt 1.6 × 10⁻¹⁹ joules per elementary charge.)

Would it be possible to use the earth's magnetic field to deflect the beam? How large a tube would you need? Assuming the earth had no magnetic field, would it be impractical to determine the mass of an electron by accelerating it horizontally through a known potential difference and subsequently observing its deflection in the earth's gravitational field?

[7] Quoted from the experiment "The Mass of the Electron," pp. 680–81, second portion of *Preliminary Edition of Laboratory Guide No. 3,* PSSC of Educational Services, Inc., April 9, 1959.

Bibliography:

books for a science library

Some of these books are recommended for the teacher's library; many others are suggested as a starting point in building a school science library for the use of both students and teachers. In general, the listing contains mainly technical references, although several excellent popularized accounts of science have been included. There are so many useful books that have recently appeared as popularized accounts that our listing would be without end if we attempted to categorize them here.

Science: general and historical

Adam, N. K., *The Physics and Chemistry of Surfaces,* Oxford U. Press, New York, 1949.

Andres, R., H. Miser, and H. Reingold, *Basic Mathematics for Science and Engineering,* Wiley, New York, 1955.

Ballentyne, D. W., and L. C. Walker, *A Dictionary of Named Effects and Laws in Chemistry, Physics and Mathematics,* Macmillan, New York, 1959.

Barnett, L., *The Universe and Dr. Einstein,* rev. ed., W. Sloane Assoc., New York, 1957.

Beeler, N., and F. Branley, *Experiments in Science,* Crowell, New York, 1955.

Bell, E. T., *Mathematics, Queen and Servant of Science,* McGraw-Hill, New York, 1951.

Berkeley, E., and L. Wainwright, *Computers: Their Operation and Applications,* Reinhold, New York, 1956.

Bohr, N., *Atomic Physics and Human Knowledge,* Wiley, New York, 1958.

Boole, G., *Calculus of Finite Differences,* 4th ed., Chelsea, New York, 1958.

Boucher, P., *Fundamentals of Photography,* 3rd ed., Van Nostrand, Princeton, N. J., 1955.

Boursnell, J., *Safety Techniques for Radioactive Tracers,* Cambridge U. Press, New York, 1958.

Butterfield, H., *The Origins of Modern Science, 1300-1800,* Macmillan, New York, 1958.

Calder, R., *Science in Our Lives,* Signet Key, New York, 1955.

Cohen, M. R., and I. E. Drabkin, *A Source Book in Greek Science,* Harvard U. Press, Cambridge, Mass., 1958.

Conant, James, *On Understanding Science,* Mentor, New York, 1951.

————, ed., *Harvard Case Histories in Experimental Science,* Harvard U. Press, Cambridge, Mass., 1957.

Cooley, H., *First Course in Calculus,* Wiley, New York, 1954.

Cox, D. R., *Planning of Experiments,* Wiley, New York, 1958.

Crane, E., A. Patterson, and E. Marr, *A Guide to the Literature of Chemistry,* 2nd ed., Wiley, New York, 1957.

Danielli, J., K. Pankhurst, and A. Riddiford, eds., *Surface Phenomena in Chemistry and Biology,* Pergamon, New York, 1959.

Delahay, Paul, *Instrumental Analysis,* Macmillan, New York, 1957.

Emberger, M., M. Hall, and W. F. Britton, eds., *Scientific Writing,* Harcourt, Brace, New York, 1955.

Estermann, I., ed., *Classical Methods,* Academic, New York, 1959.

Exner, R. M., and M. S. Rosskopf, *Logic in Elementary Math,* McGraw-Hill, New York, 1959.

Feenberg, E., *Shell Theory of the Nucleus,* Princeton U. Press, Princeton, N. J., 1958.

Finck, J., *Thermodynamics,* Bookman Assoc., New York, 1955. (Classic and generalized standpoints.)

Fraser, D., *Statistics: An Introduction,* Wiley, New York, 1958.

Gamow, G., *One, Two, Three . . . Infinity,* Mentor, New York, 1953.

Goldstein, P., *How To Do An Experiment,* Harcourt, Brace, New York, 1957.

Harwood, J., H. Hausner, S. Morse, and W. Rauch, eds., *The Effects of Radiation on Materials,* Reinhold, New York, 1958.

Heathcote, N. H. de V., *Nobel Prize Winners in Physics,* Abelard-Schuman, New York, 1954.

Hecht, Selig, *Explaining the Atom,* Viking, New York, 1954.

Heisenberg, W., *Physics and Philosophy,* Harper, New York, 1958.

Helton, F., *Introducing Mathematics,* Wiley, New York, 1958.

Hix, F., Jr., and R. Alley, *Physical Laws and Effects,* Wiley, New York, 1958.

Hodgman, C., et al., eds., *Handbook of Chemistry and Physics,* Chemical Rubber, Cleveland, O., latest ed.

Holton, G., *Introduction to Concepts and Theories in Physical Science,* Addison-Wesley, Reading, Mass., 1952.

———, and D. Roller, *Foundations of Modern Physical Science,* Addison-Wesley, Reading, Mass., 1958.

Hutten, E., *The Language of Modern Physics,* Macmillan, New York, 1956. Introduction to philosophy of science.

Langer, M., *My Hobby is Photography,* Hart, New York, 1956.

Lederer, E., and M. Lederer, *Chromatography,* 2nd ed., Van Nostrand, Princeton, N. J., 1957.

Ludovici, L., ed., *Nobel Prize Winners,* Associated Booksellers, Westport, Conn., 1957.

MacCurdy, E., ed., *The Notebooks of Leonardo da Vinci,* Braziller, New York, 1955.

Margenau, H., and G. Murphy, *The Mathematics of Physics and Chemistry,* 2nd ed., Van Nostrand, Princeton, N. J., 1956.

Meites, L., *Polarographic Techniques,* Interscience, New York, 1955.

Miner, D., and J. Seastone, eds., *Handbook of Engineering Materials,* Wiley New York, 1955.

Nagel, E., and J. Newman, *Gödel's Proof,* New York U. Press, New York, 1958.

Needham, G. H., *The Practical Use of the Microscope Including Photomicrography,* Thomas, Springfield, Ill., 1958.

Newman, James, *The World of Mathematics,* Simon and Schuster, New York, 1956.

Nicolson, M., *Science and Imagination,* Great Seal (Cornell U. Press), Ithaca, N. Y., 1956.

Pauli, W., *Theory of Relativity,* Pergamon, New York, 1958.

Pierce, J., and E. David, Jr., *Man's World of Sound,* Doubleday, New York, 1958.

Polanyi, M., *Personal Knowledge,* U. Chicago Press, Chicago, 1959.

Read, J., *Through Alchemy to Chemistry: A Procession of Ideas and Personalities,* Macmillan, New York, 1957.

Reddick, H., and D. Kibbey, *Differential Equations,* 3rd ed., Wiley, New York, 1956.

Reid, C., *Excited States in Chemistry and Biology,* Academic, New York, 1957.

Richardson, M., *Fundamentals of Mathematics,* rev. ed., Macmillan, New York, 1958.

Sarton, G., *A History of Science,* Harvard U. Press, Cambridge, Mass., 1952, 1959.

Sarton, G., *Six Wings: Men of Science in the Renaissance,* Indiana U. Press, Bloomington, Ind., 1956.

Schück, H., R. Sohlman, et al., *Nobel: The Man and His Prizes,* U. Oklahoma Press, Norman, Okla., 1951.

Schwartz, G., and P. Bishop, *Moments of Discovery,* Basic, New York, 1958.

Scientific American, *The Physics and Chemistry of Life,* Simon and Schuster, New York, 1955.

Shapley, H., S. Rapport, and H. Wright, *A Treasury of Science,* 4th ed., Harper, New York, 1958.

Siu, R., *The Tao of Science: An Essay on Western Science and Oriental Wisdom,* Wiley, New York, 1958.

Sommerville, D., *The Elements of Non-Euclidean Geometry,* Dover, New York, 1959.

Stevens, G. W., *Microphotography: Photography at Extreme Resolution,* Wiley, New York, 1957.

Taure, M., and H. Wooster, *Information Storage and Retrieval,* Columbia U. Press, New York, 1958.

Taylor, A., *Advanced Calculus,* Ginn, Boston, 1955.

Thomas, G., *Calculus and Analytic Geometry,* Addison-Wesley, Reading, Mass., 1953.

Thomas, T., *Physical Formulae,* Methuen (Wiley), New York, 1953.

Thurston, H. A., *The Number System,* Interscience, New York, 1956.

Tweney, C., and L. Hughes, eds., *Chamber's Technical Dictionary,* 3rd rev. ed., Macmillan, New York, 1958.

Van Nostrand's Scientific Encyclopedia, 3rd ed. Van Nostrand, Princeton, N. J., 1958.

Van Vlack, L. H., *Elements of Materials Science,* Addison-Wesley, Reading, Mass., 1959.

Vergara, William, *Science in Everyday Things,* Harper, New York, 1958.

Von Hippel, A., *Molecular Science and Molecular Engineering*, Wiley, New York, 1959.

Walls, H. J., *How Photography Works*, Focal Press, New York, 1959.

Wyckoff, R., *The World of the Electron Microscope*, Yale U. Press, New Haven, Conn., 1958.

———, *Purchase Guide for Programs in Science*, Ginn, Boston, 1959.

Weather and atmosphere

Best, A. C., *Physics in Meteorology*, Pitman, New York, 1957.

Cable, E., R. Getchell, W. Kodesch, W. Poppy, and H. Crull, *The Physical Sciences*, 4th ed., Prentice-Hall, Englewood Cliffs, N. J., 1959.

Fisher, R., *How To Know and Predict the Weather*, Mentor, New York, 1953.

Haltiner, G., and F. Martin, *Dynamical and Physical Meteorology*, McGraw-Hill, New York, 1957.

Hogg, J., J. Cross, and K. Vordenberg, *Physical Science, A Basic Course*, Van Nostrand, Princeton, N. J., 1959.

Houghton, H., ed., *Atmospheric Explorations*, Wiley, New York, 1958.

Hoyt, W., and W. Langbein, *Floods*, Princeton U. Press, Princeton, N. J., 1955.

Kimble, G., *Our American Weather*, McGraw-Hill, New York, 1955.

Krick, I., and R. Fleming, *Sun, Sea and Sky*, Lippincott, Philadelphia, 1954.

Laird, D. A., and E. C. Laird, *Weather Casting*, Prentice-Hall, Englewood Cliffs, 1955.

Longstretch, R., *Understanding the Weather*, Macmillan, New York, 1953.

Nakaya, U., *Snow Crystals, Natural and Artificial*, Harvard U. Press, Cambridge, Mass., 1954.

Petterssen, S., *Introduction to Meteorology*, 2nd ed., McGraw-Hill, New York, 1958.

Shapley, H., ed., *Climatic Change: Evidence, Causes and Effects*, Harvard U. Press, Cambridge, Mass., 1953.

Sloan, E., *Almanac and Weather Forecaster*, Little, Brown, Boston, 1955.

Swenson, H., and J. E. Woods, *Physical Science for Liberal Arts Students*, Wiley, New York, 1957.

U. S. Weather Bureau, *Manual of Radiosonde Applications*, U. S. Govt. Printing Office, Washington, D.C., 1957.

Weickmann, H., and W. Smith, eds., *Artificial Stimulation of Rain*, Pergamon, New York, 1958.

Willett, H., and F. Sanders, *Descriptive Meteorology*, 2nd ed., Academic, New York, 1959.

Earth's surface—land and water

Abelson, P. H., ed., *Researches in Geochemistry*, Wiley, New York, 1959.

Baity, E., *America Before Man*, Viking, New York, 1953.

Bates, D. R., ed., *The Planet Earth*, Pergamon, New York, 1957.

Buerger, M., *Vector Space*, Wiley, New York, 1959. Crystal structure.

Callison, C., ed., *America's Natural Resources*, Ronald, New York, 1957.

Cheronis, N., J. Parsons, and C. Ronneberg, *The Study of the Physical World*, Houghton Mifflin, Boston, 1957.

Dapples, E., *Basic Geology for Science and Engineering*, Wiley, New York, 1959.

Dohrs, F., L. Sommers, and D. Petterson, *Outside Readings in Geography*, Crowell, New York, 1955.

Doremus, R., B. Roberts, and D. Turnbull, eds., *Growth and Perfection of Crystals*, Wiley, New York, 1958.

Douglas, J., *The Story of the Oceans*, Dodd, Mead, New York, 1952.

Eddington, A., *The Nature of the Physical World*, Cambridge U. Press, New York, 1953.

Eiby, G., *About Earthquakes*, Harper, New York, 1957.

Emmons, W., G. Thiel, et al., *Geology: Principles and Processes*, 4th ed., McGraw-Hill, New York, 1955.

English, G., and D. Jensen, *Getting Acquainted With Minerals*, McGraw-Hill, New York, 1958.

Fenton, C., and M. Fenton, *Giants of Geology*, Doubleday, New York, 1952.

Finch, V., G. Trewartha, and M. Shearer, *The Earth and Its Resources*, 3rd ed., McGraw-Hill, New York, 1959.

Gamow, G., *Biography of the Earth*, rev. ed., New American Library, New York, 1959.

Greenhood, D., *Down to Earth: Mapping for Everybody*, Holiday House, New York, 1951.

Guy, A. G., *Elements of Physical Metallurgy*, 2nd ed., Addison-Wesley, Reading, Mass., 1959.

Hamilton, R., ed., *Venture to the Arctic*, Penguin, London, 1959.

Harker, A., *Petrology for Students*, 8th rev. ed., by C. Tilley, S. Nockolds, and M. Black, Cambridge U. Press, New York, 1954. Study rocks under microscope.

Heiskanen, W. A., and F. A. V. Meinesz, *The Earth and Its Gravitational Field*, McGraw-Hill, New York, 1958.

Himus, G. W., *A Dictionary of Geology*, Penguin, London, 1954.

Hough, J., *Geology of the Great Lakes,* U. Illinois Press, Springfield, Ill., 1958.

Howell, J. B. F., *Introduction to Geophysics,* McGraw-Hill, New York, 1959.

Howell, J. V., and A. I. Levorsen, *Directory of Geological Material in North America,* American Geological Institute, Washington, D.C., 1958.

Hoyt, W., and W. Langbein, *Floods,* Princeton U. Press, Princeton, N.J., 1955.

Hurlburt, C. S., Jr., ed., *Dana's Manual of Mineralogy,* 17th rev. ed., Wiley, New York, 1959.

Hurley, P., *How Old Is The Earth?,* Doubleday, New York, 1959.

Hyams, E., *Soil and Civilization,* Thames and Hudson, London, 1952.

Jackson, J. D., *The Physics of Elementary Particles,* Princeton U. Press, Princeton, N.J., 1958.

Jeffreys, H., *The Earth,* 4th ed., Cambridge U. Press, New York, 1959.

Johnson, J., *Physical Meteorology,* Wiley, New York, 1954.

Krause, E., W. Hunt, and L. Ramsdell, *Mineralogy,* 5th ed., McGraw-Hill, New York, 1959. Minerals and crystals.

Kraus, E., and C. Slawson, *Gems and Gem Materials,* 5th ed., McGraw-Hill, New York, 1953.

Leet, D., and S. Judson, *Physical Geology,* Prentice-Hall, Englewood Cliffs, N. J., 1954.

Longwell, C., and R. Flint, *Introduction to Physical Geology,* Wiley, New York, 1955.

Loomis, F., *Fieldbook of Common Rocks and Minerals,* Putnam, New York, 1948.

McCue, J. J. G., and K. Sherk, *The World of Atoms,* Ronald, New York, 1956.

Pearl, R., *How To Know the Minerals and Rocks,* McGraw-Hill, New York, 1955; also Signet Key, New York.

Pirsson, L., *Rocks and Rock Minerals,* 3rd rev. ed., A. Knopf, Wiley, New York, 1956.

Pough, F., *A Field Guide to Rocks and Minerals,* Houghton Mifflin, Boston, 1955.

Rapport, S., and H. Wright, eds., *The Crust of the Earth,* Signet Key, New York, 1955.

Richter, C., *Elementary Seismology,* Freeman, San Francisco, 1958.

Sinkankas, J., *Gemstones of North America,* Van Nostrand, Princeton, N. J., 1959.

Stommel, H., *The Gulf Stream,* U. California Press, Berkeley, Cal., 1958.

Swenson, H., and J. Woods, *Physical Science for Liberal Arts Students,* Wiley, New York, 1957.

U. S. Dept. of Agriculture, *Yearbook of Soil,* Govt. Printing Office, Washington, D.C., 1957.

U. S. Dept. of Interior, *Yearbook of Minerals,* Govt. Printing Office, Washington, D.C., 1957.

Wahlstrom, E., *Petrographic Mineralogy,* Wiley, New York, 1955.

Zim, H., and P. Shaffer, *Rocks and Minerals,* Simon and Schuster, New York, 1957.

Zumberge, J., *Elements of Geology,* Wiley, New York, 1958.

Astronomy and space science

Adams, C., *Space Flight,* McGraw-Hill, New York, 1958.

Adler, I., *The Stars,* New American Library, New York (n.d.).

Ambartsumyan, V. A., ed., *Theoretical Astrophysics,* Pergamon, New York, 1958.

Baker, R., *When the Stars Come Out,* Viking, New York, 1954.

———, *Astronomy,* 7th ed., Van Nostrand, Princeton, N. J., 1959.

Bernhard, H., D. Bennett, and H. Rice, *New Handbook of the Heavens,* Mentor, New York, 1954.

Bizony, M. T., ed., *The Space Encyclopedia,* Dutton, New York, 1957.

Bok, B., *The Astronomer's Universe,* Cambridge U. Press, New York, 1959.

Bondi, H., *The Universe at Large,* Doubleday, New York, 1960.

Branley, F., *Experiments in the Principles of Space Travel,* Crowell, New York, 1955.

Brown, R. H., and K. C. Lovell, *The Exploration of Space by Radio,* Wiley, New York, 1958.

Buerger, M., *Vector Space,* Wiley, New York, 1959. Crystallography.

Callaty, V. de, *Atlas of the Sky,* St. Martin's, New York, 1958.

Cohen, I. B., *The Birth of a New Physics,* Doubleday, New York, 1960.

Ehricke, K., *Space Flight: Volume I,* Van Nostrand, Princeton, N. J., 1960; Vol. II, III in prep.

Fath, E., *The Elements of Astronomy,* 5th ed., McGraw-Hill, New York, 1955.

Finlay-Freundlich, E., *Celestial Mechanics,* Pergamon, New York, 1958.

Gamow, G., *Matter, Earth, and Sky,* Prentice-Hall, Englewood Cliffs, N. J., 1958.

———, *The Creation of the Universe,* Compass Books (Viking), New York, 1956.

Gatland, K., ed., *Project Satellite,* British Book Center, New York, 1958.

Hoyle, F., *Frontiers of Astronomy,* New American Library, New York, 1957.

———, *The Nature of the Universe,* Harper, New

York, 1950; and New American Library, New York.

Ingalls, A. G., ed., *Amateur Telescope Making*, Scientific American, New York, 1953.

Jardetzky, W., *Theories of Figures of Celestial Bodies*, Interscience, New York, 1958.

Jones, H. S., *Life on Other Worlds*, Macmillan, New York, 1954.

Koestler, A., *The Watershed*, Doubleday, New York, 1960.

Kruse, W., and W. Dieckvoss, *The Stars*, U. Michigan Press, Ann Arbor, Mich., 1957.

Kuiper, G., ed., *The Earth As A Planet*, Vol. II of *Solar System*, U. Chicago Press, Chicago, 1954.

Levitt, I. M., *A Space Traveler's Guide to Mars*, Holt, New York, 1956.

Ley, W., *Rockets, Missiles and Space Travel*, Viking, New York, 1957.

———, and W. von Braun, *Exploration of Mars*, Viking, New York, 1956.

Ludlam, F., and R. Scorer, *Cloud Study: A Pictorial Guide*, Macmillan, New York, 1958.

Mehlin, T., *Astronomy*, Wiley, New York, 1959.

Menzel, D., *Flying Saucers*, Harvard U. Press, Cambridge, Mass., 1953.

Moore, P., *A Guide to the Planets*, Norton, New York, 1954.

Müller, W., *Man Among the Stars*, Criterion, New York, 1957.

Munitz, M., *Space, Time and Creation*, Free Press, Glencoe, Ill., 1958.

Opik, E. J., *Physics of Meteor Flight in the Atmosphere*, Interscience, New York, 1958.

Olcott, W., *Field Book of the Skies*, 4th ed. by R. Mayall and M. Mayall, Putnam, New York, 1954.

Payne-Gaposchkin, C., *Stars in the Making*, Harvard U. Press, Cambridge, Mass., 1952.

Schwarzchild, M., *Structure and Evolution of the Stars*, Princeton U. Press, Princeton, N. J., 1958.

Sidgwick, J., *Amateur Astronomer's Handbook*, Faber & Faber, London, 1955.

Struve, O., *The Astronomical Universe*, U. Oregon Press, Eugene, Ore., 1958.

Staff Report, 86th Congress, *Space Handbook: Astronautics and Its Applications*, U. S. Govt. Printing Office, Washington, D.C., 1959.

Sutton, O., *The Science of Flight*, Pelican, New York, 1955.

Texereau, J., *How to Make a Telescope*, Interscience, New York, 1957.

Thiel, R., *And There Was Light: The Discovery of the Universe*, trans. by R. and C. Winston, Knopf, New York, 1957.

Vaucouleurs, G. de, *Discovery of the Universe: An Outline of the History of Astronomy from the Origin to 1956*, Macmillan, 1957.

Watson, F., *Between the Planets*, rev. ed., Harvard U. Press, Cambridge, Mass., 1956.

Zinner, E., *The Stars Above Us: The Conquest of Superstition*, Scribner's, New York, 1957.

Chemistry

General

Abelson, P., ed., *Researchers in Geochemistry*, Wiley, New York, 1959.

Alyea, H., ed., *Tested Demonstrations in General Chemistry*, Journal Chemical Education, New York, 1955 and 1956.

American Chemistry Society, *Physical Properties of Chemical Compounds*, Advances in Chemistry Series, No. 15, Washington, D.C., 1955.

Arthur, P., *Analytical Chemistry*, McGraw-Hill, New York, 1957.

Asimov, I., *Building Blocks of the Universe*, Abelard-Schuman, New York, 1957.

Atack, F. W., ed., *Handbook of Chemical Data*, Reinhold, New York, 1957.

Ayres, G., *Quantitative Chemistry Analysis*, Harper, New York, 1958.

Bailey, D., *An Etymological Dictionary of Chemistry and Mineralogy*, E. Arnold, London, 1929.

Barlow, R. B., *Introduction to Chemical Pharmacology*, Wiley, New York, 1955.

Bates, R., *Electrometric pH Determinations*, Wiley, New York, 1954.

Bear, F., *Chemistry of the Soil*, Reinhold, New York, 1955.

Beeler, N., and F. Branley, *Experiments in Chemistry*, Crowell, New York, 1952.

Belcher, R., and C. Wilson, *New Methods in Analytical Chemistry*, Reinhold, New York, 1955.

Bellamy, L., *The Infra-Red Spectra of Complex Molecules*, Wiley, New York, 1958.

Benson, S., *Chemical Calculations*, Wiley, New York, 1952.

Berry, A., *From Classical to Modern Chemistry*, Cambridge U. Press, New York, 1954.

Bier, M., ed., *Electrophoresis: Theory, Methods and Applications*, Academic, New York, 1959.

Bischof, G., *Atoms at Work*, Harcourt, Brace, New York, 1951.

Boas, M., *Robert Boyle and 17th Century Chemistry*, Cambridge U. Press, New York, 1958.

Bogert, L. J., *Fundamentals of Chemistry*, 8th ed., Saunders, Philadelphia, 1958.

Boucher, P., *Fundamentals of Photography,* Van Nostrand, Princeton, N. J., 1955.

Chamot, E., and C. Mason, *Handbook of Chemical Microscopy,* vol. I, 3rd ed., Wiley, New York, 1958.

Clapp, L., *Chemistry of the Covalent Bond,* Freeman, San Francisco, 1957.

Clark, G., and G. Hawley, eds., *The Encyclopedia of Chemistry,* Reinhold, New York, 1957.

Clements, R., *Modern Chemical Discoveries,* Routledge, London, 1954.

Conant, J. B., ed., *The Overthrow of the Phlogiston Theory: Chemical Revolution of 1775-89,* Harvard U. Press, Cambridge, Mass., 1950.

Crane, E. J., A. M. Patterson, and E. Marr, *A Guide to the Literature of Chemistry,* 2nd ed., Wiley, New York, 1957.

Daggett, A., and W. Meldrum, *Quantitative Analysis,* Heath, Boston, 1955.

Daniels, F., et al., *Experimental Physical Chemistry,* 5th ed., McGraw-Hill, New York, 1956.

Davis, H. M., *Science Exhibits,* Science Service, Washington 6, D.C., 1959.

———, *Scientific Instruments You Can Make,* Science Service, Washington 6, D.C., 1959.

Deming, H., *General Chemistry,* Wiley, New York, 1955.

———, *Practical Laboratory Chemistry: A Manual for Beginners,* Wiley, New York, 1955.

Doremus, R., B. Roberts, and D. Turnbull, eds., *Growth of Perfection of Crystals,* Wiley, New York, 1958.

Duckworth, H., *Mass Spectroscopy,* Cambridge U. Press, New York, 1958.

Dyson, G., *A Short Guide to Chemical Literature,* Longmans, Green, New York, 1951.

Eley, D., *Catalysis and the Chemical Bond,* U. Notre Dame Press, Notre Dame, Ind., 1954.

Faith, W., D. Keyes, and R. Clark, *Industrial Chemicals,* 2nd ed., Wiley, New York, 1957.

Farber, E., *The Evolution of Chemistry,* Ronald, New York, 1952.

Farber, E., *Nobel Prize Winners in Chemistry 1901-50,* Abelard-Schuman, New York, 1953.

Fischer, R., and A. Basee, *Course in Quantitative Chemical Analysis,* Saunders, Philadelphia, 1956.

Fister, H. J., *Manual of Standardized Procedures for Spectrophotometric Chemistry,* Standard Scientific Supply Corp., New York, 1950.

Frey, Paul, *College Chemistry,* 2nd ed., Prentice-Hall, Englewood Cliffs, N. J., 1958.

Gaydon, A. G., *The Spectroscopy of Flames,* Wiley, New York, 1957.

Glocker, G., and R. C. Glocker, *Chemistry in Our Times,* Appleton, New York, 1958.

Gold, V., *pH Measurement,* Methuen (Wiley), New York, 1956.

Graham, R., and L. Cragg, *The Essentials of Chemistry,* Rinehart, New York, 1959.

Hamilton, L., and S. Simpson, *Quantitative Chemical Analysis,* 11th ed., Macmillan, New York, 1957.

Hartung, E. J., *The Screen Projection of Chemical Experiments,* University Press, Melbourne, Australia, 1953.

Haynes, W., *Chemical Trade Names and Commercial Synonyms,* 2nd ed., Van Nostrand, Princeton, N. J., 1955.

Hazel, J., *A Basic Laboratory Course in College Chemistry,* 2nd ed., Wiley, New York, 1957.

Hogness, T., and W. Johnson, *An Introduction to Qualitative Analysis,* Holt, New York, 1957.

———, *Qualitative Analysis and Chemical Equilibrium,* 4th ed., Holt, New York, 1954.

Holmyard, E. J., *Alchemy,* Pelican, London, 1957.

———, *Makers of Chemistry,* Oxford U. Press, New York, 1931.

Hopkins, B. Smith, and J. C. Bailar, Jr., *General Chemistry for Colleges,* 5th ed., Heath, Boston, 1956.

Huggins, M. L., *Physical Chemistry of High Polymers,* Wiley, New York, 1958.

Hutchinson, E., *Chemistry: The Elements of Their Reactions,* Saunders, Philadelphia, 1959.

Kendall, J., *Great Discoveries by Young Chemists,* Crowell, New York, 1953.

Ketelaar, J. A., *Chemical Constitution,* 2nd ed., Van Nostrand, Princeton, N. J., 1958. Chemical bond theory.

King, E., *Qualitative Analysis and Electrolytic Solutions,* Harcourt, Brace, New York, 1959.

King, W., *Semimicro Experiments in General Chemistry,* 2nd ed., Prentice-Hall, Englewood Cliffs, N. J., 1955.

Kitchener, J., *Ion-Exchange Resins,* Wiley, New York, 1957.

Kunin, R., *Ion-Exchange Resins,* 2nd ed., Wiley, New York, 1958.

Kynch, G., *Mathematics for the Chemist,* Academic, New York, 1955.

Lange, N., *Handbook of Chemistry,* 9th ed., Handbook Publishers, Sandusky, Ohio, 1956.

Langford, O., *Using Chemistry,* McGraw-Hill, New York, 1954.

Laubengayer, A. W., *General Chemistry,* Rinehart, New York, 1957.

Leicester, H., *The Historical Background of Chemistry,* Wiley, New York, 1956.

Leicester, H., and H. Klickstein, *Sourcebook in Chemistry,* Harvard U. Press, Cambridge, Mass., 1956.

Littlejohn C., and G. Meenaghan, *An Introduction to Chemical Engineering,* Reinhold, New York, 1959.

Lubs, H., ed., *The Chemistry of Synthetic Dyes and Pigments,* Reinhold, New York, 1955.

Luder, W., A. Vernon, and S. Zuffanti, *General Chemistry,* 2nd, ed., Saunders, Philadelphia, 1959.

Manufacturing Chemists Association, *Scientific Experiments in Chemistry.*

Markham, E., and S. Smith, *General Chemistry,* Houghton Mifflin, Boston, 1957.

Maron, S., and C. Prutton, *Principles of Physical Chemistry,* 3rd ed., Macmillan, New York, 1958.

Meites, L., and H. Thomas, *Advanced Analytical Chemistry,* McGraw-Hill, New York, 1958.

Mellon, M., *Quantitative Analysis: Methods of Separation and Measurement,* Crowell, New York, 1955.

Melville, Sir H., *Big Molecules,* Macmillan, New York, 1958.

Meyer, L. H., *Laboratory Manual for Introductory Chemistry,* Macmillan, New York, 1952.

Moeller, T., *Qualitative Analysis,* McGraw-Hill, New York, 1958.

Morrison, G., *Solvent Extraction in Analytical Chemistry,* Wiley, New York, 1957.

Nebergall, W. H., and F. C. Schmidt, *College Chemistry,* Heath, Boston, 1957.

———, *General Chemistry,* Heath, 1959.

Olson, A., C. Koch, and G. Pimentel, *Introductory Quantitative Chemistry,* Freeman, San Francisco, 1956.

Partington, J. R., *General and Inorganic Chemistry for University Students,* 2nd ed., Macmillan, New York, 1954.

———, *A Short History of Chemistry,* St. Martin's New York, 1957.

Pauling, L., *College Chemistry,* 3rd ed., Freeman, San Francisco, 1957.

Pecsok, R., ed., *Principles and Practice of Gas Chromatography,* Wiley, New York, 1959.

Penner, S., *Chemical Problems in Jet Propulsion,* Pergamon, New York, 1957.

Pierce, W., E. Haenisch, and D. Sawyer, *Quantitative Analysis,* 4th ed., Wiley, New York, 1958.

Read, J., *Through Alchemy to Chemistry,* Bell, London, 1957.

Riegel, E., *Industrial Chemistry,* 6th ed., Reinhold, New York, 1954.

Ritter, H., *An Introduction to Chemistry,* Wiley, New York, 1955.

Rose, Arthur, and Elizabeth Rose, *The Condensed Chemical Dictionary,* Reinhold, New York, 1956.

Routh, J., *20 Century Chemistry,* 2nd ed., Saunders, Philadelphia, 1958.

Sandell, E. B., *Colorimetric Determination of Traces of Metals,* 3rd ed., Interscience, New York, 1959.

Sanderson, R., and W. Bennett, *A Laboratory Manual for Introduction to Chemistry,* Wiley, New York, 1955.

Seaborg, G., and E. Valens, *Elements of the Universe,* Dutton, New York, 1958.

Semenov, N., *Some Problems of Chemical Kinetics and Reactivity,* transl. by J. Bradley, vol. I, Pergamon, New York, 1958.

Sienko, M., and R. Plane, *Chemistry,* McGraw-Hill, New York, 1957.

Sisler, H., C. Vanderwerf, and A. Davidson, *General Chemistry,* 2nd ed. Macmillan, New York, 1959.

Snell, C., and F. Snell, *Chemistry Made Easy,* Chemical Publishing, New York, 1959.

Steiner, L., and J. Campbell, *General Chemistry,* Macmillan, New York, 1955.

Swezey, K., *Chemistry Magic,* McGraw-Hill, New York, 1956.

Swift, E., *Introductory Quantitative Analysis,* Prentice-Hall, Englewood Cliffs, N. J., 1954.

Taylor, F. S., *A History of Industrial Chemistry,* Abelard-Schuman, New York, 1957.

Taylor Manual of Advanced Undergraduate Laboratory Experiments, Addison-Wesley, Reading, Mass., 1959.

Thornton, E., and H. Thompson, eds., *Molecular Spectroscopy,* Pergamon, New York, 1959.

Timm, J., *General Chemistry,* 3rd ed., McGraw-Hill, New York, 1956.

Venkataraman, K., *The Chemistry of Synthetic Dyes,* vols. 1 and 2, Academic, New York, 1952.

Vickerstaff, T., *The Physical Chemistry of Dyeing,* Interscience, New York, 1954.

Wagner, W., C. Hull, and G. Markle, *Advanced Analytical Chemistry,* Reinhold, New York, 1956.

Walling, C., *Free Radicals in Solution,* Wiley, New York, 1957.

Weeks, Mary Elvira, *Discovery of the Elements,* Journal of Chem. Ed., New York, 6th ed., 1956.

Wells, A. F., *The Third Dimension in Chemistry,* Oxford U. Press, New York, 1956.

Williams, E., and R. Johnson, *Stoichiometry for Chemical Engineers,* McGraw-Hill, New York, 1958.

Wilson, S., and M. Mullins, *Applied Chemistry,* Holt, New York, 1949.

Yoe, J., and H. Koch, *Trace Analysis,* Wiley, New York, 1957.

Zuffanti, S., A. Vernon, and W. Luder, *A Laboratory Manual for General Chemistry,* Saunders, Philadelphia, 1955.

Inorganic

Alexander, W., and A. Street, *Metals in the Service of Man,* Pelican, London, 1954.

Atkins, K. R., *Liquid Helium,* Cambridge U. Press, New York, 1958.

Basolo, F., and R. Pearson, *Mechanisms of Inorganic Reactions: A Study of Metal Complexes in Solution,* Wiley, New York, 1958.

Blumenthal, W., *The Chemical Behavior of Zirconium,* Van Nostrand, Princeton, N. J., 1958.

Charlot, G., and D. Bezier, *Modern Methods of Quantitative Inorganic Analysis,* Wiley, New York, 1957.

Charlot, G., *Qualitative Inorganic Analysis,* Wiley, New York, 1954.

Consultants Bureau, *The Geology of Uranium,* transl. from Russian Supplement 6 of *Soviet Journal of Atomic Energy,* New York, 1958.

Darken, L., *Physical Chemistry of Metals,* McGraw-Hill, New York, 1953.

Dodd, R. E., *Experimental Inorganic Chemistry,* Elsevier, Houston Tex., 1954.

Feigl, F., *Spot Tests in Inorganic Analysis,* 5th ed., Van Nostrand, Princeton, N. J., 1958.

Gilreath, E., *Fundamental Concepts of Inorganic Chemistry,* McGraw-Hill, New York, 1958.

Gould, E., *Inorganic Reactions and Structure,* Holt, New York, 1955.

Gray, A., ed., *Modern Electroplating,* Wiley, New York, 1953.

Guy, A. G., *Elements of Physical Metallurgy,* 2nd ed., Addison-Wesley, Reading, Mass., 1959.

Hadzi, E., ed., *Hydrogen Bonding,* Pergamon, New York, 1959.

Hamer, W., ed., *The Structure of Electrolytic Solutions,* Wiley, New York, 1959.

Harvey, H., *The Chemistry and Fertility of Sea Water,* Cambridge U. Press, New York, 1955.

Hawk, B., *Experimenting With Chemistry,* Science Service, Washington 6, D.C., 1957.

Hillebrand, W., G. Lundell, and H. Bright, *Applied Inorganic Analysis,* 2nd ed., Wiley, New York, 1953.

Iler, R., *The Colloid Chemistry of Silica and Silicates,* Cornell U. Press, Ithaca, N. Y., 1955.

Institution of Metallurgists, *The Structure of Metals,* Interscience, New York, 1959.

Jones, G., *Glass,* Methuen (Wiley), New York, 1956.

Kolthoff, I. M., and E. B. Sandell, *Textbook of Quantitative Inorganic Analysis,* Macmillan, New York, 1958.

Latimer, W., and J. Hildebrand, *Reference Book of Inorganic Chemistry,* 3rd ed., Macmillan, New York, 1951.

Lea, F. M., *The Chemistry of Cement and Concrete,* St. Martin's, New York, 1956.

Llewelyn-Jones, F., *Ionization and Breakdown in Gases,* Methuen (Wiley), New York, 1957.

Lyon, T. L., *Nature and Properties of Soil,* Macmillan, New York, 1952.

Mason, B., *Principles of Geochemistry,* 2nd ed., Wiley, New York, 1958.

Moeller, T., *Inorganic Chemistry, An Advanced Textbook,* Wiley, New York, 1952.

———, *Inorganic Synthesis,* McGraw-Hill, New York, 1956.

Nordman, J., *Qualitative Testing and Inorganic Chemistry,* Wiley, New York, 1957.

Parkes, G., *Mellor's Modern Inorganic Chemistry,* Longmans, Green, New York, 1951.

Pearson, W. B., *A Handbook of Lattice Spacing and Structures of Metals and Alloys,* Pergamon, New York, 1958.

Pollard, F. H., and J. F. McOmie, *Chromatographic Methods of Inorganic Analysis,* Academic, New York, 1953.

Riley, C., *Our Mineral Resources,* Wiley, New York, 1959.

Robinson, R., and R. Stokes, *Electrolyte Solutions,* Academic, New York, 1955.

Rochow, E., *An Introduction to the Chemistry of the Silicones,* Wiley, New York, 1951.

Sandell, E., *Colorimetric Determination of Traces of Metals,* 3rd ed., Interscience, New York, 1959.

Seaborg, G., *The Transuranium Elements,* Yale U. Press, New Haven, Conn., 1958.

Smith, M., *Principles of Physical Metallurgy,* Harper, New York, 1956.

Stock, J. T., and P. Heath, *Small Scale Inorganic Qualitative Analysis,* 2nd ed., University Tutorial Press, London, 1954.

Vival, G. W., *Storage Batteries,* 4th ed., Wiley, New York, 1955.

Organic

Adams, R., ed.-in-chief, *Organic Reactions,* 9 vols., Wiley, New York, 1944-57.

Anderson, A., and G. Pritham, *Laboratory Experiments in Physiological Chemistry,* 2nd ed., Wiley, New York, 1954.

Anfinsen, C., *The Molecular Basis of Evolution,* Wiley, New York, 1960.

Baker, J. W., *Electronic Theories of Organic Chemistry,* Oxford U. Press, New York, 1958.

Barnett, E. de Barry, *Mechanism of Organic Chemical Reactions,* Interscience, New York, 1956.

Braude, E. A., and F. C. Nachod, eds., *Determination of Organic Structures by Physical Methods,* Academic, New York, 1955.

Brauns, F., *The Chemistry of Lignin,* Academic, New York, 1952.

Bray, H. G., and K. White, *Kinetics and Thermodynamics in Biochemistry,* Academic, New York, 1957.

Brown, G., *An Introduction to Electronic Theories of Organic Chemistry,* Longmans, Green, New York, 1958.

Burr, J. G., *Tracer Applications for the Study of Organic Reactions,* Interscience, New York, 1957.

Caldwell, N. E., and D. Caldwell, *The Chemistry of Drugs,* Interscience, New York, 1959.

Calmon, C., and T. R. Kressman, eds., *Ion Exchangers in Organic and Biochemistry,* Interscience, New York, 1957.

Cason, J., *Essential Principles of Organic Chemistry,* Prentice-Hall, Englewood Cliffs, N. J., 1956.

Chaberek, S., and A. Martell, *Organic Sequestering Agents: A Discussion of the Chemical Behavior and Applications of Metal Chelate Compounds in Aqueous Systems,* Wiley, New York, 1959.

Chargaff, E., and J. Davidson, eds., *The Nucleic Acids: Chemistry and Biology,* vols. 1 and 2, Academic, New York, 1955.

Cheronis, N., and J. Entrikin, *Semimicro Qualitative Organic Analysis,* 2nd ed., Interscience, New York, 1957.

Colowick, S., and N. Kaplan, *Methods in Enzymology,* 6 vols., vols. 1 and 2, 1955; vols. 3 and 4, 1957; vols. 5 and 6 in prep. Academic, New York.

Conant, J. B., and A. H. Blatt, *The Chemistry of Organic Compounds,* 5th ed., Macmillan, New York, 1959.

Cook, A. H., ed., *The Chemistry and Biology of Yeasts,* Academic, New York, 1958.

Couzens, E. G., and R. E. Yarsley, *Plastics in the Service of Man,* Pelican, London, 1956.

Cowgill, R., and A. Pardee, *Experiments in Biochemical Research Techniques,* Wiley, New York, 1957.

Cram, D., and G. Hammond, *Organic Chemistry,* McGraw-Hill, New York, 1959.

Dartnall, H., *The Visual Pigments,* Wiley, New York, 1957.

Davidson, J. N., *The Biochemistry of Nucleic Acids,* 3rd ed., Methuen (Wiley), New York, 1958.

Duffin, D. J., *Laminated Plastics,* Reinhold, New York, 1958.

Dushman, S., and A. Joseph, *Chemistry of Petroleum,* American Institute of Petroleum, New York, 1961.

Dyson, G. M., *May's Chemistry of Synthetic Drugs,* 5th ed., Longmans, Green, New York, 1959.

Edsall, J., and J. Wyman, *Biophysical Chemistry,* vol. 1 1958; vol. 2 1959, Academic, New York.

Elkins, H., *The Chemistry of Industrial Toxicology,* 2nd ed., Wiley, New York, 1959.

Elsevier's Encyclopedia of Organic Chemistry, Elsevier, Houston, Tex., 1956.

English, J. Jr., and H. Cassidy, *Principles of Organic Chemistry,* 2nd ed., McGraw-Hill, New York, 1956.

Estok, G., *Organic Chemistry, A Short Text,* Saunders, Philadelphia, 1959.

Ferguson, L., *Textbook of Organic Chemistry,* Van Nostrand, Princeton, N. J., 1958.

Ferris, S. W., *Handbook of Hydrocarbons,* Academic, New York, 1955.

Fieser, L., *Experiments in Organic Chemistry,* 3rd ed., Heath, Boston, 1955.

———, and M. Fieser, *Basic Organic Chemistry,* Heath, Boston, 1959.

———, and M. Fieser, *Introduction to Organic Chemistry,* Heath, Boston, 1957.

———, and M. Fieser, *Organic Chemistry,* 3rd ed., Reinhold, New York, 1956.

Fisher, H., *Chemistry of Natural and Synthetic Rubbers,* Reinhold, New York, 1957.

Flagg, J. F., *Organic Reagents Used in Gravimetric and Volumetric Analysis,* Interscience, New York, 1948.

Fox, S., and J. Foster, *Introduction to Protein Chemistry,* Wiley, New York, 1957.

Frear, D. E., ed., *Agricultural Chemistry,* 2 vols., Van Nostrand, Princeton, N. J., 1950.

Fritz, J., and G. Hammond, *Quantitative Organic Analysis,* Wiley, New York, 1957.

Fruton, J., and S. Simmonds, *General Biochemistry,* 2nd ed., Wiley, New York, 1958.

Fuson, R., and H. Snyder, *Organic Chemistry,* 2nd ed., Wiley, New York, 1954.

Gattefossé, R. M., *Formulary of Perfumes and Cosmetics,* Chemical Publishing, New York, 1958.

Geissman, R. A., *Principles of Organic Chemistry,* Freeman, San Francisco, 1959.

Gillam, A. E., and E. S. Stern, *An Introduction to Electronic Absorption Spectroscopy in Organic Chemistry,* 2nd ed., E. Arnold, London, 1957.

Glascock, R. F., *Isotopic Gas Analysis for Biochemists*, Academic, New York, 1954.

Glick, D., ed., *Methods of Biochemical Analysis*, vol. 7, Interscience, New York, 1959.

Harrow, B., and A. Mazur, *Textbook of Biochemistry*, 7th ed., Saunders, Philadelphia, 1958.

Harrow, B., et. al., *Laboratory Manual of Biochemistry*, 4th ed., Saunders, Philadelphia, 1955.

Hart, H., and R. Schultz, *A Short Course in Organic Chemistry*, 2nd ed., Houghton Mifflin, Boston, 1959.

Haurowitz, F., *Biochemistry: An Introductory Textbook*, Wiley, New York, 1955.

Hawk, B., *Organic Chemistry for the Home Lab*, Science Service, Washington 6, D.C., 1956.

Hine, J. S., *Physical Organic Chemistry*, McGraw-Hill, New York, 1956.

Hollen, N., *Modern Textiles*, Burgess, Minneapolis, Minn., 1952.

Hückel, W., *Theoretical Principles of Organic Chemistry*, 7th ed., Elsevier, Houston, Tex., 1955.

Jacobs, M., *The Chemical Analysis of Food and Food Products*, 3rd ed., Van Nostrand, Princeton, N. J., 1958.

Jenkins, G. L., et al., *The Chemistry of Organic Medicinal Products*, 4th ed., Wiley, New York, 1957.

———, J. E. Christian, and G. Hager, *Quantitative Pharmaceutical Chemistry*, 5th ed., McGraw-Hill (Blakiston), New York, 1957.

Jergensons, B., *Organic Colloids*, Elsevier, Houston, Tex., 1958.

———, and M. Straumanis, *Colloidal Chemistry*, Wiley, New York, 1956.

Joseph, A., *Physics and Petroleum*, American Institute of Petroleum, New York, 1960.

Kelley, L., *Organic Chemistry*, 2nd ed., McGraw-Hill, New York, 1957.

Kharasch, M., and O. Reinmuth, *Grignard Reactions of Nonmetallic Substances*, Prentice-Hall, Englewood Cliffs, N. J., 1954.

Kinney, G., *Engineering Properties and Applications of Plastics*, Wiley, New York, 1957.

Kleiner, I., and L. Dotti, *Laboratory Instructions in Biochemistry*, 5th ed., Mosby, St. Louis, Mo., 1958.

Klotz, J., *Some Principles of Energetics in Biochemical Reactions*, Academic, New York, 1957.

Libby, W., *Radiocarbon Dating*, 2nd ed., U. Chicago Press, Chicago, 1955.

Linstead, R., J. Elridge, and M. Whalley, *A Course in Modern Techniques of Organic Chemistry*, Academic, New York, 1955.

Mann, F., and B. Saunders, *Practical Organic Chemistry*, Longmans, Green, New York, 1952.

Matthews, J. M., and H. Mauersberger, eds., *Textile Fibers: Their Physical, Microscopic and Chemical Properties*, 6th ed., Wiley, New York, 1954.

Maw, G., *Aids to Organic Chemistry*, 5th ed., Williams & Wilkins, Baltimore, Md., 1958.

Migrdichian, V., *Organic Synthesis*, Reinhold, New York, 1957.

Moncrieff, R., *Man-Made Fibers*, 3rd ed., Wiley, New York, 1957.

Noller, C., *Chemistry of Organic Compounds*, 2nd ed., Saunders, Philadelphia, 1957.

———, *Textbook of Organic Chemistry*, 2nd ed., Saunders, Philadelphia, 1958.

Neilands, J., and P. Stumpf, *Outlines of Enzyme Chemistry*, 2nd ed., Wiley, New York, 1958.

Nelson, W., *Petroleum Refinery Engineering*, 4th ed., McGraw-Hill, New York, 1958.

Packer, J., and J. Vaughan, *A Modern Approach to Organic Chemistry*, Oxford U. Press, New York, 1958.

Raphael, R. A., *Acetylenic Compounds in Organic Synthesis*, Academic, New York, 1955.

Riley, M., *Plastic Tooling*, Reinhold, New York, 1955.

Robertson, J. M., *Organic Crystals and Molecules*, Cornell U. Press, Ithaca, N. Y., 1953.

Shoppee, C., *Chemistry of the Steroids*, Academic, New York, 1957.

Shriner, R., R. Fuson, and D. Curtin, *The Systematic Identification of Organic Compounds*, 4th ed., Wiley, New York, 1956. Laboratory Manual.

Siggia, S., and H. Stolten, *An Introduction to Modern Organic Analysis*, Interscience, New York, 1956.

Smith, W., Jr., and R. Shriner, *The Examination of New Organic Compounds: Macro and Semimicro Analytical Methods*, Wiley, New York, 1956. Laboratory manual.

Spiel, H., and A. Schwarz, *Textile Chemicals and Auxiliaries*, Reinhold, New York, 1958.

Springall, H., *The Structural Chemistry of Proteins*, Academic, New York, 1954.

Sumner, J., and K. Myrbäck, eds., *The Enzymes: Chemistry and Mechanism of Action*, vol. 1, 1950-51; vol. 2, 1951-52, Academic, New York.

Surrey, A. R., *Name Reactions in Organic Chemistry*, Academic, New York, 1954.

Vogel, Arthur, *Elementary Practical Organic Chemistry*, Longmans, Green, New York, 1958.

Van Nostrand's Formulary, Van Nostrand, Princeton, N. J., 1958.

Whistler, R., and C. Smart, *Polysaccharide Chemistry*, Academic, New York, 1953.

Williams, R., *Biochemical Individuality*, Wiley, New York, 1956.

Winchell, A., *The Optical Properties of Organic Compounds*, 2nd ed., Academic, New York, 1954.

Wingate, I., *Textile Fabrics and Their Selection*, Prentice-Hall, Englewood Cliffs, N. J., 1952.

Physics

General

Andrade, E. da C., *An Approach to Modern Physics*, Doubleday, New York, 1957.

Aston, J., and J. Fritz, *Thermodynamics and Statistical Thermodynamics*, Wiley, New York, 1959.

Avery, M., *Household Physics*, 3rd ed., Macmillan, New York, 1955.

Baines, H., *The Science of Photography*, Wiley, New York, 1958. Written for the layman.

Band, W., *Introduction to Mathematical Physics*, Van Nostrand, Princeton, N. J., 1959.

Beiser, A., ed., *The World of Physics*, McGraw-Hill, New York, 1960.

Bell, C., Jr., and F. N. Hayes, eds., *Liquid Scintillation Counting*, Pergamon, New York, 1958.

Bennett, A., D. Gray, et al., eds., *American Institute of Physics Handbook*, McGraw-Hill, New York, 1957.

Bethe, H., and E. Salpeter, *Quantum Mechanics of One- and Two-Electron Atoms*, Academic, New York, 1958.

Birks, J., *Scintillation Counters*, Pergamon, New York, 1959.

Bitter, F., *Magnets: The Education of a Physicist*, Doubleday, New York, 1959.

Blackwood, O., and W. Kelley, *General Physics*, 2nd ed., Wiley, New York, 1955.

Blanchard, C., C. Burnett, R. Stoner, and R. Weber, *Introduction to Modern Physics*, Prentice-Hall, Englewood Cliffs, N. J., 1958.

Bohm, D., *Causality and Chance in Modern Physics*, Routledge and Kegan Paul London, 1957.

Bonner, F., and M. Phillips, *Principles of Physical Science*, Addison-Wesley, Reading, Mass., 1957.

Born, M., and E. Wolf, eds., *Principles of Optics*, Pergamon, New York, 1959.

Boys, C. V., *Soap Bubbles and the Forces that Mould Them*, Doubleday, New York, 1959.

Brand, L., *Vector Analysis*, Wiley, New York, 1957.

Buddenbrock, W. von, *The Senses*, U. Michigan Press, Ann Arbor, Mich., 1958.

Cable, E., R. Getchell, and W. Kadesch, *The Physical Sciences*, 3rd ed., Prentice-Hall, Englewood Cliffs, N. J., 1957.

Cohen, E. R., K. Crowe, and J. Dumond, *The Fundamental Constants of Physics*, Interscience, New York, 1957.

Condon, E., and H. Odishaw, eds., *Handbook of Physics*, McGraw-Hill, New York, 1958.

Consultants Bureau, *Russian-English Glossary of Nuclear Physics and Engineering*, 1958.

Dietrich, J., and W. Zinn, *Solid Fuel Reactors*, Addison-Wesley, Reading, Mass., 1958.

Doremus, R., B. Roberts, and D. Turnbull, *Growth and Perfection of Crystals*, Wiley, New York, 1958.

Dow, R., *Fundamentals of Advanced Missiles*, Wiley, New York, 1958.

Einstein, A., *The Meaning of Relativity*, 5th ed., Princeton U. Press, Princeton, N. J., 1955.

Etkin, B., *Dynamics of Flight: Stability and Control*, Wiley, New York, 1959.

Evans, R. M., *Eye, Film and Camera in Color Photography*, Wiley, New York, 1959.

Feller, W., *An Introduction to Probability Theory and Its Application*, Wiley, New York, 1957.

Ference, M., Jr., H. Lemon, and R. Stephenson, *Analytical Experimental Physics*, 2nd ed., U. Chicago Press, Chicago, 1956.

Finney, D., *Experimental Design and Its Statistical Bases*, U. Chicago Press, Chicago, 1955.

Forsythe, W. E., *Smithsonian Physical Tables*, 9th ed., Smithsonian Inst., Washington, D.C., 1954.

Fowler, R., and D. Meyer, *Physics for Engineers and Scientists*, Allyn & Bacon, New York, 1958.

Frank, R. G., and W. F. Zimmerman, *Materials for Rockets and Missiles*, Macmillan, New York, 1959.

Freeman, J., *Principles of Noise*, Wiley, New York, 1958.

French, A. P., *Principles of Modern Physics*, Wiley, New York, 1958.

Gilbert, William, *On the Magnet*, ed., by Derek Price, Basic Books, New York, 1958.

Gorter, I. C., ed., *Progress in Low Temperature Physics*, Interscience, New York, 1955.

Griffin, D., *Echoes of Bats and Men*, Doubleday, New York, 1959.

Hausmann, E., and E. Slack, *Physics*, 4th ed., Van Nostrand, Princeton, N. J., 1957.

Hiller, Lejaren, and L. Isaacson, *Experimental Music*, McGraw-Hill, New York, 1959.

Hoag, J. B., ed., *Nuclear Reactor Experiments*, Van Nostrand, Princeton, N. J., 1958.

Hoisington, D. B., *Nucleonics Fundamentals*, McGraw-Hill, New York, 1959.

Holton, G., and D. Roller, *Foundations of Modern*

Physical Science, Addison-Wesley, Reading, Mass., 1958.

Hooper, J., and M. Scharff, *The Cosmic Radiation,* Wiley, New York, 1958.

Horton, J. W., *Fundamentals of Sonar,* U.S. Naval Inst., Annapolis, Md., 1957.

Houstoun, R., *Physical Optics,* Interscience, New York, 1957.

Howell, B. F., *Introduction to Geophysics,* McGraw-Hill, New York, 1959.

Hunt, F., *Electroacoustics: The Analysis of Transduction and Its Historical Background,* Wiley, New York, 1954.

Ingram, D. J., *Free Radicals as Studied by Electron Spin Resonance,* Academic, New York, 1958.

Jackson, J. D., *The Physics of Elementary Particles,* Princeton U. Press, Princeton, N. J., 1958.

Jackson, L., *Low Temperature Physics,* 4th ed., Methuen (Wiley), New York, 1955.

Jaffe, B., *Michelson and the Speed of Light,* Doubleday, New York, 1960.

Jakob, M., and G. Hawkins, *Elements of Heat Transfer,* 3rd ed., Wiley, New York, 1957.

Jardetzky, W., *Theories of Figures of Celestial Bodies,* Interscience, New York, 1958.

Jelley, J., *Cerenkov Radiation and Its Applications,* Pergamon, New York, 1958.

Kac, M., *Probability and Related Topics in Physical Sciences,* Interscience, New York, 1959.

Kittel, C., *Elementary Statistical Physics,* Wiley, New York, 1958.

———, *Introduction to Solid State Physics,* 2nd ed., Wiley, New York, 1956.

Kramers, H., *The Foundations of Quantum Theory,* Interscience, New York, 1957.

Krauskopf, K., *Fundamentals of Physical Science,* 4th ed., McGraw-Hill, New York, 1959.

Kronig, R., ed., *Textbook of Physics,* 2nd ed., Pergamon, New York, 1959.

Lande, A., *Foundations of Quantum Theory,* Yale U. Press, New Haven, Conn., 1955.

Larmore, L., *Introduction to Photographic Principles,* Prentice-Hall, Englewood Cliffs, N. J., 1958.

LeGrand, Y., *Light, Color and Vision,* Wiley, New York, 1958.

Leighton, R., *Principles of Modern Physics,* McGraw-Hill, New York, 1959.

Mendenhall, C., A. S. Eve, D. A. Keys, R. M. Sutton, *College Physics,* 4th ed., Heath, Boston, 1956.

Menzel, D., ed., *Fundamental Formulas of Physics,* rev. ed., 2 vols., Dover, New York, 1960.

Miller, F., Jr., *College Physics,* Harcourt, Brace, New York, 1959.

Murray, H., *Color in Theory and Practice,* Wiley, New York, 1952.

Pauli, W., *Theory of Relativity,* Pergamon, New York, 1959.

Peierls, R. E., *The Laws of Nature,* Scribner's, New York, 1956.

———, *Quantum Theory of Solids,* Oxford U. Press, New York, 1955.

Phister, M., Jr., *Logical Design of Digital Computers,* Wiley, New York, 1958.

Physical Science Study Committee, *Physics,* Heath, Boston, 1960.

Pierce, J., and E. David, Jr., *Man's World of Sound,* Doubleday, New York, 1958.

Pokras, L., *The Properties and Structure of Matter,* McGraw-Hill, New York, 1958.

Pollack, P., *Careers and Opportunities in Engineering,* Dutton, New York, 1958.

———, *Your Career in Physics,* Dutton, New York, 1955.

Pollard, E., *The Physics of Viruses,* Academic, New York, 1953.

Randall, J., *Elements of Biophysics,* Year Book Publishers, Chicago, 1958.

Richards, P. I., *Handbook of Mathematical Physics,* Pergamon, New York, 1959.

Richtmeyer, F., E. Kennard, and T. Lauritsen, *Introduction to Modern Physics,* 5th ed., McGraw-Hill, New York, 1955.

Ridenour, L., *Modern Physics for the Engineer,* McGraw-Hill, New York, 1954.

Ruechardt, E., *Light: Visible and Invisible,* U. Michigan Press, Ann Arbor, Mich., 1958.

Scott, R., *Cryogenic Engineering,* Van Nostrand, Princeton, N. J., 1958.

Sears, F. W., *Mechanics, Wave Motion and Heat,* Addison-Wesley, Reading, Mass., 1958.

———, and M. Zemansky, *College Physics,* 2nd ed., Addison-Wesley, Reading, Mass., 1952.

———, *University Physics,* 2nd ed., Addison-Wesley, Reading, Mass., 1955. Based on Sears' 3rd vol. *Principles of Physics.*

Semat, H., and R. Katz, *Physics,* Rinehart, New York, 1958.

Smith, A., and J. Cooper, *Elements of Physics,* 6th ed., McGraw-Hill, New York, 1957.

Sokolnikoff, I. S., and R. M. Redheffer, *Mathematics of Physics and Modern Engineering,* McGraw-Hill, New York, 1958.

Spitzer, L., *Physics of Fully Ionized Gases,* Interscience, New York, 1956.

Sproull, R., *Modern Physics: A Textbook for Engineers,* Wiley, New York, 1956.

Stong, C. L., *The Amateur Scientist,* Simon and Schuster, New York, 1960.

Temple, G., *An Introduction to Fluid Dynamics,* Oxford U. Press, New York, 1958.

Tricomi, F. G., *Integral Equations,* Interscience, New York, 1958.

Trillat, J., *Exploring the Structure of Matter,* Interscience, New York, 1959.

Unified Educator Encyclopedia, *The Illustrated Encyclopedia of Modern Science,* Stuttman, New York, 1959.

Van Berge, J. K., J. R. Pierce, and E. E. David, *Waves and the Ear,* Doubleday, New York, 1960.

Von Neumann, J., *The Computer and the Brain,* Yale U. Press, New Haven, Conn., 1958.

———, *Mathematical Foundation of Quantum Mechanics,* trans. by R. Beyer, Princeton U. Press, Princeton, N. J., 1955.

Warren, F., *Rocket Propellants,* Reinhold, New York, 1958.

Weber, R., M. White, and K. Manning, *College Physics,* 3rd ed., McGraw-Hill, New York, 1959.

———, *Physics for Science and Engineering,* McGraw-Hill, New York, 1957.

White, G. K., *Experimental Techniques in Low Temperature Physics,* Oxford U. Press, New York, 1959.

White, Harvey, *Modern College Physics,* 3rd ed., Van Nostrand, Princeton, N. J., 1955.

Wood, A. B., *A Textbook of Sound,* Macmillan, New York, 1955.

Woodbury, D., *Around the World in 90 Minutes,* Harcourt, Brace, New York, 1957.

Wright, W., *The Measurement of Colour,* Macmillan, New York, 1958.

Zucrow, M., *Aircraft and Missile Propulsion,* vols. 1 and 2, Wiley, New York, 1958.

Electronics

Albert, A., *Electronics and Electronic Demonstrations,* Macmillan, New York, 1956.

Amateur Radio Relay League, *Radio Amateurs' Handbook,* Hartford, 1959.

Angelo, E., Jr., *Electronic Circuits,* McGraw-Hill, New York, 1958.

Arguimbau, L., and R. Stuart, *Frequency Modulation,* Methuen (Wiley), New York, 1956.

Attura, G., *Magnetic Amplifier Engineering,* McGraw-Hill, New York, 1959.

Bitter, F., *Currents, Fields and Particles,* Wiley, New York, 1956.

Blevins, L., and L. Crow, *Experimental Electronics for the Beginner,* Universal Scientific Co., Vincennes, Ind., 1955.

Bowen, E. G., *A Textbook of Radar,* 2nd ed., Cambridge U. Press, New York, 1954.

Carroll, J., *Modern Transistor Circuits,* McGraw-Hill, New York, 1959.

Collins, A. F., *The Radio Amateur's Handbook,* 10th ed., Crowell, New York, 1957.

Dewitt, D., and A. Rossoff, *Transistor Electronics,* McGraw-Hill, New York, 1957.

Farley, F., *Elements of Pulse Circuits,* Methuen (Wiley), New York, 1956.

Goodman, L., *Man and Automation,* Pelican, London, 1957.

Henney, K., and G. Richardson, *Principles of Radio,* 6th ed., Wiley, New York, 1952.

Hertzberg, R., *Electronics Handbook,* Fawcett, New York, 1956.

Hughes, E., *Fundamentals of Electrical Engineering,* Longmans, Green, New York, 1954.

Marcus, A., and W. Marcus, *Elements of Radio,* 3rd ed., Prentice-Hall Englewood Cliffs, N. J., 1953.

Morecroft, J., *Electron Tubes and Their Applications,* Wiley, New York, 1936.

Nett, R., and S. Hetzler, *An Introduction to Electronic Data Processing,* Free Press, Glencoe, Ill., 1959.

Newstead, G., *General Circuit Theory,* Wiley Methuen, 1959.

Pierce, J., *Electrons, Waves and Messages,* Hanover (Doubleday), New York, 1956.

Scott, W. T., *The Physics of Electricity and Magnetism,* Wiley, New York, 1959.

Shive, J., *Properties, Physics and Design of Semiconductor Devices,* Van Nostrand, Princeton, N. J., 1959.

Smyth, C., *Dielectric Behavior and Structure,* McGraw-Hill, New York, 1955.

Tall, J., *Techniques of Magnetic Recording,* Macmillan, New York, 1958.

Wass, C., *Introduction to Electronic Analogue Computers,* McGraw-Hill, New York, 1955.

Watkins, D., *Topics in Electromagnetic Theory,* Wiley, New York, 1958.

Upton, M., *Electronics for Everyone,* Signet Key, New York, 1957.

Atomic and solar energy

Allen, J., *The Neutrino,* Princeton U. Press, Princeton, N. J., 1958.

Andrews, E. R., *Nuclear Magnetic Resonance,* Cambridge U. Press, New York, 1955.

Bethe, H., and P. Morrison, *Elementary Nuclear Theory,* 2nd ed., Wiley, New York, 1956.

Cork, J., *Radioactivity and Nuclear Physics,* 3rd ed., Van Nostrand, Princeton, N. J., 1957.

Curtiss, L. F., *Introduction to Neutron Physics,* Van Nostrand, Princeton, N. J., 1959.

Daniels, B. F., *The Sun's Energy,* Stanford Research Institute, Stanford, Cal., 1955.

Eisenbud, L., and E. Wigner, *Nuclear Structure,* Princeton U. Press, Princeton, N. J., 1958.

Etherington, H., ed., *Nuclear Engineering Handbook,* McGraw-Hill, New York, 1958.

Fano, U., and L. Fano, *Basic Physics of Atoms and Molecules,* Wiley, New York, 1959.

Fermi, L., *Atoms in the Family,* U. Chicago Press, Chicago, 1954.

Glasstone, S., *Sourcebook on Atomic Energy,* 2nd ed., Van Nostrand, Princeton, N. J., 1957.

Hamilton, J., *The Theory of Elementary Particles,* Oxford U. Press, New York, 1959.

Hooper, J., and A. Scharff, *The Cosmic Radiation,* Methuen (Wiley), 1958.

Hughes, D., *On Nuclear Energy,* Harvard U. Press, Cambridge, Mass., 1957.

———, *The Neutron Story,* Doubleday, New York, 1959.

Jackson, J. D., *The Physics of Elementary Particles,* Princeton U. Press, Princeton, N. J., 1959.

Jungk, R., *Brighter Than a Thousand Suns,* Harcourt, Brace, New York, 1958.

Mather, K., and P. Swan, *Nuclear Scattering,* Cambridge U. Press, New York, 1958.

Rusk, R., *Introduction to Atomic and Nuclear Physics,* Appleton, New York, 1958.

Semat, Henry, *Introduction to Atomic and Nuclear Physics,* Rinehart, New York, 1954.

Taylor, D., *The Measurement of Radio Isotopes,* 2nd ed., Methuen (Wiley), New York, 1958.

Weinberg, A., and E. Wigner, *The Physical Theory of Chain Reactors,* U. Chicago Press, Chicago, 1958.

Wheatley, P., *The Determination of Molecular Structure,* Oxford U. Press, New York, 1959.

Whyte, G., *Principles of Radiation Dosimetry,* Wiley, New York, 1959.

Wilson, R., and R. Littauer, *Accelerators,* Doubleday, New York, 1960.

Woodburn, J., *Nuclear Science Teaching Aids and Activities,* Dept. of Health, Education and Welfare, Washington, 1959.

Young, M. E., *Radiological Physics,* Academic, New York, 1958.

Films and filmstrips

We hope that teachers will find this listing useful as a guide to films and filmstrips, recordings, and slides. Listings of films and filmstrips always seem to be incomplete or out of date; new films and filmstrips are produced regularly, and price quotations vary. This listing is subject to the same troubles; we recommend that teachers consult the reference aids listed below, and obtain catalogs from some of the distributors, also listed below.

The prices indicated here for *films* are *rental* fees; for *filmstrips, purchase* prices. (Filmstrips are not distributed on a rental basis.) Consult our directory of distributors for addresses; write to these distributors for catalogs, with purchase prices, when you want to purchase rather than rent films.

Where films are listed as "free" there is no rental fee; the school pays postal charges only. Many such films are available from industry and from state and government agencies (conservation, agriculture, forestry and wildlife, and others).

There are many techniques in showing films. A film or filmstrip need not be shown in its entirety; start the film at the place you want to use in your lesson to illustrate a point which cannot be demonstrated firsthand. A silent film may be stopped at times, so that a teacher may ask questions, direct students' observations, reverse and repeat a section for closer study and interpretation, or give students the time to ask questions while the film is still on hand. At the end of the film, students may be asked to summarize the main ideas, develop in words the concepts which were progressively developed in the film. See also the volumes, *Teaching High School Science: A Book of Methods,* Section V; and *A Sourcebook for the Biological Sciences,* Section Four.

Reference aids

3434 U.S. Government Films, Office of Education, U.S. Govt. Printing Office, Washington 25, D.C., $0.70.

Blue Book of 16-mm. Films, Educational Screen, 64 E. Lake St., Chicago 1, Ill., $1.50.

Directory of 2660 Film Libraries (16 mm), Office of Education, U.S. Govt. Printing Office, Washington 25, D.C., $0.35.

Educational Film Guide, H. W. Wilson Co., 950 University Ave., New York 52, N.Y., $3.00.

Educator's Guide to Free Films, Educator's Progress Service, Randolph, Wisc., $5.00.

Educator's Guide to Free Slidefilms, Educator's Progress Service, Randolph, Wisc., $4.00.

Evaluation of Current Films (monthly), Educational Film Library Association.

Film Library Catalogue, Dept. of Commerce, Albany 1, N.Y.

Filmstrip Guide, H. W. Wilson Co., 950 University Ave., New York 52, N.Y., $3.00.

Films for Classroom Use, Teaching Film Custodians, Inc., 25 W. 43 St., New York 36, N.Y.

Filmstrips: A Descriptive Index and User's Guide, Falconer, McGraw-Hill Book Co., New York, N.Y., $5.00.

Films, Recordings, and Slides, N. Y. State College of Agriculture, Cornell U., Ithaca, N.Y.

General Motors Motion Picture Catalog, General Motors Corp., Detroit 2; or 405 Montgomery St., San Francisco 4, Calif.

Lifelong Learning, Dept. Visual Institute, U. of California, Berkeley 4, Calif.

Modern Index and Guide to Free Educational Films from Industry, Modern Talking Picture Service, Inc., 45 Rockfeller Plaza, New York 20, N.Y.

Motion Pictures and Slide Films, General Electric Film Library, P.O. Box 5970A 840 South Canal St., Chicago, Ill.; or Peachtree Rd., Atlanta, Ga.; or 4966 Woodland Ave., Cleveland, O.; or 1801 N. Lamar St., Dallas, Tex. or 710 2d Ave., Seattle, Wash.

Reference Catalog of Medical Films and Filmstrips, Veterans' Administration, Washington, D.C.

Shell Motion Picture Catalogue, Film Library, 50 W. 50 St., New York 20, N.Y.; or 100 Bush St., San Francisco 6, Calif.

U.S. Govt. Films for Schools and Industry, United World Films, Inc., 1445 Park Ave., New York 29, N. Y. (Depository agency of U.S. Office Education films, and many government films.)

Directory of distributors

While only the central office is given for most of these film distributors, many of them have branch offices in a number of the larger cities. Before you order films, check the office nearest you.

Admiral Corporation, 1191 Merchandise Mart, Chicago 54, Ill.

Air Reduction Sales Co., 150 E. 42nd St., New York 17, N.Y.

Air Transportation Association of America, 527 Madison Ave., New York.

Allegheny Ludlum Steel Corp., 2020 Oliver Bldg., Pittsburgh 22, Pa.

Allis-Chalmers Manufacturing Co., Advertising Dept., Milwaukee 1, Wisc.

Almanac Films, Inc., 516 Fifth Ave., New York 36, N.Y.

Alturas Films, P.O. Box 940, Stanford, Calif.

Aluminum Company of America, Motion Picture Section, 1501 Alcoa Bldg., Pittsburgh 22, Pa.

American Automobile Association, Public Relations Dept., 1712 G Street, N.W., Washington 6, D.C.

American Bakers Association, 20 N. Wacker Drive, Chicago, Ill.

American Can Co., Home Economics Department, 100 Park Ave., New York 17, N.Y.

American Cyanamid Co., Lederle Laboratories Division, Film Library, Pearl River, N.Y.

American Gas Association, Film Library, 420 Lexington Ave., New York 17, N.Y.

American Iron and Steel Institute, Public Relations Dept., 150 E. 42nd St., New York 17, N.Y.

American Optical Co., Safety Products Division, 14 Mechanic St., Southbridge, Mass.

American Petroleum Institute, 50 West 50th St., New York 20, N.Y. Other branch offices.

American Telephone and Telegraph Co. Apply to regional offices.

American Viscose Corp., 350 Fifth Ave., New York 1, N.Y.

American Zinc Institute, Inc., 60 E. 42nd St., New York 17, N.Y.

Anaconda Co., Room 2148, 25 Broadway, New York 4, N.Y. Branch offices.

Arco Film Productions, 580 Fifth Ave., New York, N.Y.

Armco Steel Corp., 703 Curtis Street, Middletown, Ohio.

Association Films, Inc., 347 Madison Ave., New York 17, N.Y. Branch offices.

Athena Films, Inc., 165 W. 46th St., New York 36, N.Y.

Audio Film Center, 101 W. 31st St., New York, N.Y.

Ausable Chasm Co., Ausable Forks, N.Y.

Bailey Films, Inc., 6509 De Longpre Ave., Hollywood 28, Calif.

Bakelite Co., see Union Carbide Plastics Co.

Bausch & Lomb Optical Co., Film Distribution Service, 635 St. Paul St., Rochester 2, N.Y.

Bell Aircraft Corp. P.O. Box 1, Buffalo 5, N.Y.

Bell Telephone System. Apply to regional offices.

Bendix Aviation Corp., Bendix Products Division, 401 N. Bendix Dr., South Bend 20, Ind.

Better Vision Institute, Inc., 630 Fifth Ave., New York 20, N.Y.

Boeing Airplane Co., P.O. Box 3107, Seattle 14, Wash.

Boise Payette Lumber Co., P.O. Box 4072, Boise, Idaho.

Stanley Bowmar Co., Inc., 153 W. 166th St., New York 32, N.Y.

Brandon Films, Inc., 200 W. 57th St., New York 19, N.Y.

Bray Studios, Inc., 729 Seventh Ave., New York 19, N.Y.

Business Education Films, 630 Ninth Ave., New York 36, N.Y.

A. M. Byers Co., 200 E. 42nd St., New York 17, N.Y.

Carborundum Co., P.O. Box 337, Niagara Falls, N.Y.

J. I. Case Co., Education Division, 700 State St., Racine, Wis.

Church-Craft Pictures, Inc., 3312 Linden Blvd., St. Louis 3, Mo.

Civil Aeronautics Administration, Audio Visual Aids, Washington, D.C. Regional Offices.

Colorado Mining Association, 204 State Office Bldg., Denver, Colo.

Colorado School of Mines, Golden, Colo.

Compressed Air and Gas Institute, 1400 Terminal Tower, Cleveland, Ohio.

Contemporary Films, Inc., 267 W. 25th St., New York, N.Y.

Coronet Instructional Films, 65 E. South Water St., Chicago 1, Ill.

Coty, Inc., Public Relations Dept., 423 W. 55th St., New York, N.Y.

Current Affairs Films, 527 Madison Ave., New York 22, N.Y.

Curriculum Films, Inc., distributed by Curriculum Materials Corporation, 10031 Commerce Ave., Tujunga, Calif.

Davey Tree Expert Co., 117 S. Water St., Kent, Ohio.

Denoyer-Geppert Co., 5235 N. Ravenswood Ave., Chicago 40, Ill.

DeVry Technical Institute, 4141 W. Belmont, Chicago 41, Ill.

Walt Disney Productions, Educational Film Division, 2400 W. Alameda Ave., Burbank, Calif.

Douglas Aircraft Co., 230 Park Ave., New York.

Dow Chemical Co., Public Relations Dept., Midland, Mich.

Dow Corning Corp., Midland, Mich. Branch offices.

Dumont Television, Division of Emerson Radio Corp., 680 Fifth Ave., New York 22, N.Y.

E. I. Du Pont de Nemours and Co., Motion Picture Distribution, Advertising Dept., Wilmington 98, Dela.

Eastern Air Lines, Inc., 10 Rockefeller Plaza, New York 20, N.Y.

Eastman Kodak Co., Audio-Visual Service, 343 State St., Rochester 4, N.Y.

Educational Film Enterprises, Inc., 500 N. Wilcox Ave., Los Angeles 4, Calif.

Educational Film Library Association, 250 W. 57th St., New York 19, N.Y.

Educational Services, Inc., Physical Science Study Committee, 1329 18th St., N.W., Washington, D.C.

Encyclopaedia Britannica Films, Inc., 1150 Wilmette Ave., Wilmette, Ill. Branch offices.

Ethyl Corp., 100 Park Ave., New York 17, N.Y.

Eye Gate House, Inc., 146-01 Archer Ave., Jamaica 35, N.Y.

Film Associates of California, 10521 Santa Monica Blvd., Los Angeles 25, Calif.

Film Images, Inc., 1860 Broadway, New York 23, N.Y.

Filmstrip House, 347 Madison Ave., New York, N.Y.

Filmstrip-of-the-Month Club, Inc. (Popular Science Publg. Co.), 353 Park Avenue S., New York 10, N.Y.

Firestone Tire and Rubber Co., Public Relations Dept., Akron, Ohio.

Ford Motor Co., Motion Picture Dept., The American Rd., Dearborn, Mich. Offices also in Oakland, Calif., and New York, N.Y.

French-American Culture Services and Educational Aid, 972 Fifth Ave., New York 21, N.Y.

Gardner-Denver Co., Quincy, Ill.

Gas Appliance Manufacturers Association, 60 E. 42nd St., New York 17, N.Y.

Gateway Productions, Inc., 1859 Powell St., San Francisco 11, Calif.

Geigy Chemical Corp., Dyestuff Advertising Dept., Saw Mill River Rd., Ardsley, N.Y.

General Electric Co. Apply to regional offices.

General Motors Corp., Public Relations Dept., 3044 W. Grand Blvd., Detroit 2, Mich. Branch offices.

Glass Container Manufacturers Institute, 99 Park Ave., New York 16, N.Y.

B. F. Goodrich, Inc., 230 Park Avenue, New York 17, N.Y.

Goodyear Tire and Rubber Co., Motion Picture Dept., 1144 E. Market St., Akron 16, Ohio.

Gulf Oil Corp., P.O. Box 1166, Pittsburgh 30, Pa.

Hammermill Paper Co., Advertising Dept., 1563 East Lake Road, Erie 6, Pa.

Handel Film Corporation, 6926 Melrose Ave., Los Angeles 38, Calif.

Harcourt, Brace & World, Inc., 750 Third Ave., New York 17, N.Y.

Hercules Powder Co., Advertising Dept., Wilmington 99, Dela.

Huyck Corp., 200 E. 42nd St., New York 17, N.Y.

Ideal Pictures Co., 58 E. South Water St., Chicago 1, Ill. Regional offices.

University of Illinois, Visual Aids Service, Division of University Extension, Champaign, Ill.

Imperial Chemical Industries, Ltd., Film Library, 488 Madison Ave., New York 22, N.Y.

Indiana University Audio - Visual Center, Bloomington, Ind.

Institute of Scrap Iron and Steel, Inc., Film Section, 1729 H Street, N.W., Washington 6, D.C.

Institutional Cinema Service, Inc., 1560 Broadway, New York 19, N.Y.

Institute of Visual Training, Inc., 40 E. 49th St., New York 17, N.Y.

International Business Machines Corp., 590 Madison Ave., New York, N.Y.

International Film Bureau, Inc., 57 E. Jackson Blvd., Chicago 4, Ill.

International Film Foundation, 1 E. 42nd St., New York 17, N.Y.

International Minerals and Chemical Corp., Potash Division, 20 N. Wacker Dr., Chicago 6, Ill.

International Nickel Co., Inc., 67 Wall St., New York 5, N.Y.

International Salt Co., Inc., Public Relations Dept., Scranton Life Bldg., Scranton, Pa.

Iowa State College, Film Production Unit, Alice Norton House, Ames, Iowa.

State University of Iowa, Bureau of Audio-Visual Instruction, Iowa City, Iowa.

Jam Handy Organization, 2821 E. Grand Blvd., Detroit 11, Mich. Branch offices.

Libbey-Owens-Ford Glass Co., 608 Madison Ave., Toledo 3, Ohio.

Life Magazine, Filmstrip Division, 9 Rockefeller Plaza, New York 20, N.Y.

Massachusetts Institute of Technology, 77 Massachusetts Ave., Cambridge 39, Mass.

McGraw-Hill Book Co., Text Film Dept., 330 W. 42nd St., New York 36, N.Y. (Also distributes Popular Science filmstrips.)

Metropolitan Life Insurance Co., 1 Madison Ave., New York 10, N.Y.

University of Michigan, Audio Visual Education Center, 4028 Administration Bldg., Ann Arbor, Mich.

Minneapolis-Honeywell Regulator Co., Merchandising Division, Minneapolis 8, Minn.

University of Minnesota, Audio-Visual Education Service, Westbrook Hall, Minneapolis 14, Minn.

Modern Talking Pictures Service, Inc., 3 E. 54th St., New York 22, N.Y. Branch offices.

Moody Institute of Science, 11428 Santa Monica Blvd., Los Angeles 25, Calif.

Movies U.S.A., see Sterling-Movies U.S.A.

National Association of Manufacturers, Film Bureau, 2 E. 48th St., New York 17, N.Y.

National Committee for Careers in Medical Technology, 1785 Massachusetts Ave., N.W., Washington 6, D.C.

National Education Association, Publication Sales, 1201 16th St., N.W., Washington 6, D.C.

National Electrical Manufacturers Association, 155 E. 44th St., New York 17, N.Y.

National Film Board of Canada, Suite 2307 RKO Bldg., Sixth Ave., New York 20, N.Y.

National Plant Food Institute, 1700 K St., Suite 1004, Washington 6, D.C.

National Safety Council, 425 N. Michigan Ave., Chicago 11, Ill.

National Wholesale Druggists' Association, 60 E. 42nd St., New York 17, N.Y.

University of Nebraska, Bureau of Audio Visual Instruction, Extension Division, Lincoln 8, Neb.

NET Film Service, Indiana University, Audio-Visual Center, Bloomington, Ind.

New York State College of Agriculture, Film Library, Cornell University, Ithaca, N.Y.

New York State Dept. of Commerce, Film Library, 28 Howard St., Albany 7, N.Y.

New York State Dept. of Health, Film Library, 84 Holland Ave., Albany 8, N.Y.

New York Telephone Co., Public Relations Dept., 140 West St., New York 7, N.Y.

New York University Film Library, 26 Washington Place, New York 3, N.Y.

North American Aviation, Inc., 12214 Lakewood Drive, Downey, Calif.

Oceanic Productions, 1530 Paradise St., Modesto, Calif.

Ohio State University, Teaching Aids Laboratory, Columbus 10, Ohio.

Pacific Telephone & Telegraph Co., 85 2nd St., Room 123, San Francisco 5, Calif.

Pan American World Airways System, 28-19 Bridge Plaza, N., Long Island City 1, N.Y.

Photolab, Inc., 3825 Georgia Ave., N.W., Washington 11, D.C.

Pictura Films Corp., 41 Union Sq., W., New York 22, N.Y.

Polaroid Corp., Cambridge 39, Mass.

Popular Science. See McGraw-Hill.

Princeton Film Center, Inc., Box 431, Princeton, N.J.

Procter and Gamble Co., 6th and Sycamore, Cincinnati, Ohio.

Radio Marine Corporation of America, 75 Varick St., New York 13, N.Y.

Raytheon Manufacturing Co., Public Relations Dept., Waltham 54, Mass.

Remington Rand, Division of Sperry Rand Corp., 315 Fourth Ave., New York, N.Y.

Republic Steel Corp., Public Relations Dept., Republic Bldg., Cleveland 1, Ohio.

Reynolds Metals Co., Motion Picture Dept., 2500 S. Third St., Louisville 1, Ky.

Rothacker, Inc., 729 Seventh Ave., New York 19, N.Y.

Rutgers University, Audio-Visual Dept., 35 College Ave., New Brunswick, N.J.

Science Slides Co., 22 Oak Dr., New Hyde Park, N.Y.

Shell Oil Co., Public Relations Dept., 50 W. 50th St., New York 20, N.Y.

Sikorsky Aircraft, Public Relations Dept., Main St., Stratford, Conn.

Simmel-Meservey Inc., 9113 W. Pico Blvd., Los Angeles 35, Calif.

Sinclair Refining Co., Sales Promotion Dept., 600 Fifth Ave., New York 20, N.Y. Branch offices.

Smith, Kline & French Laboratories, 1530 Spring Garden St., Philadelphia, Pa.

Society for Visual Education, Inc., 1345 Diversey Parkway, Chicago 14, Ill.

Society of the Plastics Industry, 250 Park Ave., New York, N.Y.

Socony Mobil Oil Co., Inc., 150 E. 42nd St., New York 17, N.Y.

Spencer Chemical Co., Public Relations Dept., Dwight Bldg., Kansas City 5, Mo.

Sperry Products, Inc., Danbury, Conn.

Standard Oil Company of New Jersey, Inc., 30 Rockefeller Plaza, New York 20, N.Y.

Stanley Tools, Educational Dept., New Britain, Conn.

Sterling-Movies U.S.A., Inc., 43 W. 61st St., New York 23, N.Y.

Suburban Farm Service Co., P.O. Box 208, Whippany, N.J.

John Sutherland Productions, Inc., 136 E. 55th St., New York 22, N.Y.

Swift and Co., Public Relations Dept., Union Stock Yards, Chicago 9, Ill.

Sylvania Electric Products, Inc., 60 Boston St., Salem, Mass.

Syracuse University, Audio-Visual Center, Colvin Lane, Collendale, Syracuse 10, N.Y.

Teaching Film Custodians, Inc., 25 W. 43rd St., New York 36, N.Y.

Tektronix, Inc., P.O. Box 831, Portland 7, Ore.

Texas Co., 135 E. 42nd St., New York 17, N.Y.

Union Carbide Plastics Co., Advertising Dept., 420 Lexington Ave., New York, N.Y.

U.S. Atomic Energy Commission (AEC), 1901 Constitution Ave., Washington, D.C.

U.S. Bureau of Mines, Washington 25, D.C.

U.S. Dept. of Agriculture, Washington 25, D.C. Consult regional film library.

U.S. Dept. of Health, Education and Welfare, Washington 25, D.C.

U.S. Electrical Motors, Inc., 200 E. Slauson Ave., Los Angeles, Calif.

U.S. Public Health Service, Communicable Disease Center, Atlanta, Ga.

U.S. Rubber Co., Public Relations Dept., 1230 Avenue of the Americas, New York 20, N.Y.

U.S. Steel Corp., 525 William Penn Place, Pittsburgh 30, Pa.

United Gas Corp., P.O. Box 1407, Shreveport, La.

United World Films, Inc., 1445 Park Ave., New York 29, N.Y. Branch offices.

University of Southern California, Audio-Visual Services, Dept. of Cinema, University Park, Los Angeles 7, Calif.

Visual Sciences, Suffern, N.Y.

Visual Education Consultants, Inc. (VEC), 2066 Helena St., Madison 4, Wisc.

Venard Organization, 113 N. Madison Ave., Peoria, Ill.

Wesson Co., 1220 Woodward Heights Blvd., Ferndale 20, Mich.

Western Electric Co., Inc., Motion Picture Bureau, 195 Broadway, New York 7, N.Y.

Westinghouse Electric Corp., Film Library, No. 3 Gateway Center, Pittsburgh 30, Pa.

Wyeth Laboratories, Inc., Film Library, P.O. Box 8299, Philadelphia, Pa.

Wyckoff Steel Co., Newark, N.J.

Yale University Press Film Service, Filmstrip Dept., 386 Fourth Ave., New York 16, N.Y.

Young America, see McGraw-Hill.

Zurich-American Insurance Co., Public Relations Dept., 135 South LaSalle St., Chicago 3, Ill. Regional offices.

Selected listing of films and filmstrips

The films listed here are black-and-white unless otherwise indicated. All films have been selected for viewing within a class period of 40 to 45 minutes. As previously stated, prices are for rental unless otherwise noted; they are subject to change. For complete names, departments, and addresses of the distributors listed see the preceding directory. The following abbreviations are used throughout.

f = film	si = silent
fs = filmstrip	c = color
s = sound	rls = reels
ser = series	

General: matter and energy

Atom: How Big Is An Atom? (f, s), Indiana University, $4.75.

Atom: What Makes Atoms Stick Together? (Dr. Teller explains) (f, s), Indiana University, $4.75.

Atomic Physics (1 and 2, work of Dalton, Mendeleevf, and Faraday; 3, nuclear structure; 4, atom smashing) (f, s, 4 in series), Indiana University, $4.00 each.

Atoms for Peace (fs), Life, $2.50.

Atoms Into Molecules (f, s), Indiana University, $4.75.

Basic Principles of Analytical Balance (f, s), Communicable Disease Center, U.S. Public Health Service, free.

Characteristics of Gases (f, s), Institutional Cinema, $2.00.

Characteristics of Liquids (f, s), Institutional Cinema, $2.00.

Characteristics of Solids (f, s), Institutional Cinema, $2.00.

Chemistry Series (kinetic molecular theory, atomic theory, chemical formulas) (4 fs), McGraw-Hill, $6.00 each.

Electron Theory (fs, 2 in series), Visual Sciences, $2.00 each.

Energy and Its Transformation (f, s), EBF, $2.50.

Eye to the Unknown (mass spectrometry) (f, s, c), Modern Talking Pictures, free.

General Science (8 fs), EBF, $3.00 each.

History of the Atomic Concept (2 fs), Visual Sciences, $5.00 set.

Liquid Air (f, s), Almanac, $2.50.

Making Elements (discovery of elements 99, 100, and 101) (f, s), Indiana University, $5.25.

Matter and Energy (f, s), Indiana University, $2.00.

Molecular Forces in Matter (fs), Jam Handy, $4.50.

Molecular Theory of Matter (f, s), Indiana University, $2.00.

Physical and Chemical Changes in Everyday Living (fs, 3 in series), Popular Science through McGraw-Hill, $6.00 each.

Precisely So (measuring time, space, and weight) (f, s), General Motors, free.

Properties of Matter (f, s, 15 lessons, introductory physics), EBF, inquire rental local film library.

The Scientist Examines Life (methods, scientific procedures, and formulation of theories) (f, s), Indiana University, $4.75.

Simple Changes in Matter (f, s), Indiana University, $2.00.

The Turning Point (measurement) (f, s, c), General Motors, free.

Unlocking the Atom (f, s), U.S. AEC, free.

Weighing With the Analytical Balance (f, s), EBF, $2.50.

Why Are Atoms Unpredictable? (f, s), Indiana University, $4.75.

Earth's surface—land and water

Ausable Chasm (f, s, c), Ausable Chasm Co., free.

Birth of the Soil (f, s, c), Indiana University, $3.25.

Birth of a Volcano (Paricutin), (f, s), Institutional Cinema, $2.00.

Birthplace of Icebergs (Father Hubbard's series) (f, s), Teaching Film Custodians, free.

By Map and Compass (f, s, c), International Film Bureau, $5.00.

CaCO₃ (f, s, c), Gardner-Denver, free.

Changing Surface of the Earth (fs, c), Popular Science through McGraw-Hill, $6.00.

Continental Glaciers (f, s, c), Indiana University, $4.00.

Crystal Gazing (crystals in limestone caves and crystallization) (f, s, c), Indiana University, $3.25.

Earth and Its Wonders (fs, c, 6 in series), EBF, $6.00 each.

Earthquakes (f, s, in the series, *The Search,* filmed at Fordham University), Young America, inquire local film library.

Earth's Surface (aerial navigation terms) (fs), Audio-Visual Aids, Civil Aeronautics Administration, Washington, D.C., and regional offices, free.

Face of the Earth (f, s, c), EBF, $4.00.

From An Atom: The Earth (f, s), Nebraska University, $4.50.

Geological Work of Ice (f, s), EBF, $2.50.

Geology (fs, c), Ohio State University, Teaching Aids Lab., $4.00.

Geophysical Year (fs), Current Affairs Films, inquire rental.

Geyser Melodies (f, s, c), Bailey, $5.00.

Geysers and Hot Springs (volcanism in action) (f, s, c), Indiana University, $3.25.

Great Lakes—How They Were Formed (f, s, c), N.Y. State Dept. of Commerce, free.

Ground Water (f, s), EBF, $2.50.

How Rocks Are Formed (fs, c), Popular Science through McGraw-Hill, $6.00.

In the Beginning (Grand Canyon) (f, s, c), Modern Talking Pictures, free.

Irrigation Practices (f, s, c), Nebraska University, $5.50.

Limestone Caverns (f, s, c), Indiana University, $3.00.

Minerals and Rocks (f, s, c), EBF, $2.50.

Mountain Building (f, s), Institutional Cinema, $2.00.

Mt. Rainier (glaciers) (f, s, c), EBF, $2.50.

New Worlds of Marble (f, s, c), Vermont Marble Co., free.

The River (f, s), U.S. Dept. of Agriculture or N.Y. State Dept. of Commerce, free.

River of Ice (Alpine Valley glacier) (f, s), N.Y. State College of Agriculture, Cornell University, Ithaca, $1.00.

Rocks and Minerals (f, s, c), Indiana University, $3.25.

Tides (f, s), Almanac, $2.00.

The Universe (the elements) (f, s), Indiana University, $4.75.

Volcanoes in Action (f, s), EBF, $2.50.

Wearing Away of the Land (f, s), Indiana University, $2.00.

Wonder Trail (erosion) (f, s), Teaching Film Custodians, free.

Work of the Atmosphere (f, s), Indiana University, $2.00.

Work of Rivers (f, s), EBF, $2.50.

Work of Running Water (f, s), Ideal, $2.00.

A World Is Born (from Disney's "Fantasia") (f, s, c 3 rls), Institutional Cinema, $8.00.

World Is Built (mt. Building) (f, s), Nebraska University, $4.50.

Weather and atmosphere

Air in Action (f, s), Audio Film Center, $2.00.

Air Masses and Fronts (f, s, c), Indiana University, $6.00.

The Air We Breathe (contaminants) (f, s), Braddock, free.

The Airplane Changes Our World Map (mercator map) (f, s), EBF, $2.50.

Atmosphere and Its Circulation (f, s), EBF, inquire local film library.

The Atom and the Weather (f, s), U.S. AEC, inquire from field offices.

Basic Weather (series, 2 fs), Society for Visual Education, $3.25 each.

Birthplace of Icebergs (Father Hubbard's series) (f, s), Teaching Film Custodians, free.

Canopy of Air (fs, c), Life, $6.00.

Clouds (f, s), U.S. Dept. of Commerce, N.Y. State Dept. of Commerce, free.

Clouds of Vertical Development; High Clouds (2 fs, c) Audio-Visual Aids, Civil Aeronautics Administration, free.

Cold Front (f, s, c), Indiana University, $4.25.

Earth, Latitude and Longitude (f, s), Institutional Cinema, $2.00.

Earth and Sky Series (11 fs), Popular Science through McGraw-Hill, $3.50 each.

Earth Rotation and Revolution (f, s), Institutional Cinema, $2.00.

Everybody Talks About It (U.S. Weather Bureau) (f, s), Teaching Film Custodians, free.

Expedition to Antarctica (MGM films) (f, s, c, 2 rls), Teaching Film Custodians, free.

Flying the Weather Map; Fog; Equatorial Front (f, s, c), Civil Aeronautics Administration, U.S. Dept. of Navy, free.

Great Winds (2 fs), United World, $4.50.

Hurricane Hunters (f, s), U.S. Dept. of Navy, free.

Ice Cap II (testing clothes and equipment) (f, s), U.S. Dept. of Army, free.

It's in the Air (air conditioning) (f, s, c), Modern Talking Pictures, free.

Latitude and Longitude; Longitude and Time; Day and Night (3 fs), United World, $3.00 each.

Men, Steel and Earthquakes (f, s, c), Modern Talking Pictures, free.

Modern Weather (storms, atmospheric waves) (f, s, 2 rls), Almanac, $3.50.

Occluded Fronts (f, s, c), Indiana University, $4.50.

Operation Hurricane (f, s), Indiana University, $1.00.

Pipeline to the Clouds (f, s, c), General Electric, free.

Prophet Without Honor (MGM films; Admiral Maury and ocean currents) (f, s), Teaching Film Custodians, free.

Rain (water cycle) (fs), Filmstrip House, $3.50.

Report on Smog (f, s, c), Stanford Research Institute, free.

The Search: Weather Research (f, s), Young America, inquire local film library.

Seasons, Weather, and Climate (fs, c, 5 in series), Jam Handy, $5.70 each.

The Seasons (2 fs, c), United World, $4.50 each.

The Seasons (f, s, c, 2 rls), Teaching Film Custodians, free.

Seasons and Their Cause (f, s), Audio Film Center, $2.00.

Seasons of the Year (f, s), Coronet, inquire local film library.

Story of a Storm (f, s, c), Coronet, inquire local film library.

Thundering Water (f, s, c), New York Central System, free.

Tornadoes—What They Are and What to Do About Them (fs), VEC, $3.50.

Unchained Goddess (f, s, c), American Telephone and Telegraph, free.

Upper Atmosphere Studies (f, s), Indiana University, $3.00.

Water Front (f, s, c), Indiana University, $4.50.

The Weather (f, s), EBF, $2.50.

The Weather (fs, c, 8 in series), Curriculum Films, $24.00 set.

Weather (fs), Life, $2.50.

Winds and Their Causes (f, s), Indiana University, $2.00.

Work of the Atmosphere (f, s), EBF, $2.50.

You and the Weather (f, s, c), Texas Co., free.

Astronomy and space science

Animals in Subgravity Conditions (f, s), Indiana University, $3.00.

Constellations (fs, c), McGraw-Hill, $6.00.

Cosmic Ray Studies (f, s), Indiana University, $3.00.

Earth and Universe Series (7 fs), Society for Visual Education, $3.50 each.

Earth: Our Planet (cosmic theory of creation) (f, s), Indiana University, $4.00.

Earth and Its Seasons (f, s), EBF, $2.50.

Earth In Motion (Foucault pendulum) (f, s), EBF, $2.50.

Eclipse (f, s), Almanac, $2.00.

Exploring Space (f, s), Teaching Film Custodians, free.

Exploring the Universe (f, s), EBF, inquire rental.

Frontier to Space (series 26 f, s), Indiana University, $3.00 each.

Gyro Compass: The Gyroscope and the Earth's Rotation (f, s), Indiana University, $1.50.

How Earth Was Born (tidal theory) (f, s), Almanac, $2.00.

How Many Stars (f, s, c), Indiana University, $3.25.

How We Explore Space (f, s, c), Association Films, inquire rental.

Infinite Universe (galaxies, space, time) (f, s), Almanac, $2.00.

Introduction to Map Projection (f, s), United World, inquire film library.

Looking at the Stars (fs), McGraw-Hill, $3.50.

Man in Space (f, s, c), Disney, $12.00.

Mars (f, s), Indiana University, $3.00.

Measurement of Speed of Light (f, s), McGraw-Hill, inquire rental.

The Moon (tides) (f, s), EBF, $2.50.

Moon Is Born (f, s, c), International Business Machine, free.

Movements of the Earth and Sun (fs), United World $3.00.

Nautical Astronomy (f, s), Indiana University, $2.50.

Neighbors in Space (fs, c), Harcourt, Brace, $5.50.

Operation Hour Glass (f, s, c), Association Films, free.

Our Mr. Sun (f, s, c), local Bell Telephone Office, free.

Planet Earth (f, s), Indiana University, $4.75.

The Planets (fs), United World, $3.00.

Principles of Celestial Navigation (position finding on earth) (f, s, 2 rls), Almanac, $3.50.

Shadows and Eclipses (reflection) (f, s), United World, $2.00.

The Solar Family (f, s), EBF, $2.50.

Solar System (f, s, c), Coronet, inquire rental local film library.

Star Gazers (Galileo and his trial) (f, s), Indiana University, $1.50.

The Stars (fs), United World, $3.00.

The Starry Universe (fs, c), Life, $6.00.

Story of the Telescope (f, s), Institutional Cinema, $2.00.

The Story of Time (f, s, c), New York University film library, $3.50.

The Strange Case of the Cosmic Rays (f, s, c), local Bell Telephone Office, free.

The Sun (f, s), Indiana University, $3.00.

Sun's Family (fs, c), Popular Science through McGraw-Hill, $6.00.

This is the Moon (f, s), Institutional Cinema, $2.00.

Time—The Servant of Man (f, s), Modern Talking Pictures, free.

Trip Through Space (f, s), Institutional Cinema, $2.00.

Understanding Our Universe (f, s), Coronet, inquire rental local film library.

Chemistry

General

ABC of Chemistry (lab experiments) (f, s, c), Almanac, $5.00.

Acids, Bases and Salts (f, s, c), Coronet, inquire rental local film library.

American Frontier (current science) (f, s, c), Jam Handy, inquire rental.

Atomic Detective (f, s), Handel, $10.00.

Atoms Into Molecules (periodic table) (f, s), Indiana University, $4.75.

Bituminous Coal—Powering America's Progress (f, s, c), U.S. Bureau of Mines, free.

Black Diamonds (f, s, c), Sterling-Movies U.S.A., inquire rental.

Carbon and Its Compounds (f, s, c), Coronet, inquire rental local film library.

Catalysis (f, s), EBF, $2.00.

Chemical Bond (fs), McGraw-Hill, $6.00.

Chemical Instruments (f, s, c), University of Southern California, $4.50.

Chemical Reactions (f, s, 2 rls, or fs), Institutional Cinema, $3.00 (fs).

Chemistry of Combustion (f, s), Institutional Cinema, $2.00.

Chemistry of Fire (f, s), N. Y. State Dept. of Commerce or Ideal, $2.00.

Chemistry Series (set of 6 fs) (chemistry lab techniques, water purification, crystals, chemical bond, etc.), McGraw-Hill, $6.00 each.

Chemistry Series (set of 5 fs) (structure of atom, ionization, acids, electrolysis, periodic table), McGraw-Hill, $6.00 each.

Chemistry Series (set of 6 fs, c) (sulfuric acid, hydrocarbons, nitrogen fixation, electroplating, fluorine, etc.), McGraw-Hill, $8.00 each.

Chilean Nitrate: Gift of the Desert (f, s, c), Indiana University, $3.25.

Chlorine—A Representative Halogen (f, s), Sutherland, inquire rental.

Clean Water (f, s, c), General Electric, free.

Coal, Servant of Man (f, s, c), Modern Talking Pictures, free.

Collecting and Preparing Soil Samples for Testing (fs), Illinois University (Voc.-Agric.) inquire rental.

Colloidal State (f, s, c), Coronet, inquire rental local film library.

Colloids (f, s), EBF, $2.50.

Crystals (fs), McGraw-Hill, $6.00.

Crystals (under the microscope) (f, s), Almanac, $2.00.

Crystals at Work (quartz) (f, s), Institutional Cinema, $2.00.

Decision for Chemistry (careers) (f, s), Modern Talking Pictures, free.

Discovery of Radium (f, s), McGraw-Hill, inquire rental.

Electrochemistry (f, s), Indiana University, $2.00.

The Elements (f, s, 10 in series), Indiana University, $4.75 each.

Engineering Your Health (sanitary engineering) (f, s, c), U.S. Dept. of Health, Education and Welfare, free.

Fiery Magic (calcium carbide) (f, s), Air Reduction Co., free.

Fire Magic (combustion) (f, s, c), Modern Talking Pictures, free.

Fluoridation Story (f, s, c), U.S. Public Health Service, free.

Foundations of Chemistry (8 fs), Society for Visual Education, $3.25 each.

From Alchemy to Chemistry (f, s), Indiana University, $4.75.

Gas Laws and Their Application (f, s), Indiana University, $3.75.

Glass and You (f, s, c), Association Films, free.

Glass Center of Corning (f, s, c), Association Films, free.

The Halogens (f, s, c), Coronet, inquire rental local film library.

House of Magic (assembly program), General Electric, consult branch office.

Hydrogen (f, s, c), Coronet, inquire rental local film library.

Infinite Harvest (ammonia, dry ice) (f, s, c), Spencer Chemical Co., free.

An Introduction to Reaction Kinetics (f, s, c), Sutherland, inquire rental.

Ionization (f, s, c), Coronet, inquire rental local film library.

It Takes Coal to Make Steel (f, s, c), Armco, free.

The Laws of Gases (f, s, c), Coronet, inquire rental local film library.

Magic on a Stick (sulfur match) (f, s), Teaching Film Custodians, free.

The Missing Elements (spectroscope) (f, s), Indiana University, $4.75.

Modern Alchemy (Seaborg, Lawrence, Segré) (f, s), Indiana University, $5.25.

Mysteries of Water (f, s), Institutional Cinema, $2.00.

Nitric Acid, Compounds and the Nitrogen Cycle (f, s, c); Coronet, inquire rental local film library.

Nitrogen and Ammonia (f, s, c), Coronet, inquire rental local film library.

On to Jupiter (chemistry progress) (f, s), General Motors, free.

Oxidation and Reduction (f, s), EBF, $2.50.

Oxyacetylene Flame (f, s, c), U.S. Bureau of Mines or N. Y. State Dept. of Commerce, free.

Oxygen (f, s, c), Coronet, inquire rental local film library.

Pattern for Chemicals (f, s), Shell Oil, free.

Peat and Coal (f, s), Institutional Cinema, $2.00.

Pencil Points (f, s), Almanac, $2.00.

Preface to Chemistry (Priestley and Lavoisier) (f, s), EBF, $3.50.

Principles of Chromatography (f, s, c), McGraw-Hill, inquire rental.

Properties of Water (f, s), Indiana University, $2.00.

Putting Sulfur to Work (fs, c), Popular Science through McGraw-Hill, $6.00.

Rainbow of Stone (facts and superstitions) (f, s, c, 2 rls), Teaching Film Custodians, free.

Safety in the Chemistry Laboratory (f, s), Indiana University, $3.75.

Sand and Flame (Glass making) (f, s), General Motors, free.

Silicones (f, s), General Electric, free.

Soft as a Cloud (Water softening) (f, s, c), Modern Talking Pictures, free.

Soil Test (f, s, c), Iowa State College, $.60.

Soil Testing for Lime Requirements (f, s, c), Cornell Extension Service, Film Library, N. Y. State College of Agriculture, $2.00.

Solutions (f, s, c), Coronet, inquire rental local film library.

Story Behind a Bottle (f, s, c), Glass Container Mfg. Inst., free.

The Story of Alfred Nobel (f, s), Teaching Film Custodians, $2.00.

Story of Coal (f, s), Indiana University, $1.75.

Story of Sulfur (f, s), Institutional Cinema, $2.00.

Sulfur (f, s, c), U.S. Bureau of Mines (or Indiana University, $1.00).

Sulfur and Its Compounds (f, s, c), Coronet, inquire rental local film library.

Surface Chemistry (f, s), Indiana University, $5.50.

Testing Soils for Available Phosphorus and Interpreting the Test (fs), Illinois University (Voc.-Ag.), $1.00.

This Carbide Age (cutting tools) (f, s, c), Wesson, free.

Up From the Bed of a Desert Sea (f, s, c), International Minerals and Chemical Corp., free.

Using the Laboratory (chem. lab techniques) (f, s), Indiana University, $2.00.

Velocity of Chemical Reactions (f, s), EBF, $2.50.

Vibration of Molecules (f, s, c), Sutherland, inquire rental.

What Are Elements and Compounds? (fs, c), Popular Science through McGraw-Hill, $6.00.

What's a Silicone? (f, s, c), Dow Chemical, free.

Metals and metallurgy

Aluminum (f, s), EBF, $2.00.

Aluminum on the March (f, s, c), Association Films, free.

Art of Spark Testing (testing steel) (f, s, c), Wyckoff Steel, free.

Atomic Metallurgy (f, s), U.S. AEC, free.

Changing Ores Into Metals (fs, c), Popular Science through McGraw-Hill, $6.00.

Chemistry of Aluminum (f, s, c), Reynolds Metals, free.

Chemistry of Iron (fs, c), American Iron and Steel Inst., free.

Chemistry of Steel (fs, c) American Iron and Steel Inst., free.

Coal and Iron Ore (f, s), Indiana University, $4.75.

Copper (f, s, c), Anaconda, free.

Crystal Gazers (crystals and metals) (f, s), General Electric, free.

Eternally Yours (wrought iron) (f, s), A. M. Byers Co., free.

Highlights of Steel Making (f, s, 2 rls), Modern Talking Pictures, free.

Iron Making (f, s), International, $4.00.

Iron, Product of the Blast Furnace (f, s, c), Indiana University, $3.25.

It's Asbestos (f, s, c), Canadian Consulate General, inquire rental local film library.

Lead From Mine to Metal (f, s, c), U.S. Bureau of Mines or N. Y. State Dept. of Commerce, free.

Metallurgy Plus (f, s), Ideal, free.

Metal Magic (alloys) (f, s), General Electric, free.

Metals and Non-Metals (f, s), Ideal, $2.00.

Milling and Smelting Sudbury Nickel Ores (f, s, c), Rothacker, free.

Mining for Nickel (f, s, c), Rothacker, free.

Mining Iron Ore (f, s, c), Minneapolis University, inquire rental.

The Miracle of the Can (f, s, c), Modern Talking Pictures, free.

Ninth Element (titanium) (f, s, c), Modern Talking Pictures, free.

The Petrified River (uranium mining) (f, s, c), U.S. AEC, free.

Pioneer of Progress (steel) (f, s), Modern Talking Pictures, free.

Romance of Radium (the Curies and H. Becquerel) (f, s), Teaching Film Custodians, free.

Science of Making Brass (f, s, c), Modern Talking Pictures, free.

Steel (f, s), Almanac, $2.00.

Story of Copper (f, s, c), Indiana University, $1.00.

Story of Nickel (f, s), U. S. Bureau of Mines or N. Y. State Dept. of Commerce, free.

Story of Stainless Steel (f, s), Ideal, free.

This Is Aluminum (f, s), U.S. Bureau of Mines or N.Y. State Dept. of Commerce, free.

This Is Magnesium—Treasure from the Sea (f, s, c), Dow Chemical, free.

Tin Plate (f, s, c), U.S. Bureau of Mines or N.Y. State Dept of Commerce, free.

Unfinished Rainbows (Hall's experiments) (f, s, c), N.Y. State Dept of Commerce or Aluminum Company of America, free.

Uranium Prospecting (f, s, in series *The Search* filmed at Colorado School of Mines), Young America, inquire local film library.

What Goes Into the Blast Furnace? (f, s), International, $4.00.

Zinc Mining (f, s), N.Y. State Dept. of Commerce, free.

Organic

Another Step Forward (f, s, c), Colorado Fuel and Iron Corp., free.

Atomization (f, s), Shell Oil, free.

Basic Fibers in Cloth (f, s), N.Y. State College of Agriculture, Cornell University, $1.50.

The Big Kitchen (agricultural regions) (f, s, c), Modern Talking Pictures, free.

Canned Meat Story (f, s, c), Modern Talking Pictures, free.

Constructive Chemistry (cellulose, rubber) (f, s), Institutional Cinema, $2.00.

Crude Oil Distillation (f, s), Shell Oil, free.

Drama of Portland Cement (f, s, c), Modern Talking Pictures, free.

Food Treasure from Land and Sea (vitamins and minerals) (f, s, c), Oceanic, free.

The Fossil Story (f, s, c), Shell Oil, free.

From Atoms to Organisms (f, s), Indiana University, $4.75.

Fuels—Their Nature and Use (f, s), EBF, $2.50.

Gasoline's Amazing Molecules (f, s, c), Modern Talking Pictures, free.

The Growth of a Nation (feeding livestock) (f, s), Modern Talking Pictures, free.

Harvest of Science (crops, soil, wonder drugs) (f, s, c), Gulf, free.

House of Squibb (drugs) (f, s), N.Y. State Dept. of Commerce or Squibb, free.

How Rayon Is Made (f, s), N.Y. State Dept. of Commerce (or Indiana University, $1.00).

Infinite Harvest (ammonium nitrate fertilizer) (f, s, c), Spencer Chemical Co., free.

In These Hands (pharmaceuticals) (f, s, c), Modern Talking Pictures, free.

Kingdom of Plastics (f, s, c), General Electric, free.

Magic in Agriculture (farm chemurgy) (f, s), N.Y. State College of Agriculture, Cornell University, $1.25, or Ethyl Corp.

Men and Oil (f, s), Modern Talking Pictures, free.

Miracle Flame (natural gas) (f, s, c), American Gas Association, free.

Miracle Materials (rubber, plastics, fibers) (f, s), Almanac, $10.00.

Molding Phenolics (f, s), Bakelite Co., free.

Neoprene —The Versatile Chemical Rubber (f, s, c), Du Pont, free.

Of Men and Molecules (f, s, c), B. F. Goodrich Co., free.

Oil (f, s), Institutional Cinema, $2.00.

Oil for Aladdin's Lamp (f, s), Shell Oil, free.

Origin and Synthesis of Plastic Materials (f, s), Indiana University, $2.75.

Our Common Fuels (f, s), Indiana University, $2.00.

Our Deceiving Eyes (f, s), Indiana University, $4.75.

Paper, Pacemaker of Progress (f, s, c), Huyck, free.

Paper and Pulp Making (f, s), Indiana University, $2.00.

Paper Work (f, s, c), Modern Talking Pictures, free.

Pattern of Chemicals (cracking petroleum) (f, s), Shell Oil, free.

Pipeline (underground oil transportation) (f, s, c), Shell Oil, free.

Plastics (f, s, 1½ reels), Young America, $3.00.

Powering America's Progress (bituminous coal mining) (f, s, c), Modern Talking Pictures, free.

Prospecting for Petroleum (f, s, c), Shell Oil, free.

Put Nitrogen In Its Place (f, s, c), Suburban Farm Service Co., free.

The Questing Mind (f, s), General Motors, free.

Refining Oil for Energy (f, s, c), Shell Oil, free.

The Rival World (insecticides) (f, s, c), Shell Oil, free.

Rubber From Rock (silicone rubber) (f, s, c), Dow Corning Corp., free.

Rubber in Today's World (f, s, c), Coronet, inquire local film library.

Science of Soap (f, s), EBF, $2.50.

Soap: Production and Cleansing Action (f, s), Indiana University, $2.00.

Speaking of Rubber (f, s), Modern Talking Pictures, free.

The Story of Charles Goodyear (f, s), Teaching Film Custodians, free.

Story of Perfume (f, s, c), Coty, free.

Story of Research (orlon, acrylic fiber) (f, s, c), Du Pont, free.

Synthetic Fibers (f, s), Indiana University, $3.50.

Techniques of Organic Chemistry (solubility tests, crystallization, cholesterol, precipitates, supersaturation) (f, s, c), Young America, inquire local film library.

Techniques of Organic Chemistry (extraction, elution, chromatography) (f, s, c), Young America, inquire local film library.

Techniques of Organic Chemistry (fractional distillation, melting points, molecular weight) (f, s, c), Young America, inquire local film library.

10,000 Feet Deep (f, s), Shell Oil, free.

Testing Foods and Nutrients (fs, c), Popular Science through McGraw-Hill, $6.00.

This Is Life (meat production) (f, s, c), Modern Talking Pictures, free.

This Is Oil (f, s, c, 5 in series), Shell Oil, free.

Vitamin Rivers (frozen juices) (f, s, c), Modern Talking Pictures, free.

The Waiting Harvest (chemicals from coal) (f, s, c), U.S. Steel, free.

World That Nature Forgot (modern plastics) (f, s, c), Modern Talking Pictures, free.

Yesterday, Today and Tomorrow (food packing) (f, s), Modern Talking Pictures, free.

Physics

Pressure, heat, force, motion

Archimedes' Principle (f, s), EBF, $2.50.

Atmospheric Pressure (f, s), EBF, $2.50.

Atomization (f, s), Shell Oil, free.

Basic Hydraulics (Pascal's laws) (f, s, c), Indiana University, $2.00.

Distributing Heat Energy (f, s), Almanac, $2.00

Energy and Its Transformations (f, s), EBF, inquire rental.

Energy At Work Series (7 fs) (water power, jets and atomic power, electronics, fuels, etc.), Popular Science through McGraw-Hill, $3.25 each.

Energy From the Sun (f, s), EBF, inquire rental.

Energy in Our Business (f, s, c), N.Y. State Dept. of Commerce, free.

Exploration With the High Temperature Microscope (f, s, c), Carborundum Co., free.

Friction (f, s), Ideal, $2.00.

Galileo (f, s, c), Coronet, inquire rental local film library.

Galileo's Laws of Falling Bodies (f, s), EBF, $2.50 (or Indiana University, $1.50).

Gas Laws and Their Application (f, s), EBF, $3.00.

Harnessing Liquids (hydraulics) (f, s), Shell Oil, free.

Heat (series of 15 lessons in introductory physics) (f, s), EBF, inquire rental.

Heat (fs), Science Slides, $3.50.

Heat and Pressure (also refrigeration, liquid air) (f, s), Institutional Cinema, $2.00.

The Heat Engine (f, s), Shell Oil, free.

Heat—Its Nature and Transfer (f, s), EBF, inquire rental.

Heat Transfer—400°-750° (f, s, c), Dow Chemical, free.

Horsepower (f, s), Almanac, $2.00.

How Heat Travels (fs), Popular Science through McGraw-Hill, $3.50.

How a Watch Works (f, s, c), Association Films, free.

How We Measure Heat (fs), Filmstrip of the Month, inquire purchase.

Infrared Lamps for Better Production (heat transfer) (fs, c), General Electric, free.

Introduction to the Heat Engine (f, s), Shell Oil, free.

Introduction to Vectors: Coplanar Concurrent Forces

(f, s), Indiana University, $2.75.

Introductory Physics (H. White) (162 films, s, c), EBF, inquire rental.

Isaac Newton (f, s, c), Coronet, inquire rental.

Kitchen Physics (f, s), Minnesota University, $2.50.

Laws of Conservation of Energy and Matter (f, s, c), Coronet, inquire rental local film library.

The Laws of Gases (f, s, c), Coronet, inquire rental local film library.

Laws of Motion (f, s, c), EBF, $4.00.

Lever Age (f, s), Shell Oil, free.

Liquid Air (f, s), Almanac, $2.00.

Machines Do Work (f, s), Institutional Cinema, $2.00.

Man On the Land (power) (f, s, c), Modern Talking Pictures, free.

Mechanical Refrigeration—How It Works (f, s), Indiana University, $2.75.

Mechanics (series of 44 lessons in introductory physics) (f, s), EBF, inquire rental.

Mechanics of Liquids (f, s), Ideal, $2.00.

Modern Physics Series: Heat (5 fs), Popular Science through McGraw-Hill, $3.25 each.

Modern Physics Series: Mechanics (8 fs), Popular Science through McGraw-Hill, $3.25 each.

Nature of Energy; Nature of Heat (f, s, c), Indiana University, $2.00 each.

Oil Films in Action (in bearings), General Motors, free.

Physics At Home (f, s), Institutional Cinema, $2.00.

Preface to Physics (f, s), EBF, $3.50.

Principle of Moments (f, s), Indiana University, $2.75.

Principles of Refrigeration (f, s), Audio Film Center, $2.00.

Reaction and Momentum (f, s), Indiana University, $3.00.

Service Unseen (air conditioning) (f, s, c), Modern Talking Pictures, free.

Simple Harmonic Motion (f, s), McGraw-Hill, inquire rental.

Simple Machines (f, s), Ideal, $2.00.

Steam for Power (f, s, c), N.Y. State Dept. of Commerce, free.

Thermodynamics (f, s), EBF, inquire rental.

Thermometers; Radiation Pyrometers; Basic Automatic Control; Electronic Potentiometers (fs and lectures), Minneapolis-Honeywell, free.

To Enrich Mankind (lever, engineering) (f, s, c), Jam Handy, free.

Tragic Pursuit of Perfection (Leonardo da Vinci) (f, s), Film Images, $15.00.

Transmission of Rotary Motion (f, s), Young America, inquire rental local film library.

Uniform Circular Motion (f, s), McGraw-Hill, inquire rental local film library.

What Is Horsepower? (fs), Popular Science through McGraw-Hill, $3.50.

Whatever We Do (atmospheric gases) (f, s, c), Air Reduction Sales, free.

Whirlpool: Matter and Energy (f, s), Indiana University, $4.75.

Sound and light; music and color

Basic Physics Series: Progressive Waves; Simple Harmonic Motion; Stationary Longitude Waves; Stationary Transverse Waves (f, s), Indiana University, $2.00 each.

Behind Your Snapshot (f, s, c), Eastman Kodak Co., free.

The Case For Color (f, s, c), Du Pont, free.

Color and Light (f, s, c), Indiana University, $3.00.

The Compound Microscope (f, s, c), Bausch & Lomb, free.

Curves of Color (f, s, c), General Electric, free.

Doppler Effect (f, s), McGraw-Hill, inquire rental local film library.

Electromagnetic Radiations (f, s, c) (PSSC, Educational Services, Inc.), Modern Talking Pictures, $5.75.

Eye and the Camera (fs), Popular Science through McGraw-Hill, $3.00.

The Family Album (right and wrong ways of using light in indoor photography) (f, s, c), General Electric, free.

Faster Than Sound (f, s), Institutional Cinema, $2.00.

Fine Cameras and How They Are Made (f, s, c), Modern Talking Pictures, free.

Formulation of Crystals in Polarized Light (f, si, c), Indiana University, $2.00.

Fundamentals of Acoustics (f, s), Ideal, $2.00.

Fundamentals of Photography: Elementary Optics in Photography (f, s), Indiana University, $2.50.

How Sound Travels (fs, c), Popular Science through McGraw-Hill, $6.00.

Instruments of the Band and Orchestra (f, s, c, 5 in series), Coronet, inquire rental local film library.

Introduction to Optics (f, s, c) (PSSC, Educational Services, Inc.), Modern Talking Pictures, $5.75.

Lenses (f, s), United World, inquire rental.

Let's Take Pictures (f, s), Business Education, free.

Light (f, s, 18 lessons on optics), EBF, inquire rental.

Light (fs, c), Young America, $6.00.

Light Control Through Polarization (f, s, c), Polaroid Corp., free.

The Light in Your Life (f, s, c), General Electric, free.

Light: Lenses; Light: Refraction (f, s), Indiana University, $2.00 each.

Light and Shadow (f, s), Indiana University, $2.00.

Light Waves and Their Uses (reflection, refraction), EBF, inquire rental.

Magic of Fluorescence (f, s, c), General Electric, free.

Magic of Seeing (lenses) (f, s, c), Better Vision Institute, free.

Magic Pathway (structure and function of eye) (f, s, c), Better Vision Institute, free.

Man Within Light (lenses) (f, s), French-American Culture Services, inquire rental.

Measurement of the Speed of Light (f, s), McGraw-Hill, inquire rental local film library.

Measurement With Light Waves (f, s, 1½ rls), Ideal, $3.00.

Modern Physics Series: Light and Sound (set of 4 fs), Popular Science through McGraw-Hill, $3.25, each.

Music in Motion (f, s, c), Bell Telephone, free.

Musical Notes (f, s), United World, inquire rental.

Nature of Color (f, s, c), Indiana University, $3.25.

Nature of Light (f, s, c), Ideal, $3.50.

Nature of Sound (f, s), Ideal, $2.00.

Naval Photography in Science (f, s, c), U.S. Dept. of Navy, free.

Origins of the Motion Picture (f, s), U.S. Dept. of Navy, free.

Perfect Parallel (f, s, c), Libby-Owens-Ford, free.

Photographic Darkroom Procedures Series (6 fs), McGraw-Hill, $6.00 each.

Principles of Ultrasonics (f, s), Contemporary Films, $2.55.

Progressive Waves: Transverse and Longitudinal (f, s), McGraw-Hill, inquire rental local film library.

Quality in Photographic Lenses; Quality in Photographic Paper (2 f, s, c), Eastman Kodak Co., free.

Quiet, Please! (f, s, c), Indiana University, $3.50.

Refraction (f, s), United World, inquire rental.

Science in the Orchestra (f, s, 3 in series), Indiana University, $2.50 each.

Science of Musical Instruments (fs, 3 in series), Popular Science through McGraw-Hill, $6.00 each.

Science of Seeing (fs), General Electric, free.

Seeing Is Believing (Fastax camera) (f, s), Association Films, free.

Sound (f, s), Institutional Cinema, $2.00.

Sound (f, s, series of 11 lessons in introductory physics course), EBF, inquire rental.

Sound Recording and Reproduction (f, s), EBF, $2.50.

Sound Waves and Their Sources (f, s), EBF, $2.50.

The Sounds of Music (f, s, c), Coronet, inquire rental local film library.

The Spectrograph (f, s, c), McGraw-Hill, inquire rental local film library.

Speed of Light (f, s), EBF, $3.50.

The Speed of Sound (f, s), Indiana University, $3.00.

Spherical Mirrors; Lenses (f, s), United World, $2.00 each.

Story of Light (f, s, c), General Electric, free.

Thinnest Slice (f, s), University of Southern California, $2.50 rental.

This Is Color (f, s, c), Modern Talking Pictures, free.

Ultra Sounds (f, s), Indiana University, $2.00.

Vibrating Motions and Waves (f, s, 2 rls), Institutional Cinema, $3.00.

Waves (f, s), PSSC, Educational Services, Inc., inquire rental.

What Is Color? (Newton) (fs, c), Popular Science through McGraw-Hill, $6.50.

Wind and Water Movements in a Model Lake (f, si), International Film Bureau, inquire rental local film library.

World of Sound (f, s), Teaching Film Custodians, free.

Currents, fields, electronics

The ABC of Hand Tools (f, s, 2 in series), General Motors, free.

An Adventure in Electronics (fs, c), General Electric, inquire purchase.

Automation (f, s, in series, *The Search*), Young America, inquire local film library.

Automation in Television (f, s, c), Admiral, free.

Basic Electricity As Applied to Electronic Control Systems (f, s, c), Indiana University, $4.50.

Basic Electronics (f, s, c), Minneapolis-Honeywell, free.

Bottle of Magic (electron tube) (f, s, 2 rls), Western Electric, free.

Care and Use of the Jig Saw; Of the Drill Press (fs, c, 2 in series), Popular Science through McGraw-Hill, $6.50 each.

Cathode Ray Oscilloscope (f, s), Indiana University, $2.50.

Coils and Electric Currents (f, s), Institutional Cinema, $2.00.

The Diode (f, s), Indiana University, $2.75.

Thomas Edison (f, si), General Electric, free.

Electric Circuits (f, s), Arco, inquire rental.

Electric Motors Series (fs, 4 in series), Illinois University (Voc.-Ag.), $2.10.

Electricity and Magnetism (series of 24 lessons in introductory physics) (f, s), EBF, inquire rental.

Electrodynamics (f, s), EBF, $2.50.

Electromagnets (fs, c), Young America, $6.00.

The Electron (f, s, 2 rls), Almanac, $3.00.

Electron Theory (fs, 2 in series), Visual Sciences, $2.00 each.

Electronics (f, s, 8 lessons in introductory physics), EBF, inquire nearest regional office.

Electronics in Automation (f, s, c), DeVry Technical Inst., free.

Electrons (f, s), EBF, $2.50.

Electrostatics (f, s), EBF, $2.50.

Elements of Electrical Circuits (f, s), Ideal, $2.00.

Exploring With X-rays (f, s), General Electric, free.

Freedom and Power (Franklin to Edison) (f, s, c), General Electric, free.

Highways for the Telephone (f, s), Bell Telephone, regional offices, free.

How Color Television Works (fs, c), Popular Science through McGraw-Hill, $6.00.

Introduction to the Automotive Electrical System (fs, s, c), Delco-Remy, General Motors, free.

Loran Comes to Bataan (f, s, c), U.S. Coast Guard, free.

Magic in the Air (television) (f, s), General Motors, free.

Magic in Television Tubes (f, s), DeVry Technical Inst., free.

Magnetism (fs), General Electric, free.

Magnetism (f, s), EBF, $3.50.

Measurement of Electricity (f, s), Ideal, $2.00.

Modern Physics Series: Electricity (fs, 6 in series), Popular Science through McGraw-Hill, $3.25 each.

Mr. Bell (f, s), Association Films, free.

Naturally It's FM (f, s, c), General Electric, free.

Octopus in the House (dangers of improper electrical wiring) (f, s, c), Association Films, free.

Ohm's Law (f, s), Coronet, inquire rental local film library.

Physics Demonstrations (f, s, 5 in series, 3–5 min. each), McGraw-Hill, $17.50 each.

Piercing the Unknown (computers) (f, s, c), Modern Talking Pictures, free.

Power By Which We Live (f, s, c), General Electric, free.

Precision Cathode Ray Tube (f, s, c), Tektronix, free.

Primary Cell (f, s), EBF, $3.00.

Principle of the Generator (f, s), Indiana University, $2.00.

Principles of Electricity (f, s, c), General Electric, free.

Radio; Television (fs), Young America, $3.50 each.

Radio Antennas—Creation and Behavior of Radio Waves (f, s), Indiana University, $1.50.

Radio Receivers: Principles (f, s), Ideal, $2.20.

Radio Servicing Series (6 fs), McGraw-Hill, $6.00 each.

Receiving Radio Messages; Sending Radio Messages (f, s), Indiana University, $2.00 each.

Safe Passage (radar) (f, s, c), Raytheon, free.

Sentinel in the Sky (radar) (f, s, c) Pan American Airways, free.

Series and Parallel Circuits (f, s), EBF, $2.50.

Servant of Mankind (Edison) (f, s), Teaching Film Custodians, free.

Ships That See in the Night (radar) (f, s, c), Radio Marine Corp., free.

Sound and the Story (hi-fi) (f, s, c), Inst. Visual Training, free.

Sources of Electricity (f, s), Institutional Cinema, $2.00.

Stepping Along With Television (f, s), American Telephone and Telegraph, free.

Story of Television (f, s, c), Institute of Visual Training, free.

Telegram for America (f, s), Modern Talking Pictures, free.

Television: How It Works (f, s), Indiana University, $2.00.

Television (6 fs and 6 f, s), McGraw-Hill, inquire rental.

This Is Automation (f, s, c), General Electric, free.

Thunderbolt Hunters (f, s), General Electric, free.

Transistor (f, s), Bell Telephone Co., free.

Triode: Amplification (f, s, 2 rls), Almanac, $3.00.

Vacuum Tube (f, s), Ideal, $2.00.

Voice Sentinel (quartz crystal) (f, s, 2 rls), Western Electric, free.

Western Relay (radio relay) (f, s), Western Electric, free.

What Is Electricity? (f, s), EBF, $3.00.

What's The Story On Color Television? (f, s), Dumont, free.

Nuclear and solar energy

A is for Atom (f, s, c), General Electric, free.

Agriculture, Industry and Power (radiation of corn, radioisotopes) (f, s), U.S. AEC, free.

The Atom (fs, c), Life, $6.00.

The Atom (f, s), Almanac, $2.00.

Atom and Agriculture (f, s), EBF, $2.50.

The Atom and Industry (gauge of metals) (f, s), U.S. AEC, free.

Atom and Medicine (f, s), EBF, $2.50.

Atom and the Weather (f, s), Handel, inquire rental.

The Atom Goes to Sea (atomic submarine) (f, s), General Electric, free.

Atom Smashers (f, s), U.S. AEC, inquire rental.

The Atomic Alchemist (f, s), U.S. AEC, free.

Atomic Detective (f, s), U.S. AEC, free.

Atomic Energy (f, s), U.S. AEC, free.

Atomic Furnaces (f, s), U.S. AEC, free.

Atomic Metallurgy (alloys) (f, s), U.S. AEC, free.

Atomic Physics (f, s, 90 minutes), United World, inquire rental.

Atomic Physics (fs, 5 in series), United World, $12.50 set.

Atomic Physics (f, s, series of 9 lessons in complete course in introductory physics), EBF, inquire rental.

Atomic Power (f, s), Ideal, $3.00.

Atomic Radiation (f, s), EBF, $2.50.

Atomic Research (f, s), U.S. AEC, free.

Atoms for Power (f, s, c), Allis-Chalmers, free.

Basic Physics of an Atomic Bomb (f, s, c), Dept. of Army, free.

Bell Solar Battery (f, s, c), Bell Telephone, regional offices, free.

Beyond Uranium (f, s), Indiana University, $5.25.

Carbon-14 (f, s), EBF, inquire rental.

Cosmic Ray Studies (f, s), Indiana University, $3.00.

The Discovery of Radium (f, s, in series, *You Are There*), Young America, inquire rental local film library.

The First Atomic Pile (MGM films; Fermi, Compton) (f, s, 2 rls), Teaching Film Custodians, $2.00.

From Atoms to Organisms (f, s), Indiana University, $4.75.

How Big Is An Atom? (f, s), Indiana University, $4.75.

Linear Accelerator (f, s), McGraw-Hill, inquire rental locai film library.

Madame Curie (MGM) (f, s, 2 rls), Teaching Film Custodians, free.

The Magic of the Atom (f, s, series), Handel, inquire rental.

Medical Aspects of Nuclear Radiations (f, s), U.S. Dept. of Army, free.

Neutron Story (fs, c), Popular Science through McGraw-Hill, $6.00.

Nuclear Physics (f, s, 7 lessons in series in complete course on introductory physics), EBF, inquire rental.

Nuclear Reactors for Research (f, s, c), U.S. AEC, free.

Our Mr. Sun (f, s, c), Bell Telephone, regional offices, free.

Peacetime Uses of Atomic Energy in Medicine, Agriculture and Industry, VEC, $3.50.

Power Unlimited (breeder reactor) (f, s), U.S. AEC, free.

Radium (f, s), Institutional Cinema, $2.00.

Report on the Atom (peacetime uses) (f, s), Indiana University, $3.25.

Solar Energy (f, s), Almanac, $10.00.

Strange Case of the Cosmic Rays (f, s, c), American Telephone and Telegraph, free.

Tagging the Atom (f, s), Handel, inquire rental.

Taking the X out of X-rays (f, s), General Electric, free.

Unlocking the Atom (chain reaction) (f, s), U.S. AEC, free.

What Makes Atoms Stick? (f, s), Indiana University, $4.75.

Why Are Atoms Unpredictable? (f, s), Indiana University, $4.75.

Engines: automobile, airplane, rocket

ABC of Automobile Engine (f, s, c), General Motors, free.

ABC of Diesel Engine (f, s, c), General Motors, free.

ABC of Internal Combustion (f, s, c), General Motors, free.

ABC of Internal Combustion Engines: Automotive Engine (f, s, c), Indiana University, $4.75.

ABC of Jet Propulsion (f, s, c), General Motors, free.

Aerial Navigation (maps and the compass) (f, s), Almanac, $2.00.

Aerodynamics (forces acting on air foil) (f, s, 2 rls), Almanac, $3.50.

Aerodynamics: Airflow (f, s), Indiana University, $2.50.

Aircraft Engines (f, s, 3 rls), Almanac, $3.75.

Airplane Series (f, s, 10 in series), Massachusetts Institute of Technology, free.

Airplanes and How They Fly (f, s), Indiana University, $2.00.

And Then There Were Four (driver safety) (f, s), Modern Talking Pictures, free.

Animals in Rocket Flight (f, s), U.S. Dept. of Air Force, free.

Automatic Transmission (f, s), Ford, free.

Automotive Mechanics Series (15 fs in 2 sets), McGraw-Hill, $6.00 each.

Aviation Medicine (f, s, in series, *The Search*, filmed

at U.S. Air Force School of Aviation Medicine), Young America, inquire rental local film library.

Background of Rocketry (f, s), Indiana University, $3.00.

Carnot Cycle (Kelvin temperature scale) (f, s), McGraw-Hill, inquire rental local film library.

Diesel—The Modern Power (f, s), General Motors, free.

The Diesel Story (f, s), Shell Oil, free.

The Earth Satellite (f, s, 2 in series), Indiana University, $3.00 each.

Engineering for Tomorrow (f, s, c), North American Aviation, free.

Flight Into the Future (f, s), Bell Aircraft, free.

Flight Log (100-octane aviation gasoline) (f, s), Shell Oil, free.

Fluid Dynamics (f, s, 4 rls), PSSC, Educational Services, Inc., $23.00.

The Gas Turbine (turbojet etc.) (f, s), Shell Oil, free.

Guided Missiles (f, s), U.S. Dept. of Army, free.

Harnessed Lightning (turboprop and turbojet) (f, s, c), General Motors, free.

Helicopters (f, s), EBF, inquire rental.

The History of the Helicopter (f, s), Shell Oil, free.

How An Airplane Flies (f, s, 6 in series), Shell Oil, free.

Introduction to Rocketry (f, s), Indiana University, $3.00.

Jet Propulsion (f, s, c), General Electric, free.

Jet Propulsion (f, s, c), EBF, $3.50.

The Jet Story (f, s), General Electric, free.

Large Forces Acting on the Body (f, s), Indiana University, $3.00.

Lighter Than Air (f, s), Pictura, $10.00.

New Frontier in Space (f, s), McGraw-Hill, $4.00.

Nike (electronic brain) (f, s), Bell Telephone, regional offices, free.

Pioneer of Flight (excerpt from *Gallant Journey*, about John J. Montgomery) (f, s, 2 rls), Teaching Film Custodians, free.

Power Within (internal-combustion engine) (f, s), U.S. Bureau of Mines, free.

Principle of the Generator (f, s), Institutional Cinema, $2.00.

The Rocket (f, s), Contemporary Films, $3.50.

Safe Passage (f, s, c), Raytheon, free.

Steam Turbine; Steam Engine (f, s), Indiana University, $2.00 each.

Story of a Spark Plug (f, s), Ideal, free.

Supersonic Flight (f, s, c), Shell Oil, free.

Theory of Flight; Problems of Flight (f, s), EBF, $2.50 each.

Thermodynamics (f, s), EBF, $2.50.

Turbojets, Pulse Jets and Ramjets (f, s), Indiana University, $3.00.

We Drivers (f, s), General Motors, free.

Where Mileage Begins (gasoline engine) (f, s), General Motors, free.

Directory of manufacturers, distributors, and supply houses

Most of the companies and institutions listed here distribute useful free material on request; some charge a small sum, well under a dollar. We cannot, of course, list all the distributors, for we do not know them all. We have not attempted to list the specific materials available, since these change fairly often whereas the companies offering these materials do not usually change their public relations policies.

We recommend that the teacher send for a list of booklets, charts, films, or filmstrips available from the companies, and then select the materials useful for classwork. These can be filed in manila envelopes or file folders, properly labeled, ready for teacher or student use. We hope that individual students in class will not send for materials, for this creates a strain on any company's policy of good will.

Directory

Alconox, Inc. (detergents), 853 Broadway, New York 3, N.Y.

Allied Chemical and Dye Corp., 40 Rector St., New York 6, N.Y.

Aloe Scientific, Division of A.S. Aloe Co., 5655 Kingsbury St., St. Louis 12, Mo.

American Electronics Laboratories, Inc., 121 N. 7 St., Philadelphia 6, Pa.

J. T. Baker Chemical Co., Phillipsburg, N.J.

Bausch & Lomb Optical Co., 635 St. Paul St., Rochester 2, N.Y.

Bellco Glass Inc., Vineland, N.J.

Charles Beseler Co., Slide-o-film Division, 230 South 18 St., East Orange, N.J.

Burgess Battery Co. (Burgess kit assemblies—25 dry cells), Freeport, Ill.

California Corp., Biochemical Research, 3625 Medford St., Los Angeles 63, Calif.

California Laboratory Equipment Co., 98 Rincon Rd., Berkeley 4, Calif.

Cambosco Scientific Co., 37 Antwerp St., Brighton 35, Mass.

Cambridge Instrument Co., Inc., 3556 Grand Central Terminal, New York 17, N.Y.

Castle, Wilmont Castle Sterilizers Co., P.O. Box 629, Rochester 2, N.Y.

Central Scientific Co., 1700 N. Irving Park Rd., Chicago 13, Ill.

Chemical Rubber Co., 2310 Superior Ave., Cleveland 14, Ohio.

Coleman Instruments, Inc., Maywood, Illinois.

Corning Glass Works, 75 Crystal St., Corning, N.Y.

Difco Laboratories, Inc. (biochemicals), Detroit 1, Mich.

Duralab Equipment Corp. (laboratory furniture and equipment), 980 Linwood St., Brooklyn 8, N.Y.

Eastman Organic Chemicals, Distillation Products Industries, Eastman Kodak, Rochester 3, N.Y.

Edmund Scientific Co. (optical equipment), Barrington, N.J.

Elgeet Optical Co., Inc., 838 Smith St., Rochester 6, N.Y.

Falcon Plastics, Division of Becton, Dickenson & Co., 6016 W. Washington Blvd., Culver City, Calif.

Fisher Scientific Co. (chemicals, laboratory appliances, unitized furniture), 711 Forbes Ave., Pittsburgh 19, Pa. Offices in many cities.

General Biochemicals, Inc., 677 Laboratory Park, Chagrin Falls, Ohio.

Graf-Apsco Co., 5868 Broadway, Chicago 40, Ill. Division of Hanshaw Chemical Co., 1945 Park, Chagrin Falls, Ohio.

Harshaw Scientific, Division of Harshaw Chemical Co., 1945 E. 97 St., Cleveland 6, Ohio. Offices in many cities.

Harvard Apparatus Co., Inc., Dover, Mass.

International Equipment Co., 1219 Soldiers Field Rd., Boston 35, Mass.

Johns-Manville Corp., 22 E. 40 St., New York 16, N.Y.

Kewaunee Manufacturing Co., Adrian, Mich.

Klett Manufacturing Co. (glassware, other apparatus), 179 E. 87 St., New York 28, N.Y.

J. Klinger Scientific Apparatus, 82–87 160 St., Jamaica 32, N.Y.

Labline Inc., 3076A W. Grand Ave., Chicago 22, Ill.

Lafayette Radio Electronics Corp., P.O. Box 222, Jamaica 31, N.Y.

Charles J. Lane Corp. (cases, cabinets), 105 Chambers St., New York 7, N.Y.

E. Leitz, Inc. (optical instruments), 468 Park Ave. S, New York 16, N.Y.

Mallinckrodt Chemical Works, St. Louis, Mo., and 72 Gold St., New York, N.Y.

National Instrument Laboratories, Inc., 828 Evarts St., N.E., Washington, D.C.

New Brunswick Scientific Co., Inc., P.O. Box 606, New Brunswick, N.J.

New York Laboratory Supply Co., Inc., 76 Varick St., New York 13, N. Y.

Owens-Illinois Glassware Co., Toledo 1, Ohio.

Packard Instrument Co., Inc., P.O. Box 428A., La Grange, Ill.

Palo Laboratories Supplies, Inc., 81 Reade St., New York 7, N.Y.

Parr Instrument Co., Moline, Ill.

Perkin-Elmer Corp., Instrument Division, Norwalk, Conn.

Sargent Co., 4647 W. Foster St., Chicago 30.

Scientific Glass Apparatus Co., Inc., Bloomfield, N.J.

Scientific Products, Division of American Hospital Supply Corp., 1210 Leon Place, Evanston, Ill.

E. H. Sheldon Equipment Co., 149 Thomas St., Muskegon, Mich.

Spitz Laboratories (shadow boxes, ultraviolet orreries, planetaria), Yorklyn, Dela.

Standard Scientific Supply Corp., 808 Broadway, New York 3, N.Y.

Arthur Thomas Co. (laboratory apparatus, reagents), Vine St. at 3 St., Philadelphia 5, Pa.

Tracerlab, 1601 Trapelo Rd., Waltham, Mass.

Unitron, Instrument Division, United Scientific Co., 204–206 Milk St., Boston 9, Mass.

Universal Scientific Co., Inc., Vincennes, Ind.

Ward's Natural Science Establishment, Inc., P.O. Box 24, Beechwood Station, Rochester 9, N.Y.

Welch Scientific Co., 1515 N. Sedgwick St., Chicago 10, Ill.

Carl Zeiss, Inc. (optical equipment), 485 Fifth Ave., New York 17, N.Y.

Great Britain

Aldis Brothers, Ltd. (optical equipment), Sarehole Rd., Hall Green, Birmingham 28, Eng.

Avo, Ltd. (electrical measuring instruments), Avocet House, 92–96 Vauxhall Bridge Rd., London S.W. 1, Eng.

Cambridge Instrument Co., Ltd., 13 Grosvenor Place, London S.W. 1, Eng.

Dawe Instruments, Ltd., 99–101 Uxbridge Rd., Ealing, London W. 5, Eng.

Ekco Electronics, Ltd., Southend-on-Sea, Essex, Eng.

Electronic Instruments, Ltd., Lower Mortlake Rd., Richmond, Surrey, Eng.

A. Gallenkamp & Co., Ltd. (laboratory supplies), Sun St., London, E.C. 2, Eng.

W. F. Stanley & Co., Ltd. (surveying instruments), New Eltham, London S.E. 9, Eng.

Wray Optical Works, Ltd., Ashgrove Rd., Bromley, Kent, Eng.

These and many other British scientific instrument manufacturers have branch offices in many countries. More detailed information about overseas agents can be obtained from Scientific Instrument Manufacturers Association of Great Britain which publishes a *Directory and Buyer's Guide of British Instruments.*

Reference aids

There are many compilations of free and inexpensive materials which have been published to meet the constant search of teachers for classroom aids. For those teachers who will want to go beyond the directory we have compiled, we have added a short bibliography of publications. (Prices are given when they are known.) Be sure to check the distributors of free films and filmstrips.

Sources of Free and Inexpensive Educational Materials, Field Enterprises, Inc., Education Division, Merchandise Mart Plaza, Chicago 54, Ill., 1955, $5.00.

Free and Inexpensive Learning Materials, George Peabody College for Teachers, Division of Surveys and Field Services, Nashville 5, Tenn., 1956, $1.00.

Elementary Teachers Guide to Free Curriculum Materials, Educators' Progress Service, Randolph, Wisc., 1956, $5.50.

Sources of Teaching Materials, C. Williams, Bur. Educational Research, Ohio State U., Columbus, O., 1955.

Sources of Free and Inexpensive Pictures for the Classroom, B. Miller, Box 369, Riverside, Calif., 1956, $0.50.

Free and Inexpensive Teaching Aids for High Schools,

C. Holland, Nat. Assoc. Secondary School Principals, N.E.A., 1201 16 Street N.W., Washington 6, D.C., 1949, $1.00.

Conservation Teaching Aids, Michigan Dept. Conservation, Education Division, 1951.

1001 Valuable Things Free, 2d ed., M. Weisinger, Bantam Books, New York, 1957.

A Wonderful World for Children (free and inexpensive materials), P. Cardozo, Bantam Books, New York, 1956.

General Motors Aids to Educators, General Motors Corp., 1956.

Choosing Free Materials for Use in the Schools, Amer. Assoc. of School Administrators, N.E.A., 1201 16 Street N.W., Washington 6, D.C. 1955, $0.50.

Using Free Materials in the Classroom, Association Supervision and Curriculum Development, N.E.A., 1201 16 St., N.W., Washington 6, D.C., 1953, $0.75.

Sponsor Handbook; Thousands of Science Projects, Science Service, 1719 N St. N.W., Washington 6, D.C., 1957, $0.25 ea.

Teaching Aids, Westinghouse Electrical Corp., School Service, 306 4th Ave., Pittsburgh, Pa.

Hobby Publications, Superintendent of Documents, U.S. Govt. Printing Office, Washington 25, D.C.

Index

Numbers in italics indicate pages bearing important illustrations.

Cathode-ray oscilloscope, 432–33
Cations, 255
Caves, formation of, 60–61
Cell(s) (electrolytic), Daniell, 254–55
  dry, 254, 258
  Edison alkaline, 260
  galvanic, 253–54
  gravity, 256
  hydrogen electrode in, 255
  nickel-cadmium alkaline, 260
  sal ammoniac, 258
  standard comparison electrode for, 255
  voltaic, 237
  wet, 258
  See also Battery(ies)
Cell, photoelectric, construction of, 479
Cell potential. *See* Electrode potential
Cellulose acetate, 293–94, 295
  preparation of, 305–06
Celestial globes. *See* Globes, astronomical
Celsius temperature scale. *See* Centigrade temperature scale
Cement, 317
Center of gravity, 358–59
Centigrade (Celsius) temperature scale, 39, 393–94
Centrifugal anemometer, 51
Centrifugal pump, 334
Centripetal force, 372–73
Chain reaction, 573
Change of phase. *See* Change of state
Change of state, 29, 412–13
Changes, chemical, 29–32
  conservation of matter in, 33–34
  physical, 28–29
"Chaos" machine, 8–9
Charcoal, 197–98
Charges, electrostatic. *See* Electrostatic charges
Charles' law, 9–10, 399–400
Charts, astronomical, *90, 91,* 92–93
Chelating agents, 77
Chemical changes, 29–32
  conservation of matter in, 33–34
Chemical energy, 253–65, 376–77, 378
Chemical reactions. *See* Reactions, chemical
Chemical reagents, storage of, 606, 614
Chemically equivalent quantities, 177–78
Chemistry, safety suggestions in, 615–17
Chladni figures, *433*
Chlorate ion, test for, 316

Chloride ion, test for, 237
Chlorides, in food, testing for, 310–11
Chlorination, 75–76
Chlorine, action of, on microorganisms, 75–76, 235
  bleaching action of, 235
  burning hydrogen in, 148–49
  chemistry of, 232–37
  natural occurrence of, 230
  safety precautions for, 613, 617
Chlorine water, 171, 234
Chloroform, 284
Chlorophyll, 297*n.*
Chromatic aberration, *459*
Chromatography, adsorption, 296–97
  paper, 297
Chrome colors, 306–07
Chromium plating, 261–62
Circuit breakers, 509
Circuits, electrical, 508, 547–48
Clothing fibers. *See* Textile fibers
Cloud chambers, 563–65
  commercial alpha-track, 563
  diffusion, 563–65
Clouds, 45–46
  artificial, 45–46
Coagulation, of colloids, 162–63
  purification of water by, 74–75, 157
Coal, bituminous, 279–80
Cobalt nitrate, 171
Cobalt nitrate test, 221
Cohesion, 10
Coil spring, for demonstrating compressions and rarefactions, 427–28
Coils, induction in, 527–28
  Left-Hand Rule for, 519–20
  magnetizing with, 516
  safety precautions for, 618
Coke, 197–98
Cold cream, 315
Collections, of fossils, 69
  of minerals, 69–70
  of rocks, 69
Colligative properties, 157
Colloidal dispersions, 158–59
Colloids, 162–63
Color(s), 480–85
  additive mixing of, 483–85
  dispersion of, by prism, 480
  primary, "additive," 484
  subtractive, 485
  wave length of, 482–83
Color box, 483–84
Color television, 484, 554
Color tests, for textile fibers, 303–04
Color wheel, 483, 484–85
Colorimetric analysis, 183
Combination reactions, 124

Combustible materials, safety precautions for, 615
Combustion, Lavoisier's experiments on, 130–32
  of magnesium in carbon dioxide, 201
  Priestley's experiments on, 129–30
  of various substances in chlorine gas, 232–36
  spontaneous, 140–41
Combustion chamber, 421
Combustion mixture tubes, 422–23
Common-emitter transistor circuit, 547–48
Communication, electrical, 534–55
Commutator, 521–22
Compass, magnetic, 512–14, 516
  navigational, 513–14
"Complementary" receiver, transistor, 550–51
Complex sugar, 310
Components of a force, 353–54
Composition of forces, 353–54
Compound microscope. *See* Microscope, compound
Compounds, covalent, 108–09
  ionic (electrovalent), 108
  organic (table), 270–76
  saturated, 109–10
  separation of, 32–33
  unsaturated, 110
Compressibility, of air, 336–37
  of rocks and ores, 70
Compression and rarefaction (sound), 427–28
Concave. *See* Lenses; Mirrors
Concentration(s) of solutions, 165–73
  effect of on conductivity, 176
Concrete, 317
Condensation, heat of, 410
  of water vapor, 413
Condenser (elec.). *See* Capacitor
Condenser, Liebig, 29, 73–74
  smoke precipitation in, 264
Conduction of heat, 400–01
Conductivity, electrical, 208, 507–08
  electrolytic, 111, 263
  and flame, 141–42
  of fused NaCl, 107–08
  metallic, 111
  of solutions, 175–76
  thermal, 208
Conductometer, 208, 400–01
Conductor(s) (elec.), 507
  magnetic field around, 516–19
Conservation of matter, 33–34
Constellations. *See* Sky maps; Globes, astronomical; Charts, astronomical

Hot-water heating system, 416–17
Household chemistry, 319–21
Humidity, and evaporation, 412
    relative, 40–41
Huygens, Christian, 447, 466
Huygens' principle, 466–68
Hydraulic balance, 340
Hydraulic press, 343
    molding plastics by, 295
Hydrocarbon derivatives, 283–90
Hydrocarbons, aliphatic, 279
    aromatic, 279
    catalytic cracking of, 281
    saturated, 268–69, 276
    unsaturated (double bond), 276–77
    unsaturated (triple bond), 277–78
Hydrochloric acid, action of, on metallic oxides, 236–37
    "cleaning" action of, 237
    preparation of standard solution of, 171
    safety precautions for, 616
    See also Hydrogen chloride
Hydrochloric acid fountain, 160–61, 237
Hydrofluoric acid, etching glass with, 231–32
    safety precautions for, 231, 616
    See also Hydrogen fluoride
Hydrogen, burning, 148–49, 235
    density of, 146
    displacement of, 143–44, 209–11
    preparation of, 143–46
    properties of, 146–50
    reaction with oxygen, 146–47
    safety precautions for, 614, 615–17
    testing for, 143
Hydrogen bonds. See Bonds, hydrogen
Hydrogen bromide, 237–38, 239
Hydrogen chloride, preparation of, 172, 236
    properties of, 236–37
    reaction with ammonia, 236
    See also Hydrochloric acid
Hydrogen electrode, 255
Hydrogen fluoride, 230–31
    See also Hydrofluoric acid
"Hydrogen gun," 124, 148
Hydrogen ion (hydronium ion), 110
    and pH, 179–80
Hydrogen peroxide, 150–51, 225
    preparation of oxygen from, 136
    release of oxygen from, 32–33
Hydrogen sulfide, 188–89
Hydrolysis, of salts, 175

Hydrometer, 182–83, 349–50
Hydronium ion. See Hydrogen ion
Hydroxides, amphoteric, 213
Hydroxyl ion, and pH, 179–80
Hygrometer, 41–44
Hypo. See Sodium thiosulfate
Hypochlorites, 136–37

Ice, dry. See Dry ice
    as frictionless body, 360
    structure of, 154
Igneous rock, 65
Ignition system of automobile, 580
Illuminance, 479–80
Illumination, 478–80
    in school laboratories, 609
Image(s), in compound microscope, 476–77
    in mirrors, 452–53
Image-object relationships, for lenses, 458
    table of, 449
Impenetrability, 21
Impulse, 362
Incidence, angle of, 464
    See also Refraction; Light
Incident beam, 451
Incident waves. See Light waves
Inclined plane, 388
    motion along, 369–70
Index of refraction, 456–57, 470–71
Indicator solutions, 178–82
Indicators, acid-base, 178–82
    of diffusion, 3
Indigo carmine, 179
Induction, electromagnetic. See Electromagnetic induction
    of electrostatic charges, 499–500
Induction coils. See Coils
Inertia, 359–62
    apparatus for showing, 23
    law of. See Newton's first law
Inertial mass, 359, 360
Infrared radiation, absorption of, 405–06
    focusing of, 486
    sources of, 486
Ingrain dyes, 307
Ink eradicators, 319
Interference, of light waves, 466, 468–69, 482–83
    of sound waves (beats), 434
Intermolecular forces, 10–15
Intermolecular spaces, 21
Internal-combustion engines, 421–23
Inverse-square law, for electrostatic forces, 504
    experimental derivation of, 479–80
    for gamma radiation, 570

for light, 478
for magnetic forces, 504, 512
Iodide ion, test for, 240
Iodimetry, 195
Iodine, 30–31, 172, 239–40
    natural occurrence of, 230
    properties of, 30–31, 239–40
    safety precautions for, 616
    solid, sublimation of, 239–40
    solvents for, 240
    testing saturation of fats by, 289
Iodine number, 289
Iodoform, 283–84
Iodoform test, for ethyl alcohol, 284
Ion exchange, 125
Ion-exchange resins, 77
Ionic bonds. See Bonds, ionic
Ionization, of acids and bases, 180–82
Ions, 108
    charge of (table), 160
    metallic, tests for, 219–21
    migration of, 225–26, 263–64
    See also names of individual ions
Iron, colored ions of, 222
    extraction of, 216–18
    in liver, testing for, 311
    passivity of, 110
    rusting of, 31–32
    slow oxidation of, 138–39
    spark tests for metals alloyed with, 222
    and sulfur, 29–30
    tests for, 221–22
Isomers, 267–68
Isotherms, 52–53
Isotopes, 106
    radioactive, half-life of, 571

Javelle water, 321
Jet-propelled models, 586–87
Join (in glass tubing), 597
Joly photometer, 478
Joule's law, 413–14
J-tube barometer, 328–29

Kekulé's model of benzene, 279
Kelvin waterdrop electrostatic generator, 502
Kepler's second law, 98
Kepler's third law, 99–100
Ketones, 286–87
Kindling temperature, 140
Kinescope, 553
Kinetic theory of gases, 8
Kundt's tube, 436

Laboratory equipment, 602–04
Laboratory reagents, standard, 170–73
Laboratory tables, for students, 607

Pressure, 324–50
in air. *See* Air pressure
atmospheric, 48–49, 330–32
distinguished from force, 342
effect of on boiling point of water, 71–72, 410–12
of expanding air, 406
and gas solubility, 156
in liquids. *See* Liquid pressure
of a saturated vapor, 411–12
units of measurement of, 328
upward, in water, 347–50
vapor. *See* Vapor pressure
Pressure bottle, 341
Pressure coefficient of expansion, 397–98
Pressure cooker, safety precautions for, 618
Pressure gauges. *See* Gauges, pressure
Priestley, Joseph, 129–30
Primary colors, "additive," 484
in color television, 484, 554
for work with paint, 484–85
Print box, 487–88
Prism(s), 457
additive color mixing by, 483
color dispersion by, 480
Prism spectroscope, 96–97, 473–74, 481
Projectile motion, 370
Projection electroscope, 496
Projector, *449, 474*
Prony brake, 380–81
Propane, as fuel, 282
Proteins, in food, test for, 308–09
Protium, 106
Protons, 106
Psychrometer, sling, 41, 43
Pulleys, 384–86
movable, efficiency of, 378–79
Pump(s) (mech.), 333–34
Purification of water, 73–77, 157
Pyrex glass, 204, 599

Radiation, heat, 404–06
nuclear, 557–72
See also Beta rays; Gamma rays; X-rays; Infrared radiation; Ultraviolet radiation
Radio detection, 543–46
Radio equipment, safety precautions for, 618
Radio projects, facilities needed for, 608
Radio receiver(s), "complementary" (transistor), 550–51
crystal, 544
detection and amplification in, 544–46
regenerative (transistor), 549

solar battery-powered (transistor), 599
Radio reception, 543–47
See also Transistor
Radio transmission, 546–47
transistor, 549–50
Radio waves, amplitude-modulated (**AM**), 543–44, 546
frequency-modulated (**FM**), 546
Radioactive substances, detection of, 558–61
Radioautographs, 376, 571–72
Radiometer, 404
Rain gauge, 46–47
Rainbow, 480
Raindrops, erosion by, 63
Range finders, reflecting-image, 453
Rayon fibers, 301, 303, 304–05
Reaction balloon, 362
Reaction car, 362–63
Reactions (chemical), 119, 121–26
combination, 124
decomposition, 124–25
double replacement, 125–26
electricity in, 124
molecular, 124–26
oxidation. *See* Oxidation
oxidation-reduction, 122–24
redox, 123
reduction. *See* Reduction
single replacement, 125
in solutions, 33–35
Readings, in science. *See Bibliography in Appendix*
Reagents, chemical, storage of, 606, 614
Receivers, radio. *See* Radio receivers
Rectification, 539–41
in radio detection, 543
Rectifier, diode as, 539–41
Red phosphorus, 196
Redox reactions, 123
Reducing agents, in electromotive series, 256
metals as, 209–11
Reduction, 122
by hydrogen peroxide, 151
of metallic oxides, 149–50
Refrigeration, in school laboratories, 612
Regenerative receiver, transistor, 549
Reflected beam, 451–52
Reflection, 451–55
of circular waves, 464–65
from concave and convex surfaces, 464–65
by a parabola, 465
of plane-parallel waves, 464
of radiant energy, 404–05

of sound waves, 433
total internal, 471–72
Refracted beam, 455–56
Refraction, 455–57, 470–72
index of, 456–57, 470–71
in lenses, 458
Relative humidity. *See* Humidity, relative
Replacement (chem.). *See* Displacement
Replica diffraction grating. *See* Diffraction grating
Repulsion, electrostatic, 498–502
Research, individual, facilities for students doing, 608
Resins, phenol-formaldehyde, 292
Resistance(s) (elec.), 507, 508–509, 510–11, 525–26
Resolution of forces, 352–53
Resonance, electrical, 538
in sound waves, 434
Resonator box, 434
Resultant of forces, 352–53
Reverberations, 437
Revolution of earth, 81–82
Ripple tank, construction of, 460–62
Doppler effect and, 435
focusing by a lens in, 471
Huygens' principle and, 466–68
diffraction in, 466–68
generation of waves in, 466–68
interference patterns in, 468–69
measurement of wave length in, 465–66
propagation of waves in, 462–63
reflection in, 464–65
refraction in, 470–72
standing waves in, 466
total internal reflection in, 471–72
Ring stands, 605
Rivers, aging of, 63–64
Rockets, 585–87
Rock(s), 64–70
formation of, 65
igneous, 65
metamorphic, 65
sedimentary, 60, 64–65
Rotating apparatus, safety precautions for, 618
Rotating mirror, 430
Rotation, 370–75
of earth, 81–84
Rotational motion, 352, 370–75
Rouge, 315
Rubber, synthetic, 298
Russian leather (perfume), 312–13
Running water, for school laboratories, 609
Rust, control of, 319–20
on marble, 62
prevention of, 319–20